If $a < b$, and $c < 0$, then $ac > bc$.

If $a < b$, and $c > 0$, then $\dfrac{a}{c} < \dfrac{b}{c}$.

If $a < b$, and $c < 0$, then $\dfrac{a}{c} > \dfrac{b}{c}$.

CHAPTER 3 GRAPHING AND SOLVING SYSTEMS OF EQUATIONS AND INEQUALITIES

General form of the equation of a line:

$Ax + By = C$

Equation of a vertical line: $x = a$

Equation of a horizontal line: $y = b$

CHAPTER 4 POLYNOMIALS

Properties of exponents: If $x \neq 0$ and $y \neq 0$, then

$$x^n = \overbrace{x \cdot x \cdot x \cdots x}^{n \text{ factors of } x}$$

$$x^m x^n = x^{m+n} \qquad (x^m)^n = x^{mn}$$

$$(xy)^n = x^n y^n \qquad \left(\dfrac{x}{y}\right)^n = \dfrac{x^n}{y^n}$$

$$\dfrac{x^m}{x^n} = x^{m-n} \qquad x^0 = 1$$

$$x^{-n} = \dfrac{1}{x^n} \qquad \dfrac{x^m}{x^n} = x^{m-n}$$

Special products:

$$(x + y)^2 = x^2 + 2xy + y^2$$
$$(x - y)^2 = x^2 - 2xy + y^2$$
$$(x + y)(x - y) = x^2 - y^2$$

CHAPTER 5 FACTORING POLYNOMIALS

Factoring the difference of two squares:

$$a^2 - b^2 = (a + b)(a - b)$$

Factoring perfect-square trinomials:

$$a^2 + 2ab + b^2 = (a + b)^2$$
$$a^2 - 2ab + b^2 = (a - b)^2$$

Factoring the sum and difference of two cubes:

$$x^3 + y^3 = (x + y)(x^2 - xy + y^2)$$
$$x^3 - y^3 = (x - y)(x^2 + xy + y^2)$$

Zero-factor property: Let a and b be real numbers.

If $ab = 0$, then $a = 0$ or $b = 0$.

CHAPTER 6 PROPORTION AND RATIONAL EXPRESSIONS

If there are no divisions by 0, then

$$\dfrac{ac}{bc} = \dfrac{a}{b} \qquad \dfrac{a}{1} = a \qquad \dfrac{a}{0} \text{ is undefined} \qquad \dfrac{a}{b} \cdot \dfrac{c}{d} = \dfrac{ac}{bd}$$

$$\dfrac{a}{b} \div \dfrac{c}{d} = \dfrac{ad}{bc} \qquad \dfrac{a}{d} + \dfrac{b}{d} = \dfrac{a + b}{d}$$

$$\dfrac{a}{d} - \dfrac{b}{d} = \dfrac{a - b}{d}$$

If $\dfrac{a}{b} = \dfrac{c}{d}$, then $ad = bc$.

CHAPTER 7 MORE EQUATIONS, INEQUALITIES, AND FACTORING

If $x \geq 0$, then $|x| = x$.

If $x < 0$, then $|x| = -x$.

If $k > 0$, then

$|x| = k$ is equivalent to $x = k$ or $x = -k$.

$|x| < k$ is equivalent to $-k < x < k$.

$|x| > k$ is equivalent to $x < -k$ or $x > k$.

CHAPTER 8 WRITING EQUATIONS OF LINES, FUNCTIONS, AND VARIATION

Slope of a line: If (x_1, y_1) and (x_2, y_2) are two points on a line, the **slope** of the line is

$$m = \dfrac{y_2 - y_1}{x_2 - x_1} \quad (x_2 \neq x_1)$$

Equations of a line:

$y - y_1 = m(x - x_1)$ point-slope form

$y = mx + b$ slope-intercept form

$Ax + By = C$ general form

$y = b$ a horizontal line (slope is 0)

$x = a$ a vertical line (slope is undefined)

Two distinct lines with the same slope are parallel.

If the product of the slopes of two lines is -1, the lines are perpendicular.

Direct variation: $\qquad y = kx$

Inverse variation: $\qquad y = \dfrac{k}{x}$

Joint variation: $\qquad y = kxz$

Combined variation: $\qquad y = \dfrac{kx}{z}$

Beginning and Intermediate Accounting

Oakland Community College, Southeast Campus

R. David Gustafson | Rosemary Karr | Marilyn Massey

CENGAGE
Learning™

Australia • Brazil • Japan • Korea • Mexico • Singapore • Spain • United Kingdom • United States

CENGAGE
Learning™

**Beginning and Intermediate Accounting
Oakland Community College, Southeast
Campus**

Beginning and Intermediate Algebra: An Integrated Approach, 6th Edition
R. David Gustafson | Rosemary Karr | Marilyn Massey

© 2011 Cengage Learning. All rights reserved.

Executive Editors:
 Maureen Staudt
 Michael Stranz

Senior Project Development Manager:
 Linda deStefano

Marketing Specialist:
 Courtney Sheldon

Senior Production/Manufacturing Manager:
 Donna M. Brown

PreMedia Manager:
 Joel Brennecke

Sr. Rights Acquisition Account Manager:
 Todd Osborne

Cover Image:
 Getty Images*

*Unless otherwise noted, all cover images used by Custom
Solutions, a part of Cengage Learning, have been supplied
courtesy of Getty Images with the exception of the Earthview
cover image, which has been supplied by the National
Aeronautics and Space Administration (NASA).

Photograph taken by Anne McCarthy

For product information and technology assistance, contact us at
Cengage Learning Customer & Sales Support, 1-800-354-9706

For permission to use material from this text or product,
submit all requests online at **cengage.com/permissions**
Further permissions questions can be emailed to
permissionrequest@cengage.com

This book contains select works from existing Cengage Learning resources and
was produced by Cengage Learning Custom Solutions for collegiate use. As such,
those adopting and/or contributing to this work are responsible for editorial
content accuracy, continuity and completeness.

Compilation © 2010 Cengage Learning
ISBN-13: 978-1-111-63122-2

ISBN-10: 1-111-63122-0

Cengage Learning
5191 Natorp Boulevard
Mason, Ohio 45040
USA

Cengage Learning is a leading provider of customized learning solutions with
office locations around the globe, including Singapore, the United Kingdom,
Australia, Mexico, Brazil, and Japan. Locate your local office at:

international.cengage.com/region.
Cengage Learning products are represented in Canada by Nelson Education, Ltd.
For your lifelong learning solutions, visit **www.cengage.com/custom.**
Visit our corporate website at **www.cengage.com.**

Printed in Canada

A special thanks to the Royal Oak Campus for putting the

Beginning and Intermediate Algebra Oakland Community College

Special Edition text together.

Beginning and Intermediate Algebra 6th Edition

An Integrated Approach

R. David Gustafson
Rock Valley College

Rosemary M. Karr
Collin College

Marilyn B. Massey
Collin College

BROOKS/COLE
CENGAGE Learning

Australia · Brazil · Japan · Korea · Mexico · Singapore · Spain · United Kingdom · United States

To Craig, Jeremy, Paula, Gary, Bob,
Jennifer, John-Paul, Gary, and Charlie
RDG

To my husband and best friend Fred,
for his unwavering support of my work
RMK

To my parents, Dale and Martha,
for their lifelong encouragement, and
to Ron, for his unconditional love and support
MBM

Contents

Preface

TO THE INSTRUCTOR

This sixth edition of *Beginning and Intermediate Algebra: An Integrated Approach* is an exciting and innovative revision. The new edition reflects a thorough update, has new pedagogical features that make the text easier to read, and has an entirely new and fresh interior design. The revisions to this already successful text will further promote student achievement. This series is known for its integrated approach, for the clarity of its writing, for making algebra relevant and engaging, and for developing student skills. New coauthors Rosemary Karr and Marilyn Massey have joined David Gustafson, bringing more experience in, contributions to, developmental education.

As before, our goal has been to write a book that

1. is enjoyable to read,
2. is easy to understand,
3. is relevant, and
4. will develop the necessary skills for success in future academic courses or on the job.

In this new edition, we have developed a learning plan that helps students transition to the next level in their coursework, teaching them the problem-solving strategies that will serve them well in their everyday lives. Most textbooks share the goals of clear writing, well-developed examples, and ample exercises, whereas the Gustafson/Karr/Massey series develops student success beyond the demands of traditional required coursework.

The sixth edition's learning tools have been developed with your students in mind and include several new features:

- *Learning Objectives* appear at the beginning of each section and provide a map to the content. Objectives are keyed to Guided Practice exercises, indicating which are satisfied by specific problems.

- The addition of the *Now Try This* exercises helps students develop a deeper conceptual comprehension of the material. These exercises can also be used as questions for independent or group study, or for active classroom participation through in-class group discussions.

- The *Guided Practice* exercises are keyed both to examples and to section Learning Objectives. Students working these problems are directed to the specific section in the text where they can find help on approaches to solve these problems.

- While *Guided Practice* offers students support on their homework, the *Additional Practice* sections reinforce and stretch their newly developed skills by having them solve problems independent of examples.

Through our collective teaching experience, we have developed an acute awareness of students' approach to homework. Consequently, we have designed the problem sets to extend student learning beyond the mimicking of a previous example.

WHY A COMBINED APPROACH?

Beginning and Intermediate Algebra, Sixth Edition, combines the topics of beginning and intermediate algebra. This type of book has many advantages:

1. By combining the topics, much of the overlap and redundancy of the material can be eliminated. The instructor thus has time to teach for mastery of the material.
2. For many students, the purchase of a single book will save money.
3. A combined approach in one book will enable some colleges to cut back on the number of hours needed for mathematics remediation.

   However, there are three concerns inherent in a combined approach:

1. The first half of the book must include enough beginning algebra to ensure that students who complete the first half of the book and then transfer to another college will have the necessary prerequisites to enroll in an intermediate algebra course.
2. The beginning algebra material should not get too difficult too fast.
3. Intermediate algebra students beginning in the second half of the book must get some review of basic topics so that they can compete with students continuing on from the first course.

   Unlike many other texts, we use an integrated approach, which addresses each of the previous three concerns by

   - including a full course in beginning algebra in the first six chapters,
   - delaying the presentation of intermediate algebra topics until Chapter 7 or later,
   - providing a quick review of basic topics for those who begin in the second half of the book.

■ Organization

In the first six chapters, we present all of the topics usually associated with a first course in algebra, except for a detailed discussion of manipulating radical expressions and the quadratic formula. These topics can be omitted because they will be carefully introduced and taught in any intermediate algebra course. Harder topics, such as absolute-value inequalities and synthetic division, are left until Chapter 7.

Chapter 3 discusses graphs of linear equations and systems of two equations in two variables. Systems of three equations in three variables and the methods for solving them are left until Chapter 13.

Chapter 7 is the entry-level chapter for students enrolling in intermediate algebra. As such, it quickly reviews the topics taught in the first six chapters and extends these topics to the intermediate algebra level.

Chapters 8 through 14 are written at the intermediate algebra level, and include a quick review of important topics as needed. For example, Chapter 8 begins with a review of the rectangular coordinate system and graphing linear equations, a topic first taught in Chapter 3. It then moves on to the topics of writing equations of lines, nonlinear functions, and variation. As another example, Chapter 13 begins with a review of solving simple systems of equations, a topic first taught in Chapter 3. It then moves on to solving more difficult systems by matrices and determinants.

NEW TO THIS EDITION

- New design
- New Learning Objectives
- New Vocabulary feature
- New Glossary
- New Now Try This feature
- New Guided Practice exercises
- Retooled Exercise Sets
- Redesigned Chapter Reviews
- New Basic Calculator Keystroke Guide

■ New Tabular Structure for Easier Feature Identification

The design now incorporates a tabular structure identifying features such as Objectives, Vocabulary, Getting Ready exercises, definitions and formulas, and the new Now Try This feature. Students are visually guided through the textbook, providing for increased readability.

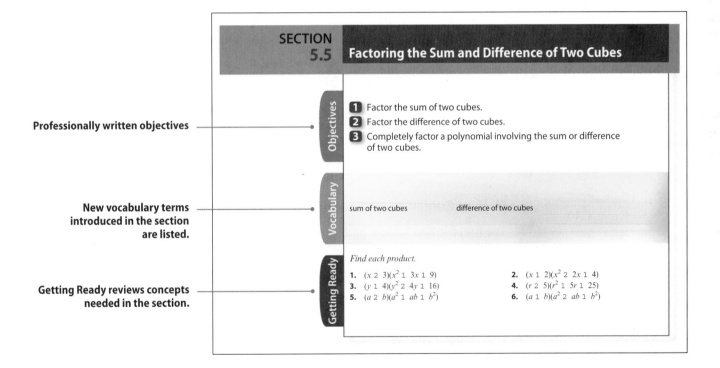

Professionally written objectives

New vocabulary terms introduced in the section are listed.

Getting Ready reviews concepts needed in the section.

■ New Learning Objectives for Measurable Outcomes

Appearing at the beginning of each section, Learning Objectives are mapped to the appropriate content, as well as to relevant exercises in the Guided Practice section. Measurable objectives allow students to identify specific mathematical processes that may need additional reinforcement. For the instructor, homework can be more easily developed with problems keyed to objectives, thus facilitating the instructors' identification of appropriate exercises.

■ New Section Vocabulary Feature plus Glossary

In order to work mathematics, one must be able to speak the language. It is this philosophy that prompted us to strengthen the treatment of vocabulary. Not only are vocabulary words identified at the beginning of each section, these words are also bolded within the section. Exercises include questions on the vocabulary words, and a glossary has been included to facilitate the students' reference to these words.

■ New Now Try This Feature at the End of Each Section

The Something to Think About feature within the exercises already serves as an excellent transition tool, but we wanted to add transitional group-work exercises. Thus, each exercise set has been preceded with Now Try This problems intended to increase conceptual understanding through active classroom participation and involvement. To discourage a student from simply looking up the answer and trying to find a process that will produce that answer, answers to these problems will be provided only in the *Annotated Instructor's Edition* of the text.

Now Try This problems can be worked independently or in small groups and transition to the Exercise Sets, as well as to material in future sections. The problems will reinforce topics, digging a little deeper than the examples.

Now Try This exercises increase understanding through classroom participation.

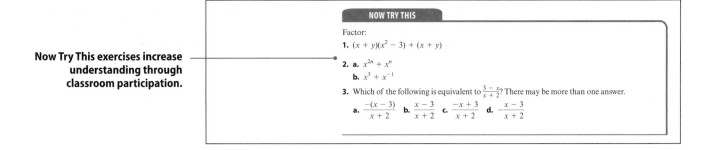

NOW TRY THIS

Factor:

1. $(x + y)(x^2 - 3) + (x + y)$

2. a. $x^{2n} + x^n$
   b. $x^3 + x^{-1}$

3. Which of the following is equivalent to $\frac{3 - x}{x + 2}$? There may be more than one answer.

   a. $\frac{-(x - 3)}{x + 2}$ **b.** $\frac{x - 3}{x + 2}$ **c.** $\frac{-x + 3}{x + 2}$ **d.** $-\frac{x - 3}{x + 2}$

■ New Guided Practice and Retooled Exercise Sets

The Exercise Sets for this sixth edition of *Beginning and Intermediate Algebra* have been retooled to transition students through progressively more difficult homework problems. Students are initially asked to work quick, basic problems on their own, then proceed to work exercises keyed to examples, and finally to complete application problems and critical thinking questions on their own.

Warm-Ups get students into the homework mindset, asking quick memory-testing questions. Review and Vocabulary and Concepts emphasize the main concepts taught in the section.

Guided Practice exercises are keyed to the objectives to increase student success by directing students to the concept covered in that group of exercises. Should a student encounter difficulties working a problem, a specific example within the objective is also cross-referenced.

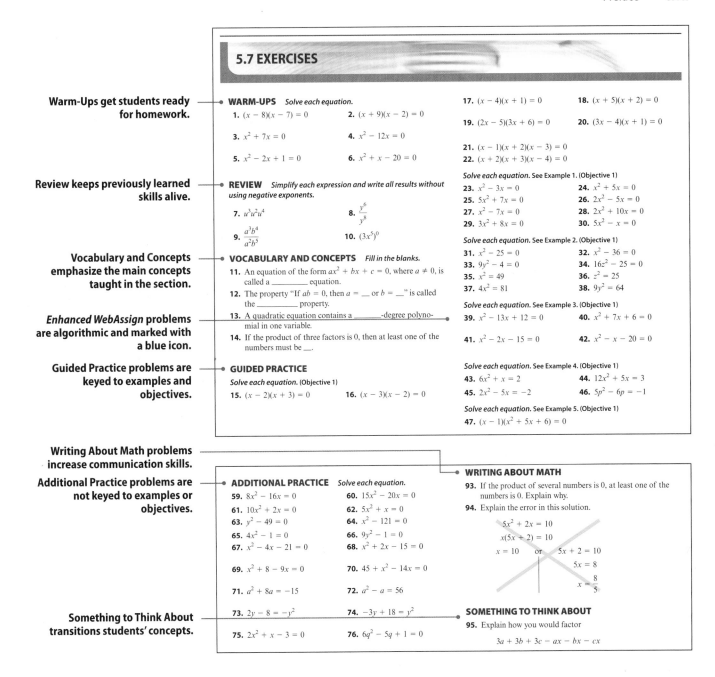

Warm-Ups get students ready for homework.

Review keeps previously learned skills alive.

Vocabulary and Concepts emphasize the main concepts taught in the section.

Enhanced WebAssign **problems are algorithmic and marked with a blue icon.**

Guided Practice problems are keyed to examples and objectives.

Writing About Math problems increase communication skills.

Additional Practice problems are not keyed to examples or objectives.

Something to Think About transitions students' concepts.

5.7 EXERCISES

WARM-UPS *Solve each equation.*

1. $(x - 8)(x - 7) = 0$
2. $(x + 9)(x - 2) = 0$
3. $x^2 + 7x = 0$
4. $x^2 - 12x = 0$
5. $x^2 - 2x + 1 = 0$
6. $x^2 + x - 20 = 0$

REVIEW *Simplify each expression and write all results without using negative exponents.*

7. $u^3 u^2 u^4$
8. $\dfrac{y^6}{y^8}$
9. $\dfrac{a^3 b^4}{a^2 b^5}$
10. $(3x^5)^0$

VOCABULARY AND CONCEPTS *Fill in the blanks.*

11. An equation of the form $ax^2 + bx + c = 0$, where $a \neq 0$, is called a _____ equation.
12. The property "If $ab = 0$, then $a =$ __ or $b =$ __" is called the _____ property.
13. A quadratic equation contains a _____-degree polynomial in one variable.
14. If the product of three factors is 0, then at least one of the numbers must be __.

GUIDED PRACTICE

Solve each equation. (Objective 1)

15. $(x - 2)(x + 3) = 0$
16. $(x - 3)(x - 2) = 0$

17. $(x - 4)(x + 1) = 0$
18. $(x + 5)(x + 2) = 0$
19. $(2x - 5)(3x + 6) = 0$
20. $(3x - 4)(x + 1) = 0$
21. $(x - 1)(x + 2)(x - 3) = 0$
22. $(x + 2)(x + 3)(x - 4) = 0$

Solve each equation. See Example 1. (Objective 1)

23. $x^2 - 3x = 0$
24. $x^2 + 5x = 0$
25. $5x^2 + 7x = 0$
26. $2x^2 - 5x = 0$
27. $x^2 - 7x = 0$
28. $2x^2 + 10x = 0$
29. $3x^2 + 8x = 0$
30. $5x^2 - x = 0$

Solve each equation. See Example 2. (Objective 1)

31. $x^2 - 25 = 0$
32. $x^2 - 36 = 0$
33. $9y^2 - 4 = 0$
34. $16z^2 - 25 = 0$
35. $x^2 = 49$
36. $z^2 = 25$
37. $4x^2 = 81$
38. $9y^2 = 64$

Solve each equation. See Example 3. (Objective 1)

39. $x^2 - 13x + 12 = 0$
40. $x^2 + 7x + 6 = 0$
41. $x^2 - 2x - 15 = 0$
42. $x^2 - x - 20 = 0$

Solve each equation. See Example 4. (Objective 1)

43. $6x^2 + x = 2$
44. $12x^2 + 5x = 3$
45. $2x^2 - 5x = -2$
46. $5p^2 - 6p = -1$

Solve each equation. See Example 5. (Objective 1)

47. $(x - 1)(x^2 + 5x + 6) = 0$

ADDITIONAL PRACTICE *Solve each equation.*

59. $8x^2 - 16x = 0$
60. $15x^2 - 20x = 0$
61. $10x^2 + 2x = 0$
62. $5x^2 + x = 0$
63. $y^2 - 49 = 0$
64. $x^2 - 121 = 0$
65. $4x^2 - 1 = 0$
66. $9y^2 - 1 = 0$
67. $x^2 - 4x - 21 = 0$
68. $x^2 + 2x - 15 = 0$
69. $x^2 + 8 - 9x = 0$
70. $45 + x^2 - 14x = 0$
71. $a^2 + 8a = -15$
72. $a^2 - a = 56$
73. $2y - 8 = -y^2$
74. $-3y + 18 = y^2$
75. $2x^2 + x - 3 = 0$
76. $6q^2 - 5q + 1 = 0$

WRITING ABOUT MATH

93. If the product of several numbers is 0, at least one of the numbers is 0. Explain why.
94. Explain the error in this solution.

$$5x^2 + 2x = 10$$
$$x(5x + 2) = 10$$
$$x = 10 \quad \text{or} \quad 5x + 2 = 10$$
$$5x = 8$$
$$x = \frac{8}{5}$$

SOMETHING TO THINK ABOUT

95. Explain how you would factor
$$3a + 3b + 3c - ax - bx - cx$$

Additional Practice problems are mixed and not linked to objectives or examples, providing the student the opportunity to distinguish between problem types and select an appropriate problem-solving strategy. This will facilitate in the transition from a guided set to a format generally seen on exams.

Applications ask students to apply their new skills to real-life situations. Writing About Math problems build students' mathematical communication skills. Something to Think About transitions students to a deeper comprehension of the section. These questions require students to take what they have learned in a section, and use those concepts to work through a problem in a new way.

Many exercises, indicated in the text by a blue triangle, are available online through *Enhanced WebAssign*. These homework problems are algorithmic, ensuring that your students will learn mathematical processes, not just how to work with specific numbers.

■ Redesigned Chapter Review

For this edition of the text, we have combined the former Chapter Summaries and Chapter Reviews into a Chapter Review grid. The grid presents material cleanly and simply, giving students an efficient means of reviewing material.

New Chapter Reviews give students an efficient means of reviewing material.

Example problems are new to this edition.

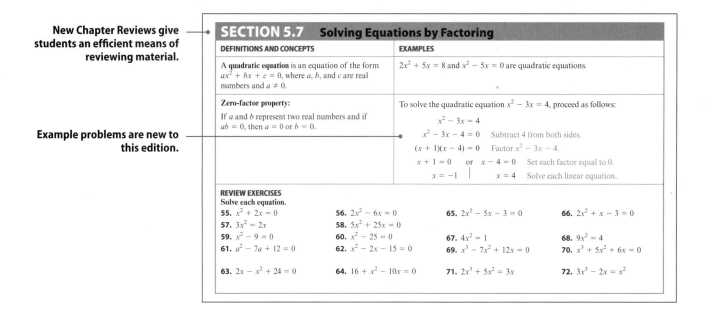

SECTION 5.7   Solving Equations by Factoring

DEFINITIONS AND CONCEPTS	EXAMPLES
A **quadratic equation** is an equation of the form $ax^2 + bx + c = 0$, where a, b, and c are real numbers and $a \neq 0$.	$2x^2 + 5x = 8$ and $x^2 - 5x = 0$ are quadratic equations.
Zero-factor property: If a and b represent two real numbers and if $ab = 0$, then $a = 0$ or $b = 0$.	To solve the quadratic equation $x^2 - 3x = 4$, proceed as follows: $x^2 - 3x = 4$ $x^2 - 3x - 4 = 0$ Subtract 4 from both sides. $(x + 1)(x - 4) = 0$ Factor $x^2 - 3x - 4$. $x + 1 = 0$ or $x - 4 = 0$ Set each factor equal to 0. $x = -1$ $\mid$ $x = 4$ Solve each linear equation.

REVIEW EXERCISES

Solve each equation.

55. $x^2 + 2x = 0$ **56.** $2x^2 - 6x = 0$ **65.** $2x^2 - 5x - 3 = 0$ **66.** $2x^2 + x - 3 = 0$

57. $3x^2 = 2x$ **58.** $5x^2 + 25x = 0$

59. $x^2 - 9 = 0$ **60.** $x^2 - 25 = 0$ **67.** $4x^2 = 1$ **68.** $9x^2 = 4$

61. $a^2 - 7a + 12 = 0$ **62.** $x^2 - 2x - 15 = 0$ **69.** $x^3 - 7x^2 + 12x = 0$ **70.** $x^3 + 5x^2 + 6x = 0$

63. $2x - x^2 + 24 = 0$ **64.** $16 + x^2 - 10x = 0$ **71.** $2x^3 + 5x^2 = 3x$ **72.** $3x^3 - 2x = x^2$

■ New Basic Calculator Keystroke Guide

This tear-out card has been provided to assist students with their calculator functionality. It will serve as a quick reference to the TI-83 and TI-84 family of calculators, aiding students in building the technology skills needed for this course.

New tear-out guide serves as a quick reference to the TI-83/84 family of calculators.

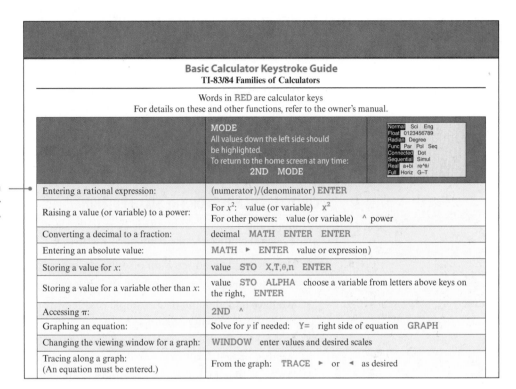

Basic Calculator Keystroke Guide
TI-83/84 Families of Calculators

Words in RED are calculator keys
For details on these and other functions, refer to the owner's manual.

MODE
All values down the left side should be highlighted.
To return to the home screen at any time:
2ND MODE

Entering a rational expression:	(numerator)/(denominator) ENTER
Raising a value (or variable) to a power:	For x^2: value (or variable) x^2 For other powers: value (or variable) ^ power
Converting a decimal to a fraction:	decimal MATH ENTER ENTER
Entering an absolute value:	MATH ▶ ENTER value or expression)
Storing a value for x:	value STO X,T,θ,n ENTER
Storing a value for a variable other than x:	value STO ALPHA choose a variable from letters above keys on the right, ENTER
Accessing π:	2ND ^
Graphing an equation:	Solve for y if needed: Y= right side of equation GRAPH
Changing the viewing window for a graph:	WINDOW enter values and desired scales
Tracing along a graph: (An equation must be entered.)	From the graph: TRACE ▶ or ◀ as desired

TRUSTED FEATURES

- **Chapter Openers** showcase the variety of career paths available in the world of mathematics. We include a brief overview of each career, as well as job outlook statistics from the U.S. Department of Labor, including potential job growth and annual earnings potential.

- **Getting Ready** questions appear at the beginning of each section, linking past concepts to the upcoming material.

- **Comment** notations alert students to common errors as well as provide helpful and pertinent information about the concepts they are learning.

- **Accent on Technology** boxes teach students the calculator skills to prepare them for using these tools in science and business classes, as well as for nonacademic purposes. Calculator examples are given in these boxes, and keystrokes are given for both scientific and graphing calculators. For instructors who do not use calculators in the classroom, the material on calculators is easily omitted without interrupting the flow of ideas.

- **Examples** are worked out in each chapter, highlighting the concept being discussed. We include Author Notes in many of the text's examples, giving students insight into the thought process one goes through when approaching a problem and working toward a solution. Most examples end with a Self Check problem, so that students may immediately apply concepts. Answers to each section's Self Checks are found at the end of that section.

- **Everyday Connections** boxes reveal the real-world power of mathematics. Each Everyday Connection invites students to see how the material covered in the chapter is relevant to their lives.
- **Perspectives** boxes highlight interesting facts from mathematics history or important mathematicians, past and present. These brief but interesting biographies connect students to discoveries of the past and their importance to the present.
- **Teaching Tips** are provided in the margins as interesting historical information, alternate approaches for teaching the material, and class activities.
- Chapter-ending **Projects** encourage in-depth exploration of key concepts.
- **Chapter Tests** allow students to pinpoint their strengths and challenges with the material. Answers to all problems are included at the back of the book.
- **Cumulative Review Exercises** follow the end of chapter material for every even-numbered chapter, and keep students' skills current before moving on to the next topic. Answers to all problems are included at the back of the book.

CONTENT CHANGES FOR THE SIXTH EDITION

Although the Table of Contents is essentially the same as the previous edition, we have made several changes to the content of the text.

1. We have added a discussion of relations before introducing functions.
2. We have included more work on the intersection and union of intervals.
3. We have added many new example problems throughout the text to better illustrate the problem-solving process.
4. In the examples, we have increased the number of Author Notes and increased the number of Self Checks.
5. We have added many new application problems throughout the text and have updated many others. The solutions to most application problems have been rewritten for better clarity.
6. We now give general ordered-pair solutions to all systems of equations involving dependent equations.
7. We have included examples in the Chapter Reviews and have made the reviews more comprehensive.
8. We have given more emphasis to factoring by grouping.
9. Throughout the text, we have given restrictions on the variable of all rational expressions to avoid any divisions by zero.
10. We now solve quadratic and rational inequalities in two ways: by constructing a sign chart and by plotting critical points and checking a test point in each interval.

CALCULATORS

The use of calculators is assumed throughout the text. We believe that students should learn calculator skills in the mathematics classroom. They will then be prepared to use calculators in science and business classes and for nonacademic purposes. The directions within each exercise set indicate which exercises require the use of a calculator.

Since most algebra students now have graphing calculators, keystrokes are given for both scientific and graphing calculators. A new, removable *Basic Calculator Keystroke Guide* is bound into the back of the book as a resource for those students learning how to use a graphing calculator

ANCILLARIES FOR THE INSTRUCTOR

■ Print Ancillaries

Annotated Instructor's Edition (0-538-73663-1)
The *Annotated Instructor's Edition* provides the complete student text with answers next to each respective exercise. Those exercises that also appear in *Enhanced WebAssign* are clearly indicated.

Complete Solutions Manual (0-538-49547-2)
The *Complete Solutions Manual* provides worked-out solutions to all of the problems in the text.

Instructor's Resource Binder (0-538-73675-5)
New! Each section of the main text is discussed in uniquely designed Teaching Guides containing instruction tips, examples, activities, worksheets, overheads, and assessments, with answers provided.

Student Workbook (0-538-73184-2)
New! The *Student Workbook* contains all of the assessments, activities, and worksheets from the *Instructor's Resource Binder* for classroom discussions, in-class activities, and group work.

■ Electronic Ancillaries

Solution Builder (0-8400-4554-9)
This online solutions manual allows instructors to create customizable solutions that they can print out to distribute or post as needed. This is a convenient and expedient way to deliver solutions to specific homework sets.

ENHANCED WebAssign

Enhanced WebAssign, used by more than one million students at more than 1,100 institutions, allows you to assign, collect, grade, and record homework assignments via the web. This proven and reliable homework system includes thousands of algorithmically generated homework problems, an eBook, links to relevant textbook sections, video examples, problem-specific tutorials, and more. Contact your local representative for ordering details.

PowerLecture with ExamView® (0-538-49598-7)
This CD-ROM provides the instructor with dynamic media tools for teaching. Create, deliver, and customize tests (both print and online) in minutes with *ExamView® Computerized Testing Featuring Algorithmic Equations*. Easily build solution sets for homework or exams using *Solution Builder's* online solutions manual. Microsoft® PowerPoint® lecture slides, figures from the book, and *Test Bank,* in electronic format, are also included on this CD-ROM.

Text Specific DVDs (0-538-73768-9)
These text-specific DVD sets, available at no charge to qualified adopters of the text, feature 10- to 20-minute problem-solving lessons that cover each section of every chapter.

Instructor Website

ANCILLARIES FOR THE STUDENT

■ Print Ancillaries

Student Solutions Manual (0-538-49533-2)
The *Student Solutions Manual* provides worked-out solutions to the odd-numbered problems in the textbook.

Student Workbook (0-538-73184-2)
Get a head-start! The *Student Workbook* contains all of the Assessments, Activities, and Worksheets from the *Instructor's Resource Binder* for classroom discussions, in-class activities, and group work.

■ Electronic Ancillaries

Enhanced WebAssign, used by more than one million students at more than 1,100 institutions, allows you to do homework assignments and get extra help and practice via the web. This proven and reliable homework system includes thousands of algorithmically generated homework problems, an eBook, links to relevant textbook sections, video examples, problem-specific tutorials, and more.

Student Website

TO THE STUDENT

Congratulations! You now own a state-of-the-art textbook that has been written especially for you. We have tried to write a book that you can read and understand. The text includes carefully written narrative and an extensive number of worked examples with Self Checks. New Now Try This problems can be worked with your classmates, and Guided Practice exercises tell you exactly which example to use as a resource for each question. These are just a few of the many changes made to this text with your success in mind.

To get the most out of this course, you must read and study the textbook properly. We recommend that you work the examples on paper first, and then work the Self Checks. Only after you thoroughly understand the concepts taught in the examples should you attempt to work the exercises. A *Student Solutions Manual* is available, which contains the worked-out solutions to the odd-numbered exercises.

Since the material presented in *Beginning and Intermediate Algebra, Sixth Edition,* will be of value to you in later years, we suggest that you keep this text. It will be a good source of reference in the future and will keep at your fingertips the material that you have learned here.

We wish you well.

■ Hints on Studying Algebra

The phrase "Practice makes perfect" is not quite true. It is "*Perfect* practice that makes perfect." For this reason, it is important that you learn how to study algebra to get the most out of this course.

Although we all learn differently, here are some hints on studying algebra that most students find useful.

Plan a Strategy for Success   To get where you want to be, you need a goal and a plan. Your goal should be to pass this course with a grade of A or B. To earn one of these grades, you must have a plan to achieve it. A good plan involves several points:

- Getting ready for class,
- Attending class,
- Doing homework,
- Making use of the extensive extra help available, if your instructor has set up a course, and
- Having a strategy for taking tests.

Getting Ready for Class

To get the most out of every class period, you will need to prepare for class. One of the best things you can do is to preview the material in the text that your instructor will be discussing in class. Perhaps you will not understand all of what you read, but you will be better able to understand your instructor when he or she discusses the material in class.

Do your work every day. If you get behind, you will become frustrated and discouraged. Make a promise that you will always prepare for class, and then keep that promise.

Attending Class

The classroom experience is your opportunity to learn from your instructor and interact with your classmates. Make the most of it by attending every class. Sit near the front of the room where you can easily see and hear. Remember that it is your responsibility to follow the discussion, even though that takes concentration and hard work.

Pay attention to your instructor, and jot down the important things that he or she says. However, do not spend so much time taking notes that you fail to concentrate on what your instructor is explaining. Listening and understanding the big picture is much better than just copying solutions to problems.

Don't be afraid to ask questions when your instructor asks for them. Asking questions will make you an active participant in the class. This will help you pay attention and keep you alert and involved.

Doing Homework

It requires practice to excel at tennis, master a musical instrument, or learn a foreign language. In the same way, it requires practice to learn mathematics. Since practice in mathematics is homework, homework is your opportunity to practice your skills and experiment with ideas.

It is important for you to pick a definite time to study and do homework. Set a formal schedule and stick to it. Try to study in a place that is comfortable and quiet. If you can, do some homework shortly after class, or at least before you forget what was discussed in class. This quick follow-up will help you remember the skills and concepts your instructor taught that day.

Each formal study session should include three parts:

1. Begin every study session with a review period. Look over previous chapters and see if you can do a few problems from previous sections. Keeping old skills alive will greatly reduce the amount of time you will need to prepare for tests.

2. After reviewing, read the assigned material. Resist the temptation of diving into the problems without reading and understanding the examples. Instead, work the examples and Self Checks with pencil and paper. Only after you completely understand the underlying principles behind them should you try to work the exercises.

Once you begin to work the exercises, check your answers with the printed answers in the back of the text. If one of your answers differs from the printed answer, see if the two can be reconciled. Sometimes, answers have more than one form. If you decide that your answer is incorrect, compare your work to the example in the text that most closely resembles the exercise, and try to find your mistake. If you cannot find an error, consult the *Student Solutions Manual.* If nothing works, mark the problem and ask about it in your next class meeting.

3. After completing the written assignment, preview the next section. This preview will be helpful when you hear that material discussed during the next class period.

You probably already know the general rule of thumb for college homework: two hours of practice for every hour you spend in class. If mathematics is hard for you, plan on spending even more time on homework.

To make doing homework more enjoyable, study with one or more friends. The interaction will clarify ideas and help you remember them. If you must study alone, a good study technique is to explain the material to yourself out loud.

Arranging for Special Help   Take advantage of any extra help that is available from your instructor. Often, your instructor can clear up difficulties in a short period of time. Find out whether your college has a free tutoring program. Peer tutors can often be of great help.

Taking Tests   Students often get nervous before taking a test because they are afraid that they will do poorly.

To build confidence in your ability to take tests, rework many of the problems in the exercise sets, work the exercises in the Chapter Reviews, and take the Chapter Tests. Check all answers with the answers printed at the back of the text.

Then guess what the instructor will ask, build your own tests, and work them. Once you know your instructor, you will be surprised at how good you can get at picking test questions. With this preparation, you will have some idea of what will be on the test, and you will have more confidence in your ability to do well.

When you take a test, work slowly and deliberately. Scan the test and work the easy problems first. Tackle the hardest problems last.

ACKNOWLEDGMENTS

We are grateful to the following people who reviewed the new edition of this series of texts. They all had valuable suggestions that have been incorporated into the texts.

Kent Aeschliman, Oakland Community College
Carol Anderson, Rock Valley College
Kristin Dillard, San Bernardino Valley College
Kirsten Dooley, Midlands Technical College
Joan Evans, Texas Southern University
Jeremiah Gilbert, San Bernardino Valley College
Harvey Hanna, Ferris State University
Kathy Holster, South Plains College
Robert McCoy, University of Alaska Anchorage
John Squires, Cleveland State Community College

■ Additional Acknowledgments

We also thank the following people who reviewed previous editions.

Cynthia Broughtou, Arizona Western College
David Byrd, Enterprise State Junior College
Pablo Chalmeta, New River Community College
Michael F. Cullinan, Glendale Community College
Lou D'Alotto, York College-CUNY
Karen Driskell, Calhoun Community College
Hamidullah Farhat, Hampton University
Harold Farmer, Wallace Community College-Hanceville
Mark Fitch, University of Alaska, Anchorage
Mark Foster, Santa Monica College
Jonathan P. Hexter, Piedmont Virginia Community College

Dorothy K. Holtgrefe, Seminole Community College
Mike Judy, Fullerton College
Lynette King, Gadsden State Community College
Janet Mazzarella, Southwestern College
Donald J. McCarthy, Glendale Community College
Andrew P. McKintosh, Glendale Community College
Christian R. Miller, Glendale Community College
Feridoon Moinian, Cameron University
Brent Monte, Irvine Valley College
Daniel F. Mussa, Southern Illinois University
Joanne Peeples, El Paso Community College
Mary Ann Petruska, Pensacola Junior College
Linda Pulsinelli, Western Kentucky University
Kimberly Ricketts, Northwest-Shoals Community College
Janet Ritchie, SUNY-Old Westbury
Joanne Roth, Oakland Community College
Richard Rupp, Del Mar College
Rebecca Sellers, Jefferson State Community College
Kathy Spradlin, Liberty University
April D. Strom, Glendale Community College
Victoria Wacek, Missouri Western State College
Judy Wells, University of Southern Indiana
Hattie White, St. Phillip's College
George J. Witt, Glendale Community College
Margaret Yoder, Eastern Kentucky University

We are grateful to the staff at Cengage Learning, especially our publisher, Charlie Van Wagner, and our editor, Marc Bove. We also thank Vernon Boes, Jennifer Risden, Meaghan Banks, and Heleny Wong.

   We are indebted to Ellen Brownstein, our production service, to Jack Morrell, who read the entire manuscript and worked every problem, and to Mike Welden, who prepared the *Student Solutions Manual.* Finally, we thank Lori Heckelman for her fine artwork and Graphic World for their excellent typesetting.

R. David Gustafson
Rosemary M. Karr
Marilyn B. Massey

Examples that are applications are shown with boldface numbers.
Exercises that are applications are shown with lightface numbers.

Real Numbers and Their Basic Properties

Careers and Mathematics

CARPENTERS

Carpenters are involved in many kinds of construction activities. They cut, fit, and assemble wood and other materials for the construction of buildings, highways, bridges, docks, industrial plants, boats, and many other structures. About 32 percent of all carpenters—the largest construction trade—are self-employed. They held about 1.5 million jobs in 2006. Future carpenters should take classes in English, algebra, geometry, physics, mechanical drawing, and blueprint reading.

Job Outlook:
Job opportunities will be the best for those with the most training and skills. Between 3 and 4 years of both on-the-job training and classroom instruction usually are needed to become a skilled carpenter. Overall, the employment of carpenters is expected to increase by 10 percent during 2006–2016, about as fast as the average for all occupations.

Hourly Earnings:
$17.57–$30.45

For More Information:
http://www.bls.gov/oco/ocos202.htm

For a Sample Application:
See Problem 154 in Section 1.2.

In this chapter ▶

In Chapter 1, we will discuss the various types of numbers that we will use throughout this course. Then we will review the basic arithmetic of fractions, explain how to add, subtract, multiply, and divide real numbers, introduce algebraic expressions, and summarize the properties of real numbers.

©Shutterstock.com/jpatava

Real Numbers and Their Graphs

1 List the numbers in a set of real numbers that are natural, whole, integers, rational, irrational, composite, prime, even, or odd.

2 Insert a symbol $<$, $>$, or $=$ to define the relationship between two rational numbers.

3 Graph a real number or a subset of real numbers on the number line.

4 Find the absolute value of a real number.

set	irrational numbers	inequality symbols
natural numbers	real numbers	variables
positive integers	prime numbers	number line
whole numbers	composite numbers	origin
ellipses	even integers	coordinate
negative numbers	odd integers	negatives
integers	sum	opposites
subsets	difference	intervals
set-builder notation	product	absolute value
rational numbers	quotient	

1. Give an example of a number that is used for counting.
2. Give an example of a number that is used when dividing a pizza.
3. Give an example of a number that is used for measuring temperatures that are below zero.
4. What other types of numbers can you think of?

We will begin by discussing various sets of numbers

1 **List the numbers in a set of real numbers that are natural, whole, integers, rational, irrational, composite, prime, even, or odd.**

A **set** is a collection of objects. For example, the set

$\{1, 2, 3, 4, 5\}$ Read as "the set with elements 1, 2, 3, 4, and 5."

contains the numbers 1, 2, 3, 4, and 5. The *members,* or *elements,* of a set are listed within braces { }.

Two basic sets of numbers are the **natural numbers** (often called the **positive integers**) and the **whole numbers.**

The Set of Natural Numbers (Positive Integers) $\{1, 2, 3, 4, 5, 6, 7, 8, 9\ 10, . . .\}$

The Set of Whole Numbers

$\{0, 1, 2, 3, 4, 5, 6, 7, 8, 9, 10, . . .\}$

The three dots in the previous definitions, called **ellipses,** indicate that each list of numbers continues on forever.

We can use whole numbers to describe many real-life situations. For example, some cars might get 30 miles per gallon (mpg) of gas, and some students might pay $1,750 in tuition.

Numbers that show a loss or a downward direction are called **negative numbers,** and they are denoted with a − sign. For example, a debt of $1,500 can be denoted as −$1,500, and a temperature of 20° below zero can be denoted as −20°.

The negatives of the natural numbers and the whole numbers together form the set of **integers.**

The Set of Integers

$\{. . . , -5, -4, -3, -2, -1, 0, 1, 2, 3, 4, 5, . . .\}$

Because the set of natural numbers and the set of whole numbers are included within the set of integers, these sets are called **subsets** of the set of integers.

Integers cannot describe every real-life situation. For example, a student might study $3\frac{1}{2}$ hours, or a television set might cost $217.37. To describe these situations, we need fractions, more formally called *rational numbers.*

We cannot list the set of rational numbers as we have listed the previous sets in this section. Instead, we will use **set-builder notation.** This notation uses a variable (or variables) to represent the elements in a set and a rule to determine the possible values of the variable.

The Set of Rational Numbers

Rational numbers are fractions that have an integer numerator and a nonzero integer denominator. Using set-builder notation, the rational numbers are

$$\left\{ \frac{a}{b} \,\middle|\, a \text{ is an integer and } b \text{ is a nonzero integer.} \right\}$$

The previous notation is read as "the set of all numbers $\frac{a}{b}$ such that a is an integer and b is a nonzero integer."

Some examples of rational numbers are

$$\frac{3}{2}, \frac{17}{12}, 5, -\frac{43}{8}, 0.25, \quad \text{and} \quad -0.66666. . .$$

The decimals 0.25 and −0.66666. . . are rational numbers, because 0.25 can be written as the fraction $\frac{1}{4}$, and −0.66666. . . can be written as the fraction $-\frac{2}{3}$.

COMMENT Because division by 0 is undefined, expressions such as $\frac{6}{0}$ and $\frac{8}{0}$ do not represent any number.

Since every integer can be written as a fraction with a denominator of 1, every integer is also a rational number. Since every integer is a rational number, the set of integers is a subset of the rational numbers.

Since π and $\sqrt{2}$ cannot be written as fractions with an integer numerator and a nonzero integer denominator, they are not rational numbers. They are called **irrational numbers.** We can find their decimal approximations with a calculator. For example,

$\pi \approx 3.141592654$ Using a scientific calculator, press $\boxed{\pi}$. Using a graphing calculator, press $\boxed{\pi}$ $\boxed{\text{ENTER}}$. Read $\approx$ as "is approximately equal to."

$\sqrt{2} \approx 1.414213562$ Using a scientific calculator, press 2 $\boxed{\sqrt{\ }}$. Using a graphing calculator, press $\boxed{\sqrt{\ }}$ 2 $\boxed{\text{ENTER}}$.

If we combine the rational and the irrational numbers, we have the set of **real numbers.**

The Set of Real Numbers	$\{x \mid x$ is either a rational number or an irrational number.$\}$

COMMENT The symbol $\mathbb{R}$ is often used to represent the set of real numbers.

The previous notation is read as "the set of all numbers x such that x is either a rational number or an irrational number."

Figure 1-1 illustrates how the various sets of numbers are interrelated.

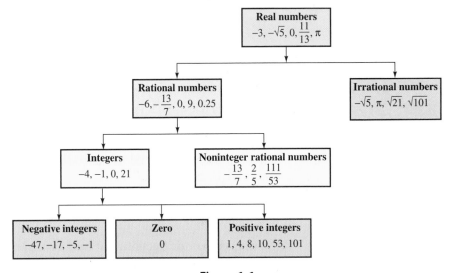

Figure 1-1

EXAMPLE 1 Which numbers in the set $\left\{-3, 0, \frac{1}{2}, 1.25, \sqrt{3}, 5\right\}$ are **a.** natural numbers
b. whole numbers **c.** negative integers **d.** rational numbers
e. irrational numbers **f.** real numbers?

Solution **a.** The only natural number is 5. **b.** The whole numbers are 0 and 5.
c. The only negative integer is -3. **d.** The rational numbers are $-3, 0, \frac{1}{2}, 1.25$, and 5. $\left(1.25 \text{ is rational, because } 1.25 \text{ can be written in the form } \frac{125}{100}.\right)$
e. The only irrational number is $\sqrt{3}$. **f.** All of the numbers are real numbers.

SELF CHECK 1 Which numbers in the set $\left\{-2, 0, 1.5, \sqrt{5}, 7\right\}$ are **a.** natural numbers
b. rational numbers?

PERSPECTIVE   The First Irrational Number

Pythagoras
(569–475 BC)
All Is Number.

The Greek mathematician and philosopher Pythagoras believed that every aspect of the natural world could be represented by ratios of whole numbers (i.e., rational numbers). However, one of his students accidentally disproved this claim by examining a surprisingly simple example. The student examined a right triangle whose legs were each 1 unit long and posed the following question. "How long is the third side of the triangle?"

Using the well-known theorem of Pythagoras, the length of the third side can be determined by using the formula $c^2 = 1^2 + 1^2$.

In other words, $c^2 = 2$. Using basic properties of arithmetic, it turns out that the numerical value of c cannot be expressed as a rational number. So we have an example of an aspect of the natural world that corresponds to an irrational number, namely $c = \sqrt{2}$.

A natural number greater than 1 that can be divided evenly only by 1 and itself is called a **prime number.**

> *The set of prime numbers*:
>
> $\{2, 3, 5, 7, 11, 13, 17, 19, 23, 29, \ldots\}$

A nonprime natural number greater than 1 is called a **composite number.**

> *The set of composite numbers*:
>
> $\{4, 6, 8, 9, 10, 12, 14, 15, 16, 18, 20, 21, 22, \ldots\}$

An integer that can be divided evenly by 2 is called an **even integer.** An integer that cannot be divided evenly by 2 is called an **odd integer.**

> *The set of even integers*:
>
> $\{\ldots, -10, -8, -6, -4, -2, 0, 2, 4, 6, 8, 10, \ldots\}$

> *The set of odd integers*:
>
> $\{\ldots, -9, -7, -5, -3, -1, 1, 3, 5, 7, 9, \ldots\}$

EXAMPLE 2   Which numbers in the set $\{-3, -2, 0, 1, 2, 3, 4, 5, 9\}$ are
   a. prime numbers   **b.** composite numbers
   c. even integers   **d.** odd integers?

Solution   **a.** The prime numbers are 2, 3, and 5.   **b.** The composite numbers are 4 and 9.
   c. The even integers are $-2, 0, 2$, and 4.   **d.** The odd integers are $-3, 1, 3, 5$, and 9.

⇨ **SELF CHECK 2**   Which numbers in the set $\{-5, 0, 1, 2, 4, 5\}$ are
   a. prime numbers   **b.** even integers?

2 **Insert a symbol $<$, $>$, or $=$ to define the relationship between two rational numbers.**

To show that two expressions represent the same number, we use an $=$ sign. Since $4 + 5$ and 9 represent the same number, we can write

$4 + 5 = 9$ Read as "the sum of 4 and 5 is equal to 9." The answer to any addition problem is called a *sum.*

Likewise, we can write

$5 - 3 = 2$ Read as "the difference between 5 and 3 equals 2," or "5 minus 3 equals 2." The answer to any subtraction problem is called a *difference.*

$4 \cdot 5 = 20$ Read as "the product of 4 and 5 equals 20," or "4 times 5 equals 20." The answer to any multiplication problem is called a *product.*

and

$30 \div 6 = 5$ Read as "the quotient obtained when 30 is divided by 6 is 5," or "30 divided by 6 equals 5." The answer to any division problem is called a *quotient.*

We can use **inequality symbols** to show that expressions are not equal.

Symbol	Read as	Symbol	Read as
$\approx$	"is approximately equal to"	$\neq$	"is not equal to"
$<$	"is less than"	$>$	"is greater than"
$\leq$	"is less than or equal to"	$\geq$	"is greater than or equal to"

EXAMPLE 3   **Inequality symbols**
a. $\pi \approx 3.14$ Read as "pi is approximately equal to 3.14."
b. $6 \neq 9$ Read as "6 is not equal to 9."
c. $8 < 10$ Read as "8 is less than 10."
d. $12 > 1$ Read as "12 is greater than 1."
e. $5 \leq 5$ Read as "5 is less than or equal to 5." (Since $5 = 5$, this is a true statement.)
f. $9 \geq 7$ Read as "9 is greater than or equal to 7." (Since $9 > 7$, this is a true statement.)

⇨ **SELF CHECK 3**   Determine whether each statement is true or false:
a. $12 \neq 12$ **b.** $7 \geq 7$ **c.** $125 < 137$

Inequality statements can be written so that the inequality symbol points in the opposite direction. For example,

$5 < 7$ and $7 > 5$

both indicate that 5 is less than 7. Likewise,

$12 \geq 3$ and $3 \leq 12$

both indicate that 12 is greater than or equal to 3.

In algebra, we use letters, called **variables,** to represent real numbers. For example,

COMMENT In algebra, we usually do not use the times sign ($\times$) to indicate multiplication. It might be mistaken for the variable x.

· If x represents 4, then $x = 4$.

· If y represents any number greater than 3, then $y > 3$.

· If z represents any number less than or equal to -4, then $z \leq -4$.

3 Graph a real number or a subset of real numbers on the number line.

We can use the **number line** shown in Figure 1-2 to represent sets of numbers. The number line continues forever to the left and to the right. Numbers to the left of 0 (the **origin**) are negative, and numbers to the right of 0 are positive.

COMMENT   The number 0 is neither positive nor negative.

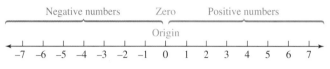

Figure 1-2

The number that corresponds to a point on the number line is called the **coordinate** of that point. For example, the coordinate of the origin is 0.

Many points on the number line do not have integer coordinates. For example, the point midway between 0 and 1 has the coordinate $\frac{1}{2}$, and the point midway between -3 and -2 has the coordinate $-\frac{5}{2}$ (see Figure 1-3).

Figure 1-3

Numbers represented by points that lie on opposite sides of the origin and at equal distances from the origin are called **negatives** (or **opposites**) of each other. For example, 5 and -5 are negatives (or opposites). We need parentheses to express the opposite of a negative number. For example, $-(-5)$ represents the opposite of -5, which we know to be 5. Thus,

$$-(-5) = 5$$

This suggests the following rule.

Double Negative Rule	If x represents a real number, then $$-(-x) = x$$

If one point lies to the *right* of a second point on a number line, its coordinate is the *greater*. Since the point with coordinate 1 lies to the right of the point with coordinate -2 (see Figure 1-4(a)), it follows that $1 > -2$.

If one point lies to the *left* of another, its coordinate is the *smaller* (see Figure 1-4(b)). The point with coordinate -6 lies to the left of the point with coordinate -3 so it follows that $-6 < -3$.

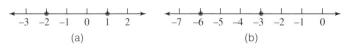

Figure 1-4

Leonardo Fibonacci
(late 12th and early 13th centuries)
Fibonacci, an Italian mathematician, is also known as Leonardo da Pisa. In his work *Liber abaci*, he advocated the adoption of Arabic numerals, the numerals that we use today. He is best known for a sequence of numbers that bears his name. Can you find the pattern in this sequence?

1, 1, 2, 3, 5, 8, 13, . . .

Figure 1-5 shows the graph of the natural numbers from 2 to 8. The points on the line are called graphs of their corresponding coordinates.

Figure 1-5

EXAMPLE 4 Graph the set of integers between -3 and 3.

Solution The integers between -3 and 3 are $-2, -1, 0, 1,$ and 2. The graph is shown in Figure 1-6.

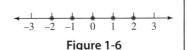

Figure 1-6

SELF CHECK 4 Graph the set of integers between -4 and 0.

Graphs of many sets of real numbers are **intervals** on the number line. For example, two graphs of all real numbers x such that $x > -2$ are shown in Figure 1-7. The parenthesis and the open circle at -2 show that this point is not included in the graph. The arrow pointing to the right shows that all numbers to the right of -2 are included.

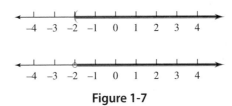

Figure 1-7

Figure 1-8 shows two graphs of the set of real numbers x between -2 and 4. This is the graph of all real numbers x such that $x > -2$ and $x < 4$. The parentheses or open circles at -2 and 4 show that these points are not included in the graph. However, all the numbers between -2 and 4 are included.

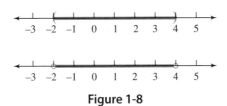

Figure 1-8

EXAMPLE 5 Graph all real numbers x such that $x < -3$ or $x > 1$.

Solution The graph of all real numbers less than -3 includes all points on the number line that are to the left of -3. The graph of all real numbers greater than 1 includes all points that are to the right of 1. The two graphs are shown in Figure 1-9.

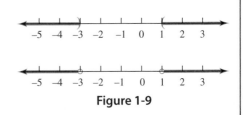

Figure 1-9

SELF CHECK 5 Graph all real numbers x such that $x < -1$ or $x > 0$. Use parentheses.

PERSPECTIVE

Algebra is an extension of arithmetic. In algebra, the operations of addition, subtraction, multiplication, and division are performed on numbers and letters, with the understanding that the letters represent numbers.

The origins of algebra are found in a papyrus written before 1600 BC by an Egyptian priest named **Ahmes.** This papyrus contains 84 algebra problems and their solutions.

Further development of algebra occurred in the ninth century in the Middle East. In AD 830, an Arabian mathematician named al-Khowarazmi wrote a book called *Ihm al-jabr wa'l muqabalah.* This title was shortened to *al-Jabr.* We now know the subject as *algebra.* The French mathematician François Vieta (1540–1603) later simplified algebra by developing the symbolic notation that we use today.

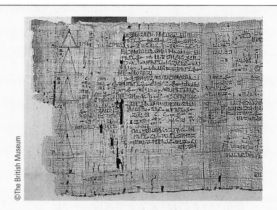

©The British Museum

The Ahmes Papyrus

EXAMPLE 6 Graph the set of all real numbers from −5 to −1.

Solution The set of all real numbers from −5 to −1 includes −5 and −1 and all the numbers in between. In the graphs shown in Figure 1-10, the brackets or the solid circles at −5 and −1 show that these points are included.

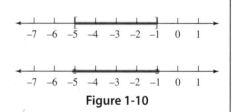

Figure 1-10

⇨ **SELF CHECK 6** Graph the set of real numbers from −2 to 1. Use brackets.

4 **Find the absolute value of a real number.**

On a number line, the distance between a number x and 0 is called the **absolute value** of x. For example, the distance between 5 and 0 is 5 units (see Figure 1-11). Thus, the absolute value of 5 is 5:

$|5| = 5$ Read as "The absolute value of 5 is 5."

Since the distance between −6 and 0 is 6,

$|-6| = 6$ Read as "The absolute value of −6 is 6."

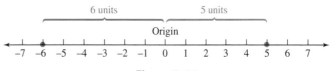

Figure 1-11

Because the absolute value of a real number represents that number's distance from 0 on the number line, the absolute value of every real number x is either positive or 0. In symbols, we say

$$|x| \geq 0 \qquad \text{for every real number } x$$

EXAMPLE 7   Evaluate: **a.** $|6|$ **b.** $|-3|$ **c.** $|0|$ **d.** $-|2 + 3|$.

Solution   **a.** $|6| = 6$, because 6 is six units from 0.   **b.** $|-3| = 3$, because -3 is three units from 0.

c. $|0| = 0$, because 0 is zero units from 0.   **d.** $-|2 + 3| = -|5| = -5$

 SELF CHECK 7   Evaluate: **a.** $|8|$ **b.** $|-8|$ **c.** $-|-8|$.

SELF CHECK ANSWERS   **1. a.** 7   **b.** $-2, 0, 1.5, 7$ **2. a.** $2, 5$ **b.** $0, 2, 4$ **3. a.** false   **b.** true   **c.** true
4. ⟨number line: -4, -3, -2, -1, 0⟩   **5.** ⟨number line: -2, -1, 0, 1⟩   **6.** ⟨number line: -3, -2, -1, 0, 1, 2⟩
7. a. 8   **b.** 8   **c.** -8

NOW TRY THIS

Given the set $\left\{ \sqrt{10}, 4.2, \sqrt{16}, 0, |-1|, 9 \right\}$, list
1. the integer(s)
2. the irrational number(s)
3. the rational number(s)
4. the prime number(s)
5. the composite number(s)

1.1 EXERCISES

WARM-UPS

Describe each set of numbers.

  1. Natural numbers   2. Whole numbers
  3. Integers   4. Rational numbers
  5. Real numbers   6. Prime numbers
  7. Composite numbers   8. Even integers
  9. Odd integers   10. Irrational numbers

Find each value.
11. $-|15|$ **12.** $|-25|$

VOCABULARY AND CONCEPTS   *Fill in the blanks.*

13. A ____ is a collection of objects.
14. The numbers 1, 2, 3, 4, 5, . . . form the set of _____ numbers. This set is also called the set of _____.
15. The set of _____ numbers is the set $\{0, 1, 2, 3, 4, 5, . . .\}$.
16. The dots following the sets in Exercises 14 and 15 are called _____.

17. The set of _____ is the set $\{.\ .\ .\ , -3, -2, -1, 0, 1, 2, 3, .\ .\ .\}$.

18. Numbers that show a loss or a downward direction are called _____.

19. Since every whole number is also an integer, the set of whole numbers is called a _____ of the set of integers.

20. The set $\{x \mid x$ is a whole number$\}$ is read as "_____."

21. Fractions that have an integer numerator and a nonzero integer denominator are called _____ numbers.

22. $\sqrt{2}$ is an example of an _____ real number.

23. The set that includes the rational and irrational numbers is called the set of _____ numbers.

24. If a natural number is greater than 1 and can be divided exactly only by 1 and itself, it is called a _____ number.

25. A composite number is a _____ number that is greater than 1 and is not _____.

26. An integer that can be evenly divided by 2 is called an _____ integer.

27. An integer that cannot be evenly divided by 2 is called an _____ integer.

28. The symbol $\neq$ means _____.

29. The symbol ___ means "is less than."

30. The symbol $\geq$ means _____.

31. In algebra, we use letters, called _____, to represent real numbers.

32. The figure $\xleftarrow{\;\;\;\underset{-3\;\;-2\;\;-1\;\;\;0\;\;\;1\;\;\;2\;\;\;3}{\;\;\;\bullet\;\;\;\bullet\;\;\;\bullet\;\;\;\bullet\;\;\;\bullet\;\;\;\bullet\;\;\;}\;\;\;}\xrightarrow{}$ is called a _____ line. The point with a coordinate of 0 is called the _____.

33. The negative, or opposite, of -7 is __.

34. The graphs of inequalities are _____ on the number line.

35. A _____ or _____ circle shows that a point is not included in a graph.

36. A _____ or _____ circle shows that a point is included in a graph.

37. The distance between 8 and 0 on a number line is called the _____ of 8.

38. The result of an addition is called the _____. The result of a subtraction is called a _____. The result of a multiplication is called a _____. The result of a division is called a _____.

GUIDED PRACTICE

Which numbers in the set $\left\{-3, -\frac{1}{2}, -1, 0, 1, 2, \frac{5}{3}, \sqrt{7}, 3.25, 6, 9\right\}$ *are in each category?* **See Examples 1–2. (Objective 1)**

39. natural numbers

40. whole numbers

41. positive integers

42. negative integers

43. integers

44. rational numbers

45. real numbers

46. irrational numbers

47. odd integers

48. even integers

49. composite numbers

50. prime numbers

Place one of the symbols =, <, or > in each box to make a true statement. **See Example 3. (Objective 2)**

51. 3 ▢ 5   **52.** 8 ▢ 8

53. 5 ▢ 3 + 2   **54.** 9 ▢ 7

55. 25 ▢ 32   **56.** 2 + 3 ▢ 17

57. 5 + 7 ▢ 10   **58.** 3 + 3 ▢ 9 − 3

Graph each pair of numbers on a number line. In each pair, indicate which number is the greater and which number lies farther to the right. **(Objective 3)**

59. 3, 6   **60.** 4, 7

61. 11, 6   **62.** 12, 10

63. 0, 2   **64.** 4, 10

65. 8, 0   **66.** 20, 30

Graph each set of numbers on a number line. Use brackets or parentheses where applicable. **See Examples 4–6. (Objective 3)**

67. The natural numbers between 2 and 8

$\xleftarrow{\;\;\;\underset{1\;\;\;2\;\;\;3\;\;\;4\;\;\;5\;\;\;6\;\;\;7\;\;\;8}{\;\;\;\mid\;\;\;\mid\;\;\;\mid\;\;\;\mid\;\;\;\mid\;\;\;\mid\;\;\;\mid\;\;\;\mid\;\;\;}\;\;\;}\xrightarrow{}$

68. The prime numbers between 5 and 15

$\xleftarrow{\;\;\;\underset{5\;\;6\;\;7\;\;8\;\;9\;\;10\;\;11\;\;12\;\;13\;\;14\;\;15}{\;\;\;\mid\;\;\;\mid\;\;\;\mid\;\;\;\mid\;\;\;\mid\;\;\;\mid\;\;\;\mid\;\;\;\mid\;\;\;\mid\;\;\;\mid\;\;\;\mid\;\;\;}\;\;\;}\xrightarrow{}$

69. The real numbers between 1 and 5

70. The odd integers between -5 and 5 that are exactly divisible by 3

$\xleftarrow{\;\;\;\underset{-5\;\;-4\;\;-3\;\;-2\;\;-1\;\;0\;\;1\;\;2\;\;3\;\;4\;\;5}{\;\;\;\mid\;\;\;\mid\;\;\;\mid\;\;\;\mid\;\;\;\mid\;\;\;\mid\;\;\;\mid\;\;\;\mid\;\;\;\mid\;\;\;\mid\;\;\;\mid\;\;\;}\;\;\;}\xrightarrow{}$

71. The real numbers greater than or equal to 8

72. The real numbers greater than or equal to 3 or less than or equal to -3

73. The prime numbers from 10 to 20

$\xleftarrow{\;\;\;\underset{10\;\;11\;\;12\;\;13\;\;14\;\;15\;\;16\;\;17\;\;18\;\;19\;\;20}{\;\;\;\mid\;\;\;\mid\;\;\;\mid\;\;\;\mid\;\;\;\mid\;\;\;\mid\;\;\;\mid\;\;\;\mid\;\;\;\mid\;\;\;\mid\;\;\;\mid\;\;\;}\;\;\;}\xrightarrow{}$

74. The even integers greater than 10 but less than 20

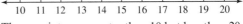

$\xleftarrow{\;\;\;\underset{10\;\;11\;\;12\;\;13\;\;14\;\;15\;\;16\;\;17\;\;18\;\;19\;\;20}{\;\;\;\mid\;\;\;\mid\;\;\;\mid\;\;\;\mid\;\;\;\mid\;\;\;\mid\;\;\;\mid\;\;\;\mid\;\;\;\mid\;\;\;\mid\;\;\;\mid\;\;\;}\;\;\;}\xrightarrow{}$

Find each absolute value. **See Example 7. (Objective 4)**

75. $|36|$ **76.** $|-30|$

77. $|0|$ **78.** $|120|$

79. $|-230|$ **80.** $|18 - 12|$

81. $|12 - 4|$ **82.** $|100 - 100|$

ADDITIONAL PRACTICE

Simplify each expression. Then classify the result as a natural number, an even integer, an odd integer, a prime number, a composite number, and/or a whole number.

83. $4 + 5$ **84.** $7 - 2$

85. $15 - 15$ **86.** $0 + 7$

87. $3 \cdot 8$ **88.** $8 \cdot 9$

89. $24 \div 8$ **90.** $3 \div 3$

Place one of the symbols =, <, or > in each box to make a true statement.

91. $3 + 9 \quad 20 - 8$ **92.** $19 - 3 \quad 8 + 6$

93. $4 \cdot 2 \quad 2 \cdot 4$ **94.** $7 \cdot 9 \quad 9 \cdot 6$

95. $8 \div 2 \quad 4 + 3$ **96.** $0 \div 7 \quad 1$

97. $45 \div 9 \quad 36 \div 12$ **98.** $5 \cdot 12 \quad 300 \div 5$

99. $3 + 2 + 5 \quad 5 + 2 + 3$ **100.** $8 + 5 + 2 \quad 5 + 2 + 8$

Write each sentence as a mathematical expression.

101. Seven is greater than three.

102. Five is less than thirty-two.

103. Eight is less than or equal to eight.

104. Twenty-five is not equal to twenty-three.

105. The sum of adding three and four is equal to seven.

106. Thirty-seven is greater than the product of multiplying three and four.

107. $\sqrt{2}$ is approximately equal to 1.41.

108. x is greater than or equal to 12.

Write each inequality as an equivalent inequality in which the inequality symbol points in the opposite direction.

109. $3 \leq 7$ **110.** $5 > 2$

111. $6 > 0$ **112.** $34 \leq 40$

113. $3 + 8 > 8$ **114.** $8 - 3 < 8$

115. $6 - 2 < 10 - 4$ **116.** $8 \cdot 2 \geq 8 \cdot 1$

117. $2 \cdot 3 < 3 \cdot 4$ **118.** $8 \div 2 \geq 9 \div 3$

119. $\dfrac{12}{4} < \dfrac{24}{6}$ **120.** $\dfrac{2}{3} \leq \dfrac{3}{4}$

Graph each set of numbers on a number line. Use brackets or parentheses where applicable.

121. The even integers that are also prime numbers

122. The numbers that are whole numbers but not natural numbers

123. The natural numbers between 15 and 25 that are exactly divisible by 6

124. The real numbers greater than -2 and less than 3

125. The real numbers greater than or equal to -5 and less than 4

126. The real numbers between -3 and 3, including 3

Find each absolute value.

127. $|21 - 19|$ **128.** $|25 - 21|$

WRITING ABOUT MATH

129. Explain why there is no greatest natural number.

130. Explain why 2 is the only even prime number.

131. Explain how to determine the absolute value of a number.

132. Explain why zero is an even integer.

SOMETHING TO THINK ABOUT *Consider the following sets: the integers, natural numbers, even and odd integers, positive and negative numbers, prime and composite numbers, and rational numbers.*

133. Find a number that fits in as many of these categories as possible.

134. Find a number that fits in as few of these categories as possible.

SECTION 1.2 Fractions

Objectives

1 Simplify a fraction.
2 Multiply and divide two fractions.
3 Add and subtract two or more fractions.
4 Add and subtract two or more mixed numbers.
5 Add, subtract, multiply, and divide two or more decimals.
6 Round a decimal to a specified number of places.
7 Apply the appropriate operation to an application problem.

Vocabulary

numerator
denominator
lowest terms
simplest form
factors of a product
prime-factored form

proper fraction
improper fraction
reciprocal
equivalent fractions
least (or lowest) common
   denominator

mixed number
terminating decimal
repeating decimal
divisor
dividend
percent

Getting Ready

1. Add:
$$\begin{array}{r}132\\45\\73\\\hline\end{array}$$

2. Subtract:
$$\begin{array}{r}321\\173\\\hline\end{array}$$

3. Multiply:
$$\begin{array}{r}437\\38\\\hline\end{array}$$

4. Divide: $37\overline{)3{,}885}$

In this section, we will review arithmetic fractions. This will help us prepare for algebraic fractions, which we will encounter later in the book.

1 Simplify a fraction.

In the fractions

$$\frac{1}{2}, \frac{3}{5}, \frac{2}{17}, \text{ and } \frac{37}{7}$$

the number above the bar is called the **numerator,** and the number below the bar is called the **denominator.**

We often use fractions to indicate parts of a whole. In Figure 1-12(a), a rectangle has been divided into 5 equal parts, and 3 of the parts are shaded. The fraction $\frac{3}{5}$ indicates how much of the figure is shaded. In Figure 1-12(b), $\frac{5}{7}$ of the rectangle is shaded. In either example, the denominator of the fraction shows the total number of equal parts into which the whole is divided, and the numerator shows how many of these equal parts are being considered.

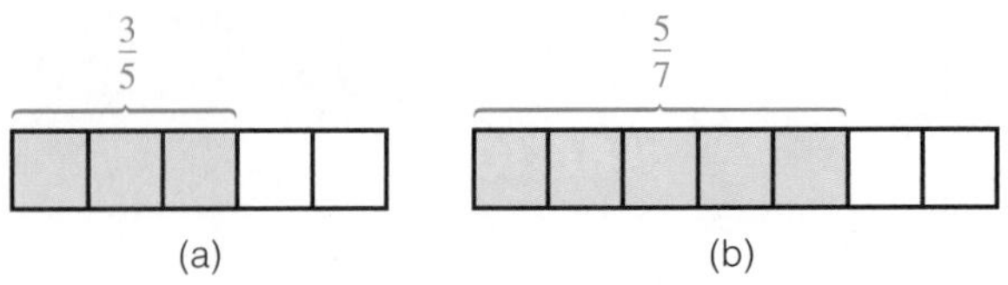

$$\frac{3}{5} \qquad \qquad \frac{5}{7}$$

(a)   (b)

Figure 1-12

We can also use fractions to indicate division. For example, the fraction $\frac{8}{2}$ indicates that 8 is to be divided by 2:

$$\frac{8}{2} = 8 \div 2 = 4$$

COMMENT   Note that $\frac{8}{2} = 4$, because $4 \cdot 2 = 8$, and that $\frac{0}{7} = 0$, because $0 \cdot 7 = 0$. However, $\frac{6}{0}$ is undefined, because no number multiplied by 0 gives 6. Remember that the denominator of a fraction cannot be 0.

A fraction is said to be in **lowest terms** (or **simplest form**) when no integer other than 1 will divide both its numerator and its denominator exactly. The fraction $\frac{6}{11}$ is in lowest terms because only 1 divides both 6 and 11 exactly. The fraction $\frac{6}{8}$ is not in lowest terms, because 2 divides both 6 and 8 exactly.

We can simplify a fraction that is not in lowest terms by dividing its numerator and its denominator by the same number. For example, to simplify $\frac{6}{8}$, we divide the numerator and the denominator by 2.

$$\frac{6}{8} = \frac{6 \div 2}{8 \div 2} = \frac{3}{4}$$

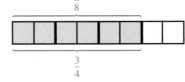

From Figure 1-13, we see that $\frac{6}{8}$ and $\frac{3}{4}$ are equal fractions, because each one represents the same part of the rectangle.

Figure 1-13

When a composite number has been written as the product of other natural numbers, we say that it has been factored. For example, 15 can be written as the product of 5 and 3.

$$15 = 5 \cdot 3$$

The numbers 5 and 3 are called **factors** of 15. When a composite number is written as the product of prime numbers, we say that it is written in **prime-factored form.**

EXAMPLE 1   Write 210 in prime-factored form.

Solution   We can write 210 as the product of 21 and 10 and proceed as follows:

$$210 = \mathbf{21 \cdot 10}$$
$$210 = \mathbf{3 \cdot 7 \cdot 2 \cdot 5} \qquad \text{Factor 21 as } 3 \cdot 7 \text{ and factor 10 as } 2 \cdot 5.$$

Since 210 is now written as the product of prime numbers, its prime-factored form is $210 = 2 \cdot 3 \cdot 5 \cdot 7$.

SELF CHECK 1   Write 70 in prime-factored form.

To simplify a fraction, we factor its numerator and denominator and divide out all factors that are common to the numerator and denominator. For example,

$$\frac{6}{8} = \frac{3 \cdot 2}{4 \cdot 2} = \frac{3 \cdot \overset{1}{\cancel{2}}}{4 \cdot \underset{1}{\cancel{2}}} = \frac{3}{4} \quad \text{and} \quad \frac{15}{18} = \frac{5 \cdot 3}{6 \cdot 3} = \frac{5 \cdot \overset{1}{\cancel{3}}}{6 \cdot \underset{1}{\cancel{3}}} = \frac{5}{6}$$

COMMENT Remember that a fraction is in lowest terms only when its numerator and denominator have no common factors.

EXAMPLE 2 Simplify, if possible: **a.** $\dfrac{6}{30}$ **b.** $\dfrac{33}{40}$

Solution **a.** To simplify $\frac{6}{30}$, we factor the numerator and denominator and divide out the common factor of 6.

$$\frac{6}{30} = \frac{6 \cdot 1}{6 \cdot 5} = \frac{\overset{1}{\cancel{6}} \cdot 1}{\underset{1}{\cancel{6}} \cdot 5} = \frac{1}{5}$$

b. To simplify $\frac{33}{40}$, we factor the numerator and denominator and divide out any common factors.

$$\frac{33}{40} = \frac{3 \cdot 11}{2 \cdot 2 \cdot 2 \cdot 5}$$

Since the numerator and denominator have no common factors, $\frac{33}{40}$ is in lowest terms.

➡ **SELF CHECK 2** Simplify: $\dfrac{14}{35}$.

The preceding examples illustrate the *fundamental property of fractions*.

The Fundamental Property of Fractions

If a, b, and x are real numbers,

$$\frac{a \cdot x}{b \cdot x} = \frac{a}{b} \quad (b \neq 0 \text{ and } x \neq 0)$$

2 **Multiply and divide two fractions.**

To multiply fractions, we use the following rule.

Multiplying Fractions

To multiply fractions, we multiply their numerators and multiply their denominators. In symbols, if a, b, c, and d are real numbers,

$$\frac{a}{b} \cdot \frac{c}{d} = \frac{a \cdot c}{b \cdot d} \quad (b \neq 0 \text{ and } d \neq 0)$$

For example,

$$\frac{4}{7} \cdot \frac{2}{3} = \frac{4 \cdot 2}{7 \cdot 3} \qquad \frac{4}{5} \cdot \frac{13}{9} = \frac{4 \cdot 13}{5 \cdot 9}$$

$$= \frac{8}{21} \qquad\qquad = \frac{52}{45}$$

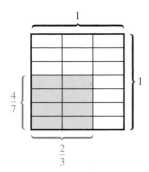

Figure 1-14

To justify the rule for multiplying fractions, we consider the square in Figure 1-14. Because the length of each side of the square is 1 unit and the area is the product of the lengths of two sides, the area is 1 square unit.

If this square is divided into 3 equal parts vertically and 7 equal parts horizontally, it is divided into 21 equal parts, and each represents $\frac{1}{21}$ of the total area. The area of the shaded rectangle in the square is $\frac{8}{21}$, because it contains 8 of the 21 parts. The width, w, of the shaded rectangle is $\frac{4}{7}$; its length, l, is $\frac{2}{3}$; and its area, A, is the product of l and w:

$$A = l \cdot w$$

$$\frac{8}{21} = \frac{2}{3} \cdot \frac{4}{7}$$

This suggests that we can find the product of

$$\frac{4}{7} \quad \text{and} \quad \frac{2}{3}$$

by multiplying their numerators and multiplying their denominators.

Fractions whose numerators are less than their denominators, such as $\frac{8}{21}$, are called **proper fractions.** Fractions whose numerators are greater than or equal to their denominators, such as $\frac{52}{45}$, are called **improper fractions.**

EXAMPLE 3 Perform each multiplication.

a. $\dfrac{3}{7} \cdot \dfrac{13}{5} = \dfrac{3 \cdot 13}{7 \cdot 5}$ Multiply the numerators and multiply the denominators. There are no common factors.

$\phantom{\dfrac{3}{7} \cdot \dfrac{13}{5}} = \dfrac{39}{35}$ Multiply in the numerator and multiply in the denominator.

b. $5 \cdot \dfrac{3}{15} = \dfrac{5}{1} \cdot \dfrac{3}{15}$ Write 5 as the improper fraction $\frac{5}{1}$.

$\phantom{5 \cdot \dfrac{3}{15}} = \dfrac{5 \cdot 3}{1 \cdot 15}$ Multiply the numerators and multiply the denominators.

$\phantom{5 \cdot \dfrac{3}{15}} = \dfrac{5 \cdot 3}{1 \cdot 5 \cdot 3}$ To simplify the fraction, factor the denominator.

$\phantom{5 \cdot \dfrac{3}{15}} = \dfrac{\overset{1}{\cancel{5}} \cdot \overset{1}{\cancel{3}}}{1 \cdot \underset{1}{\cancel{5}} \cdot \underset{1}{\cancel{3}}}$ Divide out the common factors of 3 and 5.

$\phantom{5 \cdot \dfrac{3}{15}} = 1$ $\frac{1 \cdot 1}{1 \cdot 1 \cdot 1} = 1$

⇨ **SELF CHECK 3** Multiply: $\dfrac{5}{9} \cdot \dfrac{7}{10}$.

EXAMPLE 4   **TRAVEL**   Out of 36 students in a history class, three-fourths have signed up for a trip to Europe. If there are 28 places available on the flight, will there be room for one more student?

Solution   We first find three-fourths of 36.

$$\frac{3}{4} \cdot 36 = \frac{3}{4} \cdot \frac{36}{1} \qquad \text{Write 36 as } \tfrac{36}{1}.$$

$$= \frac{3 \cdot 36}{4 \cdot 1} \qquad \text{Multiply the numerators and multiply the denominators.}$$

$$= \frac{3 \cdot 4 \cdot 9}{4 \cdot 1} \qquad \text{To simplify, factor the numerator.}$$

$$= \frac{3 \cdot \overset{1}{\cancel{4}} \cdot 9}{\underset{1}{\cancel{4}} \cdot 1} \qquad \text{Divide out the common factor of 4.}$$

$$= \frac{27}{1}$$

$$= 27$$

Twenty-seven students plan to go on the trip. Since there is room for 28 passengers, there is room for one more.

➪ **SELF CHECK 4**   If seven-ninths of the 36 students had signed up, would there be room for one more?

One number is called the **reciprocal** of another if their product is 1. For example, $\frac{3}{5}$ is the reciprocal of $\frac{5}{3}$, because

$$\frac{3}{5} \cdot \frac{5}{3} = \frac{15}{15} = 1$$

Dividing Fractions   To divide two fractions, we multiply the first fraction by the reciprocal of the second fraction. In symbols, if a, b, c, and d are real numbers,

$$\frac{a}{b} \div \frac{c}{d} = \frac{a}{b} \cdot \frac{d}{c} = \frac{a \cdot d}{b \cdot c} \qquad (b \neq 0, c \neq 0, \text{ and } d \neq 0)$$

EXAMPLE 5   Perform each division.

a. $\dfrac{3}{5} \div \dfrac{6}{5} = \dfrac{3}{5} \cdot \dfrac{5}{6} \qquad \text{Multiply } \tfrac{3}{5} \text{ by the reciprocal of } \tfrac{6}{5}.$

$$= \frac{3 \cdot 5}{5 \cdot 6} \qquad \text{Multiply the numerators and multiply the denominators.}$$

$$= \frac{3 \cdot 5}{5 \cdot 2 \cdot 3} \qquad \text{Factor the denominator.}$$

$$= \frac{\overset{1}{\cancel{3}} \cdot \overset{1}{\cancel{5}}}{\cancel{5} \cdot 2 \cdot \cancel{3}}$$ Divide out the common factors of 3 and 5.

$$= \frac{1}{2}$$

b. $\dfrac{15}{7} \div 10 = \dfrac{15}{7} \div \dfrac{10}{1}$ Write 10 as the improper fraction $\frac{10}{1}$.

$$= \frac{15}{7} \cdot \frac{1}{10}$$ Multiply $\frac{15}{7}$ by the reciprocal of $\frac{10}{1}$.

$$= \frac{15 \cdot 1}{7 \cdot 10}$$ Multiply the numerators and multiply the denominators.

$$= \frac{3 \cdot \overset{1}{\cancel{5}}}{7 \cdot 2 \cdot \underset{1}{\cancel{5}}}$$ Factor the numerator and the denominator, and divide out the common factor of 5.

$$= \frac{3}{14}$$

⇨ **SELF CHECK 5**   Divide: $\dfrac{13}{6} \div \dfrac{26}{8}$.

---

3 **Add and subtract two or more fractions.**

To add fractions with like denominators, we will use the following rule.

Adding Fractions with the Same Denominator	To add fractions with the same denominator, we add the numerators and keep the common denominator. In symbols, if a, b, and d are real numbers, $$\frac{a}{d} + \frac{b}{d} = \frac{a+b}{d} \quad (d \neq 0)$$

For example,

$$\frac{3}{7} + \frac{2}{7} = \frac{3+2}{7}$$ Add the numerators and keep the common denominator.

$$= \frac{5}{7}$$

Figure 1-15 illustrates why $\frac{3}{7} + \frac{2}{7} = \frac{5}{7}$.

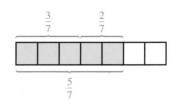

Figure 1-15

To add fractions with unlike denominators, we write the fractions so that they have the same denominator. For example, we can multiply both the numerator and denominator of $\frac{1}{3}$ by 5 to obtain an **equivalent fraction** with a denominator of 15:

$$\frac{1}{3} = \frac{1 \cdot 5}{3 \cdot 5} = \frac{5}{15}$$

To write $\frac{1}{5}$ as an equivalent fraction with a denominator of 15, we multiply the numerator and the denominator by 3:

$$\frac{1}{5} = \frac{1 \cdot 3}{5 \cdot 3} = \frac{3}{15}$$

Since 15 is the smallest number that can be used as a common denominator for $\frac{1}{3}$ and $\frac{1}{5}$, it is called the **least** (or **lowest**) **common denominator** (the **LCD**).

To add the fractions $\frac{1}{3}$ and $\frac{1}{5}$, we write each fraction as an equivalent fraction having a denominator of 15, and then we add the results:

$$\frac{1}{3} + \frac{1}{5} = \frac{1 \cdot 5}{3 \cdot 5} + \frac{1 \cdot 3}{5 \cdot 3}$$
$$= \frac{5}{15} + \frac{3}{15}$$
$$= \frac{5 + 3}{15}$$
$$= \frac{8}{15}$$

In the next example, we will add the fractions $\frac{3}{10}$ and $\frac{5}{28}$.

EXAMPLE 6   Add: $\dfrac{3}{10} + \dfrac{5}{28}$.

Solution   To find the LCD, we find the prime factorization of each denominator and use each prime factor the greatest number of times it appears in either factorization:

$$\left. \begin{array}{l} 10 = 2 \cdot 5 \\ 28 = 2 \cdot 2 \cdot 7 \end{array} \right\} \quad \text{LCD} = 2 \cdot 2 \cdot 5 \cdot 7 = 140$$

Since 140 is the smallest number that 10 and 28 divide exactly, we write both fractions as fractions with denominators of 140.

$$\frac{3}{10} + \frac{5}{28} = \frac{3 \cdot 14}{10 \cdot 14} + \frac{5 \cdot 5}{28 \cdot 5} \qquad \text{Write each fraction as a fraction with a denominator of 140.}$$
$$= \frac{42}{140} + \frac{25}{140} \qquad \text{Do the multiplications.}$$
$$= \frac{42 + 25}{140} \qquad \text{Add the numerators and keep the denominator.}$$
$$= \frac{67}{140}$$

Since 67 is a prime number, it has no common factor with 140. Thus, $\frac{67}{140}$ is in lowest terms.

⇨ **SELF CHECK 6**   Add: $\frac{3}{8} + \frac{5}{12}$.

To subtract fractions with like denominators, we will use the following rule.

Subtracting Fractions with the Same Denominator

To subtract fractions with the same denominator, we subtract their numerators and keep their common denominator. In symbols, if a, b, and d are real numbers,

$$\frac{a}{d} - \frac{b}{d} = \frac{a - b}{d} \quad (d \neq 0)$$

For example,

$$\frac{7}{9} - \frac{2}{9} = \frac{7 - 2}{9} = \frac{5}{9}$$

To subtract fractions with unlike denominators, we write them as equivalent fractions with a common denominator. For example, to subtract $\frac{2}{5}$ from $\frac{3}{4}$, we write $\frac{3}{4} - \frac{2}{5}$, find the LCD of 4 and 5, which is 20, and proceed as follows:

$$\frac{3}{4} - \frac{2}{5} = \frac{3 \cdot 5}{4 \cdot 5} - \frac{2 \cdot 4}{5 \cdot 4} \qquad \text{Write each fraction as a fraction with a denominator of 20.}$$

$$= \frac{15}{20} - \frac{8}{20} \qquad \text{Do the multiplications.}$$

$$= \frac{15 - 8}{20} \qquad \text{Add the numerators and keep the denominator.}$$

$$= \frac{7}{20}$$

EXAMPLE 7 Subtract 5 from $\dfrac{23}{3}$.

Solution

$$\frac{23}{3} - 5 = \frac{23}{3} - \frac{5}{1} \qquad \text{Write 5 as the improper fraction } \tfrac{5}{1}.$$

$$= \frac{23}{3} - \frac{5 \cdot 3}{1 \cdot 3} \qquad \text{Write } \tfrac{5}{1} \text{ as a fraction with a denominator of 3.}$$

$$= \frac{23}{3} - \frac{15}{3} \qquad \text{Do the multiplications.}$$

$$= \frac{23 - 15}{3} \qquad \text{Subtract the numerators and keep the denominator.}$$

$$= \frac{8}{3}$$

⇨ **SELF CHECK 7** Subtract: $\frac{5}{6} - \frac{3}{4}$.

4 Add and subtract two or more mixed numbers.

The **mixed number** $3\frac{1}{2}$ represents the sum of 3 and $\frac{1}{2}$. We can write $3\frac{1}{2}$ as an improper fraction as follows:

$$3\frac{1}{2} = 3 + \frac{1}{2}$$
$$= \frac{6}{2} + \frac{1}{2} \qquad 3 = \frac{6}{2}$$
$$= \frac{6+1}{2} \qquad \text{Add the numerators and keep the denominator.}$$
$$= \frac{7}{2}$$

To write the fraction $\frac{19}{5}$ as a mixed number, we divide 19 by 5 to get 3, with a remainder of 4.

$$\frac{19}{5} = 3 + \frac{4}{5} = 3\frac{4}{5}$$

EXAMPLE 8 Add: $2\frac{1}{4} + 1\frac{1}{3}$.

Solution We first change each mixed number to an improper fraction.

$$2\frac{1}{4} = 2 + \frac{1}{4} \qquad\qquad 1\frac{1}{3} = 1 + \frac{1}{3}$$
$$= \frac{8}{4} + \frac{1}{4} \qquad\qquad = \frac{3}{3} + \frac{1}{3}$$
$$= \frac{9}{4} \qquad\qquad\qquad = \frac{4}{3}$$

Then we add the fractions.

$$2\frac{1}{4} + 1\frac{1}{3} = \frac{9}{4} + \frac{4}{3}$$
$$= \frac{9 \cdot 3}{4 \cdot 3} + \frac{4 \cdot 4}{3 \cdot 4} \qquad \text{Write each fraction with the LCD of 12.}$$
$$= \frac{27}{12} + \frac{16}{12}$$
$$= \frac{43}{12}$$

Finally, we change $\frac{43}{12}$ to a mixed number.

$$\frac{43}{12} = 3 + \frac{7}{12} = 3\frac{7}{12}$$

▷ **SELF CHECK 8** Add: $5\frac{1}{7} + 4\frac{2}{3}$.

EXAMPLE 9   **FENCING LAND**   How much fencing will be needed to enclose the area within the triangular lot shown in Figure 1-16?

Solution   We can find the sum of the lengths by adding the whole-number parts and the fractional parts of the dimensions separately:

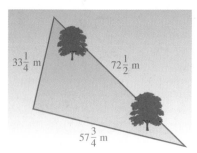

$33\frac{1}{4}$ m $72\frac{1}{2}$ m

$57\frac{3}{4}$ m

Figure 1-16

$$33\frac{1}{4} + 57\frac{3}{4} + 72\frac{1}{2} = 33 + 57 + 72 + \frac{1}{4} + \frac{3}{4} + \frac{1}{2}$$

$$= 162 + \frac{1}{4} + \frac{3}{4} + \frac{2}{4} \qquad \text{Write } \tfrac{1}{2} \text{ as } \tfrac{2}{4} \text{ to obtain a common denominator.}$$

$$= 162 + \frac{6}{4} \qquad \text{Add the fractions by adding the numerators and keeping the common denominator.}$$

$$= 162 + \frac{3}{2} \qquad \frac{6}{4} = \frac{2 \cdot 3}{2 \cdot 2} = \frac{\overset{1}{\cancel{2}} \cdot 3}{\underset{1}{\cancel{2}} \cdot 2} = \frac{3}{2}$$

$$= 162 + 1\frac{1}{2} \qquad \text{Write } \tfrac{3}{2} \text{ as a mixed number.}$$

$$= 163\frac{1}{2}$$

To enclose the area, $163\frac{1}{2}$ meters of fencing will be needed.

COMMENT   Remember to include the proper units in your answer. The Mars Climate Orbiter crashed due to lack of unit communication between the Jet Propulsion Lab and Lockheed/Martin engineers.

⇨ **SELF CHECK 9**   Find the length of fencing needed to enclose a rectangular plot that is $85\frac{1}{2}$ feet wide and $140\frac{2}{3}$ feet deep.

5   **Add, subtract, multiply, and divide two or more decimals.**

Rational numbers can always be changed to decimal form. For example, to write $\frac{1}{4}$ and $\frac{5}{22}$ as decimals, we use long division:

$$
\begin{array}{r}
0.25 \\
4\overline{)1.00} \\
\underline{8} \\
20 \\
\underline{20}
\end{array}
\qquad
\begin{array}{r}
0.22727\ldots \\
22\overline{)5.00000} \\
\underline{4\,4} \\
60 \\
\underline{44} \\
160 \\
\underline{154} \\
60 \\
\underline{44} \\
160
\end{array}
$$

The decimal 0.25 is called a **terminating decimal.** The decimal 0.2272727. . . (often written as $0.2\overline{27}$) is called a **repeating decimal,** because it repeats the block of digits 27. Every rational number can be changed into either a terminating or a repeating decimal.

Terminating decimals	*Repeating decimals*
$\dfrac{1}{2} = 0.5$	$\dfrac{1}{3} = 0.33333\ldots$ or $0.\overline{3}$
$\dfrac{3}{4} = 0.75$	$\dfrac{1}{6} = 0.16666\ldots$ or $0.1\overline{6}$
$\dfrac{5}{8} = 0.625$	$\dfrac{5}{22} = 0.2272727\ldots$ or $0.2\overline{27}$

The decimal 0.5 has one *decimal place,* because it has one digit to the right of the decimal point. The decimal 0.75 has two decimal places, and 0.625 has three.

To *add* or *subtract* decimals, we align their decimal points and then add or subtract.

EXAMPLE 10   Add 25.568 and 2.74 using a vertical format.

Solution   We align the decimal points and add the numbers, column by column,

$$
\begin{array}{r}
25.568 \\
+\ \ 2.74 \\
\hline
28.308
\end{array}
$$

⇨ **SELF CHECK 10**   Subtract 2.74 from 25.568 using a vertical format.

To perform the previous operations with a calculator, we enter these numbers and press these keys:

25.568 $+$ 2.74 $=$ and   25.568 $-$ 2.74 $=$ Using a scientific calculator

25.568 $+$ 2.74 **ENTER**   and   25.568 $-$ 2.74 **ENTER**   Using a graphing calculator

To *multiply* decimals, we multiply the numbers and place the decimal point so that the number of decimal places in the answer is equal to the sum of the decimal places in the factors.

EXAMPLE 11   Multiply: 9.25 by 3.453.

Solution   We multiply the numbers and place the decimal point so that the number of decimal places in the answer is equal to the sum of the decimal places in the factors.

$$
\begin{array}{r}
3.453 \quad \text{Here there are three decimal places.} \\
\times \quad\ \ 9.25 \quad \text{Here there are two decimal places.} \\
\hline
17265 \\
6906 \\
31\,077 \\
\hline
31.94025 \quad \text{The product has } 3 + 2 = 5 \text{ decimal places.}
\end{array}
$$

⇨ **SELF CHECK 11**   Multiply: 2.45 by 9.25.

To perform the multiplication of Example 11 with a calculator, we enter these numbers and press these keys:

3.453 $\boxed{\times}$ 9.25 $\boxed{=}$ Using a scientific calculator

3.453 $\boxed{\times}$ 9.25 $\boxed{\text{ENTER}}$ Using a graphing calculator

To *divide* decimals, we move the decimal point in the **divisor** to the right to make the divisor a whole number. We then move the decimal point in the **dividend** the same number of places to the right.

EXAMPLE 12   Divide   30.258 by 1.23.

Solution   We will write the division using a long division format in which the divisor is 1.23 and the dividend is 30.258.

$$1.23\overline{)30.258}$$ Move the decimal point in both the divisor and the dividend two places to the right.

We align the decimal point in the quotient with the repositioned decimal point in the dividend and use long division.

$$
\begin{array}{r}
24.6 \\
123\overline{)3025.8} \\
\underline{246} \\
565 \\
\underline{492} \\
73\,8 \\
\underline{73\,8}
\end{array}
$$

⇨ SELF CHECK 12   Divide 579.36 by 12.

To perform the previous division with a calculator, we enter these numbers and press these keys:

30.258 $\boxed{\div}$ 1.23 $\boxed{=}$ Using a scientific calculator

30.258 $\boxed{\div}$ 1.23 $\boxed{\text{ENTER}}$ Using a graphing calculator

6 **Round a decimal to a specified number of places.**

We often round long decimals to a specific number of decimal places. For example, the decimal 25.36124 rounded to one place (or to the nearest tenth) is 25.4. Rounded to two places (or to the nearest one-hundredth), the decimal is 25.36.

Throughout this text, we use the following rules to round decimals.

Rounding Decimals

1. Determine to how many decimal places you want to round.
2. Look at the first digit to the right of that decimal place.
3. If that digit is 4 or less, drop it and all digits that follow. If it is 5 or greater, add 1 to the digit in the position to which you want to round, and drop all digits that follow.

EXAMPLE 13   Round 2.4863 to two decimal places.

Solution   Since we are to round to two digits, we look at the digit to the right of the 8, which is 6. Since 6 is greater than 5, we add 1 to the 8 and drop all of the digits that follow. The rounded number is 2.49.

SELF CHECK 13   Round 6.5731 to three decimal places.

EVERYDAY CONNECTIONS   **2008 Presidential Election**

In the 2008 presidential election, six of the most closely contested states were North Carolina, New Hampshire, Iowa, Florida, Ohio, and Virginia.

State	John McCain total votes	Barack Obama total votes
North Carolina	2,109,698	2,123,390
New Hampshire	316,937	384,591
Iowa	677,508	818,240
Florida	3,939,380	4,143,957
Ohio	2,501,855	2,708,685
Virginia	1,726,053	1,958,370

Source: https://www.msu.edu/~sheppa28/elections.html#2008

Use the table to answer the given questions.

1. What percentage of North Carolina votes were cast for Barack Obama?

2. In which state did John McCain earn 47% of the votes cast?

Apply the appropriate operation to an application problem.

A **percent** is the numerator of a fraction with a denominator of 100. For example, $6\frac{1}{4}$ percent, written $6\frac{1}{4}\%$, is the fraction $\frac{6.25}{100}$, or the decimal 0.0625. In problems involving percent, the word *of* usually indicates multiplication. For example, $6\frac{1}{4}\%$ of 8,500 is the product 0.0625(8,500).

EXAMPLE 14   **AUTO LOANS**   Juan signs a one-year note to borrow $8,500 to buy a car. If the rate of interest is $6\frac{1}{4}\%$, how much interest will he pay?

Solution   For the privilege of using the bank's money for one year, Juan must pay $6\frac{1}{4}\%$ of $8,500. We calculate the interest, i, as follows:

$$i = 6\frac{1}{4}\% \text{ of } 8,500$$

$$= 0.0625 \cdot 8,500 \quad \text{In this case, the word } of \text{ means } times.$$

$$= 531.25$$

Juan will pay $531.25 interest.

SELF CHECK 14   If the rate is 9%, how much interest will he pay?

SELF CHECK ANSWERS   **1.** $2 \cdot 5 \cdot 7$ **2.** $\frac{2}{5}$ **3.** $\frac{7}{18}$ **4.** no   **5.** $\frac{2}{3}$ **6.** $\frac{19}{24}$ **7.** $\frac{1}{12}$ **8.** $9\frac{17}{21}$ **9.** $452\frac{1}{3}$ ft   **10.** 22.828
11. 22.6625   **12.** 48.28   **13.** 6.573   **14.** $765

 **NOW TRY THIS**

Perform each operation.

1. $\dfrac{16}{12} - 2 + \dfrac{12}{18}$

2. $25.2 - 13.58$

3. Robert's answer to a problem asking to find the length of a piece of lumber is $\frac{5}{2}$ feet. Is this the best form for the answer given the context of the problem? If not, write the answer in the most appropriate form.

4. $\dfrac{5}{x-3} - \dfrac{1}{x-3} \quad (x \neq 3)$

1.2 EXERCISES

WARM-UPS

Simplify each fraction.

1. $\dfrac{3}{6}$ **2.** $\dfrac{5}{10}$

3. $\dfrac{10}{20}$ **4.** $\dfrac{25}{75}$

Perform each operation.

5. $\dfrac{5}{6} \cdot \dfrac{1}{2}$ **6.** $\dfrac{3}{4} \cdot \dfrac{3}{5}$

7. $\dfrac{2}{3} \div \dfrac{3}{2}$ **8.** $\dfrac{3}{5} \div \dfrac{5}{2}$

9. $\dfrac{4}{9} + \dfrac{7}{9}$ **10.** $\dfrac{6}{7} - \dfrac{3}{7}$

11. $\dfrac{2}{3} - \dfrac{1}{2}$ **12.** $\dfrac{3}{4} + \dfrac{1}{2}$

13. $2.5 + 0.36$ **14.** $3.45 - 2.21$

15. $0.2 \cdot 2.5$ **16.** $0.3 \cdot 13$

Round each decimal to two decimal places.

17. 3.244993 **18.** 3.24521

REVIEW

Determine whether the following statements are true or false.

19. 6 is an integer.   **20.** $\frac{1}{2}$ is a natural number.

21. 21 is a prime number.

22. No prime number is an even number.

23. $8 > -2$ **24.** $-3 < -2$

25. $9 \leq |-9|$ **26.** $|-11| \geq 10$

Place an appropriate symbol in each box to make the statement true.

27. $3 + 7 \;\boxed{}\; 10$ **28.** $\dfrac{3}{7} \;\boxed{}\; \dfrac{2}{7} = \dfrac{1}{7}$

29. $|-2| \;\boxed{}\; 2$ **30.** $4 + 8 \;\boxed{}\; 11$

VOCABULARY AND CONCEPTS   *Fill in the blanks.*

31. The number above the bar in a fraction is called the _____.

32. The number below the bar in a fraction is called the _____.

33. The fraction $\frac{17}{0}$ is said to be _____.

34. To _____ a fraction, we divide its numerator and denominator by the same number.

35. To write a number in prime-factored form, we write it as the product of _____ numbers.

36. If the numerator of a fraction is less than the denominator, the fraction is called a _____ fraction.

37. If the numerator of a fraction is greater than the denominator, the fraction is called an _____ fraction.

38. A fraction is written in _____ or simplest form when its numerator and denominator have no common factors.

39. If the product of two numbers is __, the numbers are called reciprocals.

40. $\dfrac{ax}{bx} = $ __

41. To multiply two fractions, _____ the numerators and multiply the denominators.

42. To divide two fractions, multiply the first fraction by the _____ of the second fraction.

43. To add fractions with the same denominator, add the _____ and keep the common _____.

44. To subtract fractions with the same _____, subtract the numerators and keep the common denominator.

45. To add fractions with unlike denominators, first find the _____ and write each fraction as an _____ fraction.

46. $75\frac{2}{3}$ means 75 __ $\frac{2}{3}$. The number $75\frac{2}{3}$ is called a _____ number.

47. 0.75 is an example of a _____ decimal and it has __ decimal places.

48. $5.3\overline{27}$ is an example of a _____ decimal.

49. In the figure $2\overline{)6}^{\,3}$, 2 represents the _____, 6 represents the _____, and 3 represents the _____.

50. A _____ is the numerator of a fraction whose denominator is 100.

GUIDED PRACTICE

Write each number in prime-factored form. **See Example 1.** (Objective 1)

51. 30   **52.** 105

53. 70   **54.** 315

Write each fraction in lowest terms. If the fraction is already in lowest terms, so indicate. **See Example 2. (Objective 1)**

55. $\dfrac{6}{12}$ **56.** $\dfrac{3}{9}$

57. $\dfrac{15}{20}$ **58.** $\dfrac{22}{77}$

59. $\dfrac{24}{18}$ **60.** $\dfrac{35}{14}$

61. $\dfrac{72}{64}$ **62.** $\dfrac{26}{21}$

Perform each multiplication. Simplify each result when possible.
See Example 3. (Objective 2)

63. $\dfrac{1}{2} \cdot \dfrac{3}{5}$ **64.** $\dfrac{3}{4} \cdot \dfrac{5}{7}$

65. $\dfrac{4}{3} \cdot \dfrac{6}{5}$ **66.** $\dfrac{7}{8} \cdot \dfrac{6}{15}$

67. $12 \cdot \dfrac{5}{6}$ **68.** $9 \cdot \dfrac{7}{12}$

69. $\dfrac{10}{21} \cdot 14$ **70.** $\dfrac{5}{24} \cdot 16$

Perform each division. Simplify each result when possible.
See Example 5. (Objective 2)

71. $\dfrac{3}{5} \div \dfrac{2}{3}$ **72.** $\dfrac{4}{5} \div \dfrac{3}{7}$

73. $\dfrac{3}{4} \div \dfrac{6}{5}$ **74.** $\dfrac{3}{8} \div \dfrac{15}{28}$

75. $6 \div \dfrac{3}{14}$ **76.** $23 \div \dfrac{46}{5}$

77. $\dfrac{42}{30} \div 7$ **78.** $\dfrac{34}{8} \div 17$

Perform each operation. Simplify each result when possible.
See Examples 6–7. (Objective 3)

79. $\dfrac{3}{5} + \dfrac{3}{5}$ **80.** $\dfrac{4}{7} - \dfrac{2}{7}$

81. $\dfrac{4}{13} - \dfrac{3}{13}$ **82.** $\dfrac{2}{11} + \dfrac{9}{11}$

83. $\dfrac{1}{6} + \dfrac{1}{24}$ **84.** $\dfrac{17}{25} - \dfrac{2}{5}$

85. $\dfrac{7}{10} - \dfrac{1}{14}$ **86.** $\dfrac{7}{25} + \dfrac{3}{10}$

Perform each operation. Simplify each result when possible.
See Example 8. (Objective 4)

87. $4\dfrac{3}{5} + \dfrac{3}{5}$ **88.** $2\dfrac{1}{8} + \dfrac{3}{8}$

89. $3\dfrac{1}{3} - 1\dfrac{2}{3}$ **90.** $5\dfrac{1}{7} - 3\dfrac{2}{7}$

91. $3\dfrac{3}{4} - 2\dfrac{1}{2}$ **92.** $15\dfrac{5}{6} + 11\dfrac{5}{8}$

93. $8\dfrac{2}{9} - 7\dfrac{2}{3}$ **94.** $3\dfrac{4}{5} - 3\dfrac{1}{10}$

Change each fraction to decimal form and determine whether the decimal is a terminating or repeating decimal. (Objective 5)

95. $\dfrac{4}{5}$ **96.** $\dfrac{5}{9}$

97. $\dfrac{9}{22}$ **98.** $\dfrac{9}{5}$

Perform each operation. See Examples 10–12. (Objective 5)

99. $23.45 + 135.2$ **100.** $345.213 - 27.35$

101. $67.235 - 22.45$ **102.** $12.17 + 3.457$

103. $3.4 \cdot 13.2$ **104.** $4.21 \cdot 2.73$
105. $0.23\overline{)1.0465}$ **106.** $4.7\overline{)10.857}$

Round each of the following to two decimal places and then to three decimal places. See Example 13. (Objective 6)

107. 587.2694 **108.** 21.0721

109. $6{,}025.3982$ **110.** 1.6048

ADDITIONAL PRACTICE

Perform each operation.

111. $\dfrac{5}{12} \cdot \dfrac{18}{5}$ **112.** $\dfrac{5}{4} \cdot \dfrac{12}{10}$

113. $\dfrac{17}{34} \cdot \dfrac{3}{6}$ **114.** $\dfrac{21}{14} \cdot \dfrac{3}{6}$

115. $\dfrac{2}{13} \div \dfrac{8}{13}$ **116.** $\dfrac{4}{7} \div \dfrac{20}{21}$

117. $\dfrac{21}{35} \div \dfrac{3}{14}$ **118.** $\dfrac{23}{25} \div \dfrac{46}{5}$

119. $\dfrac{3}{5} + \dfrac{2}{3}$ **120.** $\dfrac{4}{3} + \dfrac{7}{2}$

121. $\dfrac{9}{4} - \dfrac{5}{6}$ **122.** $\dfrac{2}{15} + \dfrac{7}{9}$

123. $3 - \dfrac{3}{4}$ **124.** $5 + \dfrac{21}{5}$

125. $\dfrac{17}{3} + 4$ **126.** $\dfrac{13}{9} - 1$

Use a calculator to perform each operation and round each answer to two decimal places.

127. $323.24 + 27.2543$ **128.** $843.45213 - 712.765$

129. $25.25 \cdot 132.179$ **130.** $234.874 \cdot 242.46473$

131. $0.456\overline{)4.5694323}$ **132.** $43.225\overline{)32.465748}$

133. $55.77443 - 0.568245$ **134.** $0.62317 + 1.3316$

APPLICATIONS   See Examples 4, 9, and 14. (Objective 7)

135. Spring plowing   A farmer has plowed $12\dfrac{1}{3}$ acres of a $43\dfrac{1}{2}$-acre field. How much more needs to be plowed?

136. Fencing a garden The four sides of a garden measure $7\frac{2}{3}$ feet, $15\frac{1}{4}$ feet, $19\frac{1}{2}$ feet, and $10\frac{3}{4}$ feet. Find the length of the fence needed to enclose the garden.

137. Making clothes A designer needs $3\frac{1}{4}$ yards of material for each dress he makes. How much material will he need to make 14 dresses?

138. Track and field Each lap around a stadium track is $\frac{1}{4}$ mile. How many laps would a runner have to complete to run 26 miles?

139. Disaster relief After hurricane damage estimated at $187.75 million, a county sought relief from three agencies. Local agencies gave $46.8 million and state agencies gave $72.5 million. How much must the federal government contribute to make up the difference?

140. Minority population 26.5% of the 12,419,000 citizens of Illinois are nonwhite. How many are nonwhite?

The following circle graph shows the various sources of retirement income for a typical retired person. Use this information in Exercises 141–142.

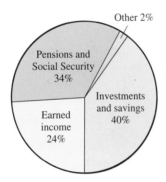

Other 2%
Pensions and Social Security 34%
Investments and savings 40%
Earned income 24%

141. Retirement income If a retiree has $36,000 of income, how much is expected to come from pensions and Social Security?

142. Retirement income If a retiree has $42,500 of income, how much is expected to come from earned income?

143. Quality control In the manufacture of active-matrix color LCD computer displays, many units must be rejected as defective. If 23% of a production run of 17,500 units is defective, how many units are acceptable?

144. Freeze-drying Almost all of the water must be removed when food is preserved by freeze-drying. Find the weight of the water removed from 750 pounds of a food that is 36% water.

145. Planning for growth This year, sales at Positronics Corporation totaled $18.7 million. If the projection of 12% annual growth is true, what will be next year's sales?

146. Speed skating In tryouts for the Olympics, a speed skater had times of 44.47, 43.24, 42.77, and 42.05 seconds. Find the average time. Give the result to the nearest hundredth. (*Hint:* Add the numbers and divide by 4.)

147. Cost of gasoline Otis drove his car 15,675.2 miles last year, averaging 25.5 miles per gallon of gasoline. If the average cost of gasoline was $2.87 per gallon, find the fuel cost to drive the car.

148. Paying taxes A woman earns $48,712.32 in taxable income. She must pay 15% tax on the first $23,000 and 28% on the rest. In addition, she must pay a Social Security tax of 15.4% on the total amount. How much tax will she need to pay?

149. Sealing asphalt A rectangular parking lot is 253.5 feet long and 178.5 feet wide. A 55-gallon drum of asphalt sealer covers 4,000 square feet and costs $97.50. Find the cost to seal the parking lot. (Sealer can be purchased only in full drums.)

150. Inventory costs Each television a retailer buys costs $3.25 per day for warehouse storage. What does it cost to store 37 television sets for three weeks?

151. Manufacturing profits A manufacturer of computer memory boards has a profit of $37.50 on each standard-capacity memory board, and $57.35 on each high-capacity board. The sales department has orders for 2,530 standard boards and 1,670 high-capacity boards. Which order will produce the greater profit?

152. Dairy production A Holstein cow will produce 7,600 pounds of milk each year, with a $3\frac{1}{2}\%$ butterfat content. Each year, a Guernsey cow will produce about 6,500 pounds of milk that is 5% butterfat. Which cow produces more butterfat?

153. Feeding dairy cows Each year, a typical dairy cow will eat 12,000 pounds of food that is 57% silage. To feed 30 cows, how much silage will a farmer use in a year?

154. Comparing bids Two carpenters bid on a home remodeling project. The first bids $9,350 for the entire job. The second will work for $27.50 per hour, plus $4,500 for materials. He estimates that the job will take 150 hours. Which carpenter has the lower bid?

155. Choosing a furnace A high-efficiency home heating system can be installed for $4,170, with an average monthly heating bill of $57.50. A regular furnace can be installed for $1,730, but monthly heating bills average $107.75. After three years, which system has cost more altogether?

156. Choosing a furnace Refer to Exercise 155. Decide which furnace system will have cost more after five years.

WRITING ABOUT MATH

157. Describe how you would find the common denominator of two fractions.

158. Explain how to convert an improper fraction into a mixed number.

159. Explain how to convert a mixed number into an improper fraction.

160. Explain how you would decide which of two decimal fractions is the larger.

SOMETING TO THINK ABOUT

161. In what situations would it be better to leave an answer in the form of an improper fraction?

162. When would it be better to change an improper-fraction answer into a mixed number?

163. Can the product of two proper fractions be larger than either of the fractions?

164. How does the product of one proper and one improper fraction compare with the two factors?

SECTION 1.3

Exponents and Order of Operations

Objectives

1. Identify the base and the exponent to simplify an exponential expression.
2. Evaluate a numeric expression following the order of operations.
3. Apply the correct geometric formula to an application problem.

Vocabulary

base
exponent
exponential expression
power of x
grouping symbol

perimeter
area
circumference
diameter

radius
volume
square units
cubic units

Getting Ready

Perform the operations.

1. $2 \cdot 2$
2. $3 \cdot 3$
3. $3 \cdot 3 \cdot 3$
4. $2 \cdot 2 \cdot 2$
5. $\frac{1}{2} \cdot \frac{1}{2}$
6. $\frac{1}{3} \cdot \frac{1}{3} \cdot \frac{1}{3}$
7. $\frac{2}{5} \cdot \frac{2}{5} \cdot \frac{2}{5}$
8. $\frac{3}{10} \cdot \frac{3}{10} \cdot \frac{3}{10}$

In algebra, we will encounter many expressions that contain exponents, a shortcut method of showing repeated multiplication. In this section, we will introduce exponential notation and discuss the rules for the order of operations.

1 **Identify the base and the exponent to simplify an exponential expression.**

To show how many times a number is to be used as a factor in a product, we use exponents. In the expression 2^3, 2 is called the **base** and 3 is called the **exponent.**

$$\text{Base} \rightarrow 2^3 \leftarrow \text{Exponent}$$

COMMENT   Note that $2^3 = 8$. This is not the same as $2 \cdot 3 = 6$.

The exponent of 3 indicates that the base of 2 is to be used as a factor three times:

$$\overbrace{}^{3 \text{ factors of } 2}$$
$$2^3 = 2 \cdot 2 \cdot 2 = 8$$

In the expression x^5 (called an **exponential expression** or a **power of x**), x is the base and 5 is the exponent. The exponent of 5 indicates that a base of x is to be used as a factor five times.

$$\overbrace{}^{5 \text{ factors of } x}$$
$$x^5 = x \cdot x \cdot x \cdot x \cdot x$$

In expressions such as 7, x, or y, the exponent is understood to be 1:

$$7 = 7^1 \qquad x = x^1 \qquad y = y^1$$

In general, we have the following definition.

Natural-Number Exponents

If n is a natural number, then

$$\overbrace{}^{n \text{ factors of } x}$$
$$x^n = x \cdot x \cdot x \cdot \cdots \cdot x$$

EXAMPLE 1   Write each expression without exponents.

a. $4^2 = 4 \cdot 4 = 16$ Read 4^2 as "4 squared" or as "4 to the second power."

b. $5^3 = 5 \cdot 5 \cdot 5 = 125$ Read 5^3 as "5 cubed" or as "5 to the third power."

c. $6^4 = 6 \cdot 6 \cdot 6 \cdot 6 = 1{,}296$ Read 6^4 as "6 to the fourth power."

d. $\left(\dfrac{2}{3}\right)^5 = \dfrac{2}{3} \cdot \dfrac{2}{3} \cdot \dfrac{2}{3} \cdot \dfrac{2}{3} \cdot \dfrac{2}{3} = \dfrac{32}{243}$ Read $\left(\dfrac{2}{3}\right)^5$ as "$\dfrac{2}{3}$ to the fifth power."

⇨ **SELF CHECK 1**   Evaluate: **a.** 7^2 **b.** $\left(\dfrac{3}{4}\right)^3$.

We can find powers using a calculator. For example, to find 2.35^4, we enter these numbers and press these keys:

2.35 y^x 4 $=$ Using a scientific calculator

2.35 $\wedge$ 4 **ENTER**   Using a graphing calculator

Either way, the display will read 30.49800625 . Some scientific calculators have an x^y key rather than a y^x key.

In the next example, the base of an exponential expression is a variable.

EXAMPLE 2   Write each expression without exponents.

a. $y^6 = y \cdot y \cdot y \cdot y \cdot y \cdot y$ Read y^6 as "y to the sixth power."

b. $x^3 = x \cdot x \cdot x$ Read x^3 as "x cubed" or as "x to the third power."

c. $z^2 = z \cdot z$ Read z^2 as "z squared" or as "z to the second power."

d. $a^1 = a$ Read a^1 as "a to the first power."

e. $2(3x)^2 = 2(3x)(3x)$ Read $2(3x)^2$ as "2 times $(3x)$ to the second power."

⇨ **SELF CHECK 2**   Write each expression without exponents: **a.** a^3 **b.** b^4.

---

2 **Evaluate a numeric expression following the order of operations.**

Suppose you are asked to contact a friend if you see a Rolex watch for sale while traveling in Switzerland. After locating the watch, you send the following message to your friend.

ROLEX WATCH $10,800. SHOULD I BUY IT FOR YOU?

The next day, you receive this response.

NO PRICE TOO HIGH! REPEAT...NO! PRICE TOO HIGH.

The first statement says to buy the watch at any price. The second says not to buy it, because it is too expensive. The placement of the exclamation point makes these statements read differently, resulting in different interpretations.

When reading a mathematical statement, the same kind of confusion is possible. To illustrate, we consider the expression $2 + 3 \cdot 4$, which contains the operations of addition and multiplication. We can calculate this expression in two different ways. We can perform the multiplication first and then perform the addition. Or we can perform the addition first and then perform the multiplication. However, we will get different results.

Multiply first		*Add first*	
$2 + 3 \cdot 4 = 2 + 12$	Multiply 3 and 4.	$2 + 3 \cdot 4 = 5 \cdot 4$	Add 2 and 3.
$= 14$	Add 2 and 12.	$= 20$	Multiply 5 and 4.

└────────── Different results ──────────┘

To eliminate the possibility of getting different answers, we will agree to perform multiplications before additions. The correct calculation of $2 + 3 \cdot 4$ is

$$2 + 3 \cdot 4 = 2 + 12 \qquad \text{Do the multiplication first.}$$
$$= 14$$

To indicate that additions should be done before multiplications, we use **grouping symbols** such as parentheses ( ), brackets [ ], or braces { }. The operational symbols $\sqrt{}$, $|\ |$, and fraction bars are also grouping symbols. In the expression $(2 + 3)4$, the parentheses indicate that the addition is to be done first:

$$(2 + 3)4 = 5 \cdot 4 \qquad \text{Do the addition within the parentheses first.}$$
$$= 20$$

To guarantee that calculations will have one correct result, we will always perform calculations in the following order.

Rules for the Order of Operations	Use the following steps to perform all calculations within each pair of grouping symbols, working from the innermost pair to the outermost pair. **1.** Find the values of any exponential expressions. **2.** Perform all multiplications and divisions, working from left to right. **3.** Perform all additions and subtractions, working from left to right. **4.** Because a fraction bar is a grouping symbol, simplify the numerator and the denominator in a fraction separately. Then simplify the fraction, whenever possible.

COMMENT Note that $4(2)^3 \neq (4 \cdot 2)^3$:

$$4(2)^3 = 4 \cdot 2 \cdot 2 \cdot 2 = 4(8) = 32 \quad \text{and} \quad (4 \cdot 2)^3 = 8^3 = 8 \cdot 8 \cdot 8 = 512$$

Likewise, $4x^3 \neq (4x)^3$ because

$$4x^3 = 4xxx \quad \text{and} \quad (4x)^3 = (4x)(4x)(4x) = 64xxx$$

EXAMPLE 3   Evaluate: $5^3 + 2(8 - 3 \cdot 2)$.

Solution   We perform the work within the parentheses first and then simplify.

$$5^3 + 2(8 - 3 \cdot 2) = 5^3 + 2(8 - 6) \qquad \text{Do the multiplication within the parentheses.}$$
$$= 5^3 + 2(2) \qquad \text{Do the subtraction within the parentheses.}$$
$$= 125 + 2(2) \qquad \text{Find the value of the exponential expression.}$$
$$= 125 + 4 \qquad \text{Do the multiplication.}$$
$$= 129 \qquad \text{Do the addition.}$$

⇨ **SELF CHECK 3**   Evaluate: $5 + 4 \cdot 3^2$.

EXAMPLE 4   Evaluate: $\dfrac{3(3 + 2) + 5}{17 - 3(4)}$.

Solution   We simplify the numerator and denominator separately and then simplify the fraction.

$$\frac{3(3+2)+5}{17-3(4)} = \frac{3(5)+5}{17-3(4)} \qquad \text{Do the addition within the parentheses.}$$

$$= \frac{15+5}{17-12} \qquad \text{Do the multiplications.}$$

$$= \frac{20}{5} \qquad \text{Do the addition and the subtraction.}$$

$$= 4 \qquad \text{Do the division.}$$

⇨ **SELF CHECK 4**   Evaluate: $\dfrac{4+2(5-3)}{2+3(2)}$.

EXAMPLE 5   Evaluate: $\dfrac{3(4^2)-2(3)}{2(4+3)}$.

Solution $\dfrac{3(4^2)-2(3)}{2(4+3)} = \dfrac{3(16)-2(3)}{2(7)}$ Find the value of 4^2 in the numerator and do the addition in the denominator.

$$= \frac{48-6}{14} \qquad \text{Do the multiplications.}$$

$$= \frac{42}{14} \qquad \text{Do the subtraction.}$$

$$= 3 \qquad \text{Do the division.}$$

⇨ **SELF CHECK 5**   Evaluate: $\dfrac{2^2+6(5)}{2(2+5)+3}$.

3 Apply the correct geometric formula to an application problem.

To find perimeters and areas of geometric figures, we often must substitute numbers for variables in a formula. The **perimeter** of a geometric figure is the distance around it, and the **area** of a geometric figure is the amount of surface that it encloses. The perimeter of a circle is called its **circumference.**

EXAMPLE 6   **CIRCLES**   Use the information in Figure 1-17 to find:
a. the circumference   **b.** the area of the circle

Solution   **a.** The formula for the circumference of a circle is

$$C = \pi D$$

where C is the circumference, π can be approximated by $\frac{22}{7}$, and D is the **diameter**—a line segment that passes through the center of the circle and joins two points on the circle. We can approximate the circumference by substituting $\frac{22}{7}$ for π and 14 for D in the formula and simplifying.

$$C = \pi D$$

$$C \approx \frac{22}{7} \cdot 14 \qquad \text{Read } \approx \text{ as "is approximately equal to."}$$

14 cm

Figure 1-17

$$C \approx \frac{22 \cdot \overset{2}{\cancel{14}}}{\underset{1}{\cancel{7}} \cdot 1}$$ Multiply the fractions and simplify.

$$C \approx 44$$

The circumference is approximately 44 centimeters. To use a calculator, we enter these numbers and press these keys:

π $\boxed{\times}$ 14 $\boxed{=}$ Using a scientific calculator

π $\boxed{\times}$ 14 $\boxed{\textbf{ENTER}}$ Using a graphing calculator

Either way, the display will read 43.98229715. The result is not 44, because a calculator uses a better approximation for π than $\frac{22}{7}$.

COMMENT   A segment drawn from the **center** of a circle to a point on the circle is called a **radius.** Since the diameter D of a circle is twice as long as its radius r, we have $D = 2r$. If we substitute $2r$ for D in the formula $C = \pi D$, we obtain an alternate formula for the circumference of a circle: $C = 2\pi r$.

b. The formula for the area of a circle is

$$A = \pi r^2$$

where A is the area, $\pi \approx \frac{22}{7}$, and r is the radius of the circle. We can approximate the area by substituting $\frac{22}{7}$ for π and 7 for r in the formula and simplifying.

$$A = \pi r^2$$

$$A \approx \frac{22}{7} \cdot 7^2$$

$$A \approx \frac{22}{7} \cdot \frac{49}{1}$$ Evaluate the exponential expression.

$$A \approx \frac{22 \cdot \overset{7}{\cancel{49}}}{\underset{1}{\cancel{7}} \cdot 1}$$ Multiply the fractions and simplify.

$$A \approx 154$$

The area is approximately 154 square centimeters.

To use a calculator, we enter these numbers and press these keys:

π $\boxed{\times}$ 7 $\boxed{x^2}$ $\boxed{=}$ Using a scientific calculator

π $\boxed{\times}$ 7 $\boxed{x^2}$ $\boxed{\textbf{ENTER}}$ Using a graphing calculator

The display will read 153.93804.

⇨ **SELF CHECK 6**   Given a circle with a diameter of 28 meters, find an estimate of
a. the circumference   **b.** the area.
(Use $\frac{22}{7}$ to estimate π.) Check your results with a calculator.

Table 1-1 shows the formulas for the perimeter and area of several geometric figures.

Euclid
325–265 BC

Although Euclid is best known for his study of geometry, many of his writings deal with number theory. In about 300 BC, the Greek mathematician Euclid proved that the number of prime numbers is unlimited—that there are infinitely many prime numbers. This is an important branch of mathematics called number theory.

Figure	Name	Perimeter	Area
Square	Square	$P = 4s$	$A = s^2$
Rectangle	Rectangle	$P = 2l + 2w$	$A = lw$
Triangle	Triangle	$P = a + b + c$	$A = \frac{1}{2}bh$
Trapezoid	Trapezoid	$P = a + b + c + d$	$A = \frac{1}{2}h(b + d)$
Circle	Circle	$C = \pi D = 2\pi r$	$A = \pi r^2$

Table 1-1

The **volume** of a three-dimensional geometric solid is the amount of space it encloses. Table 1-2 shows the formulas for the volume of several solids.

Figure	Name	Volume
	Rectangular solid	$V = lwh$
	Cylinder	$V = Bh$, where B is the area of the base
	Pyramid	$V = \frac{1}{3}Bh$, where B is the area of the base
	Cone	$V = \frac{1}{3}Bh$, where B is the area of the base
	Sphere	$V = \frac{4}{3}\pi r^3$

Table 1-2

When working with geometric figures, measurements are often given in **linear units** such as feet (ft), centimeters (cm), or meters (m). If the dimensions of a two-dimensional geometric figure are given in feet, we can calculate its perimeter by finding the sum of the lengths of its sides. This sum will be in feet.

If we calculate the area of a two-dimensional figure, the result will be in **square units.** For example, if we calculate the area of the figure whose sides are measured in centimeters, the result will be in square centimeters (cm^2).

If we calculate the volume of a three-dimensional figure, the result will be in **cubic units.** For example, the volume of a three-dimensional geometric figure whose sides are measured in meters will be in cubic meters (m^3).

EXAMPLE 7   **WINTER DRIVING**   Find the number of cubic feet of road salt in the conical pile shown in Figure 1-18. Round the answer to two decimal places.

Figure 1-18

Solution   We can find the area of the circular base by substituting $\frac{22}{7}$ for π and 14.3 for the radius.

$$A = \pi r^2$$

$$\approx \frac{22}{7}(14.3)^2$$

$$\approx 642.6828571 \quad \text{Use a calculator.}$$

We then substitute 642.6828571 for B and 18.75 for h in the formula for the volume of a cone.

$$V = \frac{1}{3}Bh$$

$$\approx \frac{1}{3}(642.6828571)(18.75)$$

$$\approx 4{,}016.767857 \quad \text{Use a calculator.}$$

To two decimal places, there are 4,016.77 cubic feet of salt in the pile.

⇨ **SELF CHECK 7**   To the nearest hundredth, find the number of cubic feet of water that can be contained in a spherical tank that has a radius of 9 feet. (Use $\pi \approx \frac{22}{7}$.)

⇨ **SELF CHECK ANSWERS**   **1. a.** 49 **b.** $\frac{27}{64}$ **2. a.** $a \cdot a \cdot a$ **b.** $b \cdot b \cdot b \cdot b$ **3.** 41 **4.** 1 **5.** 2 **6. a.** 88 m **b.** 616 m^2
7. 3,054.86 ft^2

NOW TRY THIS

Simplify each expression.

1. $28 - 7(4 - 1)$

2. $\dfrac{5 - |4 - 1|}{2}$

3. Insert the appropriate operations and one set of parentheses so that the expression yields the given value.
   a. 16   3   5 =   2
   b. 4   2   6 = 12

1.3 EXERCISES

WARM-UPS

Find the value of each expression.

1. 2^5
2. 3^4
3. 4^3
4. 5^3

Simplify each expression.

5. $3(2)^3$
6. $(3 \cdot 2)^2$
7. $3 + 2 \cdot 4$
8. $10 - 3^2$
9. $4 + 2^2 \cdot 3$
10. $2 \cdot 3 + 2 \cdot 3^2$

REVIEW

11. On the number line, graph the prime numbers between 10 and 20.

$$\overset{\longleftarrow\!\!\mid\!\!\mid\!\!\mid\!\!\mid\!\!\mid\!\!\mid\!\!\mid\!\!\mid\!\!\mid\!\!\mid\!\!\mid\!\!\longrightarrow}{\qquad 10\ \ 11\ \ 12\ \ 13\ \ 14\ \ 15\ \ 16\ \ 17\ \ 18\ \ 19\ \ 20}$$

12. Write the inequality $7 \le 12$ as an inequality using the symbol $\ge$.

13. Classify the number 17 as a prime number or a composite number.

14. Evaluate: $\dfrac{3}{5} - \dfrac{1}{2}$.

VOCABULARY AND CONCEPTS   *Fill in the blanks.*

15. An _____ indicates how many times a base is to be used as a factor in a product.

16. In the exponential expression (power of x) x^7, x is called the _____ and 7 is called an _____.

17. Parentheses, brackets, and braces are called _____ symbols.

18. A line segment that passes through the center of a circle and joins two points on the circle is called a _____. A line segment drawn from the center of a circle to a point on the circle is called a _____.

19. The distance around a rectangle is called the _____, and the distance around a circle is called the _____.

20. The region enclosed by a two-dimensional geometric figure is called the _____ and is designated by _____ units, and the region enclosed by a three-dimensional geometric figure is called the _____ and is designated by _____ units.

Write the appropriate formula to find each quantity and state the correct units.

21. The perimeter of a square _____; _____

22. The area of a square _____; _____

23. The perimeter of a rectangle _____; _____

24. The area of a rectangle _____; _____

25. The perimeter of a triangle _____; _____

26. The area of a triangle _____; _____

27. The perimeter of a trapezoid _____; _____

28. The area of a trapezoid _____; _____

29. The circumference of a circle _____; _____

30. The area of a circle _____; _____

31. The volume of a rectangular solid _____; _____

32. The volume of a cylinder _____; _____

33. The volume of a pyramid _____; _____

34. The volume of a cone _____; _____

35. The volume of a sphere _____; _____

36. In Exercises 32–34, B is the _____ of the base.

GUIDED PRACTICE

Write each expression without using exponents and find the value of each expression. See Example 1. (Objective 1)

37. 4^2
38. 5^2

39. $\left(\dfrac{1}{10}\right)^4$

40. $\left(\dfrac{1}{2}\right)^6$

Write each expression without using exponents. **See Example 2.**
(Objective 1)

41. x^2

42. y^3

43. $3z^4$

44. $5t^2$

45. $(5t)^2$

46. $(3z)^4$

47. $5(2x)^3$

48. $7(3t)^2$

Find the value of each expression. **See Examples 3–5. (Objective 2)**

49. $4(3^2)$

50. $4(2^3)$

51. $(5 \cdot 2)^3$

52. $(2 \cdot 2)^4$

53. $2(3^2)$

54. $3(2^3)$

55. $(3 \cdot 2)^3$

56. $(2 \cdot 3)^2$

57. $3 \cdot 5 - 4$

58. $6 + 4 \cdot 3$

59. $3(5 - 4)$

60. $4(6 + 5)$

61. $2 + 3 \cdot 5 - 4$

62. $12 + 2 \cdot 3 + 2$

63. $64 \div (3 + 1)$

64. $16 \div (5 + 3)$

65. $3^2 + 2(1 + 4) - 2$

66. $4 \cdot 3 + 2(5 - 2) - 2^3$

67. $\dfrac{3}{5} \cdot \dfrac{10}{3} + \dfrac{1}{2} \cdot 12$

68. $\dfrac{15}{4}\left(1 + \dfrac{3}{5}\right)$

69. $\left[\dfrac{1}{3} - \left(\dfrac{1}{2}\right)^2\right]^2$

70. $\left[\left(\dfrac{2}{3}\right)^2 - \dfrac{1}{3}\right]^2$

71. $\dfrac{(3 + 5)^2 + 2}{2(8 - 5)}$

72. $\dfrac{25 - (2 \cdot 3 - 1)}{2 \cdot 9 - 8}$

73. $\dfrac{(5 - 3)^2 + 2}{4^2 - (8 + 2)}$

74. $\dfrac{(4^2 - 2) + 7}{5(2 + 4) - 3^2}$

75. $\dfrac{3 \cdot 7 - 5(3 \cdot 4 - 11)}{4(3 + 2) - 3^2 + 5}$

76. $\dfrac{2 \cdot 5^2 - 2^2 + 3}{2(5 - 2)^2 - 11}$

Find the perimeter of each figure. **(Objective 3)**

77.

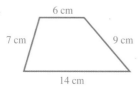

4 in.
4 in.   4 in.
4 in.

78.

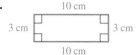

10 cm
3 cm   3 cm
10 cm

79.

3 m   5 m
7 m

80.

6 cm
7 cm   9 cm
14 cm

Find the area of each figure. **(Objective 3)**

81.

5 m
5 m

82.

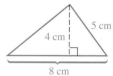

5 cm
4 cm
8 cm

83.

6 ft
10 ft

84.

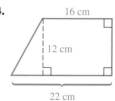

16 cm
12 cm
22 cm

Find the circumference of each circle. Use $\pi \approx \dfrac{22}{7}$. **See Example 6.**
(Objective 3)

85.

14 m

86.

21 cm

Find the area of each circle. Use $\pi \approx \dfrac{22}{7}$. **See Example 6.**
(Objective 3)

87.

42 ft

88.

7 m

Find the volume of each solid. Use $\pi \approx \dfrac{22}{7}$ where applicable.
See Example 7. (Objective 3)

89.

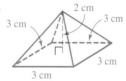

2 cm
3 cm   3 cm
3 cm
3 cm
3 cm

90.

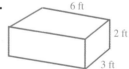

6 ft
2 ft
3 ft

91.

6 m

92.

14 in.
12 in.

93.

94.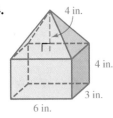

ADDITIONAL PRACTICE

Simplify each expression.

95. 6^2
96. 7^3
97. $3 + 5^2$
98. $4^2 - 2^2$
99. $(3 + 5)^2$
100. $(5 - 2)^3$
101. $(7 + 9) \div (2 \cdot 4)$
102. $(7 + 9) \div 2 \cdot 4$
103. $(5 + 7) \div 3 \cdot 4$
104. $(5 + 7) \div (3 \cdot 4)$
105. $24 \div 4 \cdot 3 + 3$
106. $36 \div 9 \cdot 4 - 2$
107. $5^2 - (7 - 3)^2$
108. $3^3 + (3 - 1)^3$
109. $(2 \cdot 3 - 4)^3$
110. $(3 \cdot 5 - 2 \cdot 6)^2$
111. $\dfrac{2[4 + 2(3 - 1)]}{3[3(2 \cdot 3 - 4)]}$
112. $\dfrac{3[9 - 2(7 - 3)]}{(8 - 5)(9 - 7)}$

 Use a calculator to find each power.

113. 7.9^3
114. 0.45^4
115. 25.3^2
116. 7.567^3

Insert parentheses in the expression $3 \cdot 8 + 5 \cdot 3$ to make its value equal to the given number.

117. 39
118. 117
119. 87
120. 69

 APPLICATIONS *Use a calculator. For π, use the $\boxed{\pi}$ key. Round to two decimal places.* See Example 7. (Objective 3)

121. Volume of a tank Find the number of cubic feet of water in the spherical tank at the top of the water tower.

21.35 ft

122. Storing solvents A hazardous solvent fills a rectangular tank with dimensions of 12 inches by 9.5 inches by 7.3 inches. For disposal, it must be transferred to a cylindrical canister 7.5 inches in diameter and 18 inches high. How much solvent will be left over?

123. Buying fencing How many meters of fencing are needed to enclose the square pasture shown in the illustration?

$30\frac{2}{5}$ m

124. Installing carpet What will it cost to carpet the area shown in the illustration with carpet that costs $29.79 per square yard? (One square yard is 9 square feet.)

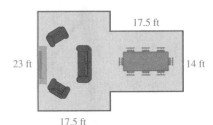
17.5 ft
23 ft
14 ft
17.5 ft

125. Volume of a classroom Thirty students are in a classroom with dimensions of 40 feet by 40 feet by 9 feet. How many cubic feet of air are there for each student?

126. Wallpapering One roll of wallpaper covers about 33 square feet. At $27.50 per roll, how much would it cost to paper two walls 8.5 feet high and 17.3 feet long? (*Hint:* Wallpaper can be purchased only in full rolls.)

127. Focal length The focal length f of a double-convex thin lens is given by the formula

$$f = \frac{rs}{(r + s)(n - 1)}$$

If $r = 8$, $s = 12$, and $n = 1.6$, find f.

128. Resistance The total resistance R of two resistors in parallel is given by the formula

$$R = \frac{rs}{r + s}$$

If $r = 170$ and $s = 255$, find R.

WRITING ABOUT MATH

129. Explain why the symbols $3x$ and x^3 have different meanings.

130. Students often say that x^n means "x multiplied by itself n times." Explain why this is not correct.

SOMETHING TO THINK ABOUT

131. If x were greater than 1, would raising x to higher and higher powers produce bigger numbers or smaller numbers?

132. What would happen in Exercise 131 if x were a positive number that was less than 1?

SECTION 1.4

Adding and Subtracting Real Numbers

Objectives

1 Add two or more real numbers with like signs.
2 Add two or more real numbers with unlike signs.
3 Subtract two real numbers.
4 Use signed numbers and one or more operations to model an application problem.
5 Use a calculator to add or subtract two real numbers.

Vocabulary

like signs   unlike signs

Getting Ready

Perform each operation.

1. $14.32 + 3.2$ **2.** $5.54 - 2.6$
3. $4.2 - (3 - 0.8)$ **4.** $(5.42 - 4.22) - 0.2$
5. $(437 - 198) - 143$ **6.** $437 - (198 - 143)$

In this section, we will discuss how to add and subtract real numbers. Recall that the result of an addition problem is called a *sum* and the result of a subtraction problem is called a *difference.* To develop the rules for adding real numbers, we will use the number line.

1 Add two or more real numbers with like signs.

Since the positive direction on the number line is to the right, positive numbers can be represented by arrows pointing to the right. Negative numbers can be represented by arrows pointing to the left.

To add $+2$ and $+3$, we can represent $+2$ with an arrow the length of 2, pointing to the right. We can represent $+3$ with an arrow of length 3, also pointing to the right. To add the numbers, we place the arrows end to end, as in Figure 1-19. Since the endpoint of the second arrow is the point with coordinate $+5$, we have

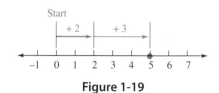

Figure 1-19

$$(+2) + (+3) = +5$$

As a check, we can think of this problem in terms of money. If you had \$2 and earned \$3 more, you would have a total of \$5.

The addition

$$(-2) + (-3)$$

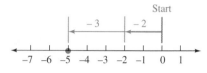

Figure 1-20

can be represented by the arrows shown in Figure 1-20. Since the endpoint of the final arrow is the point with coordinate -5, we have

$$(-2) + (-3) = -5$$

As a check, we can think of this problem in terms of money. If you lost \$2 and then lost \$3 more, you would have lost a total of \$5.

Because two real numbers with like signs can be represented by arrows pointing in the same direction, we have the following rule.

| **Adding Real Numbers with Like Signs** | **1.** *To add two positive numbers,* add their absolute values and the answer is positive. |
| | **2.** *To add two negative numbers,* add their absolute values and the answer is negative. |

EXAMPLE 1   **ADDING REAL NUMBERS**

a. $(+4) + (+6) = +(4 + 6)$
$$= 10$$

b. $(-4) + (-6) = -(4 + 6)$
$$= -10$$

c. $+5 + (+10) = +(5 + 10)$
$$= 15$$

d. $-\dfrac{1}{2} + \left(-\dfrac{3}{2}\right) = -\left(\dfrac{1}{2} + \dfrac{3}{2}\right)$
$$= -\dfrac{4}{2}$$
$$= -2$$

⇨ **SELF CHECK 1**   Add: **a.** $(+0.5) + (+1.2)$ **b.** $(-3.7) + (-2.3)$.

2 Add two or more real numbers with unlike signs.

Real numbers with **unlike signs** can be represented by arrows on a number line pointing in opposite directions. For example, the addition

$$(-6) + (+2)$$

COMMENT We do not need to write a + sign in front of a positive number.

$$+4 = 4 \quad \text{and} \quad +5 = 5$$

However, we must always write a − sign in front of a negative number.

can be represented by the arrows shown in Figure 1-21. Since the endpoint of the final arrow is the point with coordinate −4, we have

$$(-6) + (+2) = -4$$

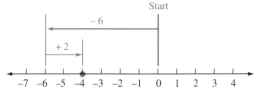

Figure 1-21

As a check, we can think of this problem in terms of money. If you lost $6 and then earned $2, you would still have a loss of $4.

The addition

$$(+7) + (-4)$$

can be represented by the arrows shown in Figure 1-22. Since the endpoint of the final arrow is the point with coordinate +3, we have

$$(+7) + (-4) = +3$$

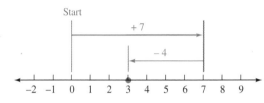

Figure 1-22

As a check, you can think of this problem in terms of money. If you had $7 and then lost $4, you would still have a gain of $3.

Because two real numbers with unlike signs can be represented by arrows pointing in opposite directions, we have the following rule.

Adding Real Numbers with Unlike Signs	*To add a positive and a negative number,* subtract the smaller absolute value from the larger.
	1. If the positive number has the larger absolute value, the answer is positive.
	2. If the negative number has the larger absolute value, the answer is negative.

EXAMPLE 2   **ADDING REAL NUMBERS**

a. $(+6) + (-5) = +(6 - 5)$
$= 1$

b. $(-2) + (+3) = +(3 - 2)$
$= 1$

c. $+6 + (-9) = -(9 - 6)$
$= -3$

d. $-\dfrac{2}{3} + \left(+\dfrac{1}{2}\right) = -\left(\dfrac{2}{3} - \dfrac{1}{2}\right)$
$= -\left(\dfrac{4}{6} - \dfrac{3}{6}\right)$
$= -\dfrac{1}{6}$

 **SELF CHECK 2**   Add: **a.** $(+3.5) + (-2.6)$ **b.** $(-7.2) + (+4.7)$.

When adding three or more real numbers, we use the rules for the order of operations.

EXAMPLE 3   **WORKING WITH GROUPING SYMBOLS**

  a. $[(+3) + (-7)] + (-4) = [-4] + (-4)$ Do the work within the brackets first.
            $= -8$

  b. $-3 + [(-2) + (-8)] = -3 + [-10]$ Do the work within the brackets first.
           $= -13$

  c. $2.75 + [8.57 + (-4.8)] = 2.75 + 3.77$ Do the work within the brackets first.
           $= 6.52$

⇨ **SELF CHECK 3** Add: $-2 + [(+5.2) + (-12.7)]$.

Sometimes numbers are added vertically, as shown in the next example.

EXAMPLE 4   **ADDING NUMBERS IN A VERTICAL FORMAT**

  a. $\begin{array}{r} +5 \\ +2 \\ \hline +7 \end{array}$ **b.** $\begin{array}{r} +5 \\ -2 \\ \hline +3 \end{array}$ **c.** $\begin{array}{r} -5 \\ +2 \\ \hline -3 \end{array}$ **d.** $\begin{array}{r} -5 \\ -2 \\ \hline -7 \end{array}$

⇨ **SELF CHECK 4** Add: **a.** $\begin{array}{r} +3.2 \\ -5.4 \\ \hline \end{array}$ **b.** $\begin{array}{r} -13.5 \\ -4.3 \\ \hline \end{array}$

3 **Subtract two real numbers.**

In arithmetic, subtraction is a take-away process. For example,

  $7 - 4 = 3$

can be thought of as taking 4 objects away from 7 objects, leaving 3 objects.
  For algebra, a better approach treats the subtraction problem

  $7 - 4$

as the equivalent addition problem:

  $7 + (-4)$

In either case, the answer is 3.

  $7 - 4 = 3$ and $7 + (-4) = 3$

Thus, to subtract 4 from 7, we can add the negative (or opposite) of 4 to 7. In general, to subtract one real number from another, we add the negative (or opposite) of the number that is being subtracted.

Subtracting Real Numbers

If a and b are two real numbers, then

  $a - b = a + (-b)$

EXAMPLE 5   Evaluate: **a.** $12 - 4$ **b.** $-13 - 5$ **c.** $-14 - (-6)$

Solution   **a.** $12 - 4 = 12 + (-4)$ To subtract 4, add the opposite of 4.
$= 8$

b. $-13 - 5 = -13 + (-5)$ To subtract 5, add the opposite of 5.
$= -18$

c. $-14 - (-6) = -14 + [-(-6)]$ To subtract -6, add the opposite of -6. The opposite of -6 is 6.

$= -14 + 6$
$= -8$

⇨ **SELF CHECK 5**   Evaluate: **a.** $-12.7 - 8.9$ **b.** $15.7 - (-11.3)$

To use a vertical format for subtracting real numbers, we add the opposite of the number that is to be subtracted by changing the sign of the lower number and proceeding as in addition.

EXAMPLE 6   Perform each subtraction by doing an equivalent addition.

$$5 \qquad\qquad 5$$
a. The subtraction $\underline{-\ -4}$ becomes the addition $\underline{+\ +4}$
$$9$$

$$-8 \qquad\qquad -8$$
b. The subtraction $\underline{-\ +3}$ becomes the addition $\underline{+\ -3}$
$$-11$$

⇨ **SELF CHECK 6**   Perform the subtraction: $\begin{array}{r} 5.8 \\ \underline{-\ -4.6} \end{array}$

When dealing with three or more real numbers, we use the rules for the order of operations.

EXAMPLE 7   Simplify: **a.** $3 - [4 + (-6)]$ **b.** $[-5 + (-3)] - [-2 - (+5)]$.

Solution   **a.** $3 - [4 + (-6)] = 3 - (-2)$ Do the addition within the brackets first.
$= 3 + [-(-2)]$ To subtract -2, add the opposite of -2.
$= 3 + 2$ $-(-2) = 2$
$= 5$

b. $[-5 + (-3)] - [-2 - (+5)]$
$= [-5 + (-3)] - [-2 + (-5)]$ To subtract -5, add the opposite of 5.
$= -8 - (-7)$ Do the work within the brackets.
$= -8 + [-(-7)]$ To subtract -7, add the opposite of -7.   •

$$= -8 + 7 \qquad\qquad -(-7) = 7$$
$$= -1$$

⇨ **SELF CHECK 7**   Simplify: $[7.2 - (-3)] - [3.2 + (-1.7)]$.

EXAMPLE 8   Evaluate: **a.** $\dfrac{-3 - (-5)}{7 + (-5)}$ **b.** $\dfrac{6 + (-5)}{-3 - (-5)} - \dfrac{-3 - 4}{7 + (-5)}$.

Solution   **a.** $\dfrac{-3 - (-5)}{7 + (-5)} = \dfrac{-3 + [-(-5)]}{7 + (-5)}$ To subtract -5, add the opposite of -5.

$$= \dfrac{-3 + 5}{2} \qquad\qquad -(-5) = 5; \ 7 + (-5) = 2$$

$$= \dfrac{2}{2}$$

$$= 1$$

b. $\dfrac{6 + (-5)}{-3 - (-5)} - \dfrac{-3 - 4}{7 + (-5)} = \dfrac{1}{-3 + 5} - \dfrac{-3 + (-4)}{2}$ $6 + (-5) = 1; \ -(-5) = +5;$
$-3 - 4 = -3 + (-4);$
$7 + (-5) = 2$

$$= \dfrac{1}{2} - \dfrac{-7}{2} \qquad\qquad -3 + (-4) = -7; \ -3 + 5 = 2$$

$$= \dfrac{1 - (-7)}{2} \qquad\qquad \text{Subtract the numerators and keep the denominator.}$$

$$= \dfrac{1 + [-(-7)]}{2} \qquad\qquad \text{To subtract } -7, \text{ add the opposite of } -7.$$

$$= \dfrac{1 + 7}{2} \qquad\qquad -(-7) = 7$$

$$= \dfrac{8}{2}$$

$$= 4$$

⇨ **SELF CHECK 8**   Evaluate: $\dfrac{7 - (-3)}{-5 - (-3) + 3}$.

4   ## Use signed numbers and one or more operations to model an application problem.

Words such as *found, gain, credit, up, increase, forward, rises, in the future,* and *to the right* indicate a positive direction. Words such as *lost, loss, debit, down, decrease, backward, falls, in the past,* and *to the left* indicate a negative direction.

EXAMPLE 9   **ACCOUNT BALANCES**   The treasurer of a math club opens a checking account by depositing $350 in the bank. The bank debits the account $9 for check printing, and the treasurer writes a check for $22. Find the balance after these transactions.

Solution The deposit can be represented by $+350$. The debit of \$9 can be represented by -9, and the check written for \$22 can be represented by -22. The balance in the account after these transactions is the sum of 350, -9, and -22.

$$350 + (-9) + (-22) = 341 + (-22) \quad \text{Work from left to right.}$$
$$= 319$$

The balance is \$319.

 SELF CHECK 9   Find the balance if another deposit of \$17 is made.

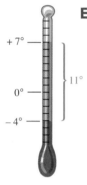

Figure 1-23

EXAMPLE 10   **TEMPERATURE CHANGES**   At noon, the temperature was 7° above zero. At midnight, the temperature was 4° below zero. Find the difference between these two temperatures.

Solution A temperature of 7° above zero can be represented as $+7$. A temperature of 4° below zero can be represented as -4. To find the difference between these temperatures, we can set up a subtraction problem and simplify.

$$7 - (-4) = 7 + [-(-4)] \quad \text{To subtract } -4, \text{ add the opposite of } -4.$$
$$= 7 + 4 \qquad -(-4) = 4$$
$$= 11$$

The difference between the temperatures is 11°. Figure 1-23 shows this difference.

 SELF CHECK 10   Find the difference between temperatures of 32° and $-10°$.

5 Use a calculator to add or subtract two real numbers.

COMMENT   A common error is to use the subtraction key $\boxed{-}$ on a calculator rather than the negative key $(-)$.

A calculator can add positive and negative numbers.

- You do not have to do anything special to enter positive numbers. When you press 5, for example, a positive 5 is entered.
- To enter -5 into a calculator with a $\boxed{+/-}$ key, called the *plus-minus* or *change-of-sign* key, you must enter 5 and then press the $\boxed{+/-}$ key. To enter -5 into a calculator with a $\boxed{(-)}$ key, you must press the $\boxed{(-)}$ key and then press 5.

EXAMPLE 11   To evaluate $-345.678 + (-527.339)$, we enter these numbers and press these keys:

$$345.678 \boxed{+/-} \boxed{+} 527.339 \boxed{+/-} \boxed{=} \quad \text{Using a calculator with a } \boxed{+/-} \text{ key}$$

$$\boxed{(-)}\ 345.678 \boxed{+} \boxed{(-)}\ 527.339 \boxed{\text{ENTER}} \quad \text{Using a graphing calculator}$$

The display will read $\boxed{-873.017}$.

 SELF CHECK 11   Evaluate: $-783.291 - (-28.3264)$.

SELF CHECK ANSWERS   **1. a.** 1.7   **b.** -6 **2. a.** 0.9   **b.** -2.5 **3.** -9.5 **4. a.** -2.2 **b.** -17.8 **5. a.** -21.6 **b.** 27   **6.** 10.4   **7.** 8.7   **8.** 10   **9.** \$336   **10.** 42°   **11.** -754.9646

NOW TRY THIS

1. Evaluate each expression.

   a. $-2 - |5 - 8|$ b. $\dfrac{|6 - (-4)|}{|-1 - 9|}$

2. Determine the signs necessary to obtain the given value.
   a. $\boxed{+}3 + (\boxed{-})5 = -2$
   b. $\boxed{}6 + (\boxed{-})8 = -14$
   c. $\boxed{-}56 + (\boxed{+})24 = -32$

1.4 EXERCISES

WARM-UPS   *Find each value.*

1. $2 + 3$ **2.** $2 + (-5)$

3. $-4 + 7$ **4.** $-5 + (-6)$

5. $6 - 2$ **6.** $-8 - 4$

7. $-5 - (-7)$ **8.** $12 - (-4)$

REVIEW   *Simplify each expression.*

9. $5 + 3(7 - 2)$ **10.** $(5 + 3)(7 - 2)$

11. $5 + 3(7) - 2$ **12.** $(5 + 3)7 - 2$

VOCABULARY AND CONCEPTS   *Fill in the blanks.*

13. Positive and negative numbers can be represented by _____ on the number line.

14. The numbers $+5$ and $+8$ and the numbers -5 and -8 are said to have ____ signs.

15. The numbers $+7$ and -9 are said to have _____ signs.

16. To find the sum of two real numbers with like signs, ____ their absolute values and ____ their common sign.

17. To find the sum of two real numbers with unlike signs, _____ their absolute values and use the sign of the number with the _____ absolute value.

18. $a - b = $ _____

19. To subtract a number, we ____ its _____.

20. The difference

$$\begin{array}{r} 35 \\ \underline{-45} \end{array}$$

is equivalent to the subtraction 35 ____.

GUIDED PRACTICE

Find each sum. See Example 1. (Objective 1)

21. $4 + 8$ **22.** $(-4) + (-2)$

23. $(-3) + (-7)$ **24.** $(+4) + 11$

25. $\dfrac{1}{5} + \left(+\dfrac{1}{7}\right)$ **26.** $-\dfrac{2}{5} + \left(-\dfrac{3}{5}\right)$

27. $44.902 + 33.098$ **28.** $-421.377 + (-122.043)$

Find each sum. See Example 2. (Objective 2)

29. $6 + (-4)$ **30.** $5 + (-3)$

31. $(-0.4) + 0.9$ **32.** $(-1.2) + (-5.3)$

33. $\dfrac{2}{3} + \left(-\dfrac{1}{4}\right)$ **34.** $-\dfrac{1}{2} + \dfrac{1}{3}$

35. $87.63 + (-102.6)$ **36.** $-721.964 + (38.291)$

Evaluate each expression. See Example 3. (Objectives 1 and 2)

37. $5 + [4 + (-2)]$ **38.** $-6 + [(-3) + 8]$

39. $-2 + (-4 + 5)$ **40.** $5 + [-4 + (-6)]$

41. $(-3 + 5) + 2$ **42.** $-7 + [-3 + (-7)]$

43. $-15 + (-4 + 12)$ **44.** $-27 + [-12 + (-13)]$

Add vertically. See Example 4. (Objectives 1 and 2)

45. $\begin{array}{r} 5 \\ \underline{+-4} \end{array}$ **46.** $\begin{array}{r} -20 \\ \underline{+-17} \end{array}$

47. $\begin{array}{r} -1.3 \\ \underline{+\ \ 3.5} \end{array}$ **48.** $\begin{array}{r} 1.3 \\ \underline{+-2.5} \end{array}$

Find each difference. See Example 5. (Objective 3)

49. $8 - 4$ **50.** $-8 - 4$

51. $8 - (-4)$ **52.** $-9 - (-5)$

53. $0 - (-5)$ **54.** $0 - 75$

55. $\dfrac{5}{3} - \dfrac{7}{6}$ **56.** $-\dfrac{5}{9} - \dfrac{5}{3}$

Subtract vertically. See Example 6. (Objective 3)

57. $\begin{array}{r} 8 \\ \underline{-4} \end{array}$ **58.** $\begin{array}{r} 8 \\ \underline{--3} \end{array}$

59. $\begin{array}{r} -10 \\ -\underline{-3} \end{array}$ **60.** $\begin{array}{r} -13 \\ -\underline{5} \end{array}$

Simplify each expression. See Examples 7–8. (Objective 3)

61. $+3 - [(-4) - 3]$ **62.** $-5 - [4 - (-2)]$

63. $(5 - 3) + (3 - 5)$ **64.** $(3 - 5) - [5 - (-3)]$

65. $5 - [4 + (-2) - 5]$ **66.** $3 - [-(-2) + 5]$

67. $\dfrac{5 - (-4)}{3 - (-6)}$ **68.** $\dfrac{2 + (-3)}{-3 - (-4)}$

69. $\left(\dfrac{5}{2} - 3\right) - \left(\dfrac{3}{2} - 5\right)$

70. $\left(\dfrac{7}{3} - \dfrac{5}{6}\right) - \left[\dfrac{5}{6} - \left(-\dfrac{7}{3}\right)\right]$

71. $(5.2 - 2.5) - (5.25 - 5)$

72. $(3.7 - 8.25) - (3.75 + 2.5)$

Use a calculator to evaluate each quantity. Round the answers to two decimal places. See Example 11. (Objective 5)

73. $2.34 - 3.47 + 0.72$

74. $3.47 - 0.72 - 2.34$

75. $(2.34)^2 - (3.47)^2 - (0.72)^2$

76. $(0.72)^2 - (2.34)^2 + (3.47)^3$

ADDITIONAL PRACTICE   *Simplify each expression.*

77. $9 + (-11)$ **78.** $10 + (-13)$

79. $[-4 + (-3)] + [2 + (-2)]$

80. $[3 + (-1)] + [-2 + (-3)]$

81. $-4 + (-3 + 2) + (-3)$ **82.** $5 + [2 + (-5)] + (-2)$

83. $-|8 + (-4)| + 7$ **84.** $\left|\dfrac{3}{5} + \left(-\dfrac{4}{5}\right)\right|$

85. $-5.2 + |-2.5 + (-4)|$ **86.** $6.8 + |8.6 + (-1.1)|$

87. $-3\dfrac{1}{2} - 5\dfrac{1}{4}$ **88.** $2\dfrac{1}{2} - \left(-3\dfrac{1}{2}\right)$

89. $-6.7 - (-2.5)$ **90.** $25.3 - 17.5$

91. $\dfrac{-4 - 2}{-[2 + (-3)]}$ **92.** $\dfrac{5}{-4 - (-6)} - \dfrac{-4}{8 + (-6)}$

93. $\left(\dfrac{3}{4} - \dfrac{4}{5}\right) - \left(\dfrac{2}{3} + \dfrac{1}{4}\right)$

94. $\left(3\dfrac{1}{2} - 2\dfrac{1}{2}\right) - \left[5\dfrac{1}{3} - \left(-5\dfrac{2}{3}\right)\right]$

APPLICATIONS

Use the appropriate signed numbers and operations for each problem. See Examples 9–10. (Objective 4)

95. College tuition   A student owes $575 in tuition. If she is awarded a scholarship that will pay $400 of the bill, what will she still owe?

96. Dieting   Scott weighed 212 pounds but lost 24 pounds during a three-month diet. What does Scott weigh now?

97. Temperatures   The temperature rose 13 degrees in 1 hour and then dropped 4 degrees in the next hour. What signed number represents the net change in temperature?

98. Mountain climbing   A team of mountaineers climbed 2,347 feet one day and then came down 597 feet to a good spot to make camp. What signed number represents their net change in altitude?

99. Temperatures   The temperature fell from zero to 14° below one night. By 5:00 P.M. the next day, the temperature had risen 10 degrees. What was the temperature at 5:00 P.M.?

100. History   In 1897, Joseph Thompson discovered the electron. Fifty-four years later, the first fission reactor was built. Nineteen years before the reactor was erected, James Chadwick discovered the neutron. In what year was the neutron discovered?

101. History   The Greek mathematician Euclid was alive in 300 BC. The English mathematician Sir Isaac Newton was alive in AD 1700. How many years apart did they live?

102. Banking   A student deposited $212 in a new checking account, wrote a check for $173, and deposited another $312. Find the balance in his account.

103. Military science   An army retreated 2,300 meters. After regrouping, it moved forward 1,750 meters. The next day it gained another 1,875 meters. What was the army's net gain?

104. Football   A football player gained and lost the yardage shown in the illustration on six consecutive plays. How many total yards were gained or lost on the six plays?

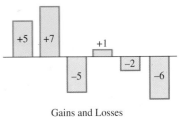

Gains and Losses

105. Aviation   A pilot flying at 32,000 feet is instructed to descend to 28,000 feet. How many feet must he descend?

106. Stock market   Tuesday's high and low prices for Transitronics stock were 37.125 and 31.625. Find the range of prices for this stock.

107. Temperatures   Find the difference between a temperature of 32° above zero and a temperature of 27° above zero.

108. Temperatures   Find the difference between a temperature of 3° below zero and a temperature of 21° below zero.

109. Stock market   At the opening bell on Monday, the Dow Jones Industrial Average was 12,153. At the close, the Dow was down 23 points, but news of a half-point drop in interest rates on Tuesday sent the market up 57 points. What was the Dow average after the market closed on Tuesday?

110. Stock market   On a Monday morning, the Dow Jones Industrial Average opened at 11,917. For the week, the Dow rose 29 points on Monday and 12 points on Wednesday. However, it fell 53 points on Tuesday and 27 points on both Thursday and Friday. Where did the Dow close on Friday?

111. Buying stock   A woman owned 500 shares of Microsoft stock, bought another 500 shares on a price dip, and then sold 300 shares when the price rose. How many shares does she now own?

112. Small business   Maria earned $2,532 in a part-time business. However, $633 of the earnings went for taxes. Find Maria's net earnings.

Use a calculator to help answer each question.

113. Balancing the books   On January 1, Sally had $437.45 in the bank. During the month, she had deposits of $25.17, $37.93, and $45.26, and she had withdrawals of $17.13, $83.44, and $22.58. How much was in her account at the end of the month?

114. Small business   The owner of a small business has a gross income of $97,345.32. However, he paid $37,675.66 in expenses plus $7,537.45 in taxes, $3,723.41 in health-care premiums, and $5,767.99 in pension payments. What was his profit?

115. Closing real estate transactions   A woman sold her house for $115,000. Her fees at closing were $78 for preparing a deed, $446 for title work, $216 for revenue stamps, and a sales commission of $7,612.32. In addition, there was a deduction of $23,445.11 to pay off her old mortgage. As part of the deal, the buyer agreed to pay half of the title work. How much money did the woman receive after closing?

116. Winning the lottery   Mike won $500,000 in a state lottery. He will get $\frac{1}{20}$ of the sum each year for the next 20 years. After he receives his first installment, he plans to pay off a car loan of $7,645.12 and give his son $10,000 for college. By paying off the car loan, he will receive a rebate of 2% of the loan. If he must pay income tax of 28% on his first installment, how much will he have left to spend?

WRITING ABOUT MATH

117. Explain why the sum of two negative numbers is always negative, and the sum of two positive numbers is always positive.

118. Explain why the sum of a negative number and a positive number could be either negative or positive.

SOMETHING TO THINK ABOUT

119. Think of two numbers. First, add the absolute values of the two numbers, and write your answer. Second, add the two numbers, take the absolute value of that sum, and write that answer. Do the two answers agree? Can you find two numbers that produce different answers? When do you get answers that agree, and when don't you?

120. "Think of a very small number," requests the teacher. "One one-millionth," answers Charles. "Negative one million," responds Mia. Explain why either answer might be considered correct.

SECTION 1.5   Multiplying and Dividing Real Numbers

Objectives

1 Multiply two or more real numbers.
2 Divide two real numbers.
3 Use signed numbers and an operation to model an application problem.
4 Use a calculator to multiply or divide two real numbers.

Getting Ready

Find each product or quotient.

1. $8 \cdot 7$ **2.** $9 \cdot 6$ **3.** $8 \cdot 9$ **4.** $7 \cdot 9$

5. $\dfrac{81}{9}$ **6.** $\dfrac{48}{8}$ **7.** $\dfrac{64}{8}$ **8.** $\dfrac{56}{7}$

In this section, we will develop the rules for multiplying and dividing real numbers. We will see that the rules for multiplication and division are very similar.

1 **Multiply two or more real numbers.**

Because the times sign, $\times$, looks like the letter x, it is seldom used in algebra. Instead, we will use a dot, parentheses, or no symbol at all to denote multiplication. Each of the following expressions indicates the *product* obtained when two real numbers x and y are multiplied.

$$x \cdot y \qquad (x)(y) \qquad x(y) \qquad (x)y \qquad xy$$

To develop rules for multiplying real numbers, we rely on the definition of multiplication. The expression $5 \cdot 4$ indicates that 4 is to be used as a term in a sum five times.

$5(4) = 4 + 4 + 4 + 4 + 4 = 20$ Read 5(4) as "5 times 4."

Likewise, the expression $5(-4)$ indicates that -4 is to be used as a term in a sum five times.

$5(-4) = (-4) + (-4) + (-4) + (-4) + (-4) = -20$ Read 5(−4) as "5 times negative 4."

If multiplying by a positive number indicates repeated addition, it is reasonable that multiplication by a negative number indicates repeated subtraction. The expression $(-5)4$, for example, means that 4 is to be used as a term in a repeated subtraction five times.

$$\begin{aligned}
(-5)4 &= -(4) - (4) - (4) - (4) - (4) \\
&= (-4) + (-4) + (-4) + (-4) + (-4) \\
&= -20
\end{aligned}$$

Likewise, the expression $(-5)(-4)$ indicates that -4 is to be used as a term in a repeated subtraction five times.

$$\begin{aligned}
(-5)(-4) &= -(-4) - (-4) - (-4) - (-4) - (-4) \\
&= -(-4) + [-(-4)] + [-(-4)] + [-(-4)] + [-(-4)] \\
&= 4 + 4 + 4 + 4 + 4 \\
&= 20
\end{aligned}$$

The expression $0(-2)$ indicates that -2 is to be used zero times as a term in a repeated addition. Thus,

$$0(-2) = 0$$

Finally, the expression $(-3)(1) = -3$ suggests that the product of any number and 1 is the number itself.

The previous results suggest the following rules.

Rules for Multiplying Signed Numbers

To multiply two real numbers, multiply their absolute values.

1. *If the numbers are positive,* the product is positive.

2. *If the numbers are negative,* the product is positive.

3. *If one number is positive and the other is negative,* the product is negative.

4. Any number multiplied by 0 is 0: $a \cdot 0 = 0 \cdot a = 0$.

5. Any number multiplied by 1 is the number itself: $a \cdot 1 = 1 \cdot a = a$.

EXAMPLE 1 Find each product: **a.** $4(-7)$ **b.** $(-5)(-4)$ **c.** $(-7)(6)$ **d.** $8(6)$ **e.** $(-3)^2$ **f.** $(-3)^3$ **g.** $(-3)(5)(-4)$ **h.** $(-4)(-2)(-3)$.

Solution **a.** $4(-7) = (-4 \cdot 7)$
$= -28$

b. $(-5)(-4) = +(5 \cdot 4)$
$= +20$

c. $(-7)(6) = -(7 \cdot 6)$
$= -42$

d. $8(6) = +(8 \cdot 6)$
$= +48$

e. $(-3)^2 = (-3)(-3)$
$= +9$

f. $(-3)^3 = (-3)(-3)(-3)$
$= 9(-3)$
$= -27$

g. $(-3)(5)(-4) = (-15)(-4)$
$= +60$

h. $(-4)(-2)(-3) = 8(-3)$
$= -24$

⇨ **SELF CHECK 1** Find each product: **a.** $-7(5)$ **b.** $-12(-7)$ **c.** $(-5)^2$ **d.** $-2(-4)(-9)$.

EXAMPLE 2 Evaluate: **a.** $2 + (-3)(4)$ **b.** $-3(2-4)$ **c.** $(-2)^2 - 3^2$ **d.** $-(-2)^2 + 4$.

Solution **a.** $2 + (-3)(4) = 2 + (-12)$
$= -10$

b. $-3(2-4) = -3[2 + (-4)]$
$= -3(-2)$
$= 6$

c. $(-2)^2 - 3^2 = 4 - 9$
$= -5$

d. $-(-2)^2 + 4 = -4 + 4$
$= 0$

⇨ **SELF CHECK 2** Evaluate: **a.** $-4 - (-3)(5)$ **b.** $(-3.2)^2 - 2(-5)^3$.

EXAMPLE 3 Find each product: **a.** $\left(-\dfrac{2}{3}\right)\left(-\dfrac{6}{5}\right)$ **b.** $\left(\dfrac{3}{10}\right)\left(-\dfrac{5}{9}\right)$.

Solution **a.** $\left(-\dfrac{2}{3}\right)\left(-\dfrac{6}{5}\right) = +\left(\dfrac{2}{3} \cdot \dfrac{6}{5}\right)$
$= \dfrac{2 \cdot 6}{3 \cdot 5}$
$= \dfrac{12}{15}$
$= \dfrac{4}{5}$

b. $\left(\dfrac{3}{10}\right)\left(-\dfrac{5}{9}\right) = -\left(\dfrac{3}{10} \cdot \dfrac{5}{9}\right)$
$= -\dfrac{3 \cdot 5}{10 \cdot 9}$
$= -\dfrac{15}{90}$
$= -\dfrac{1}{6}$

⇨ **SELF CHECK 3** Evaluate: **a.** $\dfrac{3}{5}\left(-\dfrac{10}{9}\right)$ **b.** $-\left(\dfrac{15}{8}\right)\left(-\dfrac{16}{5}\right)$.

2 **Divide two real numbers.**

Recall that the result in a division is called a *quotient.* We know that 8 divided by 4 has a quotient of 2, and 18 divided by 6 has a quotient of 3.

$$\frac{8}{4} = 2, \text{ because } 2 \cdot 4 = 8 \qquad \frac{18}{6} = 3, \text{ because } 3 \cdot 6 = 18$$

These examples suggest that the following rule

$$\frac{a}{b} = c \quad \text{if and only if} \quad c \cdot b = a$$

is true for the division of any real number a by any nonzero real number b. For example,

$$\frac{+10}{+2} = +5, \text{ because } (+5)(+2) = +10.$$

$$\frac{-10}{-2} = +5, \text{ because } (+5)(-2) = -10.$$

$$\frac{+10}{-2} = -5, \text{ because } (-5)(-2) = +10.$$

$$\frac{-10}{+2} = -5, \text{ because } (-5)(+2) = -10.$$

Furthermore,

$$\frac{-10}{0} \text{ is undefined, because no number multiplied by 0 gives } -10.$$

$$\frac{0}{-10} = 0, \text{ because } 0(-10) = 0.$$

These examples suggest the rules for dividing real numbers.

Rules for Dividing Signed Numbers

To divide two real numbers, find the quotient of their absolute values.

1. *If the numbers are positive,* the quotient is positive.

2. *If the numbers are negative,* the quotient is positive.

3. *If one number is positive and the other is negative,* the quotient is negative.

4. $\frac{a}{0}$ is undefined.   **5.** $\frac{a}{1} = a$

6. If $a \neq 0$, then $\frac{0}{a} = 0$.   **7.** If $a \neq 0$, then $\frac{a}{a} = 1$.

EXAMPLE 4   Find each quotient: **a.** $\frac{36}{18}$ **b.** $\frac{-44}{11}$ **c.** $\frac{27}{-9}$ **d.** $\frac{-64}{-8}$.

Solution   **a.** $\frac{36}{18} = +\frac{36}{18} = 2$ The quotient of two numbers with like signs is positive.

b. $\frac{-44}{11} = -\frac{44}{11} = -4$ The quotient of two numbers with unlike signs is negative.

c. $\dfrac{27}{-9} = -\dfrac{27}{9} = -3$ The quotient of two numbers with unlike signs is negative.

d. $\dfrac{-64}{-8} = +\dfrac{64}{8} = 8$ The quotient of two numbers with like signs is positive.

⇨ **SELF CHECK 4**   Find each quotient: **a.** $\dfrac{-72.6}{12.1}$ **b.** $\dfrac{-24.51}{-4.3}$.

EXAMPLE 5   Evaluate: **a.** $\dfrac{16(-4)}{-(-64)}$ **b.** $\dfrac{(-4)^3(16)}{-64}$.

Solution   **a.** $\dfrac{16(-4)}{-(-64)} = \dfrac{-64}{+64}$

$= -1$

b. $\dfrac{(-4)^3(16)}{-64} = \dfrac{(-64)(16)}{(-64)}$

$= 16$

⇨ **SELF CHECK 5**   Evaluate: $\dfrac{-64 + 16}{-(-4)^2}$.

When dealing with three or more real numbers, we use the rules for the order of operations.

EXAMPLE 6   Evaluate: **a.** $\dfrac{(-50)(10)(-5)}{-50 - 5(-5)}$ **b.** $\dfrac{3(-50)(10) + 2(10)(-5)}{2(-50 + 10)}$.

Solution   **a.** $\dfrac{(-50)(10)(-5)}{-50 - 5(-5)} = \dfrac{(-500)(-5)}{-50 + 25}$ Multiply.

$= \dfrac{2{,}500}{-25}$ Multiply and add.

$= -100$ Divide.

b. $\dfrac{3(-50)(10) + 2(10)(-5)}{2(-50 + 10)} = \dfrac{-150(10) + (20)(-5)}{2(-40)}$ Multiply and add.

$= \dfrac{-1{,}500 - 100}{-80}$ Multiply.

$= \dfrac{-1{,}600}{-80}$ Subtract.

$= 20$ Divide.

⇨ **SELF CHECK 6**   Evaluate: $\dfrac{2(-50)(10) - 3(-5) - 5}{3[10 - (-5)]}$.

3 Use signed numbers and an operation to model an application problem.

EXAMPLE 7   **TEMPERATURE CHANGES** If the temperature is dropping 4° each hour, how much warmer was it 3 hours ago?

Solution   A temperature drop of 4° per hour can be represented by −4° per hour. "Three hours ago" can be represented by −3. The temperature 3 hours ago is the product of −3 and −4.

$$(-3)(-4) = +12$$

The temperature was 12° warmer 3 hours ago.

SELF CHECK 7   How much colder will it be after 5 hours?

EXAMPLE 8   **STOCK REPORTS** In its annual report, a corporation reports its performance on a per-share basis. When a company with 35 million shares loses $2.3 million, find the per-share loss.

Solution   A loss of $2.3 million can be represented by −2,300,000. Because there are 35 million shares, the per-share loss can be represented by the quotient $\frac{-2,300,000}{35,000,000}$.

$$\frac{-2,300,000}{35,000,000} \approx -0.065714286 \qquad \text{Use a calculator.}$$

The company lost about 6.6¢ per share.

SELF CHECK 8   If the company earns $1.5 million in the following year, find its per-share gain for that year.

4 Use a calculator to multiply or divide two real numbers.

A calculator can be used to multiply and divide positive and negative numbers. To evaluate $(-345.678)(-527.339)$, we enter these numbers and press these keys:

345.678 | +/− | × | 527.339 | +/− | = | Using a calculator with a | +/− | key

| (−) | 345.678 | × | − | 527.339 | ENTER | Using a graphing calculator

The display will read | 182289.4908 |.

To evaluate $\frac{-345.678}{-527.339}$, we enter these numbers and press these keys:

345.678 | +/− | ÷ | 527.339 | +/− | = | Using a calculator with a | +/− | key

| (−) | 345.678 | ÷ | (−) | 527.339 | ENTER | Using a graphing calculator

The display will read | 0.655513815 |.

SELF CHECK ANSWERS   **1. a.** −35 **b.** 84 **c.** 25 **d.** −72 **2. a.** 11 **b.** 260.24 **3. a.** $-\frac{2}{3}$ **b.** 6 **4. a.** −6 **b.** 5.7 **5.** 3 **6.** −22 **7.** 20° colder **8.** about 4.3¢

NOW TRY THIS

Perform the operations.

1. $-2 - 3(1 - 6)$

2. $-3^2 - 4(3)(-1)$

3. $\dfrac{5^2 - 2(6)(-1)}{45 - 5 \cdot 9}$

Determine the value of x that will make the fraction undefined.

4. $\dfrac{12}{x}$ **5.** $\dfrac{7}{x + 1}$

1.5 EXERCISES

WARM-UPS   *Find each product or quotient.*

1. $1(-3)$

2. $-2(-5)$

3. $-2(3)(-4)$

4. $-2(-3)(-4)$

5. $\dfrac{-12}{6}$

6. $\dfrac{-10}{-5}$

7. $\dfrac{3(6)}{-2}$

8. $\dfrac{(-2)(-3)}{-6}$

9. $12 \div 4(-3)$

10. $-16 \div 2(-4)$

REVIEW

11. A concrete block weighs $37\frac{1}{2}$ pounds. How much will 30 of these blocks weigh?

12. If one brick weighs 1.3 pounds, how much will 500 bricks weigh?

13. Evaluate: $3^3 - 8(3)^2$.

14. Place $<$, $=$, or $>$ in the box to make a true statement:

$-2(-3 + 4)$ ▢ $-3[3 - (-4)]$

VOCABULARY AND CONCEPTS   *Fill in the blanks.*

15. The product of two positive numbers is _____.

16. The product of a _____ number and a negative number is negative.

17. The product of two negative numbers is _____.

18. The quotient of a _____ number and a positive number is negative.

19. The quotient of two negative numbers is _____.

20. Any number multiplied by __ is 0.

21. $a \cdot 1 =$ __

22. The quotient $\dfrac{a}{0}$ is _____.

23. If $a \neq 0$, $\dfrac{0}{a} =$ __.

24. If $a \neq 0$, $\dfrac{a}{a} =$ __.

GUIDED PRACTICE

Perform the operations. See Example 1. (Objective 1)

25. $(+6)(+8)$

26. $(-9)(-7)$

27. $(-8)(-7)$

28. $(9)(-6)$

29. $(+12)(-12)$

30. $(-9)(12)$

31. $(-32)(-14)$

32. $(-27)(14)$

33. $(-2)(3)(4)$

34. $(5)(0)(-3)$

35. $(-2)^2$

36. $(-1)^3$

37. $(-4)^3$

38. $(-6)^2$

39. $(3)(-4)(-6)$

40. $(-1)(-3)(-6)$

Perform the operations. See Example 2. (Objective 1)

41. $2 + (-1)(-3)$

42. $-3 - (-1)(2)$

43. $(-1 + 2)(-3)$

44. $2[-1 - (-3)]$

45. $[-1 + (+3)][-1 + (-3)]$

46. $[2 + (-3)][-1 - (-3)]$

47. $-1(2) + 2(-3)^2$

48. $(-1)^2(2) + (-3)$

Perform the operation. See Example 3. (Objective 1)

49. $\left(\dfrac{1}{2}\right)(-32)$

50. $\left(-\dfrac{3}{4}\right)(12)$

51. $\left(-\dfrac{3}{4}\right)\left(-\dfrac{8}{3}\right)$

52. $\left(-\dfrac{2}{5}\right)\left(\dfrac{15}{2}\right)$

Perform the operation. See Example 4. (Objective 2)

53. $\dfrac{80}{-20}$

54. $\dfrac{-66}{33}$

55. $\dfrac{-110}{-55}$

56. $\dfrac{200}{40}$

57. $\dfrac{-160}{40}$

58. $\dfrac{-250}{-25}$

59. $\dfrac{320}{-16}$

60. $\dfrac{180}{-36}$

Perform the operation. See Example 5. (Objective 2)

61. $\dfrac{3(4)}{-2}$

62. $\dfrac{4(5)}{-2}$

63. $\dfrac{5(-18)}{3}$

64. $\dfrac{-18}{-2(3)}$

Perform the operations. If the result is undefined, so indicate. See Example 6. (Objective 2)

65. $\dfrac{8 - 12}{-2}$

66. $\dfrac{16 - 2}{2 - 9}$

67. $\dfrac{20 - 25}{7 - 12}$

68. $\dfrac{2(15)^2 - 2}{-2^3 + 1}$

69. $\dfrac{6 - 2(3)}{-3(8 - 4)}$

70. $\dfrac{2(-25)(10) + 4(5)(-5)}{5(125 - 25)}$

71. $\dfrac{-4(3) - 5}{3(2) - 6}$

72. $\dfrac{-5(-2) + 4}{-4(2) + 8}$

 Use a calculator to evaluate each expression. (Objective 4)

73. $\dfrac{(-6) + 4(-3)}{4 - 6}$

74. $\dfrac{4 - 2(4)(-3) + (-3)}{4 - (-6) - 3}$

75. $\dfrac{4(-6)^2(-3) + 4^2(-6)}{2(-6) - 2(-3)}$

76. $\dfrac{[4^2 - 2(-6)](-3)^2}{-4(-3)}$

ADDITIONAL PRACTICE   *Simplify each expression.*

77. $(-3)\left(-\dfrac{1}{3}\right)$

78. $(5)\left(-\dfrac{2}{5}\right)$

79. $(-1)(2^3)$

80. $[2(-3)]^2$

81. $(-2)(-2)(-2)(-3)(-4)$

82. $(-5)(4)(3)(-2)(-1)$

83. $(2)(-5)(-6)(-7)$

84. $(-3)(-5)(-5)(-2)$

85. $(-7)^2$

86. $(-2)^3$

87. $-(-3)^2$

88. $-(-1)(-3)^2$

89. $(-1)^2[2 - (-3)]$

90. $2^2[-1 - (-3)]$

91. $-3(-1) - (-3)(2)$

92. $-1(2)(-3) + 6$

93. $(-1)^3(-2)^2 + (-3)^2$

94. $(-2)^3[3 - (-5)]$

95. $\dfrac{4 + (-18)}{-2}$

96. $\dfrac{-2(3)(4)}{3 - 1}$

97. $\dfrac{-2(5)(4)}{-3 + 1}$

98. $\dfrac{-2 + 3 - (-18)}{4(-5) + 1}$

99. $\dfrac{1}{2} - \dfrac{2}{3} - \dfrac{3}{4}$

100. $-\dfrac{2}{3} + \dfrac{1}{2} + \dfrac{3}{4}$

101. $\dfrac{1}{2} - \dfrac{2}{3}$

102. $-\dfrac{2}{3} - \dfrac{3}{4}$

103. $\left(\dfrac{1}{2} - \dfrac{2}{3}\right)\left(\dfrac{1}{2} + \dfrac{2}{3}\right)$

104. $\left(\dfrac{1}{2} + \dfrac{3}{4}\right)\left(\dfrac{1}{2} - \dfrac{3}{4}\right)$

105. $\left(\dfrac{1}{3} - \dfrac{1}{2}\right)\left(\dfrac{2}{3} - \dfrac{1}{2}\right)$

106. $\left(\dfrac{2}{5} - \dfrac{1}{4}\right)\left(\dfrac{1}{5} - \dfrac{3}{4}\right)$

APPLICATIONS   *Use signed numbers and one or more operations to answer each question. See Examples 7–8. (Objective 3)*

107. Temperature changes   If the temperature is increasing 2 degrees each hour for 3 hours, what product of signed numbers represents the temperature change?

108. Temperature changes   If the temperature is decreasing 2 degrees each hour for 3 hours, what product of signed numbers represents the temperature change?

109. Loss of revenue   A manufacturer's website normally produces sales of $350 per hour, but was offline for 15 hours due to a systems virus. What product of signed numbers represents the loss of revenue during this time?

110. Draining pools   A pool is emptying at the rate of 12 gallons per minute. What product of signed numbers would represent how much more water was in the pool 2 hours ago?

111. Filling pools   Water from a pipe is filling a pool at the rate of 23 gallons per minute. What product of signed numbers represents how much less water was in the pool 2 hours ago?

112. Mowing lawns   Justin worked all day mowing lawns and was paid $8 per hour. If he had $94 at the end of an 8-hour day, how much did he have before he started working?

113. Temperatures   Suppose that the temperature is dropping at the rate of 3 degrees each hour. If the temperature has dropped 18 degrees, what signed number expresses how many hours the temperature has been falling?

114. Dieting   A man lost 37.5 pounds. If he lost 2.5 pounds each week, how long has he been dieting?

115. Inventories   A spreadsheet is used to record inventory losses at a warehouse. The items, their cost, and the number missing are listed in the table.

a. Find the value of the lost MP3 players.

b. Find the value of the lost cell phones.

c. Find the value of the lost GPS systems.

d. Find the total losses.

	A	B	C	D
	Item	**Cost**	**Number of units**	**$ Losses**
1	MP3 player	75	-32	
2	Cell phone	57	-17	
3	GPS system	87	-12	

116. Inventories   A spreadsheet is used to record inventory losses at a warehouse. The item, the number of units, and the dollar losses are listed in the table.

   a. Find the cost of a truck.

   b. Find the cost of a drum.

   c. Find the cost of a ball.

	A	**B**	**C**	**D**
	Item	**Cost**	**Number of units**	**$ Losses**
1	Truck		-12	$-$60$
2	Drum		-7	$-$49$
3	Ball		-13	$-$39$

 Use a calculator to help answer each question.

117. Stock market   Over a 7-day period, the Dow Jones Industrial Average had gains of 26, 35, and 17 points. In that period, there were also losses of 25, 31, 12, and 24 points. What is the average daily performance over the 7-day period?

118. Astronomy   Light travels at the rate of 186,000 miles per second. How long will it take light to travel from the Sun to Venus?   (*Hint:* The distance from the Sun to Venus is 67,000,000 miles.)

119. Saving for school   A student has saved $15,000 to attend graduate school. If she estimates that her expenses will be $613.50 a month while in school, does she have enough to complete an 18-month master's degree program?

120. Earnings per share   Over a five-year period, a corporation reported profits of $18 million, $21 million, and $33 million. It also reported losses of $5 million and $71 million. What is the average gain (or loss) each year?

WRITING ABOUT MATH

121. Explain how you would decide whether the product of several numbers is positive or negative.

122. Describe two situations in which negative numbers are useful.

SOMETHING TO THINK ABOUT

123. If the quotient of two numbers is undefined, what would their product be?

124. If the product of five numbers is negative, how many of the factors could be negative?

125. If x^5 is a negative number, can you determine whether x is also negative?

126. If x^6 is a positive number, can you determine whether x is also positive?

SECTION 1.6   Algebraic Expressions

Objectives

1 Translate an English phrase into an algebraic expression.

2 Evaluate an algebraic expression when given values for its variables.

3 Identify the number of terms in an algebraic expression and identify the numerical coefficient of each term.

Vocabulary

algebraic expression   constant   term   numerical coefficient

Identify each of the following as a sum, difference, product, or quotient.

1. $x + 3$ **2.** $57x$

3. $\dfrac{x}{9}$ **4.** $19 - y$

5. $\dfrac{x - 7}{3}$ **6.** $x - \dfrac{7}{3}$

7. $5(x + 2)$ **8.** $5x + 10$

Algebraic expressions are a fundamental concept in the study of algebra. They convey mathematical operations and are the building blocks of many equations, the main topic of the next chapter.

①   Translate an English phrase into an algebraic expression.

Variables and numbers can be combined with the operations of arithmetic to produce algebraic expressions. For example, if x and y are variables, the **algebraic expression** $x + y$ represents the sum of x and y, and the algebraic expression $x - y$ represents their difference.

There are many other ways to express addition or subtraction with algebraic expressions, as shown in Tables 1-3 and 1-4.

The phrase	translates into the algebraic expression
the *sum* of t and 12	$t + 12$
5 *plus* s	$5 + s$
7 *added to* a	$a + 7$
10 *more than* q	$q + 10$
12 *greater than* m	$m + 12$
l *increased by* m	$l + m$
exceeds p *by* 50	$p + 50$

Table 1-3

The phrase	translates into the algebraic expression
the *difference* of 50 and r	$50 - r$
1,000 *minus* q	$1{,}000 - q$
15 *less than* w	$w - 15$
t *decreased by* q	$t - q$
12 *reduced by* m	$12 - m$
l *subtracted from* 250	$250 - l$
2,000 *less* p	$2{,}000 - p$

Table 1-4

EXAMPLE 1   Let x represent a certain number. Write an expression that represents   **a.** the number that is 5 more than x **b.** the number 12 decreased by x.

Solution   **a.** The number "5 more than x" is the number found by adding 5 to x. It is represented by $x + 5$.

b. The number "12 decreased by x" is the number found by subtracting x from 12. It is represented by $12 - x$.

 **SELF CHECK 1**   Let y represent a certain number. Write an expression that represents y increased by 25.

EXAMPLE 2   **INCOME TAXES**   Bob worked x hours preparing his income tax return. He worked 3 hours less than that on his son's return. Write an expression that represents
a. the number of hours he spent preparing his son's return
b. the total number of hours he worked.

Solution   **a.** Because he worked x hours on his own return and 3 hours less on his son's return, he worked $(x - 3)$ hours on his son's return.

b. Because he worked x hours on his own return and $(x - 3)$ hours on his son's return, the total time he spent on taxes was $[x + (x - 3)]$ hours.

⇨ **SELF CHECK 2**   Javier deposited $\$d$ in a bank account. Later, he withdrew \$500. Write an expression that represents the number of dollars in his account.

There are several ways to indicate the **product** of two numbers with algebraic expressions, as shown in Table 1-5.

The phrase	translates into the algebraic expression
the *product* of a and b	ab
25 *times* B	$25B$
twice x	$2x$
$\frac{1}{2}$ *of* z	$\frac{1}{2}z$
12 *multiplied by* m	$12m$

Table 1-5

EXAMPLE 3   Let x represent a certain number. Denote a number that is   **a.** twice as large as x
b. 5 more than 3 times x **c.** 4 less than $\frac{1}{2}$ of x.

Solution   **a.** The number "twice as large as x" is found by multiplying x by 2. It is represented by $2x$.

b. The number "5 more than 3 times x" is found by adding 5 to the product of 3 and x. It is represented by $3x + 5$.

c. The number "4 less than $\frac{1}{2}$ of x" is found by subtracting 4 from the product of $\frac{1}{2}$ and x. It is represented by $\frac{1}{2}x - 4$.

⇨ **SELF CHECK 3**   Find the product of 40 and t.

EXAMPLE 4   **STOCK VALUATIONS**   Jim owns x shares of Transitronics stock, valued at \$29 a share; y shares of Positone stock, valued at \$32 a share; and 300 shares of Baby Bell, valued at \$42 a share.
a. How many shares of stock does he own?
b. What is the value of his stock?

Solution   **a.** Because there are x shares of Transitronics, y shares of Positone, and 300 shares of Baby Bell, his total number of shares is $x + y + 300$.

b. The value of x shares of Transitronics is $\$29x$, the value of y shares of Positone is $\$32y$, and the value of 300 shares of Baby Bell is $\$42(300)$. The total value of the stock is $\$(29x + 32y + 12{,}600)$.

⇨ **SELF CHECK 4**   If water softener salt costs $\$p$ per bag, find the cost of 25 bags.

There are also several ways to indicate the quotient of two numbers with algebraic expressions, as shown in Table 1-6.

The phrase	translates into the algebraic expression
the *quotient* of 470 and *A*	$\dfrac{470}{A}$
B divided by C	$\dfrac{B}{C}$
the *ratio* of *h to* 5	$\dfrac{h}{5}$
x split into 5 equal parts	$\dfrac{x}{5}$

Table 1-6

EXAMPLE 5   Let x and y represent two numbers. Write an algebraic expression that represents the sum obtained when 3 times the first number is added to the quotient obtained when the second number is divided by 6.

Solution   Three times the first number x is denoted as $3x$. The quotient obtained when the second number y is divided by 6 is the fraction $\frac{y}{6}$. Their sum is expressed as $3x + \frac{y}{6}$.

⇨ SELF CHECK 5   If the cost c of a meal is split equally among 4 people, what is each person's share?

EXAMPLE 6   **CUTTING ROPES**   A 5-foot section is cut from the end of a rope that is l feet long. If the remaining rope is divided into three equal pieces, find an expression for the length of each of the equal pieces.

Solution   After a 5-foot section is cut from one end of l feet of rope, the rope that remains is $(l - 5)$ feet long. When that remaining rope is cut into 3 equal pieces, each piece will be $\dfrac{l - 5}{3}$ feet long. See Figure 1-24.

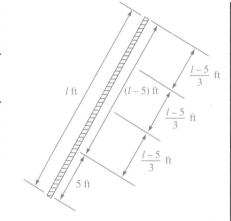

Figure 1-24

⇨ SELF CHECK 6   If a 7-foot section is cut from a rope that is l feet long and the remaining rope is divided into two equal pieces, find an expression for the length of each piece.

2   **Evaluate an algebraic expression when given values for its variables.**

Since variables represent numbers, algebraic expressions also represent numbers. We can evaluate algebraic expressions when we know the values of the variables.

EXAMPLE 7 If $x = 8$ and $y = 10$, evaluate **a.** $x + y$ **b.** $y - x$ **c.** $3xy$ **d.** $\dfrac{5x}{y - 5}$.

Solution We substitute 8 for x and 10 for y in each expression and simplify.

a. $x + y = 8 + 10$ **b.** $y - x = 10 - 8$
$= 18$ $= 2$

c. $3xy = (3)(8)(10)$
$= (24)(10)$ Do the multiplications from left to right.
$= 240$

d. $\dfrac{5x}{y - 5} = \dfrac{5(8)}{10 - 5}$

$= \dfrac{40}{5}$ Simplify the numerator and the denominator separately.

$= 8$ Simplify the fraction.

COMMENT When substituting a number for a variable in an expression, it is a good idea to write the number within parentheses. This will avoid mistaking 5(8) for 58.

⇨ **SELF CHECK 7** If $a = -2$ and $b = 5$, evaluate $\dfrac{6b + 2}{a + 2b}$.

EXAMPLE 8 If $x = -4$, $y = 8$, and $z = -6$, evaluate **a.** $\dfrac{7x^2 y}{2(y - z)}$ **b.** $\dfrac{3xz^2}{y(x + z)}$.

Solution We substitute -4 for x, 8 for y, and -6 for z in each expression and simplify.

a. $\dfrac{7x^2 y}{2(y - z)} = \dfrac{7(-4)^2(8)}{2[8 - (-6)]}$

$= \dfrac{7(16)(8)}{2(14)}$ $(-4)^2 = 16; 8 - (-6) = 14$

$= \dfrac{\overset{1}{\cancel{7}}\overset{1}{(\cancel{2})}\overset{1}{(\cancel{2})}(4)(8)}{\underset{1}{\cancel{2}}\underset{1}{(\cancel{2})}\underset{1}{(\cancel{7})}}$ Factor the numerator and denominator and divide out all common factors.

$= 32$ $4 \cdot 8 = 32$

b. $\dfrac{3xz^2}{y(x + z)} = \dfrac{3(-4)(-6)^2}{8[-4 + (-6)]}$

$= \dfrac{3(-4)(36)}{8(-10)}$ $(-6)^2 = 36; -4 + (-6) = -10$

$= \dfrac{3(\cancel{-2})\overset{1}{(\cancel{2})}\overset{1}{(\cancel{4})}(9)}{\underset{1}{(\cancel{4})}\underset{1}{(\cancel{-2})}(5)}$ Factor the numerator and denominator and divide out all common factors.

$= \dfrac{27}{5}$ $3(9) = 27; 1(5) = 5$

⇨ **SELF CHECK 8** If $a = -3$, $b = -2$, and $c = -5$, evaluate $\dfrac{b(a + c^2)}{abc}$.

3 Identify the number of terms in an algebraic expression and identify the numerical coefficient of each term.

Numbers without variables, such as 7, 21, and 23, are called **constants.** Expressions such as 37, xyz, and $32t$, which are constants, variables, or products of constants and variables, are called algebraic **terms.**

- The expression $3x + 5y$ contains two terms. The first term is $3x$, and the second term is $5y$.
- The expression $xy + (-7)$ contains two terms. The first term is xy, and the second term is -7.
- The expression $3 + x + 2y$ contains three terms. The first term is 3, the second term is x, and the third term is $2y$.

Numbers and variables that are part of a product are called **factors.** For example,

- The product $7x$ has two factors, which are 7 and x.
- The product $-3xy$ has three factors, which are -3, x, and y.
- The product $\frac{1}{2}abc$ has four factors, which are $\frac{1}{2}$, a, b, and c.

The number factor of a product is called its **numerical coefficient.** The numerical coefficient (or just the *coefficient*) of $7x$ is 7. The coefficient of $-3xy$ is -3, and the coefficient of $\frac{1}{2}abc$ is $\frac{1}{2}$. The coefficient of terms such as x, ab, and rst is understood to be 1.

$$x = 1x, \qquad ab = 1ab, \qquad \text{and} \qquad rst = 1rst$$

EXAMPLE 9
  a. The expression $5x + y$ has two terms. The coefficient of its first term is 5. The coefficient of its second term is 1.
  b. The expression $-17wxyz$ has one term, which contains the five factors -17, w, x, y, and z. Its coefficient is -17.
  c. The expression 37 has one term, the constant 37. Its coefficient is 37.
  d. The expression $3x^2 - 2x$ has two terms. The coefficient of the first term is 3. Since $3x^2 - 2x$ can be written as $3x^2 + (-2x)$, the coefficient of the second term is -2.

▷ **SELF CHECK 9**   How many terms does the expression $3x^2 - 2x + 7$ have? Find the sum of the coefficients.

▷ **SELF CHECK ANSWERS**   **1.** $y + 25$ **2.** $d - 500$ **3.** $40t$ **4.** $\$25p$ **5.** $\frac{c}{4}$ **6.** $\frac{l-7}{2}$ ft   **7.** 4   **8.** $\frac{22}{15}$ **9.** 3, 8

NOW TRY THIS

If $a = -2$, $b = -1$, and $c = 8$, evaluate the expressions.

1. $3b^2$

2. $\dfrac{a - b}{c - a}$

3. $b^2 - 4ac$

4. Write $2(a - b)$ as an English phrase.

1.6 EXERCISES

WARM-UPS   *If $x = -2$ and $y = 3$, find the value of each expression.*

1. $x + y$ **2.** $7x$

3. $7x + y$ **4.** $7(x + y)$

5. $4x^2$ **6.** $(4x)^2$

7. $-3x^2$ **8.** $(-3x)^2$

REVIEW   *Evaluate each expression.*

9. $0.14 \cdot 3{,}800$ **10.** $\dfrac{3}{5}$ of $4{,}765$

11. $\dfrac{-4 + (7 - 9)}{(-9 - 7) + 4}$ **12.** $\dfrac{5}{4}\left(1 - \dfrac{3}{5}\right)$

VOCABULARY AND CONCEPTS   *Fill in the blanks.*

13. The answer to an addition problem is called a _____.

14. The answer to a _____ problem is called a difference.

15. The answer to a _____ problem is called a product.

16. The answer to a division problem is called a _____.

17. An _____ expression is a combination of variables, numbers, and the operation symbols for addition, subtraction, multiplication, or division.

18. To _____ an algebraic expression, we substitute values for the variables and simplify.

19. A _____ is the product of constants and/or variables and the numerical part is called the _____.

20. Terms that have no variables are called _____.

GUIDED PRACTICE

Let x and y represent two real numbers. Write an algebraic expression to denote each quantity. See Example 1. (Objective 1)

21. The sum of x and y

22. The sum of twice x and twice y

23. The difference obtained when x is subtracted from y

24. The difference obtained when twice x is subtracted from y

Let x, y, and z represent three real numbers. Write an algebraic expression to denote each quantity. See Example 3. (Objective 1)

25. The product of x and y

26. The product of x and twice y

27. The product of 3, x, and y

28. The product of 7 and $2z$

Let x, y, and z represent three real numbers. Write an algebraic expression to denote each quantity. Assume that no denominators are 0. See Example 5. (Objective 1)

29. The quotient obtained when y is divided by x

30. The quotient obtained when the sum of x and y is divided by z

31. The quotient obtained when the product of 3 and z is divided by the product of 4 and x

32. The quotient obtained when the sum of x and y is divided by the sum of y and z

Evaluate each expression if $x = -2$, $y = 5$, and $z = -3$. See Examples 7–8. (Objective 2)

33. $x + y$ **34.** $x - z$

35. xyz **36.** $x^2 z$

37. $\dfrac{yz}{x}$ **38.** $\dfrac{xy - 2}{z}$

39. $\dfrac{3(x + z)}{y}$ **40.** $\dfrac{x + y + z}{y^2}$

41. $\dfrac{x(y + z) - 25}{(x + z)^2 - y^2}$ **42.** $\dfrac{(x + y)(y + z)}{x + z + y}$

43. $\dfrac{3(x + z^2) + 4}{y(x - z)}$ **44.** $\dfrac{x(y^2 - 2z) - 1}{z(y - x^2)}$

Give the number of terms in each algebraic expression and also give the numerical coefficient of the first term. See Example 9. (Objective 3)

45. $6d$ **46.** $-4c + 3d$

47. $-xy - 4t + 35$ **48.** xy

49. $3ab + bc - cd - ef$ **50.** $-2xyz + cde - 14$

51. $-4xyz + 7xy - z$ **52.** $5uvw - 4uv + 8uw$

53. $3x + 4y + 2z + 2$

54. $7abc - 9ab + 2bc + a - 1$

ADDITIONAL PRACTICE

Let x, y, and z represent three real numbers. Write an algebraic expression to denote each quantity. Assume that no denominators are 0.

55. The sum obtained when the quotient of x divided by y is added to z

56. y decreased by x

57. z less the product of x and y

58. z less than the product of x and y

59. The quotient obtained when the product of x and y is divided by the sum of x and z

60. The sum of the product xy and the quotient obtained when y is divided by z

61. The number obtained when x decreased by 4 is divided by the product of 3 and y

62. The number obtained when $2z$ minus $5y$ is divided by the sum of x and $3y$

Let x, y, and z represent three real numbers. Write each algebraic expression as an English phrase. Assume that no denominators are 0.

63. $\dfrac{3 + x}{y}$

64. $3 + \dfrac{x}{y}$

65. $xy(x + y)$

66. $(x + y + z)(xyz)$

67. $x + 3$

68. $y - 2$

69. $\dfrac{x}{y}$

70. xz

71. $2xy$

72. $\dfrac{x + y}{2}$

73. $\dfrac{5}{x + y}$

74. $\dfrac{3x}{y + z}$

Let x = 8, y = 4, and z = 2. Write each phrase as an algebraic expression, and evaluate it. Assume that no denominators are 0.

75. The sum of x and z

76. The product of x, y, and z

77. z less than y

78. The quotient obtained when y is divided by z

79. 3 less than the product of y and z

80. 7 less than the sum of x and y

81. The quotient obtained when the product of x and y is divided by z

82. The quotient obtained when 10 greater than x is divided by z

Consider the algebraic expression $29xyz + 23xy + 19x$.

83. What are the factors of the third term?

84. What are the factors of the second term?

85. What factor is common to the first and third terms?

86. What factor is common to all three terms?

Consider the algebraic expression $3xyz + 5xy + 17xz$.

87. What are the factors of the first term?

88. What are the factors of the second term?

89. What are the factors of the third term?

90. What factor is common to all three terms?

Consider the algebraic expression $5xy + yt + 8xyt$.

91. Find the numerical coefficients of each term.

92. What factor is common to all three terms?

93. What factors are common to the first and third terms?

94. What factors are common to the second and third terms?

Consider the algebraic expression $3xy + y + 25xyz$.

95. Find the numerical coefficient of each term and find their product.

96. Find the numerical coefficient of each term and find their sum.

97. What factors are common to the first and third terms?

98. What factor is common to all three terms?

APPLICATIONS   *Write an algebraic expression to denote each quantity. Assume that no denominators are 0. See Examples 2, 4, and 6. (Objective 1)*

99. Course loads   A man enrolls in college for c hours of credit, and his sister enrolls for 4 more hours than her brother. Write an expression that represents the number of hours the sister is taking.

100. Antique cars   An antique Ford has 25,000 more miles on its odometer than a newer car. If the newer car has traveled m miles, find an expression that represents the mileage on the Ford.

101. Heights of trees

    a. If h represents the height (in feet) of the oak tree, write an expression that represents the height of the crab apple tree.

    b. If c represents the height (in feet) of the crab apple tree, write an expression that represents the height of the oak.

crab apple   oak

102. T-bills   Write an expression that represents the value of t T-bills, each worth $9,987.

103. Real estate   Write an expression that represents the value of n vacant lots if each lot is worth $35,000.

104. Cutting ropes   A rope x feet long is cut into 5 equal pieces. Find an expression for the length of each piece.

105. Invisible tape   If x inches of tape have been used off the roll shown below, how many inches of tape are left on the roll?

106. Plumbing   A plumber cuts a pipe that is 12 feet long into x equal pieces. Find an expression for the length of each piece.

107. Comparing assets   A girl had d dollars, and her brother had $5 more than three times that amount. How much did the brother have?

108. Comparing investments   Wendy has x shares of stock. Her sister has 2 fewer shares than twice Wendy's shares. How many shares does her sister have?

109. Sorting records   In electronic data processing, the process of sorting records into sequential order is a common task. One sorting technique, called a **selection sort,** requires C comparisons to sort N records, where C and N are related by the formula

$$C = \frac{N(N-1)}{2}$$

How many comparisons are necessary to sort 10,000 records?

110. Sorting records   How many comparisons are necessary to sort 50,000 records? See Exercise 109.

WRITING ABOUT MATH

111. Distinguish between the meanings of these two phrases: "3 less than x" and "3 is less than x."

112. Distinguish between *factor* and *term.*

113. What is the purpose of using variables? Why aren't ordinary numbers enough?

114. In words, xy is "the product of x and y." However, $\frac{x}{y}$ is "the quotient obtained when x is divided by y." Explain why the extra words are needed.

SOMETHING TO THINK ABOUT

115. If the value of x were doubled, what would happen to the value of $37x$?

116. If the values of both x and y were doubled, what would happen to the value of $5xy^2$?

SECTION 1.7   Properties of Real Numbers

Objectives

1 Apply the closure properties by evaluating an expression for given values for variables.

2 Apply the commutative and associative properties.

3 Apply the distributive property of multiplication over addition to rewrite an expression.

4 Recognize the identity elements and find the additive and multiplicative inverse of a nonzero real number.

5 Identify the property that justifies a given statement.

closure properties   distributive property   reciprocal
commutative properties   identity elements   multiplicative inverse
associative properties   additive inverse

Perform the operations.

1. $3 + (5 + 9)$ **2.** $(3 + 5) + 9$
3. $23.7 + 14.9$ **4.** $14.9 + 23.7$
5. $7(5 + 3)$ **6.** $7 \cdot 5 + 7 \cdot 3$
7. $125.3 + (-125.3)$ **8.** $125.3\left(\dfrac{1}{125.3}\right)$
9. $777 + 0$ **10.** $777 \cdot 1$

To understand algebra, we must know the properties that govern the operations of addition, subtraction, multiplication, and division of real numbers. These properties enable us to write expressions in equivalent forms, often making our work easier.

1 **Apply the closure properties by evaluating an expression for given values for variables.**

The **closure properties** guarantee that the sum, difference, product, or quotient (except for division by 0) of any two real numbers is also a real number.

Closure Properties

If a and b are real numbers, then

$a + b$ is a real number. $a - b$ is a real number.

ab is a real number. $\dfrac{a}{b}$ is a real number $(b \neq 0)$.

EXAMPLE 1   Let $x = 8$ and $y = -4$. Find the real-number answers to show that each expression represents a real number.
a. $x + y$ **b.** $x - y$ **c.** xy **d.** $\frac{x}{y}$

Solution   We substitute 8 for x and -4 for y in each expression and simplify.

a. $x + y = 8 + (-4)$ **b.** $x - y = 8 - (-4)$
$ = 4$ $ = 8 + 4$
$ = 12$

c. $xy = 8(-4)$ **d.** $\dfrac{x}{y} = \dfrac{8}{-4}$
$ = -32$ $\phantom{\dfrac{x}{y}} = -2$

 **SELF CHECK 1**   Assume that $a = -6$ and $b = 3$. Find the real-number answers to show that each expression represents a real number.

a. $a - b$ **b.** $\frac{a}{b}$ are real numbers.

---

2 ### Apply the commutative and associative properties.

The **commutative properties** (from the word *commute*, which means to go back and forth) guarantee that addition or multiplication of two real numbers can be done in either order.

Commutative Properties	If a and b are real numbers, then
	$a + b = b + a$ commutative property of addition
	$ab = ba$ commutative property of multiplication

EXAMPLE 2   Let $x = -3$ and $y = 7$. Show that **a.** $x + y = y + x$ **b.** $xy = yx$

Solution   **a.** We can show that the sum $x + y$ is the same as the sum $y + x$ by substituting -3 for x and 7 for y in each expression and simplifying.

$$x + y = -3 + 7 = 4 \quad \text{and} \quad y + x = 7 + (-3) = 4$$

COMMENT Since
$5 - 3 \neq 3 - 5$ and
$5 \div 3 \neq 3 \div 5$, the
commutative property cannot
be applied to a subtraction or
a division.

b. We can show that the product xy is the same as the product yx by substituting -3 for x and 7 for y in each expression and simplifying.

$$xy = -3(7) = -21 \quad \text{and} \quad yx = 7(-3) = -21$$

 **SELF CHECK 2**   Let $a = 6$ and $b = -5$. Show that **a.** $a + b = b + a$
b. $ab = ba$

The **associative properties** guarantee that three real numbers can be regrouped in an addition or multiplication.

Associative Properties	If a, b, and c are real numbers, then
	$(a + b) + c = a + (b + c)$ associative property of addition
	$(ab)c = a(bc)$ associative property of multiplication

Because of the associative property of addition, we can group (or associate) the numbers in a sum in any way that we wish. For example,

$$(3 + 4) + 5 = 7 + 5 \qquad 3 + (4 + 5) = 3 + 9$$
$$= 12 \qquad\qquad\qquad = 12$$

The answer is 12 regardless of how we group the three numbers.

COMMENT Since
$(2 - 5) - 3 \neq 2 - (5 - 3)$
and
$(2 \div 5) \div 3 \neq 2 \div (5 \div 3)$,
the associative property
cannot be applied to
subtraction or division.

The associative property of multiplication permits us to group (or associate) the numbers in a product in any way that we wish. For example,

$$(3 \cdot 4) \cdot 7 = 12 \cdot 7 \qquad\qquad 3 \cdot (4 \cdot 7) = 3 \cdot 28$$
$$= 84 \qquad\qquad\qquad\qquad = 84$$

The answer is 84 regardless of how we group the three numbers.

3 **Apply the distributive property of multiplication over addition to rewrite an expression.**

The **distributive property** shows how to multiply the sum of two numbers by a third number. Because of this property, we can often add first and then multiply, or multiply first and then add.

For example, $2(3 + 7)$ can be calculated in two different ways. We can add and then multiply, or we can multiply each number within the parentheses by 2 and then add.

$$2(3 + 7) = 2(10) \qquad\qquad 2(3 + 7) = 2 \cdot 3 + 2 \cdot 7$$
$$= 20 \qquad\qquad\qquad\qquad = 6 + 14$$
$$= 20$$

Either way, the result is 20.

In general, we have the following property.

Distributive Property of Multiplication Over Addition	If a, b, and c are real numbers, then $$a(b + c) = ab + ac$$

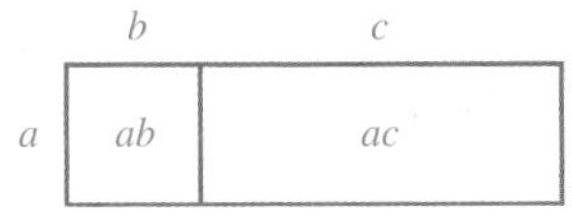

Figure 1-25

Because multiplication is commutative, the distributive property also can be written in the form

$$(b + c)a = ba + ca$$

We can interpret the distributive property geometrically. Since the area of the largest rectangle in Figure 1-25 is the product of its width a and its length $b + c$, its area is $a(b + c)$. The areas of the two smaller rectangles are ab and ac. Since the area of the largest rectangle is equal to the sum of the areas of the smaller rectangles, we have $a(b + c) = ab + ac$.

The previous discussion shows that multiplication distributes over addition. Multiplication also distributes over subtraction. For example, $2(3 - 7)$ can be calculated in two different ways. We can subtract and then multiply, or we can multiply each number within the parentheses by 2 and then subtract.

$$2(3 - 7) = 2(-4) \qquad\qquad 2(3 - 7) = 2 \cdot 3 - 2 \cdot 7$$
$$= -8 \qquad\qquad\qquad\qquad = 6 - 14$$
$$= -8$$

Either way, the result is -8. In general, we have

$$a(b - c) = ab - ac$$

EXAMPLE 3 Evaluate each expression in two different ways:
a. $3(5 + 9)$ **b.** $4(6 - 11)$ **c.** $-2(-7 + 3)$

Solution **a.** $3(5 + 9) = 3(14)$ $\qquad$ $3(5 + 9) = 3 \cdot 5 + 3 \cdot 9$
$\qquad\qquad\qquad = 42$ $\qquad\qquad\qquad\qquad = 15 + 27$
$\qquad\qquad\qquad\qquad\qquad\qquad\qquad\qquad\qquad = 42$

b. $4(6 - 11) = 4(-5)$ $\qquad$ $4(6 - 11) = 4 \cdot 6 - 4 \cdot 11$
$\qquad\qquad\qquad\quad = -20$ $\qquad\qquad\qquad\qquad\quad = 24 - 44$
$\qquad\qquad\qquad\qquad\qquad\qquad\qquad\qquad\qquad\quad = -20$

c. $-2(-7 + 3) = -2(-4)$ $\qquad$ $-2(-7 + 3) = -2(-7) + (-2)(3)$
$\qquad\qquad\qquad\qquad = 8$ $\qquad\qquad\qquad\qquad\qquad\quad = 14 + (-6)$
$\qquad\qquad\qquad\qquad\qquad\qquad\qquad\qquad\qquad\qquad\quad = 8$

➡ **SELF CHECK 3** Evaluate $-5(-7 + 20)$ in two different ways.

The distributive property can be extended to three or more terms. For example, if a, b, c, and d are real numbers, then

$$a(b + c + d) = ab + ac + ad$$

EXAMPLE 4 Write $3.2(x + y + 2.7)$ without using parentheses.

Solution $3.2(x + y + 2.7) = 3.2x + 3.2y + (3.2)(2.7)$ $\quad$ Distribute the multiplication by 3.2.
$\qquad\qquad\qquad\qquad\quad = 3.2x + 3.2y + 8.64$

➡ **SELF CHECK 4** Write $-6.3(a + 2b + 3.7)$ without using parentheses.

4 **Recognize the identity elements and find the additive and multiplicative inverse of a nonzero real number.**

The numbers 0 and 1 play special roles in mathematics. The number 0 is the only number that can be added to another number (say, a) and give an answer that is the same number a:

$$0 + a = a + 0 = a$$

The number 1 is the only number that can be multiplied by another number (say, a) and give an answer that is the same number a:

$$1 \cdot a = a \cdot 1 = a$$

Because adding 0 to a number or multiplying a number by 1 leaves that number the same (identical), the numbers 0 and 1 are called **identity elements.**

Identity Elements | 0 is the **identity element for addition.**
1 is the **identity element for multiplication.**

If the sum of two numbers is 0, the numbers are called **negatives** (or **opposites** or **additive inverses**) of each other. Since $3 + (-3) = 0$, the numbers 3 and -3 are negatives (or opposites or additive inverses) of each other. In general, because

$$a + (-a) = 0$$

the numbers represented by a and $-a$ are negatives (or opposites or additive inverses) of each other.

If the product of two numbers is 1, the numbers are called **reciprocals,** or **multiplicative inverses,** of each other. Since $7\left(\frac{1}{7}\right) = 1$, the numbers 7 and $\frac{1}{7}$ are reciprocals. Since $(-0.25)(-4) = 1$, the numbers -0.25 and -4 are reciprocals. In general, because

$$a\left(\frac{1}{a}\right) = 1 \qquad \text{provided } a \neq 0$$

the numbers represented by a and $\frac{1}{a}$ are reciprocals (or multiplicative inverses) of each other.

Additive and Multiplicative Inverses	Because $a + (-a) = 0$, the numbers a and $-a$ are called **negatives, opposites,** or **additive inverses.** Because $a\left(\frac{1}{a}\right) = 1$ $(a \neq 0)$, the numbers a and $\frac{1}{a}$ are called **reciprocals** or **multiplicative inverses.**

EXAMPLE 5   Find the additive and multiplicative inverses of $\frac{2}{3}$.

Solution   The additive inverse of $\frac{2}{3}$ is $-\frac{2}{3}$ because $\frac{2}{3} + \left(-\frac{2}{3}\right) = 0$.

The multiplicative inverse of $\frac{2}{3}$ is $\frac{3}{2}$ because $\frac{2}{3}\left(\frac{3}{2}\right) = 1$.

⇨ **SELF CHECK 5**   Find the additive and multiplicative inverses of $-\frac{1}{5}$.

5   **Identify the property that justifies a given statement.**

EXAMPLE 6   The property in the right column justifies the statement in the left column.

a. $3 + 4$ is a real number   closure property of addition

b. $\frac{8}{3}$ is a real number   closure property of division

c. $3 + 4 = 4 + 3$ commutative property of addition
d. $-3 + (2 + 7) = (-3 + 2) + 7$ associative property of addition
e. $(5)(-4) = (-4)(5)$ commutative property of multiplication
f. $(ab)c = a(bc)$ associative property of multiplication

g. $3(a + 2) = 3a + 3 \cdot 2$ distributive property

h. $3 + 0 = 3$ additive identity property

i. $3(1) = 3$ multiplicative identity property

j. $2 + (-2) = 0$ additive inverse property

k. $\left(\dfrac{2}{3}\right)\left(\dfrac{3}{2}\right) = 1$ multiplicative inverse property

SELF CHECK 6 Which property justifies each statement?

a. $a + 7 = 7 + a$

b. $3(y + 2) = 3y + 3 \cdot 2$

c. $3 \cdot (2 \cdot p) = (3 \cdot 2) \cdot p$

The properties of the real numbers are summarized as follows.

Properties of Real Numbers

For all real numbers a, b, and c,

Closure properties $a + b$ is a real number. $a \cdot b$ is a real number.
$a - b$ is a real number. $a \div b$ is a real number $(b \neq 0)$.

	Addition	*Multiplication*
Commutative properties	$a + b = b + a$	$a \cdot b = b \cdot a$
Associative properties	$(a + b) + c = a + (b + c)$	$(ab)c = a(bc)$
Identity properties	$a + 0 = a$	$a \cdot 1 = a$
Inverse properties	$a + (-a) = 0$	$a\left(\dfrac{1}{a}\right) = 1 \quad (a \neq 0)$
Distributive property		$a(b + c) = ab + ac$

NOW TRY THIS

1. Give the additive and multiplicative inverses of 1.2.

2. Use the commutative property of multiplication to write the expression $x(y + w)$.

3. Simplify: $-4(2a - 3b + 5)$.

4. Use the distributive property to complete the following multiplication:
$9x - 12y - 3 = 3(\boxed{\ } - \boxed{\ } - \boxed{\ })$

5. Find the additive inverse of $x - y$. Try to find a second way to write it (there are three).

1.7 EXERCISES

WARM-UPS

Give an example of each property.

1. The associative property of multiplication
2. The additive identity property
3. The distributive property
4. The inverse property for multiplication

Provide an example to illustrate each statement.

5. Subtraction is not commutative.
6. Division is not associative.

REVIEW

7. Write as a mathematical inequality: The sum of x and the square of y is greater than or equal to z.
8. Write as an English phrase: $3(x + z)$.

Fill each box with an appropriate symbol.

9. For any number x, $|x|$ ▢ 0.
10. $x - y = x + (▢)$

Fill in the blanks.

11. The product of two negative numbers is a _____ number.
12. The sum of two negative numbers is a _____ number.

VOCABULARY AND CONCEPTS   *Fill in the blanks.*

13. **Closure property:** If a and b are real numbers, $a + b$ is a _____ number.
14. **Closure property:** If a and b are real numbers, $\frac{a}{b}$ is a real number, provided that _____.
15. **Commutative property of addition:** $a + b = b + $ __
16. **Commutative property of multiplication:** $a \cdot b = $ __ $\cdot a$
17. **Associative property of addition:** $(a + b) + c = a + $ _____
18. **Associative property of multiplication:** $(ab)c = $ __ $\cdot (bc)$
19. **Distributive property:** $a(b + c) = ab + $ ___
20. $0 + a = $ __
21. $a \cdot 1 = $ __
22. 0 is the _____ element for _____.
23. 1 is the identity _____ for _____.
24. If $a + (-a) = 0$, then a and $-a$ are called _____ inverses.
25. If $a\left(\dfrac{1}{a}\right) = 1$, then __ and __ are called *reciprocals* or _____ inverses.
26. $a(b + c + d) = ab + $ _____

GUIDED PRACTICE

Assume that $x = 12$ and $y = -2$. Show that each expression represents a real number by finding the real-number answer. See Example 1. (Objective 1)

27. $x + y$
28. $y - x$
29. xy
30. $\dfrac{x}{y}$
31. x^2
32. y^2
33. $\dfrac{x}{y^2}$
34. $\dfrac{2x}{3y}$

Let $x = 5$, $y = 7$, and $z = -1$. Show that the two expressions have the same value. See Example 2. (Objective 2)

35. $x + y$; $y + x$
36. xy; yx
37. $3x + 2y$; $2y + 3x$
38. $3xy$; $3yx$
39. $x(x + y)$; $(x + y)x$
40. $xy + y^2$; $y^2 + xy$
41. $x^2(yz^2)$; $(x^2y)z^2$
42. $x(y^2z^3)$; $(xy^2)z^3$

Use the distributive property to write each expression without parentheses. Simplify each result, if possible. See Examples 3–4. (Objective 3)

43. $4(x + 2)$
44. $5(y + 4)$
45. $2(z - 3)$
46. $3(b - 4)$
47. $3(x + y)$
48. $4(a + b)$
49. $x(x + 3)$
50. $y(y + z)$
51. $-x(a + b)$
52. $-a(x + y)$
53. $-4(x^2 + x + 2)$
54. $-2(a^2 - a + 3)$

Give the additive and the multiplicative inverses of each number, if possible. See Example 5. (Objective 4)

55. 2
56. 3
57. $\dfrac{1}{3}$
58. $-\dfrac{1}{2}$
59. 0
60. -2
61. $-\dfrac{5}{2}$
62. 0.5
63. -0.2
64. 0.75
65. $\dfrac{4}{3}$
66. -1.25

Use the given property to rewrite the expression in a different form. See Example 6. (Objective 5)

67. $3(x + 2)$; distributive property

68. $x + y$; commutative property of addition
69. y^2x; commutative property of multiplication
70. $x + (y + z)$; associative property of addition
71. $(x + y)z$; commutative property of addition
72. $x(y + z)$; distributive property
73. $(xy)z$; associative property of multiplication
74. $1x$; multiplicative identity property

ADDITIONAL PRACTICE

Let $x = 2, y = -3$, and $z = 1$. Show that the two expressions have the same value.

75. $(x + y) + z$; $x + (y + z)$
76. $(xy)z$; $x(yz)$
77. $(xz)y$; $x(yz)$
78. $(x + y) + z$; $y + (x + z)$

Use the distributive property to write each expression without parentheses.

79. $-5(t + 2)$ **80.** $2x(a - x)$
81. $-2a(x - a)$ **82.** $-p(p - q)$

Which property of real numbers justifies each statement?

83. $3 + x = x + 3$
84. $(3 + x) + y = 3 + (x + y)$
85. $xy = yx$
86. $(3)(2) = (2)(3)$
87. $-2(x + 3) = -2x + (-2)(3)$

88. $x(y + z) = (y + z)x$
89. $(x + y) + z = z + (x + y)$
90. $3(x + y) = 3x + 3y$
91. $5 \cdot 1 = 5$ **92.** $x + 0 = x$

93. $3 + (-3) = 0$ **94.** $9 \cdot \dfrac{1}{9} = 1$

95. $0 + x = x$ **96.** $5 \cdot \dfrac{1}{5} = 1$

WRITING ABOUT MATH

97. Explain why division is not commutative.
98. Describe two ways of calculating the value of $3(12 + 7)$.

SOMETHING TO THINK ABOUT

99. Suppose there were no numbers other than the odd integers.

- Would the closure property for addition still be true?
- Would the closure property for multiplication still be true?
- Would there still be an identity for addition?
- Would there still be an identity for multiplication?

100. Suppose there were no numbers other than the even integers. Answer the four parts of Exercise 99 again.

PROJECTS

Project 1

The circumference of any circle and its diameter are related. When you divide the circumference by the diameter, the quotient is always the same number, **pi,** denoted by the Greek letter π.

- Carefully measure the circumference of several circles—a quarter, a dinner plate, a bicycle tire—whatever you can find that is round. Then calculate approximations of π by dividing each circle's circumference by its diameter.
- Use the $\boxed{\pi}$ key on the calculator to obtain a more accurate value of π. How close were your approximations?

Project 2

a. The fraction $\frac{22}{7}$ is often used as an approximation of π. To how many decimal places is this approximation accurate?

b. Experiment with your calculator and try to do better. Find another fraction (with no more than three digits in either its numerator or its denominator) that is closer to π. Who in your class has done best?

Project 3

Write an essay answering this question.

When three professors attending a convention in Las Vegas registered at the hotel, they were told that the room rate was $120. Each professor paid his $40 share.

Later the desk clerk realized that the cost of the room should have been $115. To fix the mistake, she sent a bellhop to the room to refund the $5 overcharge. Realizing that $5 could not be evenly divided among the three professors, the bellhop refunded only $3 and kept the other $2.

Since each professor received a $1 refund, each paid $39 for the room, and the bellhop kept $2. This gives $39 + $39 + $39 + $2, or $119. What happened to the other $1?

Chapter 1   REVIEW

SECTION 1.1   Real Numbers and Their Graphs

DEFINITIONS AND CONCEPTS	EXAMPLES
Natural numbers: $\{1, 2, 3, 4, 5, \ldots\}$ **Whole numbers:** $\{0, 1, 2, 3, 4, 5, \ldots\}$ **Integers:** $\{\ldots, -3, -2, -1, 0, 1, 2, 3, \ldots\}$ **Rational numbers:** $\left\{\dfrac{a}{b} \,\middle|\, a \text{ is an integer and } b \text{ is a nonzero integer}\right\}$ **Irrational numbers:** $\{x \mid x \text{ is a number such as } \pi \text{ or } \sqrt{2} \text{ that cannot be written as a fraction with an integer numerator and a nonzero integer denominator.}\}$ **Real numbers:** {Rational numbers or irrational numbers} **Prime numbers:** $\{2, 3, 5, 7, 11, 13, 17, \ldots\}$ **Composite numbers:** $\{4, 6, 8, 9, 10, 12, 14, 15, \ldots\}$ **Even integers:** $\{\ldots, -6, -4, -2, 0, 2, 4, 6, \ldots\}$ **Odd integers:** $\ldots, -5, -3, -1, 1, 3, 5, \ldots\}$	Which numbers in the set $\left\{-5, 0, \frac{2}{3}, 1.5, \sqrt{9}, \pi, 6\right\}$ are **a.** natural numbers, **b.** whole numbers, **c.** integers, **d.** rational numbers, **e.** irrational numbers, **f.** real numbers, **g.** prime numbers, **h.** composite numbers, **i.** even integers, **j.** odd integers? **a.** $\sqrt{9}, 6, \sqrt{9}$ is a natural number since $\sqrt{9} = 3$ **b.** $0, \sqrt{9}, 6$ **c.** $-5, 0, \sqrt{9}, 6$ **d.** $-5, 0, \frac{2}{3}, 1.5, \sqrt{9}, 6$ **e.** π **f.** $-5, 0, \frac{2}{3}, 1.5, \sqrt{9}, \pi, 6$ **g.** $\sqrt{9}$ **h.** 6 **i.** $0, 6$ **j.** $-5, \sqrt{9}$
Double negative rule: $-(-x) = x$	$-(-3) = 3$

Sets of numbers can be graphed on the number line.	**1.** Graph the set of integers between -2 and 4.
	
	    $-3 \;\; -2 \;\; -1 \;\;\; 0 \;\;\; 1 \;\;\; 2 \;\;\; 3 \;\;\; 4$
	
	2. Graph all real numbers x such that $x < -2$ or $x > 1$.
	
	    $-3 \;\; -2 \;\; -1 \;\;\; 0 \;\;\; 1 \;\;\; 2 \;\;\; 3$

The **absolute value** of x, denoted as $|x|$, is the distance between x and 0 on the number line. $|x| \geq 0$	Evaluate: $-|-8|$. $-|-8| = -(8) = -8$

REVIEW EXERCISES

Consider the set $\{0, 1, 2, 3, 4, 5\}$.

1. Which numbers are natural numbers?

2. Which numbers are prime numbers?

3. Which numbers are odd natural numbers?

4. Which numbers are composite numbers?

Consider the set $\left\{-6, -\frac{2}{3}, 0, \sqrt{2}, 2.6, \pi, 5\right\}$.

5. Which numbers are integers?

6. Which numbers are rational numbers?

7. Which numbers are prime numbers?

8. Which numbers are real numbers?

9. Which numbers are even integers?

10. Which numbers are odd integers?

11. Which numbers are irrational?

12. Which numbers are negative numbers?

Place one of the symbols $=$, $<$, or $>$ in each box to make a true statement.

13. $-5 \;\boxed{}\; 12 - 12$

14. $\dfrac{24}{6} \;\boxed{}\; 5$

15. $13 - 13 \;\boxed{}\; 5 - \dfrac{25}{5}$

16. $\dfrac{21}{7} \;\boxed{}\; -33$

Simplify each expression.

17. $-(-8)$

18. $-(12 - 4)$

Draw a number line and graph each set of numbers.

19. The composite numbers from 14 to 20

20. The whole numbers between 19 and 25

21. The real numbers less than or equal to -3 or greater than 2

22. The real numbers greater than -4 and less than 3

Find each absolute value.

23. $|53 - 42|$

24. $|-31|$

SECTION 1.2   Fractions

DEFINITIONS AND CONCEPTS	EXAMPLES
To simplify a fraction, factor the numerator and the denominator. Then divide out all common factors.	Simplify: $\dfrac{12}{32}$. $\dfrac{12}{32} = \dfrac{4 \cdot 3}{4 \cdot 8} = \dfrac{\overset{1}{\cancel{4}} \cdot 3}{\underset{1}{\cancel{4}} \cdot 8} = \dfrac{3}{8}$
To multiply two fractions, multiply their numerators and multiply their denominators.	$4 \cdot \dfrac{5}{6} = \dfrac{4}{1} \cdot \dfrac{5}{6}$ $= \dfrac{4 \cdot 5}{1 \cdot 6}$ $= \dfrac{2 \cdot 2 \cdot 5}{1 \cdot 2 \cdot 3}$ $= \dfrac{10}{3}$
To divide two fractions, multiply the first by the reciprocal of the second.	$\dfrac{2}{3} \div \dfrac{5}{6} = \dfrac{2}{3} \cdot \dfrac{6}{5}$ $= \dfrac{2 \cdot 6}{3 \cdot 5}$ $= \dfrac{2 \cdot 2 \cdot \cancel{3}}{\cancel{3} \cdot 5}$ $= \dfrac{4}{5}$
To add (or subtract) two fractions with like denominators, add (or subtract) their numerators and keep their common denominator.	$\dfrac{9}{11} + \dfrac{2}{11} = \dfrac{9 + 2}{11}$ $= \dfrac{11}{11}$ $= 1$

To add (or subtract) two fractions with unlike denominators, rewrite the fractions with the same denominator, add (or subtract) their numerators, and use the common denominator.

Subtract: $\dfrac{11}{12} - \dfrac{3}{4}$.

Begin by finding the LCD.

$$\left.\begin{array}{r} 12 = 2 \cdot 2 \cdot 3 \\ 4 = 2 \cdot 2 \end{array}\right\} \text{LCD} = 2 \cdot 2 \cdot 3 = 12$$

Write $\dfrac{3}{4}$ as a fraction with a denominator of 12 and then do the subtraction.

$$\begin{aligned} \frac{11}{12} - \frac{3}{4} &= \frac{11}{12} - \frac{3 \cdot 3}{4 \cdot 3} \\ &= \frac{11}{12} - \frac{9}{12} \\ &= \frac{11 - 9}{12} \\ &= \frac{2}{12} \\ &= \frac{\cancel{2}}{\cancel{2} \cdot 6} \\ &= \frac{1}{6} \end{aligned}$$

Before working with mixed numbers, convert them to improper fractions.

Write $5\dfrac{7}{9}$ as an improper fraction.

$$5\frac{7}{9} = 5 + \frac{7}{9} = \frac{45}{9} + \frac{7}{9} = \frac{52}{9}$$

A **percent** is the numerator of a fraction with a denominator of 100.

$5\frac{1}{2}\%$ can be written as $\dfrac{550}{100}$, or as the decimal 5.50.

REVIEW EXERCISES
Simplify each fraction.

25. $\dfrac{45}{27}$ **26.** $\dfrac{121}{11}$

Perform each operation and simplify the answer, if possible.

27. $\dfrac{31}{15} \cdot \dfrac{10}{62}$ **28.** $\dfrac{25}{36} \cdot \dfrac{12}{15} \cdot \dfrac{3}{5}$

29. $\dfrac{18}{21} \div \dfrac{6}{7}$ **30.** $\dfrac{14}{24} \div \dfrac{7}{12} \div \dfrac{2}{5}$

31. $\dfrac{7}{12} + \dfrac{9}{12}$ **32.** $\dfrac{13}{24} - \dfrac{5}{24}$

33. $\dfrac{1}{3} + \dfrac{1}{7}$ **34.** $\dfrac{5}{7} + \dfrac{4}{9}$

35. $\dfrac{2}{3} - \dfrac{1}{7}$ **36.** $\dfrac{4}{5} - \dfrac{2}{3}$

37. $3\dfrac{2}{3} + 5\dfrac{1}{4}$ **38.** $7\dfrac{5}{12} - 4\dfrac{1}{2}$

Perform the operations.

39. $32.71 + 15.9$ **40.** $27.92 - 14.93$

41. $5.3 \cdot 3.5$ **42.** $21.83 \div 5.9$

Perform each operation and round to two decimal places.

43. $2.7(4.92 - 3.18)$ **44.** $\dfrac{3.3 + 2.5}{0.22}$

45. $\dfrac{12.5}{14.7 - 11.2}$ **46.** $(3 - 0.7)(3.63 - 2)$

47. Farming One day, a farmer plowed $17\frac{1}{2}$ acres and on the second day, $15\frac{3}{4}$ acres. How much is left to plow if the fields total 100 acres?

48. Study times Four students recorded the time they spent working on a take-home exam: 5.2, 4.7, 9.5, and 8 hours. Find the average time spent. (*Hint:* Add the numbers and divide by 4.)

49. Absenteeism During the height of the flu season, 15% of the 380 university faculty members were sick. How many were ill?

50. Packaging Four steel bands surround the shipping crate in the illustration. Find the total length of strapping needed.

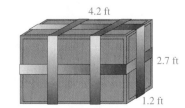

4.2 ft

2.7 ft

1.2 ft

SECTION 1.3   Exponents and Order of Operations

DEFINITIONS AND CONCEPTS	EXAMPLES
If n is a natural number, then n factors of x $x^n = x \cdot x \cdot x \cdot x \cdot \;\cdots\; \cdot x$	$x^5 = x \cdot x \cdot x \cdot x \cdot x$ $b^7 = b \cdot b \cdot b \cdot b \cdot b \cdot b \cdot b$

Order of operations

Within each pair of grouping symbols (working from the innermost pair to the outermost pair), perform the following operations:

1. Evaluate all exponential expressions.
2. Perform multiplications and divisions, working from left to right.
3. Perform additions and subtractions, working from left to right.
4. Because the bar in a fraction is a grouping symbol, simplify the numerator and the denominator of a fraction separately. Then simplify the fraction, whenever possible.

Evaluate: $6^2 - 5(12 - 2 \cdot 5)$.

$6^2 - 5(12 - 2 \cdot 5) = 6^2 - 5(12 - 10)$ Do the multiplication within the parentheses.

$= 6^2 - 5(2)$ Do the subtraction within the parentheses.

$= 36 - 5(2)$ Find the value of the exponential expression.

$= 36 - 10$ Do the multiplication.

$= 26$ Do the subtraction.

To simplify $\dfrac{2^3 + 4 \cdot 2}{2 + 6}$, we first simplify the numerator and the denominator.

$\dfrac{2^3 + 4 \cdot 2}{2 + 6} = \dfrac{8 + 8}{8}$ Find the power. Then find the product. Find the sum in the denominator.

$= \dfrac{16}{8}$ Find the sum in the numerator.

$= 2$ Find the quotient.

To find perimeters, areas, and volumes of geometric figures, substitute numbers for variables in the formulas. Be sure to include the proper units in the answer.

Find the perimeter of a rectangle whose length is 4 feet and whose width is 1 foot.

$P = 2l + 2w$ This is the formula for the perimeter of a rectangle.

$= 2(4) + 2(1)$ Substitute 4 for l and 1 for w.

$= 8 + 2$

$= 10$

The perimeter is 10 feet.

REVIEW EXERCISES

Find the value of each expression.

51. 3^4

52. $\left(\dfrac{2}{3}\right)^2$

53. $(0.5)^2$

54. $5^2 + 2^3$

55. $3^2 + 4^2$

56. $(3 + 4)^2$

57. Geometry Find the area of a triangle with a base of $6\frac{1}{2}$ feet and a height of 7 feet.

58. 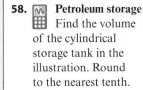 **Petroleum storage** Find the volume of the cylindrical storage tank in the illustration. Round to the nearest tenth.

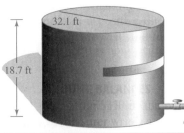

32.1 ft

18.7 ft

Simplify each expression.

59. $5 + 3^3$

60. $7 \cdot 2 - 7$

61. $4 + (8 \div 4)$

62. $(4 + 8) \div 4$

63. $5^3 - \dfrac{81}{3}$

64. $(5 - 2)^2 + 5^2 + 2^2$

65. $\dfrac{4 \cdot 3 + 3^4}{31}$

66. $\dfrac{4}{3} \cdot \dfrac{9}{2} + \dfrac{1}{2} \cdot 18$

Evaluate each expression.

67. $8^2 - 6$

68. $(8 - 6)^2$

69. $\dfrac{6 + 8}{6 - 4}$

70. $\dfrac{6(8) - 12}{4 + 8}$

71. $2^2 + 2(3^2)$

72. $\dfrac{2^2 + 3}{2^3 - 1}$

SECTION 1.4 Adding and Subtracting Real Numbers

DEFINITIONS AND CONCEPTS	EXAMPLES
To add two positive numbers, add their absolute values and make the answer positive.	$(+1) + (+6) = +7$
To add two negative numbers, add their absolute values and make the answer negative.	$(-1) + (-6) = -7$
To add a positive and a negative number, subtract the smaller absolute value from the larger.	
1. If the positive number has the larger absolute value, the answer is positive.	$(-1) + (+6) = +5$
2. If the negative number has the larger absolute value, the answer is negative.	$(+1) + (-6) = -5$
If a and b are two real numbers, then $$a - b = a + (-b)$$	$-8 - 2 = -8 + (-2)$ To subtract 2, add the opposite of 2. $\qquad = -10$

REVIEW EXERCISES
Evaluate each expression.

73. $(+7) + (+8)$ **74.** $(-25) + (-32)$

75. $(-2.7) + (-3.8)$ **76.** $\dfrac{1}{3} + \dfrac{1}{6}$

77. $(+12) + (-24)$ **78.** $(-44) + (+60)$

79. $3.7 + (-2.5)$ **80.** $-5.6 + (+2.06)$

81. $15 - (-4)$ **82.** $-12 - (-13)$

83. $[-5 + (-5)] - (-5)$ **84.** $1 - [5 - (-3)]$

85. $\dfrac{5}{6} - \left(-\dfrac{2}{3}\right)$ **86.** $\dfrac{2}{3} - \left(\dfrac{1}{3} - \dfrac{2}{3}\right)$

87. $\left|\dfrac{3}{7} - \left(-\dfrac{4}{7}\right)\right|$ **88.** $\dfrac{3}{7} - \left|-\dfrac{4}{7}\right|$

SECTION 1.5 Multiplying and Dividing Real Numbers

DEFINITIONS AND CONCEPTS	EXAMPLES
To multiply two real numbers, multiply their absolute values.	
1. If the numbers are positive, the product is positive.	$3(7) = 21$
2. If the numbers are negative, the product is positive.	$-3(-7) = 21$
3. If one number is positive and the other is negative, the product is negative.	$-3(7) = -21 \qquad 3(-7) = -21$
4. $a \cdot 0 = 0 \cdot a = 0$	$5(0) = 0$
5. $a \cdot 1 = 1 \cdot a = a$	$-7(1) = -7$
To divide two real numbers, find the quotient of their absolute values.	
1. If the numbers are positive, the quotient is positive.	$\dfrac{+6}{+2} = +3$ because $(+2)(+3) = +6$
2. If the numbers are negative, the quotient is positive.	$\dfrac{-6}{-2} = +3$ because $(-2)(+3) = -6$
3. If one number is positive and the other is negative, the quotient is negative.	$\dfrac{+6}{-2} = -3$ because $(-2)(-3) = +6$ $\dfrac{-6}{+2} = -3$ because $(+2)(-3) = -6$

4. $\frac{a}{0}$ is undefined.

$\frac{2}{0}$ is undefined   because no number multiplied by 0 gives 2

5. If $a \neq 0$, then $\frac{0}{a} = 0$.

$\frac{0}{2} = 0$ because $(2)(0) = 0$

REVIEW EXERCISES
Simplify each expression.

89. $(+3)(+4)$

90. $(-5)(-12)$

91. $\left(-\frac{3}{14}\right)\left(-\frac{7}{6}\right)$

92. $(3.75)(0.37)$

93. $5(-7)$

94. $(-15)(7)$

95. $\left(-\frac{1}{2}\right)\left(\frac{4}{3}\right)$

96. $(-12.2)(3.7)$

97. $\frac{+25}{+5}$

98. $\frac{-14}{-2}$

99. $\frac{(-2)(-7)}{4}$

100. $\frac{-22.5}{-3.75}$

101. $\frac{-25}{5}$

102. $\frac{(-3)(-4)}{-6}$

103. $\left(\frac{-10}{2}\right)^2 - (-1)^3$

104. $\frac{[-3 + (-4)]^2}{10 + (-3)}$

105. $\left(\frac{-3 + (-3)}{3}\right)\left(\frac{-15}{5}\right)$

106. $\frac{-2 - (-8)}{5 + (-1)}$

SECTION 1.6   Algebraic Expressions

DEFINITIONS AND CONCEPTS	EXAMPLES
Variables and numbers can be combined with operations of arithmetic to produce **algebraic expressions**.	$5x \qquad 3x^2 + 7x \qquad 5(3x - 8)$
We can **evaluate** algebraic expressions when we know the values of the variables.	Evaluate: $5x - 2$ when $x = 3$. $5x + 2 = 5(3) - 2$ Substitute 3 for x. $\qquad\quad = 15 - 2$ $\qquad\quad = 13$
Numbers written without variables are called **constants**.	Identify the constant in $6x^2 - 4x + 2$. The constant is 2.
Expressions that are constants, variables, or products of constants and variables are called **algebraic terms**.	Identify the algebraic terms: $6x^2 - 4x + 2$. The terms are $6x^2$, $-4x$, and 2.
Numbers and variables that are part of a product are called **factors**.	Identify the factors in $7x$. The factors are 7 and x.
The number factor of a product is called its **numerical coefficient**.	Identify the numerical coefficient of $7x$. The numerical coefficient is 7.

REVIEW EXERCISES
Let x, y, and z represent three real numbers. Write an algebraic expression that represents each quantity.

107. The product of x and z

108. The sum of x and twice y

109. Twice the sum of x and y

110. x decreased by the product of y and z

Write each algebraic expression as an English phrase.

111. $3xy$

112. $5 - yz$

113. $yz - 5$

114. $\frac{x + y + z}{2xyz}$

Let $x = 2$, $y = -3$, and $z = -1$ and evaluate each expression.

115. $y + z$

116. $x + y$

117. $x + (y + z)$

118. $x - y$

119. $x - (y - z)$

120. $(x - y) - z$

Let $x = 2$, $y = -3$, and $z = -1$ and evaluate each expression.

121. xy

122. yz

123. $x(x + z)$

124. xyz

125. $y^2z + x$

126. $yz^3 + (xy)^2$

127. $\dfrac{xy}{z}$ **128.** $\dfrac{|xy|}{3z}$

129. How many terms does the expression $3x + 4y + 9$ have?

130. What is the numerical coefficient of the term $7xy$?

131. What is the numerical coefficient of the term xy?

132. Find the sum of the numerical coefficients in $2x^3 + 4x^2 + 3x$.

SECTION 1.7   Properties of Real Numbers

DEFINITIONS AND CONCEPTS	EXAMPLES
The closure properties: $a + b$ is a real number. $a - b$ is a real number. ab is a real number. $\dfrac{a}{b}$ is a real number $(b \neq 0)$.	$5 + (-2) = 3$ is a real number. $5 - 2 = 3$ is a real number. $5(-2) = -10$ is a real number. $\dfrac{10}{-5} = -2$ is a real number.
The commutative properties: $a + b = b + a$ for addition. $ab = ba$ for multiplication.	The commutative property of addition justifies the statement $x + 3 = 3 + x$. The commutative property of multiplication justifies the statement $x \cdot 3 = 3 \cdot x$.
The associative properties: $(a + b) + c = a + (b + c)$ of addition. $(ab)c = a(bc)$ of multiplication.	The associative property of addition justifies the statement $(x + 3) + 4 = x + (3 + 4)$. The associative property of multiplication justifies the statement $(x \cdot 3) \cdot 4 = x \cdot (3 \cdot 4)$.
The distributive property of multiplication over addition: $a(b + c) = ab + ac$ $a(b - c) = ab - ac$	Use the distributive property to write the expression $7(2x - 8)$ without parentheses. $7(2x - 8) = 7(2x) - 7(8) = 14x - 56$
The identity elements: 0 is the identity for addition. 1 is the identity for multiplication.	$0 + 5 = 5$ $1 \cdot 5 = 5$
The additive and multiplicative inverse properties: $a + (-a) = 0$ $a\left(\dfrac{1}{a}\right) = 1$ $(a \neq 0)$	The additive inverse of -2 is 2 because $-2 + 2 = 0$. The multiplicative inverse of -2 is $-\dfrac{1}{2}$ because $-2\left(-\dfrac{1}{2}\right) = 1$.

REVIEW EXERCISES
Determine which property of real numbers justifies each statement. Assume that all variables represent real numbers.

133. $x + y$ is a real number
134. $3 \cdot (4 \cdot 5) = (4 \cdot 5) \cdot 3$
135. $3 + (4 + 5) = (3 + 4) + 5$
136. $5(x + 2) = 5 \cdot x + 5 \cdot 2$
137. $a + x = x + a$
138. $3 \cdot (4 \cdot 5) = (3 \cdot 4) \cdot 5$
139. $3 + (x + 1) = (x + 1) + 3$
140. $x \cdot 1 = x$
141. $17 + (-17) = 0$
142. $x + 0 = x$

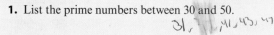

Chapter 1   TEST

1. List the prime numbers between 30 and 50.

2. What is the only even prime number?

3. Graph the composite numbers less than 10 on a number line.

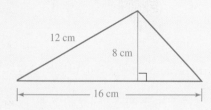

4. Graph the real numbers from 5 to 15 on a number line.

5. Evaluate: $-|23|$.

6. Evaluate: $-|7| + |-7|$.

Place one of the symbols = , <, or > in each box to make a true statement.

7. $3(4 - 2)$ ▢ $-2(2 - 5)$

8. $1 + 4 \cdot 3$ ▢ $-2(-7)$

9. 25% of 136 ▢ $\dfrac{1}{2}$ of 66

10. -13.7 ▢ $-|-13.7|$

Simplify each expression.

11. $\dfrac{26}{40}$

12. $\dfrac{7}{8} \cdot \dfrac{24}{21}$

13. $\dfrac{18}{35} \div \dfrac{9}{14}$

14. $\dfrac{24}{16} + 3$

15. $\dfrac{17 - 5}{36} - \dfrac{2(13 - 5)}{12}$

16. $\dfrac{|-7 - (-6)|}{-7 - |-6|}$

17. Find 17% of 457 and round the answer to one decimal place.

18. Find the area of a rectangle 12.8 feet wide and 23.56 feet long. Round the answer to two decimal places.

19. Find the area of the triangle in the illustration.

12 cm

8 cm

16 cm

20. To the nearest cubic inch, find the volume of the solid in the illustration.

14 in.

← 10 in. →

Let x = −2, y = 3, and z = 4. Evaluate each expression.

21. $xy + z$

22. $x(y + z)$

23. $\dfrac{z + 4y}{2x}$

24. $|x^3 - z|$

25. $x^3 + y^2 + z$

26. $|x| - 3|y| - 4|z|$

27. Let x and y represent two real numbers. Write an algebraic expression to denote the quotient obtained when the product of the two numbers is divided by their sum.

28. Let x and y represent two real numbers. Write an algebraic expression to denote the difference obtained when the sum of x and y is subtracted from the product of 5 and y.

29. A man lives 12 miles from work and 7 miles from the grocery store. If he made x round trips to work and y round trips to the store, write an expression to represent how many miles he drove.

30. A baseball costs \$$a$ and a glove costs \$$b$. Write an expression to represent how much it will cost a community center to buy 12 baseballs and 8 gloves.

31. What is the numerical coefficient of the term $3xy^2$?

32. How many terms are in the expression $3x^2y + 5xy^2 + x + 7$?

Write each expression without using parentheses.

33. $3(x + 2)$

34. $-p(r - t)$

35. What is the identity element for addition?

36. What is the multiplicative inverse of $\frac{1}{5}$?

Determine which property of the real numbers justifies each statement.

37. $(xy)z = z(xy)$

38. $3(x + y) = 3x + 3y$

39. $2 + x = x + 2$

40. $7 \cdot \dfrac{1}{7} = 1$

CHAPTER **2**

Equations and Inequalities

Careers and Mathematics

SECURITIES AND FINANCIAL SERVICES SALES AGENTS

Many investors use securities and financial sales agents when buying or selling stocks, bonds, shares in mutual funds, annuities, or other financial products. Securities and financial services sales agents held about 320,000 jobs in 2006.

The overwhelming majority of workers in this occupation are college graduates, with courses in business administration, economics, mathematics, and finance. After working for a few years, many agents get a Master's degree in Business Administration (MBA).

Job Outlook:
Employment of workers in this field is expected to grow rapidly over the next decade, especially in banking. However, there will be keen competition for these jobs.

Annual Earnings:
$42,630–$126,290

For More Information:
http://www.bls.gov/oco/ocos122.htm

For a Sample Application:
See Problem 59 in Section 2.5.

In this chapter ▶

In this chapter, we will learn how to solve basic linear equations and apply that knowledge to solving many types of problems. We also will consider special equations called **formulas** *and conclude by solving linear inequalities.*

Solving Basic Linear Equations in One Variable

Objectives

1 Determine whether a statement is an expression or an equation.

2 Determine whether a number is a solution of an equation.

3 Solve a linear equation in one variable by applying the addition or subtraction property of equality.

4 Solve a linear equation in one variable by applying the multiplication or division property of equality.

5 Solve a linear equation in one variable involving markdown and markup.

6 Solve a percent problem involving a linear equation in one variable using the formula $rb = a$.

7 Solve an application problem involving percents.

Vocabulary

equation	linear equation	discount
expression	addition property of equality	markup
variable	equivalent equations	percent
solution	multiplication property	rate
root	of equality	base
solution set	markdown	amount

Getting Ready

Fill in the blanks.

1. $3 + \boxed{} = 0$

2. $(-7) + \boxed{} = 0$

3. $(-x) + \boxed{} = 0$

4. $\dfrac{1}{3} \cdot 3 = \boxed{}$

5. $x \cdot \boxed{} = 1 \quad x \neq 0$

6. $\dfrac{-6}{-6} = \boxed{}$

7. $\dfrac{4(2)}{\boxed{}} = 2$

8. $5 \cdot \dfrac{4}{5} = \boxed{}$

9. $\dfrac{-5(3)}{-5} = \boxed{}$

To answer questions such as "How many?", "How far?", "How fast?", and "How heavy?", we will often use mathematical statements called *equations*. In this chapter, we will discuss this important idea.

1 Determine whether a statement is an expression or an equation.

An **equation** is a statement indicating that two quantities are equal. Some examples of equations are

$$x + 5 = 21 \qquad 2x - 5 = 11 \qquad \text{and} \qquad 3x^2 - 4x + 5 = 0$$

The **expression** $3x + 2$ is not an equation, because it does not contain an $=$ sign. Some examples of expressions are

$$6x - 1 \qquad 3x^2 - x - 2 \qquad \text{and} \qquad -8(x + 1)$$

EXAMPLE 1 Determine whether the following are expressions or equations.
a. $9x^2 - 5x = 4$ **b.** $3x + 2$ **c.** $6(2x - 1) + 5$

Solution **a.** $9x^2 - 5x = 4$ is an equation because it contains an $=$ sign.

b. $3x + 2$ is an expression. It does not contain an $=$ sign.

c. $6(2x - 1) + 5$ is an expression. It does not contain an $=$ sign.

⇨ **SELF CHECK 1** Is $8(x + 1) = 4$ an expression or an equation?

2 Determine whether a number is a solution of an equation.

In the equation $x + 5 = 21$, the expression $x + 5$ is called the *left side* and 21 is called the *right side*. The letter x is called the **variable** (or the **unknown**).

An equation can be true or false. The equation $16 + 5 = 21$ is true, but the equation $10 + 5 = 21$ is false. The equation $2x - 5 = 11$ might be true or false, depending on the value of x. For example, when $x = 8$, the equation is true, because when we substitute 8 for x we get 11.

$$2(8) - 5 = 16 - 5$$
$$= 11$$

Any number that makes an equation true when substituted for its variable is said to *satisfy* the equation. A number that makes an equation true is called a **solution** or a **root** of the equation. Since 8 is the only number that satisfies the equation $2x - 5 = 11$, it is the only solution.

The **solution set** of an equation is the set of numbers that make the equation true. In the previous equation, the solution set is $\{8\}$.

EXAMPLE 2 Determine whether 6 is a solution of $3x - 5 = 2x$.

Solution To see whether 6 is a solution, we can substitute 6 for x and simplify.

$$3x - 5 = 2x$$
$$3 \cdot 6 - 5 \overset{?}{=} 2 \cdot 6 \qquad \text{Substitute 6 for } x.$$
$$18 - 5 \overset{?}{=} 12 \qquad \text{Do the multiplication.}$$
$$13 = 12 \qquad \text{False.}$$

Since $13 = 12$ is a false statement, 6 is not a solution.

⇨ **SELF CHECK 2** Determine whether 1 is a solution of $2x + 3 = 5$.

3 Solve a linear equation in one variable by applying the addition or subtraction property of equality.

To solve an equation means to find its solutions. To develop an understanding of how to solve basic equation of the form $ax + b = c$, called **linear equations,** we will refer to the scales shown in Figure 2-1. We can think of the scale shown in Figure 2-1(a) as representing the equation $x - 5 = 2$. The weight on the left side of the scale is $(x - 5)$ grams, and the weight on the right side is 2 grams. Because these weights are equal, the scale is in balance. To find x, we need to isolate it by adding 5 grams to the left side of the scale. To keep the scale in balance, we must also add 5 grams to the right side. After adding 5 grams to both sides of the scale, we can see from Figure 2-1(b) that x grams will be balanced by 7 grams. We say that we have solved the equation and that the solution is 7, or we can say that the solution set is $\{7\}$.

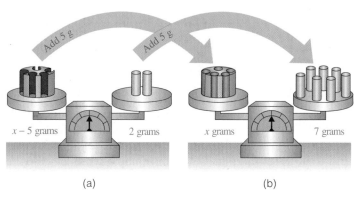

(a)   (b)

Figure 2-1

Figure 2-1 suggests the ***addition property of equality:*** *If the same quantity is added to equal quantities, the results will be equal quantities.*

We can think of the scale shown in Figure 2-2(a) as representing the equation $x + 4 = 9$. The weight on the left side of the scale is $(x + 4)$ grams, and the weight on the right side is 9 grams. Because these weights are equal, the scale is in balance. To find x, we need to isolate it by removing 4 grams from the left side. To keep the scale in balance, we must also remove 4 grams from the right side. In Figure 2-2(b), we can see that x grams will be balanced by 5 grams. We have found that the solution is 5, or that the solution set is $\{5\}$.

François Vieta (Viete)
(1540–1603)

By using letters in place of unknown numbers, Vieta simplified algebra and brought its notation closer to the notation that we use today. The one symbol he didn't use was the equal sign.

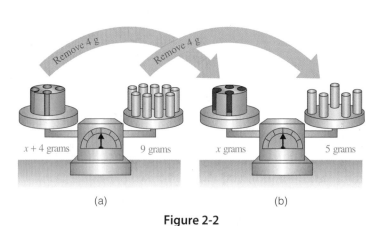

(a)   (b)

Figure 2-2

Figure 2-2 suggests the *subtraction property of equality: If the same quantity is subtracted from equal quantities, the results will be equal quantities.*

The previous discussion justifies the following properties.

Addition Property of Equality	Suppose that a, b, and c are real numbers. Then,
	If $a = b$, then $a + c = b + c$.
Subtraction Property of Equality	Suppose that a, b, and c are real numbers. Then,
	If $a = b$, then $a - c = b - c$.

COMMENT The subtraction property of equality is a special case of the addition property. Instead of subtracting a number from both sides of an equation, we could just as well add the opposite of the number to both sides.

When we use the properties described above, the resulting equation will have the same solution set as the original one. We say that the equations are *equivalent*.

Equivalent Equations	Two equations are called **equivalent equations** when they have the same solution set.

Using the scales shown in Figures 2-1 and 2-2, we found that $x - 5 = 2$ is equivalent to $x = 7$ and $x + 4 = 9$ is equivalent to $x = 5$. In the next two examples, we use properties of equality to solve these equations algebraically.

EXAMPLE 3 Solve: $x - 5 = 2$.

Solution To isolate x on one side of the $=$ sign, we will use the addition property of equality to undo the subtraction of 5 by adding 5 to both sides of the equation.

$$x - 5 = 2$$
$$x - 5 + 5 = 2 + 5 \quad \text{Add 5 to both sides of the equation.}$$
$$x = 7 \quad \quad -5 + 5 = 0 \text{ and } 2 + 5 = 7.$$

We check by substituting 7 for x in the original equation and simplifying.

$$x - 5 = 2$$
$$7 - 5 \stackrel{?}{=} 2 \quad \text{Substitute 7 for } x.$$
$$2 = 2 \quad \text{True.}$$

Since the previous statement is true, 7 is a solution. The solution set of this equation is $\{7\}$.

⇨ **SELF CHECK 3** Solve: $b - 21.8 = 13$.

EXAMPLE 4 Solve: $x + 4 = 9$.

Solution To isolate x on one side of the $=$ sign, we will use the subtraction property of equality to undo the addition of 4 by subtracting 4 from both sides of the equation.

COMMENT Note that Example 4 can be solved by using the addition property of equality. We could simply add −4 to both sides to undo the addition of 4.

$$x + 4 = 9$$
$$x + 4 - 4 = 9 - 4 \qquad \text{Subtract 4 from both sides.}$$
$$x = 5 \qquad 4 - 4 = 0 \text{ and } 9 - 4 = 5.$$

We can check by substituting 5 for x in the original equation and simplifying.

$$x + 4 = 9$$
$$5 + 4 \stackrel{?}{=} 9 \qquad \text{Substitute 5 for } x.$$
$$9 = 9 \qquad \text{True.}$$

Since the solution 5 checks, the solution set is $\{5\}$.

SELF CHECK 4 Solve: $a + 17.5 = 12.2$

4 **Solve a linear equation in one variable by applying the multiplication or division property of equality.**

We can think of the scale shown in Figure 2-3(a) as representing the equation $\frac{x}{3} = 12$. The weight on the left side of the scale is $\frac{x}{3}$ grams, and the weight on the right side is 12 grams. Because these weights are equal, the scale is in balance. To find x, we can triple (or multiply by 3) the weight on each side. When we do this, the scale will remain in balance. From the scale shown in Figure 2-3(b), we can see that x grams will be balanced by 36 grams. Thus, $x = 36$. Since 36 is the solution of the equation, the solution set is $\{36\}$.

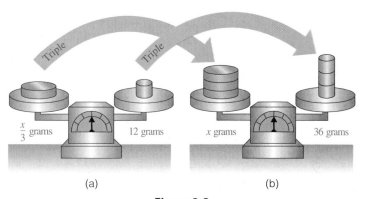

(a)   (b)

Figure 2-3

PERSPECTIVE

To answer questions such as How many?, How far?, How fast?, and How heavy?, we often make use of equations. This concept has a long history, and the techniques that we will study in this chapter have been developed over many centuries.

The mathematical notation that we use today to solve equations is the result of thousands of years of development. The ancient Egyptians used a word for variables, best translated as *heap*. Others used the word *res*, which is Latin for *thing*. In the fifteenth century, the letters *p:* and *m:* were used for *plus* and *minus*. What we would now write as $2x + 3 = 5$ might have been written by those early mathematicians as

2 res p:3 aequalis 5

Figure 2–3 suggests the ***multiplication property of equality:*** *If equal quantities are multiplied by the same quantity, the results will be equal quantities.*

We will now consider how to solve the equation $2x = 6$. Since $2x$ means $2 \cdot x$, the equation can be written as $2 \cdot x = 6$. We can think of the scale shown in Figure 2-4(a) as representing this equation. The weight on the left side of the scale is $2 \cdot x$ grams, and the weight on the right side is 6 grams. Because these weights are equal, the scale is in balance. To find x, we remove half of the weight from each side. This is equivalent to dividing the weight on both sides by 2. When we do this, the scale will remain in balance. From the scale shown in Figure 2-4(b), we can see that x grams will be balanced by 3 grams. Thus, $x = 3$. Since 3 is a solution of the equation, the solution set is $\{3\}$.

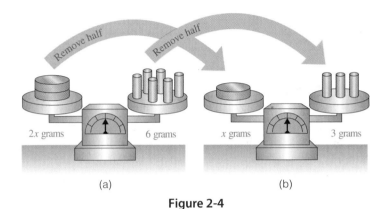

(a)   (b)

Figure 2-4

Figure 2-4 suggests the *division property of equality: If equal quantities are divided by the same quantity, the results will be equal quantities.*

The previous discussion justifies the following properties.

Multiplication Property of Equality	Suppose that a, b, and c are real numbers. Then, If $a = b$, then $ca = cb$.
Division Property of Equality	Suppose that a, b, and c are real numbers and $c \neq 0$. Then, If $a = b$, then $\dfrac{a}{c} = \dfrac{b}{c}$.

COMMENT   Since dividing by a number is the same as multiplying by its reciprocal, the division property is a special case of the multiplication property. However, because the reciprocal of 0 is undefined, we must exclude the possibility of division by 0.

When we use the multiplication and division properties, the resulting equations will be equivalent to the original ones.

To solve the previous equations algebraically, we proceed as in the next examples.

EXAMPLE 5   Solve: $\dfrac{x}{3} = 12$.

Solution   To isolate x on one side of the $=$ sign, we use the multiplication property of equality to undo the division by 3 by multiplying both sides of the equation by 3.

$$\frac{x}{3} = 12$$

$$3 \cdot \frac{x}{3} = 3 \cdot 12 \qquad \text{Multiply both sides by 3.}$$

$$x = 36 \qquad 3 \cdot \frac{x}{3} = x \text{ and } 3 \cdot 12 = 36.$$

Since 36 is a solution, the solution set is {36}. Verify that the solution checks.

➡ **SELF CHECK 5**   Solve: $\dfrac{x}{5} = -7$.

EXAMPLE 6   Solve: $2x = 6$.

Solution   To isolate x on one side of the = sign, we use the division property of equality to undo the multiplication by 2 by dividing both sides by 2.

$$2x = 6$$

$$\frac{2x}{2} = \frac{6}{2} \qquad \text{Divide both sides by 2.}$$

$$x = 3 \qquad \frac{2}{2} = 1 \text{ and } \frac{6}{2} = 3.$$

Since 3 is a solution, the solution set is {3}. Verify that the solution checks.

COMMENT   Note that we could have solved the equation in Example 6 by using the multiplication property of equality. To isolate x, we could have multiplied both sides by $\frac{1}{2}$.

➡ **SELF CHECK 6**   Solve: $-5x = 15$.

EXAMPLE 7   Solve: $3x = \dfrac{1}{5}$.

Solution   To isolate x on the left side of the equation, we could undo the multiplication by 3 by dividing both sides by 3. However, it is easier to isolate x by multiplying both sides by the reciprocal of 3, which is $\frac{1}{3}$.

$$3x = \frac{1}{5}$$

$$\frac{1}{3}(3x) = \frac{1}{3}\left(\frac{1}{5}\right) \qquad \text{Multiply both sides by } \frac{1}{3}.$$

$$\left(\frac{1}{3} \cdot 3\right)x = \frac{1}{15} \qquad \text{Use the associative property of multiplication.}$$

$$1x = \frac{1}{15} \qquad \tfrac{1}{3} \cdot 3 = 1$$

$$x = \frac{1}{15}$$

Since the solution is $\frac{1}{15}$, the solution set is $\left\{\frac{1}{15}\right\}$. Verify that the solution checks.

⇨ **SELF CHECK 7**   Solve: $-5x = \frac{1}{3}$

5   ## Solve a linear equation in one variable involving markdown and markup.

When the price of merchandise is reduced, the amount of reduction is called the **markdown** or the **discount**. To find the sale price of an item, we subtract the markdown from the regular price.

EXAMPLE 8   **BUYING FURNITURE**   A sofa is on sale for $650. If it has been marked down $325, find its regular price.

Solution   We can let r represent the regular price and substitute 650 for the sale price and 325 for the markdown in the following formula.

Sale price	equals	regular price	minus	markdown.
650	=	r	−	325

We can use the addition property of equality to solve the equation.

$$650 = r - 325$$
$$650 + 325 = r - 325 + 325 \qquad \text{Add 325 to both sides.}$$
$$975 = r \qquad\qquad 650 + 325 = 975 \text{ and } -325 + 325 = 0.$$

The regular price is $975.

⇨ **SELF CHECK 8**   Find the regular price of the sofa if the discount is $275.

To make a profit, a merchant must sell an item for more than he paid for it. The retail price of the item is the sum of its wholesale cost and the **markup.**

EXAMPLE 9   **BUYING CARS**   A car with a sticker price of $17,500 has a markup of $3,500. Find the invoice price (the wholesale price) to the dealer.

Solution   We can let w represent the wholesale price and substitute 17,500 for the retail price and 3,500 for the markup in the following formula.

Retail price	equals	wholesale cost	plus	markup.
17,500	=	w	+	3,500

We can use the subtraction property of equality to solve the equation.

$$17,500 = w + 3,500$$

$$17,500 - \textbf{3,500} = w + 3,500 - \textbf{3,500} \qquad \text{Subtract 3,500 from both sides.}$$

$$14,000 = w \qquad\qquad\qquad \text{17,500} - 3,500 = 14,000 \text{ and}$$
$$\text{3,500} - 3,500 = 0.$$

The invoice price is $14,000.

⇨ **SELF CHECK 9**   Find the invoice price of the car if the markup is $6,700.

---

6 **Solve a percent problem involving a linear equation in one variable using the formula** $rb = a$**.**

A **percent** is the numerator of a fraction with a denominator of 100. For example, $6\frac{1}{4}$ percent $\left(\text{written as } 6\frac{1}{4}\%\right)$ is the fraction $\frac{6.25}{100}$, or the decimal 0.0625. In problems involving percent, the word *of* usually means multiplication. For example, $6\frac{1}{4}\%$ of 8,500 is the product of 0.0625 and 8,500.

$$6\frac{1}{4}\% \text{ of } 8,500 = 0.0625 \cdot 8,500$$

$$= 531.25$$

In the statement $6\frac{1}{4}\%$ of $8,500 = 531.25$, the percent $6\frac{1}{4}\%$ is called a **rate,** 8,500 is called the **base,** and their product, 531.25, is called the **amount.** Every percent problem is based on the equation rate · base = amount.

Percent Formula	If r is the rate, b is the base, and a is the amount, then
	$rb = a$

COMMENT Note that the previous formula can be written in the equivalent form $a = rb$.

Percent problems involve questions such as the following.

- What is 30% of 1,000?   In this problem, we must find the amount.
- 45% of what number is 405?   In this problem, we must find the base.
- What percent of 400 is 60?   In this problem, we must find the rate.

When we substitute the values of the rate, base, and amount into the percent formula, we will obtain an equation that we can solve.

EXAMPLE 10   What is 30% of 1,000?

Solution   In this problem, the rate r is 30% and the base is 1,000. We must find the amount.

Rate	·	base	=	amount
30%	of	1,000	is	the amount

We can substitute these values into the percent formula and solve for a.

$$rb = a$$

$30\% \cdot 1{,}000 = a$ Substitute 30% for r and 1,000 for b.

$0.30 \cdot 1{,}000 = a$ Change 30% to the decimal 0.30.

$300 = a$ Multiply.

Thus, 30% of 1,000 is 300.

SELF CHECK 10   Find 45% of 800.

EXAMPLE 11   45% of what number is 405?

Solution   In this problem, the rate r is 45% and the amount a is 405. We must find the base.

Rate	·	base	=	amount
45%	of	what number	is	405?

We can substitute these values into the percent formula and solve for b.

$$rb = a$$

$45\% \cdot b = 405$ Substitute 45% for r and 405 for a.

$0.45 \cdot b = 405$ Change 45% to a decimal.

$\dfrac{0.45b}{0.45} = \dfrac{405}{0.45}$ To undo the multiplication by 0.45, divide both sides by 0.45.

$b = 900$ $\frac{0.45}{0.45} = 1$ and $\frac{405}{0.45} = 900$.

Thus, 45% of 900 is 405.

SELF CHECK 11   35% of what number is 306.25?

EXAMPLE 12   What percent of 400 is 60?

Solution   In this problem, the base b is 400 and the amount a is 60. We must find the rate.

Rate	·	base	=	amount
What percent	of	400	is	60?

We can substitute these values in the percent formula and solve for r.

$$rb = a$$

$r \cdot 400 = 60$ Substitute 400 for b and 60 for a.

$\dfrac{400r}{400} = \dfrac{60}{400}$ To undo the multiplication by 400, divide both sides by 400.

$r = 0.15$ $\frac{400}{400} = 1$ and $\frac{60}{400} = 0.15$.

$r = 15\%$ To change the decimal into a percent, we multiply by 100 and insert a % sign.

Thus, 15% of 400 is 60.

▷ **SELF CHECK 12**   What percent of 600 is 150?

7   **Solve an application problem involving percents.**

The ability to solve linear equations enables us to solve many application problems. This is what makes the algebra relevant to our lives.

EXAMPLE 13   **INVESTING**   At a stockholders meeting, members representing 4.5 million shares voted in favor of a proposal for a mandatory retirement age for the members of the board of directors. If this represented 75% of the number of shares outstanding, how many shares were outstanding?

Solution   Let b represent the number of outstanding shares. Then 75% of b is 4.5 million. We can substitute 75% for r and 4.5 million for a in the percent formula and solve for b.

$$rb = a$$
$$75\% \cdot b = \mathbf{4,500,000} \qquad \text{4.5 million} = 4,500,000$$
$$0.75b = 4,500,000 \qquad \text{Change 75\% to a decimal.}$$
$$\frac{0.75b}{0.75} = \frac{4,500,000}{0.75} \qquad \text{To undo the multiplication of 0.75, divide both sides by 0.75.}$$
$$b = 6,000,000 \qquad \tfrac{0.75}{0.75} = 1 \text{ and } \tfrac{4,500,000}{0.75} = 6,000,000.$$

There were 6 million shares outstanding.

▷ **SELF CHECK 13**   If 60% of the shares outstanding were voted in favor of the proposal, how many shares were voted in favor?

EXAMPLE 14   **QUALITY CONTROL**   After examining 240 sweaters, a quality-control inspector found 5 with defective stitching, 8 with mismatched designs, and 2 with incorrect labels. What percent were defective?

Solution   Let r represent the percent that are defective. Then the base b is 240 and the amount a is the number of defective sweaters, which is $5 + 8 + 2 = 15$. We can find r by using the percent formula.

$$rb = a$$
$$r \cdot 240 = 15 \qquad \text{Substitute 240 for } b \text{ and 15 for } a.$$
$$\frac{240r}{240} = \frac{15}{240} \qquad \text{To undo the multiplication of 240, divide both sides by 240.}$$
$$r = 0.0625 \qquad \tfrac{240}{240} = 1 \text{ and } \tfrac{15}{240} = 0.0625.$$
$$r = 6.25\% \qquad \text{To change 0.0625 to a percent, multiply by 100 and insert a \% sign.}$$

The defect rate is 6.25%.

▷ **SELF CHECK 14**   If a second inspector found 3 sweaters with faded colors in addition to the defects found by inspector 1, what percent were defective?

⇨ **SELF CHECK ANSWERS** **1.** equation **2.** yes **3.** 34.8 **4.** −5.3 **5.** −35 **6.** −3 **7.** −$\frac{1}{15}$ **8.** $925 **9.** $10,800
10. 360 **11.** 875 **12.** 25% **13.** 3.6 million **14.** 7.5%

NOW TRY THIS

Solve each equation.

1. $\dfrac{x}{12} = 0$

2. $\dfrac{2}{3}x = 24$

3. $-25 + x = 25$

2.1 EXERCISES

WARM-UPS *Find the solution of each equation.*

1. $x - 9 = 11$

2. $x - 3 = 13$

3. $w + 5 = 7$

4. $x + 32 = 36$

5. $3x = 3$

6. $-7x = 14$

7. $\dfrac{x}{5} = 2$

8. $\dfrac{x}{2} = -10$

REVIEW *Perform the operations. Simplify the result when possible.*

9. $\dfrac{4}{5} + \dfrac{2}{3}$

10. $\dfrac{5}{6} \cdot \dfrac{12}{25}$

11. $\dfrac{5}{9} \div \dfrac{3}{5}$

12. $\dfrac{15}{7} - \dfrac{10}{3}$

13. $2 + 3 \cdot 4$

14. $3 \cdot 4^2$

15. $3 + 4^3(-5)$

16. $\dfrac{5(-4) - 3(-2)}{10 - (-4)}$

VOCABULARY AND CONCEPTS *Fill in the blanks.*

17. An _____ is a statement that two quantities are equal.
An _____ is a mathematical statement without an = sign.

18. A _____ or _____ of an equation is a number that satisfies the equation.

19. If two equations have the same solutions, they are called _____ equations.

20. To solve an equation, we isolate the _____, or unknown, on one side of the equation.

21. If the same quantity is added to _____ quantities, the results will be equal quantities.

22. If the same quantity is subtracted from equal quantities, the results will be _____ quantities.

23. If equal quantities are multiplied or divided by the same nonzero quantity, the results are _____ quantities.

24. An equation in the form $x + b = c$ is called a _____ equation.

25. Sale price = _____ − markdown

26. Retail price = wholesale cost + _____

27. A *percent* is the numerator of a fraction whose denominator is _____.

28. Rate · _____ = amount

GUIDED PRACTICE

Determine whether each statement is an expression or an equation. See Example 1. (Objective 1)

29. $x = 2$

30. $y = 3$

31. $6x + 7$

32. $8 - x$

33. $x + 7 = 0$

34. $7 + x = 2$

35. $3(x - 4)$

36. $5(2 + x)$

Determine whether the given number is a solution of the equation. See Example 2. (Objective 2)

37. $x + 2 = 3; 1$

38. $x - 2 = 4; 6$

39. $a - 7 = 0; -7$

40. $x + 4 = 4; 0$

41. $\dfrac{y}{7} = 4; 28$

42. $\dfrac{c}{-5} = -2; -10$

43. $\dfrac{x}{5} = x;\ 0$

44. $\dfrac{x}{7} = 7x;\ 0$

45. $3k + 5 = 5k - 1;\ 3$

46. $2s - 1 = s + 7;\ 6$

47. $\dfrac{5 + x}{10} - x = \dfrac{1}{2};\ 0$

48. $\dfrac{x - 5}{6} = 12 - x;\ 11$

Use the addition property of equality to solve each equation.
Check all solutions. See Example 3. (Objective 3)

49. $y - 7 = 12$

50. $c - 11 = 22$

51. $a - 4 = -12$

52. $m - 5 = -12$

53. $p - 404 = 115$

54. $1 = y - 5$

55. $r - \dfrac{1}{5} = \dfrac{3}{10}$

56. $\dfrac{4}{3} = -\dfrac{2}{3} + x$

Use the subtraction property of equality to solve each equation.
Check all solutions. See Example 4. (Objective 3)

57. $x + 7 = 13$

58. $y + 3 = 7$

59. $b + 3 = -10$

60. $n + 8 = -16$

61. $41 = 45 + q$

62. $0 = r + 10$

63. $k + \dfrac{2}{3} = \dfrac{1}{5}$

64. $b + \dfrac{4}{7} = \dfrac{15}{14}$

Use the multiplication property of equality to solve each equation.
Check all solutions. See Example 5. (Objective 4)

65. $\dfrac{x}{5} = 5$

66. $\dfrac{x}{15} = 3$

67. $\dfrac{b}{3} = 5$

68. $\dfrac{a}{5} = -3$

69. $\dfrac{b}{3} = \dfrac{1}{3}$

70. $\dfrac{a}{13} = \dfrac{1}{26}$

71. $\dfrac{u}{5} = -\dfrac{3}{10}$

72. $\dfrac{t}{-7} = \dfrac{1}{2}$

Use the division property of equality to solve each equation.
Check all solutions. See Example 6. (Objective 4)

73. $6x = 18$

74. $25x = 625$

75. $11x = -121$

76. $-9y = -9$

77. $-4x = 36$

78. $-16y = 64$

79. $4w = 108$

80. $-66 = -6w$

Use the multiplication or division property of equality to solve
each equation. Check all solutions. See Example 7. (Objective 4)

81. $5x = \dfrac{5}{8}$

82. $6x = \dfrac{2}{3}$

83. $\dfrac{1}{7}w = 14$

84. $-19x = -57$

85. $-1.2w = -102$

86. $1.5a = -15$

87. $0.25x = 1{,}228$

88. $-0.2y = 51$

Solve each problem involving markdown or markup. See
Examples 8–9. (Objective 5)

89. Buying boats   A boat is on sale for $7,995. Find its
regular price if it has been marked down $1,350.

90. Buying houses   A house that was priced at $105,000 has
been discounted $7,500. Find the new asking price.

91. Buying clothes   A sport jacket that sells for $175 has a
markup of $85. Find the wholesale price.

92. Buying vacuum cleaners   A vacuum that sells for $97 has a
markup of $37. Find the wholesale price.

Use the formula $rb = a$ or $a = rb$ to find each value.
See Examples 10–12. (Objective 6)

93. What number is 40% of 200?

94. What number is 35% of 520?

95. What number is 50% of 38?

96. What number is 25% of 300?

97. 15% of what number is 48?

98. 26% of what number is 78?

99. 133 is 35% of what number?

100. 13.3 is 3.5% of what number?

101. 28% of what number is 42?

102. 44% of what number is 143?

103. What percent of 357.5 is 71.5?

104. What percent of 254 is 13.208?

ADDITIONAL PRACTICE   *Solve each equation. Be sure to*
check each answer.

105. $p + 0.27 = 3.57$

106. $m - 5.36 = 1.39$

107. $\dfrac{x}{32} = -2$

108. $\dfrac{y}{16} = -5$

109. $-57 = b - 29$

110. $-93 = 67 + y$

111. $y - 2.63 = -8.21$

112. $s + 8.56 = 5.65$

113. $\dfrac{y}{-3} = -\dfrac{5}{6}$

114. $\dfrac{y}{-8} = -\dfrac{3}{16}$

115. $-37 + w = 37$

116. $-43 + a = -43$

117. $-3 = \dfrac{x}{11}$

118. $\dfrac{w}{-12} = 4$

119. $b + 7 = \dfrac{20}{3}$

120. $x + \dfrac{5}{7} = -\dfrac{2}{7}$

121. $2x = \dfrac{1}{7}$

122. $-8x + 1 = -7$

123. $-\dfrac{3}{5} = x - \dfrac{2}{5}$

124. $d + \dfrac{2}{3} = \dfrac{3}{2}$

125. $\dfrac{1}{7}x = \dfrac{5}{7}$

126. $-17x = -51$

127. $-32r = 64$

128. $15 = \dfrac{r}{-5}$

129. $18x = -9$

130. $-12x = 3$

Find each value.

131. 0.32 is what percent of 4?

132. 3.6 is what percent of 28.8?

133. 34 is what percent of 17?

134. 39 is what percent of 13?

APPLICATIONS

Solve each application problem involving percents.
See Examples 13–14. (Objective 7)

135. Selling microwave ovens   The 5% sales tax on a microwave oven amounts to $13.50. What is the microwave's selling price?

136. Hospitals   18% of hospital patients stay for less than 1 day. If 1,008 patients in January stayed for less than 1 day, what total number of patients did the hospital treat in January?

137. Sales taxes   Sales tax on a $12 compact disc is $0.72. At what rate is sales tax computed?

138. Home prices   The average price of homes in one neighborhood decreased 8% since last year, a drop of $7,800. What was the average price of a home last year?

Solve each problem.

139. Banking   The amount A in an account is given by the formula

$$A = p + i$$

where p is the principal and i is the interest. How much interest was earned if an original deposit (the principal) of $4,750 has grown to be $5,010?

140. Selling real estate   The money m received from selling a house is given by the formula

$$m = s - c$$

where s is the selling price and c is the agent's commission. Find the selling price of a house if the seller received $217,000 and the agent received $13,020.

141. Customer satisfaction   One-third of the movie audience left the theater in disgust. If 78 angry patrons walked out, how many were there originally?

142. Off-campus housing   One-seventh of the senior class is living in off-campus housing. If 217 students live off campus, how large is the senior class?

143. Shopper dissatisfaction   Refer to the survey results shown in the table. What percent of those surveyed were not pleased?

Shopper survey results	
First-time shoppers	1,731
Major purchase today	539
Shopped within previous month	1,823
Satisfied with service	4,140
Seniors	2,387
Total surveyed	9,200

144. Shopper satisfaction   Refer to the survey results shown in the table above. What percent of those surveyed were satisfied with their service?

145. Union membership   If 2,484 union members represent 90% of a factory's work force, how many workers are employed?

146. Charities   Out of $237,000 donated to a certain charity, $5,925 is used to pay for fund-raising expenses. What percent of the donations is overhead?

147. Stock splits   After a 3-for-2 stock split, each shareholder will own 1.5 times as many shares as before. If 555 shares are owned after the split, how many were owned before?

148. Stock splits   After a 2-for-1 stock split, each shareholder owned twice as many shares as before. If 2,570 shares are owned after the split, how many were owned before?

149. Depreciation   Find the original cost of a car that is worth $10,250 after depreciating $7,500.

150. Appreciation   Find the original purchase price of a house that is worth $150,000 and has appreciated $57,000.

151. Taxes   Find the tax paid on an item that was priced at $37.10 and cost $39.32.

152. Buying carpets   How much did it cost to install $317 worth of carpet that cost $512?

153. Buying paint   After reading this ad, a decorator bought 1 gallon of primer, 1 gallon of paint, and a brush. If the total cost was $30.44, find the cost of the brush.

154. Painting a room   After reading the ad above, a woman bought 2 gallons of paint, 1 gallon of primer, and a brush. If the total cost was $46.94, find the cost of the brush.

155. Buying real estate   The cost of a condominium is $57,595 less than the cost of a house. If the house costs $202,744, find the cost of the condominium.

156. Buying airplanes   The cost of a twin-engine plane is $175,260 less than the cost of a 2-seater jet. If the jet cost $321,435, find the cost of the twin-engine plane.

WRITING ABOUT MATH

157. Explain what it means for a number to satisfy an equation.

158. How can you tell whether a number is the solution to an equation?

SOMETHING TO THINK ABOUT

159. The Ahmes papyrus mentioned on page 9 contains this statement: *A circle nine units in diameter has the same area as a square eight units on a side.* From this statement, determine the ancient Egyptians' approximation of π.

160. Calculate the Egyptians' *percent of error*: What percent of the actual value of π is the difference of the estimate obtained in Exercise 159 and the actual value of π?

SECTION 2.2   Solving More Linear Equations in One Variable

Objectives

1 Solve a linear equation in one variable requiring more than one property of equality.

2 Solve an application problem requiring more than one property of equality.

3 Solve an application problem involving percent of increase or decrease.

Vocabulary

percent of increase   percent of decrease

Getting Ready

Perform the operations.

1. $7 + 3 \cdot 5$

2. $3(5 + 7)$

3. $\dfrac{3 + 7}{2}$

4. $3 + \dfrac{7}{2}$

5. $\dfrac{3(5 - 8)}{9}$

6. $3 \cdot \dfrac{5 - 8}{9}$

7. $\dfrac{3 \cdot 5 - 8}{9}$

8. $3 \cdot \dfrac{5}{9} - 8$

We have solved equations by using the addition, subtraction, multiplication, and division properties of equality. To solve more complicated equations, we need to use several of these properties in succession.

1 Solve a linear equation in one variable requiring more than one property of equality.

To solve many equations, we must use more than one property of equality. In the following examples, we will combine the addition or subtraction property with the multiplication or division property to solve more complicated equations.

EVERYDAY CONNECTIONS   Renting a Car

Rental car rates for various cars are given for three different companies. In each formula, x represents the number of days the rental car is used.

Economy car from Dan's Rentals

$C = 19.14x + 65.48$

Luxury car from Spencer's Cars

$C = 55x + 124.15$

SUV from Tyler's Auto Rentals

$C = 35.87x + 89.08$

We can solve an equation to compare the companies to one another.

Suppose you have $900 available to spend on a rental car. Find the number of days you can afford to rent from each company.   (*Hint:* Substitute 900 for C.)

Dan's Rentals

Spencer's Cars

Tyler's Auto Rentals

EXAMPLE 1   Solve: $-12x + 5 = 17$.

Solution   The left side of the equation indicates that x is to be multiplied by -12 and then 5 is to be added to that product. To isolate x, we must undo these operations in the reverse order.

- To undo the addition of 5, we subtract 5 from both sides.
- To undo the multiplication by -12, we divide both sides by -12.

$$-12x + 5 = 17$$
$$-12x + 5 - 5 = 17 - 5 \qquad \text{To undo the addition of 5, subtract 5 from both sides.}$$
$$-12x = 12 \qquad 5 - 5 = 0 \text{ and } 17 - 5 = 12.$$
$$\frac{-12x}{-12} = \frac{12}{-12} \qquad \text{To undo the multiplication by } -12, \text{ divide both sides by } -12.$$
$$x = -1 \qquad \frac{-12}{-12} = -1 \text{ and } \frac{12}{-12} = -1.$$

Check: $-12x + 5 = 17$
$$-12(-1) + 5 \stackrel{?}{=} 17 \qquad \text{Substitute } -1 \text{ for } x.$$
$$12 + 5 \stackrel{?}{=} 17 \qquad \text{Simplify.}$$
$$17 = 17 \qquad \text{True.}$$

Since $17 = 17$, the solution -1 checks and the solution set is $\{-1\}$.

⇨ SELF CHECK 1   Solve: $2x + 3 = 15$.

EXAMPLE 2   Solve: $\dfrac{x}{3} - 7 = -3$.

Solution   The left side of the equation indicates that x is to be divided by 3 and then 7 is to be subtracted from that quotient. To isolate x, we must undo these operations in the reverse order.

- To undo the subtraction of 7, we add 7 to both sides.
- To undo the division by 3, we multiply both sides by 3.

$$\frac{x}{3} - 7 = -3$$

$$\frac{x}{3} - 7 + 7 = -3 + 7 \qquad \text{To undo the subtraction of 7, add 7 to both sides.}$$

$$\frac{x}{3} = 4 \qquad -7 + 7 = 0 \text{ and } -3 + 7 = 4.$$

$$3 \cdot \frac{x}{3} = 3 \cdot 4 \qquad \text{To undo the division by 3, multiply both sides by 3.}$$

$$x = 12 \qquad 3 \cdot \tfrac{1}{3} = 1 \text{ and } 3 \cdot 4 = 12.$$

Check: $\dfrac{x}{3} - 7 = -3$

$$\frac{12}{3} - 7 \stackrel{?}{=} -3 \qquad \text{Substitute 12 for } x.$$

$$4 - 7 \stackrel{?}{=} -3 \qquad \text{Simplify.}$$

$$-3 = -3$$

Since $-3 = -3$, the solution 12 checks and the solution set is $\{12\}$.

⇨ **SELF CHECK 2**   Solve: $\frac{x}{4} - 3 = 5$.

EXAMPLE 3   Solve: $\dfrac{x - 7}{3} = 9$.

Solution   The left side of the equation indicates that 7 is to be subtracted from x and that the difference is to be divided by 3. To isolate x, we must undo these operations in the reverse order.

- To undo the division by 3, we multiply both sides by 3.
- To undo the subtraction of 7, we add 7 to both sides.

$$\frac{x - 7}{3} = 9$$

$$3\left(\frac{x - 7}{3}\right) = 3(9) \qquad \text{To undo the division by 3, multiply both sides by 3.}$$

$$x - 7 = 27 \qquad 3 \cdot \tfrac{1}{3} = 1 \text{ and } 3(9) = 27.$$

$$x - 7 + 7 = 27 + 7 \qquad \text{To undo the subtraction of 7, add 7 to both sides.}$$

$$x = 34 \qquad -7 + 7 = 0 \text{ and } 27 + 7 = 34.$$

Since the solution is 34, the solution set is $\{34\}$. Verify that the solution checks.

⇨ **SELF CHECK 3**   Solve: $\frac{a - 3}{5} = -2$.

EXAMPLE 4   Solve: $\dfrac{3x}{4} + \dfrac{2}{3} = -7$.

Solution   The left side of the equation indicates that x is to be multiplied by 3, then $3x$ is to be divided by 4, and then $\dfrac{2}{3}$ is to be added to that result. To isolate x, we must undo these operations in the reverse order.

- To undo the addition of $\dfrac{2}{3}$, we subtract $\dfrac{2}{3}$ from both sides.
- To undo the division by 4, we multiply both sides by 4.
- To undo the multiplication by 3, we multiply both sides by $\dfrac{1}{3}$.

$$\frac{3x}{4} + \frac{2}{3} = -7$$

$$\frac{3x}{4} + \frac{2}{3} - \frac{2}{3} = -7 - \frac{2}{3} \qquad \text{To undo the addition of } \tfrac{2}{3}, \text{ subtract } \tfrac{2}{3} \text{ from both sides.}$$

$$\frac{3x}{4} = -\frac{23}{3} \qquad \tfrac{2}{3} - \tfrac{2}{3} = 0 \text{ and } -7 - \tfrac{2}{3} = -\tfrac{23}{3}.$$

$$4\left(\frac{3x}{4}\right) = 4\left(-\frac{23}{3}\right) \qquad \text{To undo the division by 4, multiply both sides by 4.}$$

$$3x = -\frac{92}{3} \qquad 4 \cdot \tfrac{3x}{4} = 3x \text{ and } 4\left(-\tfrac{23}{3}\right) = -\tfrac{92}{3}.$$

$$\frac{1}{3}(3x) = \frac{1}{3}\left(-\frac{92}{3}\right) \qquad \text{To undo the multiplication by 3, multiply both sides by } \tfrac{1}{3}.$$

$$x = -\frac{92}{9} \qquad \tfrac{1}{3} \cdot 3x = x \text{ and } \tfrac{1}{3}\left(-\tfrac{92}{3}\right) = -\tfrac{92}{9}.$$

Since the solution is $-\dfrac{92}{9}$, the solution set is $\left\{-\dfrac{92}{9}\right\}$. Verify that the solution checks.

SELF CHECK 4   Solve: $\dfrac{2x}{3} - \dfrac{4}{5} = 3$.

EXAMPLE 5   Solve: $\dfrac{0.6x - 1.29}{0.33} - 3.67 = -6.67$.

Solution   The left side of the equation indicates that x is to be multiplied by 0.6, then 1.29 is to be subtracted from $0.6x$, then that difference is to be divided by 0.33, and finally 3.67 is to be subtracted from the result. To isolate x, we must undo these operations in the reverse order.

- To undo the subtraction of 3.67, we add 3.67 to both sides.
- To undo the division by 0.33, we multiply both sides by 0.33.
- To undo the subtraction of 1.29, we add 1.29 to both sides.
- To undo the multiplication by 0.6, we divide both sides by 0.6.

$$\frac{0.6x - 1.29}{0.33} - 3.67 = -6.67$$

$$\frac{0.6x - 1.29}{0.33} - 3.67 + \mathbf{3.67} = -6.67 + \mathbf{3.67} \qquad \text{To undo the subtraction of 3.67, add 3.67 to both sides.}$$

$$\frac{0.6x - 1.29}{0.33} = -3$$ Do the additions.

$$0.33\left(\frac{0.6x - 1.29}{0.33}\right) = 0.33(-3)$$ To undo the division by 0.33, multiply both sides by 0.33.

$$0.6x - 1.29 = -0.99$$ Do the multiplications; $\frac{0.33}{0.33} = 1$

$$0.6x - 1.29 + 1.29 = -0.99 + 1.29$$ To undo the subtraction of 1.29, add 1.29 to both sides.

$$0.6x = 0.3$$ Do the additions.

$$\frac{0.6x}{0.6} = \frac{0.3}{0.6}$$ To undo the multiplication by 0.6, divide both sides by 0.6.

$$x = 0.5$$ Do the divisions.

The solution set is {0.5}. Verify that the solution checks.

⇨ **SELF CHECK 5** Solve: $\frac{0.5x + 5.1}{0.45} + 4.71 = 16.71$.

2 Solve an application problem requiring more than one property of equality.

EXAMPLE 6 **ADVERTISING** A store manager hires a student to distribute advertising circulars door to door. The student will be paid $24 a day plus 12¢ for every ad she distributes. How many circulars must she distribute to earn $42 in one day?

Solution We can let a represent the number of circulars that the student must distribute. Her earnings can be expressed in two ways: as $24 plus the 12¢-apiece pay for distributing the circulars, and as $42.

| $24 | plus | a ads at $0.12 each | is | $42. | 12¢ = $0.12 |

$$24 \quad + \quad 0.12a \quad = \quad 42$$

We can solve this equation as follows:

$$24 + 0.12a = 42$$

$$24 - 24 + 0.12a = 42 - 24$$ To undo the addition of 24, subtract 24 from both sides.

$$0.12a = 18$$ $24 - 24 = 0$ and $42 - 24 = 18$.

$$\frac{0.12a}{0.12} = \frac{18}{0.12}$$ To undo the multiplication by 0.12, divide both sides by 0.12.

$$a = 150$$ $\frac{0.12}{0.12} = 1$ and $\frac{18}{0.12} = 150$.

The student must distribute 150 ads. Check the result.

⇨ **SELF CHECK 6** How many circulars must the student deliver in one day to earn $48?

3 **Solve an application problem involving percent of increase or decrease.**

We have seen that the retail price of an item is the sum of the cost and the markup.

| Retail price | equals | cost | plus | markup |

Often, the markup is expressed as a percent of the cost.

| Markup | equals | percent of markup | times | cost |

Suppose a store manager buys toasters for $21 and sells them at a 17% markup. To find the retail price, the manager begins with his cost and adds 17% of that cost.

$$
\begin{aligned}
\text{Retail price} \;=\; & \text{cost} \;+\; \text{markup} \\
=\; & \text{cost} \;+\; \text{percent of markup} \cdot \text{cost} \\
=\; & 21 \;+\; 0.17 \;\cdot\; 21 \\
=\; & 21 + 3.57 \\
=\; & 24.57
\end{aligned}
$$

The retail price of a toaster is $24.57.

EXAMPLE 7   **ANTIQUE CARS**   In 1956, a Chevrolet BelAir automobile sold for $4,000. Today, it is worth about $28,600. Find the percent that its value has increased, called the **percent of increase**.

Solution   We let p represent the percent of increase, expressed as a decimal.

| Current price | equals | original price | plus | p(original price) |

$$28{,}600 = 4{,}000 + p(4{,}000)$$

$28{,}600 - \mathbf{4{,}000} = 4{,}000 - \mathbf{4{,}000} + 4{,}000p$	To undo the addition of 4,000, subtract 4,000 from both sides.
$24{,}600 = 4{,}000p$	$28{,}600 - 4{,}000 = 24{,}600$ and $4{,}000 - 4{,}000 = 0$.
$\dfrac{24{,}600}{\mathbf{4{,}000}} = \dfrac{4{,}000p}{\mathbf{4{,}000}}$	To undo the multiplication by 4,000, divide both sides by 4,000.
$6.15 = p$	Simplify.

To convert 6.15 to a percent, we multiply by 100 and insert a % sign. Since the percent of increase is 615%, the car has appreciated 615%.

⇨ **SELF CHECK 7**   Find the percent of increase if the car sells for $30,000.

We have seen that when the price of merchandise is reduced, the amount of reduction is the markdown (also called the *discount*).

| Sale price | equals | regular price | minus | markdown |

Usually, the markdown is expressed as a percent of the regular price.

| Markdown | equals | percent of markdown | times | regular price |

Suppose that a television set that regularly sells for $570 has been marked down 25%. That means the customer will pay 25% less than the regular price. To find the sale price, we use the formula

| Sale price | = | regular price | − | markdown |

$$= \quad \text{regular price} \quad - \quad \text{percent of markdown} \quad \cdot \quad \text{regular price}$$

$$= \quad \$570 \quad - \quad 25\% \quad \text{of} \quad \$570$$

$$= \$570 - (0.25)(\$570) \qquad 25\% = 0.25$$

$$= \$570 - \$142.50$$

$$= \$427.50$$

The television set is selling for $427.50.

EXAMPLE 8 **BUYING CAMERAS** A camera that was originally priced at $452 is on sale for $384.20. Find the percent of markdown.

Solution We let p represent the percent of markdown, expressed as a decimal, and substitute $384.20 for the sale price and $452 for the regular price.

| Sale price | equals | regular price | minus | percent of markdown | times | regular price |

$$384.20 \quad = \quad 452 \quad - \quad p \quad \cdot \quad 452$$

$$384.20 - 452 = 452 - 452 - p(452) \qquad \text{To undo the addition of 452, subtract 452 from both sides.}$$

$$-67.80 = -p(452) \qquad 384.20 - 452 = -67.80; 452 - 452 = 0$$

$$\frac{-67.80}{-452} = \frac{-p(452)}{-452} \qquad \text{To undo the multiplication by } -452, \text{ divide both sides by } -452.$$

$$0.15 = p \qquad \frac{-67.80}{-452} = 0.15 \text{ and } \frac{-452}{-452} = 1.$$

The camera is on sale at a 15% markdown.

▷ **SELF CHECK 8** If the camera is reduced another $22.60, find the percent of discount.

COMMENT When a price increases from $100 to $125, the percent of increase is 25%. When the price *decreases* from $125 to $100, the **percent of decrease** is 20%. These different results occur because the percent of increase is a percent of the original (smaller) price, $100. The percent of decrease is a percent of the original (larger) price, $125.

▷ **SELF CHECK ANSWERS**   **1.** 6   **2.** 32   **3.** −7   **4.** $\frac{57}{10}$ **5.** 0.6   **6.** 200   **7.** 650%   **8.** 20%

NOW TRY THIS

Solve each equation.

1. $\frac{2}{7}x + 3 = 3$

2. $10 - \frac{2}{3}x = -6$

3. $-0.2x - 4.3 = -10.7$

2.2 EXERCISES

WARM-UPS

What would you do first when solving each equation?

1. $5x - 7 = -12$

2. $15 = \frac{x}{5} + 3$

3. $\frac{x}{7} - 3 = 0$

4. $\frac{x - 3}{7} = -7$

5. $\frac{x - 7}{3} = 5$

6. $\frac{3x - 5}{2} + 2 = 0$

Solve each equation.

7. $7z - 7 = 14$

8. $\frac{p - 1}{2} = 6$

REVIEW   *Refer to the formulas given in Section 1.3.*

9. Find the perimeter of a rectangle with sides measuring 8.5 and 16.5 cm.

10. Find the area of a rectangle with sides measuring 2.3 in. and 3.7 in.

11. Find the area of a trapezoid with a height of 8.5 in. and bases measuring 6.7 in. and 12.2 in.

12. Find the volume of a rectangular solid with dimensions of 8.2 cm by 7.6 cm by 10.2 cm.

VOCABULARY AND CONCEPTS   *Fill in the blanks.*

13. Retail price = _____ + markup

14. Markup = percent of markup · _____.

15. Markdown = _____ of markdown · regular price

16. Another word for markdown is _____.

17. The percent that an object has increased in value is called the _____.

18. The percent that an object has deceased in value is called the _____.

GUIDED PRACTICE

Solve each equation. Check all solutions. **See Example 1.** (Objective 1)

19. $5x - 1 = 4$

20. $5x + 3 = 8$

21. $-6x + 2 = 14$

22. $4x - 4 = 8$

23. $6x + 2 = -4$

24. $4x - 4 = 4$

25. $3x - 8 = 1$

26. $7x - 19 = 2$

Solve each equation. Check all solutions. **See Example 2.** (Objective 1)

27. $\frac{z}{9} + 5 = -1$

28. $\frac{y}{5} - 3 = 3$

29. $\frac{b}{3} + 5 = 2$

30. $\frac{a}{5} - 3 = -4$

31. $\frac{x}{3} - 3 = -2$

32. $\frac{x}{7} + 3 = 5$

33. $\frac{p}{11} + 9 = 6$

34. $\frac{r}{12} + 2 = 4$

Solve each equation. Check all solutions. **See Example 3.** (Objective 1)

35. $\frac{b + 5}{3} = 11$

36. $\frac{a + 2}{13} = 3$

37. $\frac{r + 7}{3} = 4$

38. $\frac{q - 2}{7} = -3$

39. $\frac{3x - 12}{2} = 9$

40. $\frac{5x + 10}{7} = 0$

41. $\frac{5k - 8}{9} = 1$

42. $\frac{2k - 1}{3} = -5$

Solve each equation. Check all solutions. **See Example 4.** (Objective 1)

43. $\frac{k}{5} - \frac{1}{2} = \frac{3}{2}$

44. $\frac{y}{5} - \frac{8}{7} = -\frac{1}{7}$

45. $\frac{w}{16} + \frac{5}{4} = 1$

46. $\frac{m}{7} - \frac{1}{14} = \frac{1}{14}$

47. $\dfrac{3x}{2} - 6 = 9$ **48.** $\dfrac{5x}{7} + 3 = 8$

49. $\dfrac{3y}{2} + 5 = 11$ **50.** $\dfrac{5z}{3} + 3 = -2$

Solve each equation. Check all solutions. See Example 5.
(Objective 1)

51. $\dfrac{2.4x + 4.8}{1.2} = 8$ **52.** $\dfrac{1.5x - 15}{2.5} = -5.1$

53. $\dfrac{2.1x - 0.13}{0.8} + 2.5 = 0.5$

54. $\dfrac{8.4x + 4.8}{0.24} + 50.5 = -52$

ADDITIONAL PRACTICE *Solve each equation. Check all solutions.*

55. $11x + 17 = -5$ **56.** $13x - 29 = -3$

57. $43p + 72 = 158$ **58.** $96q + 23 = -265$

59. $-47 - 21n = 58$ **60.** $-151 + 13m = -229$

61. $2y - \dfrac{5}{3} = \dfrac{4}{3}$ **62.** $9y + \dfrac{1}{2} = \dfrac{3}{2}$

63. $-0.4y - 12 = -20$ **64.** $-0.8y + 64 = -32$

65. $\dfrac{2x}{3} + \dfrac{1}{2} = 3$ **66.** $\dfrac{4x}{5} - \dfrac{1}{3} = 1$

67. $\dfrac{3x}{4} - \dfrac{2}{5} = 2$ **68.** $\dfrac{5x}{6} + \dfrac{3}{5} = 3$

69. $\dfrac{u - 2}{5} = 1$ **70.** $\dfrac{v - 7}{3} = -1$

71. $\dfrac{x - 4}{4} = -3$ **72.** $\dfrac{3 + y}{5} = -3$

73. $\dfrac{3z + 2}{17} = 0$ **74.** $\dfrac{10n - 4}{2} = 1$

75. $\dfrac{17k - 28}{21} + \dfrac{4}{3} = 0$ **76.** $\dfrac{5a - 2}{3} = \dfrac{1}{6}$

77. $-\dfrac{x}{3} - \dfrac{1}{2} = -\dfrac{5}{2}$ **78.** $\dfrac{17 - 7a}{8} = 2$

79. $\dfrac{9 - 5w}{15} = \dfrac{2}{5}$ **80.** $\dfrac{3p - 5}{5} + \dfrac{1}{2} = -\dfrac{19}{2}$

APPLICATIONS

Solve each problem. See Example 6. (Objective 2)

81. Apartment rentals A student moves into a bigger apartment that rents for $400 per month. That rent is $100 less than twice what she had been paying. Find her former rent.

82. Auto repairs A mechanic charged $20 an hour to repair the water pump on a car, plus $95 for parts. If the total bill was $155, how many hours did the repair take?

83. Boarding dogs A sportsman boarded his dog at a kennel for a $16 registration fee plus $12 a day. If the stay cost $100, how many days was the owner gone?

84. Water billing The city's water department charges $7 per month, plus 42¢ for every 100 gallons of water used. Last month, one homeowner used 1,900 gallons and received a bill for $17.98. Was the billing correct?

Solve each problem. See Examples 7–8. (Objective 3)

85. Clearance sales Sweaters already on sale for 20% off the regular price cost $36 when purchased with a promotional coupon that allows an additional 10% discount. Find the original price. (*Hint:* When you save 20%, you are paying 80%.)

86. Furniture sales A $1,250 sofa is marked down to $900. Find the percent of markdown.

87. Value of coupons The percent discount offered by this coupon depends on the amount purchased. Find the range of the percent discount.

Value coupon

Save $15

on purchases of $100 to $250.

88. Furniture pricing A bedroom set selling for $1,900 cost $1,000 wholesale. Find the percent markup.

Solve each problem.

89. Integer problem Six less than 3 times a number is 9. Find the number.

90. Integer problem Seven less than 5 times a number is 23. Find the number.

91. Integer problem If a number is increased by 7 and that result is divided by 2, the number 5 is obtained. Find the original number.

92. Integer problem If twice a number is decreased by 5 and that result is multiplied by 4, the result is 36. Find the number.

93. Telephone charges A call to Tucson from a pay phone in Chicago costs 85¢ for the first minute and 27¢ for each additional minute or portion of a minute. If a student has $8.68 in change, how long can she talk?

94. Monthly sales A clerk's sales in February were $2,000 less than 3 times her sales in January. If her February sales were $7,000, by what amount did her sales increase?

95. Ticket sales A music group charges $1,500 for each performance, plus 20% of the total ticket sales. After a concert, the group received $2,980. How much money did the ticket sales raise?

96. Getting an A To receive a grade of A, the average of four 100-point exams must be 90 or better. If a student received scores of 88, 83, and 92 on the first three exams, what minimum score does he need on the fourth exam to earn an A?

97. Getting an A   The grade in history class is based on the average of five 100-point exams. One student received scores of 85, 80, 95, and 78 on the first four exams. With an average of 90 needed, what chance does he have for an A?

98. Excess inventory   From the portion of the following ad, determine the sale price of a shirt.

Clearance Sale
Save 40%

	Regularly	Sale
Sweaters	$45.95	$27.57
Shirts	$37.50	$

WRITING ABOUT MATH

99. In solving the equation $5x - 3 = 12$, explain why you would add 3 to both sides first, rather than dividing by 5 first.

100. To solve the equation $\frac{3x - 4}{7} = 2$, what operations would you perform, and in what order?

SOMETHING TO THINK ABOUT

101. Suppose you must solve the following equation but you can't read one number. If the solution of the equation is 1, what is the equation?

$$\frac{7x + \bullet}{22} = \frac{1}{2}$$

102. A store manager first increases his prices by 30% to get a new retail price and then advertises as shown at the right. What is the real percent discount to customers?

SALE
30% savings
off retail price!!

SECTION 2.3   Simplifying Expressions to Solve Linear Equations in One Variable

Objectives

1 Simplify an expression using the order of operations and combining like terms.

2 Solve a linear equation in one variable requiring simplifying one or both sides.

3 Solve a linear equation in one variable that is an identity or a contradiction.

Vocabulary

numerical coefficient   conditional equation   empty set
like terms   identity
unlike terms   contradiction

Getting Ready

Use the distributive property to remove parentheses.

1. $(3 + 4)x$ **2.** $(7 + 2)x$
3. $(8 - 3)w$ **4.** $(10 - 4)y$

Simplify each expression by performing the operations within the parentheses.

5. $(3 + 4)x$ **6.** $(7 + 2)x$
7. $(8 - 3)w$ **8.** $(10 - 4)y$

When algebraic expressions with the same variables occur, we can combine them.

1 Simplify an expression using the order of operations and combining like terms.

Recall that a *term* is either a number or the product of numbers and variables. Some examples of terms are $7x$, $-3xy$, y^2, and 8. The number part of each term is called its **numerical coefficient** (or just the *coefficient*).

· The coefficient of $7x$ is 7.

· The coefficient of $-3xy$ is -3.

· The coefficient of y^2 is the understood factor of 1.

· The coefficient of 8 is 8.

Like Terms	**Like terms,** or *similar terms,* are terms with the same variables having the same exponents.

COMMENT Terms are separated by $+$ and $-$ signs.

The terms $3x$ and $5x$ are **like terms,** as are $9x^2$ and $-3x^2$. The terms $4xy$ and $3x^2$ are **unlike terms,** because they have different variables. The terms $4x$ and $5x^2$ are unlike terms, because the variables have different exponents.

The distributive property can be used to combine terms of algebraic expressions that contain sums or differences of like terms. For example, the terms in $3x + 5x$ and $9xy^2 - 11xy^2$ can be combined as follows:

$$\underbrace{3x + 5x}_{\substack{\text{expressions with} \\ \text{like terms}}} = (3 + 5)x \qquad \underbrace{9xy^2 - 11xy^2}_{\substack{\text{expressions with} \\ \text{like terms}}} = (9 - 11)xy^2$$
$$= 8x \qquad\qquad\qquad\qquad = -2xy^2$$

These examples suggest the following rule.

Combining Like Terms	To combine like terms, add their coefficients and keep the same variables and exponents.

COMMENT If the terms of an expression are unlike terms, they cannot be combined. For example, since the terms in $9xy^2 - 11x^2y$ have variables with different exponents, they are unlike terms and cannot be combined.

EXAMPLE 1 Simplify: $3(x + 2) + 2(x - 8)$.

Solution To simplify the expression, we will use the distributive property to remove parentheses and then combine like terms.

$$3(x + 2) + 2(x - 8)$$
$$= 3x + 3 \cdot 2 + 2x - 2 \cdot 8 \quad \text{Use the distributive property to remove parentheses.}$$

$$= 3x + 6 + 2x - 16 \qquad 3 \cdot 2 = 6 \text{ and } 2 \cdot 8 = 16.$$

$$= 3x + 2x + 6 - 16 \qquad \text{Use the commutative property of addition:}$$
$$6 + 2x = 2x + 6.$$

$$= 5x - 10 \qquad \text{Combine like terms.}$$

⇨ **SELF CHECK 1**   Simplify: $-5(a + 3) + 2(a - 5)$.

EXAMPLE 2   Simplify: $3(x - 3) - 5(x + 4)$.

Solution   To simplify the expression, we will use the distributive property to remove parentheses and then combine like terms.

$$3(x - 3) - 5(x + 4)$$
$$= 3(x - 3) + (-5)(x + 4) \qquad a - b = a + (-b)$$
$$= 3x - 3 \cdot 3 + (-5)x + (-5)4 \qquad \text{Use the distributive property to remove}$$
$$\text{parentheses.}$$
$$= 3x - 9 + (-5x) + (-20) \qquad 3 \cdot 3 = 9 \text{ and } (-5)(4) = -20.$$
$$= -2x - 29 \qquad \text{Combine like terms.}$$

⇨ **SELF CHECK 2**   Simplify: $-3(b - 2) - 4(b - 4)$.

COMMENT   In algebra, you will simplify expressions and solve equations. Recognizing which one to do is a skill that we will apply throughout this course.

Since an expression does not contain an = sign, it can be simplified only by combining its like terms. Since an equation contains an = sign, it can be solved. Remember that

Expressions are to be simplified. Equations are to be solved.

2   **Solve a linear equation in one variable requiring simplifying one or both sides.**

To solve a linear equation in one variable, we must isolate the variable on one side. This is often a multistep process that may require combining like terms. As we solve equations, we will follow these steps, if necessary.

Solving Equations

1. Clear the equation of any fractions.
2. Use the distributive property to remove any grouping symbols.
3. Combine like terms on each side of the equation.
4. Undo the operations of addition and subtraction to get the variables on one side and the constants on the other.
5. Combine like terms and undo the operations of multiplication and division to isolate the variable.
6. Check the solution.

EXAMPLE 3   Solve: $3(x + 2) - 5x = 0$.

Solution   To solve the equation, we will remove parentheses, combine like terms, and solve for x.

$$3(x + 2) - 5x = 0$$
$$3x + 3 \cdot 2 - 5x = 0 \qquad \text{Use the distributive property to remove parentheses.}$$
$$3x - 5x + 6 = 0 \qquad \text{Rearrange terms and simplify.}$$
$$-2x + 6 = 0 \qquad \text{Combine like terms.}$$
$$-2x + 6 - 6 = 0 - 6 \qquad \text{Subtract 6 from both sides.}$$
$$-2x = -6 \qquad \text{Combine like terms.}$$
$$\frac{-2x}{-2} = \frac{-6}{-2} \qquad \text{Divide both sides by } -2.$$
$$x = 3 \qquad \text{Simplify.}$$

Check:
$$3(x + 2) - 5x = 0$$
$$3(3 + 2) - 5 \cdot 3 \stackrel{?}{=} 0 \qquad \text{Substitute 3 for } x.$$
$$3 \cdot 5 - 5 \cdot 3 \stackrel{?}{=} 0$$
$$15 - 15 \stackrel{?}{=} 0$$
$$0 = 0 \qquad \text{True.}$$

Since the solution 3 checks, the solution set is {3}.

⇨ **SELF CHECK 3**   Solve: $-2(y - 3) - 4y = 0$.

EXAMPLE 4   Solve: $3(x - 5) = 4(x + 9)$.

Solution   To solve the equation, we will remove parentheses, get all like terms involving x on one side, combine like terms, and solve for x.

$$3(x - 5) = 4(x + 9)$$
$$3x - 15 = 4x + 36 \qquad \text{Remove parentheses.}$$
$$3x - 15 - 3x = 4x + 36 - 3x \qquad \text{Subtract } 3x \text{ from both sides.}$$
$$-15 = x + 36 \qquad \text{Combine like terms.}$$
$$-15 - 36 = x + 36 - 36 \qquad \text{Subtract 36 from both sides.}$$
$$-51 = x \qquad \text{Combine like terms.}$$
$$x = -51$$

Check:
$$3(x - 5) = 4(x + 9)$$
$$3(-51 - 5) \stackrel{?}{=} 4(-51 + 9) \qquad \text{Substitute } -51 \text{ for } x.$$
$$3(-56) \stackrel{?}{=} 4(-42)$$
$$-168 = -168 \qquad \text{True.}$$

Since the solution -51 checks, the solution set is $\{-51\}$.

⇨ **SELF CHECK 4**   Solve: $4(z + 3) = -3(z - 4)$.

EXAMPLE 5   Solve: $\dfrac{3x + 11}{5} = x + 3.$

Solution   We first multiply both sides by 5 to clear the equation of fractions. When we multiply the right side by 5, we must multiply the *entire* right side by 5.

COMMENT   Remember that when you multiply one side of an equation by a nonzero number, you must multiply the other side by the same number to maintain the equality.

$$\dfrac{3x + 11}{5} = x + 3$$

$$5\left(\dfrac{3x + 11}{5}\right) = 5(x + 3) \qquad \text{Multiply both sides by 5.}$$

$$3x + 11 = 5x + 15 \qquad \text{Remove parentheses.}$$

$$3x + 11 - 11 = 5x + 15 - 11 \qquad \text{Subtract 11 from both sides.}$$

$$3x = 5x + 4 \qquad \text{Combine like terms.}$$

$$3x - 5x = 5x + 4 - 5x \qquad \text{Subtract } 5x \text{ from both sides.}$$

$$-2x = 4 \qquad \text{Combine like terms.}$$

$$\dfrac{-2x}{-2} = \dfrac{4}{-2} \qquad \text{Divide both sides by } -2.$$

$$x = -2 \qquad \text{Simplify.}$$

Check: $\dfrac{3x + 11}{5} = x + 3$

$$\dfrac{3(-2) + 11}{5} \stackrel{?}{=} (-2) + 3 \qquad \text{Substitute } -2 \text{ for } x.$$

$$\dfrac{-6 + 11}{5} \stackrel{?}{=} 1 \qquad \text{Simplify.}$$

$$\dfrac{5}{5} \stackrel{?}{=} 1$$

$$1 = 1 \qquad \text{True.}$$

Since the solution -2 checks, the solution set is $\{-2\}$.

➡ SELF CHECK 5   Solve: $\dfrac{2x - 5}{4} = x - 2.$

EXAMPLE 6   Solve: $0.2x + 0.4(50 - x) = 19.$

Solution   Since $0.2 = \dfrac{2}{10}$ and $0.4 = \dfrac{4}{10}$, this equation contains fractions. To clear the fractions, we will multiply both sides by 10.

$$0.2x + 0.4(50 - x) = 19$$

$$10[0.2x + 0.4(50 - x)] = 10(19) \qquad \text{Multiply both sides by 10.}$$

$$10[0.2x] + 10[0.4(50 - x)] = 10(19) \qquad \text{Use the distributive property on the left side.}$$

$$2x + 4(50 - x) = 190 \qquad \text{Do the multiplications.}$$

$$2x + 200 - 4x = 190 \qquad \text{Remove parentheses.}$$

$$-2x + 200 = 190 \qquad \text{Combine like terms.}$$

$$-2x = -10 \qquad \text{Subtract 200 from both sides.}$$

$$x = 5 \qquad \text{Divide both sides by } -2.$$

Since the solution is 5, the solution set is {5}. Verify that the solution checks.

⇨ **SELF CHECK 6**   Solve: $0.3(20 - x) + 0.5x = 15$.

3 **Solve a linear equation in one variable that is an identity or a contradiction.**

The equations solved in Examples 3–6 are called **conditional equations.** For these equations, each has exactly one solution.

An equation that is true for all values of its variable is called an **identity.** For example, the equation $x + x = 2x$ is an identity because it is true for all values of x. The solution of an identity is the set of *all real numbers* and is denoted by the symbol $\mathbb{R}$.

An equation that is not true for any value of its variable is called a **contradiction.** For example, the equation $x = x + 1$ is a contradiction because there is no value of x that will make the statement true. Since there are no solutions to a contradiction, its set of solutions is empty. This is denoted by the symbol $\varnothing$ or { } and is called the **empty set.**

Type of equation	Examples		Solution sets
Conditional	$2x + 4 = 8$	$\dfrac{x}{2} - 4 = 12$	{2} and {32}
Identity	$x + x = 2x$	$2(x + 3) = 2x + 6$	$\mathbb{R}$ and $\mathbb{R}$
Contradiction	$x = x - 1$	$2(x + 3) = 2x + 5$	$\varnothing$ and $\varnothing$

Table 2-1

EXAMPLE 7   Solve: $3(x + 8) + 5x = 2(12 + 4x)$.

Solution   To solve this equation, we will remove parentheses, combine terms, and solve for x.

$$3(x + 8) + 5x = 2(12 + 4x)$$
$$3x + 24 + 5x = 24 + 8x \qquad \text{Remove parentheses.}$$
$$8x + 24 = 24 + 8x \qquad \text{Combine like terms.}$$
$$8x + 24 - \mathbf{8x} = 24 + 8x - \mathbf{8x} \qquad \text{Subtract } 8x \text{ from both sides.}$$
$$24 = 24 \qquad \text{Combine like terms.}$$

Since the result $24 = 24$ is true for every number x, every number is a solution of the original equation. The solution set is the set of real numbers, $\mathbb{R}$. This equation is an identity.

⇨ **SELF CHECK 7**   Solve: $-2(x + 3) - 18x = 5(9 - 4x) - 51$.

EXAMPLE 8   Solve: $3(x + 7) - x = 2(x + 10)$.

Solution   To solve this equation, we will remove parentheses, combine terms, and solve for x.

$$3(x + 7) - x = 2(x + 10)$$
$$3x + 21 - x = 2x + 20 \qquad \text{Remove parentheses.}$$
$$2x + 21 = 2x + 20 \qquad \text{Combine like terms.}$$
$$2x + 21 - \mathbf{2x} = 2x + 20 - \mathbf{2x} \qquad \text{Subtract } 2x \text{ from both sides.}$$
$$21 = 20 \qquad \text{Combine like terms.}$$

Since the result $21 = 20$ is false, the original equation is a contradiction. Since the original equation has no solution, the solution set is $\varnothing$.

⇨ **SELF CHECK 8**   Solve: $5(x - 2) - 2x = 3(x + 7)$.

⇨ **SELF CHECK ANSWERS**   **1.** $-3a - 25$ **2.** $-7b + 22$ **3.** 1   **4.** 0   **5.** $\frac{3}{2}$ **6.** 45   **7.** identity, $\mathbb{R}$ **8.** contradiction, $\varnothing$

NOW TRY THIS

Identify each of the following as an expression or an equation. Simplify or solve as appropriate.

1. $4\left(x - \dfrac{7}{4}\right) + 3(x + 2)$

2. $4\left(x - \dfrac{7}{4}\right) = 3(x + 2)$

3. $6x - 2(3x - 9)$

2.3 EXERCISES

WARM-UPS

Simplify by combining like terms.

1. $3x + 5x$

2. $-2y + 3y$

3. $3x + 2x - 5x$

4. $3y + 2y - 7y$

5. $3(x + 2) - 3x + 6$

6. $3(x + 2) + 3x - 6$

Solve each equation.

7. $5x = 4x + 3$

8. $2(x - 1) = 2(x + 1)$

9. $3x = 2(x + 1)$

10. $x + 2(x + 1) = 3$

REVIEW

Evaluate each expression when $x = -3$, $y = -5$, and $z = 0$.

11. $x^2 z(y^3 - z)$

12. $z - y^3$

13. $\dfrac{x - y^2}{2y - 1 + x}$

14. $\dfrac{2y + 1}{x} - x$

Perform the operations.

15. $\dfrac{6}{7} - \dfrac{5}{8}$

16. $\dfrac{6}{7} \cdot \dfrac{5}{8}$

17. $\dfrac{6}{7} \div \dfrac{5}{8}$

18. $\dfrac{6}{7} + \dfrac{5}{8}$

VOCABULARY AND CONCEPTS   *Fill in the blanks.*

19. If terms have the same _____ with the same exponents, they are called _____ terms. Terms that have different variables or have a variable with different exponents are called _____ terms. The number part of a term is called its _____ coefficient.

20. To combine like terms, _____ their numerical coefficients and _____ the same variables and exponents.

21. If an equation is true for all values of its variable, it is called an _____. If an equation is true for no values of its variable, it is called a _____.

22. If an equation is true for some values of its variable, but not all, it is called a _____ equation.

GUIDED PRACTICE

Simplify each expression, when possible. See Example 1. (Objective 1)

23. $3x + 17x$
24. $12y - 15y$
25. $8x^2 - 5x^2$
26. $17x^2 + 3x^2$
27. $9x + 3y$
28. $5x + 5y$
29. $3(x + 2) + 4x$
30. $9(y - 3) + 2y$

Simplify each expression. See Example 2. (Objective 1)

31. $5(z - 3) + 2z$
32. $4(y + 9) - 6y$
33. $12(x + 11) - 11$
34. $-3(3 + z) + 2z$
35. $8(y + 7) - 2(y - 3)$
36. $9(z + 2) + 5(3 - z)$
37. $2x + 4(y - x) + 3y$
38. $3y - 6(y + z) + y$

Solve each equation. Check all solutions. See Example 3. (Objective 2)

39. $9(x + 11) + 5(13 - x) = 0$
40. $3(x + 15) + 4(11 - x) = 0$
41. $11x + 6(3 - x) = 3$
42. $5(x - 6) - 8x = 15$

Solve each equation. Check all solutions. See Example 4. (Objective 2)

43. $3x + 2 = 2x$
44. $5x + 7 = 4x$
45. $5x - 3 = 4x$
46. $4x + 3 = 5x$
47. $9y - 3 = 6y$
48. $8y + 4 = 4y$
49. $8y - 7 = y$
50. $9y - 8 = y$
51. $3(a + 2) = 4a$
52. $4(a - 5) = 3a$
53. $5(b + 7) = 6b$
54. $8(b + 2) = 9b$
55. $2 + 3(x - 5) = 4(x - 1)$
56. $2 - (4x + 7) = 3 + 2(x + 2)$
57. $3(a + 2) = 2(a - 7)$
58. $9(n - 1) = 6(n + 2) - n$

Solve each equation. Check all solutions. See Example 5. (Objective 2)

59. $\dfrac{3(t - 7)}{2} = t - 6$
60. $\dfrac{2(p + 9)}{3} = p - 8$
61. $\dfrac{2(t - 1)}{6} - 2 = \dfrac{t + 2}{6}$
62. $\dfrac{2(2r - 1)}{6} + 5 = \dfrac{3(r + 7)}{6}$

Solve each equation. Check all solutions. See Example 6. (Objective 2)

63. $3.1(x - 2) = 1.3x + 2.8$
64. $0.6x - 0.8 = 0.8(2x - 1) - 0.7$
65. $2.7(y + 1) = 0.3(3y + 33)$
66. $1.5(5 - y) = 3y + 12$

Solve each equation. If it is an identity or a contradiction, so indicate. See Examples 7–8. (Objective 3)

67. $8x + 3(2 - x) = 5(x + 2) - 4$
68. $21(b - 1) + 3 = 3(7b - 6)$
69. $2(s + 2) = 2(s + 1) + 3$
70. $2(3z + 4) = 2(3z - 2) + 13$
71. $\dfrac{5(x + 3)}{3} - x = \dfrac{2(x + 8)}{3}$
72. $5(x + 2) = 5x - 2$
73. $x + 7 = \dfrac{2x + 6}{2} + 4$
74. $2(y - 3) - \dfrac{y}{2} = \dfrac{3}{2}(y - 4)$

ADDITIONAL PRACTICE

Identify each statement as an expression or an equation, and then either simplify or solve as appropriate.

75. $(x + 2) - (x - y)$
76. $3z + 2(y - z) + y$
77. $\dfrac{4(2x - 10)}{3} = 2(x - 4)$
78. $\dfrac{11(x - 12)}{2} = 9 - 2x$
79. $2\left(4x + \dfrac{9}{2}\right) - 3\left(x + \dfrac{2}{3}\right)$
80. $\dfrac{5(2 - m)}{3} = m + 6$
81. $\dfrac{8(5 - q)}{5} = -2q$
82. $\dfrac{20 - a}{2} = \dfrac{3}{2}(a + 4)$
83. $\dfrac{3x + 14}{2} = x - 2 + \dfrac{x + 18}{2}$
84. $7\left(3x - \dfrac{2}{7}\right) - 5\left(2x - \dfrac{3}{5}\right) + x$
85. $5 - 7r = 8r$
86. $y + 4 = -7y$
87. $22 - 3r = 8r$
88. $14 + 7s = s$
89. $8(x + 3) - 3x$
90. $2x + 2(x + 3)$
91. $19.1x - 4(x + 0.3) = -46.5$
92. $18.6x + 7.2 = 1.5(48 - 2x)$
93. $3.2(m + 1.3) - 2.5(m - 7.2)$
94. $6.7(t - 2.1) + 5.5(t + 1)$
95. $14.3(x + 2) + 13.7(x - 3) = 15.5$

96. $1.25(x - 1) = 0.5(3x - 1) - 1$
97. $10x + 3(2 - x) = 5(x + 2) - 4$
98. $19.1x - 4(x + 0.3)$

Solve each equation and round the result to the nearest tenth.

99. $\dfrac{3.7(2.3x - 2.7)}{1.5} = 5.2(x - 1.2)$

100. $\dfrac{-2.1(1.7x + 0.9)}{3.1} = -7.1(x - 1.3)$

WRITING ABOUT MATH

101. Explain why $3x^2y$ and $5x^2y$ are like terms.
102. Explain why $3x^2y$ and $3xy^2$ are unlike terms.
103. Discuss whether $7xxy^3$ and $5x^2yyy$ are like terms.
104. Discuss whether $\frac{3}{2}x$ and $\frac{3x}{2}$ are like terms.

SOMETHING TO THINK ABOUT

105. What number is equal to its own double?
106. What number is equal to one-half of itself?

Objectives

1 Solve a formula for an indicated variable using the properties of equality.
2 Evaluate a formula for specified values for the variables.
3 Solve an application problem using a given formula and specified values for the variables.

Vocabulary

literal equations   formulas

Getting Ready

Fill in the blanks.

1. $\dfrac{3x}{\boxed{}} = x$
2. $\dfrac{-5y}{\boxed{}} = y$
3. $\dfrac{rx}{\boxed{}} = x$
4. $\dfrac{-ay}{\boxed{}} = y$

5. $\boxed{} \cdot \dfrac{x}{7} = x$
6. $\boxed{} \cdot \dfrac{y}{12} = y$
7. $\boxed{} \cdot \dfrac{x}{d} = x$
8. $\boxed{} \cdot \dfrac{y}{s} = y$

Equations with several variables are called **literal equations.** Often these equations are **formulas** such as $A = lw$, the formula for finding the area of a rectangle.

Suppose that we want to find the lengths of several rectangles whose areas and widths are known. It would be tedious to substitute values for A and w into the formula and then repeatedly solve the formula for l. It would be much easier to solve the formula $A = lw$ for l first, then substitute values for A and w, and compute l directly.

Solve a formula for an indicated variable using the properties of equality.

To **solve a formula for a variable** means to isolate that variable on one side of the equation, with all other numbers and variables on the opposite side. We can isolate the variable by using the equation-solving techniques we have learned in the previous three sections.

EXAMPLE 1 Solve $A = lw$ for l.

Solution To isolate l on the left side, we undo the multiplication by w by dividing both sides of the equation by w.

$$A = lw$$

$$\frac{A}{w} = \frac{lw}{w} \qquad \text{To undo the multiplication by } w, \text{ divide both sides by } w.$$

$$\frac{A}{w} = l \qquad \frac{w}{w} = 1$$

$$l = \frac{A}{w}$$

SELF CHECK 1 Solve $A = lw$ for w.

EXAMPLE 2 Recall that the formula $A = \frac{1}{2}bh$ gives the area of a triangle with base b and height h. Solve the formula for b.

Solution To isolate b on the left side, we will undo the multiplication by $\frac{1}{2}$ by multiplying both sides by 2. Then we will undo the multiplication by h by dividing both sides by h.

$$A = \frac{1}{2}bh$$

$$2A = 2 \cdot \frac{1}{2}bh \qquad \text{To eliminate the fraction, multiply both sides by 2.}$$

$$2A = bh \qquad 2 \cdot \frac{1}{2} = 1$$

$$\frac{2A}{h} = \frac{bh}{h} \qquad \text{To undo the multiplication by } h, \text{ divide both sides by } h.$$

$$\frac{2A}{h} = b \qquad \frac{h}{h} = 1$$

If the area A and the height h of a triangle are known, the base b is given by the formula $b = \frac{2A}{h}$.

SELF CHECK 2 Solve $A = \frac{1}{2}bh$ for h.

EXAMPLE 3 The formula $C = \frac{5}{9}(F - 32)$ is used to convert Fahrenheit temperature readings into their Celsius equivalents. Solve the formula for F.

Solution   To isolate F on the left side, we will undo the multiplication by $\frac{5}{9}$ by multiplying both sides by the reciprocal of $\frac{5}{9}$, which is $\frac{9}{5}$. Then we will use the distributive property to remove parentheses and finally undo the subtraction of 32 by adding 32 to both sides.

$$C = \frac{5}{9}(F - 32)$$

$$\frac{9}{5}C = \frac{9}{5} \cdot \frac{5}{9}(F - 32) \qquad \text{To eliminate } \tfrac{5}{9}, \text{ multiply both sides by } \tfrac{9}{5}.$$

$$\frac{9}{5}C = 1(F - 32) \qquad \frac{9}{5} \cdot \frac{5}{9} = \frac{9 \cdot 5}{5 \cdot 9} = 1$$

$$\frac{9}{5}C = F - 32 \qquad \text{Remove parentheses.}$$

$$\frac{9}{5}C + 32 = F - 32 + 32 \qquad \text{To undo the subtraction of 32, add 32 to both sides.}$$

$$\frac{9}{5}C + 32 = F \qquad \text{Combine like terms.}$$

$$F = \frac{9}{5}C + 32$$

The formula $F = \frac{9}{5}C + 32$ is used to convert degrees Celsius to degrees Fahrenheit.

⇨ SELF CHECK 3   Solve $x = \frac{2}{3}(y + 5)$ for y.

EXAMPLE 4   Recall that the area A of the trapezoid shown in Figure 2-5 is given by the formula

$$A = \frac{1}{2}h(B + b)$$

where B and b are its bases and h is its height. Solve the formula for b.

Solution   There are two different ways to solve this formula.

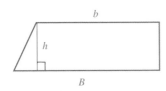

Figure 2-5

Method 1:
$$A = \frac{1}{2}(B + b)h$$

$$2A = 2 \cdot \frac{1}{2}(B + b)h \qquad \text{Multiply both sides by 2.}$$

$$2A = Bh + bh \qquad \text{Simplify and remove parentheses.}$$

$$2A - Bh = Bh + bh - Bh \qquad \text{Subtract } Bh \text{ from both sides.}$$

$$2A - Bh = bh \qquad \text{Combine like terms.}$$

$$\frac{2A - Bh}{h} = \frac{bh}{h} \qquad \text{Divide both sides by } h.$$

$$\frac{2A - Bh}{h} = b \qquad \frac{h}{h} = 1$$

Method 2:
$$A = \frac{1}{2}(B + b)h$$

$$2 \cdot A = 2 \cdot \frac{1}{2}(B + b)h \qquad \text{Multiply both sides by 2.}$$

$$2A = (B + b)h \qquad \text{Simplify.}$$

$$\frac{2A}{h} = \frac{(B + b)h}{h} \qquad \text{Divide both sides by } h.$$

$$\frac{2A}{h} = B + b \qquad \frac{h}{h} = 1$$

$$\frac{2A}{h} - B = B + b - B \qquad \text{Subtract } B \text{ from both sides.}$$

$$\frac{2A}{h} - B = b \qquad \text{Combine like terms.}$$

Although they look different, the results of Methods 1 and 2 are equivalent.

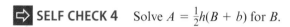 **SELF CHECK 4**   Solve $A = \frac{1}{2}h(B + b)$ for B.

2 **Evaluate a formula for specified values for the variables.**

EXAMPLE 5   Solve the formula $P = 2l + 2w$ for l and find l when $P = 56$ and $w = 11$.

Solution   We first solve the formula $P = 2l + 2w$ for l.

$$P = 2l + 2w$$

$$P - 2w = 2l + 2w - 2w \qquad \text{Subtract } 2w \text{ from both sides.}$$

$$P - 2w = 2l \qquad \text{Combine like terms.}$$

$$\frac{P - 2w}{2} = \frac{2l}{2} \qquad \text{Divide both sides by 2.}$$

$$\frac{P - 2w}{2} = l \qquad \frac{2}{2} = 1$$

$$l = \frac{P - 2w}{2}$$

Albert Einstein (1879–1955)

Einstein was a theoretical physicist best known for his theory of relativity. Although Einstein was born in Germany, he became a Swiss citizen and earned his doctorate at the University of Zurich in 1905. In 1910, he returned to Germany to teach. He fled Germany because of the Nazi government and became a United States citizen in 1940. He is famous for his formula $E = mc^2$.

We will then substitute 56 for P and 11 for w and simplify.

$$l = \frac{P - 2w}{2}$$

$$l = \frac{56 - 2(11)}{2}$$

$$= \frac{56 - 22}{2}$$

$$= \frac{34}{2}$$

$$= 17$$

Thus, $l = 17$.

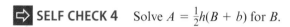 **SELF CHECK 5**   Solve $P = 2l + 2w$ for w and find w when $P = 46$ and $l = 16$.

3 **Solve an application problem using a given formula and specified values for the variables.**

EXAMPLE 6 Recall that the volume V of the right-circular cone shown in Figure 2-6 is given by the formula

$$V = \frac{1}{3}Bh$$

where B is the area of its circular base and h is its height. Solve the formula for h and find the height of a right-circular cone with a volume of 64 cubic centimeters and a base area of 16 square centimeters.

Solution We first solve the formula for h.

$$V = \frac{1}{3}Bh$$

$3V = 3 \cdot \frac{1}{3}Bh$ Multiply both sides by 3.

$3V = Bh$ $3 \cdot \frac{1}{3} = 1$

$\dfrac{3V}{B} = \dfrac{Bh}{B}$ Divide both sides by B.

$\dfrac{3V}{B} = h$ $\frac{B}{B} = 1$

$h = \dfrac{3V}{B}$

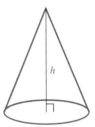

Figure 2-6

We then substitute 64 for V and 16 for B and simplify.

$$h = \frac{3V}{B}$$

$$h = \frac{3(64)}{16}$$

$$= 3(4)$$

$$= 12$$

The height of the cone is 12 centimeters.

⇨ SELF CHECK 6 Solve $V = \frac{1}{3}Bh$ for B, and find the area of the base when the volume is 42 cubic feet and the height is 6 feet.

⇨ SELF CHECK ANSWERS   **1.** $w = \frac{A}{l}$ **2.** $h = \frac{2A}{b}$ **3.** $y = \frac{3}{2}x - 5$ **4.** $B = \frac{2A - hb}{h}$ or $B = \frac{2A}{h} - b$ **5.** $w = \frac{P - 2l}{2}, 7$

   6. $B = \frac{3V}{h}, 21 \text{ ft}^2$

NOW TRY THIS

A student's test average for four tests can be modeled by the equation

$$A = \frac{T_1 + T_2 + T_3 + T_4}{4}$$

where T_1 is the grade for Test 1, T_2 is the grade for Test 2, and so on.

1. Solve the equation for T_4.
2. Julio has test grades of 82, 88, and 71. What grade would he need on Test 4 to have a test average of 80?
3. Melinda has test grades of 75, 80, and 89. What grade would she need on Test 4 to have a test average of 90? Interpret your answer.

2.4 EXERCISES

WARM-UPS

Solve the equation ab + c = 0.

1. for a
2. for c

Solve the equation $a = \dfrac{b}{c}$.

3. for b
4. for c

REVIEW   *Simplify each expression, if possible.*

5. $2x - 5y + 3x$
6. $2x^2y + 5x^2y^2$

7. $\dfrac{3}{5}(x + 5) - \dfrac{8}{5}(10 + x)$
8. $\dfrac{2}{11}(22x - y) + \dfrac{9}{11}y$

VOCABULARY AND CONCEPTS   *Fill in the blanks.*

9. Equations that contain several variables are called _____ equations.
10. The equation $A = lw$ is an example of a _____.
11. To solve a formula for a variable means to _____ the variable on one side of the equation.
12. To solve the formula $d = rt$ for t, divide both sides of the formula by __.
13. To solve $A = p + i$ for p, _____ i from both sides.
14. To solve $t = \dfrac{d}{r}$ for d, _____ both sides by r.

GUIDED PRACTICE

Solve for the indicated variable. See Example 1. (Objective 1)

15. $E = IR$ for I
16. $i = prt$ for r

17. $V = lwh$ for w
18. $C = 2\pi r$ for r
19. $K = A + 32$ for A
20. $P = a + b + c$ for b

Solve for the indicated variable. See Example 2. (Objective 1)

21. $V = \dfrac{1}{3}Bh$ for h
22. $V = \dfrac{1}{3}Bh$ for B
23. $V = \dfrac{1}{3}\pi r^2 h$ for h
24. $I = \dfrac{E}{R}$ for R

Solve for the indicated variable. See Examples 3–4. (Objective 1)

25. $y = \dfrac{1}{2}(x + 2)$ for x
26. $x = \dfrac{1}{5}(y - 7)$ for y

27. $A = \dfrac{B + 4}{8}$ for B
28. $y = mx + b$ for x

29. $A = \dfrac{3}{2}(B + 5)$ for B

30. $y = \dfrac{5}{2}(x - 10)$ for x

31. $p = \dfrac{h}{2}(q + r)$ for q

32. $p = \dfrac{h}{2}(q + r)$ for r

33. $G = 2b(r - 1)$ for r

34. $F = f(1 - M)$ for M

Solve each formula for the indicated variable. Then evaluate the new formula for the values given. See Example 5. (Objective 2)

35. $d = rt$ Find t if $d = 135$ and $r = 45$.

36. $d = rt$ Find r if $d = 275$ and $t = 5$

37. $P = a + b + c$ Find c if $P = 37$, $a = 15$, and $b = 19$.

38. $y = mx + b$ Find x if $y = 30$, $m = 3$, and $b = 0$.

ADDITIONAL PRACTICE   *Solve each formula for the indicated variable.*

39. $P = 4s$ for s

40. $P = I^2R$ for R

41. $P = 2l + 2w$ for w

42. $d = rt$ for t

43. $A = P + Prt$ for t

44. $A = \frac{1}{2}(B + b)h$ for h

45. $K = \frac{wv^2}{2g}$ for w

46. $V = \pi r^2 h$ for h

47. $K = \frac{wv^2}{2g}$ for g

48. $P = \frac{RT}{mV}$ for V

49. $F = \frac{GMm}{d^2}$ for M

50. $C = 1 - \frac{A}{a}$ for A

51. Given that $i = prt$, find t if $i = 12$, $p = 100$, and $r = 0.06$.

52. Given that $i = prt$, find r if $i = 120$, $p = 500$, and $t = 6$.

53. Given that $K = \frac{1}{2}h(a + b)$, find h if $K = 48$, $a = 7$, and $b = 5$.

54. Given that $\frac{x}{2} + y = z^2$, find x if $y = 3$ and $z = 3$.

APPLICATIONS   *Solve.* See Example 6 (Objective 3)

55. Volume of a cone   The volume V of a cone is given by the formula $V = \frac{1}{3}\pi r^2 h$. Solve the formula for h, and then calculate the height h if V is 36π cubic inches and the radius r is 6 inches.

56. Circumference of a circle   The circumference C of a circle is given by $C = 2\pi r$, where r is the radius of the circle. Solve the formula for r, and then calculate the radius of a circle with a circumference of 14.32 feet. Round to the nearest hundredth of a foot.

57. Ohm's law   The formula $E = IR$, called **Ohm's law,** is used in electronics. Solve for I, and then calculate the current I if the voltage E is 48 volts and the resistance R is 12 ohms. Current has units of *amperes*.

58. Growth of money   At a simple interest rate r, an amount of money P grows to an amount A in t years according to the formula $A = P(1 + rt)$. Solve the formula for P. After $t = 3$ years, a girl has an amount $A = \$4,357$ on deposit. What amount P did she start with? Assume an interest rate of 6%.

59. Power loss   The power P lost when an electric current I passes through a resistance R is given by the formula $P = I^2R$. Solve for R. If P is 2,700 watts and I is 14 amperes, calculate R to the nearest hundredth of an ohm.

60. Geometry   The perimeter P of a rectangle with length l and width w is given by the formula $P = 2l + 2w$. Solve this formula for w. If the perimeter of a certain rectangle is 58.37 meters and its length is 17.23 meters, find its width. Round to two decimal places.

61. Force of gravity   The masses of the two objects in the illustration are m and M. The force of gravitation F between the masses is given by

$$F = \frac{GmM}{d^2}$$

where G is a constant and d is the distance between them. Solve for m.

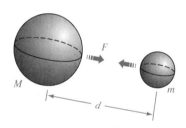

62. Thermodynamics   In thermodynamics, the Gibbs free-energy equation is given by

$$G = U - TS + pV$$

Solve this equation for the pressure, p.

63. Pulleys   The approximate length L of a belt joining two pulleys of radii r and R feet with centers D feet apart is given by the formula

$$L = 2D + 3.25(r + R)$$

Solve the formula for D. If a 25-foot belt joins pulleys with radii of 1 foot and 3 feet, how far apart are their centers?

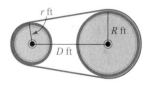

64. Geometry   The measure a of an interior angle of a regular polygon with n sides is given by $a = 180°\left(1 - \frac{2}{n}\right)$. Solve the formula for n. How many sides does a regular polygon have if an interior angle is 108°?   (*Hint:* Distribute first.)

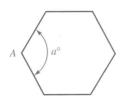

One common retirement plan for self-employed people is called a Simplified Employee Pension Plan. It allows for a maximum annual contribution of 15% of taxable income (earned income minus deductible expenses). However, since the Internal Revenue Service considers the SEP contribution to be a deductible expense, the taxable income must be reduced by the amount of the contribution. Therefore, to calculate the maximum contribution C, we take 15% of what's left after we subtract the contribution C from the taxable income T.

$$C = 0.15(T - C)$$

65. Calculating SEP contributions   Find the maximum allowable contribution to a SEP plan by solving the equation $C = 0.15(T - C)$ for C.

66. Calculating SEP contributions   Find the maximum allowable contribution to a SEP plan for a person who earns $75,000 and has deductible expenses of $27,540. See problem 65.

WRITING ABOUT MATH

67. The formula $P = 2l + 2w$ is also an equation, but an equation such as $2x + 3 = 5$ is not a formula. What equations do you think should be called formulas?

68. To solve the equation $s - A(s - 5) = r$ for the variable s, one student simply added $A(s - 5)$ to both sides to get $s = r + A(s - 5)$. Explain why this is not correct.

SOMETHING TO THINK ABOUT

69. The energy of an atomic bomb comes from the conversion of matter into energy, according to Einstein's formula $E = mc^2$. The constant c is the speed of light, about 300,000 meters per second. Find the energy in a mass m of 1 kilogram. Energy has units of **joules.**

70. When a car of mass m collides with a wall, the energy of the collision is given by the formula $E = \frac{1}{2}mv^2$. Compare the energy of two collisions: a car striking a wall at 30 mph, and at 60 mph.

SECTION 2.5   Introduction to Problem Solving

Objectives

1 Solve a number application using a linear equation in one variable.

2 Solve a geometry application using a linear equation in one variable.

3 Solve an investment application using a linear equation in one variable.

Vocabulary

angle	complementary angles	vertex angle of an isosceles
degree	supplementary angles	triangle
right angle	isosceles triangle	base angles of an isosceles
straight angle		triangle

Getting Ready

1. If one part of a pipe is x feet long and the other part is $(x + 2)$ feet long, find an expression that represents the total length of the pipe.
2. If one part of a board is x feet long and the other part is three times as long, find an expression that represents the length of the board.
3. What is the formula for the perimeter of a rectangle?
4. Define a triangle.

In this section, we will use the equation-solving skills we have learned in the previous four sections to solve many types of problems. The key to successful problem solving is to understand the problem thoroughly and then devise a plan to solve it. To do so, we will use the following problem-solving strategy.

Problem Solving

1. **Analyze the problem** and **identify a variable** by asking yourself "What am I asked to find?" Choose a variable to represent the quantity to be found and then express all other unknown quantities in the problem as expressions involving that variable.
2. **Form an equation** by expressing a quantity in two different ways. This may require reading the problem several times to understand the given facts. What information is given? Is there a formula that applies to this situation? Often a sketch, chart, or diagram will help you visualize the facts of the problem.
3. **Solve the equation** found in Step 2.
4. **State the conclusion.**
5. **Check the result.**

In this section, we will use this five-step strategy to solve many types of applications.

1   Solve a number application using a linear equation in one variable.

EXAMPLE 1   **PLUMBING**   A plumber wants to cut a 17-foot pipe into three parts. (See Figure 2-7.) If the longest part is to be 3 times as long as the shortest part, and the middle-sized part is to be 2 feet longer than the shortest part, how long should each part be?

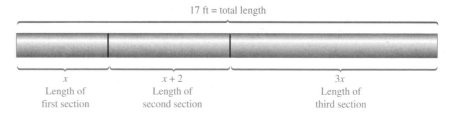

17 ft = total length

| x | $x + 2$ | $3x$ |
| Length of first section | Length of second section | Length of third section |

Figure 2-7

Analyze the problem   We are asked to find the length of three pieces of pipe. The information is given in terms of the length of the shortest part. Therefore, we let x represent the length of the shortest part and express the other lengths in terms of x. Then $3x$ represents the length of the longest part, and $x + 2$ represents the length of the middle-sized part.

Form an equation   The sum of the lengths of these three parts is equal to the total length of the pipe.

The length of part 1	plus	the length of part 2	plus	the length of part 3	equals	the total length.
x	$+$	$x + 2$	$+$	$3x$	$=$	17

Solve the equation   We can solve this equation as follows.

$$x + x + 2 + 3x = 17 \qquad \text{This is the equation to solve.}$$
$$5x + 2 = 17 \qquad \text{Combine like terms.}$$
$$5x = 15 \qquad \text{Subtract 2 from both sides.}$$
$$x = 3 \qquad \text{Divide both sides by 5.}$$

State the conclusion   The shortest part is 3 feet long. Because the middle-sized part is 2 feet longer than the shortest, it is 5 feet long. Because the longest part is 3 times longer than the shortest, it is 9 feet long.

Check the result   Because the sum of 3 feet, 5 feet, and 9 feet is 17 feet, the solution checks.

COMMENT   Remember to include any units (feet, inches, pounds, etc.) when stating the conclusion to an application problem.

2   **Solve a geometry application using a linear equation in one variable.**

The geometric figure shown in Figure 2-8(a) is an **angle.** Angles are measured in **degrees.** The angle shown in Figure 2-8(b) measures 45 degrees (denoted as 45°). If an angle measures 90°, as in Figure 2-8(c), it is a **right angle.** If an angle measures 180°, as in Figure 2-8(d), it is a **straight angle.**

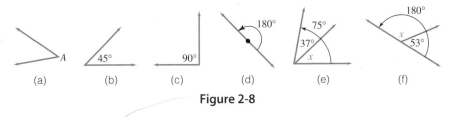

Figure 2-8

EXAMPLE 2   **GEOMETRY**   Refer to Figure 2-8(e) and find x.

Analyze the problem   In Figure 2-8(e), we have two angles that are side by side. The unknown angle measure is designated as x.

Form an equation   From the figure, we can see that the sum of their measures is 75°. Since the sum of x and 37° is equal to 75°, we can form the equation.

The angle that measures x	plus	the angle that measures 37°	equals	the angle that measures 75°.
x	$+$	37	$=$	75

Solve the equation   We can solve this equation as follows.

$$x + 37 = 75 \qquad \text{This is the equation to solve.}$$
$$x + 37 - 37 = 75 - 37 \qquad \text{Subtract 37 from both sides.}$$
$$x = 38 \qquad 37 - 37 = 0 \text{ and } 75 - 37 = 38.$$

State the conclusion   The value of x is 38°.

Check the result   Since the sum of 38° and 37° is 75°, the solution checks.

EXAMPLE 3   **GEOMETRY**   Refer to Figure 2-8(f) and find x.

Analyze the problem   In Figure 2-8(f), we have two angles that are side by side. The unknown angle measure is designated as x.

Form an equation   From the figure, we can see that the sum of their measures is 180°. Since the sum of x and 53° is equal to 180°, we can form the equation.

The angle that measures x	plus	the angle that measures 53°	equals	the angle that measures 180°.
x	+	53	=	180

Solve the equation   We can solve this equation as follows.

$$x + 53 = 180 \qquad \text{This is the equation to solve.}$$
$$x + 53 - \mathbf{53} = 180 - \mathbf{53} \qquad \text{Subtract 53 from both sides.}$$
$$x = 127 \qquad 53 - 53 = 0 \text{ and } 180 - 53 = 127.$$

State the conclusion   The value of x is 127°.

Check the result   Since the sum of 127° and 53° is 180°, the solution checks.

If the sum of two angles is 90°, the angles are **complementary angles** and either angle is the *complement* of the other. If the sum of two angles is 180°, the angles are **supplementary angles** and either angle is the *supplement* of the other.

EXAMPLE 4   **COMPLEMENTARY ANGLES**   Find the complement of an angle measuring 30°.

Analyze the problem   To find the complement of a 30° angle, we must find an angle whose measure plus 30° equals 90°. We can let x represent the complement of 30°.

Form an equation   Since the sum of two complementary angles is 90°, we can form the equation.

The angle that measures x	plus	the angle that measures 30°	equals	90°.
x	+	30	=	90

Solve the equation   We can solve this equation as follows.

$$x + 30 = 90 \qquad \text{This is the equation to solve.}$$
$$x + 30 - \mathbf{30} = 90 - \mathbf{30} \qquad \text{Subtract 30 from both sides.}$$
$$x = 60 \qquad 30 - 30 = 0 \text{ and } 90 - 30 = 60.$$

State the conclusion   The complement of a 30° angle is a 60° angle.

Check the result   Since the sum of 60° and 30° is 90°, the solution checks.

EXAMPLE 5   **SUPPLEMENTARY ANGLES**   Find the supplement of an angle measuring 50°.

Analyze the problem

To find the supplement of a 50° angle, we must find an angle whose measure plus 50° equals 180°. We can let x represent the supplement of 50°.

Form an equation

Since the sum of two supplementary angles is 180°, we can form the equation.

The angle that measures x	plus	the angle that measures 50°	equals	180°.
x	$+$	50	$=$	180

Solve the equation

We can solve this equation as follows.

$$x + 50 = 180 \qquad \text{This is the equation to solve.}$$
$$x + 50 - 50 = 180 - 50 \qquad \text{Subtract 50 from both sides.}$$
$$x = 130 \qquad 50 - 50 = 0 \text{ and } 180 - 50 = 130.$$

State the conclusion

The supplement of a 50° angle is a 130° angle.

Check the result

Since the sum of 50° and 130° is 180°, the solution checks.

EXAMPLE 6   **RECTANGLES**   The length of a rectangle is 4 meters longer than twice its width. If the perimeter of the rectangle is 26 meters, find its dimensions.

Analyze the problem

Because we are asked to find the dimensions of the rectangle, we will need to find both the width and the length. If we let w represent the width of the rectangle, then $4 + 2w$ will represent its length.

Form an equation

To visualize the problem, we sketch the rectangle as shown in Figure 2-9. Recall that the formula for finding the perimeter of a rectangle is $P = 2l + 2w$. Therefore, the perimeter of the rectangle in the figure is $2(4 + 2w) + 2w$. We also are told that the perimeter is 26.

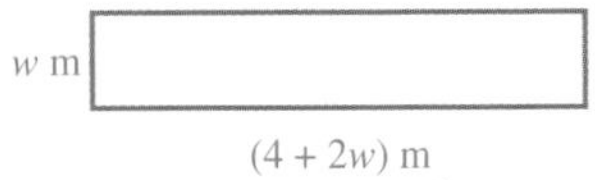

w m

$(4 + 2w)$ m

Figure 2-9

We can form the equation as follows.

2	times	the length	plus	2	times	the width	equals	the perimeter.
2	$\cdot$	$(4 + 2w)$	$+$	2	$\cdot$	w	$=$	26

Solve the equation

We can solve this equation as follows.

$$2(4 + 2w) + 2w = 26 \qquad \text{This is the equation to solve.}$$
$$8 + 4w + 2w = 26 \qquad \text{Remove parentheses.}$$
$$6w + 8 = 26 \qquad \text{Combine like terms.}$$
$$6w = 18 \qquad \text{Subtract 8 from both sides.}$$
$$w = 3 \qquad \text{Divide both sides by 6.}$$

State the conclusion

The width of the rectangle is 3 meters, and the length, $4 + 2w$, is 10 meters.

Check the result

If the rectangle has a width of 3 meters and a length of 10 meters, the length is 4 meters longer than twice the width ($4 + 2 \cdot 3 = 10$), and the perimeter is 26 meters. The solution checks.

EXAMPLE 7   **ISOSCELES TRIANGLES**   The vertex angle of an isosceles triangle is 56°. Find the measure of each base angle.

Analyze the problem   An **isosceles triangle** has two sides of equal length, which meet to form the **vertex angle.** See Figure 2-10. The angles opposite those sides, called **base angles,** are also equal. If we let x represent the measure of one base angle, the measure of the other base angle is also x.

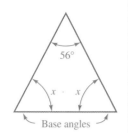

Form an equation   From geometry, we know that in any triangle the sum of the measures of its three angles is 180°. Therefore, we can form the equation.

Figure 2-10

One base angle	plus	the other base angle	plus	the vertex angle	equals	180°.
x	$+$	x	$+$	56	$=$	180

Solve the equation   We can solve this equation as follows.

$$x + x + 56 = 180 \quad \text{This is the equation to solve.}$$
$$2x + 56 = 180 \quad \text{Combine like terms.}$$
$$2x = 124 \quad \text{Subtract 56 from both sides.}$$
$$x = 62 \quad \text{Divide both sides by 2.}$$

State the conclusion   The measure of each base angle is 62°.

Check the result   The measure of each base angle is 62°, and the vertex angle measures 56°. Since $62° + 62° + 56° = 180°$, the sum of the measures of the three angles is 180°. The solution checks.

---

3   **Solve an investment application using a linear equation in one variable.**

EXAMPLE 8   **INVESTMENTS**   A teacher invests part of $12,000 at 6% annual simple interest, and the rest at 9%. If the annual income from these investments was $945, how much did the teacher invest at each rate?

Analyze the problem   We are asked to find the amount of money the teacher has invested in two different accounts. If we let x represent the amount of money invested at 6% annual interest, the remainder, $12,000 - x$, represents the amount invested at 9% annual interest.

Form an equation   The interest i earned by an amount p invested at an annual rate r for t years is given by the formula $i = prt$. In this example, $t = 1$ year. Hence, if x dollars were invested at 6%, the interest earned would be $0.06x$ dollars. If x dollars were invested at 6%, the rest of the money, $(12,000 - x)$ dollars, would be invested at 9%. The interest earned on that money would be $0.09(12,000 - x)$ dollars. The total interest earned in dollars can be expressed in two ways: as 945 and as the sum $0.06x + 0.09(12,000 - x)$.

We can form an equation as follows.

The interest earned at 6%	plus	the interest earned at 9%	equals	the total interest.
$0.06x$	$+$	$0.09(12,000 - x)$	$=$	945

Solve the equation We can solve this equation as follows.

$0.06x + 0.09(12,000 - x) = 945$	This is the equation to solve.
$6x + 9(12,000 - x) = 94,500$	Multiply both sides by 100 to clear the equation of decimals.
$6x + 108,000 - 9x = 94,500$	Remove parentheses.
$-3x + 108,000 = 94,500$	Combine like terms.
$-3x = -13,500$	Subtract 108,000 from both sides.
$x = 4,500$	Divide both sides by -3.

State the conclusion The teacher invested \$4,500 at 6% and \$12,000 − \$4,500 or \$7,500 at 9%.

Check the result The first investment earned 6% of \$4,500, or \$270. The second investment earned 9% of \$7,500, or \$675. Because the total return was \$270 + \$675, or \$945, the solutions check.

NOW TRY THIS

1. Mark invested \$100,000 in two accounts. Part was in bonds that paid 7% annual interest and the rest in stocks that lost 5% of their value. How much did he originally invest in each account if his total earned interest for the year was \$2,200? How much money does he have in each account now?

2.5 EXERCISES

WARM-UPS

1. Find the complement of a 20° angle.

2. Find the supplement of a 70° angle.

3. Find the perimeter of a rectangle 4 feet wide and 6 feet long.

4. Find an expression that represents one year's interest on \$18,000, invested at an annual rate r.

REVIEW

Refer to the formulas in Section 1.3.

5. Find the volume of a pyramid that has a height of 6 centimeters and a square base, 10 centimeters on each side.

6. Find the volume of a cone with a height of 6 centimeters and a circular base with radius 6 centimeters. Use $\pi \approx \frac{22}{7}$.

Simplify each expression.

7. $3(x + 2) + 4(x - 3)$

8. $4(x - 2) - 3(x + 1)$

9. $\frac{1}{2}(x + 1) - \frac{1}{2}(x + 4)$

10. $\frac{3}{2}\left(x + \frac{2}{3}\right) + \frac{1}{2}(x + 8)$

11. The amount A on deposit in a bank account bearing simple interest is given by the formula

$$A = P + Prt$$

Find A when $P = \$1,200$, $r = 0.08$, and $t = 3$.

12. The distance s that a certain object falls from a height of 350 ft in t seconds is given by the formula

$$s = 350 - 16t^2 + vt$$

Find s when $t = 4$ and $v = -3$.

VOCABULARY AND CONCEPTS   *Fill in the blanks.*

13. The perimeter of a rectangle is given by the formula $P =$ _____.

14. An _____ triangle is a triangle with two sides of equal length.

15. The sides of equal length of an isosceles triangle meet to form the _____ angle.

16. The angles opposite the sides of equal length of an isosceles triangle are called _____ angles.

17. Angles are measured in _____.

18. If an angle measures 90°, it is called a _____ angle.

19. If an angle measures 180°, it is called a _____ angle.

20. If the sum of the measures of two angles is 90°, the angles are called _____ angles.

21. If the sum of the measures of two angles is 180°, the angles are called _____ angles.

22. The sum of the measures of the angles of any triangle is _____.

APPLICATIONS

See Example 1. (Objective 1)

23. Carpentry   The 12-foot board in the illustration has been cut into two parts, one twice as long as the other. How long is each part?

24. Plumbing   A 20-foot pipe has been cut into two parts, one 3 times as long as the other. How long is each part?

25. Robotics   If the robotic arm shown in the illustration will extend a total distance of 30 feet, how long is each section?

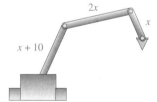

26. Statue of Liberty   If the figure part of the Statue of Liberty is 3 feet shorter than the height of its pedestal base, find the height of the figure.

305 ft

27. Window designs   The perimeter of the triangular window shown in the illustration is 24 feet. How long is each section?

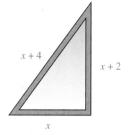

$x + 4$

$x + 2$

x

28. Football   In 1967, Green Bay beat Kansas City by 25 points in the first Super Bowl. If a total of 45 points were scored, what was the final score of the game?

29. Publishing   A book can be purchased in hardcover for $15.95 or in paperback for $4.95. How many of each type were printed if 11 times as many paperbacks were printed as hardcovers and a total of 114,000 books were printed?

30. Concert tours   A rock group plans three concert tours over a period of 38 weeks. The tour in Britain will be 4 weeks longer than the tour in France and the tour in Germany will be 2 weeks shorter than the tour in France. How many weeks will they be in France?

Find x. **See Examples 2–3. (Objective 2)**

31.

50° x 40°

32.

123° x 32°

33.

180° x 21°

34.

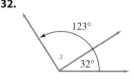

x 80°   180°

35.

12°   59° x

36.

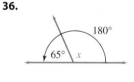

65° x 180°

37.

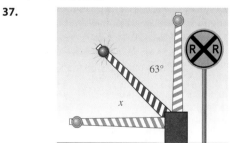

63° x

38.

Find each value. See Examples 4–5. (Objective 2)

39. Find the complement of an angle measuring 37°.

40. Find the supplement of an angle measuring 37°.

41. Find the supplement of the complement of an angle measuring 40°.

42. Find the complement of the supplement of an angle measuring 140°.

Solve each problem. See Example 6. (Objective 2)

43. Circuit boards The perimeter of the circuit board in the illustration is 90 centimeters. Find the dimensions of the board.

44. Swimming pools The width of a rectangular swimming pool is 11 meters less than the length, and the perimeter is 94 meters. Find its dimensions.

45. Framing pictures The length of a rectangular picture is 5 inches greater than twice the width. If the perimeter is 112 inches, find the dimensions of the frame.

46. Land areas The perimeter of a square piece of land is twice the perimeter of an equilateral (equal-sided) triangular lot. If one side of the square is 60 meters, find the length of a side of the triangle.

Solve each problem. See Example 7. (Objective 2)

47. Triangular bracing The outside perimeter of the triangular brace shown in the illustration is 57 feet. If all three sides are of equal length, find the length of each side.

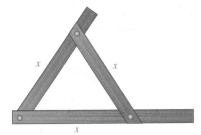

48. Trusses The truss in the illustration is in the form of an isosceles triangle. Each of the two equal sides is 4 feet less than the third side. If the perimeter is 25 feet, find the length of each side.

49. Guy wires The two guy wires in the illustration form an isosceles triangle. One of the two equal angles of the triangle is 4 times the third angle (the vertex angle). Find the measure of the vertex angle.

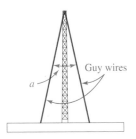

50. Equilateral triangles Find the measure of each angle of an equilateral triangle. (*Hint:* The three angles of an equilateral triangle are equal.)

Solve each problem. See Example 8. (Objective 3)

51. Investments A student invested some money at an annual rate of 5%. If the annual income from the investment is $300, how much did he invest?

52. Investments A student invested 90% of her savings in the stock market. If she invested $4,050, what are her total savings?

53. Investments A broker invested $24,000 in two mutual funds, one earning 9% annual interest and the other earning 14%. After 1 year, his combined interest is $3,135. How much was invested at each rate?

54. Investments A rollover IRA of $18,750 was invested in two mutual funds, one earning 12% interest and the other earning 10%. After 1 year, the combined interest income is $2,117. How much was invested at each rate?

55. Investments One investment pays 8% and another pays 11%. If equal amounts are invested in each, the combined interest income for 1 year is $712.50. How much is invested at each rate?

56. Investments When equal amounts are invested in each of three accounts paying 7%, 8%, and 10.5%, one year's combined interest income is $1,249.50. How much is invested in each account?

57. Investments   A college professor wants to supplement her retirement income with investment interest. If she invests $15,000 at 6% annual interest, how much more would she have to invest at 7% to achieve a goal of $1,250 in supplemental income?

58. Investments   A teacher has a choice of two investment plans: an insured fund that has paid an average of 11% interest per year, or a riskier investment that has averaged a 13% return. If the same amount invested at the higher rate would generate an extra $150 per year, how much does the teacher have to invest?

59. Investments   A financial counselor recommends investing twice as much in CDs (certificates of deposit) as in a bond fund. A client follows his advice and invests $21,000 in CDs paying 1% more interest than the fund. The CDs would generate $840 more interest than the fund. Find the two rates.   (*Hint:* 1% = 0.01.)

60. Investments   The amount of annual interest earned by $8,000 invested at a certain rate is $200 less than $12,000 would earn at a 1% lower rate. At what rate is the $8,000 invested?

WRITING ABOUT MATH

61. Write a paragraph describing the problem-solving process.

62. List as many types of angles as you can think of. Then define each type.

SOMETHING TO THINK ABOUT

63. If two lines intersect as in the illustration, angle 1 (denoted as ∠1) and ∠2, and ∠3 and ∠4, are called **vertical angles.** Let the measure of ∠1 be various numbers and compute the values of the other three angles. What do you discover?

64. If two lines meet and form a right angle, the lines are said to be **perpendicular.** See the illustration. Find the measures of ∠1, ∠2, and ∠3. What do you discover?

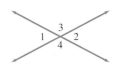

SECTION
2.6   Motion and Mixture Problems

Objectives

1 Solve a motion application using a linear equation in one variable.

2 Solve a liquid mixture application using a linear equation in one variable.

3 Solve a dry mixture application using a linear equation in one variable.

Getting Ready

1. At 30 mph, how far would a bus go in 2 hours?
2. At 55 mph, how far would a car travel in 7 hours?
3. If 8 gallons of a mixture of water and alcohol is 70% alcohol, how much alcohol does the mixture contain?
4. At $7 per pound, how many pounds of chocolate would be worth $63?

In this section, we continue the discussion of applications by considering uniform motion and mixture problems. In these problems, we will use the following three formulas:

$$r \cdot t = d$$ The rate multiplied by the time equals the distance.

$$r \cdot b = a$$ The rate multiplied by the base equals the amount.

$$v = p \cdot n$$ The value equals the price multiplied by the number.

Solve a motion application using a linear equation in one variable.

EXAMPLE 1

TRAVELING   Chicago and Green Bay are about 200 miles apart. If a car leaves Chicago traveling toward Green Bay at 55 mph at the same time as a truck leaves Green Bay bound for Chicago at 45 mph, how long will it take them to meet?

Analyze the problem   We are asked to find the amount of time it takes for the two vehicles to meet, so we will let t represent the time in hours.

Form an equation   Motion problems are based on the formula $d = rt$, where d is the distance traveled, r is the rate, and t is the time. We can organize the information of this problem in a chart or a diagram, as shown in Figure 2-11.

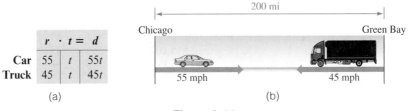

	r	$\cdot \ t$	$= d$
Car	55	t	$55t$
Truck	45	t	$45t$

(a)   (b)

Figure 2-11

We know that the two vehicles travel for the same amount of time, t hours. The faster car will travel $55t$ miles, and the slower truck will travel $45t$ miles. At the time they meet, the total distance traveled can be expressed in two ways: as the sum $55t + 45t$, and as 200 miles.

After referring to Figure 2-11, we can form the equation.

The distance the car goes	plus	the distance the truck goes	equals	the total distance.
$55t$	$+$	$45t$	$=$	200

Solve the equation   We can solve this equation as follows.

$$55t + 45t = 200 \quad \text{This is the equation to solve.}$$
$$100t = 200 \quad \text{Combine like terms.}$$
$$t = 2 \quad \text{Divide both sides by 100.}$$

State the conclusion   The vehicles will meet in 2 hours.

Check the result   In 2 hours, the car will travel $55 \cdot 2 = 110$ miles, while the truck will travel $45 \cdot 2 = 90$ miles. The total distance traveled will be $110 + 90 = 200$ miles. Since this is the total distance between Chicago and Green Bay, the solution checks.

EXAMPLE 2

SHIPPING   Two ships leave port, one heading east at 12 mph and one heading west at 10 mph. How long will it take before they are 33 miles apart?

Analyze the problem   We are asked to find the amount of time in hours, so we will let t represent the time.

Form an equation   In this problem, the ships leave port at the same time and travel in opposite directions. We know that both travel for the same amount of time, t hours. The faster ship will travel 12*t* miles, and the slower ship will travel 10*t* miles. We can organize the information of this problem in a chart or a diagram, as shown in Figure 2-12. When they are 33 miles apart, the total distance traveled can be expressed in two ways: as the sum 12*t* + 10*t*, and as 33 miles.

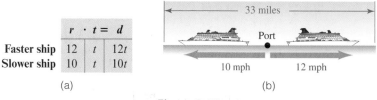

r	$\cdot$	t	$=$	d
Faster ship	12	t		12t
Slower ship	10	t		10t

(a)

(b)

Figure 2-12

After referring to Figure 2-12, we can form the equation.

The distance the faster ship goes	plus	The distance the slower ship goes	equals	the total distance.
12t	$+$	10t	$=$	33

Solve the equation   We can solve this equation as follows.

$$12t + 10t = 33 \qquad \text{This is the equation to solve.}$$
$$22t = 33 \qquad \text{Combine like terms.}$$
$$t = \frac{33}{22} \qquad \text{Divide both sides by 22.}$$
$$t = \frac{3}{2} \qquad \text{Simplify the fractions: } \frac{33}{22} = \frac{3 \cdot \cancel{11}}{2 \cdot \cancel{11}} = \frac{3}{2}.$$

State the conclusion   The ships will be 33 miles apart in $\frac{3}{2}$ hours (or $1\frac{1}{2}$ hours.)

Check the result   In 1.5 hours, the faster ship travels $12 \cdot 1.5 = 18$ miles, while the slower ship travels $10 \cdot 1.5 = 15$ miles. Since the total distance traveled is $18 + 15 = 33$ miles, the solution checks.

EXAMPLE 3   **TRAVELING**   A car leaves Beloit, heading east at 50 mph. One hour later, a second car leaves Beloit, heading east at 65 mph. How long will it take for the second car to overtake the first car?

Analyze the problem   In this problem, the cars travel different amounts of time. In fact, the first car travels for one extra hour because it had a 1-hour head start. It is convenient to let the variable *t* represent the time traveled by the second car. Then *t* + 1 represents the number of hours the first car travels.

Form an equation   We know that car 1 travels at 50 mph and car 2 travels at 65 mph. Using the formula $r \cdot t = d$, when car 2 overtakes car 1, car 2 will have traveled 65*t* miles and car 1 will have traveled 50(*t* + 1) hours.

We can organize the information in a chart or a diagram, as shown in Figure 2-13.

	r	$\cdot$ t	$=$ d
Car 1	50	$(t + 1)$	$50(t + 1)$
Car 2	65	t	$65t$

(a)

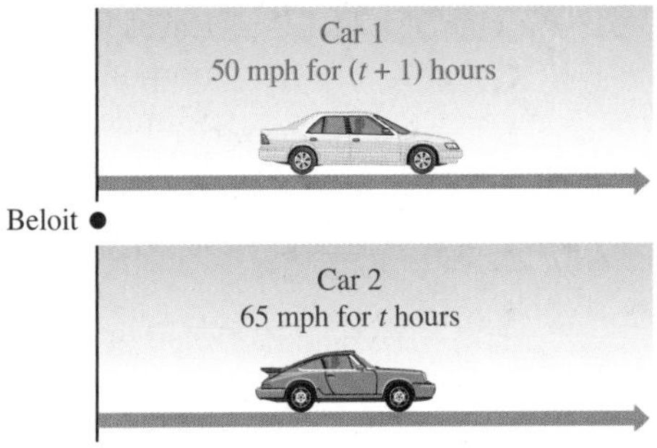

(b)

Figure 2-13

The distance the cars travel can be expressed in two ways: as $50(t + 1)$ miles, and as $65t$ miles.

Since these distances are equal when car 2 overtakes car 1, we can form the equation:

The distance that car 1 goes	equals	the distance that car 2 goes.
$50(t + 1)$	$=$	$65t$

Solve the equation   We can solve this equation as follows.

$50(t + 1) = 65t$ This is the equation to solve.

$50t + 50 = 65t$ Use the distributive property to remove parentheses.

$50 = 15t$ Subtract $50t$ from both sides.

$\dfrac{50}{15} = t$ Divide both sides by 15.

$t = \dfrac{10}{3}$ Simplify the fraction: $\frac{50}{15} = \frac{10 \cdot \overset{1}{\cancel{5}}}{3 \cdot \underset{1}{\cancel{5}}} = \frac{10}{3}$.

State the conclusion   Car 2 will overtake car 1 in $\frac{10}{3}$, or $3\frac{1}{3}$ hours.

Check the result   In $3\frac{1}{3}$ hours, car 2 will have traveled $65\left(\frac{10}{3}\right)$, or $\frac{650}{3}$ miles. With a 1-hour head start, car 1 will have traveled $50\left(\frac{10}{3} + 1\right) = 50\left(\frac{13}{3}\right)$, or $\frac{650}{3}$ miles. Since these distances are equal, the solution checks.

COMMENT   In this problem, we could let t represent the time traveled by the first car. Then $t - 1$ would represent the time traveled by the second car.

---

2 **Solve a liquid mixture application using a linear equation in one variable.**

EXAMPLE 4   **MIXING ACID**   A chemist has one solution that is 50% sulfuric acid and another that is 20% sulfuric acid. How much of each should she use to make 12 liters of a solution that is 30% sulfuric acid?

Analyze the problem   We will let x represent the number of liters of the 50% sulfuric acid solution. Since there must be 12 liters of the final mixture, $12 - x$ represents the number of liters of 20% sulfuric acid solution to use.

Form an equation   Liquid mixture problems are based on the percent formula $rb = a$, where b is the base, r is the rate, and a is the amount.

If x represents the number of liters of 50% solution to use, the amount of sulfuric acid in the solution will be $0.50x$ liters. The amount of sulfuric acid in the 20% solution will be $0.20(12 - x)$ liters. The amount of sulfuric acid in the final mixture will be $0.30(12)$ liters. We can organize this information in a chart or a diagram, as shown in Figure 2-14.

	r	$\cdot$	b	$=$	a
50% solution	0.50		x		$0.50x$
20% solution	0.20		$12 - x$		$0.20(12 - x)$
30% solution	0.30		12		$0.30(12)$

(a)

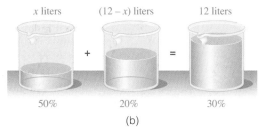

(b)

Figure 2-14

Since the number of liters of sulfuric acid in the 50% solution plus the number of liters of sulfuric acid in the 20% solution will equal the number of liters of sulfuric acid in the mixture, we can form the equation:

The amount of sulfuric acid in the 50% solution	plus	the amount of sulfuric acid in the 20% solution	equals	the amount of sulfuric acid in the final mixture.
50% of x	+	20% of $(12 - x)$	=	30% of 12

Solve the equation   We can solve this equation as follows.

$0.5x + 0.2(12 - x) = 0.3(12)$ This is the equation to solve. $50\% = 0.5$, $20\% = 0.2$, and $30\% = 0.3$.

$5x + 2(12 - x) = 3(12)$ Multiply both sides by 10 to clear the equation of decimals.

$5x + 24 - 2x = 36$ Remove parentheses.

$3x + 24 = 36$ Combine like terms.

$3x = 12$ Subtract 24 from both sides.

$x = 4$ Divide both sides by 3.

State the conclusion   The chemist must mix 4 liters of the 50% solution and $12 - 4 = 8$ liters of the 20% solution.

Check the result   The amount of acid in 4 liters of 50% solution is $4(0.50) = 2$ liters.

The amount of acid in 8 liters of 20% solution is $8(0.20) = 1.6$ liters.

The amount of acid in 12 liters of 30% solution is $12(0.30) = 3.6$ liters.

Since $2 + 1.6 = 3.6$, the results check.

3 Solve a dry mixture application using a linear equation in one variable.

EXAMPLE 5 **MIXING NUTS** Fancy cashews are not selling at $9 per pound, because they are too expensive. However, filberts are selling well at $6 per pound. How many pounds of filberts should be combined with 50 pounds of cashews to obtain a mixture that can be sold at $7 per pound?

Analyze the problem We will let x represent the number of pounds of filberts in the mixture. Since we will be adding the filberts to 50 pounds of cashews, the total number of pounds of the mixture will be $50 + x$.

Form an equation Dry mixture problems are based on the formula $v = pn$, where v is the value of the mixture, p is the price per pound, and n is the number of pounds. At $6 per pound, x pounds of the filberts are worth $6x. At $9 per pound, the 50 pounds of cashews are worth $9 · 50, or $450. The mixture will weigh $(50 + x)$ pounds, and at $7 per pound, it will be worth $7(50 + x). The *value* of the filberts (in dollars) $6x$ plus the *value* of the cashews (in dollars) 450, is equal to the *value* of the mixture (in dollars) $7(50 + x)$. We can organize this information in a table or a diagram, as shown in Figure 2-15.

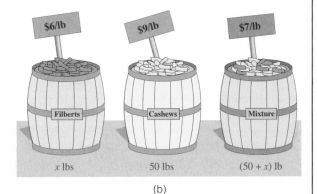

	p ·	n	=	v
Filberts	6	x		$6x$
Cashews	9	50		$9(50)$
Mixture	7	$50 + x$		$7(50 + x)$

(a)

(b)

Figure 2-15

We can form the equation:

The value of the filberts	plus	the value of the cashews	equals	the value of the mixture.
$6x$	+	$9(50)$	=	$7(50 + x)$

Solve the equation We can solve this equation as follows.

$$6x + 9(50) = 7(50 + x) \quad \text{This is the equation to solve.}$$
$$6x + 450 = 350 + 7x \quad \text{Remove parentheses and simplify.}$$
$$100 = x \quad \text{Subtract } 6x \text{ and } 350 \text{ from both sides.}$$

State the conclusion The storekeeper should use 100 pounds of filberts in the mixture.

Check the result

The value of 100 pounds of filberts at $6 per pound is	$ 600
The value of 50 pounds of cashews at $9 per pound is	$ 450
The value of the mixture is	$ 1,050

The value of 150 pounds of mixture at $7 per pound is also $1,050.

NOW TRY THIS

1. A nurse has 5 ml of a 10% solution of benzalkonium chloride. If a doctor orders a 40% solution, how much pure benzalkonium chloride must he add to the solution to obtain the desired strength?

2. A paramedic has 5 ml of a 5% saline solution. If she needs a 4% saline solution, how much water must she add to obtain the desired strength?

2.6 EXERCISES

WARM-UPS

1. How far will a car travel in h hours at a speed of 50 mph?

2. Two cars leave Midtown at the same time, one at 55 mph and the other at 65 mph. If they travel in the same direction, how far apart will they be in h hours?

3. How many ounces of alcohol are there in 12 ounces of a solution that is 40% alcohol?

4. Find the value of 7 pounds of coffee worth $\$d$ per pound.

REVIEW

Simplify each expression.

5. $3 + 4(-5)$

6. $\dfrac{-5(3) - 2(-2)}{6 - (-5)}$

7. $2^3 - 3^2$

8. $3^2 + 3(2) - (-5)$

Solve each equation.

9. $-2x + 3 = 9$

10. $\dfrac{1}{3}y - 4 = 2$

11. $\dfrac{2}{3}p + 1 = 5$

12. $2(z + 3) = 4(z - 1)$

VOCABULARY AND CONCEPTS   *Fill in the blanks.*

13. Motion problems are based on the formula _____.
14. Liquid mixture problems are based on the formula _____.
15. Dry mixture problems are based on the formula _____.
16. The information in motion and mixture problems can be organized in the form of a _____ or a _____.

APPLICATIONS

Solve each problem. **See Examples 1–2. (Objective 1)**

17. **Travel times**   Ashford and Bartlett are 315 miles apart. A car leaves Ashford bound for Bartlett at 50 mph. At the same time, another car leaves Bartlett bound for Ashford at 55 mph. How long will it take them to meet?

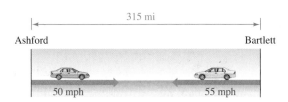

18. **Travel times**   Granville and Preston are 535 miles apart. A car leaves Preston bound for Granville at 47 mph. At the same time, another car leaves Granville bound for Preston at 60 mph. How long will it take them to meet?

19. **Paving highways**   Two crews working toward each other are 9.45 miles apart. One crew paves 1.5 miles of highway per day, and the other paves 1.2 miles per day. How long will it take them to meet?

20. **Biking**   Two friends who live 33 miles apart ride bikes toward each other. One averages 12 mph, and the other averages 10 mph. How long will it take for them to meet?

21. **Travel times**   Two cars leave Peoria at the same time, one heading east at 60 mph and the other west at 50 mph. How long will it take them to be 715 miles apart?

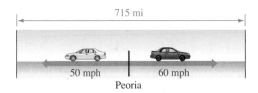

22. **Boating**   Two boats leave port at the same time, one heading north at 35 knots (nautical miles per hour) and the other south at 47 knots. How long will it take them to be 738 nautical miles apart?

23. **Hiking**   Two boys with two-way radios that have a range of 2 miles leave camp and walk in opposite directions. If one boy walks 3 mph and the other walks 4 mph, how long will it take before they lose radio contact?

24. Biking Two cyclists leave a park and ride in opposite directions, one averaging 9 mph and the other 6 mph. If they have two-way radios with a 5-mile range, for how many minutes will they remain in radio contact?

Solve each problem. **See Example 3. (Objective 1)**

25. Chasing a bus Complete the table and compute how long it will take the car to overtake the bus if the bus had a 2-hour head start.

	r	$\cdot$	t	$= d$
Car	60 mph		t	
Bus	50 mph		$t + 2$	

26. Hot pursuit Two crooks rob a bank and flee to the east at 66 mph. In 30 minutes, the police follow them in a helicopter, flying at 132 mph. How long will it take for the police to overtake the robbers?

27. Travel times Two cars start together and head east, one averaging 42 mph and the other averaging 53 mph. See the illustration. In how many hours will the cars be 82.5 miles apart?

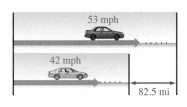

28. Aviation A plane leaves an airport and flies south at 180 mph. Later, a second plane leaves the same airport and flies south at 450 mph. If the second plane overtakes the first one in $1\frac{1}{2}$ hours, how much of a head start did the first plane have?

29. Speed of trains Two trains are 330 miles apart, and their speeds differ by 20 mph. They travel toward each other and meet in 3 hours. Find the speed of each train.

30. Speed of airplanes Two planes are 6,000 miles apart, and their speeds differ by 200 mph. They travel toward each other and meet in 5 hours. Find the speed of the slower plane.

31. Average speeds An automobile averaged 40 mph for part of a trip and 50 mph for the remainder. If the 5-hour trip covered 210 miles, for how long did the car average 40 mph?

32. Vacation driving A family drove to the Grand Canyon, averaging 45 mph. They returned using the same route, averaging 60 mph. If they spent a total of 7 hours of driving time, how far is their home from the Grand Canyon?

Solve each problem. **See Example 4. (Objective 2)**

33. Chemistry A solution contains 0.3 liters of sulfuric acid. If this represents 12% of the total amount, find the total amount.

34. Medicine A laboratory has a solution that contains 3 ounces of benzalkonium chloride. If this is 15% of the total solution, how many ounces of solution does the lab have?

35. Mixing fuels How many gallons of fuel costing $1.15 per gallon must be mixed with 20 gallons of a fuel costing $0.85 per gallon to obtain a mixture costing $1 per gallon?

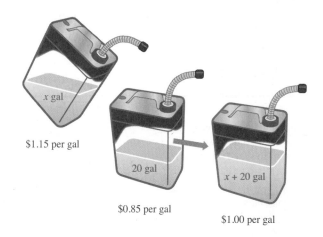

36. Mixing paint Paint costing $19 per gallon is to be mixed with 5 gallons of paint thinner costing $3 per gallon to make a paint that can be sold for $14 per gallon. Refer to the table and compute how much paint will be produced.

	p	$\cdot$	n	$=$	r
Paint	$19		x gal		$19x
Thinner	$3		5 gal		$3(5)
Mixture	$14		$(x + 5)$ gal		$14(x + 5)

37. Brine solutions How many gallons of a 3% salt solution must be mixed with 50 gallons of a 7% solution to obtain a 5% solution?

38. Making cottage cheese To make low-fat cottage cheese, milk containing 4% butterfat is mixed with 10 gallons of milk containing 1% butterfat to obtain a mixture containing 2% butterfat. How many gallons of the fattier milk must be used?

39. Antiseptic solutions A nurse wants to add water to 30 ounces of a 10% solution of benzalkonium chloride to dilute it to an 8% solution. How much water must she add?

40. Mixing photographic chemicals A photographer wants to mix 2 liters of a 5% acetic acid solution with a 10% solution to get a 7% solution. How many liters of 10% solution must be added?

Solve each problem. **See Example 5. (Objective 3)**

41. Mixing candy Lemon drops are to be mixed with jelly beans to make 100 pounds of mixture. Refer to the illustration and compute how many pounds of each candy should be used.

Lemon Drops
$1.90/lb

Jelly Beans
$1.20/lb

Mixture
$1.48/lb

42. Blending gourmet tea One grade of tea, worth $3.20 per pound, is to be mixed with another grade worth $2 per pound to make 20 pounds that will sell for $2.72 per pound. How much of each grade of tea must be used?

43. Mixing nuts A bag of peanuts is worth 30¢ less than a bag of cashews. Equal amounts of peanuts and cashews are used to make 40 bags of a mixture that sells for $1.05 per bag. How much would a bag of cashews be worth?

44. Mixing candy Twenty pounds of lemon drops are to be mixed with cherry chews to make a mixture that will sell for $1.80 per pound. How much of the more expensive candy should be used? See the table.

	Price per pound
Peppermint patties	$1.35
Lemon drops	$1.70
Licorice lumps	$1.95
Cherry chews	$2.00

45. Coffee blends A store sells regular coffee for $4 a pound and a gourmet coffee for $7 a pound. To get rid of 40 pounds of the gourmet coffee, the shopkeeper plans to make a gourmet blend to sell for $5 a pound. How many pounds of regular coffee should be used?

46. Lawn seed blends A garden store sells Kentucky bluegrass seed for $6 per pound and ryegrass seed for $3 per pound. How much rye must be mixed with 100 pounds of bluegrass to obtain a blend that will sell for $5 per pound?

47. Mixing coffee A shopkeeper sells chocolate coffee beans for $7 per pound. A customer asks the shopkeeper to mix 2 pounds of chocolate beans with 5 pounds of hazelnut coffee beans. If the customer paid $6 per pound for the mixture, what is the price per pound of the hazelnut beans?

48. Trail mix Fifteen pounds of trail mix are made by mixing 2 pounds of raisins worth $3 per pound with peanuts worth $4 per pound and M&Ms worth $5 per pound. How many pounds of peanuts must be used if the mixture is to be worth $4.20 per pound?

WRITING ABOUT MATH

49. Describe the steps you would use to analyze and solve a problem.

50. Create a mixture problem that could be solved by using the equation $4x + 6(12 - x) = 5(12)$.

51. Create a mixture problem of your own, and solve it.

52. In mixture problems, explain why it is important to distinguish between the quantity and the value (or strength) of the materials being combined.

SOMETHING TO THINK ABOUT

53. Is it possible for the equation of a problem to have a solution, but for the problem to have no solution? For example, is it possible to find two consecutive even integers whose sum is 16?

54. Invent a motion problem that leads to an equation that has a solution, although the problem does not.

55. Consider the problem: How many gallons of a 10% and a 20% solution should be mixed to obtain a 30% solution? Without solving it, how do you know that the problem has no solution?

56. What happens if you try to solve Exercise 55?

Solving Linear Inequalities in One Variable

Objectives

1 Solve a linear inequality in one variable using the properties of inequality and graph the solution on a number line.

2 Solve a compound linear inequality in one variable.

3 Solve an application problem involving a linear inequality in one variable.

Vocabulary

inequality double inequality interval
solution of an inequality compound inequality

Getting Ready

Graph each set on the number line.

1. All real numbers greater than −1

2. All real numbers less than or equal to 5

3. All real numbers between −2 and 4

4. All real numbers less than −2 or greater than or equal to 4

Many times, we will encounter mathematical statements indicating that two quantities are not necessarily equal. These statements are called *inequalities*.

 Solve a linear inequality in one variable using the properties of inequality and graph the solution on a number line.

Recall the meaning of the following symbols.

Inequality Symbols

$<$	means	"is less than"
$>$	means	"is greater than"
$\leq$	means	"is less than or equal to"
$\geq$	means	"is greater than or equal to"

An **inequality** is a statement that indicates that two quantities are not necessarily equal. A **solution of an inequality** is any number that makes the inequality true. The number 2 is a solution of the inequality

$$x \leq 3$$

because $2 \leq 3$.

This inequality has many more solutions, because any real number that is less than or equal to 3 will satisfy it. We can use a graph on the number line to represent the solutions of the inequality. The red arrow in Figure 2-16 indicates all those points with coordinates that satisfy the inequality $x \leq 3$.

The bracket at the point with coordinate 3 indicates that the number 3 is a solution of the inequality $x \leq 3$.

The graph of the inequality $x > 1$ appears in Figure 2-17. The red arrow indicates all those points whose coordinates satisfy the inequality. The parenthesis at the point with coordinate 1 indicates that 1 is not a solution of the inequality $x > 1$.

Figure 2-16

Figure 2-17

To solve more complicated inequalities, we need to use the addition, subtraction, multiplication, and division properties of inequalities. When we use any of these properties, the resulting inequality will have the same solutions as the original one.

Addition Property of Inequality	If a, b, and c are real numbers, and If $a < b$, then $a + c < b + c$.
Subtraction Property of Inequality	If a, b, and c are real numbers, and If $a < b$, then $a - c < b - c$. Similar statements can be made for the symbols $>$, $\le$, and $\ge$.

The **addition property of inequality** can be stated this way: *If any quantity is added to both sides of an inequality, the resulting inequality has the same direction as the original inequality.*

The **subtraction property of inequality** can be stated this way: *If any quantity is subtracted from both sides of an inequality, the resulting inequality has the same direction as the original inequality.*

COMMENT   The subtraction property of inequality is included in the addition property: To *subtract* a number a from both sides of an inequality, we could just as well *add* the *negative* of a to both sides.

EXAMPLE 1   Solve $2x + 5 > x - 4$ and graph the solution on a number line.

Solution   To isolate the x on the left side of the $>$ sign, we proceed as if we were solving an equation.

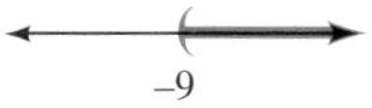

Figure 2-18

$$2x + 5 > x - 4$$
$$2x + 5 - 5 > x - 4 - 5 \qquad \text{Subtract 5 from both sides.}$$
$$2x > x - 9 \qquad \text{Combine like terms.}$$
$$2x - x > x - 9 - x \qquad \text{Subtract } x \text{ from both sides.}$$
$$x > -9 \qquad \text{Combine like terms.}$$

The graph of the solution (see Figure 2-18) includes all points to the right of -9 but does not include -9 itself. For this reason, we use a parenthesis at -9.

SELF CHECK 1   Graph the solution of $2x - 2 < x + 1$.

If both sides of the true inequality $6 < 9$ are multiplied or divided by a *positive* number, such as 3, another true inequality results.

$$6 < 9$$
$$3 \cdot 6 < 3 \cdot 9 \qquad \text{Multiply both sides by 3.}$$
$$18 < 27 \qquad \text{True.}$$

$$6 < 9$$
$$\frac{6}{3} < \frac{9}{3} \qquad \text{Divide both sides by 3.}$$
$$2 < 3 \qquad \text{True.}$$

The inequalities $18 < 27$ and $2 < 3$ are true.

However, if both sides of $6 < 9$ are multiplied or divided by a negative number, such as -3, the direction of the inequality symbol must be reversed to produce another true inequality.

$$6 < 9$$

$$-3 \cdot 6 > -3 \cdot 9$$ Multiply both sides by -3 and reverse the direction of the inequality.

$$-18 > -27$$ True.

$$6 < 9$$

$$\frac{6}{-3} > \frac{9}{-3}$$ Divide both sides by -3 and reverse the direction of the inequality.

$$-2 > -3$$ True.

The inequality $-18 > -27$ is true, because -18 lies to the right of -27 on the number line. The inequality $-2 > -3$ is true, because -2 lies to the right of -3 on the number line. This example suggests the multiplication and division properties of inequality.

Multiplication Property of Inequality	If a, b, and c are real numbers, and If $a < b$ and $c > 0$, then $ac < bc$. If $a < b$ and $c < 0$, then $ac > bc$.
Division Property of Inequality	If a, b, and c are real numbers, and If $a < b$ and $c > 0$, then $\dfrac{a}{c} < \dfrac{b}{c}$. If $a < b$ and $c < 0$, then $\dfrac{a}{c} > \dfrac{b}{c}$.

Similar statements can be made for the symbols $>$, $\leq$, and $\geq$.

COMMENT In the previous definitions, we did not consider the case of $c = 0$. If $a < b$ and $c = 0$, then $ac = bc$, and $\frac{a}{c}$ and $\frac{b}{c}$ are not defined.

The multiplication property of inequality can be stated this way:

If unequal quantities are multiplied by the same positive quantity, the results will be unequal and in the same direction.

If unequal quantities are multiplied by the same negative quantity, the results will be unequal but in the opposite direction.

The division property of inequality can be stated this way:

If unequal quantities are divided by the same positive quantity, the results will be unequal and in the same direction.

If unequal quantities are divided by the same negative quantity, the results will be unequal but in the opposite direction.

To *divide* both sides of an inequality by a nonzero number c, we could instead *multiply* both sides by $\frac{1}{c}$.

COMMENT Remember that if both sides of an inequality are multiplied by a *positive* number, the direction of the resulting inequality remains the same. However, if both sides of an inequality are multiplied by a *negative* number, the direction of the resulting inequality must be reversed.

Note that the procedures for solving inequalities are the same as for solving equations, except that we must reverse the inequality symbol whenever we multiply or divide by a negative number.

EXAMPLE 2 Solve $3x + 7 \leq -5$, and graph the solution on the number line.

Solution To isolate x on the left side, we proceed as if we were solving an equation.

$$3x + 7 \leq -5$$
$$3x + 7 - 7 \leq -5 - 7 \qquad \text{Subtract 7 from both sides.}$$
$$3x \leq -12 \qquad \text{Combine like terms.}$$
$$\frac{3x}{3} \leq \frac{-12}{3} \qquad \text{Divide both sides by 3.}$$
$$x \leq -4$$

Figure 2-19

The solution consists of all real numbers that are less than or equal to -4. The bracket at -4 in the graph of Figure 2-19 indicates that -4 is one of the solutions.

SELF CHECK 2 Graph the solution of $2x - 5 \geq -3$ on the number line.

EXAMPLE 3 Solve $5 - 3x \leq 14$, and graph the solution on the number line.

Solution To isolate x on the left side, we proceed as if we were solving an equation. This time, we will have to reverse the inequality symbol.

$$5 - 3x \leq 14$$
$$5 - 3x - 5 \leq 14 - 5 \qquad \text{Subtract 5 from both sides.}$$
$$-3x \leq 9 \qquad \text{Combine like terms.}$$
$$\frac{-3x}{-3} \geq \frac{9}{-3} \qquad \text{Divide both sides by } -3 \text{ and reverse the direction of the } \leq \text{ symbol.}$$
$$x \geq -3$$

Figure 2-20

Since both sides of the inequality were divided by -3, the direction of the inequality was *reversed*. The graph of the solution appears in Figure 2-20. The bracket at -3 indicates that -3 is one of the solutions.

SELF CHECK 3 Graph the solution of $6 - 7x \geq -15$ on the number line.

---

2 **Solve a compound linear inequality in one variable.**

Two inequalities often can be combined into a **double inequality** or **compound inequality** to indicate that numbers lie *between* two fixed values. For example, the inequality $2 < x < 5$ indicates that x is greater than 2 and that x is also less than 5. The solution of $2 < x < 5$ consists of all numbers that lie *between* 2 and 5. The graph of this set (called an **interval**) appears in Figure 2-21.

Figure 2-21

EXAMPLE 4 Solve $-4 < 2(x - 1) \leq 4$, and graph the solution on the number line.

Solution To isolate x in the center, we proceed as if we were solving an equation with three parts: a left side, a center, and a right side.

$$-4 < 2(x - 1) \leq 4$$
$$-4 < 2x - 2 \leq 4 \quad \text{Remove parentheses.}$$
$$-2 < 2x \leq 6 \quad \text{Add 2 to all three parts.}$$
$$-1 < x \leq 3 \quad \text{Divide all three parts by 2.}$$

Figure 2-22   The graph of the solution appears in Figure 2-22.

⇨ **SELF CHECK 4**   Graph the solution of $0 \leq 4(x + 5) < 26$ on the number line.

3 **Solve an application problem involving a linear inequality in one variable.**

When solving application problems, there are certain words that help us translate a sentence into a mathematical inequality.

Words	Sentence	Inequality
at least	To earn a grade of A, you must score at least 90%.	$S \geq 90\%$
is less than	The perimeter is less than 30 feet.	$P < 30$ ft
is no less than	The perimeter is no less than 100 centimeters.	$P \geq 100$ cm
is more than	The area is more than 30 square inches.	$A > 30$ sq in.
exceeds	The car's speed exceeded the limit of 45 mph.	$S > 45$ mph
cannot exceed	The salary cannot exceed $50,000.	$S \leq \$50,000$
at most	The perimeter is at most 75 feet.	$P \leq 75$ ft
is between	The altitude was between 10,000 and 15,000 feet.	$10,000 < A < 15,000$

EXAMPLE 5   **GRADES**   A student has scores of 72, 74, and 78 points on three mathematics examinations. How many points does he need on his last exam to earn a B or better, an average of at least 80 points?

Solution   We can let x represent the score on the fourth (last) exam. To find the average grade, we add the four scores and divide by 4. To earn a B, this average must be greater than or equal to 80 points.

The average of the four grades	is greater than or equal to	80.
$\dfrac{72 + 74 + 78 + x}{4}$	$\geq$	80

We can solve this inequality for x.

$$\frac{224 + x}{4} \geq 80 \quad 72 + 74 + 78 = 224$$

$$224 + x \geq 320 \quad \text{Multiply both sides by 4.}$$

$$x \geq 96 \quad \text{Subtract 224 from both sides.}$$

To earn a B, the student must score at least 96 points.

EXAMPLE 6   **EQUILATERAL TRIANGLES**   If the perimeter of an equilateral triangle is less than 15 feet, how long could each side be?

Solution   Recall that each side of an equilateral triangle is the same length and that the perimeter of a triangle is the sum of the lengths of its three sides. If we let x represent the length of one of the sides, then $x + x + x$ represents the perimeter. Since the perimeter is to be less than 15 feet, we have the following inequality:

$$x + x + x < 15$$
$$3x < 15 \qquad \text{Combine like terms.}$$
$$x < 5 \qquad \text{Divide both sides by 3.}$$

Each side of the triangle must be less than 5 feet long.

SELF CHECK ANSWERS   **1.** 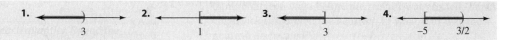   **2.** ·   **3.** ·   **4.** ·

NOW TRY THIS

Solve each inequality and graph the solution.

1. $2(x - 3) \le 2x - 1$

2. $-5x - 7 > 5(3 - x)$

3. A person's body-mass index (BMI) determines the amount of body fat. BMI is represented by the formula $B = 703\frac{w}{h^2}$, where w is weight (in pounds) and h is height (in inches). A 5′8″ gymnast must maintain a normal body-mass index. If the normal range for men is represented by $18.5 < 703\frac{w}{h^2} < 25$, within what range should the gymnast maintain his weight? Give the answer to the nearest tenth of a pound.

2.7 EXERCISES

WARM-UPS   *Solve each inequality.*

1. $2x < 4$

2. $x + 5 \ge 6$

3. $-3x \le -6$

4. $-x > 2$

5. $2x - 5 < 7$

6. $5 - 2x < 7$

REVIEW   *Simplify each expression.*

7. $3x^2 - 2(y^2 - x^2)$

8. $5(xy + 2) - 3xy - 8$

9. $\frac{1}{3}(x + 6) - \frac{4}{3}(x - 9)$

10. $\frac{4}{5}x(y + 1) - \frac{9}{5}y(x - 1)$

VOCABULARY AND CONCEPTS   *Fill in the blanks.*

11. The symbol $<$ means _____. The symbol $>$ means _____.

12. The symbol ___ means "is greater than or equal to." The symbol ___ means "is less than or equal to."

13. Two inequalities often can be combined into a _____ or *compound inequality*.

14. The graph of the solution of $2 < x < 5$ on the number line is called an _____.

15. An _____ is a statement indicating that two quantities are not necessarily equal.

16. A _____ of an inequality is any number that makes the inequality true.

GUIDED PRACTICE

Solve each inequality and graph the solution on the number line.
See Example 1. (Objective 1)

17. $x + 2 > 5$

18. $x + 5 \geq 2$

19. $2x + 9 \leq x + 8$

20. $3 + x < 2$

Solve each inequality and graph the solution on the number line.
See Example 2. (Objective 1)

21. $2x - 3 \leq 5$

22. $9x + 13 \geq 8x$

23. $8x + 4 > 6x - 2$

24. $7x + 6 \geq 4x$

25. $7x + 2 > 4x - 1$

26. $5x + 7 < 2x + 1$

27. $\frac{5}{2}(7x - 15) + x \geq \frac{13}{2}x - \frac{3}{2}$

28. $\frac{5}{3}(x + 1) \leq -x + \frac{2}{3}$

Solve each inequality and graph the solution on the number line.
See Example 3. (Objective 1)

29. $-x - 3 \leq 7$

30. $-x - 9 > 3$

31. $-3x - 5 < 4$

32. $3x + 7 \leq 4x - 2$

33. $-3x - 7 > -1$

34. $-5x + 7 \leq 12$

35. $-4x + 1 > 17$

36. $7x - 9 > 5$

37. $9 - 2x > 24 - 7x$

38. $13 - 17x < 34 - 10x$

39. $3(x - 8) < 5x + 6$

40. $9(x - 11) > 13 + 7x$

Solve each inequality and graph the solution on the number line.
See Example 4. (Objective 2)

41. $2 < x - 5 < 5$

42. $3 < x - 2 < 7$

43. $-5 < x + 4 \leq 7$

44. $-9 \leq x + 8 < 1$

45. $0 \leq x + 10 \leq 10$

46. $-8 < x - 8 < 8$

47. $-6 < 3(x + 2) < 9$

48. $-18 \leq 9(x - 5) < 27$

ADDITIONAL PRACTICE   *Solve each inequality and graph the solution on the number line.*

49. $5 + x \geq 3$

50. $7x - 16 < 6x$

51. $7 - x \leq 3x - 1$

52. $2 - 3x \geq 6 + x$

53. $8(5 - x) \leq 10(8 - x)$

54. $17(3 - x) \geq 3 - 13x$

55. $\frac{3x - 3}{2} < 2x + 2$

56. $\frac{x + 7}{3} \geq x - 3$

57. $\dfrac{2(x + 5)}{3} \leq 3x - 6$ **58.** $\dfrac{3(x - 1)}{4} > x + 1$

59. $4 < -2x < 10$ **60.** $-4 \leq -4x < 12$

61. $-3 \leq \dfrac{x}{2} \leq 5$ **62.** $-12 \leq \dfrac{x}{3} < 0$

63. $3 \leq 2x - 1 < 5$ **64.** $4 < 3x - 5 \leq 7$

65. $0 < 10 - 5x \leq 15$ **66.** $1 \leq -7x + 8 \leq 15$

67. $-4 < \dfrac{x - 2}{2} < 6$ **68.** $-1 \leq \dfrac{x + 1}{3} \leq 3$

APPLICATIONS

Express each solution as an inequality. **See Examples 5–6.**
(Objective 3)

69. Calculating grades   A student has test scores of 68, 75, and 79 points. What must she score on the fourth exam to have an average score of at least 80 points?

70. Calculating grades   A student has test scores of 70, 74, and 84 points. What must he score on the fourth exam to have an average score of at least 70 points?

71. Geometry   The perimeter of a square is no less than 68 centimeters. How long can a side be?

72. Geometry   The perimeter of an equilateral triangle is at most 57 feet. What could be the length of a side?   (*Hint:* All three sides of an equilateral triangle are equal.)

Express each solution as an inequality.

73. Fleet averages   An automobile manufacturer produces three light trucks in equal quantities. One model has an economy rating of 17 miles per gallon, and the second model is rated for 19 mpg. If the manufacturer is required to have a fleet average of at least 21 mpg, what economy rating is required for the third model?

74. Avoiding service charges   When the average daily balance of a customer's checking account is less than $500 in any business week, the bank assesses a $5 service charge. Bill's account balances for the week were as shown in the table. What must Friday's balance be to avoid the service charge?

Monday	$540.00
Tuesday	$435.50
Wednesday	$345.30
Thursday	$310.00

75. Land elevations   The land elevations in Nevada fall from the 13,143-foot height of Boundary Peak to the Colorado River at 470 feet. To the nearest tenth, what is the range of these elevations in miles?   (*Hint:* 1 mile is 5,280 feet.)

76. Homework   A teacher requires that students do homework at least 2 hours a day. How many minutes should a student work each week?

77. Plane altitudes   A pilot plans to fly at an altitude of between 17,500 and 21,700 feet. To the nearest tenth, what will be the range of altitudes in miles?   (*Hint:* There are 5,280 feet in 1 mile.)

78. Getting exercise   A certain exercise program recommends that your daily exercise period should exceed 15 minutes but should not exceed 30 minutes per day. In hours, find the range of exercise time for one week.

79. Comparing temperatures   To hold the temperature of a room between 19° and 22° Celsius, what Fahrenheit temperatures must be maintained?   (*Hint:* Fahrenheit temperature (F) and Celsius temperature (C) are related by the formula $C = \frac{5}{9}(F - 32)$.)

80. Melting iron   To melt iron, the temperature of a furnace must be at least $1{,}540°C$ but at most $1{,}650°C$. What range of Fahrenheit temperatures must be maintained?

81. Phonograph records   The radii of old phonograph records lie between 5.9 and 6.1 inches. What variation in circumference can occur?   (*Hint:* The circumference of a circle is given by the formula $C = 2\pi r$, where r is the radius. Use 3.14 to approximate π.)

82. Pythons   A large snake, the African Rock Python, can grow to a length of 25 feet. To the nearest hundredth, find the snake's range of lengths in meters.   (*Hint:* There are about 3.281 feet in 1 meter.)

83. Comparing weights   The normal weight of a 6 foot 2 inch man is between 150 and 190 pounds. To the nearest hundredth, what would such a person weigh in kilograms?   (*Hint:* There are approximately 2.2 pounds in 1 kilogram.)

84. Manufacturing The time required to assemble a television set at the factory is 2 hours. A stereo receiver requires only 1 hour. The labor force at the factory can supply at least 644 and at most 805 hours of assembly time per week. When the factory is producing 3 times as many television sets as stereos, how many stereos could be manufactured in 1 week?

85. Geometry A rectangle's length is 3 feet less than twice its width, and its perimeter is between 24 and 48 feet. What might be its width?

86. Geometry A rectangle's width is 8 feet less than 3 times its length, and its perimeter is between 8 and 16 feet. What might be its length?

WRITING ABOUT MATH

87. Explain why multiplying both sides of an inequality by a negative constant reverses the direction of the inequality.

88. Explain the use of parentheses and brackets in the graphing of the solution of an inequality.

SOMETHING TO THINK ABOUT

89. To solve the inequality $1 < \frac{1}{x}$, one student multiplies both sides by x to get $x < 1$. Why is this not correct?

90. Find the solution of $1 < \frac{1}{x}$. (*Hint:* Will any negative values of x work?)

PROJECTS

Project 1

Build a scale similar to the one shown in Figure 2-1. Demonstrate to your class how you would use the scale to solve the following equations.

a. $x - 4 = 6$ **b.** $x + 3 = 2$ **c.** $2x = 6$

d. $\frac{x}{2} = 3$ **e.** $3x - 2 = 5$ **f.** $\frac{x}{3} + 1 = 2$

Project 2

Use a calculator to determine whether the following statements are true or false.

1. $7^5 = 5^7$

2. $2^3 + 7^3 = (2 + 7)^3$

3. $(-4)^4 = -4^4$

4. $\frac{10^3}{5^3} = 2^3$

5. $8^4 \cdot 9^4 = (8 \cdot 9)^4$

6. $2^3 \cdot 3^3 = 6^3$

7. $\frac{3^{10}}{3^2} = 3^5$

8. $[(1.2)^3]^2 = [(1.2)^2]^3$

9. $(7.2)^2 - (5.1)^2 = (7.2 - 5.1)^2$

Chapter 2   REVIEW

SECTION 2.1   Solving Basic Linear Equations in One Variable

DEFINITIONS AND CONCEPTS	EXAMPLES
An **equation** is a statement indicating that two quantities are equal.	**Equations:** $3x = 5$ $3x - 4 = 10$ $8x - 7 = -2x$
An **expression** is a mathematical statement that does not contain an = sign.	**Expressions:** $5x + 1$ $5x^2 + 3x - 2$ $-8(2x - 4)$

A number is said to *satisfy* an equation if it makes the equation true when substituted for the variable.	To determine whether 3 is a solution of the equation $2x + 5 = 11$, substitute 3 for x and determine whether the result is a true statement. $$2x + 5 = 11$$ $$2(3) + 5 \stackrel{?}{=} 11$$ $$6 + 5 \stackrel{?}{=} 11$$ $$11 = 11$$ Since the result is a true statement, 3 satisfies the equation.
Addition and subtraction properties of equality: Any real number can be added to (or subtracted from) both sides of an equation to form another equation with the same solutions as the original equation.	To solve $x - 3 = 8$, add 3 to both sides. To solve $x + 3 = 8$, subtract 3 from both sides. $$x - 3 = 8 \qquad\qquad x + 3 = 8$$ $$x - 3 + 3 = 8 + 3 \qquad x - 3 - 3 = 8 - 3$$ $$x = 11 \qquad\qquad x = 5$$ Verify that each result satisfies its corresponding equation.
Two equations are **equivalent equations** when they have the same solutions.	$3x + 4 = 10$ and $3x = 6$ are equivalent equations because 2 is the only solution of each equation.
Multiplication and division properties of equality: Both sides of an equation can be multiplied (or divided) by any *nonzero* real number to form another equation with the same solutions as the original equation.	To solve $\frac{x}{3} = 4$, multiply both sides by 3. To solve $3x = 12$, divide both sides by 3. $$\frac{x}{3} = 4 \qquad\qquad 3x = 12$$ $$3\left(\frac{x}{3}\right) = 3(4) \qquad \frac{3x}{3} = \frac{12}{3}$$ $$x = 12 \qquad\qquad x = 4$$ Verify that each result satisfies its corresponding equation.
Sales price = regular price − markdown	If a coat regularly costs $150 and is marked down $25, its selling price is $150 − $25 = $125.
Retail price = wholesale cost + markup	If the wholesale cost of a television is $500 and it is marked up $200, its retail price is $500 + $200 = $700.
A **percent** is the numerator of a fraction with a denominator of 100.	$$6\% = \frac{6}{100} = 0.06 \qquad 8\% = \frac{8}{100} = 0.08$$
Amount = rate · base	An amount of $150 will be earned when a base of $3,000 is invested at a rate of 5%. $$a = rb$$ $$150 = 0.05 \cdot 3{,}000$$ $$150 = 150$$

REVIEW EXERCISES

Determine whether the given number is a solution of the equation.

1. $3x + 7 = 1$; -2 **2.** $5 - 2x = 3$; -1

3. $2(x + 3) = x$; -3 **4.** $5(3 - x) = 2 - 4x$; 13

5. $3(x + 5) = 2(x - 3)$; -21 **6.** $2(x - 7) = x + 14$; 0

Solve each equation and check all solutions.

7. $x - 7 = -6$ **8.** $y - 4 = 5$

9. $p + 4 = 20$

10. $x + \dfrac{3}{5} = \dfrac{3}{5}$

11. $y - \dfrac{7}{2} = \dfrac{1}{2}$

12. $z + \dfrac{5}{3} = -\dfrac{1}{3}$

13. Retail sales A necklace is on sale for $69.95. If it has been marked down $35.45, what is its regular price?

14. Retail sales A suit that has been marked up $115.25 sells for $212.95. Find its wholesale price.

Solve each equation and check all solutions.

15. $3x = 15$

16. $8r = -16$

17. $10z = 5$

18. $14q = 21$

19. $\dfrac{y}{3} = 6$

20. $\dfrac{w}{7} = -5$

21. $\dfrac{a}{-7} = \dfrac{1}{14}$

22. $\dfrac{p}{12} = \dfrac{1}{2}$

Solve each problem.

23. What number is 35% of 700?

24. 72% of what number is 936?

25. What percent of 2,300 is 851?

26. 72 is what percent of 576?

SECTION 2.2 Solving More Linear Equations in One Variable

DEFINITIONS AND CONCEPTS	EXAMPLES
Solving a linear equation may require the use of several properties of equality.	To solve $\dfrac{x}{3} - 4 = -8$, proceed as follows: $\dfrac{x}{3} - 4 + 4 = -8 + 4$ To undo the subtraction of 4, add 4 to both sides. $\dfrac{x}{3} = -4$ $3\left(\dfrac{x}{3}\right) = 3(-4)$ To undo the division of 3, multiply both sides by 3. $x = -12$
Retail price = cost + $\dfrac{\text{percent of}}{\text{markup}} \cdot$ cost Markup = percent of markup $\cdot$ cost	A wholesale cost of a necklace is \$125. If its retail price is \$150, find the percent of markup. $150 = 125 + p \cdot 125$ $25 = 125p$ Subtract 125 from both sides. $0.20 = p$ Divide both sides by 125. The percent of markup is 20%.
$\dfrac{\text{Sale}}{\text{price}}$ = regular price $- \dfrac{\text{percent of}}{\text{markdown}} \cdot$ regular price $\dfrac{\text{Markdown}}{\text{(discount)}} = \dfrac{\text{percent of}}{\text{markdown}} \cdot$ regular price	A used textbook that was originally priced at \$95 is now priced at \$57. Find the percent of markdown. $57 = 95 - p \cdot 95$ $-38 = -95p$ Subtract 95 from both sides. $0.40 = p$ Divide both sides by -95. The used textbook has a markdown of 40%.

REVIEW EXERCISES

Solve each equation and check all solutions.

27. $5y + 6 = 21$

28. $5y - 9 = 1$

29. $-12z + 4 = -8$

30. $17z + 3 = 20$

31. $13 - 13p = 0$

32. $10 + 7p = -4$

33. $23a - 43 = 3$

34. $84 - 21a = -63$

35. $3x + 7 = 1$

36. $7 - 9x = 16$

37. $\dfrac{b + 3}{4} = 2$

38. $\dfrac{b - 7}{2} = -2$

39. $\dfrac{x - 8}{5} = 1$

40. $\dfrac{x + 10}{2} = -1$

41. $\dfrac{2y - 2}{4} = 2$

42. $\dfrac{3y + 12}{11} = 3$

43. $\dfrac{x}{2} + 7 = 11$

44. $\dfrac{r}{3} - 3 = 7$

45. $\dfrac{a}{2} + \dfrac{9}{4} = 6$

46. $\dfrac{x}{8} - 2.3 = 3.2$

47. Retail sales An iPod is on sale for \$240, a 25% savings from the regular price. Find the regular price.

48. Tax rates A \$38 dictionary costs \$40.47 with sales tax. Find the tax rate.

49. Percent of increase A Turkish rug was purchased for \$560. If it is now worth \$1,100, find the percent of increase to the nearest 10th.

50. Percent of discount A clock on sale for \$215 was regularly priced at \$465. Find the percent of discount.

SECTION 2.3   Simplifying Expressions to Solve Linear Equations in One Variable

DEFINITIONS AND CONCEPTS	EXAMPLES
Like terms are terms with the same variables having the same exponents. They can be combined by adding their numerical coefficients and using the same variables and exponents.	Combine like terms. $4(x + 3) + 6(x - 5)$ $\quad = 4x + 12 + 6x - 30$ Use the distributive property to remove parentheses. $\quad = 10x - 18$ Combine like terms: $4x + 6x = 10x$, $12 - 30 = -18$.
An **identity** is an equation that is true for all values of its variable.	Show that the following equation is an identity. $\quad 2(x - 5) + 6x = 8(x - 1) - 2$ $\quad 2x - 10 + 6x = 8x - 8 - 2$ Remove parentheses. $\qquad 8x - 10 = 8x - 10$ Combine like terms. $\qquad\quad -10 = -10$ Subtract $8x$ from both sides. Since the final result is always true, the equation is an identity and its solution set is $\mathbb{R}$.
A **contradiction** is an equation that is true for no values of its variable.	Show that the following equation is a contradiction. $\quad 6x - 2(x + 5) = 4x - 1$ $\quad 6x - 2x - 10 = 4x - 1$ Remove parentheses. $\qquad 4x - 10 = 4x - 1$ Combine like terms. $\qquad\quad -10 = -1$ Subtract $4x$ from both sides. Since the final result is false, the equation is a contradiction and its solution set is $\varnothing$.

REVIEW EXERCISES

Simplify each expression, if possible.

51. $5x + 9x$

52. $7a + 12a$

53. $18b - 13b$

54. $21x - 23x$

55. $5y - 7y$

56. $19x - 19$

57. $7(x + 2) + 2(x - 7)$

58. $2(3 - x) + x - 6x$

59. $y^2 + 3(y^2 - 2)$

60. $2x^2 - 2(x^2 - 2)$

Solve each equation and check all solutions.

61. $2x - 19 = 2 - x$

62. $5b - 19 = 2b + 20$

63. $3x + 20 = 5 - 2x$

64. $0.9x + 10 = 0.7x + 1.8$

65. $10(p - 3) = 3(p + 11)$

66. $2(5x - 7) = 2(x - 35)$

67. $\dfrac{3u - 6}{5} = 3$

68. $\dfrac{5v - 35}{3} = -5$

69. $\dfrac{7x - 28}{4} = -21$

70. $\dfrac{27 + 9y}{5} = -27$

Classify each equation as an identity or a contradiction and give the solution.

71. $2x - 5 = x - 5 + x$

72. $-3(a + 1) - a = -4a + 3$

73. $2(x - 1) + 4 = 4(1 + x) - (2x + 2)$

74. $3(2x + 1) + 3 = 9(x + 2) + 9 - 3x$

SECTION 2.4 Formulas

DEFINITIONS AND CONCEPTS	EXAMPLES
A **literal equation** or **formula** often can be solved for any of its variables.	Solve $2x + 3y = 6$ for y. $$2x + 3y = 6$$ $$3y = -2x + 6 \quad \text{Subtract } 2x \text{ from both sides.}$$ $$y = -\frac{2}{3}x + 2 \quad \text{Divide both sides by 3.}$$

REVIEW EXERCISES

Solve each equation for the indicated variable.

75. $E = IR$; for R **76.** $i = prt$; for t **81.** $V = \pi r^2 h$; for h **82.** $a = 2\pi rh$; for r

77. $P = I^2 R$; for R **78.** $d = rt$; for r **83.** $F = \dfrac{GMm}{d^2}$; for G **84.** $P = \dfrac{RT}{mV}$; for m

79. $V = lwh$; for h **80.** $y = mx + b$; for m

SECTION 2.5 Introduction to Problem Solving

DEFINITIONS AND CONCEPTS	EXAMPLES
To solve application problems, follow these steps: **1.** Analyze the problem and choose a variable. **2.** Form an equation. **3.** Solve the equation. **4.** State the conclusion. **5.** Check the result.	The length of a rectangular frame is 4 in. longer than twice the width. If the perimeter is 38 in., find the width of the frame. **1.** Analyze the problem and let w represent the width of the frame. **2.** The width of the frame is w and since the length is 4 in. longer than twice the width, the length is $2w + 4$. Since the frame is a rectangle, its perimeter is the sum of two widths and two lengths. This perimeter is 38. So $$2w + 2(2w + 4) = 38$$ **3.** To solve the equation, proceed as follows: $$2w + 2(2w + 4) = 38$$ $$2w + 4w + 8 = 38$$ $$6w + 8 = 38$$ $$6w = 30$$ $$w = 5$$ **4.** The frame is 5 inches wide. **5.** If the width is 5 in., the length is $2 \cdot 5 + 4 = 14$ in. The perimeter is $2 \cdot 5 + 2 \cdot 14 = 10 + 28 = 38$. The result checks.
If the sum of the measures of two angles is 90°, the angles are called **complementary angles**.	Find the complement of an angle measuring 42°. $$x + 42 = 90$$ $$x + 42 - 42 = 90 - 42$$ $$x = 58°$$
If the sum of the measures of two angles is 180°, the angles are called **supplementary angles**.	Find the supplement of an angle measuring 42°. $$x + 42 = 180$$ $$x + 42 - 42 = 180 - 42$$ $$x = 138°$$

REVIEW EXERCISES

85. Carpentry   A carpenter wants to cut an 8-foot board into two pieces so that one piece is 7 feet shorter than twice the longer piece. Where should he make the cut?

86. Find x.

87. Find x.

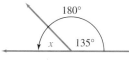

88. Find the complement of an angle that measures 69°.

89. Find the supplement of an angle that measures 69°.

90. Rectangles   If the length of the rectangular painting in the illustration is 3 inches more than twice the width, how wide is the rectangle?

©Shutterstock.com/Laurin Rinder

84 in.

91. Investing   A woman has $27,000. Part is invested for 1 year in a certificate of deposit paying 7% interest, and the remaining amount in a cash management fund paying 9%. The total interest on the two investments is $2,110. How much does she invest at each rate?

SECTION 2.6   Motion and Mixture Problems

DEFINITIONS AND CONCEPTS	EXAMPLES
Distance = rate · time $d = rt$	How far will a car go traveling at 40 mph for 3 hours? $d = rt = 40(3) = 120$ The car will go 120 miles.
Value = price · number $v = pn$	How much will 3 lb of peanuts cost if the cost is $2 per lb? $v = pn = 3(2) = 6$ The cost will be $6.

REVIEW EXERCISES

92. Riding bicycles   A bicycle path is 5 miles long. A man walks from one end at the rate of 3 mph. At the same time, a friend bicycles from the other end, traveling at 12 mph. In how many minutes will they meet?

93. Tornadoes   During a storm, two teams of scientists leave a university at the same time in specially designed vans to search for tornadoes. The first team travels east at 20 mph and the second travels west at 25 mph. If their radios have a range of up to 90 miles, how long will it be before they lose radio contact?

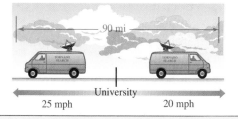

90 mi

University
25 mph   20 mph

94. Band trips   A bus carrying the members of a marching band and a truck carrying their instruments leave a high school at the same time and travel in the same direction. The bus travels at 65 mph and the truck at 55 mph. In how many hours will they be 75 miles apart?

95. Mixing milk   A container is partly filled with 12 liters of whole milk containing 4% butterfat. How much 1% milk must be added to get a mixture that is 2% butterfat?

96. Photography   A photographer wants to mix 2 liters of a 6% acetic acid solution with a 12% solution to get an 8% solution. How many liters of 12% solution must be added?

97. Mixing candy   A store manager mixes candy worth 90¢ per pound with gumdrops worth $1.50 per pound to make 20 pounds of a mixture worth $1.20 per pound. How many pounds of each kind of candy must he use?

SECTION 2.7   Solving Linear Inequalities in One Variable

DEFINITIONS AND CONCEPTS	EXAMPLES
Inequalities are solved by techniques similar to those used to solve equations, with this exception: *If both sides of an inequality are multiplied or divided by a negative number, the direction of the inequality must be reversed.* The solution of an inequality can be graphed on the number line.	To solve the inequality $-3x - 8 < 7$, proceed as follows: $$-3x - 8 < 7$$ $$-3x < 15$$ $$x > -5 \quad \text{Divide both sides by } -3 \text{ and reverse the inequality symbol.}$$ The graph of $x > -5$ is  -5

REVIEW EXERCISES

Graph the solution to each inequality.

98. $3x + 2 < 5$

99. $-5x - 8 > 7$

104. $8 < x + 2 < 13$

105. $0 \le 2 - 2x < 4$

100. $5x - 3 \ge 2x + 9$

101. $7x + 1 \le 8x - 5$

102. $5(3 - x) \le 3(x - 3)$

103. $3(5 - x) \ge 2x$

106. Swimming pools   By city ordinance, the perimeter of a rectangular swimming pool cannot exceed 68 feet. The width is 6 feet shorter than the length. What possible lengths will meet these conditions?

Chapter 2   TEST

Determine whether the given number is a solution of the equation.

1. $5x + 3 = -2; -1$

2. $3(x + 2) = 2x; -6$

3. $-3(2 - x) = 0; -2$

4. $3(x + 2) = 2x + 7; 1$

Solve each equation.

5. $x + 17 = -19$

6. $a - 15 = 32$

7. $12x = -144$

8. $\dfrac{x}{7} = -1$

9. $8x + 2 = -14$

10. $3 = 5 - 2x$

11. $\dfrac{2x - 5}{3} = 3$

12. $23 - 5(x + 10) = -12$

Simplify each expression.

13. $x + 5(x - 3)$

14. $3x - 5(2 - x)$

15. $-3(x + 3) + 3(x - 3)$

16. $-4(2x - 5) - 7(4x + 1)$

Solve each equation.

17. $\dfrac{3x - 18}{2} = 6x$

18. $\dfrac{7}{8}(x - 4) = 5x - \dfrac{7}{2}$

Solve each equation for the variable indicated.

19. $d = rt$; for t

20. $P = 2l + 2w$; for l

21. $A = 2\pi rh$; for h

22. $A = P + Prt$; for r

23. Find x.

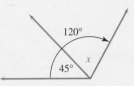

24. Find the supplement of a $105°$ angle.

25. Investing   A student invests part of $10,000 at 6% annual interest and the rest at 5%. If the annual income from these investments is $560, how much was invested at each rate?

26. Traveling   A car leaves Rockford at the rate of 65 mph, bound for Madison. At the same time, a truck leaves Madison at the rate of 55 mph, bound for Rockford. If the cities are 72 miles apart, how long will it take for the car and the truck to meet?

27. Mixing solutions   How many liters of water must be added to 30 liters of a 10% brine solution to dilute it to an 8% solution?

28. Mixing nuts   Twenty pounds of cashews are to be mixed with peanuts to make a mixture that will sell for $4 per pound. How many pounds of peanuts should be used?

	Price per pound
Cashews	$6
Peanuts	$3

Graph the solution of each inequality.

29. $8x - 20 \geq 4$

30. $x - 2(x + 7) > 14$

31. $-4 \leq 2(x + 1) < 10$

32. $-2 < 5(x - 1) \leq 10$

Cumulative Review Exercises

Classify each number as an integer, a rational number, an irrational number, and/or a real number. Each number may be in several classifications.

1. $\dfrac{27}{9}$

2. -0.25

Graph each set of numbers on the number line.

3. The natural numbers between 2 and 7

$$\overset{1\quad 2\quad 3\quad 4\quad 5\quad 6\quad 7}{\xleftarrow{\hspace{4cm}}}$$

4. The real numbers between 2 and 7

Simplify each expression.

5. $\dfrac{|-3| - |3|}{|-3 - 3|}$

  $2\dfrac{3}{5} + 5\dfrac{1}{2}$

6. $\dfrac{5}{7} \cdot \dfrac{14}{3}$

  $35.7 - 0.05$

Let $x = -5$, $y = 3$, and $z = 0$, and evaluate each expression.

9. $(3x - 2y)z$

10. $\dfrac{x - 3y + |z|}{2 - x}$

11. $x^2 - y^2 + z^2$

12. $\dfrac{x}{y} + \dfrac{y + 2}{3 - z}$

13. What is $7\frac{1}{2}\%$ of 330?

14. 1,688 is 32% of what number?

Consider the algebraic expression $3x^3 + 5x^2y + 37y$.

15. Find the coefficient of the second term.

16. List the factors of the third term.

Simplify each expression.

17. $3x - 5x + 2y$

18. $3(x - 7) + 2(8 - x)$

19. $2x^2y^3 - 4x^2y^3$

20. $2(3 - x) + 5(x + 2)$

Solve each equation and check the result.

21. $3(x - 5) + 2 = 2x$

22. $\dfrac{x - 5}{3} - 5 = 7$

23. $\dfrac{2x - 1}{5} = \dfrac{1}{2}$

24. $2(a - 3) - 3(a - 2) = -a$

Solve each formula for the variable indicated.

25. $A = \dfrac{1}{2}h(b + B)$; for h

26. $y = mx + b$; for x

27. Auto sales   An auto dealer's promotional ad appears in the illustration. One car is selling for $23,499. What was the dealer's invoice?

28. Furniture pricing   A sofa and a $300 chair are discounted 35%, and are priced at $780 for both. Find the original price of the sofa.

29. Cost of a car   The total cost of a new car, including an 8.5% sales tax, is $13,725.25. Find the cost before tax.

30. Manufacturing concrete   Concrete contains 3 times as much gravel as cement. How many pounds of cement are in 500 pounds of dry concrete mix?

31. Building construction   A 35-foot beam, 1 foot wide and 2 inches thick, is cut into three sections. One section is 14 feet long. Of the remaining two sections, one is twice as long as the other. Will the shortest section span an 8-foot-wide doorway?

32. Installing solar heating   One solar panel in the illustration is 3.4 feet wider than the other. Find the width of each panel.

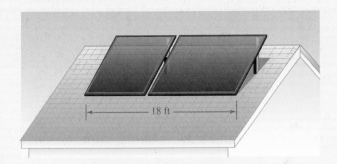

33. Electric bills   An electric company charges $17.50 per month, plus 18¢ for every kwh of energy used. One resident's bill was $43.96. How many kwh were used that month?

34. Installing gutters   A contractor charges $35 for the installation of rain gutters, plus $1.50 per foot. If one installation cost $162.50, how many feet of gutter were required?

Evaluate each expression.

35. $4^2 - 5^2$

36. $(4 - 5)^2$

37. $5(4^3 - 2^3)$

38. $-2(5^4 - 7^3)$

Graph the solutions of each inequality.

39. $8(4 + x) > 10(6 + x)$

40. $-9 < 3(x + 2) \le 3$

©Shutterstock.com/Gina Sanders

Graphing and Solving Systems of Linear Equations and Linear Inequalities

Careers and Mathematics

MARKET AND SURVEY RESEARCHERS

Market and survey researchers gather information about what people think. They help companies understand what types of products people want to buy and at what price. Gathering statistical data on competitors and examining prices, sales, and methods of marketing and distribution, they analyze statistical data on past sales to predict future sales.

Market and survey researchers held about 261,000 jobs in 2006. Prospective researchers should study mathematics, statistics, sampling theory, and survey design. Computer science courses are extremely helpful.

Job Outlook:
Employment of market and survey researchers is projected to grow by 20% in the decade from 2006 to 2016. This is faster than the average for all occupations.

Annual Earnings:
$42,190–$84,070

For More Information:
http://www.bls.gov/oco/ocos013.htm

For a Sample Application:
See Problem 61 in Section 3.6.

In this chapter ▶

Many problems involve linear equations with two variables. In this chapter, we will use the rectangular coordinate system to graph these equations and then consider three methods to solve systems of these equations. Finally, we will use these methods to solve many application problems.

1. Graph ordered pairs and mathematical relationships.
2. Interpret the meaning of graphed data.
3. Interpret information from a step graph.

rectangular coordinate system	y-axis	x-coordinate
Cartesian coordinate system	origin	y-coordinate
perpendicular lines	coordinate plane	coordinates
x-axis	Cartesian plane	ordered pairs
	quadrants	

Graph each set of numbers on the number line.

1. $-2, 1, 3$

2. All numbers greater than -2

3. All numbers less than or equal to 3

4. All numbers between -3 and 2

It is often said, "A picture is worth a thousand words." In this section, we will show how numerical relationships can be described by using mathematical pictures called *graphs*. We also will show how we can obtain important information by reading graphs.

1. Graph ordered pairs and mathematical relationships.

When designing the Gateway Arch in St. Louis, shown in Figure 3-1(a), architects created a mathematical model of the arch called a *graph*. This graph, shown in Figure 3-1(b), is drawn on a grid called the **rectangular coordinate system.** This coordinate system is sometimes called a **Cartesian coordinate system** after the 17th-century French mathematician René Descartes.

A rectangular coordinate system (see Figure 3-2) is formed by two perpendicular number lines. Recall that **perpendicular lines** are lines that meet at a 90° angle.

- The horizontal number line is called the *x*-axis.
- The vertical number line is called the *y*-axis.

The positive direction on the x-axis is to the right, and the positive direction on the y-axis is upward. The scale on each axis should fit the data. For example, the axes of the graph of the arch shown in Figure 3-1(b) are scaled in units of 100 feet. If no scale is indicated on the axes, we assume that the axes are scaled in units of 1.

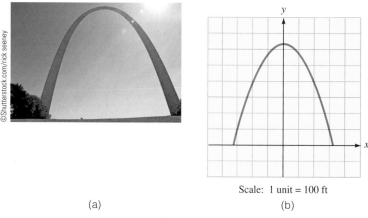

Scale: 1 unit = 100 ft

(a)   (b)

Figure 3-1

The point where the axes cross is called the **origin.** This is the 0 point on each axis. The two axes form a **coordinate plane** (often referred to as the **Cartesian plane**) and divide it into four regions called **quadrants,** which are numbered as shown in Figure 3-2.

**René Descartes
(1596–1650)**

Descartes is famous for his work in philosophy as well as for his work in mathematics. His philosophy is expressed in the words "I think, therefore I am." He is best known in mathematics for his invention of a coordinate system and his work with conic sections.

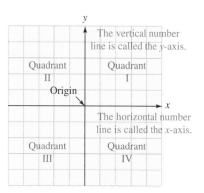

Figure 3-2

Each point in a coordinate plane can be identified by a pair of real numbers x and y, written as (x, y). The first number in the pair is the **x-coordinate,** and the second number is the **y-coordinate.** The numbers are called the **coordinates** of the point. Some examples of ordered pairs are $(3, -4)$, $\left(-1, -\frac{3}{2}\right)$, and $(0, 2.5)$.

$$(3, \ -4)$$
↑   ↑

In an ordered pair, the   The y-coordinate
x-coordinate is listed first.   is listed second.

The process of locating a point in the coordinate plane is called *graphing* or *plotting* the point. In Figure 3-3(a), we show how to graph the point A with coordinates of $(3, -4)$. Since the x-coordinate is positive, we start at the origin and move 3 units to the right along the x-axis. Since the y-coordinate is negative, we then move down 4 units to locate point A. Point A is the *graph* of $(3, -4)$ and lies in quadrant IV.

To plot the point $B(-4, 3)$, we start at the origin, move 4 units to the left along the x-axis, and then move up 3 units to locate point B. Point B lies in quadrant II.

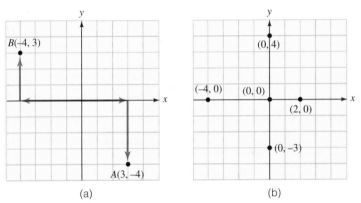

Figure 3-3

COMMENT Note that point A with coordinates of $(3, -4)$ is not the same as point B with coordinates $(-4, 3)$. Since the order of the coordinates of a point is important, we call them **ordered pairs.**

In Figure 3-3(b), we see that the points $(-4, 0)$, $(0, 0)$, and $(2, 0)$ lie on the x-axis. In fact, all points with a y-coordinate of 0 will lie on the x-axis.

From Figure 3-3(b), we also see that the points $(0, -3)$, $(0, 0)$, and $(0, 4)$ lie on the y-axis. All points with an x-coordinate of 0 lie on the y-axis. From the figure, we also can see that the coordinates of the origin are $(0, 0)$.

EXAMPLE 1 **GRAPHING POINTS** Plot the points

a. $A(-2, 3)$ **b.** $B\left(-1, -\frac{3}{2}\right)$ **c.** $C(0, 2.5)$ **d.** $D(4, 2)$

Solution

a. To plot point A with coordinates $(-2, 3)$, we start at the origin, move 2 units to the *left* on the x-axis, and move 3 units *up*. Point A lies in quadrant II. (See Figure 3-4.)

b. To plot point B with coordinates of $\left(-1, -\frac{3}{2}\right)$, we start at the origin and move 1 unit to the *left* and $\frac{3}{2}$ (or $1\frac{1}{2}$) units *down*. Point B lies in quadrant III, as shown in Figure 3-4.

c. To graph point C with coordinates of $(0, 2.5)$, we start at the origin and move 0 units on the x-axis and 2.5 units *up*. Point C lies on the y-axis, as shown in Figure 3-4.

d. To graph point D with coordinates of $(4, 2)$, we start at the origin and move 4 units to the *right* and 2 units *up*. Point D lies in quadrant I, as shown in Figure 3-4.

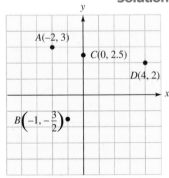

Figure 3-4

➡ **SELF CHECK 1** Plot the points. **a.** $E(2, -2)$ **b.** $F(-4, 0)$ **c.** $G\left(1.5, \frac{5}{2}\right)$ **d.** $H(0, 5)$

EXAMPLE 2   **ORBITS**   The circle shown in Figure 3-5 is an approximate graph of the orbit of the Earth. The graph is made up of infinitely many points, each with its own *x*- and *y*-coordinates. Use the graph to find the approximate coordinates of the Earth's position during the months of February, May, and August.

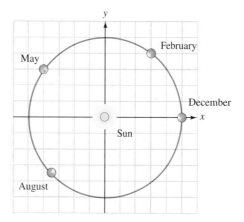

Figure 3-5

Solution   To find the coordinates of each position, we start at the origin and move left or right along the *x*-axis to find the *x*-coordinate and then up or down to find the *y*-coordinate. See Table 3-1.

Month	Position of the Earth on the graph	Coordinates
February	3 units to the *right,* then 4 units *up*	$(3, 4)$
May	4 units to the *left,* then 3 units *up*	$(-4, 3)$
August	3.5 units to the *left,* then 3.5 units *down*	$(-3.5, -3.5)$

Table 3-1

 **SELF CHECK 2**   Find the coordinates of the Earth's position in December.

PERSPECTIVE

As a child, René Descartes was frail and often sick. To improve his health, eight-year-old René was sent to a Jesuit school. The headmaster encouraged him to sleep in the morning as long as he wished. As a young man, Descartes spent several years as a soldier and world traveler, but his interests included mathematics and philosophy, as well as science, literature, writing, and taking it easy. The habit of sleeping late continued throughout his life. He claimed that his most productive thinking occurred when he was lying in bed. According to one story, Descartes first thought of analytic geometry as he watched a fly walking on his bedroom ceiling.

Descartes might have lived longer if he had stayed in bed. In 1649, Queen Christina of Sweden decided that she needed a tutor in philosophy, and she requested the services of Descartes. Tutoring would not have been difficult, except that the queen scheduled her lessons before dawn in her library with her windows open. The cold Stockholm mornings were too much for a man who was used to sleeping past noon. Within a few months, Descartes developed a fever and died, probably of pneumonia.

Every day, we deal with quantities that are related.

- The distance that we travel depends on how fast we are going.
- Our weight depends on how much we eat.
- The amount of water in a tub depends on how long the water has been running.

We often can use graphs to visualize relationships between two quantities. For example, suppose that we know the number of gallons of water that are in a tub at several time intervals after the water has been turned on. We can list that information in a *table of values*. (See Figure 3-6.)

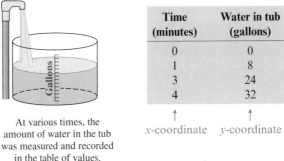

Time (minutes)	Water in tub (gallons)	
0	0	→ (0, 0)
1	8	→ (1, 8)
3	24	→ (3, 24)
4	32	→ (4, 32)

At various times, the amount of water in the tub was measured and recorded in the table of values.

↑ *x*-coordinate   ↑ *y*-coordinate   ↑ The data in the table can be expressed as ordered pairs (x, y).

Figure 3-6

The information in the table can be used to construct a graph that shows the relationship between the amount of water in the tub and the time the water has been running. Since the amount of water in the tub *depends* on the time, we will associate *time* with the *x*-axis and the *amount of water* with the *y*-axis.

To construct the graph in Figure 3-7, we plot the four ordered pairs and draw a line through the resulting data points.

COMMENT Note that the scale for the gallons of water (*y*-axis) is 4 units while the scale for minutes (*x*-axis) is 1 unit. The scales on both axes do not have to be the same, but remember to label them!

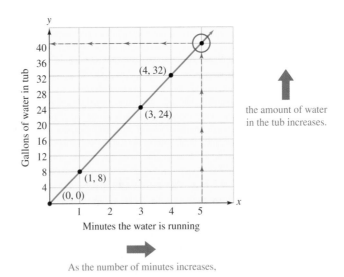

the amount of water in the tub increases.

As the number of minutes increases,

Figure 3-7

From the graph, we can see that the amount of water in the tub increases as the water is allowed to run. We also can use the graph to make observations about the amount of water in the tub at other times. For example, the dashed line on the graph shows that in 5 minutes, the tub will contain 40 gallons of water.

2 Interpret the meaning of graphed data.

In the next example, we show that valuable information can be obtained from reading a graph.

EXAMPLE 3 **READING GRAPHS** The graph in Figure 3-8 shows the number of people in an audience before, during, and after the taping of a television show. On the *x*-axis, 0 represents the time when taping began. Use the graph to answer the following questions, and record each result in a table of values.

a. How many people were in the audience when taping began?

b. What was the size of the audience 10 minutes before taping began?

c. At what times were there exactly 100 people in the audience?

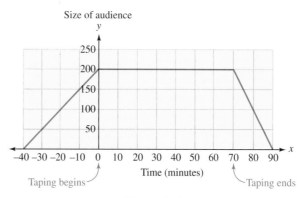

Figure 3-8

Solution

a. The time when taping began is represented by 0 on the *x*-axis. Since the point on the graph directly above 0 has a *y*-coordinate of 200, the point (0, 200) is on the graph. The *y*-coordinate of this point indicates that 200 people were in the audience when the taping began.

Time	Audience
0	200

b. Ten minutes before taping began is represented by −10 on the *x*-axis. Since the point on the graph directly above −10 has a *y*-coordinate of 150, the point (−10, 150) is on the graph. The *y*-coordinate of this point indicates that 150 people were in the audience 10 minutes before the taping began.

Time	Audience
−10	150

c. We can draw a horizontal line passing through 100 on the *y*-axis. Since this line intersects the graph twice, there were two times when 100 people were in the audience. The points (−20, 100) and (80, 100) are on the graph. The *y*-coordinates of these points indicate that there were 100 people in the audience 20 minutes before and 80 minutes after taping began.

Time	Audience
−20	100
80	100

⇨ SELF CHECK 3 Use the graph in Figure 3-8 to answer the following questions.

a. At what times were there exactly 50 people in the audience?

b. What was the size of the audience that watched the taping?

c. How long did it take for the audience to leave the studio after taping ended?

3 **Interpret information from a step graph.**

The graph in Figure 3-9 shows the cost of renting a trailer for different periods of time. For example, the cost of renting the trailer for 4 days is $60, which is the *y*-coordinate of the point with coordinates of (4, 60). For renting the trailer for a period lasting over 4 and up to 5 days, the cost jumps to $70. Since the jumps in cost form steps in the graph, we call the graph a *step graph*.

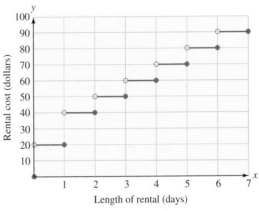

Length of rental (days)

Figure 3-9

EXAMPLE 4   **STEP GRAPHS**   Use the information in Figure 3-9 to answer the following questions. Write the results in a table of values.

a. Find the cost of renting the trailer for 2 days.

b. Find the cost of renting the trailer for $5\frac{1}{2}$ days.

c. How long can you rent the trailer if you have $50?

d. Is the rental cost per day the same?

Solution   **a.** We locate 2 days on the *x*-axis and move up to locate the point on the graph directly above the 2. Since the point has coordinates (2, 40), a two-day rental would cost $40. We enter this ordered pair in Table 3-2.

b. We locate $5\frac{1}{2}$ days on the *x*-axis and move straight up to locate the point on the graph with coordinates $\left(5\frac{1}{2}, 80\right)$, which indicates that a $5\frac{1}{2}$-day rental would cost $80. We enter this ordered pair in Table 3-2.

c. We draw a horizontal line through the point labeled 50 on the *y*-axis. Since this line intersects one step of the graph, we can look down to the *x*-axis to find the *x*-values that correspond to a *y*-value of 50. From the graph, we see that the trailer can be rented for more than 2 and up to 3 days for $50. We write (3, 50) in Table 3-2.

d. No, the cost per day is not the same. If we look at the *y*-coordinates, we see that for the first day, the rental fee is $20. For the second day, the cost jumps another $20. For the third day, and all subsequent days, the cost jumps only $10.

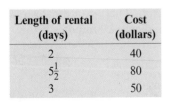

Length of rental (days)	Cost (dollars)
2	40
$5\frac{1}{2}$	80
3	50

Table 3-2

⇨ **SELF CHECK ANSWERS**

1.

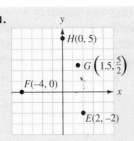

2. (5, 0)   **3. a.** 30 min before and 85 min after taping began   **b.** 200
c. 20 min

NOW TRY THIS

1. Find three ordered pairs that represent the information stated below.

Damon paid $1,150 for 2 airline tickets. Javier paid $1,250 for 3 tickets, and Caroline paid $1,400 for 4 tickets.

Because the size of some data is large, we sometimes insert a // (break) symbol on the x- and/or y-axis of the rectangular coordinate system near the origin to indicate that the designated scale does not begin until the first value is listed.

2. Plot the points from Problem 1 on a single set of coordinate axes with an appropriate scale.

3.1 EXERCISES

WARM-UPS

1. Explain why the pair $(-2, 4)$ is called an ordered pair.
2. At what point do the coordinate axes intersect?
3. In which quadrant does the graph of $(3, -5)$ lie?
4. On which axis does the point $(0, 5)$ lie?

REVIEW

5. Evaluate: $-3 - 3(-5)$.
6. Evaluate: $(-5)^2 + (-5)$.
7. What is the opposite of -8?
8. Simplify: $|-1 - 9|$.
9. Solve: $-4x + 7 = -21$.
10. Solve $P = 2l + 2w$ for w.
11. Evaluate $(x + 1)(x + y)^2$ for $x = -2$ and $y = -5$.
12. Simplify: $-6(x - 3) - 2(1 - x)$.

VOCABULARY AND CONCEPTS

Fill in the blanks.

13. The pair of numbers $(-1, -5)$ is called an _____.
14. In the _____ $\left(-\frac{3}{2}, -5\right)$, $-\frac{3}{2}$ is called the ___coordinate and -5 is called the ___coordinate.
15. The point with coordinates $(0, 0)$ is the _____.
16. The x- and y-axes divide the _____ into four regions called _____.
17. The point with coordinates $(4, 2)$ can be graphed on a _____ or _____ coordinate system.
18. The rectangular coordinate system is formed by two _____ number lines called the ___ and ___axes.
19. The values x and y in the ordered pair (x, y) are called the _____ of its corresponding point.
20. The process of locating the position of a point on a coordinate plane is called _____ the point.

Answer the question or fill in the blanks.

21. Do $(3, 2)$ and $(2, 3)$ represent the same point?
22. In the ordered pair $(4, 5)$, is 4 associated with the horizontal or the vertical axis?

23. To plot the point with coordinates $(-5, 4.5)$, we start at the _____, move 5 units to the ____, and then move 4.5 units ___.

24. To plot the point with coordinates $\left(6, -\frac{3}{2}\right)$, we start at the _____, move 6 units to the _____, and then move $\frac{3}{2}$ units _____.

25. In which quadrant do points with a negative x-coordinate and a positive y-coordinate lie?

26. In which quadrant do points with a positive x-coordinate and a negative y-coordinate lie?

GUIDED PRACTICE

Graph each point on the coordinate grid. **See Example 1.** (Objective 1)

27. $A(-3, 4)$, $B(4, 3.5)$, $C\left(-2, -\frac{5}{2}\right)$, $D(0, -4)$, $E\left(\frac{3}{2}, 0\right)$, $F(3, -4)$

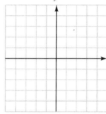

28. $G(4, 4)$, $H(0.5, -3)$, $I(-4, -4)$, $J(0, -1)$, $K(0, 0)$, $L(0, 3)$, $M(-2, 0)$

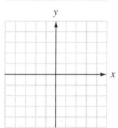

Use each graph to complete the table. **See Example 2.** (Objective 1)

29. Use the graph to complete the table.

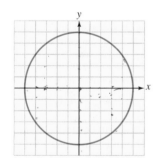

x	y
4	3
0	5
-3	4
5	0
-4	-3
0	-5
3	-4

30. Use the graph to complete the table.

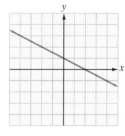

x	y
	0
	2
	-1
-4	
	1

The graph in the illustration gives the heart rate of a woman before, during, and after an aerobic workout. Use the graph to answer the following questions. **See Example 3.** (Objective 2)

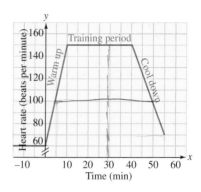

31. What information does the point $(-10, 60)$ give us?

32. After beginning the workout, how long did it take the woman to reach her training-zone heart rate?

33. What was her heart rate one-half hour after beginning the workout?

34. For how long did she work out at the training-zone level?

35. At what times was her heart rate 100 beats per minute?

36. How long was her cool-down period?

37. What was the difference in her heart rate before the workout and after the cool-down period?

38. What was her approximate heart rate 8 minutes after beginning?

Use the corresponding graphs to answer the questions. **See Example 4.** (Objective 3)

DVD rentals   The charges for renting a movie are shown in the graph in the illustration.

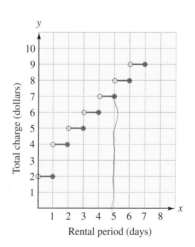

39. Find the charge for a 1-day rental.

40. Find the charge for a 2-day rental.

41. Find the charge if the DVD is kept for 5 days.

42. Find the charge if the DVD is kept for a week.

Postage rates   The graph shown in the illustration gives the first-class postage rates for mailing letters weighing up to 3.5 ounces.

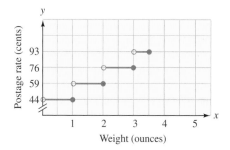

43. Find the cost of postage to mail each of the following letters first class: 1-ounce; $2\frac{1}{2}$-ounce.

44. Find the cost of postage to mail each of the following letters first class: 1.5-ounce; 3.25-ounce.

45. Find the difference in postage for a 0.75-ounce letter and a 2.75-ounce letter.

46. What is the heaviest letter that can be mailed for 59¢?

APPLICATIONS

47. Road maps   Road maps usually have a coordinate system to help locate cities. Use the map in the illustration to locate Carbondale, Champaign, Chicago, Peoria, Rockford, Springfield, and St. Louis. Express each answer in the form (number, letter).

48. Battling Ships   In a computer game of Battling Ships, players use coordinates to drop depth charges from a battle-ship to hit a hidden submarine. What coordinates should be used to make three hits on the exposed submarine shown in the illustration? Express each answer in the form (letter, number).

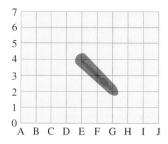

49. Water pressure   The graphs in the illustration show the paths of two streams of water from the same hose held at two different angles.

   a. At which angle does the stream of water shoot higher? How much higher?

   b. At which angle does the stream of water shoot out farther? How much farther?

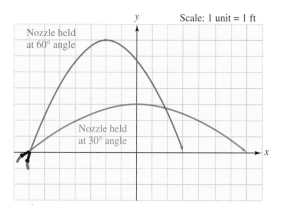

50. Golf swings   To correct her swing, a golfer was videotaped and then had her image displayed on a computer monitor so that it could be analyzed by a golf pro. See the illustration. Give the coordinates of the points that are highlighted on the arc of her swing.

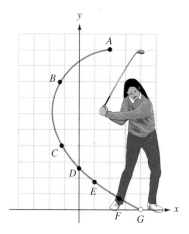

51. Gas mileage The table in the illustration gives the number of miles (y) that a truck can be driven on x gallons of gasoline. Plot the ordered pairs and draw a line connecting the points.

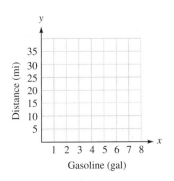

Gallons	Miles
2	10
3	15
5	25

a. Estimate how far the truck can go on 7 gallons of gasoline.

b. How many gallons of gas are needed to travel a distance of 20 miles?

c. Estimate how far the truck can go on 6.5 gallons of gasoline.

52. Wages The table in the illustration gives the amount y (in dollars) that a student can earn by working x hours. Plot the ordered pairs and draw a line connecting the points.

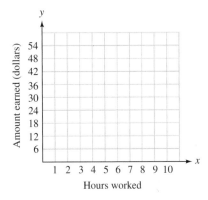

Hours	Dollars
3	18
6	36
7	42

a. How much will the student earn in 5 hours?

b. How long would the student have to work to earn $12?

c. Estimate how much the student will earn in 3.5 hours.

53. Value of a car The table in the illustration shows the value y (in thousands of dollars) of a car that is x years old. Plot the ordered pairs and draw a line connecting the points.

a. What does the point (3, 7) on the graph tell you?

b. Estimate the value of the car when it is 7 years old.

c. After how many years will the car be worth $2,500?

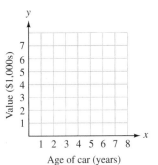

Years	Value (in thousands)
3	7
4	5.5
5	4

54. Depreciation As a piece of farm machinery gets older, it loses value. The table in the illustration shows the value y of a tractor that is x years old. Plot the ordered pairs and draw a line connecting them.

a. What does the point (0, 9) on the graph tell you?

b. Estimate the value of the tractor in 3 years.

c. When will the tractor's value fall below $30,000?

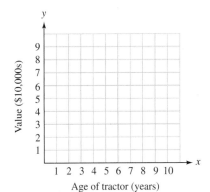

Years	Value
0	9
6	5
9	3

WRITING ABOUT MATH

55. Explain why the point with coordinates $(-3, 3)$ is not the same as the point with coordinates $(3, -3)$.

56. Explain what is meant when we say that the rectangular coordinate graph of the St. Louis Arch is made up of *infinitely many* points.

57. Explain how to plot the point with coordinates $(-2, 5)$.

58. Explain why the coordinates of the origin are $(0, 0)$.

SOMETHING TO THINK ABOUT

59. Could you have a coordinate system in which the coordinate axes were not perpendicular? How would it be different?

60. René Descartes is famous for saying, "I think, therefore I am." What do you think he meant by that?

**SECTION
3.2**

Graphing Linear Equations

Objectives

1. Determine whether an ordered pair satisfies an equation in two variables.
2. Construct a table of values given an equation.
3. Graph a linear equation in two variables by constructing a table of values.
4. Graph a linear equation in two variables using the intercept method.
5. Graph a horizontal line and a vertical line.
6. Write a linear equation in two variables from given information, graph the equation, and interpret the graphed data.

Vocabulary

input value   independent variable y-intercept
output value x-intercept   general form
dependent variable

Getting Ready

In Problems 1–4, let $y = 2x + 1$.

1. Find y when $x = 0$.
2. Find y when $x = 2$.
3. Find y when $x = -2$.
4. Find y when $x = \frac{1}{2}$.
5. Find five pairs of numbers with a sum of 8.
6. Find five pairs of numbers with a difference of 5.

In this section, we will discuss how to graph linear equations. We will then show how to make tables and graphs with a graphing calculator.

1   Determine whether an ordered pair satisfies an equation in two variables.

The equation $x + 2y = 5$ contains the two variables x and y. The solutions of such equations are ordered pairs of numbers. For example, the ordered pair $(1, 2)$ is a solution, because the equation is satisfied when $x = 1$ and $y = 2$.

$$x + 2y = 5$$
$$1 + 2(2) = 5 \quad \text{Substitute 1 for } x \text{ and 2 for } y.$$
$$1 + 4 = 5$$
$$5 = 5$$

EXAMPLE 1   Is the pair $(-2, 4)$ a solution of $y = 3x + 9$?

Solution   We substitute -2 for x and 4 for y and see whether the resulting equation is true.

$$y = 3x + 9 \qquad \text{This is the original equation.}$$
$$4 \stackrel{?}{=} 3(-2) + 9 \qquad \text{Substitute } -2 \text{ for } x \text{ and } 4 \text{ for } y.$$
$$4 \stackrel{?}{=} -6 + 9 \qquad \text{Do the multiplication: } 3(-2) = -6.$$
$$4 = 3 \qquad \text{Do the addition: } -6 + 9 = 3.$$

Since the equation $4 = 3$ is false, the pair $(-2, 4)$ is not a solution.

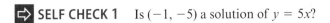 **SELF CHECK 1**   Is $(-1, -5)$ a solution of $y = 5x$?

---

2 **Construct a table of values given an equation.**

To find solutions of equations in x and y, we can pick numbers at random, substitute them for x, and find the corresponding values of y. For example, to find some ordered pairs that satisfy $y = 5 - x$, we can let $x = 1$ (called the **input value**), substitute 1 for x, and solve for y (called the **output value**).

(1)

$y = 5 - x$		
x	y	(x, y)
1	4	$(1, 4)$

$$y = 5 - x \qquad \text{This is the original equation.}$$
$$y = 5 - 1 \qquad \text{Substitute the input value of 1 for } x.$$
$$y = 4 \qquad \text{The output is 4.}$$

The ordered pair $(1, 4)$ is a solution. As we find solutions, we will list them in a *table of values* like Table (1) at the left.
    If $x = 2$, we have

(2)

$y = 5 - x$		
x	y	(x, y)
1	4	$(1, 4)$
2	3	$(2, 3)$

$$y = 5 - x \qquad \text{This is the original equation.}$$
$$y = 5 - 2 \qquad \text{Substitute the input value of 2 for } x.$$
$$y = 3 \qquad \text{The output is 3.}$$

A second solution is $(2, 3)$. We list it in Table (2) at the left.
    If $x = 5$, we have

(3)

$y = 5 - x$		
x	y	(x, y)
1	4	$(1, 4)$
2	3	$(2, 3)$
5	0	$(5, 0)$

$$y = 5 - x \qquad \text{This is the original equation.}$$
$$y = 5 - 5 \qquad \text{Substitute the input value of 5 for } x.$$
$$y = 0 \qquad \text{The output is 0.}$$

A third solution is $(5, 0)$. We list it in Table (3) at the left.
    If $x = -1$, we have

(4)

$y = 5 - x$		
x	y	(x, y)
1	4	$(1, 4)$
2	3	$(2, 3)$
5	0	$(5, 0)$
-1	6	$(-1, 6)$

$$y = 5 - x \qquad \text{This is the original equation.}$$
$$y = 5 - (-1) \qquad \text{Substitute the input value of } -1 \text{ for } x.$$
$$y = 6 \qquad \text{The output is 6.}$$

A fourth solution is $(-1, 6)$. We list it in Table (4) at the left.
    If $x = 6$, we have

(5)

$y = 5 - x$		
x	y	(x, y)
1	4	$(1, 4)$
2	3	$(2, 3)$
5	0	$(5, 0)$
-1	6	$(-1, 6)$
6	-1	$(6, -1)$

$$y = 5 - x \qquad \text{This is the original equation.}$$
$$y = 5 - 6 \qquad \text{Substitute the input value of 6 for } x.$$
$$y = -1 \qquad \text{The output is } -1.$$

A fifth solution is $(6, -1)$. We list it in Table (5) at the left.
    Since we can choose any real number for x, and since any choice of x will give a corresponding value of y, we can see that the equation $y = 5 - x$ has *infinitely many solutions*.

3 **Graph a linear equation in two variables by constructing a table of values.**

A *linear equation* is any equation that can be written in the form $Ax + By = C$, where A, B, and C are real numbers and A and B are not both 0. To graph the equation $y = 5 - x$, we plot the ordered pairs listed in the table on a rectangular coordinate system, as in Figure 3-10. From the figure, we can see that the five points lie on a line.

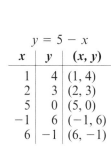

$y = 5 - x$		
x	y	(x, y)
1	4	$(1, 4)$
2	3	$(2, 3)$
5	0	$(5, 0)$
-1	6	$(-1, 6)$
6	-1	$(6, -1)$

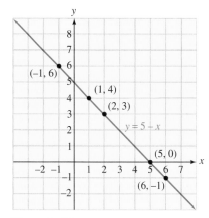

Figure 3-10

We draw a line through the points. The arrowheads on the line show that the graph continues forever in both directions. Since the graph of any solution of $y = 5 - x$ will lie on this line, the line is a picture of all of the solutions of the equation. The line is said to be the *graph* of the equation.

Any equation, such as $y = 5 - x$, whose graph is a line is called a **linear equation in two variables.** Any point on the line has coordinates that satisfy the equation, and the graph of any pair (x, y) that satisfies the equation is a point on the line.

Since we usually will choose a number for x first and then find the corresponding value of y, the value of y depends on x. For this reason, we call y the **dependent variable** and x the **independent variable.** The value of the independent variable is the input value, and the value of the dependent variable is the output value.

Although only two points are needed to graph a linear equation, we often plot a third point as a check. If the three points do not lie on a line, at least one of them is in error.

Graphing Linear Equations

1. Find two pairs (x, y) that satisfy the equation by picking arbitrary input values for x and solving for the corresponding output values of y. A third point provides a check.
2. Plot each resulting pair (x, y) on a rectangular coordinate system. If they do not lie on a line, check your calculations.
3. Draw the line passing through the points.

EXAMPLE 2   Graph by constructing a table of values and plotting points: $y = 3x - 4$.

Solution   We find three ordered pairs that satisfy the equation.

$$\textbf{If } x = 1 \qquad \textbf{If } x = 2 \qquad \textbf{If } x = 3$$

If x = 1	If x = 2	If x = 3
$y = 3x - 4$	$y = 3x - 4$	$y = 3x - 4$
$y = 3(1) - 4$	$y = 3(2) - 4$	$y = 3(3) - 4$
$y = -1$	$y = 2$	$y = 5$

We enter the results in a table of values, plot the points, and draw a line through the points. The graph appears in Figure 3-11.

$y = 3x - 4$

x	y	(x, y)
1	-1	$(1, -1)$
2	2	$(2, 2)$
3	5	$(3, 5)$

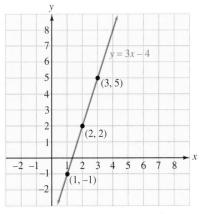

Figure 3-11

➡ **SELF CHECK 2**   Graph: $y = 3x$.

EXAMPLE 3   Graph by constructing a table of values and plotting points: $y = -0.4x + 2$.

Solution   We find three ordered pairs that satisfy the equation.

If x = −5	If x = 0	If x = 5
$y = -0.4x + 2$	$y = -0.4x + 2$	$y = -0.4x + 2$
$y = -0.4(-5) + 2$	$y = -0.4(0) + 2$	$y = -0.4(5) + 2$
$y = 2 + 2$	$y = 2$	$y = -2 + 2$
$y = 4$		$y = 0$

We enter the results in a table of values, plot the points, and draw a line through the points. The graph appears in Figure 3-12.

$y = -0.4x + 2$

x	y	(x, y)
-5	4	$(-5, 4)$
0	2	$(0, 2)$
5	0	$(5, 0)$

Figure 3-12

➡ **SELF CHECK 3**   Graph: $y = 1.5x - 2$.

EXAMPLE 4   Graph by constructing a table of values and plotting points: $y - 4 = \frac{1}{2}(x - 8)$.

Solution   We first solve for y and simplify.

$$y - 4 = \frac{1}{2}(x - 8)$$

$$y - 4 = \frac{1}{2}x - 4 \qquad \text{Use the distributive property to remove parentheses.}$$

$$y = \frac{1}{2}x \qquad \text{Add 4 to both sides.}$$

We now find three ordered pairs that satisfy the equation.

If $x = 0$	**If $x = 2$**	**If $x = -4$**
$y = \frac{1}{2}x$	$y = \frac{1}{2}x$	$y = \frac{1}{2}x$
$y = \frac{1}{2}(0)$	$y = \frac{1}{2}(2)$	$y = \frac{1}{2}(-4)$
$y = 0$	$y = 1$	$y = -2$

We enter the results in a table of values, plot the points, and draw a line through the points. The graph appears in Figure 3-13.

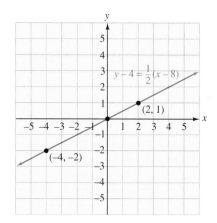

$$y - 4 = \frac{1}{2}(x - 8)$$

x	y	(x, y)
0	0	$(0, 0)$
2	1	$(2, 1)$
-4	-2	$(-4, -2)$

Figure 3-13

⇨ **SELF CHECK 4**   Graph: $y + 3 = \frac{1}{3}(x - 6)$.

4   Graph a linear equation in two variables using the intercept method.

The points where a line intersects the x- and y-axes are called **intercepts** of the line.

x- and y-Intercepts

The **x-intercept** of a line is a point $(a, 0)$ where the line intersects the x-axis. (See Figure 3-14.) To find a, substitute 0 for y in the equation of the line and solve for x.

A **y-intercept** of a line is a point $(0, b)$ where the line intersects the y-axis. To find b, substitute 0 for x in the equation of the line and solve for y.

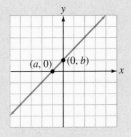

Figure 3-14

Plotting the x- and y-intercepts and drawing a line through them is called the **intercept method of graphing a line.** This method is useful for graphing equations written in *general form.*

General Form of the Equation of a Line

If A, B, and C are real numbers and A and B are not both 0, then the equation

$$Ax + By = C$$

is called the **general form** of the equation of a line.

COMMENT Whenever possible, we will write the general form $Ax + By = C$ so that A, B, and C are integers and $A \geq 0$. We also will make A, B, and C as small as possible. For example, the equation $6x + 12y = 24$ can be changed to $x + 2y = 4$ by dividing both sides by 6.

EXAMPLE 5 Graph by using the intercept method: $3x + 2y = 6$.

Solution To find the y-intercept, we let $x = 0$ and solve for y.

$$3x + 2y = 6$$
$$3(0) + 2y = 6 \qquad \text{Substitute 0 for } x.$$
$$2y = 6 \qquad \text{Simplify.}$$
$$y = 3 \qquad \text{Divide both sides by 2.}$$

The y-intercept is the point with coordinates $(0, 3)$. To find the x-intercept, we let $y = 0$ and solve for x.

$$3x + 2y = 6$$
$$3x + 2(0) = 6 \qquad \text{Substitute 0 for } y.$$
$$3x = 6 \qquad \text{Simplify.}$$
$$x = 2 \qquad \text{Divide both sides by 3.}$$

The x-intercept is the point with coordinates $(2, 0)$. As a check, we plot one more point. If $x = 4$, then

$$3x + 2y = 6$$
$$3(4) + 2y = 6 \qquad \text{Substitute 4 for } x.$$
$$12 + 2y = 6 \qquad \text{Simplify.}$$

$$2y = -6 \quad \text{Subtract 12 from both sides.}$$

$$y = -3 \quad \text{Divide both sides by 2.}$$

The point $(4, -3)$ is on the graph. We plot these three points and join them with a line. The graph of $3x + 2y = 6$ is shown in Figure 3-15.

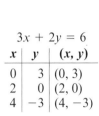

$$3x + 2y = 6$$

x	y	(x, y)
0	3	$(0, 3)$
2	0	$(2, 0)$
4	-3	$(4, -3)$

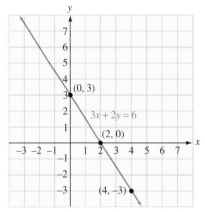

Figure 3-15

⇨ **SELF CHECK 5**   Graph: $4x + 3y = 6$.

---

5   **Graph a horizontal line and a vertical line.**

Equations such as $y = 3$ and $x = -2$ are linear equations, because they can be written in the general form $Ax + By = C$.

$$y = 3 \qquad \text{is equivalent to} \qquad 0x + 1y = 3$$

$$x = -2 \qquad \text{is equivalent to} \qquad 1x + 0y = -2$$

Next, we discuss how to graph these types of linear equations.

EXAMPLE 6   Graph: **a.** $y = 3$ **b.** $x = -2$.

Solution   **a.** We can write the equation $y = 3$ in general form as $0x + y = 3$. Since the coefficient of x is 0, the numbers chosen for x have no effect on y. The value of y is always 3. For example, if we substitute -3 for x, we get

$$0x + y = 3$$

$$0(-3) + y = 3$$

$$0 + y = 3$$

$$y = 3$$

The table in Figure 3-16(a) on the next page gives several pairs that satisfy the equation $y = 3$. After plotting these pairs and joining them with a line, we see that the graph of $y = 3$ is a horizontal line that intersects the y-axis at 3. The y-intercept is $(0, 3)$. There is no x-intercept.

b. We can write $x = -2$ in general form as $x + 0y = -2$. Since the coefficient of y is 0, the values of y have no effect on x. The value of x is always -2. A table of values and the graph are shown in Figure 3-16(b). The graph of $x = -2$ is a vertical line that intersects the x-axis at -2. The x-intercept is $(-2, 0)$. There is no y-intercept.

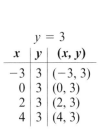

x	y	(x, y)
-3	3	$(-3, 3)$
0	3	$(0, 3)$
2	3	$(2, 3)$
4	3	$(4, 3)$

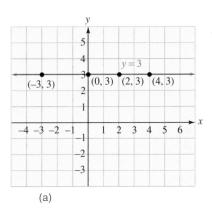

(a)

$x = -2$

x	y	(x, y)
-2	-2	$(-2, -2)$
-2	0	$(-2, 0)$
-2	2	$(-2, 2)$
-2	3	$(-2, 3)$

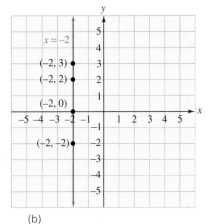

(b)

Figure 3-16

⇨ **SELF CHECK 6**   Identify the graph of each equation as a horizontal or a vertical line:
a. $x = 5$ **b.** $y = -3$ **c.** $x = 0$

From the results of Example 6, we have the following facts.

Equations of Horizontal and Vertical Lines	The equation $y = b$ represents a horizontal line that intersects the y-axis at $(0, b)$. If $b = 0$, the line is the x-axis.
	The equation $x = a$ represents a vertical line that intersects the x-axis at $(a, 0)$. If $a = 0$, the line is the y-axis.

6   **Write a linear equation in two variables from given information, graph the equation, and interpret the graphed data.**

In Chapter 2, we solved application problems using one variable. In the next example, we will write an equation containing two variables to describe an application problem and then graph the equation.

EXAMPLE 7   **BIRTHDAY PARTIES**   A restaurant offers a party package that includes food, drinks, cake, and party favors for a cost of $25 plus $3 per child. Write a linear equation that will give the cost for a party of any size. Then graph the equation.

Solution   We can let c represent the cost of the party and n represent the number of children attending. Then c will be the sum of the basic charge of $25 and the cost per child times the number of children attending.

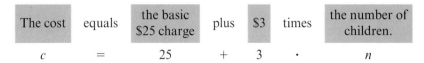

The cost	equals	the basic $25 charge	plus	$3	times	the number of children.
c	$=$	25	$+$	3	$\cdot$	n

For the equation $c = 25 + 3n$, the independent variable (input) is n, the number of children. The dependent variable (output) is c, the cost of the party. We will find three points on the graph of the equation by choosing n-values of 0, 5, and 10 and finding the corresponding c-values. The results are recorded in the table.

$c = 25 + 3n$

n	c
0	25
5	40
10	55

If $n = 0$
$c = 25 + 3(0)$
$c = 25$

If $n = 5$
$c = 25 + 3(5)$
$c = 25 + 15$
$c = 40$

If $n = 10$
$c = 25 + 3(10)$
$c = 25 + 30$
$c = 55$

Next, we graph the points in Figure 3-17 and draw a line through them. We don't draw an arrowhead on the left, because it doesn't make sense to have a *negative* number of children attend a party.

We can use the graph to determine the cost of a party of any size. For example, to use the graph to find the cost of a party with 8 children, we locate 8 on the horizontal axis and then move up to find a point on the graph directly above the 8. Since the coordinates of that point are (8, 49), the cost for 8 children would be $49.

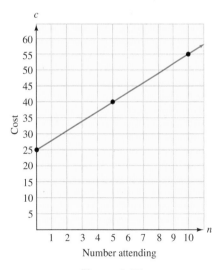

Figure 3-17

COMMENT   The scale for the cost (y-axis) is 5 units and the scale for the number attending (x-axis) is 1. Since the scales on the x- and y-axes are not the same, you must label them!

Making Tables and Graphs

The TI-84 Plus graphing calculator, shown above, is keystroke-for-keystroke compatible with the TI-83 Plus.

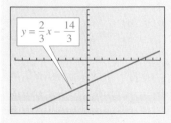

Figure 3-19

So far, we have graphed equations by making tables and plotting points. This method is often tedious and time-consuming. Fortunately, making tables and graphing equations is easier when we use a graphing calculator.

Although we will use calculators to make tables and graph equations, we will not show complete keystrokes for any specific brand of calculator. For these details, please consult your owner's manual.

All graphing calculators have a *viewing window* that is used to display tables and graphs. We will first discuss how to make tables and then discuss how to draw graphs.

MAKING TABLES To construct a table of values for the equation $y = x^2$, simply press the **Y =** key, enter the expression x^2, and press the **2nd** and **TABLE** keys to get a screen similar to Figure 3-18(a). You can use the up and down keys to scroll through the table to obtain a screen like Figure 3-18(b).

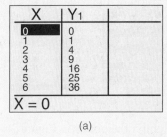

(a)   (b)

Figure 3-18

DRAWING GRAPHS To see the proper picture of a graph, we must often set the minimum and maximum values for the x- and y-coordinates. The standard window settings of

$$Xmin = -10 \qquad Xmax = 10 \qquad Ymin = -10 \qquad Ymax = -10$$

indicate that -10 is the minimum x- and y-coordinate to be used in the graph, and that 10 is the maximum x- and y-coordinate to be used. We will usually express window values in interval notation. In this notation, the standard settings are

$$X = [-10, 10] \qquad Y = [-10, 10]$$

To graph the equation $2x - 3y = 14$ with a calculator, we must first solve the equation for y.

$$2x - 3y = 14$$
$$-3y = -2x + 14 \qquad \text{Subtract } 2x \text{ from both sides.}$$
$$y = \frac{2}{3}x - \frac{14}{3} \qquad \text{Divide both sides by } -3.$$

We now set the standard window values of $X = [-10, 10]$ and $Y = [-10, 10]$, press the **Y =** key and enter the equation as $(2/3)x - 14/3$, and press **GRAPH** to get the line shown in Figure 3-19.

COMMENT To graph an equation with a graphing calculator, the equation must be solved for y.

USING THE TRACE AND ZOOM FEATURES With the trace feature, we can approximate the coordinates of any point on a graph. For example, to find the x-intercept of the line shown in Figure 3-19, we press the **TRACE** key and move the flashing cursor along the line until we approach the x-intercept, as shown in Figure 3-20(a). The x- and y-coordinates of the flashing cursor appear at the bottom of the screen.

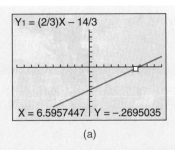
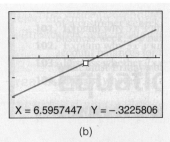
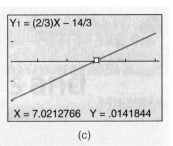

(a)   (b)   (c)

Figure 3-20

To get better results, we can press the **ZOOM** key to see a magnified picture of the line, as shown in Figure 3-20(b). We can trace again and move the cursor even closer to the *x*-intercept, as shown in Figure 3-20(c). Since the *y*-coordinate shown on the screen is close to 0, the *x*-coordinate shown on the screen is close to the *x*-value of the *x*-intercept. Repeated zooms will show that the *x*-intercept is (7, 0).

To get exact results, we can use the ZERO (ROOT) or INTERSECT feature of the calculator. Keystrokes for the TI-83/84 family of calculators can be found in the removeable card attached to the book. For other calculators, refer to the owner's manual for specific keystrokes.

⇨ **SELF CHECK ANSWERS**   **1.** yes   **2.**   **3.**   **4.**

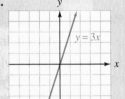

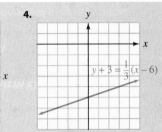

5.   **6. a.** vertical   **b.** horizontal   **c.** vertical

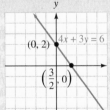

NOW TRY THIS

1. Given $8x - 7y = 12$, complete the ordered pair $(-2,)$ that satisfies the equation.

2. Graph $y - 5 = 0$.

3. Graph $y = x$.

4. Identify the *x*-intercept and the *y*-intercept of $y = \frac{2}{3}x + 8$.

3.2 EXERCISES

WARM-UPS

1. How many points should be plotted to graph a line?
2. Define the intercepts of a line.
3. Find three pairs (x, y) that satisfy $x + y = 8$.
4. Find three pairs (x, y) that satisfy $x - y = 6$.
5. Which lines have no y-intercepts?
6. Which lines have no x-intercepts?

REVIEW

7. Solve: $\dfrac{x}{8} = -12$.
8. Combine like terms: $3t - 4T + 5T - 6t$.
9. Is $\dfrac{x + 5}{6}$ an expression or an equation?
10. Write the formula used to find the perimeter of a rectangle.

11. What number is 0.5% of 250?
12. Solve: $-3x + 5 > 17$.
13. Subtract: $-2.5 - (-2.6)$.
14. Evaluate: $(-5)^3$.

VOCABULARY AND CONCEPTS   *Fill in the blanks.*

15. The equation $y = x + 1$ is an equation in _____ variables.
16. An ordered pair is a _____ of an equation if the numbers in the ordered pair satisfy the equation.
17. In equations containing the variables x and y, x is called the _____ variable and y is called the _____ variable.
18. When constructing a _____ of values, the values of x are the _____ values and the values of y are the _____ values.
19. An equation whose graph is a line and whose variables are to the first power is called a _____ equation.
20. The equation $Ax + By = C$ is the _____ form of the equation of a line.
21. The _____ of a line is the point $(0, b)$, where the line intersects the y-axis.
22. The _____ of a line is the point $(a, 0)$, where the line intersects the x-axis.

GUIDED PRACTICE

Determine whether the ordered pair satisfies the equation.
See Example 1. (Objective 1)

23. $x - 2y = -4$; $(4, 4)$
24. $y = 8x - 5$; $(4, 26)$

25. $y = \dfrac{2}{3}x + 5$; $(6, 12)$
26. $y = -\dfrac{1}{2}x - 2$; $(4, -4)$

Complete each table of values. Check your work with a graphing calculator. (Objective 2)

27. $y = x - 3$

x	y	(x, y)
0		
1		
-2		
-4		

28. $y = x + 2$

x	y	(x, y)
0		
-1		
-2		
3		

29. $y = -2x$

x	y	(x, y)
0		
1		
3		
-2		

30. $y = -1.7x + 2$

x	y	(x, y)
-3		
-1		
0		
3		

 Graph each equation by constructing a table of values and then plotting the points. Check your work with a graphing calculator. See Example 2. (Objective 3)

31. $y = 2x$

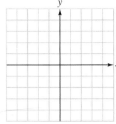

32. $y = -\dfrac{1}{2}x$

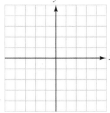

33. $y = 2x - 1$

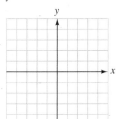

34. $y = 3x + 1$

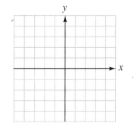

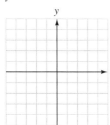 *Graph each equation by constructing a table of values and then plotting the points. Check your work with a graphing calculator.* See Example 3. (Objective 3)

35. $y = 1.2x - 2$

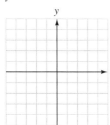

36. $y = -2.4x + 1$

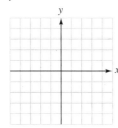

37. $y = 2.5x - 5$

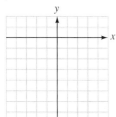

38. $y = x$

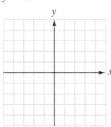

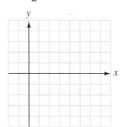 *Graph each equation by constructing a table of values and then plotting the points. Check your work with a graphing calculator.* See Example 4. (Objective 3)

39. $y = \dfrac{x}{2} - 2$

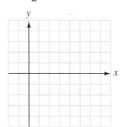

40. $y = \dfrac{x}{3} - 3$

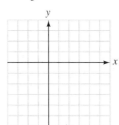

41. $y - 3 = -\dfrac{1}{2}\left(2x + 4\right)$

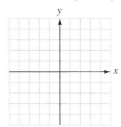

42. $y + 1 = 3\left(x - 1\right)$

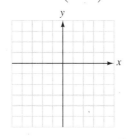

Graph each equation using the intercept method. Write the equation in general form, if necessary. See Example 5. (Objective 4)

43. $x + y = 7$

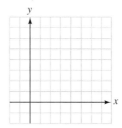

44. $x + y = -2$

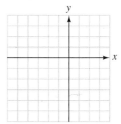

45. $x - y = 7$

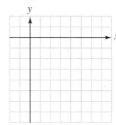

46. $x - y = -2$

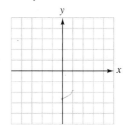

47. $y = -2x + 5$

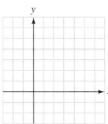

48. $y = -3x - 1$

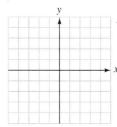

49. $2x + 3y = 12$

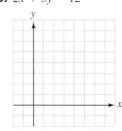

50. $3x - 2y = 6$

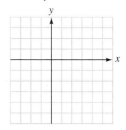

Graph each equation. See Example 6. (Objective 5)

51. $y = -5$

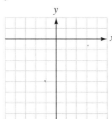

52. $x = 4$

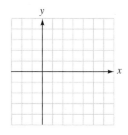

53. $x = 5$

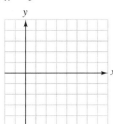

54. $y = 4$

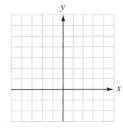

55. $y = 0$

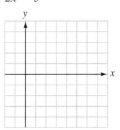

56. $x = 0$

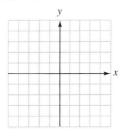

57. $2x = 5$

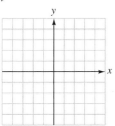

58. $3y = 7$

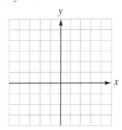

APPLICATIONS   See Example 7. (Objective 6)

59. Educational costs   Each semester, a college charges a service fee of $50 plus $25 for each unit taken by a student.

  a. Write a linear equation that gives the total enrollment cost c for a student taking u units.

  b. Complete the table of values and graph the equation. See the illustration.

  c. What does the y-intercept of the line tell you?

  d. Use the graph to find the total cost for a student taking 18 units the first semester and 12 units the second semester.

u	c	(u, c)
4		
8		
14		

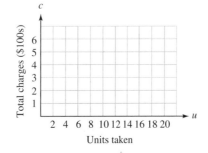

60. Group rates   To promote the sale of tickets for a cruise to Alaska, a travel agency reduces the regular ticket price of $3,000 by $5 for each individual traveling in the group.

  a. Write a linear equation that would find the ticket price T for the cruise if a group of p people travel together.

  b. Complete the table of values and then graph the equation. See the illustration.

  c. As the size of the group increases, what happens to the ticket price?

  d. Use the graph to determine the cost of an individual ticket if a group of 25 will be traveling together.

p	T	(p, T)
10		
30		
60		

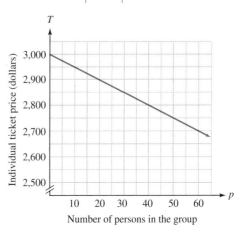

Number of persons in the group

61. Physiology   Physiologists have found that a woman's height h in inches can be approximated using the linear equation $h = 3.9r + 28.9$, where r represents the length of her radius bone in inches.

  a. Complete the table of values (round to the nearest tenth), and then graph the equation on the illustration.

  b. Complete this sentence: From the graph, we see that the longer the radius bone, the . . .

  c. From the graph, estimate the height of a girl whose radius bone is 7.5 inches long.

r	h	(r, h)
7		$(7, \quad)$
8.5		$(8.5, \quad)$
9		$(9, \quad)$

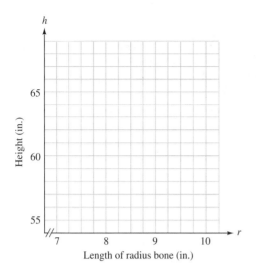

Height (in.)

Length of radius bone (in.)

62. Research A psychology major found that the time t in seconds that it took a white rat to complete a maze was related to the number of trials n the rat had been given by the equation $t = 25 - 0.25n$.

   a. Complete the table of values and then graph the equation on the illustration.

   b. Complete this sentence: From the graph, we see that the more trials the rat had, the . . .

   c. From the graph, estimate the time it will take the rat to complete the maze on its 32nd trial.

n	t	(n, t)
4		
12		
16		

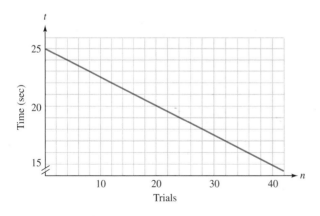

WRITING ABOUT MATH

63. From geometry, we know that two points determine a line. Explain why it is good practice when graphing linear equations to find and plot three points instead of just two.

64. Explain the process used to find the x- and y-intercepts of the graph of a line.

65. What is a table of values? Why is it often called a table of solutions?

66. When graphing an equation in two variables, how many solutions of the equation must be found?

67. Give examples of an equation in one variable and an equation in two variables. How do their solutions differ?

68. What does it mean when we say that an equation in two variables has infinitely many solutions?

SOMETHING TO THINK ABOUT

If points P(a, b) and Q(c, d) are two points on a rectangular coordinate system and point M is midway between them, then point M is called the midpoint of the line segment joining P and Q. (See the illustration.) To find the coordinates of the midpoint $M(x_M, y_M)$ of the segment PQ, we find the average of the x-coordinates and the average of the y-coordinates of P and Q.

$$x_M = \frac{a + c}{2} \quad \text{and} \quad y_M = \frac{b + d}{2}$$

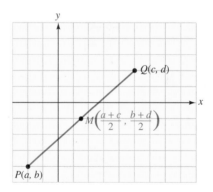

Find the coordinates of the midpoint of the line segment with the given endpoints.

69. $P(5, 3)$ and $Q(7, 9)$ **70.** $P(5, 6)$ and $Q(7, 10)$

71. $P(2, -7)$ and $Q(-3, 12)$ **72.** $P(-8, 12)$ and $Q(3, -9)$

73. $A(4, 6)$ and $B(10, 6)$ **74.** $A(8, -6)$ and the origin

Objectives

1 Determine whether an ordered pair is a solution to a given system of linear equations.

2 Solve a system of linear equations by graphing.

3 Recognize that an inconsistent system has no solution.

4 Recognize that a dependent system has infinitely many solutions that can be expressed as a general ordered pair.

Vocabulary

system of equations	independent equations	inconsistent system
simultaneous solution	consistent system	dependent equations

Getting Ready

If $y = x^2 - 3$, find y when

1. $x = 0$ **2.** $x = 1$ **3.** $x = -2$ **4.** $x = 3$

The lines graphed in Figure 3-21 approximate the per-person consumption of chicken and beef by Americans for the years 1985 to 2005. We can see that over this period, consumption of chicken increased, while that of beef decreased.

By graphing this information on the same coordinate system, it is apparent that Americans consumed equal amounts of chicken and beef in 1992—about 66 pounds each. In this section, we will work with pairs of linear equations whose graphs often will be intersecting lines.

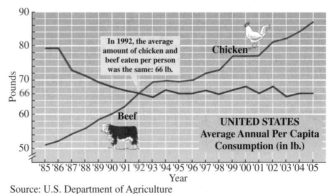

Source: U.S. Department of Agriculture

Figure 3-21

1 **Determine whether an ordered pair is a solution to a given system of linear equations.**

Recall that we have considered equations such as $x + y = 3$ that contain two variables. Because there are infinitely many pairs of numbers whose sum is 3, there are infinitely many pairs (x, y) that will satisfy this equation. Some of these pairs are listed in Table 3-3(a). Likewise, there are infinitely many pairs (x, y) that will satisfy the equation $3x - y = 1$. Some of these pairs are listed in Table 3-3(b).

$x + y = 3$		$3x - y = 1$	
x	y	x	y
0	3	0	-1
1	2	1	2
2	1	2	5
3	0	3	8
(a)		(b)	

Table 3-3

Although there are infinitely many pairs that satisfy each of these equations, only the pair $(1, 2)$ satisfies both equations. We can see that this is true because the pair $(1, 2)$ appears in both tables.

The pair of equations

$$\begin{cases} x + y = 3 \\ 3x - y = 1 \end{cases}$$

is called a **system of equations.** Because the ordered pair $(1, 2)$ satisfies both equations, it is called a **simultaneous solution** or just a *solution of the system of equations.* In this chapter, we will discuss three methods for finding the solution of a system of two linear equations. In this section, we consider the graphing method.

2 **Solve a system of linear equations by graphing.**

To use the method of graphing to solve the system

$$\begin{cases} x + y = 3 \\ 3x - y = 1 \end{cases}$$

we will graph both equations on one set of coordinate axes using the intercept method. Recall that to find the y-intercept, we let $x = 0$ and solve for y and to find the x-intercept, we let $y = 0$ and solve for x. We will also plot one extra point as a check. See Figure 3-22.

$x + y = 3$			$3x - y = 1$		
x	y	(x, y)	x	y	(x, y)
0	3	$(0, 3)$	0	-1	$(0, -1)$
3	0	$(3, 0)$	$\frac{1}{3}$	0	$\left(\frac{1}{3}, 0\right)$
2	1	$(2, 1)$	2	5	$(2, 5)$

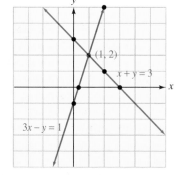

Figure 3-22

PERSPECTIVE

To schedule a company's workers, managers must consider several factors to match a worker's ability to the demands of various jobs and to match company resources to the requirements of the job. To design bridges or office buildings, engineers must analyze the effects of thousands of forces to ensure that structures won't collapse. A telephone switching network decides which of thousands of possible routes is the most efficient and then rings the correct telephone in seconds. Each of these tasks requires solving systems of equations—not just two equations in two variables, but hundreds of equations in hundreds of variables. These tasks are common in every business, industry, educational institution, and government in the world. All would be much more difficult without a computer.

One of the earliest computers in use was the Mark I, which resulted from a collaboration between IBM and a Harvard mathematician, Howard Aiken. The Mark I was started in 1939 and finished in 1944. It was 8 feet tall, 2 feet thick, and more than 50 feet long. It contained more than 750,000 parts and performed 3 calculations per second.

Ironically, Aiken could not envision the importance of his invention. He advised the National Bureau of Standards that there was no point in building a better computer, because "there will never be enough work for more than one or two of these machines."

©Courtesy of IBM

Mark I Relay Computer (1944)

Although there are infinitely many pairs (x, y) that satisfy $x + y = 3$ and infinitely many pairs (x, y) that satisfy $3x - y = 1$, only the coordinates of the point where their graphs intersect satisfy both equations. The solution of the system is $x = 1$ and $y = 2$, or $(1, 2)$.

To check the solution, we substitute 1 for x and 2 for y in each equation and verify that the pair $(1, 2)$ satisfies each equation.

First equation	*Second equation*
$x + y = 3$	$3x - y = 1$
$1 + 2 \stackrel{?}{=} 3$	$3(1) - 2 \stackrel{?}{=} 1$
$3 = 3$	$3 - 2 \stackrel{?}{=} 1$
	$1 = 1$

When the graphs of two equations in a system are different lines, the equations are called **independent equations.** When a system of equations has a solution, the system is called a **consistent system.**

To solve a system of equations in two variables by graphing, we follow these steps.

The Graphing Method
1. Carefully graph each equation.
2. Find the coordinates of the point where the graphs intersect, if possible.
3. Check the solution in the equations of the original system.

EXAMPLE 1   Solve the system $\begin{cases} 2x + 3y = 2 \\ 3x = 2x + 16 \end{cases}$.

Solution   Using the intercept method, we graph both equations on one set of coordinate axes, as shown in Figure 3-23. We also plot a third point as a check.

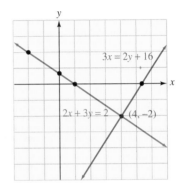

2x + 3y = 2		
x	*y*	(*x*, *y*)
0	$\frac{2}{3}$	$\left(0, \frac{2}{3}\right)$
1	0	(1, 0)
−2	2	(−2, 2)

3x = 2y + 16		
x	*y*	(*x*, *y*)
0	−8	(0, −8)
$\frac{16}{3}$	0	$\left(\frac{16}{3}, 0\right)$
4	−2	(4, −2)

Figure 3-23

Although there are infinitely many pairs (*x*, *y*) that satisfy $2x + 3y = 2$ and infinitely many pairs (*x*, *y*) that satisfy $3x = 2y + 16$, only the coordinates of the point where the graphs intersect satisfy both equations. The solution is $x = 4$ and $y = -2$, or (4, −2).

To check, we substitute 4 for *x* and −2 for *y* in each equation and verify that the pair (4, −2) satisfies each equation.

$$2x + 3y = 2 \qquad\qquad 3x = 2y + 16$$
$$2(4) + 3(-2) \overset{?}{=} 2 \qquad\qquad 3(4) \overset{?}{=} 2(-2) + 16$$
$$8 - 6 \overset{?}{=} 2 \qquad\qquad 12 \overset{?}{=} -4 + 16$$
$$2 = 2 \qquad\qquad 12 = 12$$

The equations in this system are independent equations, and the system is a consistent system of equations.

⇨ SELF CHECK 1   Solve: $\begin{cases} 2x = y - 5 \\ x + y = -1 \end{cases}$.

---

3   **Recognize that an inconsistent system has no solution.**

Sometimes a system of equations will have no solution. These systems are called **inconsistent systems**.

EXAMPLE 2   Solve: $\begin{cases} 2x + y = -6 \\ 4x + 2y = 8 \end{cases}$.

Solution   We graph both equations on one set of coordinate axes, as in Figure 3-24.

$$2x + y = -6$$

x	y	(x, y)
-3	0	$(-3, 0)$
0	-6	$(0, -6)$
-2	-2	$(-2, -2)$

$$4x + 2y = 8$$

x	y	(x, y)
2	0	$(2, 0)$
0	4	$(0, 4)$
1	2	$(1, 2)$

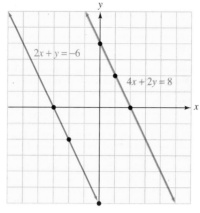

Figure 3-24

In the figure, we can see that the lines appear to be parallel. Since the lines are indeed parallel and parallel lines do not intersect, the system is inconsistent and has no solution. Its solution set is $\varnothing$. Because the graphs are different lines, the equations of the system are independent.

When using the graphing method, it may be difficult to determine whether two lines are almost parallel or exactly parallel. For now, we will use our best judgment. Later in the text, we will develop methods that will enable us to determine exactly whether two lines are parallel.

⇨ **SELF CHECK 2**   Solve: $\begin{cases} 2y = 3x \\ 3x - 2y = 6 \end{cases}$.

In Example 1, we saw that a system of equations can have a single solution. In Example 2, we saw that a system can have no solution. In Example 3, we will see that a system can have infinitely many solutions.

4   **Recognize that a dependent system has infinitely many solutions that can be expressed as a general ordered pair.**

Sometimes a system will have infinitely many solutions. In this case, we say that the equations of the system are **dependent equations.**

EXAMPLE 3   Solve: $\begin{cases} y - 2x = 4 \\ 4x + 8 = 2y \end{cases}$.

Solution   We graph each equation on one set of axes, as in Figure 3-25 shown on the next page.

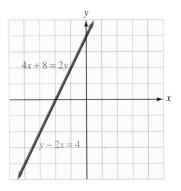

$y - 2x = 4$

x	y	(x, y)
0	4	$(0, 4)$
-2	0	$(-2, 0)$
1	6	$(1, 6)$

$4x + 8 = 2y$

x	y	(x, y)
0	4	$(0, 4)$
-2	0	$(-2, 0)$
-3	-2	$(-3, -2)$

Figure 3-25

Since the lines in the figure are the same line, they intersect at infinitely many points and there are infinitely many solutions. To describe these solutions, we can solve either equation for y. If we choose the first equation, we have

$$y - 2x = 4$$

$$y = 2x + 4 \qquad \text{Add } 2x \text{ to both sides.}$$

Because $2x + 4$ is equal to y, every solution (x, y) of the system will have the form $(x, 2x + 4)$. This solution can also be written in set-builder notation, $[(x, y) | y = 2x + 4]$.

To find some specific solutions, we can substitute 0, 1, and -1 for x in the general ordered pair $(x, 2x + 4)$ to get $(0, 4)$, $(1, 6)$, and $(-1, 2)$. From the graph, we can see that each point lies on the one line that is the graph of both equations.

⇨ SELF CHECK 3   Solve: $\begin{cases} 6x - 2y = 4 \\ y + 2 = 3x \end{cases}$.

Table 3-4 summarizes the possibilities that can occur when two equations, each with two variables, are graphed.

Possible graph	If the	then
	lines are different and intersect,	the equations are independent and the system is consistent. One solution exists.
	lines are different and parallel,	the equations are independent and the system is inconsistent. No solution exists.
	lines coincide (are the same line),	the equations are dependent and the system is consistent. Infinitely many solutions exist.

Table 3-4

EXAMPLE 4   Solve: $\begin{cases} \frac{2}{3}x - \frac{1}{2}y = 1 \\ \frac{1}{10}x + \frac{1}{15}y = 1 \end{cases}$.

Solution We can multiply both sides of the first equation by 6 to clear it of fractions.

$$\frac{2}{3}x - \frac{1}{2}y = 1$$

$$6\left(\frac{2}{3}x - \frac{1}{2}y\right) = 6(1)$$

(1) $\qquad 4x - 3y = 6$

We then multiply both sides of the second equation by 30 to clear it of fractions.

$$\frac{1}{10}x + \frac{1}{15}y = 1$$

$$30\left(\frac{1}{10}x + \frac{1}{15}y\right) = 30(1)$$

(2) $\qquad 3x + 2y = 30$

Equations 1 and 2 form the following equivalent system of equations, which has the same solutions as the original system.

$$\begin{cases} 4x - 3y = 6 \\ 3x + 2y = 30 \end{cases}$$

We can graph each equation of the previous system (see Figure 3-26) and find that their point of intersection has coordinates of (6, 6). The solution of the given system is $x = 6$ and $y = 6$, or (6, 6).

To verify that (6, 6) satisfies each equation of the original system, we substitute 6 for x and 6 for y in each of the original equations and simplify.

$$\frac{2}{3}x - \frac{1}{2}y = 1 \qquad\qquad \frac{1}{10}x + \frac{1}{15}y = 1$$

$$\frac{2}{3}(6) - \frac{1}{2}(6) \stackrel{?}{=} 1 \qquad\qquad \frac{1}{10}(6) + \frac{1}{15}(6) \stackrel{?}{=} 1$$

$$4 - 3 \stackrel{?}{=} 1 \qquad\qquad\qquad \frac{3}{5} + \frac{2}{5} \stackrel{?}{=} 1$$

$$1 = 1 \qquad\qquad\qquad\qquad 1 = 1$$

The equations in this system are independent and the system is consistent.

4x − 3y = 6		
x	y	(x, y)
0	−2	(0, −2)
3	2	(3, 2)
6	6	(6, 6)

3x + 2y = 30		
x	y	(x, y)
10	0	(10, 0)
8	3	(8, 3)
6	6	(6, 6)

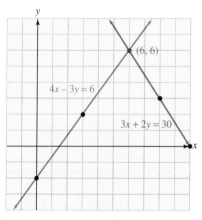

Figure 3-26

⇨ **SELF CHECK 4** Solve the system: $\begin{cases} -\dfrac{x}{2} = \dfrac{y}{4} \\ \dfrac{1}{4}x - \dfrac{3}{8}y = -2 \end{cases}$.

ACCENT ON TECHNOLOGY

Solving Systems of Equations

We can use a graphing calculator to solve the system $\begin{cases} 2x + y = 12 \\ 2x - y = -2 \end{cases}$.

However, before we can enter the equations into the calculator, we must solve them for y.

$$2x + y = 12 \qquad\qquad 2x - y = -2$$
$$y = -2x + 12 \qquad\qquad -y = -2x - 2$$
$$y = 2x + 2$$

We can now enter the resulting equations into a calculator and graph them. If we use standard window settings of $x = [-10, 10]$ and $y = [-10, 10]$, their graphs will look like Figure 3-27(a). We can trace to see that the coordinates of the intersection point are approximately

$$x = 2.5531915 \qquad \text{and} \qquad y = 6.893617$$

See Figure 3-27(b). For better results, we can zoom in on the intersection point and trace again to find that

$$x = 2.5 \qquad \text{and} \qquad y = 7$$

See Figure 3-27(c). Check the solution.

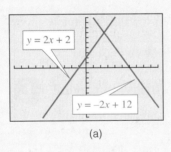

(a)

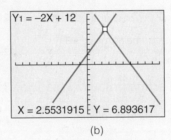

(b)

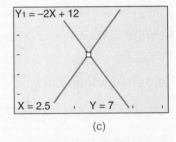

(c)

Figure 3-27

You also can find the intersection point by using the INTERSECT command, found in the CALC menu.

⇨ **SELF CHECK ANSWERS**

1. $(-2, 1)$ **2.** $\varnothing$ **3.** infinitely many solutions of the form $(x, 3x - 2)$ **4.** $(-2, 4)$

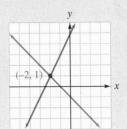

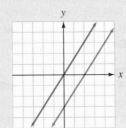

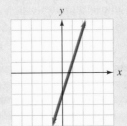

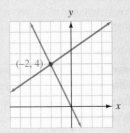

NOW TRY THIS

Solve each system by graphing.

1. $\begin{cases} y = -1 \\ x = 4 \end{cases}$

2. $\begin{cases} x = y \\ y = 0 \end{cases}$

Solve using a graphing calculator.

3. $\begin{cases} y = \frac{3}{4}x - 2 \\ 2x + 4y = 24 \end{cases}$

3.3 EXERCISES

WARM-UPS   *Determine whether the pair is a solution of the system.*

1. $(3, 2)$, $\begin{cases} x + y = 5 \\ x - y = 1 \end{cases}$

2. $(1, 2)$, $\begin{cases} x - y = -1 \\ x + y = 3 \end{cases}$

3. $(4, 1)$, $\begin{cases} x + y = 5 \\ x - y = 2 \end{cases}$

4. $(5, 2)$, $\begin{cases} x - y = 3 \\ x + y = 6 \end{cases}$

REVIEW   *Evaluate each expression. Assume that $x = -3$.*

5. $(-2)^4$

6. -2^4

7. $3x - x^2$

8. $\dfrac{-3 + 2x}{6x}$

VOCABULARY AND CONCEPTS   *Fill in the blanks.*

9. The pair of equations $\begin{cases} x - y = -1 \\ 2x - y = 1 \end{cases}$ is called a _____ of equations.

10. Because the ordered pair $(2, 3)$ satisfies both equations in Exercise 9, it is called a _____ of the system.

11. When the graphs of two equations in a system are different lines, the equations are called _____ equations.

12. When a system of equations has a solution, the system is called a _____.

13. If a systems of equations is _____, there is no solution and the solution set is ___.

14. When a system has infinitely many solutions, the equations of the system are said to be _____ equations.

GUIDED PRACTICE

Determine whether the ordered pair is a solution of the given system. (Objective 1)

15. $(1, 1)$, $\begin{cases} x + y = 2 \\ 2x - y = 1 \end{cases}$

16. $(1, 3)$, $\begin{cases} 2x + y = 5 \\ 3x - y = 0 \end{cases}$

17. $(3, -2)$, $\begin{cases} 2x + y = 4 \\ x + y = 1 \end{cases}$

18. $(-2, 4)$, $\begin{cases} 2x + 2y = 4 \\ x + 3y = 10 \end{cases}$

19. $(4, 5)$, $\begin{cases} 2x - 3y = -7 \\ 4x - 5y = 25 \end{cases}$

20. $(2, 3)$, $\begin{cases} 3x - 2y = 0 \\ 5x - 3y = -1 \end{cases}$

21. $(-2, -3)$, $\begin{cases} 4x + 5y = -23 \\ -3x + 2y = 0 \end{cases}$

22. $(-5, 1)$, $\begin{cases} -2x + 7y = 17 \\ 3x - 4y = -19 \end{cases}$

23. $\left(\frac{1}{2}, 3\right)$, $\begin{cases} 2x + y = 4 \\ 4x - 3y = 11 \end{cases}$

24. $\left(2, \frac{1}{3}\right)$, $\begin{cases} x - 3y = 1 \\ -2x + 6y = -6 \end{cases}$

25. $\left(-\frac{2}{5}, \frac{1}{4}\right)$, $\begin{cases} 5x - 4y = -6 \\ 8y = 10x + 12 \end{cases}$

26. $\left(-\frac{1}{3}, \frac{3}{4}\right)$, $\begin{cases} 3x + 4y = 2 \\ 12y = 3(2 - 3x) \end{cases}$

Solve each system by graphing. See Example 1. (Objective 2)

27. $\begin{cases} x + y = 2 \\ x - y = 0 \end{cases}$

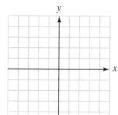

28. $\begin{cases} x + y = 4 \\ x - y = 0 \end{cases}$

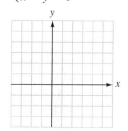

29. $\begin{cases} x + y = 2 \\ x - y = 4 \end{cases}$

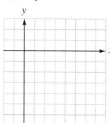

30. $\begin{cases} x + y = 1 \\ x - y = -5 \end{cases}$

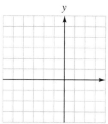

31. $\begin{cases} y = 2x \\ x + y = 0 \end{cases}$

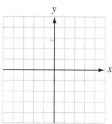

32. $\begin{cases} y = -x \\ x - y = 0 \end{cases}$

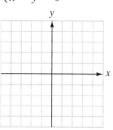

33. $\begin{cases} 3x + 2y = -8 \\ 2x - 3y = -1 \end{cases}$

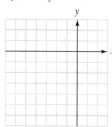

34. $\begin{cases} x + 4y = -2 \\ x + y = -5 \end{cases}$

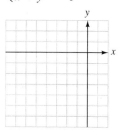

Solve each system by graphing. If a system is inconsistent, so indicate. See Example 2. (Objective 3)

35. $\begin{cases} 3x - 6y = 18 \\ x = 2y + 3 \end{cases}$

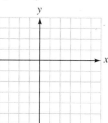

36. $\begin{cases} 5x - 4y = 20 \\ 4y = 5x + 12 \end{cases}$

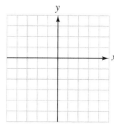

37. $\begin{cases} y = x \\ x - y = 7 \end{cases}$

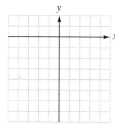

38. $\begin{cases} x = 2y - 8 \\ y = \frac{1}{2}x - 5 \end{cases}$

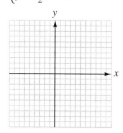

Solve each system by graphing. Give each answer as a general ordered pair. If a system is dependent, so indicate. See Example 3. (Objective 4)

39. $\begin{cases} 4x - 2y = 8 \\ y = 2x - 4 \end{cases}$

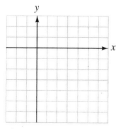

40. $\begin{cases} 2x = 3(2 - y) \\ 3y = 2(3 - x) \end{cases}$

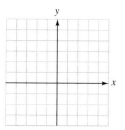

41. $\begin{cases} 6x + 3y = 9 \\ y + 2x = 3 \end{cases}$

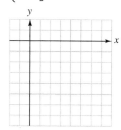

42. $\begin{cases} x = y \\ y - x = 0 \end{cases}$

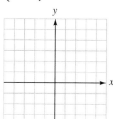

Solve each system by graphing. See Example 4. (Objective 2)

43. $\begin{cases} x + 2y = -4 \\ x - \frac{1}{2}y = 6 \end{cases}$

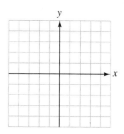

44. $\begin{cases} \frac{2}{3}x - y = -3 \\ 3x + y = 3 \end{cases}$

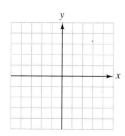

45. $\begin{cases} -\frac{3}{4}x + y = 3 \\ \frac{1}{4}x + y = -1 \end{cases}$

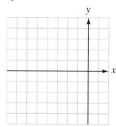

46. $\begin{cases} \frac{1}{3}x + y = 7 \\ \frac{2}{3}x - y = -4 \end{cases}$

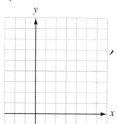

ADDITIONAL PRACTICE

Solve each system by graphing. If the equations of a system are dependent or if a system is inconsistent, so indicate.

47. $\begin{cases} 2x - 3y = -18 \\ 3x + 2y = -1 \end{cases}$

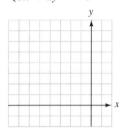

48. $\begin{cases} -x + 3y = -11 \\ 3x - y = 17 \end{cases}$

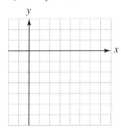

49. $\begin{cases} 4x = 3(4 - y) \\ 2y = 4(3 - x) \end{cases}$

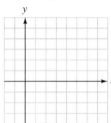

50. $\begin{cases} 8x = 2y - 9 \\ 4y = -x - 16 \end{cases}$

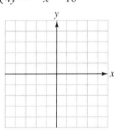

51. $\begin{cases} \frac{1}{2}x + \frac{1}{4}y = 0 \\ \frac{1}{4}x - \frac{3}{8}y = -2 \end{cases}$

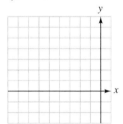

52. $\begin{cases} \frac{1}{2}x + \frac{2}{3}y = -5 \\ \frac{3}{2}x - y = 3 \end{cases}$

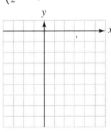

53. $\begin{cases} \frac{1}{3}x - \frac{1}{2}y = \frac{1}{6} \\ \frac{2}{5}x + \frac{1}{2}y = \frac{13}{10} \end{cases}$

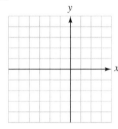

54. $\begin{cases} \frac{3}{4}x + \frac{2}{3}y = -\frac{19}{6} \\ y - x = -\frac{4}{3}x \end{cases}$

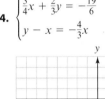

 *Use a graphing calculator to solve each system.*

55. $\begin{cases} y = 4 - x \\ y = 2 + x \end{cases}$

56. $\begin{cases} y = x - 2 \\ y = x + 2 \end{cases}$

57. $\begin{cases} 3x - 6y = 4 \\ 2x + y = 1 \end{cases}$

58. $\begin{cases} 4x + 9y = 4 \\ 6x + 3y = -1 \end{cases}$

APPLICATIONS

59. Transplants See the illustration. In what year was the number of donors and the number of people waiting for a transplant the same? Estimate the number.

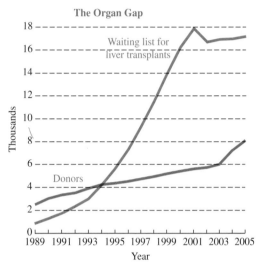

Source: Organ Procurement and Transportation Network

60. Daily tracking polls See the illustration.
   a. Which candidate was ahead on October 28 and by how much?
   b. On what day did the challenger pull even with the incumbent?
   c. If the election was held November 4, whom did the poll predict as the winner and by how many percentage points?

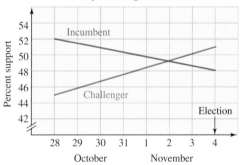

61. Latitude and longitude See the illustration.
  a. Name three American cities that lie on the latitude line of 30° north.
  b. Name three American cities that lie on the longitude line of 90° west.
  c. What city lies on both lines?

62. Economics The graph in the illustration illustrates the law of supply and demand.
  a. Complete this sentence: "As the price of an item increases, the *supply* of the item _____."
  b. Complete this sentence: "As the price of an item increases, the *demand* for the item _____."
  c. For what price will the supply equal the demand? How many items will be supplied for this price?

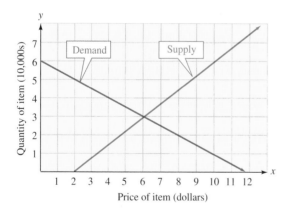

63. Traffic control The equations describing the paths of two airplanes are $y = -\frac{1}{2}x + 3$ and $3y = 2x + 2$. Graph each equation on the radar screen shown. Is there a possibility of a midair collision? If so, where?

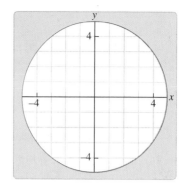

64. TV coverage A television camera is located at $(-2, 0)$ and will follow the launch of a space shuttle, as shown in the graph. (Each unit in the illustration is 1 mile.) As the shuttle rises vertically on a path described by $x = 2$, the farthest the camera can tilt back is a line of sight given by $y = \frac{5}{2}x + 5$. For how many miles of the shuttle's flight will it be in view of the camera?

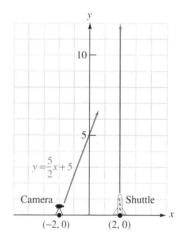

WRITING ABOUT MATH

65. Explain what we mean when we say "inconsistent system."
66. Explain what we mean when we say, "The equations of a system are dependent."

SOMETHING TO THINK ABOUT

67. Use a graphing calculator to solve the system

$$\begin{cases} 11x - 20y = 21 \\ -4x + 7y = 21 \end{cases}$$

What problems did you encounter?

68. Can the equations of an inconsistent system with two equations in two variables be dependent?

Solving Systems of Linear Equations by Substitution

Objectives

1. Solve a system of linear equations by substitution.
2. Identify an inconsistent system of linear equations.
3. Identify a dependent system of linear equations.

Getting Ready

Remove parentheses.

1. $2(3x + 2)$ **2.** $5(-5 - 2x)$

Substitute $x - 2$ for y and remove parentheses.

3. $2y$ **4.** $3(y - 2)$

The graphing method for solving systems of equations does not always provide exact solutions. For example, if the solution of a system is $x = \frac{11}{97}$ and $y = \frac{13}{97}$, it is unlikely we could read this solution exactly from a graph. Fortunately, there are other methods that provide exact solutions. We now consider one of them, called the *substitution method*.

1 **Solve a system of linear equations by substitution.**

To solve the system

$$\begin{cases} y = 3x - 2 \\ 2x + y = 8 \end{cases}$$

by the substitution method, we note that $y = 3x - 2$. Because $y = 3x - 2$, we can substitute $3x - 2$ for y in the equation $2x + y = 8$ to get

$$2x + y = 8$$
$$2x + (3x - 2) = 8$$

The resulting equation has only one variable and can be solved for x.

$$2x + (3x - 2) = 8$$

$2x + 3x - 2 = 8$	Remove parentheses.
$5x - 2 = 8$	Combine like terms.
$5x = 10$	Add 2 to both sides.
$x = 2$	Divide both sides by 5.

We can find y by substituting 2 for x in either equation of the given system. Because $y = 3x - 2$ is already solved for y, it is easier to substitute in this equation.

$$y = 3x - 2$$
$$= 3(2) - 2$$

$$= 6 - 2$$
$$= 4$$

The solution of the given system is $x = 2$ and $y = 4$, written as $(2, 4)$.

Check:

$$
\begin{array}{ll}
y = 3x - 2 & 2x + y = 8 \\
4 \stackrel{?}{=} 3(2) - 2 & 2(2) + 4 \stackrel{?}{=} 8 \\
4 \stackrel{?}{=} 6 - 2 & 4 + 4 \stackrel{?}{=} 8 \\
4 = 4 & 8 = 8
\end{array}
$$

Since the pair $x = 2$ and $y = 4$ is a solution, the lines represented by the equations of the given system intersect at the point $(2, 4)$. The equations of this system are independent, and the system is consistent.

    To solve a system of equations in x and y by the substitution method, we follow these steps.

The Substitution Method

1. If necessary, solve one of the equations for x or y, preferably a variable with a coefficient of 1.
2. Substitute the resulting expression for the variable obtained in Step 1 into the other equation, and solve that equation.
3. Find the value of the other variable by substituting the solution found in Step 2 into any equation containing both variables.
4. Check the solution in the equations of the original system.

EXAMPLE 1   Solve the system by substitution: $\begin{cases} 2x + y = -5 \\ 3x + 5y = -4 \end{cases}$.

Solution   We first solve one of the equations for one of its variables. Since the term y in the first equation has a coefficient of 1, we solve the first equation for y.

$$
\begin{array}{ll}
2x + y = -5 & \\
y = -5 - 2x & \text{Subtract } 2x \text{ from both sides.}
\end{array}
$$

We then substitute $-5 - 2x$ for y in the second equation and solve for x.

$$
\begin{array}{ll}
3x + 5y = -4 & \\
3x + 5(-5 - 2x) = -4 & \\
3x - 25 - 10x = -4 & \text{Remove parentheses.} \\
-7x - 25 = -4 & \text{Combine like terms.} \\
-7x = 21 & \text{Add 25 to both sides.} \\
x = -3 & \text{Divide both sides by } -7.
\end{array}
$$

We can find y by substituting -3 for x in the equation $y = -5 - 2x$.

$$
\begin{array}{l}
y = -5 - 2x \\
 = -5 - 2(-3) \\
 = -5 + 6 \\
 = 1
\end{array}
$$

The solution is $x = -3$ and $y = 1$, written as $(-3, 1)$.

Check: $2x + y = -5$ $3x + 5y = -4$

$2(-3) + 1 \overset{?}{=} -5$ $3(-3) + 5(1) \overset{?}{=} -4$

$-6 + 1 \overset{?}{=} -5$ $-9 + 5 \overset{?}{=} -4$

$-5 = -5$ $-4 = -4$

⇨ **SELF CHECK 1**   Solve by substitution: $\begin{cases} 2x - 3y = 13 \\ 3x + y = 3 \end{cases}$.

EXAMPLE 2   Solve the system by substitution: $\begin{cases} 2x + 3y = 5 \\ 3x + 2y = 0 \end{cases}$.

Solution   We can solve the second equation for x:

$3x + 2y = 0$

$3x = -2y$ Subtract $2y$ from both sides.

$x = \dfrac{-2y}{3}$ Divide both sides by 3.

We then substitute $\dfrac{-2y}{3}$ for x in the other equation and solve for y.

$2x + 3y = 5$

$2\left(\dfrac{-2y}{3}\right) + 3y = 5$

$\dfrac{-4y}{3} + 3y = 5$ Remove parentheses.

$3\left(\dfrac{-4y}{3}\right) + 3(3y) = 3(5)$ Multiply both sides by 3.

$-4y + 9y = 15$ Remove parentheses.

$5y = 15$ Combine like terms.

$y = 3$ Divide both sides by 5.

We can find x by substituting 3 for y in the equation $x = \dfrac{-2y}{3}$.

$x = \dfrac{-2y}{3}$

$= \dfrac{-2(3)}{3}$

$= -2$

Check the solution $(-2, 3)$ in each equation of the original system.

⇨ **SELF CHECK 2**   Solve by substitution: $\begin{cases} 3x - 2y = -19 \\ 2x + 5y = 0 \end{cases}$.

EXAMPLE 3   Solve the system by substitution: $\begin{cases} 3(x - y) = 5 \\ x + 3 = -\frac{5}{2}y \end{cases}$.

Solution   We begin by solving the second equation for x because it has a coefficient of 1.

$$x + 3 = -\frac{5}{2}y$$

(1) $$x = -\frac{5}{2}y - 3 \qquad \text{Subtract 3 from both sides.}$$

We can now substitute $-\frac{5}{2}y - 3$ for x in the first equation.

$$3(x - y) = 5 \qquad \text{This is the first equation of the system.}$$

$$3\left(-\frac{5}{2}y - 3 - y\right) = 5 \qquad \text{Substitute.}$$

$$-\frac{15}{2}y - 9 - 3y = 5 \qquad \text{Remove parentheses.}$$

$$2\left(-\frac{15}{2}y - 9 - 3y\right) = (5)2 \qquad \text{Multiply both sides by 2 to clear the fractions.}$$

$$-15y - 18 - 6y = 10 \qquad \text{Remove parentheses.}$$

$$-21y - 18 = 10 \qquad \text{Combine like terms.}$$

$$-21y = 28 \qquad \text{Add 18 to both sides.}$$

$$y = -\frac{28}{21} \qquad \text{Divide both sides by } -21.$$

$$y = -\frac{4}{3} \qquad \text{Simplify the fraction.}$$

To find x, we substitute $-\frac{4}{3}$ for y in Equation 1 and simplify.

$$x = -\frac{5}{2}y - 3$$

$$= -\frac{5}{2}\left(-\frac{4}{3}\right) - 3$$

$$= \frac{20}{6} - 3$$

$$= \frac{10}{3} - \frac{9}{3}$$

$$= \frac{1}{3}$$

Because we performed operations on the original equations, it is important that we check the solution $\left(\frac{1}{3}, -\frac{4}{3}\right)$ in each original equation.

⇨ **SELF CHECK 3**   Solve by substitution: $\begin{cases} 2(x + y) = -5 \\ x + 2 = -\frac{3}{5}y \end{cases}$.

---

2   **Identify an inconsistent system of linear equations.**

EXAMPLE 4   Solve the system by substitution: $\begin{cases} x = 4(3 - y) \\ 2x = 4(3 - 2y) \end{cases}$.

Solution   Since $x = 4(3 - y)$, we can substitute $4(3 - y)$ for x in the second equation and solve for y.

$$2x = 4(3 - 2y)$$
$$2[4(3 - y)] = 4(3 - 2y)$$
$$2(12 - 4y) = 4(3 - 2y) \qquad \text{Distribute the 4: } 4(3 - y) = 12 - 4y.$$
$$24 - 8y = 12 - 8y \qquad \text{Remove parentheses.}$$
$$24 = 12 \qquad \text{Add } 8y \text{ to both sides.}$$

This impossible result indicates that the equations in this system are independent, but that the system is inconsistent. If each equation in this system were graphed, these graphs would be parallel lines. Since there are no solutions to this system, the solution set is $\varnothing$.

⇨ **SELF CHECK 4**   Solve by substitution: $\begin{cases} 0.1x - 0.4 = 0.1y \\ -2y = 2(2 - x) \end{cases}.$

3   **Identify a dependent system of linear equations.**

EXAMPLE 5   Solve the system by substitution: $\begin{cases} 3x = 4(6 - y) \\ 4y + 3x = 24 \end{cases}.$

Solution   We can substitute $4(6 - y)$ for $3x$ in the second equation and proceed as follows:

$$4y + 3x = 24$$
$$4y + 4(6 - y) = 24$$
$$4y + 24 - 4y = 24 \qquad \text{Remove parentheses.}$$
$$24 = 24 \qquad \text{Combine like terms.}$$

Although $24 = 24$ is true, we did not find y. This result indicates that the equations of this system are dependent. If either equation were graphed, the same line would result.

Because any ordered pair that satisfies one equation satisfies the other also, the system has infinitely many solutions. To obtain a general solution, we can solve the second equation of the system for y:

$$4y + 3x = 24$$
$$4y = -3x + 24 \qquad \text{Subtract } 3x \text{ from both sides.}$$
$$y = \frac{-3x + 24}{4} \qquad \text{Divide both sides by 4.}$$

A general solution (x, y) is $\left(x, \frac{-3x + 24}{4}\right)$.

⇨ **SELF CHECK 5**   Solve by substitution: $\begin{cases} 3y = -3(x + 4) \\ 3x + 3y = -12 \end{cases}.$

⇨ **SELF CHECK ANSWERS**   **1.** $(2, -3)$ **2.** $(-5, 2)$ **3.** $\left(-\frac{5}{4}, -\frac{5}{4}\right)$ **4.** $\varnothing$ **5.** infinitely many solutions of the form $(x, -x - 4)$

> **NOW TRY THIS**
>
> Use substitution to solve each of the systems.
>
> **1.** $\begin{cases} y = x \\ 5x - 2y = -12 \end{cases}$
>
> **2.** $\begin{cases} \dfrac{1}{3}a + \dfrac{1}{3}b = 2 \\ 5a + 7b = 12 \end{cases}$
>
> **3.** $\begin{cases} 6x = 5 - 3y \\ y = -2x + 1 \end{cases}$

3.4 EXERCISES

WARM-UPS *Let y = x + 1. Substitute each expression for x and simplify.*

1. $2z$

2. $z + 1$

3. $3t + 2$

4. $\dfrac{t}{3} + 3$

REVIEW *Let x = −2 and y = 3 and evaluate each expression.*

5. $y^2 - x^2$

6. $-x^2 + y^3$

7. $\dfrac{3x - 2y}{2x + y}$

8. $-2x^2y^2$

9. $-x(3y - 4)$

10. $-2y(4x - y)$

VOCABULARY AND CONCEPTS *Fill in the blanks.*

11. We say the equation $y = 2x + 4$ is solved for __ or that y is expressed in _____ of x.

12. To _____ a solution of a system means to see whether the coordinates of the ordered pair satisfy both equations.

13. The solution set of the contradiction $2(x - 6) = 2x - 15$ is __.

14. In mathematics, to _____ means to replace an expression with one that is equivalent to it.

15. A system with dependent equations has _____ solutions. Its solutions can be described by a general ordered pair or in set-builder notation.

16. In the term y, the _____ is understood to be 1.

GUIDED PRACTICE

Use substitution to solve each system. (Objective 1)

17. $\begin{cases} y = 2x \\ x + y = 6 \end{cases}$

18. $\begin{cases} y = 3x \\ x + y = 4 \end{cases}$

19. $\begin{cases} y = 2x - 6 \\ 2x + y = 6 \end{cases}$

20. $\begin{cases} y = 2x - 9 \\ x + 3y = 8 \end{cases}$

21. $\begin{cases} y = 2x + 5 \\ x + 2y = -5 \end{cases}$

22. $\begin{cases} y = -2x \\ 3x + 2y = -1 \end{cases}$

23. $\begin{cases} 4x + 5y = 2 \\ 3x - y = 11 \end{cases}$

24. $\begin{cases} 5u + 3v = 5 \\ 4u - v = 4 \end{cases}$

Use substitution to solve each system. See Examples 1–2. (Objective 1)

25. $\begin{cases} 2x + y = 0 \\ 3x + 2y = 1 \end{cases}$

26. $\begin{cases} 3x - y = 7 \\ 2x + 3y = 1 \end{cases}$

27. $\begin{cases} 2x + 3y = 5 \\ 3x + 2y = 5 \end{cases}$

28. $\begin{cases} 3x - 2y = -1 \\ 2x + 3y = -5 \end{cases}$

29. $\begin{cases} 2x + 5y = -2 \\ 4x + 3y = 10 \end{cases}$

30. $\begin{cases} 3x + 4y = -6 \\ 2x - 3y = -4 \end{cases}$

31. $\begin{cases} 2a = 3b - 13 \\ b = 2a + 7 \end{cases}$

32. $\begin{cases} a = 3b - 1 \\ b = 2a + 2 \end{cases}$

Use substitution to solve each system. See Example 3. (Objective 1)

33. $\begin{cases} 3(x - 1) + 3 = 8 + 2y \\ 2(x + 1) = 4 + 3y \end{cases}$

34. $\begin{cases} 4(x - 2) = 19 - 5y \\ 3(x + 1) - 2y = 2y \end{cases}$

35. $\begin{cases} 6a = 5(3 + b + a) - a \\ 3(a - b) + 4b = 5(1 + b) \end{cases}$

36. $\begin{cases} 5(x + 1) + 7 = 7(y + 1) \\ 5(y + 1) = 6(1 + x) + 5 \end{cases}$

Use substitution to solve each system. If the equations of a system are dependent or if a system is inconsistent, so indicate. •
See Example 4. (Objective 2)

37. $\begin{cases} 8y = 15 - 4x \\ x + 2y = 4 \end{cases}$

38. $\begin{cases} 2a + 4b = -24 \\ a = 20 - 2b \end{cases}$

39. $\begin{cases} a = \frac{3}{2}b + 5 \\ 2a - 3b = 8 \end{cases}$

40. $\begin{cases} 3x - 6y = 18 \\ x = 2y + 3 \end{cases}$

Use substitution to solve each system. If the equations of a system are dependent or if a system is inconsistent, so indicate.
See Example 5. (Objective 3)

41. $\begin{cases} 9x = 3y + 12 \\ 4 = 3x - y \end{cases}$

42. $\begin{cases} x = \frac{1}{2}y + \frac{5}{4} \\ 4x - 2y = 5 \end{cases}$

43. $\begin{cases} 3a + 6b = -15 \\ a = -2b - 5 \end{cases}$

44. $\begin{cases} y - 2x = 4 \\ 4x + 8 = 2y \end{cases}$

ADDITIONAL PRACTICE   *Use substitution to solve each system. If the equations of a system are dependent or if a system is inconsistent, so indicate.*

45. $\begin{cases} 2x + y = 4 \\ 4x + y = 5 \end{cases}$

46. $\begin{cases} x + 3y = 3 \\ 2x + 3y = 4 \end{cases}$

47. $\begin{cases} r + 3s = 9 \\ 3r + 2s = 13 \end{cases}$

48. $\begin{cases} x - 2y = 2 \\ 2x + 3y = 11 \end{cases}$

49. $\begin{cases} y - x = 3x \\ 2(x + y) = 14 - y \end{cases}$

50. $\begin{cases} y + x = 2x + 2 \\ 2(3x - 2y) = 21 - y \end{cases}$

51. $\begin{cases} 3x + 4y = -7 \\ 2y - x = -1 \end{cases}$

52. $\begin{cases} 4x + 5y = -2 \\ x + 2y = -2 \end{cases}$

53. $\begin{cases} 2x - 3y = -3 \\ 3x + 5y = -14 \end{cases}$

54. $\begin{cases} 4x - 5y = -12 \\ 5x - 2y = 2 \end{cases}$

55. $\begin{cases} 7x - 2y = -1 \\ -5x + 2y = -1 \end{cases}$

56. $\begin{cases} -8x + 3y = 22 \\ 4x + 3y = -2 \end{cases}$

57. $\begin{cases} 2a + 3b = 2 \\ 8a - 3b = 3 \end{cases}$

58. $\begin{cases} 3a - 2b = 0 \\ 9a + 4b = 5 \end{cases}$

59. $\begin{cases} \frac{1}{2}x + \frac{1}{2}y = -1 \\ \frac{1}{3}x - \frac{1}{2}y = -4 \end{cases}$

60. $\begin{cases} \frac{2}{3}y + \frac{1}{5}z = 1 \\ \frac{1}{3}y - \frac{2}{5}z = 3 \end{cases}$

61. $\begin{cases} 5x = \frac{1}{2}y - 1 \\ \frac{1}{4}y = 10x - 1 \end{cases}$

62. $\begin{cases} \frac{2}{3}x = 1 - 2y \\ 2(5y - x) + 11 = 0 \end{cases}$

63. $\begin{cases} \frac{6x - 1}{3} - \frac{5}{3} = \frac{3y + 1}{2} \\ \frac{1 + 5y}{4} + \frac{x + 3}{4} = \frac{17}{2} \end{cases}$

64. $\begin{cases} \frac{5x - 2}{4} + \frac{1}{2} = \frac{3y + 2}{2} \\ \frac{7y + 3}{3} = \frac{x}{2} + \frac{7}{3} \end{cases}$

APPLICATIONS

65. Geometry   In the illustration, $x + y = 90°$ and $y = 2x$. Find x and y.

66. Geometry   In the illustration, $x + y = 180°$ and $y = 5x$. Find x and y.

WRITING ABOUT MATH

67. Explain how to use substitution to solve a system of equations.

68. If the equations of a system are written in general form, why is it to your advantage to solve for a variable whose coefficient is 1?

SOMETHING TO THINK ABOUT

69. Could you use substitution to solve the system

$$\begin{cases} y = 2y + 4 \\ x = 3x - 5 \end{cases}$$

How would you solve it?

70. What are the advantages and disadvantages of
  a. the graphing method?
  b. the substitution method?

SECTION 3.5   **Solving Systems of Linear Equations by Elimination (Addition)**

Objectives

1 Solve a system of linear equations by elimination (addition).
2 Identify an inconsistent system of linear equations.
3 Identify a dependent system of linear equations.

Vocabulary

elimination

Getting Ready

Add the left sides and the right sides of the equations in each system.

1. $\begin{cases} 2x + 3y = 4 \\ 3x - 3y = 6 \end{cases}$ **2.** $\begin{cases} 4x - 2y = 1 \\ -4x + 3y = 5 \end{cases}$

3. $\begin{cases} 6x - 5y = 23 \\ -4x + 5y = 10 \end{cases}$ **4.** $\begin{cases} -5x + 6y = 18 \\ 5x + 12y = 10 \end{cases}$

We now consider a second algebraic method for solving systems of equations that will provide exact solutions. It is called the *elimination* or *addition method*.

1 Solve a system of linear equations by elimination (addition).

To solve the system

$$\begin{cases} x + y = 8 \\ x - y = -2 \end{cases}$$

by the **elimination** (addition method), we first note that the coefficients of y are 1 and -1, which are negatives (opposites). We then add the left and right sides of the equations to eliminate the variable y.

$$\begin{array}{ll} x + y = 8 & \text{Equal quantities, } x - y \text{ and } -2, \text{ are added to both sides of the equation} \\ \underline{x - y = -2} & x + y = 8. \text{ By the addition property of equality, the results will be equal.} \end{array}$$

Now, column by column, we add like terms.

Combine like terms.

$$\begin{array}{ll} x + y = 8 & \\ \underline{x - y = -2} & \\ 2x = 6 & \leftarrow \text{Write each result here.} \end{array}$$

We can then solve the resulting equation for x.

$$\begin{array}{ll} 2x = 6 & \\ x = 3 & \text{Divide both sides by 2.} \end{array}$$

To find y, we substitute 3 for x in either equation of the system and solve it for y.

$$\begin{array}{ll} x + y = 8 & \text{The first equation of the system.} \\ 3 + y = 8 & \text{Substitute 3 for } x. \\ y = 5 & \text{Subtract 3 from both sides.} \end{array}$$

We check the solution by verifying that the pair $(3, 5)$ satisfies each equation of the original system.

To solve a system of equations in x and y by the elimination (addition) method, we follow these steps.

The Elimination (Addition) Method

1. If necessary, write both equations in general form: $Ax + By = C$.
2. If necessary, multiply one or both of the equations by nonzero quantities to make the coefficients of x (or the coefficients of y) opposites.
3. Add the equations to eliminate the term involving x (or y).
4. Solve the equation resulting from Step 3.
5. Find the value of the other variable by substituting the solution found in Step 4 into any equation containing both variables.
6. Check the solution in the equations of the original system.

EXAMPLE 1 Solve the system by elimination: $\begin{cases} 3y = 14 + x \\ x + 22 = 5y \end{cases}$.

Solution We begin by writing the equations in general form:

$$\begin{cases} -x + 3y = 14 \\ x - 5y = -22 \end{cases}$$

When these equations are added, the terms involving x are eliminated and we can solve the resulting equation for y.

$$\begin{array}{r} -x + 3y = 14 \\ \underline{x - 5y = -22} \\ -2y = -8 \end{array}$$

$$y = 4 \qquad \text{Divide both sides by } -2.$$

To find x, we substitute 4 for y in either equation of the system. If we substitute 4 for y in the equation $-x + 3y = 14$, we have

$$\begin{aligned} -x + 3y &= 14 \\ -x + 3(\mathbf{4}) &= 14 \\ -x + 12 &= 14 \qquad \text{Simplify.} \\ -x &= 2 \qquad \text{Subtract 12 from both sides.} \\ x &= -2 \qquad \text{Divide both sides by } -1. \end{aligned}$$

Since we performed operations on the equations, it is important to verify that $(-2, 4)$ satisfies each original equation.

SELF CHECK 1 Solve by elimination: $\begin{cases} 3y = 7 - x \\ 2x - 3y = -22 \end{cases}$.

Sometimes we need to multiply both sides of one equation in a system by a number to make the coefficients of one of the variables opposites.

EXAMPLE 2   Solve the system by elimination: $\begin{cases} 3x + y = 7 \\ x + 2y = 4 \end{cases}$.

Solution   If we add the equations as they are, neither variable will be eliminated. We must write the equations so that the coefficients of one of the variables are opposites. To eliminate x, we can multiply both sides of the second equation by -3 to get

$$\begin{cases} 3x + y = 7 \\ -3(x + 2y) = -3(4) \end{cases} \quad \rightarrow \quad \begin{cases} 3x + y = 7 \\ -3x - 6y = -12 \end{cases}$$

The coefficients of the terms $3x$ and $-3x$ are opposites. When the equations are added, x is eliminated.

$$\begin{array}{r} 3x + y = 7 \\ -3x - 6y = -12 \\ \hline -5y = -5 \end{array}$$

$$y = 1 \qquad \text{Divide both sides by } -5.$$

To find x, we substitute 1 for y in the equation $3x + y = 7$.

$$3x + y = 7$$
$$3x + (1) = 7 \qquad \text{Substitute 1 for } y.$$
$$3x = 6 \qquad \text{Subtract 1 from both sides.}$$
$$x = 2 \qquad \text{Divide both sides by 3.}$$

Check the solution $(2, 1)$ in the original system of equations.

 **SELF CHECK 2**   Solve by elimination: $\begin{cases} 3x + 4y = 25 \\ 2x + y = 10 \end{cases}$.

COMMENT   In Example 2, we could have multiplied the first equation by -2 and eliminated y. The result would be the same.

In some instances, we must multiply both equations by nonzero quantities to make the coefficients of one of the variables opposites.

EXAMPLE 3   Solve the system by elimination: $\begin{cases} 2a - 5b = 10 \\ 3a - 2b = -7 \end{cases}$.

Solution   The equations in the system must be written so that one of the variables will be eliminated when the equations are added.

To eliminate a, we can multiply the first equation by 3 and the second equation by -2 to get

$$\begin{cases} 3(2a - 5b) = 3(10) \\ -2(3a - 2b) = -2(-7) \end{cases} \quad \rightarrow \quad \begin{cases} 6a - 15b = 30 \\ -6a + 4b = 14 \end{cases}$$

When these equations are added, the terms $6a$ and $-6a$ are eliminated.

$$\begin{array}{r} 6a - 15b = 30 \\ -6a + 4b = 14 \\ \hline -11b = 44 \end{array}$$

$$b = -4 \qquad \text{Divide both sides by } -11.$$

To find a, we substitute -4 for b in the equation $2a - 5b = 10$.

$$2a - 5b = 10$$

$$2a - 5(-4) = 10 \qquad \text{Substitute } -4 \text{ for } b.$$

$$2a + 20 = 10 \qquad \text{Simplify.}$$

$$2a = -10 \qquad \text{Subtract 20 from both sides.}$$

$$a = -5 \qquad \text{Divide both sides by 2.}$$

COMMENT Note that solving Example 3 by the substitution method would involve fractions. In these cases, the elimination method is usually easier.

Check the solution $(-5, -4)$ in the original equations.

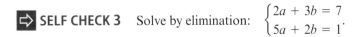 **SELF CHECK 3** Solve by elimination: $\begin{cases} 2a + 3b = 7 \\ 5a + 2b = 1 \end{cases}$.

EXAMPLE 4 Solve the system by elimination: $\begin{cases} \frac{5}{6}x + \frac{2}{3}y = \frac{7}{6} \\ \frac{10}{7}x - \frac{4}{9}y = \frac{17}{21} \end{cases}$.

Solution To clear the equations of fractions, we multiply both sides of the first equation by 6 and both sides of the second equation by 63. This gives the system

(1)
(2)
$$\begin{cases} 5x + 4y = 7 \\ 90x - 28y = 51 \end{cases}$$

We can solve for x by eliminating the terms involving y. To do so, we multiply Equation 1 by 7 and add the result to Equation 2.

$$\begin{array}{r} 35x + 28y = 49 \\ 90x - 28y = 51 \\ \hline 125x \qquad = 100 \end{array}$$

$$x = \frac{100}{125} \qquad \text{Divide both sides by 125.}$$

$$x = \frac{4}{5} \qquad \text{Simplify.}$$

To solve for y, we substitute $\frac{4}{5}$ for x in Equation 1 and simplify.

$$5x + 4y = 7$$

$$5\left(\frac{4}{5}\right) + 4y = 7$$

$$4 + 4y = 7 \qquad \text{Simplify.}$$

$$4y = 3 \qquad \text{Subtract 4 from both sides.}$$

$$y = \frac{3}{4} \qquad \text{Divide both sides by 4.}$$

Check the solution of $\left(\frac{4}{5}, \frac{3}{4}\right)$ in the original equations.

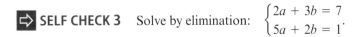 **SELF CHECK 4** Solve by elimination: $\begin{cases} \frac{1}{3}x + \frac{1}{6}y = 1 \\ \frac{1}{2}x - \frac{1}{4}y = 0 \end{cases}$.

2 **Identify an inconsistent system of linear equations.**

In the next example, the system has no solution.

EXAMPLE 5   Solve the system by elimination: $\begin{cases} x - \frac{2y}{3} = \frac{8}{3} \\ -\frac{3x}{2} + y = -6 \end{cases}$.

Solution   We can multiply both sides of the first equation by 3 and both sides of the second equation by 2 to clear the equations of fractions.

$$\begin{cases} 3\left(x - \frac{2y}{3}\right) = 3\left(\frac{8}{3}\right) \\ 2\left(-\frac{3x}{2} + y\right) = 2(-6) \end{cases} \;\rightarrow\; \begin{cases} 3x - 2y = 8 \\ -3x + 2y = -12 \end{cases}$$

We can add the resulting equations to eliminate the term involving x.

$$\begin{array}{r} 3x - 2y = 8 \\ -3x + 2y = -12 \\ \hline 0 = -4 \end{array}$$

Here, the terms involving both x and y drop out, and a false result is obtained. This shows that the equations of the system are independent, but the system itself is inconsistent. If we graphed these two equations, they would be parallel. This system has no solution; its solution set is $\varnothing$.

SELF CHECK 5   Solve by elimination: $\begin{cases} x - \frac{y}{3} = \frac{10}{3} \\ 3x - y = \frac{5}{2} \end{cases}$.

3 **Identify a dependent system of linear equations.**

In the next example, the system has infinitely many solutions.

EXAMPLE 6   Solve the system by elimination: $\begin{cases} \frac{2x - 5y}{2} = \frac{19}{2} \\ -0.2x + 0.5y = -1.9 \end{cases}$.

Solution   We can multiply both sides of the first equation by 2 to clear it of fractions and both sides of the second equation by 10 to clear it of decimals.

$$\begin{cases} 2\left(\frac{2x - 5y}{2}\right) = 2\left(\frac{19}{2}\right) \\ 10(-0.2x + 0.5y) = 10(-1.9) \end{cases} \;\rightarrow\; \begin{cases} 2x - 5y = 19 \\ -2x + 5y = -19 \end{cases}$$

We add the resulting equations to get

$$\begin{array}{r} 2x - 5y = 19 \\ -2x + 5y = -19 \\ \hline 0 = 0 \end{array}$$

As in Example 5, both x and y drop out. However, this time a true result is obtained. This shows that the equations are dependent and the system has infinitely many solutions. Any ordered pair that satisfies one equation satisfies the other. To find a general solution, we can solve the equation $-2x + 5y = -19$ for y,

$$-2x + 5y = -19$$
$$5y = 2x - 19 \quad \text{Add } 2x \text{ to both sides.}$$
$$y = \frac{2x - 19}{5} \quad \text{Divide both sides by 5.}$$

A general solution is given by an ordered pair of the form $\left(x, \frac{2x - 19}{5}\right)$.

⇨ **SELF CHECK 6**   Solve by elimination: $\begin{cases} \frac{3x + y}{6} = \frac{1}{3} \\ -0.3x - 0.1y = -0.2 \end{cases}$.

⇨ **SELF CHECK ANSWERS**   **1.** $(-5, 4)$ **2.** $(3, 4)$ **3.** $(-1, 3)$ **4.** $\left(\frac{3}{2}, 3\right)$ **5.** $\varnothing$
6. infinitely many solutions of the form $(x, -3x + 2)$

NOW TRY THIS

Solve each system by elimination.

1. $\begin{cases} x + y = 8 \\ 0.70x + 0.30y = 3.04 \end{cases}$

2. $\begin{cases} 5x - 4y = 16 \\ 3y + 2x = -12 \end{cases}$

3.5 EXERCISES

WARM-UPS

Use elimination to solve each system for x.

1. $\begin{cases} x + y = 1 \\ x - y = 1 \end{cases}$ **2.** $\begin{cases} 2x + y = 4 \\ x - y = 2 \end{cases}$

Use elimination to solve each system for y.

3. $\begin{cases} -x + y = 3 \\ x + y = 3 \end{cases}$ **4.** $\begin{cases} x + 2y = 4 \\ -x - y = 1 \end{cases}$

REVIEW

Solve each equation.

5. $8(3x - 5) - 12 = 4(2x + 3)$ **6.** $5x - 13 = x - 1$

7. $x - 2 = \frac{x + 2}{3}$ **8.** $\frac{3}{2}(y + 4) = \frac{20 - y}{2}$

Solve each inequality and graph the solution.

9. $7x - 9 \le 5$ **10.** $-2x + 6 > 16$

VOCABULARY AND CONCEPTS   *Fill in the blanks.*

11. The numerical _____ of $-3x$ is -3.

12. The _____ of 4 is -4.

13. $Ax + By = C$ is the _____ form of the equation of a line.

14. The process of adding the equations

$$5x - 6y = 10$$
$$\underline{-3x + 6y = 24}$$

to eliminate the variable y is called the _____ method.

15. To clear the equation $\frac{2}{3}x + 4y = -\frac{4}{5}$ of fractions, we must multiply both sides by ___.

16. To solve the system

$$\begin{cases} 3x + 12y = 4 \\ 6x - 4y = 8 \end{cases}$$

we would multiply the second equation by ___ and add to eliminate the y.

GUIDED PRACTICE

Use elimination to solve each system. See Example 1. (Objective 1)

17. $\begin{cases} x + y = 5 \\ x - y = -3 \end{cases}$

18. $\begin{cases} x - y = 1 \\ x + y = 7 \end{cases}$

19. $\begin{cases} x - y = -5 \\ x + y = 1 \end{cases}$

20. $\begin{cases} x + y = 1 \\ x - y = 5 \end{cases}$

21. $\begin{cases} 2x + y = -1 \\ -2x + y = 3 \end{cases}$

22. $\begin{cases} 3x + y = -6 \\ x - y = -2 \end{cases}$

23. $\begin{cases} 2x - 3y = -11 \\ 3x + 3y = 21 \end{cases}$

24. $\begin{cases} 3x - 2y = 16 \\ -3x + 8y = -10 \end{cases}$

Use elimination to solve each system. See Example 2. (Objective 1)

25. $\begin{cases} x + y = 5 \\ x + 2y = 8 \end{cases}$

26. $\begin{cases} x + 2y = 0 \\ x - y = -3 \end{cases}$

27. $\begin{cases} 2x + y = 4 \\ 2x + 3y = 0 \end{cases}$

28. $\begin{cases} 2x + 5y = -13 \\ 2x - 3y = -5 \end{cases}$

29. $\begin{cases} 3x + 29 = 5y \\ 4y - 34 = -3x \end{cases}$

30. $\begin{cases} 3x - 16 = 5y \\ 33 - 5y = 4x \end{cases}$

31. $\begin{cases} 2x + y = 10 \\ x + 2y = 10 \end{cases}$

32. $\begin{cases} 2x - y = 16 \\ 3x + 2y = 3 \end{cases}$

Use elimination to solve each system. See Example 3. (Objective 1)

33. $\begin{cases} 3x + 2y = 0 \\ 2x - 3y = -13 \end{cases}$

34. $\begin{cases} 3x + 4y = -17 \\ 4x - 3y = -6 \end{cases}$

35. $\begin{cases} 4x + 5y = -20 \\ 5x - 4y = -25 \end{cases}$

36. $\begin{cases} 3x - 5y = 4 \\ 7x + 3y = 68 \end{cases}$

37. $\begin{cases} 6x = -3y \\ 5y = 2x + 12 \end{cases}$

38. $\begin{cases} 3y = 4x \\ 5x = 4y - 2 \end{cases}$

39. $\begin{cases} 3x - 2y = -1 \\ 2x + 3y = -5 \end{cases}$

40. $\begin{cases} 2x - 3y = -3 \\ 3x + 5y = -14 \end{cases}$

Use elimination to solve each system. See Example 4. (Objective 1)

41. $\begin{cases} \frac{3}{5}x + \frac{4}{5}y = 1 \\ -\frac{1}{4}x + \frac{3}{8}y = 1 \end{cases}$

42. $\begin{cases} \frac{1}{2}x - \frac{1}{4}y = 1 \\ \frac{1}{3}x + y = 3 \end{cases}$

43. $\begin{cases} \frac{3}{5}x + y = 1 \\ \frac{4}{5}x - y = -1 \end{cases}$

44. $\begin{cases} \frac{1}{2}x + \frac{4}{7}y = -1 \\ 5x - \frac{4}{5}y = -10 \end{cases}$

Use elimination to solve each system. See Example 5. (Objective 2)

45. $\begin{cases} 2x = 3(y - 2) \\ 2(x + 4) = 3y \end{cases}$

46. $\begin{cases} 3(x + 3) + 2(y - 4) = 5 \\ 3(x - 1) = -2(y + 2) \end{cases}$

47. $\begin{cases} 4x = 3(4 - y) \\ 3y = 4(2 - x) \end{cases}$

48. $\begin{cases} 4(x + 2y) = 15 \\ x + 2y = 4 \end{cases}$

Use elimination to solve each system. See Example 6. (Objective 3)

49. $\begin{cases} 3(x - 2) = 4y \\ 2(2y + 3) = 3x \end{cases}$

50. $\begin{cases} -2(x + 1) = 3(y - 2) \\ 3(y + 2) = 6 - 2(x - 2) \end{cases}$

51. $\begin{cases} 3(x - 2y) = 12 \\ x = 2(y + 2) \end{cases}$

52. $\begin{cases} 9x = 3y + 12 \\ 4 = 3x - y \end{cases}$

ADDITIONAL PRACTICE   Solve each system.

53. $\begin{cases} 2x + y = -2 \\ -2x - 3y = -6 \end{cases}$

54. $\begin{cases} 3x + 4y = 8 \\ 5x - 4y = 24 \end{cases}$

55. $\begin{cases} 4x + 3y = 24 \\ 4x - 3y = -24 \end{cases}$

56. $\begin{cases} 5x - 4y = 8 \\ -5x - 4y = 8 \end{cases}$

57. $\begin{cases} 5(x - 1) = 8 - 3(y + 2) \\ 4(x + 2) - 7 = 3(2 - y) \end{cases}$

58. $\begin{cases} 4(x + 1) = 17 - 3(y - 1) \\ 2(x + 2) + 3(y - 1) = 9 \end{cases}$

59. $\begin{cases} 2x + 3y = 2 \\ 4x - 9y = -1 \end{cases}$

60. $\begin{cases} 4x + 5y = 2 \\ 16x - 15y = 1 \end{cases}$

61. $\begin{cases} 4(2x - y) = 18 \\ 3(x - 3) = 2y - 1 \end{cases}$

62. $\begin{cases} 2(2x + 3y) = 5 \\ 8x = 3(1 + 3y) \end{cases}$

63. $\begin{cases} \frac{x}{2} - \frac{y}{3} = -2 \\ \frac{2x - 3}{2} + \frac{6y + 1}{3} = \frac{17}{6} \end{cases}$

64. $\begin{cases} \frac{x + 2}{4} + \frac{y - 1}{3} = \frac{1}{12} \\ \frac{x + 4}{5} - \frac{y - 2}{2} = \frac{5}{2} \end{cases}$

65. $\begin{cases} \frac{x - 3}{2} + \frac{y + 5}{3} = \frac{11}{6} \\ \frac{x + 3}{3} - \frac{5}{12} = \frac{y + 3}{4} \end{cases}$

66. $\begin{cases} \frac{x + 2}{3} = \frac{3 - y}{2} \\ \frac{x + 3}{2} = \frac{2 - y}{3} \end{cases}$

APPLICATIONS

67. Boating   Use the information in the table to find x and y.

	Rate	·	Time	=	Distance (mi)
Downstream	$x + y$		2		10
Upstream	$x - y$		5		5

68. Flying   Use the information in the table to find x and y.

	Rate	·	Time	=	Distance (mi)
Downwind	$x + y$		3		1,800
Upwind	$x - y$		5		2,400

WRITING ABOUT MATH

69. Why is it usually best to write the equations of a system in general form before using the elimination method to solve it?

70. How would you decide whether to use substitution or elimination to solve a system of equations?

SOMETHING TO THINK ABOUT

71. If possible, find a solution to the system

$$\begin{cases} x + y = 5 \\ x - y = -3 \\ 2x - y = -2 \end{cases}$$

72. If possible, find a solution to the system

$$\begin{cases} x + y = 5 \\ x - y = -3 \\ x - 2y = 0 \end{cases}$$

SECTION 3.6   Solving Applications of Systems of Linear Equations

Objective

1 Solve an application problem using a system of linear equations.

Getting Ready

Let x and y represent two numbers. Use an algebraic expression to denote each phrase.

1. The sum of x and y

2. The difference when y is subtracted from x

3. The product of x and y

4. The quotient x divided by y

5. Give the formula for the area of a rectangle.

6. Give the formula for the perimeter of a rectangle.

We have previously set up equations involving one variable to solve problems. In this section, we consider ways to solve problems by using equations in two variables.

1   Solve an application problem using a system of linear equations.

The following steps are helpful when solving problems involving two unknown quantities.

Problem Solving

1. Read the problem and *analyze* the facts. Identify the variables by asking yourself "What am I asked to find?" Pick different variables to represent two unknown quantities. Write a sentence to define each variable.

2. Form two equations involving each of the two variables. This will give a system of two equations in two variables. This may require reading the problem several times to understand the given facts. What information is given? Is there a formula that applies to this situation? Occasionally, a sketch, chart, or diagram will help you visualize the facts of the problem.

3. Solve the system using the most convenient method: graphing, substitution, or elimination (addition).

4. State the conclusion.

5. Check the solution in the words of the problem.

EXAMPLE 1   **FARMING**   A farmer raises wheat and soybeans on 215 acres. If he wants to plant 31 more acres in wheat than in soybeans, how many acres of each should he plant?

Analyze the problem   The farmer plants two fields, one in wheat and one in soybeans. We are asked to find how many acres of each he should plant. So, we let w represent the number of acres of wheat and s represent the number of acres of soybeans.

Form two equations   We know that the *number of acres* of wheat planted plus the *number of acres* of soybeans planted will equal a total of 215 *acres*. So we can form the equation

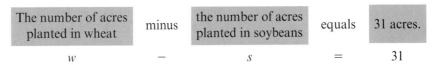

The number of acres planted in wheat	plus	the number of acres planted in soybeans	equals	215 acres.
w	$+$	s	$=$	215

Since the farmer wants to plant 31 more acres in wheat than in soybeans, we can form the equation

The number of acres planted in wheat	minus	the number of acres planted in soybeans	equals	31 acres.
w	$-$	s	$=$	31

Solve the system   We can now solve the system

$$(1) \quad \begin{cases} w + s = 215 \\ w - s = 31 \end{cases}$$
$$(2)$$

by the elimination method.

$$\begin{array}{r} w + s = 215 \\ \underline{w - s = 31} \\ 2w = 246 \\ w = 123 \end{array} \quad \text{Divide both sides by 2.}$$

To find s, we substitute 123 for w in Equation 1.

$$\begin{array}{rl} w + s = 215 & \\ \mathbf{123} + s = 215 & \text{Substitute 123 for } w. \\ s = 92 & \text{Subtract 123 from both sides.} \end{array}$$

State the conclusion   The farmer should plant 123 acres of wheat and 92 acres of soybeans.

Check the result   The total acreage planted is $123 + 92$, or 215 acres. The area planted in wheat is 31 acres greater than that planted in soybeans, because $123 - 92 = 31$. The answers check.

EXAMPLE 2   **LAWN CARE**   An installer of underground irrigation systems wants to cut a 20-foot length of plastic tubing into two pieces. The longer piece is to be 2 feet longer than twice the shorter piece. Find the length of each piece.

Analyze the problem   Refer to Figure 3-28, which shows the pipe. We need to find the length of each pipe, so we let s represent the *length* of the shorter piece and l represent the *length* of the longer piece.

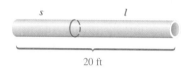

20 ft

Figure 3-28

Form two equations   Since the length of the plastic tube is 20 ft, we can form the equation

The length of the shorter piece	plus	the length of the longer piece	equals	20 feet.
s	$+$	l	$=$	20

Since the longer piece is 2 feet longer than twice the shorter piece, we can form the equation

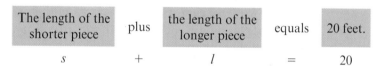

The length of the longer piece	equals	2	times	the length of the shorter piece	plus	2 feet.
l	$=$	2	$\cdot$	s	$+$	2

Solve the system   We can use the substitution method to solve the system

$$(1) \quad \begin{cases} s + l = 20 \\ (2) \quad l = 2s + 2 \end{cases}$$

$$s + (2s + 2) = 20 \quad \text{Substitute } 2s + 2 \text{ for } l \text{ in Equation 1.}$$
$$3s + 2 = 20 \quad \text{Remove parentheses and combine like terms.}$$
$$3s = 18 \quad \text{Subtract 2 from both sides.}$$
$$s = 6 \quad \text{Divide both sides by 3.}$$

State the conclusion   The shorter piece should be 6 feet long. To find the length of the longer piece, we substitute 6 for s in Equation 1 and solve for l.

$$s + l = 20$$
$$6 + l = 20 \quad \text{Substitute 6 for } s.$$
$$l = 14 \quad \text{Subtract 6 from both sides.}$$

The longer piece should be 14 feet long.

Check the result   The sum of 6 and 14 is 20 and 14 is 2 more than twice 6. The answers check.

EXAMPLE 3   **GARDENING**   Tom has 150 feet of fencing to enclose a rectangular garden. If the length is to be 5 feet less than 3 times the width, find the area of the garden.

Analyze the problem   To find the area of a rectangle, we need to know its length and width, so we can let l represent the length of the garden and w represent the width. See Figure 3-29.

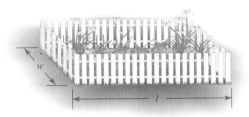

Figure 3-29

Form two equations   Since the perimeter of the rectangle is 150 ft, and this is two lengths plus two widths, we can form the equation:

2	times	the length of the garden	plus	2	times	the width of the garden	equals	150 feet.
2	$\cdot$	l	+	2	$\cdot$	w	=	150

Since the length is 5 feet less than 3 times the width, we can form the equation

The length of the garden	equals	3	times	the width of the garden	minus	5 feet.
l	=	3	$\cdot$	w	−	5

Solve the system   We can use the substitution method to solve this system.

$$(1) \quad \begin{cases} 2l + 2w = 150 \\ (2) \quad l = 3w - 5 \end{cases}$$

$2(3w - 5) + 2w = 150$ Substitute $3w - 5$ for l in Equation 1.

$6w - 10 + 2w = 150$ Remove parentheses.

$8w - 10 = 150$ Combine like terms.

$8w = 160$ Add 10 to both sides.

$w = 20$ Divide both sides by 8.

The width of the garden is 20 feet. To find the length, we substitute 20 for w in Equation 2 and simplify.

$l = 3w - 5$

$ = 3(20) - 5$ Substitute 20 for w.

$ = 60 - 5$

$ = 55$

Since the dimensions of the rectangle are 55 feet by 20 feet, and the area of a rectangle is given by the formula

$A = l \cdot w$ Area = length times width.

we have

$$A = 55 \cdot 20$$
$$= 1{,}100$$

State the conclusion   The garden covers an area of 1,100 square feet.

Check the result   Because the dimensions of the garden are 55 feet by 20 feet, the perimeter is

$$P = 2l + 2w$$
$$= 2(55) + 2(20) \quad \text{Substitute for } l \text{ and } w.$$
$$= 110 + 40$$
$$= 150$$

It is also true that 55 feet is 5 feet less than 3 times 20 feet. The answers check.

EXAMPLE 4   **MANUFACTURING**   The set-up cost of a machine that mills brass plates is $750. After set-up, it costs $0.25 to mill each plate. Management is considering the use of a larger machine that can produce the same plates at a cost of $0.20 per plate. If the set-up cost of the larger machine is $1,200, how many plates would the company have to produce to make the switch worthwhile?

Analyze the problem   We can let p represent the number of brass plates produced. Then, we will let c represent the total cost of milling p plates (set-up cost plus cost per plate).

Form two equations   To determine whether the switch is worthwhile, we need to know if the larger machine can produce the plates cheaper than the old machine and if so, when that occurs. We begin by finding the number of plates (called the *break point*) that will cost the same to produce on either machine.

If we call the machine currently being used machine 1, and the larger one machine 2, we can form the two equations

The cost of making p plates on machine 1	equals	the set-up cost of machine 1	plus	the cost per plate on machine 1	times	the number of plates p to be made.
c_1	$=$	750	$+$	0.25	$\cdot$	p

EVERYDAY CONNECTIONS   Olympic Medals

©Shutterstock.com/Aneta Skoczewska

According to specifications set by the International Olympic Committee, all Olympic medals must be at least 60 millimeters in diameter and three millimeters thick. Gold medals must be of 92.5% pure silver and gilded with at least six grams of gold.

In 2008, a gold medal consisting of 6 grams of gold and 74 grams of silver was worth $219.40. A gold medal consisting of 8 grams of gold and 85.75 grams of silver was worth $282.20.

Source: http://www.bargaineering.com/articles/how-much-is-an-olympic-medal-worth.html

1. What was the price of 1 gram of gold in 2008?

2. What was the price of 1 gram of silver in 2008?

The cost of making p plates on machine 2	equals	the set-up cost of machine 2	plus	the cost per plate on machine 2	times	the number of plates p to be made.
c_2	$=$	1,200	$+$	0.20	$\cdot$	p

Solve the system   Since the costs at the break point are equal ($c_1 = c_2$), we can use the substitution method to solve the system

$$\begin{cases} c_1 = \mathbf{750 + 0.25}p \\ c_2 = 1{,}200 + 0.20p \end{cases}$$

$$750 + 0.25p = 1{,}200 + 0.20p \quad \text{Substitute } 750 + 0.25p \text{ for } c_2 \text{ in the second equation.}$$
$$0.25p = 450 + 0.20p \quad \text{Subtract 750 from both sides.}$$
$$0.05p = 450 \quad \text{Subtract } 0.20p \text{ from both sides.}$$
$$p = 9{,}000 \quad \text{Divide both sides by 0.05.}$$

State the conclusion   If 9,000 plates are milled, the cost will be the same on either machine. If more than 9,000 plates are milled, the cost will be less on the larger machine, because it mills the plates less expensively than the smaller machine.

Check the solution   Figure 3-30 verifies that the break point is 9,000 plates. It also interprets the solution graphically.

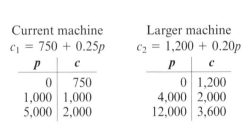

Current machine
$c_1 = 750 + 0.25p$

p	c
0	750
1,000	1,000
5,000	2,000

Larger machine
$c_2 = 1,200 + 0.20p$

p	c
0	1,200
4,000	2,000
12,000	3,600

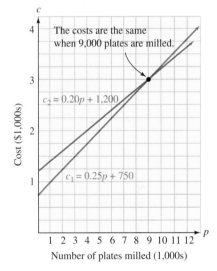

Figure 3-30

EXAMPLE 5   **INVESTING**   Terri and Juan earned $650 from a one-year investment of $15,000. If Terri invested some of the money at 4% interest and Juan invested the rest at 5%, how much did each invest?

Analyze the problem   We are asked to find how much money Terri and Juan invested. We can let x represent the amount invested by Terri and y represent the amount of money invested by Juan. We are told that Terri invested an unknown part of the $15,000 at 4% interest and Juan invested the rest at 5% interest. Together, these investments earned $650 in interest.

Form two equations   Because the total investment is $15,000, we have

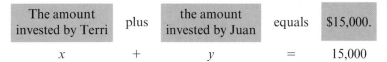

The amount invested by Terri	plus	the amount invested by Juan	equals	$15,000.
x	$+$	y	$=$	15,000

Since the income on x dollars invested at 4% is $0.04x$, the income on y dollars invested at 5% is $0.05y$, and the combined income is $650, we have

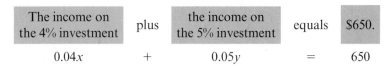

The income on the 4% investment	plus	the income on the 5% investment	equals	$650.
$0.04x$	$+$	$0.05y$	$=$	650

Thus, we have the system

(1) $\begin{cases} x + y = 15{,}000 \\ 0.04x + 0.05y = 650 \end{cases}$
(2)

Solve the system   To solve the system, we use the elimination method.

$$\begin{aligned} -4x - 4y &= -60{,}000 \quad &\text{Multiply both sides of Equation 1 by } -4. \\ \underline{4x + 5y} &= \underline{65{,}000} \quad &\text{Multiply both sides of Equation 2 by 100.} \\ y &= 5{,}000 \quad &\text{Add the equations together.} \end{aligned}$$

To find x, we substitute 5,000 for y in Equation 1 and simplify.

$$\begin{aligned} x + y &= 15{,}000 \\ x + \mathbf{5{,}000} &= 15{,}000 \quad &\text{Substitute 5,000 for } y. \\ x &= 10{,}000 \quad &\text{Subtract 5,000 from both sides.} \end{aligned}$$

State the conclusion   Terri invested $10,000, and Juan invested $5,000.

Check the result
$$\begin{aligned} \$10{,}000 + \$5{,}000 &= \$15{,}000 \quad &\text{The two investments total \$15,000.} \\ 0.04(\$10{,}000) &= \$400 \quad &\text{Terri earned \$400.} \\ 0.05(\$5{,}000) &= \$250 \quad &\text{Juan earned \$250.} \end{aligned}$$

The combined interest is $400 + $250 = $650. The answers check.

EXAMPLE 6   **BOATING**   A boat traveled 30 kilometers downstream in 3 hours and made the return trip in 5 hours. Find the speed of the boat in still water.

Analyze the problem   We are asked to find the speed of the boat, so we let s represent the speed of the boat in still water. Recall from earlier problems that when traveling upstream or downstream, the current affects that speed. Therefore, we let c represent the speed of the current.

Form two equations   Traveling downstream, the rate of the boat will be the speed of the boat in still water, s, plus the speed of the current, c. Thus, the rate of the boat going downstream is $s + c$.

Traveling upstream, the rate of the boat will be the speed of the boat in still water, s, minus the speed of the current, c. Thus, the rate of the boat going upstream is $s - c$.

We can organize the information of the problem as in Table 3-5.

	Distance	=	Rate	·	Time
Downstream	30		$s + c$		3
Upstream	30		$s - c$		5

Table 3-5

Because $d = r \cdot t$, the information in the table gives two equations in two variables.

$$\begin{cases} 30 = 3(s + c) \\ 30 = 5(s - c) \end{cases}$$

After removing parentheses and rearranging terms, we have

(1) $\quad \begin{cases} 3s + 3c = 30 \end{cases}$
(2) $\quad \begin{cases} 5s - 5c = 30 \end{cases}$

Solve the system   To solve this system by elimination, we multiply Equation 1 by 5, multiply Equation 2 by 3, add the equations, and solve for s.

$$\begin{array}{r} 15s + 15c = 150 \\ 15s - 15c = 90 \\ \hline 30s = 240 \end{array}$$

$\qquad\qquad s = 8 \qquad$ Divide both sides by 30.

State the conclusion   The speed of the boat in still water is 8 kilometers per hour.

Check the result   Verify the answer checks.

EXAMPLE 7   **MEDICAL TECHNOLOGY**   A laboratory technician has one batch of antiseptic that is 40% alcohol and a second batch that is 60% alcohol. She would like to make 8 liters of solution that is 55% alcohol. How many liters of each batch should she use?

Analyze the problem   We need to know how many liters of each type of alcohol she should use, so we can let x represent the number of liters to be used from batch 1 and let y represent the number of liters to be used from batch 2.

Form two equations   Some 60% alcohol solution must be added to some 40% alcohol solution to make a 55% alcohol solution. We can organize the information of the problem as in Table 3-6.

	Fractional part that is alcohol	·	Number of liters of solution	=	Number of liters of alcohol
Batch 1	0.40		x		$0.40x$
Batch 2	0.60		y		$0.60y$
Mixture	0.55		8		0.55(8)

Table 3-6

The information in Table 3-6 provides two equations.

(1) $\quad x + y = 8$ The *number of liters* of batch 1 plus the *number of liters* of batch 2 equals the *total number of liters* in the mixture.

(2) $\quad 0.40x + 0.60y = 0.55(8)$ The *amount of alcohol* in batch 1 plus the *amount of alcohol* in batch 2 equals the *amount of alcohol* in the mixture.

Solve the system   We can use elimination to solve this system.

$$\begin{array}{r} -40x - 40y = -320 \\ 40x + 60y = 440 \\ \hline 20y = 120 \end{array}$$

Multiply both sides of Equation 1 by −40.
Multiply both sides of Equation 2 by 100.

$\qquad\qquad y = 6 \qquad$ Divide both sides by 20.

To find x, we substitute 6 for y in Equation 1 and simplify:

$x + y = 8$

$x + 6 = 8$ Substitute 6 for y.

$x = 2$ Subtract 6 from both sides.

State the conclusion   The technician should use 2 liters of the 40% solution and 6 liters of the 60% solution.

Check the result   Verify the answer checks.

NOW TRY THIS

1. A chemist has 20 ml of a 30% alcohol solution. How much pure alcohol must she add so that the resulting solution contains 50% alcohol?

3.6 EXERCISES

WARM-UPS

If x and y are integers, express each quantity.

1. Twice x
2. One more than y
3. The sum of twice x and three times y.
4. The quotient when x is divided by $3y$.

If a book costs $x and a calculator costs $y, find

5. The cost of 3 books and 2 calculators
6. The cost of 4 books and 5 calculators

REVIEW

Graph each inequality.

7. $x < 4$
8. $x \geq -3$

9. $-1 < x \leq 2$
10. $-2 \leq x \leq 0$

Write each product using exponents.

11. $8 \cdot 8 \cdot 8 \cdot c$
12. $5(\pi)(r)(r)$
13. $a \cdot a \cdot b \cdot b$
14. $(-2)(-2)$

VOCABULARY AND CONCEPTS   *Fill in the blanks.*

15. A _____ is a letter that stands for a number.
16. An _____ is a statement indicating that two quantities are equal.
17. $\begin{cases} a + b = 20 \\ a = 2b + 4 \end{cases}$ is a _____ of linear equations.
18. A _____ of a system of two linear equations satisfies both equations simultaneously.

APPLICATIONS

Use two equations in two variables to solve each problem.
See Example 1. (Objective 1)

19. **Government** The salaries of the President and Vice President of the United States total $592,600 a year. If the President makes $207,400 more than the Vice President, find each of their salaries.

20. **Splitting the lottery** Chayla and Lena pool their resources to buy several lottery tickets. They win $250,000! They agree that Lena should get $50,000 more than Chayla, because she gave most of the money. How much will Chayla get?

21. **Figuring inheritances** In his will, a man left his older son $10,000 more than twice as much as he left his younger son. If the estate is worth $497,500, how much did the younger son get?

22. Selling radios   An electronics store put two types of car radios on sale. One model sold for $87, and the other sold for $119. During the sale, the receipts for 25 radios sold were $2,495. How many of the less expensive radios were sold?

Use two equations in two variables to solve each problem. **See Example 2. (Objective 1)**

23. Cutting pipe   A plumber wants to cut the pipe shown in the illustration into two pieces so that one piece is 5 feet longer than the other. How long should each piece be?

25 ft

24. Cutting lumber   A carpenter wants to cut a 20-foot board into two pieces so that one piece is 4 times as long as the other. How long should each piece be?

25. Buying baseball equipment   One catcher's mitt and ten out-fielder's gloves cost $239.50. How much does each cost if one catcher's mitt and five outfielder's gloves cost $134.50?

26. Buying painting supplies   Two partial receipts for paint supplies appear in the illustration. How much did each gallon of paint and each brush cost?

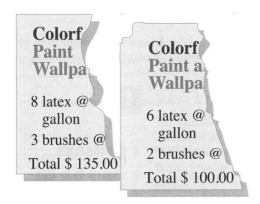

Colorf
Paint
Wallpa

8 latex @
gallon
3 brushes @
Total $ 135.00

Colorf
Paint a
Wallpa

6 latex @
gallon
2 brushes @
Total $ 100.00

Use two equations in two variables to solve each problem. **See Example 3. (Objective 1)**

27. Geometry   The perimeter of the rectangle shown in the illustration is 110 feet. Find its dimensions.

w

$l = w + 5$

28. Geometry   A rectangle is 3 times as long as it is wide, and its perimeter is 80 centimeters. Find its dimensions.

29. Geometry   The length of a rectangle is 2 feet more than twice its width. If its perimeter is 34 feet, find its area.

30. Geometry   A 50-meter path surrounds a rectangular garden. The width of the garden is two-thirds its length. Find its area.

Use two equations in two variables to solve each problem. **See Example 4. (Objective 1)**

31. Choosing a furnace   A high-efficiency 90+ furnace costs $2,250 and costs an average of $412 per year to operate in Rockford, IL. An 80+ furnace costs only $1,715 but costs $466 per year to operate. Find the break point.

32. Making tires   A company has two molds to form tires. One mold has a set-up cost of $600 and the other a set-up cost of $1,100. The cost to make each tire on the first machine is $15, and the cost per tire on the second machine is $13. Find the break point.

33. Choosing a furnace   See Exercise 31. If you intended to live in a house for seven years, which furnace would you choose?

34. Making tires   See Exercise 32. If you planned a production run of 500 tires, which mold would you use?

Use two equations in two variables to solve each problem. **See Example 5. (Objective 1)**

35. Investing money   Bill invested some money at 5% annual interest, and Janette invested some at 7%. If their combined interest was $310 on a total investment of $5,000, how much did Bill invest?

36. Investing money   Peter invested some money at 6% annual interest, and Martha invested some at 12%. If their combined investment was $6,000 and their combined interest was $540, how much money did Martha invest?

37. Buying tickets   Students can buy tickets to a basketball game for $1. The admission for nonstudents is $2. If 350 tickets are sold and the total receipts are $450, how many student tickets are sold?

38. Buying tickets   If receipts for the movie advertised in the illustration were $720 for an audience of 190 people, how many senior citizens attended?

TICKETS

Admissions: $4
Seniors: $3
Showtimes: 7, 9,11

Use two equations in two variables to solve each problem.
See Example 6. (Objective 1)

39. Boating A boat can travel 24 miles downstream in 2 hours and can make the return trip in 3 hours. Find the speed of the boat in still water.

40. Aviation With the wind, a plane can fly 3,000 miles in 5 hours. Against the same wind, the trip takes 6 hours. Find the airspeed of the plane (the speed in still air).

41. Aviation An airplane can fly downwind a distance of 600 miles in 2 hours. However, the return trip against the same wind takes 3 hours. Find the speed of the wind.

42. Finding the speed of a current It takes a motorboat 4 hours to travel 56 miles down a river, and it takes 3 hours longer to make the return trip. Find the speed of the current.

Use two equations in two variables to solve each problem.
See Example 7. (Objective 1)

43. Mixing chemicals A chemist has one solution that is 40% alcohol and another that is 55% alcohol. How much of each must she use to make 15 liters of a solution that is 50% alcohol?

44. Mixing pharmaceuticals A nurse has a solution that is 25% alcohol and another that is 50% alcohol. How much of each must he use to make 20 liters of a solution that is 40% alcohol?

45. Mixing nuts A merchant wants to mix the peanuts with the cashews shown in the illustration to get 48 pounds of mixed nuts to sell at $4 per pound. How many pounds of each should the merchant use?

46. Mixing peanuts and candy A merchant wants to mix peanuts worth $3 per pound with jelly beans worth $1.50 per pound to make 30 pounds of a mixture worth $2.10 per pound. How many pounds of each should he use?

Use two equations in two variables to solve each problem.

47. Integer problem One integer is twice another, and their sum is 96. Find the integers.

48. Integer problem The sum of two integers is 38, and their difference is 12. Find the integers.

49. Integer problem Three times one integer plus another integer is 29. If the first integer plus twice the second is 18, find the integers.

50. Integer problem Twice one integer plus another integer is 21. If the first integer plus 3 times the second is 33, find the integers.

51. Buying contact lens cleaner Two bottles of contact lens cleaner and three bottles of soaking solution cost $29.40, and three bottles of cleaner and two bottles of soaking solution cost $28.60. Find the cost of each.

52. Buying clothes Two pairs of shoes and four pairs of socks cost $109, and three pairs of shoes and five pairs of socks cost $160. Find the cost of a pair of socks.

53. At the movies At an IMAX theater, the giant rectangular movie screen has a width 26 feet less than its length. If its perimeter is 332 feet, find the area of the screen.

54. Raising livestock A rancher raises five times as many cows as horses. If he has 168 animals, how many cows does he have?

55. Grass seed mixture A landscaper used 100 pounds of grass seed containing twice as much bluegrass as rye. He added 15 more pounds of bluegrass to the mixture before seeding a lawn. How many pounds of bluegrass did he use?

56. Television programming The producer of a 30-minute documentary about World War I divided it into two parts. Four times as much program time was devoted to the causes of the war as to the outcome. How long was each part of the documentary?

57. Causes of death In 2005, the number of American women dying from cancer was seven times the number that died from diabetes. If the number of deaths from these two causes was 308,000, how many American women died from each cause?

58. Selling ice cream At a store, ice cream cones cost $1.90 and sundaes cost $2.65. One day, the receipts for a total of 148 cones and sundaes were $328.45. How many cones were sold?

59. Investing money An investment of $950 at one rate of interest and $1,200 at a higher rate together generate an annual income of $88.50. If the investment rates differ by 2%, find the lower rate.

60. Motion problem A man drives for a while at 45 mph. Realizing that he is running late, he increases his speed to 60 mph and completes his 405-mile trip in 8 hours. How long does he drive at 45 mph?

61. Equilibrium price The number of canoes sold at a marina depends on price. As the price gets higher, fewer canoes will be sold. The equation that relates the price of a canoe to the number sold is called a **demand equation.** Suppose that the demand equation for canoes is

$$p = -\frac{1}{2}q + 1,300$$

where p is the price and q is the number sold at that price.

The number of canoes produced also depends on price. As the price gets higher, more canoes will be manufactured. The equation that relates the number of canoes produced to the price is called a **supply equation.** Suppose that the supply equation for canoes is

$$p = \frac{1}{3}q + \frac{1,400}{3}$$

where p is the price and q is the number produced at that price. The **equilibrium price** is the price at which supply equals demand. Find the equilibrium price.

WRITING ABOUT MATH

62. Which problem in the preceding set did you find the hardest? Why?

63. Which problem in the preceding set did you find the easiest? Why?

SOMETHING TO THINK ABOUT

64. In the illustration below, how many nails will balance one nut?

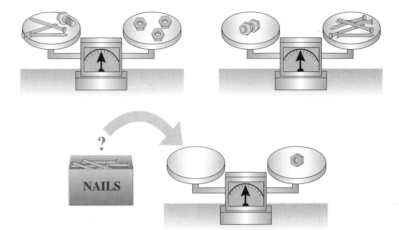

SECTION 3.7

Solving Systems of Linear Inequalities

Objectives

1 Determine whether an ordered pair is a solution to a given linear inequality.

2 Graph a linear inequality in one or two variables.

3 Solve an application problem involving a linear inequality in two variables.

4 Graph the solution set of a system of linear inequalities in one or two variables.

5 Solve an application problem using a system of linear inequalities.

linear inequality	half-plane	doubly shaded region

Graph $y = \frac{1}{3}x + 3$ and determine whether the given point lies on the line, above the line, or below the line.

1. $(0, 0)$ **2.** $(0, 4)$ **3.** $(2, 2)$ **4.** $(6, 5)$
5. $(-3, 2)$ **6.** $(6, 8)$ **7.** $(-6, 0)$ **8.** $(-9, 5)$

We now discuss how to solve a linear inequality in two variables graphically. Then we will show how to solve systems of inequalities.

1 **Determine whether an ordered pair is a solution to a given linear inequality.**

A **linear inequality** in x and y is an inequality that can be written in one of the following forms:

$$Ax + By > C \qquad Ax + By < C \qquad Ax + By \geq C \qquad Ax + By \leq C$$

where A, B, and C are real numbers and A and B are not both 0. Some examples of linear inequalities are

$$2x - y > -3 \qquad y < 3 \qquad x + 47 \geq 6 \qquad x \leq -2$$

An ordered pair (x, y) is a solution of an inequality in x and y if a true statement results when the values of x and y are substituted into the inequality.

EXAMPLE 1   Determine whether each ordered pair is a solution of $y \geq x - 5$:
a. $(4, 2)$ **b.** $(0, -6)$ **c.** $(5, 0)$

Solution   **a.** To determine whether $(4, 2)$ is a solution, we substitute 4 for x and 2 for y.

$$y \geq x - 5$$
$$2 \geq 4 - 5$$
$$2 \geq -1$$

Since $2 \geq -1$ is a true inequality, $(4, 2)$ is a solution.

b. To determine whether $(0, -6)$ is a solution, we substitute 0 for x and -6 for y.

$$y \geq x - 5$$
$$-6 \geq 0 - 5$$
$$-6 \geq -5$$

Since $-6 \geq -5$ is a false inequality, $(0, -6)$ is not a solution.

c. To determine whether $(5, 0)$ is a solution, we substitute 5 for x and 0 for y.

$$y \geq x - 5$$
$$0 \geq 5 - 5$$
$$0 \geq 0$$

Since $0 \geq 0$ is a true inequality, $(5, 0)$ is a solution.

SELF CHECK 1 Use the inequality in Example 1 and determine whether each ordered pair is a solution:
a. $(8, 2)$ **b.** $(-4, 3)$

---

2 **Graph a linear inequality in one or two variables.**

The graph of $y = x - 5$ is a line consisting of the points whose coordinates satisfy the equation. The graph of the inequality $y \geq x - 5$ is not a line but rather an area bounded by a line, called a **half-plane.** The half-plane consists of the points whose coordinates satisfy the inequality.

EXAMPLE 2 Graph the inequality: $y \geq x - 5$.

Solution Because equality is included in the inequality, we begin by graphing the equation $y = x - 5$ with a solid line, as in Figure 3-31(a). Because the graph of $y \geq x - 5$ also indicates that y can be greater than $x - 5$, the coordinates of points other than those shown in Figure 3-31(a) satisfy the inequality. For example, the coordinates of the origin satisfy the inequality. We can verify this by letting x and y be 0 in the given inequality:

$$y \geq x - 5$$
$$0 \geq 0 - 5 \qquad \text{Substitute 0 for } x \text{ and 0 for } y.$$
$$0 \geq -5$$

Because $0 \geq -5$ is true, the coordinates of the origin satisfy the original inequality. In fact, the coordinates of every point on the same side of the line as the origin satisfy the inequality. The graph of $y \geq x - 5$ is the half-plane that is shaded in Figure 3-31(b).

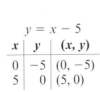

$y = x - 5$		
x	y	(x, y)
0	-5	$(0, -5)$
5	0	$(5, 0)$

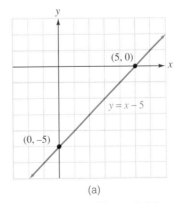

(a)

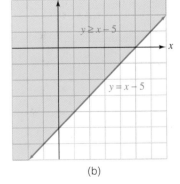

(b)

Figure 3-31

SELF CHECK 2 Graph: $y \geq -x - 2$.

EXAMPLE 3   Graph: $x + 2y < 6$.

Solution   We find the boundary by graphing the equation $x + 2y = 6$. Since the symbol $<$ does not include an $=$ sign, the points on the graph of $x + 2y = 6$ will not be a part of the graph. To show this, we draw the boundary line as a dashed line. See Figure 3-32.

To determine which half-plane to shade, we substitute the coordinates of some point that lies on one side of the boundary line into $x + 2y < 6$. The origin is a convenient choice.

$$x + 2y < 6$$
$$0 + 2(0) < 6 \qquad \text{Substitute 0 for } x \text{ and 0 for } y.$$
$$0 < 6$$

Since $0 < 6$ is true, we shade the side of the line that includes the origin. The graph is shown in Figure 3-32.

Sophie Germain
(1776–1831)

Sophie Germain was 13 years old during the French Revolution. Because of dangers caused by the insurrection in Paris, she was kept indoors and spent most of her time reading about mathematics in her father's library. Since interest in mathematics was considered inappropriate for a woman at that time, much of her work was written under the pen name of M. LeBlanc.

$x + 2y = 6$

x	y	(x, y)
0	3	(0, 3)
6	0	(6, 0)
4	1	(4, 1)

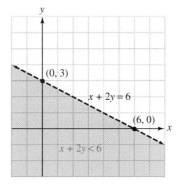

Figure 3-32

⇨ **SELF CHECK 3**   Graph: $2x - y < 4$.

COMMENT   The decision to use a dashed line or solid line is determined by the inequality symbol. If the symbol is $<$ or $>$, the line is dashed. If it is $\leq$ or $\geq$, the line is solid.

EXAMPLE 4   Graph: $y > 2x$.

Solution   To find the boundary line, we graph the equation $y = 2x$. Since the symbol $>$ does not include an equal sign, the points on the boundary are not a part of the graph of $y > 2x$. To show this, we draw the boundary as a dashed line. See Figure 3-33(a).

To determine which half-plane to shade, we substitute the coordinates of some point that lies on one side of the boundary into $y > 2x$. Point $T(0, 2)$, for example, is below the boundary line. See Figure 3-33(a) on the next page. To see if point $T(2, 0)$ satisfies $y > 2x$, we substitute 2 for x and 0 for y in the inequality.

$$y > 2x$$
$$0 > 2(2) \qquad \text{Substitute 2 for } x \text{ and 0 for } y.$$
$$0 > 4$$

Since $0 > 4$ is false, the coordinates of point T do not satisfy the inequality, and point T is not on the side of the line we want to shade. Instead, we shade the other side of the boundary line. The graph of the solution set of $y > 2x$ is shown in Figure 3-33(b).

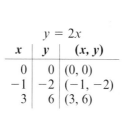

$$y = 2x$$

x	y	(x, y)
0	0	$(0, 0)$
-1	-2	$(-1, -2)$
3	6	$(3, 6)$

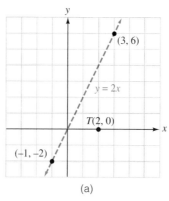

(a)

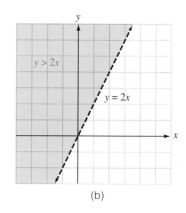

(b)

Figure 3-33

➡️ **SELF CHECK 4**   Graph: $y < 3x$.

3   **Solve an application problem involving a linear inequality in two variables.**

EXAMPLE 5   **EARNING MONEY**   Chen has two part-time jobs, one paying $5 per hour and the other paying $6 per hour. He must earn at least $120 per week to pay his expenses while attending college. Write an inequality that shows the various ways he can schedule his time to achieve his goal.

Solution   If we let x represent the number of hours Chen works on the first job and y the number of hours he works on the second job, we have

The hourly rate on the first job	times	the hours worked on the first job	plus	the hourly rate on the second job	times	the hours worked on the second job	is at least	$120.
$5	·	x	+	$6	·	y	≥	$120

The graph of the inequality $5x + 6y \geq 120$ is shown in Figure 3-34. Any point in the shaded region indicates a possible way Chen can schedule his time and earn $120 or more per week. For example, if he works 20 hours on the first job and 10 hours on the second job, he will earn

$$\$5(20) + \$6(10) = \$100 + \$60$$
$$= \$160$$

Since Chen cannot work a negative number of hours, the graph in the figure has no meaning when either x or y is negative.

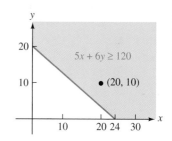

Figure 3-34

Graph the solution set of a system of linear inequalities in one or two variables.

We have seen that the graph of a linear inequality in two variables is a half-plane. Therefore, we would expect the graph of a system of two linear inequalities to be two overlapping half-planes. For example, to solve the system

$$\begin{cases} x + y \geq 1 \\ x - y \geq 1 \end{cases}$$

we graph each inequality and then superimpose the graphs on one set of coordinate axes.

The graph of $x + y \geq 1$ includes the graph of the equation $x + y = 1$ and all points above it. Because the boundary line is included, we draw it with a solid line. See Figure 3-35(a).

The graph of $x - y \geq 1$ includes the graph of the equation $x - y = 1$ and all points below it. Because the boundary line is included, we draw it with a solid line. See Figure 3-35(b).

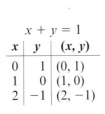

$x + y = 1$

x	y	(x, y)
0	1	$(0, 1)$
1	0	$(1, 0)$
2	-1	$(2, -1)$

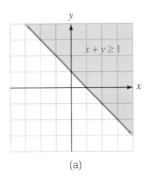

$x - y = 1$

x	y	(x, y)
0	-1	$(0, -1)$
1	0	$(1, 0)$
2	1	$(2, 1)$

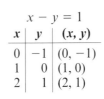

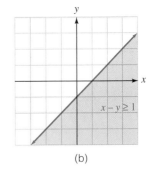

(a)

(b)

Figure 3-35

In Figure 3-36, we show the result when the graphs are superimposed on one coordinate system. The area that is shaded twice represents the set of solutions of the given system. Any point in the **doubly shaded region** has coordinates that satisfy both of the inequalities.

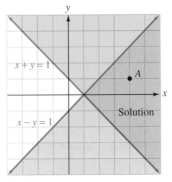

Figure 3-36

To see that this is true, we can pick a point, such as point A, that lies in the doubly shaded region and show that its coordinates satisfy both inequalities. Because point A has coordinates (4, 1), we have

$$x + y \geq 1 \qquad x - y \geq 1$$
$$4 + 1 \geq 1 \qquad 4 - 1 \geq 1$$
$$5 \geq 1 \qquad 3 \geq 1$$

Since the coordinates of point A satisfy each inequality, point A is a solution. If we pick a point that is not in the doubly shaded region, its coordinates will not satisfy both of the inequalities.

In general, to solve systems of linear inequalities, we will take the following steps.

Solving Systems of Inequalities

1. Graph each inequality in the system on the same coordinate axes using solid or dashed lines as appropriate.
2. Find the region where the graphs overlap.
3. Pick a test point from the region to verify the solution.

EXAMPLE 6   Graph the solution set: $\begin{cases} 2x + y < 4 \\ -2x + y > 2 \end{cases}$.

Solution   We graph each inequality on one set of coordinate axes, as in Figure 3-37.

- The graph of $2x + y < 4$ includes all points below the line $2x + y = 4$. Since the boundary is not included, we draw it as a dashed line.
- The graph of $-2x + y > 2$ includes all points above the line $-2x + y = 2$. Since the boundary is not included, we draw it as a dashed line.

The area that is shaded twice represents the set of solutions of the given system.

$2x + y = 4$		
x	y	(x, y)
0	4	$(0, 4)$
1	2	$(1, 2)$
2	0	$(2, 0)$

$-2x + y = 2$		
x	y	(x, y)
-1	0	$(-1, 0)$
0	2	$(0, 2)$
2	6	$(2, 6)$

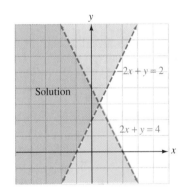

Figure 3-37

Pick a point in the doubly shaded region and show that it satisfies both inequalities.

SELF CHECK 6   Graph the solution set: $\begin{cases} x + 3y \leq 6 \\ -x + 3y < 6 \end{cases}$.

EXAMPLE 7   Graph the solution set: $\begin{cases} x \leq 2 \\ y > 3 \end{cases}$.

Solution   We graph each inequality on one set of coordinate axes, as in Figure 3-38.

- The graph of $x \leq 2$ includes all points on the line $x = 2$ and all points to the left of the line. Since the boundary line is included, we draw it as a solid line.
- The graph $y > 3$ includes all points above the line $y = 3$. Since the boundary is not included, we draw it as a dashed line.

The area that is shaded twice represents the set of solutions of the given system. Pick a point in the doubly shaded region and show that this is true.

$x = 2$

x	y	(x, y)
2	0	(2, 0)
2	2	(2, 2)
2	4	(2, 4)

$y = 3$

x	y	(x, y)
0	3	(0, 3)
1	3	(1, 3)
4	3	(4, 3)

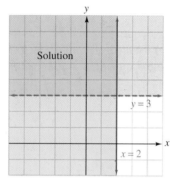

Figure 3-38

⇨ **SELF CHECK 7**   Graph the solution set: $\begin{cases} y \geq 1 \\ x > 2 \end{cases}$.

EXAMPLE 8   Graph the solution set: $\begin{cases} y < 3x - 1 \\ y \geq 3x + 1 \end{cases}$.

Solution   We graph each inequality, as in Figure 3-39.

- The graph of $y < 3x - 1$ includes all of the points below the dashed line $y = 3x - 1$.
- The graph of $y \geq 3x + 1$ includes all of the points on and above the solid line $y = 3x + 1$.

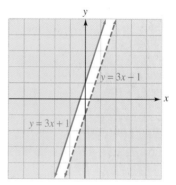

Figure 3-39

Since the graphs of these inequalities do not intersect, the solution set is $\varnothing$.

⇨ **SELF CHECK 8**   Graph the solution set: $\begin{cases} y \geq -\frac{1}{2} + 1 \\ y \leq -\frac{1}{2}x - 1 \end{cases}$.

5 Solve an application problem using a system of linear inequalities.

EXAMPLE 9   **LANDSCAPING**   A man budgets from $300 to $600 for trees and bushes to landscape his yard. After shopping around, he finds that good trees cost $150 and mature bushes cost $75. What combinations of trees and bushes can he afford to buy?

Analyze the problem   The man wants to spend *at least* $300 but *not more than* $600 for trees and bushes.

Form two inequalities   We can let x represent the number of trees purchased and y the number of bushes purchased. We can then form the following system of inequalities.

The cost of a tree	times	the number of trees purchased	plus	the cost of a bush	times	the number of bushes purchased	should be at least	$300.
$150	$\cdot$	x	+	$75	$\cdot$	y	$\geq$	$300

The cost of a tree	times	the number of trees purchased	plus	the cost of a bush	times	the number of bushes purchased	should not be more than	$600.
$150	$\cdot$	x	+	$75	$\cdot$	y	$\leq$	$600

Solve the system   We graph the system

$$\begin{cases} 150x + 75y \geq 300 \\ 150x + 75y \leq 600 \end{cases}$$

as in Figure 3-40. The coordinates of each point shown in the graph give a possible combination of the number of trees (x) and the number of bushes (y) that can be purchased. These possibilities are

(0, 4), (0, 5), (0, 6), (0, 7), (0, 8)

(1, 2), (1, 3), (1, 4), (1, 5), (1, 6)

(2, 0), (2, 1), (2, 2), (2, 3), (2, 4)

(3, 0), (3, 1), (3, 2), (4, 0)

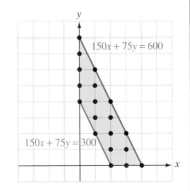

Figure 3-40

Only these points can be used, because the man cannot buy part of a tree or part of a bush.

➡ **SELF CHECK ANSWERS**

1. a. no   **b.** yes   **2.**   **3.**   **4.**

6.   **7.**   **8.** ∅

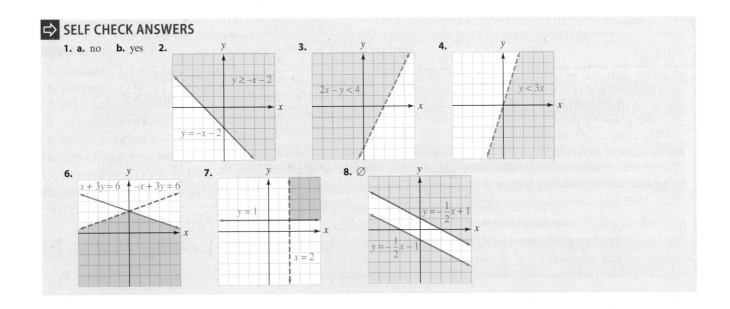

NOW TRY THIS

Solve each system by graphing.

1. $\begin{cases} y \geq x \\ x < -y + 2 \end{cases}$

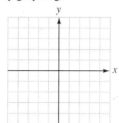

2. $\begin{cases} x - y > 4 \\ y < x + 5 \end{cases}$

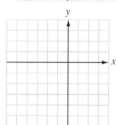

3. $\begin{cases} x - y > 0 \\ x \geq 3 \\ -y > 2 \end{cases}$

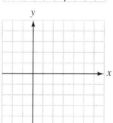

3.7 EXERCISES

WARM-UPS

Determine whether the following coordinates satisfy y > 3x + 2.

1. $(0, 0)$ **2.** $(5, 5)$

3. $(-2, 4)$ **4.** $(-3, -6)$

Determine whether the following coordinates satisfy the inequality $y \leq \frac{1}{2}x - 1$.

5. $(0, 0)$ **6.** $(2, 0)$

7. $(4, 3)$ **8.** $(-4, -3)$

REVIEW

9. Solve: $3x + 5 = 14$.

10. Solve: $2(x - 4) \leq -12$.

11. Solve: $A = P + Prt$ for t.

12. Does the graph of $y = -x$ pass through the origin?

Simplify each expression.

13. $2a + 5(a - 3)$

14. $2t - 3(3 + t)$

15. $4(b - a) + 3b + 2a$

16. $3p + 2(q - p) + q$

VOCABULARY AND CONCEPTS   *Fill in the blanks.*

17. $2x - y \leq 4$ is a linear _____ in x and y.

18. The symbol $\leq$ means _____ or _____.

19. In the accompanying graph, the line $2x - y = 4$ is the _____ of the graph $2x - y \leq 4$.

20. In the accompanying graph, the line $2x - y = 4$ divides the rectangular coordinate system into two _____.

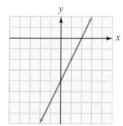

21. $\begin{cases} x + y > 2 \\ x + y < 4 \end{cases}$ is a system of linear _____.

22. The _____ of a system of linear inequalities are all the ordered pairs that make all of the inequalities of the system true at the same time.

23. Any point in the _____ region of the graph of the solution of a system of two linear inequalities has coordinates that satisfy both of the inequalities of the system.

24. To graph a linear inequality such as $x + y > 2$, first graph the boundary with a dashed line. Then pick a test _____ to determine which half-plane to shade.

25. Determine whether the graph of each linear inequality includes the boundary line.
    a. $y > -x$ **b.** $5x - 3y \leq -2$

26. If a false statement results when the coordinates of a test point are substituted into a linear inequality, which half-plane should be shaded to represent the solution of the inequality?

GUIDED PRACTICE

Determine whether each ordered pair is a solution of the given inequality. See Example 1. (Objective 1)

27. Determine whether each ordered pair is a solution of $5x - 3y \geq 0$.
    a. $(1, 1)$ **b.** $(-2, -3)$
    c. $(0, 0)$ **d.** $\left(\frac{1}{5}, \frac{4}{3}\right)$

28. Determine whether each ordered pair is a solution of $x + 4y < -1$.
    a. $(3, 1)$ **b.** $(-2, 0)$
    c. $(0.5, 0.2)$ **d.** $\left(-2, \frac{1}{4}\right)$

29. Determine whether each ordered pair is a solution of $x + y < 2$.
    a. $(2, 1)$ **b.** $(-2, -5)$
    c. $(-0.1, 0.3)$ **d.** $\left(-3, \frac{3}{4}\right)$

30. Determine whether each ordered pair is a solution of $2x - y < 3$.
    a. $(0, 3)$ **b.** $(-2, 0)$
    c. $(0.8, -1.5)$ **d.** $\left(-\frac{2}{3}, \frac{1}{3}\right)$

Graph each inequality. See Example 2. (Objective 2)

31. $y \leq x + 2$

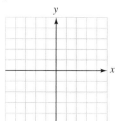

32. $y \leq -x + 1$

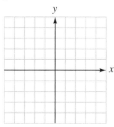

33. $y \leq 4x$

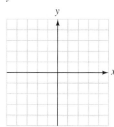

34. $y \geq 3 - x$

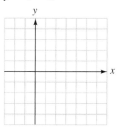

Graph each inequality. See Example 3. (Objective 2)

35. $y > x - 3$

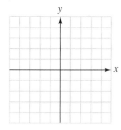

36. $y + 2x < 0$

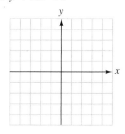

37. $y > 2x - 4$

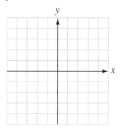

38. $y < 2 - x$

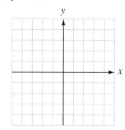

Graph each inequality. See Example 4. (Objective 2)

39. $y \geq 2x$

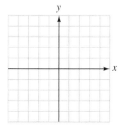

40. $y < 3x$

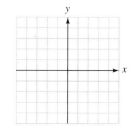

41. $x < 2$

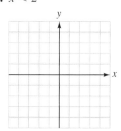

42. $y > -3$

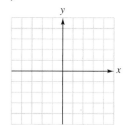

Graph the solution set of each system of inequalities, when possible. See Example 6. (Objective 4)

43. $\begin{cases} x + 2y \le 3 \\ 2x - y \ge 1 \end{cases}$

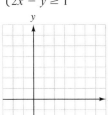

44. $\begin{cases} 2x + y \ge 3 \\ x - 2y \le -1 \end{cases}$

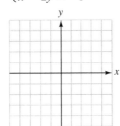

45. $\begin{cases} x + y < -1 \\ x - y > -1 \end{cases}$

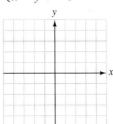

46. $\begin{cases} x + y > 2 \\ x - y < -2 \end{cases}$

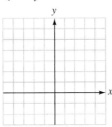

Graph the solution set of each system of inequalities, when possible. See Example 7. (Objective 4)

47. $\begin{cases} x > 2 \\ y \le 3 \end{cases}$

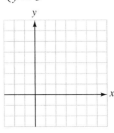

48. $\begin{cases} x \ge -1 \\ y > -2 \end{cases}$

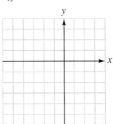

49. $\begin{cases} x \le 0 \\ y < 0 \end{cases}$

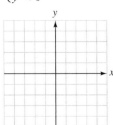

50. $\begin{cases} x < -2 \\ y \ge 3 \end{cases}$

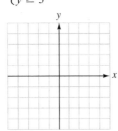

Graph the solution set of each system of inequalities, when possible. See Example 8. (Objective 4)

51. $\begin{cases} x + y < 1 \\ x + y > 3 \end{cases}$

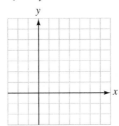

52. $\begin{cases} y < 2x - 1 \\ 2x - y < -4 \end{cases}$

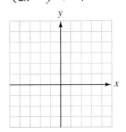

53. $\begin{cases} y \le -\frac{4}{3}x - 2 \\ 4x + 3y > 15 \end{cases}$

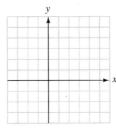

54. $\begin{cases} 3x + y < -2 \\ y > 3(1 - x) \end{cases}$

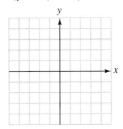

ADDITIONAL PRACTICE

Graph each inequality.

55. $x - 2y \le 4$

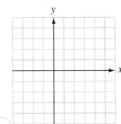

56. $3x + 2y \ge 12$

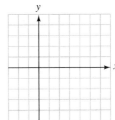

57. $y < 2 - 3x$

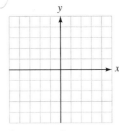

58. $y \ge 5 - 2x$

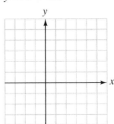

59. $2y - x < 8$

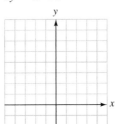

60. $y + 9x \ge 3$

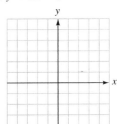

61. $3x - 4y > 12$

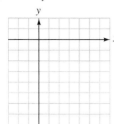

62. $4x + 3y \leq 12$

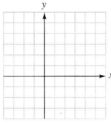

63. $5x + 4y \geq 20$

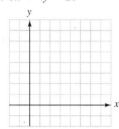

64. $7x - 2y < 21$

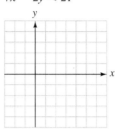

65. $y \leq 1$

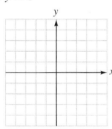

66. $x \geq -4$

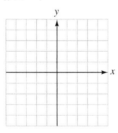

Graph the solution set of each system of inequalities, when possible.

67. $\begin{cases} 2x - y < 4 \\ x + y \geq -1 \end{cases}$

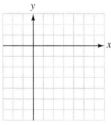

68. $\begin{cases} x - y \geq 5 \\ x + 2y < -4 \end{cases}$

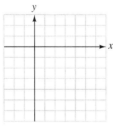

69. $\begin{cases} 3x + 4y > -7 \\ 2x - 3y \geq 1 \end{cases}$

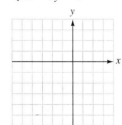

70. $\begin{cases} 3x + y \leq 1 \\ 4x - y > -8 \end{cases}$

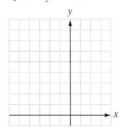

71. $\begin{cases} 2x - 4y > -6 \\ 3x + y \geq 5 \end{cases}$

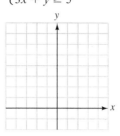

72. $\begin{cases} 2x - 3y < 0 \\ 2x + 3y \geq 12 \end{cases}$

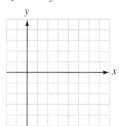

73. $\begin{cases} \frac{x}{2} + \frac{y}{3} \geq 2 \\ \frac{x}{2} - \frac{y}{2} < -1 \end{cases}$

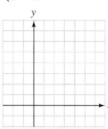

74. $\begin{cases} \frac{x}{3} - \frac{y}{2} < -3 \\ \frac{x}{3} + \frac{y}{2} > -1 \end{cases}$

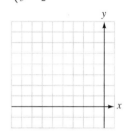

APPLICATIONS

Graph each inequality for nonnegative values of x and y. Then give some ordered pairs that satisfy the inequality. **See Example 5.** **(Objective 3)**

75. Production planning   It costs a bakery $3 to make a cake and $4 to make a pie. Production costs cannot exceed $120 per day. Find an inequality that shows the possible combinations of cakes, x, and pies, y, that can be made, and graph it in the illustration.

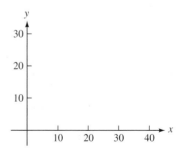

76. Hiring baby sitters
Tomiko has a choice of two babysitters. Sitter 1 charges $6 per hour, and sitter 2 charges $7 per hour. Tomiko can afford no more than $42 per week for sitters. Find an inequality that shows the possible ways that she can hire sitter 1 (x) and sitter 2 (y), and graph it in the illustration.

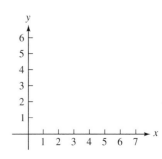

77. Inventory A clothing store advertises that it maintains an inventory of at least \$4,400 worth of men's jackets. A leather jacket costs \$100, and a nylon jacket costs \$88. Find an inequality that shows the possible ways that leather jackets, x, and nylon jackets, y, can be stocked, and graph it in the illustration.

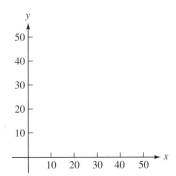

78. Making sporting goods To keep up with demand, a sporting goods manufacturer allocates at least 2,400 units of time per day to make baseballs and footballs. It takes 20 units of time to make a baseball and 30 units of time to make a football. Find an inequality that shows the possible ways to schedule the time to make baseballs, x, and footballs, y, and graph it in the illustration.

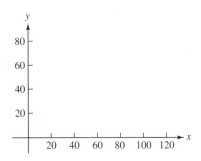

79. Investing Robert has up to \$8,000 to invest in two companies. Stock in Robotronics sells for \$40 per share, and stock in Macrocorp sells for \$50 per share. Find an inequality that shows the possible ways that he can buy shares of Robotronics, x, and Macrocorp, y, and graph it in the illustration.

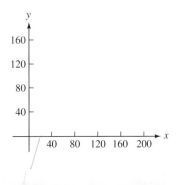

80. Buying tickets Tickets to the Rockford Rox baseball games cost \$6 for reserved seats and \$4 for general admission. Nightly receipts must be at least \$10,200 to meet expenses. Find an inequality that shows the possible ways that the Rox can sell reserved seats, x, and general admission tickets, y, and graph it in the illustration.

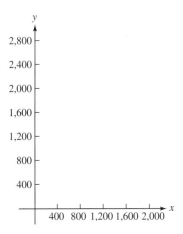

Graph each system of inequalities and give two possible solutions to each problem. **See Example 9. (Objective 5)**

81. Buying compact discs Melodic Music has compact discs on sale for either \$10 or \$15. A customer wants to spend at least \$30 but no more than \$60 on CDs. Find a system of inequalities whose graph will show the possible combinations of \$10 CDs, x, and \$15 CDs, y, that the customer can buy, and graph it in the illustration.

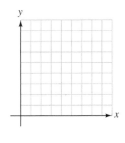

82. Buying boats Dry Boatworks wholesales aluminum boats for \$800 and fiberglass boats for \$600. Northland Marina wants to order at least \$2,400 but no more than \$4,800 worth of boats. Find a system of inequalities whose graph will show the possible combinations of aluminum boats, x, and fiberglass boats, y, that can be ordered, and graph it in the illustration.

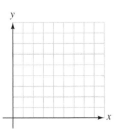

83. Buying furniture A distributor wholesales desk chairs for $150 and side chairs for $100. Best Furniture wants to order no more than $900 worth of chairs and wants to order more side chairs than desk chairs. Find a system of inequalities whose graph will show the possible combinations of desk chairs, x, and side chairs, y, that can be ordered, and graph it in the illustration.

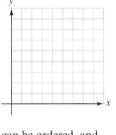

84. Ordering furnace equipment J. Bolden Heating Company wants to order no more than $2,000 worth of electronic air cleaners and humidifiers from a wholesaler that charges $500 for air cleaners and $200 for humidifiers. Bolden wants more humidifiers than air cleaners. Find a system of inequalities whose graph will show the possible combinations of air cleaners, x, and humidifiers, y, that can be ordered, and graph it in the illustration.

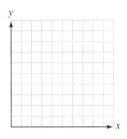

WRITING ABOUT MATH

85. Explain how to find the boundary for the graph of an inequality.

86. Explain how to decide which side of the boundary line to shade.

87. Explain how to use graphing to solve a system of inequalities.

88. Explain when a system of inequalities will have no solutions.

SOMETHING TO THINK ABOUT

89. What are some limitations of the graphing method for solving inequalities?

90. Graph $y = 3x + 1$, $y < 3x + 1$, and $y > 3x + 1$. What do you discover?

91. Can a system of inequalities have
a. no solutions?
b. exactly one solution?
c. infinitely many solutions?

92. Find a system of two inequalities that has a solution of $(2, 0)$ but no solutions of the form (x, y) where $y < 0$.

PROJECTS

Project 1

The graphing method of solving a system of equations is not as accurate as algebraic methods, and some systems are more difficult than others to solve accurately. For example, the two lines in Illustration 1(a) could be drawn carelessly, and the point of intersection would not be far from the correct location. If the lines in Illustration 1(b) were drawn carelessly, the point of intersection could move substantially from its correct location.

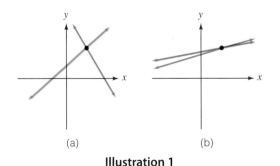

(a)　　　　　(b)

Illustration 1

■ Carefully solve each of these systems of equations graphically (by hand, not with a graphing calculator). Indicate your best estimate of the solution of each system.

$$\begin{cases} 2x - 4y = -7 \\ 4x + 2y = 11 \end{cases} \qquad \begin{cases} 5x - 4y = -1 \\ 12x - 10y = -3 \end{cases}$$

■ Solve each system algebraically. How close were your graphical solutions to the actual solutions? Write a paragraph explaining any differences.

■ Create a system of equations with the solutions $x = 3$, $y = 2$ for which an accurate solution could be obtained graphically.

■ Create a system of equations with the solutions $x = 3$, $y = 2$ that is more difficult to solve graphically than the previous system, and write a paragraph explaining why.

Project 2

Find the solutions of the following system of linear inequalities by graphing the inequalities of the given coordinate system.

$$\begin{cases} x + \frac{2}{3}y < \frac{4}{3} \\ y \le \frac{3}{5}x + 2 \end{cases}$$

For each point, A through G, on the graph, determine whether its coordinates satisfy the first inequality, the second inequality, neither inequality, or both. Present your results in a table like the one shown below.

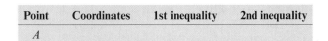

Point	Coordinates	1st inequality	2nd inequality
A			

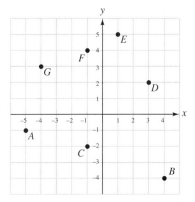

Illustration 2

Chapter 3 REVIEW

SECTION 3.1 The Rectangular Coordinate System

DEFINITIONS AND CONCEPTS	EXAMPLES
Any **ordered pair of real numbers** represents a point on the rectangular coordinate system.	Plot $(2, 6)$, $(-2, 6)$, $(-2, -6)$, $(2, -6)$, and $(0, 0)$.
The point where the axes cross is called the **origin**.	The origin is represented by the ordered pair $(0, 0)$.
The four regions of a coordinate plane are called **quadrants**.	The ordered pair $(2, 6)$ is found in quadrant I.
	The ordered pair $(-2, 6)$ is found in quadrant II.
	The ordered pair $(-2, -6)$ is found in quadrant III.
	The ordered pair $(2, -6)$ is found in quadrant IV.

REVIEW EXERCISES

Plot each point on the rectangular coordinate system in the illustration.

1. $A(1, 3)$ **2.** $B(1, -3)$
3. $C(-3, 1)$ **4.** $D(-3, -1)$
5. $E(0, 5)$ **6.** $F(-5, 0)$

Find the coordinates of each point in the illustration.

7. A **8.** B
9. C **10.** D
11. E **12.** F
13. G **14.** H

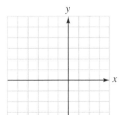

SECTION 3.2   Graphing Linear Equations

DEFINITIONS AND CONCEPTS	EXAMPLES
An ordered pair of real numbers is a **solution** to an equation in two variables if it satisfies the equation.	The ordered pair $(-1, 5)$ satisfies the equation $x - 2y = -11$. $(-1) - 2(5) \overset{?}{=} -11$ Substitute -1 for x and 5 for y. $-1 - 10 \overset{?}{=} -11$ $-11 = -11$ True. Since the results are equal, $(-1, 5)$ is a solution.

To graph a linear equation,

1. Find three pairs (x, y) that satisfy the equation.
2. Plot each pair on the rectangular coordinate system.
3. Draw a line passing through the three points.

General form of an equation of a line:

$$Ax + By = C$$
(A and B are not both 0.)

Graph: $x - y = -2$.

We first solve for y.

$x - y = -2$	This is the original equation.
$-y = -x - 2$	Subtract x from both sides.
$y = x + 2$	Divide both sides by -1.

Then find three ordered pairs that satisfy the equation.

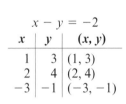

$$x - y = -2$$

x	y	(x, y)
1	3	$(1, 3)$
2	4	$(2, 4)$
-3	-1	$(-3, -1)$

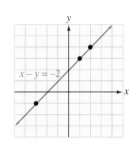

We then plot the points and draw a line passing through them.

The equation $y = b$ represents a horizontal line that intersects the y-axis at $(0, b)$.	The graph of $y = 5$ is a horizontal line passing through $(0, 5)$.
The equation $x = a$ represents a vertical line that intersects the x-axis at $(a, 0)$.	The graph of $x = 3$ is a vertical line passing through $(3, 0)$.

REVIEW EXERCISES

Determine whether each pair satisfies the equation $3x - 4y = 12$.

15. $(2, 1)$ **16.** $\left(3, -\frac{3}{4}\right)$

Graph each equation on a rectangular coordinate system.

17. $y = x - 5$ **18.** $y = 2x + 1$

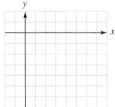

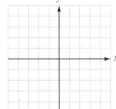

19. $y = \frac{x}{2} + 2$

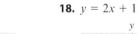

20. $y = 3$

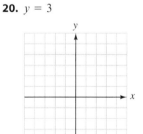

21. $x + y = 4$

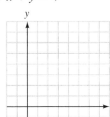

22. $x - y = -3$

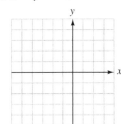

23. $3x + 5y = 15$

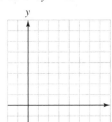

24. $7x - 4y = 28$

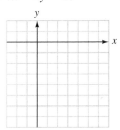

SECTION 3.3   Solving Systems of Linear Equations by Graphing

DEFINITIONS AND CONCEPTS	EXAMPLES
An *ordered pair* is a solution of a system of equations if it satisfies both equations.	To determine whether $(5, -1)$ is a solution of the following system, we proceed as follows: $$\begin{cases} x + y = 4 \\ 2x - y = 11 \end{cases}$$ $x + y = 4$ $5 + (-1) \overset{?}{=} 4$ Substitute 5 for x and -1 for y. $\qquad 4 = 4$ Add. $2x - y = 11$ $2(5) - (-1) \overset{?}{=} 11$ Substitute 5 for x and -1 for y. $\qquad 10 + 1 \overset{?}{=} 11$ Multiply 2 and 5, change sign of -1. $\qquad\qquad 11 = 11$ Add. Because the ordered pair $(5, -1)$ satisfies both equations, it is a solution of the system of equations.
To solve a system of equations graphically, carefully graph each equation of the system. If the lines intersect, the coordinates of the point of intersection give the solution of the system.	To solve the system $\begin{cases} x + y = 8 \\ 2x - 3y = 6 \end{cases}$ by graphing, we graph both equations on one set of coordinate axes using the intercept method.

$x + y = 8$

x	y	(x, y)
0	8	(0, 8)
8	0	(8, 0)

$2x - 3y = 6$

x	y	(x, y)
0	-2	(0, -2)
3	0	(3, 0)

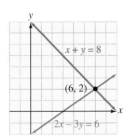

The solution of the system is the ordered pair $(6, 2)$.

If a system of equations has infinitely many solutions, the equations of the system are *dependent equations*.

To solve the system $\begin{cases} x + y = 8 \\ 2x + 2y = 16 \end{cases}$ by graphing, we graph both equations on one set of coordinate axes using the intercept method.

$x + y = 8$		
x	y	(x, y)
0	8	$(0, 8)$
8	0	$(8, 0)$

$2x + 2y = 16$		
x	y	(x, y)
0	8	$(0, 8)$
8	0	$(8, 0)$

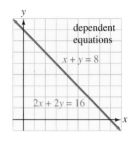

Since the lines in the illustration are the same line, there are infinitely many solutions, which can be written in the general form $(x, 8 - x)$.

If a system of equations has no solutions, it is an *inconsistent system* and we write the solution set as $\varnothing$.

To solve the system $\begin{cases} x + y = 8 \\ 2x + 2y = 6 \end{cases}$ by graphing, we graph both equations on one set of coordinate axes using the intercept method.

$x + y = 8$		
x	y	(x, y)
0	8	$(0, 8)$
8	0	$(8, 0)$

$2x + 2y = 6$		
x	y	(x, y)
0	3	$(0, 3)$
3	0	$(3, 0)$

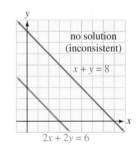

Since the lines in the figure are parallel, there are no solutions and the solution set is $\varnothing$.

REVIEW EXERCISES

Determine whether the ordered pair is a solution of the system.

25. $(1, 5)$, $\begin{cases} 3x - y = -2 \\ 2x + 3y = 17 \end{cases}$

26. $(-2, 4)$, $\begin{cases} 5x + 3y = 2 \\ -3x + 2y = 16 \end{cases}$

27. $\left(14, \frac{1}{2}\right)$, $\begin{cases} 2x + 4y = 30 \\ \frac{x}{4} - y = 3 \end{cases}$

28. $\left(\frac{7}{2}, -\frac{2}{3}\right)$, $\begin{cases} 4x - 6y = 18 \\ \frac{x}{3} + \frac{y}{2} = \frac{5}{6} \end{cases}$

Use the graphing method to solve each system.

29. $\begin{cases} x + y = 7 \\ 2x - y = 5 \end{cases}$ **30.** $\begin{cases} \frac{x}{3} + \frac{y}{5} = -1 \\ x - 3y = -3 \end{cases}$ **31.** $\begin{cases} 3x + 6y = 6 \\ x + 2y = 2 \end{cases}$ **32.** $\begin{cases} 6x + 3y = 12 \\ 2x + y = 2 \end{cases}$

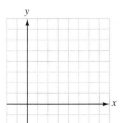 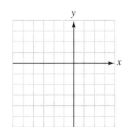 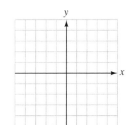 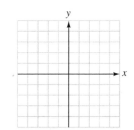

SECTION 3.4   Solving Systems of Linear Equations by Substitution

DEFINITIONS AND CONCEPTS	EXAMPLES

DEFINITIONS AND CONCEPTS

To solve a system of equations by substitution, solve one of the equations of the system for one of the variables, substitute the resulting expression into the other equation, and solve for the other variable.

EXAMPLES

To solve the system $\begin{cases} x + y = 8 \\ 2x - 3y = 6 \end{cases}$ by substitution, we solve one of the equations for one of its variables. If we solve $x + y = 8$ for y, we have

$\qquad y = 8 - x \qquad$ Subtract x from both sides.

We then substitute $8 - x$ for y in the second equation and solve for x.

$$2x - 3y = 6$$
$$2x - 3(8 - x) = 6 \qquad \text{Substitute } 8 - x \text{ for } y.$$
$$2x - 24 + 3x = 6 \qquad \text{Use the distributive property.}$$
$$5x - 24 = 6 \qquad \text{Combine like terms.}$$
$$5x = 30 \qquad \text{Add 24 to both sides.}$$
$$x = 6 \qquad \text{Divide by 5.}$$

We can find y by substituting 6 for x in the equation $y = 8 - x$.

$$y = 8 - x$$
$$y = 8 - 6 \qquad \text{Substitute 6 for } x.$$
$$y = 2 \qquad \text{Add.}$$

The solution is the ordered pair (6, 2).

REVIEW EXERCISES
Use substitution to solve each system.

33. $\begin{cases} x = 3y + 5 \\ 5x - 4y = 3 \end{cases}$

34. $\begin{cases} 3x - \frac{2y}{5} = 2(x - 2) \\ 2x - 3 = 3 - 2y \end{cases}$

35. $\begin{cases} 8x + 5y = 3 \\ 5x - 8y = 13 \end{cases}$

36. $\begin{cases} 6(x + 2) = y - 1 \\ 5(y - 1) = x + 2 \end{cases}$

SECTION 3.5   Solving Systems of Linear Equations by Elimination (Addition)

DEFINITIONS AND CONCEPTS	EXAMPLES

To solve a system of equations by elimination (addition), first multiply one or both of the equations by suitable constants, if necessary, to eliminate one of the variables when the equations are added. The equation that results can be solved for its single variable. Then substitute the value obtained back into one of the original equations and solve for the other variable.

To solve the system $\begin{cases} x + y = 8 \\ 2x - 3y = 6 \end{cases}$ by elimination, we can eliminate x by multiplying the first equation by -2 to get

$$\begin{cases} -2(x + y) = -2(8) \\ 2x - 3y = 6 \end{cases} \quad \rightarrow \quad \begin{cases} -2x - 2y = -16 \\ 2x - 3y = 6 \end{cases}$$

When these equations are added, the terms $-2x$ and $2x$ are eliminated.

$$\begin{array}{r} -2x - 2y = -16 \\ \underline{2x - 3y = 6} \\ -5y = -10 \end{array}$$

$$y = 2 \qquad \text{Divide both sides by } -5.$$

To find x, we substitute 2 for y in the equation $x + y = 8$.

$$x + y = 8$$
$$x + 2 = 8 \qquad \text{Substitute 2 for } y.$$
$$x = 6 \qquad \text{Subtract 2 from both sides.}$$

The solution is the ordered pair (6, 2).

REVIEW EXERCISES

Use elimination to solve each system.

37. $\begin{cases} 2x + y = 1 \\ 5x - y = 20 \end{cases}$

38. $\begin{cases} x + 8y = 7 \\ x - 4y = 1 \end{cases}$

39. $\begin{cases} 5x + y = 2 \\ 3x + 2y = 11 \end{cases}$

40. $\begin{cases} x + y = 3 \\ 3x = 2 - y \end{cases}$

41. $\begin{cases} 11x + 3y = 27 \\ 8x + 4y = 36 \end{cases}$

42. $\begin{cases} 9x + 3y = 5 \\ 3x = 4 - y \end{cases}$

43. $\begin{cases} 9x + 3y = 5 \\ 3x + y = \frac{5}{3} \end{cases}$

44. $\begin{cases} \frac{x}{3} + \frac{y+2}{2} = 1 \\ \frac{x+8}{8} + \frac{y-3}{3} = 0 \end{cases}$

SECTION 3.6   Solving Applications of Systems of Linear Equations

DEFINITIONS AND CONCEPTS	EXAMPLES

Systems of equations are useful in solving many types of application problems.

Boating   A boat traveled 30 kilometers downstream in 3 hours and traveled 12 kilometers in 3 hours against the current. Find the speed of the boat in still water.

Analyze the problem   We can let s represent the speed of the boat in still water and let c represent the speed of the current.

Form two equations   The rate of speed of the boat while going downstream is $s + c$. The rate of the boat while going upstream is $s - c$. Because $d = r \cdot t$, the information gives two equations in two variables.

$$\begin{cases} 30 = 3(s + c) \\ 12 = 3(s - c) \end{cases}$$

After removing parentheses and rearranging terms, we have

(1) $\begin{cases} 3s + 3c = 30 \\ 3s - 3c = 12 \end{cases}$
(2)

Solve the system   To solve this system by elimination (addition), we add the equations, and solve for *s*.

$$\begin{array}{rl} 3s + 3c &= 30 \\ 3s - 3c &= 12 \\ \hline 6s \quad\;\; &= 42 \\ s \quad\;\; &= 7 \end{array}$$ Divide both sides by 6.

State the conclusion   The speed of the boat in still water is 7 kilometers per hour.

REVIEW EXERCISES

45. Integer problem   One number is 5 times another, and their sum is 18. Find the numbers.

46. Geometry   The length of a rectangle is 3 times its width, and its perimeter is 24 feet. Find its dimensions.

47. Buying grapefruit   A grapefruit costs 15 cents more than an orange. Together, they cost 85 cents. Find the cost of a grapefruit.

48. Utility bills   A man's electric bill for January was $23 less than his gas bill. The two utilities cost him a total of $109. Find the amount of his gas bill.

49. Buying groceries   Two gallons of milk and 3 dozen eggs cost $6.80. Three gallons of milk and 2 dozen eggs cost $7.35. How much does each gallon of milk cost?

50. Investing money   Carlos invested part of $3,000 in a 10% certificate of deposit account and the rest in a 6% passbook account. If the total annual interest from both accounts is $270, how much did he invest at 6%?

51. Boating   It takes a boat 4 hours to travel 56 miles down a river and 3 hours longer to make the return trip. Find the speed of the current.

52. Medical technology   A laboratory technician has one batch of solution that is 10% saline and a second batch that is 60% saline. He would like to make 50 milliliters of solution that is 30% saline. How many liters of each batch should he use?

SECTION 3.7   Solving Systems of Linear Inequalities

DEFINITIONS AND CONCEPTS	EXAMPLES

DEFINITIONS AND CONCEPTS

To graph a system of linear inequalities, first graph the individual inequalities of the system. The final solution, if one exists, is that region where all the individual graphs intersect.

If a given inequality is $<$ or $>$, the boundary line is dashed.

If a given inequality is $\leq$ or $\geq$, the boundary line is solid.

EXAMPLES

Graph the solution set: $\begin{cases} x + y < 4 \\ 2x - y \geq 6 \end{cases}$

$x + y = 4$

x	y	(x, y)
0	4	(0, 4)
1	3	(1, 3)
2	2	(2, 2)

$2x - y = 6$

x	y	(x, y)
0	-6	(0, -6)
1	-4	(1, -4)
2	-2	(2, -2)

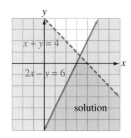

The graph of $x + y < 4$ includes all points below the line $x + y = 4$. Since the boundary is not included, we draw it as a dashed line.

The graph of $2x - y \geq 6$ includes all points below the line $2x - y = 6$. Since the boundary is included, we draw it as a solid line.

REVIEW EXERCISES

Graph each inequality.

53. $y \geq x + 2$

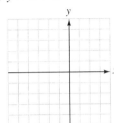

54. $x < 3$

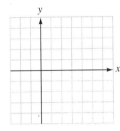

57. $\begin{cases} x \geq 3y \\ y < 3x \end{cases}$

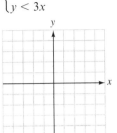

58. $\begin{cases} x \geq 0 \\ x \leq 3 \end{cases}$

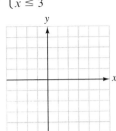

Solve each system of inequalities.

55. $\begin{cases} 5x + 3y < 15 \\ 3x - y > 3 \end{cases}$

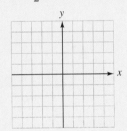

56. $\begin{cases} 5x - 3y \geq 5 \\ 3x + 2y \geq 3 \end{cases}$

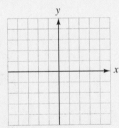

59. Shopping   A mother wants to spend at least $40 but no more than $60 on her child's school clothes. If shirts sell for $10 and pants sell for $20, find a system of inequalities that describe the possible numbers of shirts, x, and pants, y, that she can buy. Graph the system and give two possible solutions.

Chapter 3   TEST

Graph each equation.

1. $y = \dfrac{x}{2} + 1$

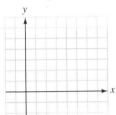

2. $2(x + 1) - y = 4$

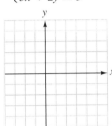

3. $x = 1$

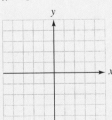

4. $2y = 8$

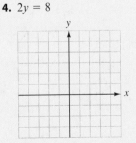

Determine whether the given ordered pair is a solution of the given system.

5. $(2, -3)$, $\begin{cases} 3x - 2y = 12 \\ 2x + 3y = -5 \end{cases}$

6. $(-2, -1)$, $\begin{cases} 4x + y = -9 \\ 2x - 3y = -7 \end{cases}$

Solve each system by graphing.

7. $\begin{cases} 3x + y = 7 \\ x - 2y = 0 \end{cases}$

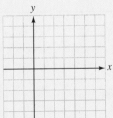

8. $\begin{cases} x + \frac{y}{2} = 1 \\ y = 1 - 3x \end{cases}$

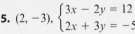
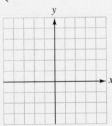

Solve each system by substitution.

9. $\begin{cases} y = x - 1 \\ x + y = -7 \end{cases}$

10. $\begin{cases} \frac{x}{6} + \frac{y}{10} = 3 \\ \frac{5x}{16} - \frac{3y}{16} = \frac{15}{8} \end{cases}$

Solve each system by elimination (addition).

11. $\begin{cases} 3x - y = 2 \\ 2x + y = 8 \end{cases}$

12. $\begin{cases} 4x + 3 = -3y \\ \frac{-x}{7} + \frac{4y}{21} = 1 \end{cases}$

Classify each system as consistent or inconsistent.

13. $\begin{cases} 2x + 3(y - 2) = 0 \\ -3y = 2(x - 4) \end{cases}$

14. $\begin{cases} \frac{x}{3} + y - 4 = 0 \\ -3y = x - 12 \end{cases}$

Use a system of equations in two variables to solve each problem.

15. The sum of two numbers is -18. One number is 2 greater than 3 times the other. Find the product of the numbers.

16. Water parks   A father paid $119 for his family of 7 to spend the day at Magic Waters water park. How many adult tickets did he buy?

Admission	
Adult ticket	$21
Child ticket	$14

17. Investing   A woman invested some money at 3% and some at 4%. The interest on the combined investment of $10,000 was $340 for one year. How much was invested at 4%?

18. Kayaking   A kayaker can paddle 8 miles down a river in 2 hours and make the return trip in 4 hours. Find the speed of the current in the river.

Solve each system of inequalities by graphing.

19. $\begin{cases} x + y < 3 \\ x - y < 1 \end{cases}$

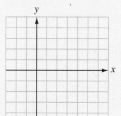

20. $\begin{cases} 2x + 3y \le 6 \\ x \ge 2 \end{cases}$

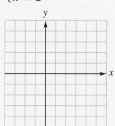

Polynomials

Careers and Mathematics

MEDICAL SCIENTISTS

Medical scientists research human diseases to improve human health. Most conduct biomedical research to gain knowledge of the life processes of living organisms, including viruses, bacteria, and other infectious agents. They study biological systems to understand the causes of disease and develop treatments. Medical scientists try to identify changes in cells or chromosomes that signal the development of medical problems, such as various types of cancer. They held about 92,000 jobs in 2006.

Job Outlook:
Employment of medical scientists is expected to increase 20 percent from 2006 to 2016. This is faster than the average for all occupations.

Annual Earnings:
$44,830–$88,130

For More Information:
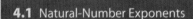
http://www.bls.gov/oco/ocos008.htm

For a Sample Application:
See Problem 67 in Section 4.3.

In this chapter ▶

In this chapter, we will develop rules for integer exponents and use them to express very large and small numbers in scientific notation. We then discuss special algebraic expressions, called polynomials, and show how to add, subtract, multiply, and divide them.

Natural-Number Exponents

Objectives

1. Write an exponential expression without exponents.
2. Write an expression using exponents.
3. Simplify an expression by using the product rule for exponents.
4. Simplify an expression by using the power rules for exponents.
5. Simplify an expression by using the quotient rule for exponents.

Vocabulary

base   exponent   power

Getting Ready

Evaluate each expression.

1. 2^3

2. 3^2

3. $3(2)$

4. $2(3)$

5. $2^3 + 2^2$

6. $2^3 \cdot 2^2$

7. $3^3 - 3^2$

8. $\dfrac{3^3}{3^2}$

In this section, we will revisit the topic of exponents. This time we will develop the basic rules used to manipulate exponential expressions.

1 Write an exponential expression without exponents.

We have used natural-number exponents to indicate repeated multiplication. For example,

$$2^5 = 2 \cdot 2 \cdot 2 \cdot 2 \cdot 2 = 32 \qquad (-7)^3 = (-7)(-7)(-7) = -343$$
$$x^4 = x \cdot x \cdot x \cdot x \qquad\qquad -y^5 = -y \cdot y \cdot y \cdot y \cdot y$$

These examples suggest a definition for x^n, where n is a natural number.

Natural-Number Exponents

If n is a natural number, then

$$x^n = \overset{n \text{ factors of } x}{\overbrace{x \cdot x \cdot x \cdot \,\cdots\, \cdot x}}$$

In the exponential expression x^n, x is called the **base** and n is called the **exponent.** The entire expression is called a **power of x.**

$$\text{Base} \rightarrow x^n \leftarrow \text{Exponent}$$

If an exponent is a natural number, it tells how many times its base is to be used as a factor. An exponent of 1 indicates that its base is to be used one time as a factor, an exponent of 2 indicates that its base is to be used two times as a factor, and so on.

$$3^1 = 3 \qquad (-y)^1 = -y \qquad (-4z)^2 = (-4z)(-4z) \qquad (t^2)^3 = t^2 \cdot t^2 \cdot t^2$$

EXAMPLE 1　Find each value to show that　**a.** -2^4　and　**b.** $(-2)^4$ have different values.

Solution　We find each power and show that the results are different.

$$-2^4 = -(2^4) \qquad\qquad (-2)^4 = (-2)(-2)(-2)(-2)$$
$$= -(2 \cdot 2 \cdot 2 \cdot 2) \qquad\qquad = 16$$
$$= -16$$

Since $-16 \neq 16$, it follows that $-2^4 \neq (-2)^4$.

▷ **SELF CHECK 1**　Show that $(-4)^3$ and -4^3 have the same value.

EXAMPLE 2　Write each expression without exponents.

a. r^3　　**b.** $(-2s)^4$　　**c.** $\left(\dfrac{1}{3}ab\right)^5$

Solution　**a.** $r^3 = r \cdot r \cdot r$

b. $(-2s)^4 = (-2s)(-2s)(-2s)(-2s)$

c. $\left(\dfrac{1}{3}ab\right)^5 = \left(\dfrac{1}{3}ab\right)\left(\dfrac{1}{3}ab\right)\left(\dfrac{1}{3}ab\right)\left(\dfrac{1}{3}ab\right)\left(\dfrac{1}{3}ab\right)$

▷ **SELF CHECK 2**　Write each expression without exponents.　**a.** x^4
b. $\left(-\dfrac{1}{2}xy\right)^3$

COMMENT　There is a pattern regarding even and odd exponents. If the exponent is even, the result is positive. If the exponent is odd, the result will be the same sign as the original base.

2　Write an expression using exponents.

Many expressions can be written more compactly by using exponents.

EXAMPLE 3　Write each expression using one exponent.
a. $3 \cdot 3 \cdot 3 \cdot 3 \cdot 3$　　**b.** $(5z)(5z)(5z)$

Solution   **a.** Since 3 is used as a factor five times,

$$3 \cdot 3 \cdot 3 \cdot 3 \cdot 3 = 3^5$$

b. Since $5z$ is used as a factor three times,

$$(5z)(5z)(5z) = (5z)^3$$

⇨ **SELF CHECK 3**   Write the expression $\left(\frac{1}{3}xy\right)\left(\frac{1}{3}xy\right)$ using one exponent.

3 **Simplify an expression by using the product rule for exponents.**

To develop a rule for multiplying exponential expressions with the same base, we consider the product $x^2 \cdot x^3$. Since the expression x^2 means that x is to be used as a factor two times and the expression x^3 means that x is to be used as a factor three times, we have

$$x^2 x^3 = \overbrace{x \cdot x}^{2 \text{ factors of } x} \cdot \overbrace{x \cdot x \cdot x}^{3 \text{ factors of } x}$$

$$= \overbrace{x \cdot x \cdot x \cdot x \cdot x}^{5 \text{ factors of } x}$$

$$= x^5$$

In general,

$$x^m \cdot x^n = \overbrace{x \cdot x \cdot x \cdot \cdots \cdot x}^{m \text{ factors of } x} \cdot \overbrace{x \cdot x \cdot x \cdot x \cdot \cdots \cdot x}^{n \text{ factors of } x}$$

$$= \overbrace{x \cdot x \cdot x \cdot x \cdot x \cdot x \cdot \cdots \cdot x \cdot x \cdot x}^{m + n \text{ factors of } x}$$

$$= x^{m+n}$$

This discussion suggests the following rule: *To multiply two exponential expressions with the same base, keep the base and add the exponents.*

Product Rule for Exponents	If m and n are natural numbers, then $$x^m x^n = x^{m+n}$$

EXAMPLE 4   Simplify each expression.

a. $x^3 x^4 = x^{3+4}$ Keep the base and add the exponents.

$\quad\quad = x^7$ $3 + 4 = 7$

b. $y^2 y^4 y = (y^2 y^4)y$ Use the associative property to group y^2 and y^4 together.

$\quad\quad = (y^{2+4})y$ Keep the base and add the exponents.

$\quad\quad = y^6 y$ $2 + 4 = 6$

$\quad\quad = y^{6+1}$ Keep the base and add the exponents: $y = y^1$.

$\quad\quad = y^7$ $6 + 1 = 7$

⇨ **SELF CHECK 4**   Simplify each expression.   **a.** zz^3 **b.** $x^2 x^3 x^6$

EXAMPLE 5   Simplify: $(2y^3)(3y^2)$.

Solution $(2y^3)(3y^2) = 2(3)y^3y^2$ Use the commutative and associative properties to group the coefficients together and the variables together.

$= 6y^{3+2}$ Multiply the coefficients. Keep the base and add the exponents.

$= 6y^5$ $3 + 2 = 5$

⇨ **SELF CHECK 5**   Simplify $(4x)(-3x^2)$.

COMMENT   The product rule for exponents applies only to exponential expressions with the same base. An expression such as x^2y^3 cannot be simplified, because x^2 and y^3 have different bases.

4   **Simplify an expression by using the power rules for exponents.**

To find another rule of exponents, we consider the expression $(x^3)^4$, which can be written as $x^3 \cdot x^3 \cdot x^3 \cdot x^3$. Because each of the four factors of x^3 contains three factors of x, there are $4 \cdot 3$ (or 12) factors of x. Thus, the expression can be written as x^{12}.

$$(x^3)^4 = x^3 \cdot x^3 \cdot x^3 \cdot x^3$$

$$= \overbrace{x \cdot x \cdot x \cdot x \cdot x \cdot x \cdot x \cdot x \cdot x \cdot x \cdot x \cdot x}^{12 \text{ factors of } x}$$
$$\underbrace{\quad}_{x^3} \underbrace{\quad}_{x^3} \underbrace{\quad}_{x^3} \underbrace{\quad}_{x^3}$$

$$= x^{12}$$

In general,

$$(x^m)^n = \overbrace{x^m \cdot x^m \cdot x^m \cdot \cdots \cdot x^m}^{n \text{ factors of } x^m}$$

$$= \overbrace{x \cdot x \cdot x \cdot x \cdot x \cdot x \cdot x \cdot \cdots \cdot x}^{m \cdot n \text{ factors of } x}$$

$$= x^{m \cdot n}$$

The previous discussion suggests the following rule: *To raise an exponential expression to a power, keep the base and multiply the exponents.*

Power Rule for Exponents

If m and n are natural numbers, then

$$(x^m)^n = x^{mn}$$

EXAMPLE 6   Write each expression using one exponent.

a. $(2^3)^7 = 2^{3 \cdot 7}$ Keep the base and multiply the exponents.

$= 2^{21}$ $3 \cdot 7 = 21$

b. $(z^7)^7 = z^{7 \cdot 7}$ Keep the base and multiply the exponents.

$= z^{49}$ $7 \cdot 7 = 49$

⇨ **SELF CHECK 6** Write each expression using one exponent.
a. $(y^5)^2$ **b.** $(u^x)^y$

In the next example, the product and power rules of exponents are both used.

EXAMPLE 7 Write each expression using one exponent.

a. $(x^2x^5)^2 = (x^7)^2$
$= x^{14}$

b. $(y^6y^2)^3 = (y^8)^3$
$= y^{24}$

c. $(z^2)^4(z^3)^3 = z^8z^9$
$= z^{17}$

d. $(x^3)^2(x^5x^2)^3 = x^6(x^7)^3$
$= x^6x^{21}$
$= x^{27}$

⇨ **SELF CHECK 7** Write each expression using one exponent.
a. $(a^4a^3)^3$ **b.** $(a^3)^3(a^4)^2$

To find more rules for exponents, we consider the expressions $(2x)^3$ and $\left(\frac{2}{x}\right)^3$.

$(2x)^3 = (2x)(2x)(2x)$

$= (2 \cdot 2 \cdot 2)(x \cdot x \cdot x)$

$= 2^3x^3$

$= 8x^3$

$\left(\frac{2}{x}\right)^3 = \left(\frac{2}{x}\right)\left(\frac{2}{x}\right)\left(\frac{2}{x}\right)$ $(x \neq 0)$

$= \frac{2 \cdot 2 \cdot 2}{x \cdot x \cdot x}$

$= \frac{2^3}{x^3}$

$= \frac{8}{x^3}$

These examples suggest the following rules: *To raise a product to a power, we raise each factor of the product to that power, and to raise a quotient to a power, we raise both the numerator and denominator to that power.*

Product to a Power Rule for Exponents	If n is a natural number, then $$(xy)^n = x^ny^n$$
Quotient to a Power Rule for Exponents	If n is a natural number, and if $y \neq 0$, then $$\left(\frac{x}{y}\right)^n = \frac{x^n}{y^n}$$

EXAMPLE 8 Write each expression without parentheses. Assume no division by zero.

a. $(ab)^4 = a^4b^4$

b. $(3c)^3 = 3^3c^3$
$= 27c^3$

c. $(x^2y^3)^5 = (x^2)^5(y^3)^5$
$= x^{10}y^{15}$

d. $(-2x^3y)^2 = (-2)^2(x^3)^2y^2$
$= 4x^6y^2$

e. $\left(\dfrac{4}{k}\right)^3 = \dfrac{4^3}{k^3}$

$= \dfrac{64}{k^3}$

f. $\left(\dfrac{3x^2}{2y^3}\right)^5 = \dfrac{3^5(x^2)^5}{2^5(y^3)^5}$

$= \dfrac{243x^{10}}{32y^{15}}$

➡ **SELF CHECK 8**   Write each expression without parentheses. Assume no division by zero.
a. $(3x^2y)^2$ **b.** $\left(\dfrac{2x^3}{3y^2}\right)^4$

---

5 **Simplify an expression by using the quotient rule for exponents.**

To find a rule for dividing exponential expressions, we consider the fraction $\dfrac{4^5}{4^2}$, where the exponent in the numerator is greater than the exponent in the denominator. We can simplify the fraction as follows:

$$\dfrac{4^5}{4^2} = \dfrac{4 \cdot 4 \cdot 4 \cdot 4 \cdot 4}{4 \cdot 4}$$

$$= \dfrac{\overset{1}{\cancel{4}} \cdot \overset{1}{\cancel{4}} \cdot 4 \cdot 4 \cdot 4}{\underset{1}{\cancel{4}} \cdot \underset{1}{\cancel{4}}}$$

$$= 4^3$$

The result of 4^3 has a base of 4 and an exponent of $5 - 2$ (or 3). This suggests that *to divide exponential expressions with the same base, we keep the base and subtract the exponents.*

Quotient Rule for Exponents	If m and n are natural numbers, $m > n$ and $x \neq 0$, then $$\dfrac{x^m}{x^n} = x^{m-n}$$

EXAMPLE 9   Simplify each expression. Assume no division by zero.

a. $\dfrac{x^4}{x^3} = x^{4-3}$

$= x^1$

$= x$

b. $\dfrac{8y^2y^6}{4y^3} = \dfrac{8y^8}{4y^3}$

$= \dfrac{8}{4}y^{8-3}$

$= 2y^5$

c. $\dfrac{a^3a^5a^7}{a^4a} = \dfrac{a^{15}}{a^5}$

$= a^{15-5}$

$= a^{10}$

d. $\dfrac{(a^3b^4)^2}{ab^5} = \dfrac{a^6b^8}{ab^5}$

$= a^{6-1}b^{8-5}$

$= a^5b^3$

➡ **SELF CHECK 9**   Simplify.   **a.** $\dfrac{a^5}{a^3}$ **b.** $\dfrac{6b^2b^3}{2b^4}$ **c.** $\dfrac{(x^2y^3)^2}{x^3y^4}$

We summarize the rules for positive exponents as follows.

Properties of Exponents

If n is a natural number, then

$$x^n = \overbrace{x \cdot x \cdot x \cdot \cdots \cdot x}^{n \text{ factors of } x}$$

If m and n are natural numbers and there is no division by 0, then

$$x^m x^n = x^{m+n} \qquad (x^m)^n = x^{mn} \qquad (xy)^n = x^n y^n \qquad \left(\frac{x}{y}\right)^n = \frac{x^n}{y^n}$$

$$\frac{x^m}{x^n} = x^{m-n} \quad \text{provided that } m > n$$

SELF CHECK ANSWERS

1. both are -64 2. **a.** $x \cdot x \cdot x \cdot x$ **b.** $\left(-\frac{1}{2}xy\right)\left(-\frac{1}{2}xy\right)\left(-\frac{1}{2}xy\right)$ 3. $\left(\frac{1}{3}xy\right)^2$ 4. **a.** z^4 **b.** x^{11}
5. $-12x^3$ 6. **a.** y^{10} **b.** u^{xy} 7. **a.** a^{21} **b.** a^{17} 8. **a.** $9x^4y^2$ **b.** $\frac{16x^{12}}{81y^8}$ 9. **a.** a^2 **b.** $3b$
c. xy^2

NOW TRY THIS

Simplify each expression.
1. If $x^{1/2}$ has meaning, find $(x^{1/2})^2$.

2. $-3^2(x^2 - 2^2)$

3. **a.** $x^{p+1}x^p$ **b.** $(x^{p+1})^2$ **c.** $\dfrac{x^{2p+1}}{x^p}$

4.1 EXERCISES

WARM-UPS

Find the base and the exponent in each expression.

1. x^3 **2.** 3^x

3. ab^c **4.** $(ab)^c$

Evaluate each expression.

5. 6^2 **6.** $(-6)^2$
7. $2^3 + 1^3$ **8.** $(2 + 1)^3$

REVIEW

9. Graph the real numbers $-3, 0, 2$, and $-\frac{3}{2}$ on a number line.

10. Graph the real numbers $-2 < x \leq 3$ on a number line.

Write each algebraic expression as an English phrase.

11. $3(x + y)$
12. $3x + y$

Write each English phrase as an algebraic expression.

13. Three greater than the absolute value of twice x

14. The sum of the numbers y and z decreased by the sum of their squares

VOCABULARY AND CONCEPTS

Fill in the blanks.

15. The _____ of the exponential expression $(-5)^3$ is _____. The exponent is __.

16. The base of the exponential expression -5^3 is __. The _____ is 3.

17. $(3x)^4$ means _____.

18. Write $(-3y)(-3y)(-3y)$ as a power. _____

19. $y^5 =$ _____

20. $x^m x^n =$ _____

21. $(xy)^n =$ _____

22. $\left(\dfrac{a}{b}\right)^n =$ _____

23. $(a^b)^c =$ _____

24. $\dfrac{x^m}{x^n} =$ _____

25. The area of the square is $s \cdot s$. Why do you think the symbol s^2 is called "s squared"?

26. The volume of the cube is $s \cdot s \cdot s$. Why do you think the symbol s^3 is called "s cubed"?

Identify the base and the exponent in each expression.

27. 4^3

28. $(-5)^2$

29. x^5

30. y^8

31. $(2y)^3$

32. $(-3x)^2$

33. $-x^4$

34. $(-x)^4$

35. x

36. $(xy)^3$

37. $2x^3$

38. $-3y^6$

GUIDED PRACTICE

Evaluate each expression. See Example 1. (Objective 1)

39. 5^4

40. $(-3)^3$

41. $2^2 + 3^2$

42. $2^3 - 2^2$

43. $5^4 - 4^3$

44. $2(4^3 + 3^2)$

45. $-5(3^4 + 4^3)$

46. $-5(4^3 - 2^6)$

Write each expression without using exponents. See Example 2. (Objective 1)

47. 5^3

48. -4^5

49. x^7

50. $3x^3$

51. $-4x^5$

52. $(-2y)^4$

53. $(3t)^5$

54. a^3b^2

Write each expression using exponents. See Example 3. (Objective 2)

55. $2 \cdot 2 \cdot 2$

56. $5 \cdot 5$

57. $x \cdot x \cdot x \cdot x$

58. $y \cdot y \cdot y \cdot y \cdot y \cdot y$

59. $(2x)(2x)(2x)$

60. $(-4y)(-4y)$

61. $-4 \cdot t \cdot t \cdot t \cdot t$

62. $5 \cdot u \cdot u$

Write each expression as an expression involving only one exponent. See Example 4. (Objective 3)

63. x^4x^3

64. y^5y^2

65. x^5x^5

66. yy^3

67. $a^3a^4a^5$

68. $b^2b^3b^5$

69. $y^3(y^2y^4)$

70. $(y^4y)y^6$

Write each expression involving only one exponent. See Example 5. (Objective 3)

71. $4x^2(3x^5)$

72. $-2y(y^3)$

73. $(-y^2)(4y^3)$

74. $(-4x^3)(-5x)$

Write each expression using one exponent. See Example 6. (Objective 4)

75. $(3^2)^4$

76. $(4^3)^3$

77. $(y^5)^3$

78. $(b^3)^6$

Write each expression using one exponent. See Example 7. (Objective 4)

79. $(x^2x^3)^5$

80. $(y^3y^4)^4$

81. $(a^2a^7)^3$

82. $(q^2q^3)^5$

83. $(x^5)^2(x^7)^3$

84. $(y^3y)^2(y^2)^2$

85. $(r^3r^2)^4(r^3r^5)^2$

86. $(yy^3)^3(y^2y^3)^4(y^3y^3)^2$

Write each expression without parentheses. Assume no division by 0. See Example 8. (Objective 4)

87. $(xy)^3$

88. $(uv^2)^4$

89. $(r^3s^2)^2$

90. $(a^3b^2)^3$

91. $(4ab^2)^2$

92. $(3x^2y)^3$

93. $(-2r^2s^3t)^3$

94. $(-3x^2y^4z)^2$

95. $\left(\dfrac{a}{b}\right)^3$

96. $\left(\dfrac{r^2}{s}\right)^4$

97. $\left(\dfrac{x^2}{y^3}\right)^5$

98. $\left(\dfrac{u^4}{v^2}\right)^6$

Simplify each expression. Assume no division by 0. See Example 9. (Objective 5)

99. $\dfrac{x^5}{x^3}$

100. $\dfrac{a^6}{a^3}$

101. $\dfrac{y^3y^4}{yy^2}$

102. $\dfrac{b^4b^5}{b^2b^3}$

103. $\dfrac{12a^2a^3a^4}{4(a^4)^2}$

104. $\dfrac{16(aa^2)^3}{2a^2a^3}$

105. $\dfrac{(ab^3)^3}{(ab)^2}$

106. $\dfrac{(m^3n^4)^3}{(mn^2)^3}$

ADDITIONAL PRACTICE   *Simplify each expression.*
Assume no division by 0.

107. tt^2

108. w^3w^5

109. $6x^3(-x^2)(-x^4)$

110. $-2x(-x^2)(-3x)$

111. $(a^3)^7$

112. $(b^2)^3$

113. $(3zz^2z^5)^5$

114. $(4t^3t^6t^2)^2$

115. $(s^3)^3(s^2)^2(s^5)^4$

116. $(s^2)^3(s^3)^2(s^4)^4$

117. $\left(\dfrac{-2a}{b}\right)^5$

118. $\left(\dfrac{2t}{3}\right)^4$

119. $\left(\dfrac{b^2}{3a}\right)^3$

120. $\left(\dfrac{a^3b}{c^4}\right)^5$

121. $\dfrac{17(x^4y^3)^8}{34(x^5y^2)^4}$

122. $\dfrac{35(r^3s^2)^2}{49r^2s^3}$

123. $\left(\dfrac{y^3y}{2yy^2}\right)^3$

124. $\left(\dfrac{3t^3t^4t^5}{4t^2t^6}\right)^3$

125. $\left(\dfrac{-2r^3r^3}{3r^4r}\right)^3$

126. $\left(\dfrac{-6y^4y^5}{5y^3y^5}\right)^2$

127. $\dfrac{20(r^4s^3)^4}{6(rs^3)^3}$

128. $\dfrac{15(x^2y^5)^5}{21(x^3y)^2}$

APPLICATIONS

129. Bouncing balls   When a certain ball is dropped, it always rebounds to one-half of its previous height. If the ball is dropped from a height of 32 feet, explain why the expression $32\left(\frac{1}{2}\right)^4$ represents the height of the ball on the fourth bounce. Find the height of the fourth bounce.

130. Having babies   The probability that a couple will have *n* baby boys in a row is given by the formula $\left(\frac{1}{2}\right)^n$. Find the probability that a couple will have four baby boys in a row.

131. Investing   If an investment of $1,000 doubles every seven years, find the value of the investment after 28 years.

If P dollars are invested at a rate r, compounded annually, it will grow to A dollars in t years according to the formula.

$$A = P(1 + r)^t$$

132. 📟 **Compound interest**   How much will be in an account at the end of 2 years if $12,000 is invested at 5%, compounded annually?

133. 📟 **Compound interest**   How much will be in an account at the end of 30 years if $8,000 is invested at 6%, compounded annually?

134. 📟 **Investing**   Guess the answer to the following question. Then use a calculator to find the correct answer. Were you close?

If the value of 1¢ is to double every day, what will the penny be worth after 31 days?

WRITING ABOUT MATH

135. Describe how you would multiply two exponential expressions with like bases.

136. Describe how you would divide two exponential expressions with like bases.

SOMETHING TO THINK ABOUT

137. Is the operation of raising to a power commutative? That is, is $a^b = b^a$? Explain.

138. Is the operation of raising to a power associative? That is, is $(a^b)^c = a^{(b^c)}$? Explain.

SECTION 4.2   Zero and Negative-Integer Exponents

Objectives

1 Simplify an expression containing an exponent of zero.

2 Simplify an expression containing a negative-integer exponent.

3 Simplify an expression containing a variable exponent.

Vocabulary

present value

Getting Ready

Simplify by dividing out common factors.

1. $\dfrac{3 \cdot 3 \cdot 3}{3 \cdot 3 \cdot 3 \cdot 3}$ **2.** $\dfrac{2yy}{2yyy}$ **3.** $\dfrac{3xx}{3xx}$ **4.** $\dfrac{xxy}{xxxyy}$

In the previous section, we discussed natural-number exponents. We now continue the discussion and include 0 and negative-integer exponents.

1 Simplify an expression containing an exponent of zero.

When we discussed the quotient rule for exponents in the previous section, the exponent in the numerator was always greater than the exponent in the denominator. We now consider what happens when the exponents are equal.

If we apply the quotient rule to the fraction $\frac{5^3}{5^3}$, where the exponents in the numerator and denominator are equal, we obtain 5^0. However, because any nonzero number divided by itself equals 1, we also obtain 1.

$$\frac{5^3}{5^3} = 5^{3-3} = 5^0 \qquad \frac{5^3}{5^3} = \frac{\overset{1}{\cancel{5}} \cdot \overset{1}{\cancel{5}} \cdot \overset{1}{\cancel{5}}}{\underset{1}{\cancel{5}} \cdot \underset{1}{\cancel{5}} \cdot \underset{1}{\cancel{5}}} = 1$$

These are equal.

For this reason, we define 5^0 to be equal to 1. In general, the following is true.

Zero Exponents

If x is any nonzero real number, then

$$x^0 = 1$$

Since $x \neq 0$, 0^0 is undefined.

EXAMPLE 1   Write each expression without exponents.

a. $\left(\dfrac{1}{13}\right)^0 = 1$ **b.** $\dfrac{x^5}{x^5} = x^{5-5} \quad (x \neq 0)$
$$= x^0$$
$$= 1$$

c. $3x^0 = 3(1)$
$= 3$

d. $(3x)^0 = 1$

e. $\dfrac{6^n}{6^n} = 6^{n-n}$
$= 6^0$
$= 1$

f. $\dfrac{y^m}{y^m} = y^{m-m}$ $(y \neq 0)$
$= y^0$
$= 1$

Parts c and d point out that $3x^0 \neq (3x)^0$.

⇨ **SELF CHECK 1**   Write each expression without exponents.
a. $(-0.115)^0$ **b.** $\dfrac{4^2}{4^2}$ **c.** $\dfrac{x^m}{x^m}$ $(x \neq 0)$

2   **Simplify an expression containing a negative-integer exponent.**

If we apply the quotient rule to $\dfrac{6^2}{6^5}$, where the exponent in the numerator is less than the exponent in the denominator, we obtain 6^{-3}. However, by dividing out two factors of 6, we also obtain $\dfrac{1}{6^3}$.

$$\dfrac{6^2}{6^5} = 6^{2-5} = \mathbf{6^{-3}} \qquad \dfrac{6^2}{6^5} = \dfrac{\overset{1}{\cancel{6}} \cdot \overset{1}{\cancel{6}}}{\underset{1}{\cancel{6}} \cdot \underset{1}{\cancel{6}} \cdot 6 \cdot 6 \cdot 6} = \dfrac{1}{6^3}$$

These are equal.

For these reasons, we define 6^{-3} to be $\dfrac{1}{6^3}$. In general, the following is true.

Negative Exponents

If x is any nonzero number and n is a natural number, then

$$x^{-n} = \dfrac{1}{x^n}$$

EXAMPLE 2   Express each quantity without negative exponents or parentheses. Assume that no variables are zero.

a. $3^{-5} = \dfrac{1}{3^5}$
$= \dfrac{1}{243}$

b. $x^{-4} = \dfrac{1}{x^4}$

c. $(2x)^{-2} = \dfrac{1}{(2x)^2}$
$= \dfrac{1}{4x^2}$

d. $2x^{-2} = 2\left(\dfrac{1}{x^2}\right)$
$= \dfrac{2}{x^2}$

e. $(-3a)^{-4} = \dfrac{1}{(-3a)^4}$

$= \dfrac{1}{81a^4}$

f. $(x^3x^2)^{-3} = (x^5)^{-3}$

$= \dfrac{1}{(x^5)^3}$

$= \dfrac{1}{x^{15}}$

⇨ **SELF CHECK 2**   Write each expression without negative exponents or parentheses. Assume that no variable is zero.   **a.** a^{-5} **b.** $(3y)^{-3}$ **c.** $(a^4a^3)^{-2}$

Because of the definitions of negative and zero exponents, the product, power, and quotient rules are true for all integer exponents.

Properties of Exponents

If m and n are integers and there are no divisions by 0, then

$$x^m x^n = x^{m+n} \qquad (x^m)^n = x^{mn} \qquad (xy)^n = x^n y^n \qquad \left(\dfrac{x}{y}\right)^n = \dfrac{x^n}{y^n}$$

$$x^0 = 1 \quad (x \neq 0) \qquad x^{-n} = \dfrac{1}{x^n} \qquad \dfrac{x^m}{x^n} = x^{m-n}$$

EXAMPLE 3   Simplify and write the result without negative exponents. Assume that no variables are 0.

a. $(x^{-3})^2 = x^{-6}$

$= \dfrac{1}{x^6}$

b. $\dfrac{x^3}{x^7} = x^{3-7}$

$= x^{-4}$

$= \dfrac{1}{x^4}$

c. $\dfrac{y^{-4}y^{-3}}{y^{-20}} = \dfrac{y^{-7}}{y^{-20}}$

$= y^{-7-(-20)}$

$= y^{-7+20}$

$= y^{13}$

d. $\dfrac{12a^3b^4}{4a^5b^2} = 3a^{3-5}b^{4-2}$

$= 3a^{-2}b^2$

$= \dfrac{3b^2}{a^2}$

e. $\left(-\dfrac{x^3y^2}{xy^{-3}}\right)^{-2} = (-x^{3-1}y^{2-(-3)})^{-2}$

$= (-x^2y^5)^{-2}$

$= \dfrac{1}{(-x^2y^5)^2}$

$= \dfrac{1}{x^4y^{10}}$

⇨ **SELF CHECK 3**   Simplify and write the result without negative exponents. Assume that no variables are 0.
a. $(x^4)^{-3}$ **b.** $\dfrac{a^4}{a^8}$ **c.** $\dfrac{a^{-4}a^{-5}}{a^{-3}}$ **d.** $\dfrac{20x^5y^3}{5x^3y^6}$

3   **Simplify an expression containing a variable exponent.**

These properties of exponents are also true when the exponents are algebraic expressions.

EXAMPLE 4   Simplify each expression. Assume that no variables are 0.

a. $x^{2m}x^{3m} = x^{2m+3m}$
$\qquad\qquad = x^{5m}$

b. $\dfrac{y^{2m}}{y^{4m}} = y^{2m-4m}$ $(y \neq 0)$
$\qquad\quad = y^{-2m}$
$\qquad\quad = \dfrac{1}{y^{2m}}$

c. $a^{2m-1}a^{2m} = a^{2m-1+2m}$
$\qquad\qquad = a^{4m-1}$

d. $(b^{m+1})^2 = b^{(m+1)2}$
$\qquad\qquad = b^{2m+2}$

 **SELF CHECK 4**   Simplify. Assume that no variables are 0.

a. $z^{3n}z^{2n}$ **b.** $\dfrac{z^{3n}}{z^{5n}}$ **c.** $(x^{m+2})^3$

ACCENT ON TECHNOLOGY

Finding Present Value

To find out how much money P (called the **present value**) must be invested at an annual rate i (expressed as a decimal) to have $\$A$ in n years, we use the formula $P = A(1 + i)^{-n}$. To find out how much we must invest at 6% to have $50,000 in 10 years, we substitute 50,000 for A, 0.06 (6%) for i, and 10 for n to get

$$P = A(1 + i)^{-n}$$
$$P = 50{,}000(1 + 0.06)^{-10}$$

To evaluate P with a calculator, we enter these numbers and press these keys:

(1 + .06) **y^x** 10 +/− × 50000   Using a calculator with a y^x and a +/− key.

50000 (1 + .06) ∧ ((−) 10) **ENTER**   Using a graphing calculator.

Either way, we see that we must invest $27,919.74 to have $50,000 in 10 years.

 **SELF CHECK ANSWERS**   **1. a.** 1   **b.** 1   **c.** 1   **2. a.** $\frac{1}{a^5}$ **b.** $\frac{1}{27y^3}$ **c.** $\frac{1}{a^{14}}$ **3. a.** $\frac{1}{x^{12}}$ **b.** $\frac{1}{a^4}$ **c.** $\frac{1}{a^6}$ **d.** $\frac{4x^2}{y^3}$ **4. a.** z^{5n}
b. $\frac{1}{z^{2n}}$ **c.** x^{3m+6}

NOW TRY THIS

Simplify each expression. Write your answer with positive exponents only. Assume no variable is 0.

1. $-2(x^2y^5)^0$

2. $-3x^{-2}$

3. $9^2 - 9^0$

4. Explain why the instructions above include the statement "Assume no variable is 0."

4.2 EXERCISES

WARM-UPS   *Simplify each quantity. Assume there are no divisions by 0.*

1. 2^{-1}

2. 2^{-2}

3. $\left(\dfrac{1}{2}\right)^{-1}$

4. $\left(\dfrac{7}{9}\right)^{0}$

5. $x^{-1}x^2$

6. $y^{-2}y^{-5}$

7. $\dfrac{x^5x^2}{x^7}$

8. $\left(\dfrac{x}{y}\right)^{-1}$

REVIEW

9. If $a = -2$ and $b = 3$, evaluate $\dfrac{3a^2 + 4b + 8}{a + 2b^2}$.

10. Evaluate: $|-3 + 5 \cdot 2|$.

Solve each equation.

11. $5\left(x - \dfrac{1}{2}\right) = \dfrac{7}{2}$

12. $\dfrac{5(2 - x)}{6} = \dfrac{x + 6}{2}$

13. Solve $P = L + \dfrac{s}{f}i$ for s.

14. Solve $P = L + \dfrac{s}{f}i$ for i.

VOCABULARY AND CONCEPTS   *Fill in the blanks.*

15. If x is any nonzero real number, then $x^0 = \_\_$. If x is any nonzero real number, then $x^{-n} = \_\_$.

16. Since $\dfrac{6^4}{6^4} = 6^{4-4} = 6^0$ and $\dfrac{6^4}{6^4} = 1$, we define 6^0 to be $\_\_$.

17. Since $\dfrac{8^3}{8^5} = 8^{3-5} = 8^{-2}$ and $\dfrac{8^3}{8^5} = \dfrac{8 \cdot 8 \cdot 8}{8 \cdot 8 \cdot 8 \cdot 8 \cdot 8} = \dfrac{1}{8^2}$, we define 8^{-2} to be $\_\_$.

18. The amount P that must be deposited now to have A dollars in the future is called the _____.

GUIDED PRACTICE

Write each expression without exponents. Assume that no variable is 0. See Example 1. (Objective 1).

19. 14^0

20. $\dfrac{a^4}{a^4}$

21. $2x^0$

22. $(2x)^0$

23. $\left(\dfrac{a^2b^3}{ab^4}\right)^0$

24. $\dfrac{2}{3}\left(\dfrac{xyz}{x^2y}\right)^0$

25. $\dfrac{8^y}{8^y}$

26. $\dfrac{a^n}{a^n}$

Simplify each expression by writing it as an expression without negative exponents or parentheses. Assume that no variables are 0. See Example 2. (Objective 2)

27. 5^{-4}

28. 7^{-2}

29. x^{-2}

30. y^{-3}

31. $(2y)^{-4}$

32. $(-3x)^{-1}$

33. $(-5p)^{-3}$

34. $(7z)^{-2}$

35. $(y^2y^4)^{-2}$

36. $(x^3x^2)^{-3}$

37. $3x^{-3}$

38. $-7y^{-2}$

Simplify and write the result without negative exponents. Assume that no variable is 0. See Example 3. (Objective 2)

39. $\dfrac{y^4}{y^5}$

40. $\dfrac{t^7}{t^{10}}$

41. $\dfrac{p^3}{p^6}$

42. $\dfrac{z^5}{z^8}$

43. $\dfrac{x^{-2}x^{-3}}{x^{-10}}$

44. $\dfrac{a^{-4}a^{-2}}{a^{-12}}$

45. $\dfrac{15a^3b^8}{3a^4b^4}$

46. $\dfrac{14b^5c^4}{21b^3c^5}$

47. $(a^{-4})^3$

48. $(b^{-5})^2$

49. $\left(\dfrac{a^3}{a^{-4}}\right)^{-2}$

50. $\left(\dfrac{a^4}{a^{-3}}\right)^{3}$

51. $\left(\dfrac{6a^2b^3}{2ab^2}\right)^{-2}$

52. $\left(\dfrac{15r^2s^{-2}t}{3r^{-3}s^3}\right)^{-3}$

53. $\left(\dfrac{18a^2b^3c^{-4}}{3a^{-1}b^2c}\right)^{-3}$

54. $\left(\dfrac{21x^{-2}y^2z^{-2}}{7x^3y^{-1}}\right)^{-2}$

Simplify each expression. Assume that $x \ne 0, y \ne 0$. See Example 4. (Objective 3)

55. $x^{2m}x^m$

56. $y^{3m}y^{2m}$

57. $\dfrac{x^{3n}}{x^{6n}}$

58. $\dfrac{x^m}{x^{5m}}$

59. $y^{3m+2}y^{-m}$

60. $x^{m+1}x^m$

61. $(y^{n+2})^2$

62. $(y^{m-3})^4$

ADDITIONAL PRACTICE *Simplify each expression and write the result without using parentheses or negative exponents. Assume that no variable base is 0.*

63. $2^5 \cdot 2^{-2}$

64. $10^2 \cdot 10^{-4} \cdot 10^5$

65. $4^{-3} \cdot 4^{-2} \cdot 4^5$

66. $3^{-4} \cdot 3^5 \cdot 3^{-3}$

67. $\dfrac{3^5 \cdot 3^{-2}}{3^3}$

68. $\dfrac{6^2 \cdot 6^{-3}}{6^{-2}}$

69. $\dfrac{2^5 \cdot 2^7}{2^6 \cdot 2^{-3}}$

70. $\dfrac{5^{-2} \cdot 5^{-4}}{5^{-6}}$

71. $(-x)^0$

72. $-x^0$

73. $\dfrac{x^0 - 5x^0}{2x^0}$

74. $\dfrac{4a^0 + 2a^0}{3a^0}$

75. b^{-5}

76. c^{-4}

77. $u^{2m}v^{3n}u^{3m}v^{-3n}$

78. $r^{2m}s^{-3}r^{3m}s^3$

79. $(x^{3-2n})^{-4}$

80. $(y^{1-n})^{-3}$

81. $(y^{2-n})^{-4}$

82. $(x^{3-4n})^{-2}$

83. $\dfrac{y^{3m}}{y^{2m}}$

84. $\dfrac{z^{4m}}{z^{2m}}$

85. $(4t)^{-3}$

86. $(-6r)^{-2}$

87. $(ab^2)^{-3}$

88. $(m^2n^3)^{-2}$

89. $(x^2y)^{-2}$

90. $(m^3n^4)^{-3}$

91. $\dfrac{(r^2)^3}{(r^3)^4}$

92. $\dfrac{(b^3)^4}{(b^5)^4}$

93. $\dfrac{y^4y^3}{y^4y^{-2}}$

94. $\dfrac{x^{12}x^{-7}}{x^3x^4}$

95. $\dfrac{a^4a^{-2}}{a^2a^0}$

96. $\dfrac{b^0b^3}{b^{-3}b^4}$

97. $(ab^2)^{-2}$

98. $(c^2d^3)^{-2}$

99. $(x^2y)^{-3}$

100. $(-xy^2)^{-4}$

101. $(x^{-4}x^3)^3$

102. $(y^{-2}y)^3$

103. $(y^3y^{-2})^{-2}$

104. $(x^{-3}x^{-2})^2$

105. $(a^{-2}b^{-3})^{-4}$

106. $(y^{-3}z^5)^{-6}$

107. $(-2x^3y^{-2})^{-5}$

108. $(-3u^{-2}v^3)^{-3}$

109. $\left(\dfrac{b^5}{b^{-2}}\right)^{-2}$

110. $\left(\dfrac{b^{-2}}{b^3}\right)^{-3}$

111. $\left(\dfrac{4x^2}{3x^{-5}}\right)^4$

112. $\left(\dfrac{-3r^4r^{-3}}{r^{-3}r^7}\right)^3$

113. $\left(\dfrac{12y^3z^{-2}}{3y^{-4}z^3}\right)^2$

114. $\left(\dfrac{6xy^3}{3x^{-1}y}\right)^3$

115. $\left(\dfrac{2x^3y^{-2}}{4xy^2}\right)^7$

116. $\left(\dfrac{9u^2v^3}{18u^{-3}v}\right)^4$

117. $\left(\dfrac{14u^{-2}v^3}{21u^{-3}v}\right)^4$

118. $\left(\dfrac{-27u^{-5}v^{-3}w}{18u^3v^{-2}}\right)^4$

119. $\dfrac{(2x^{-2}y)^{-3}}{(4x^2y^{-1})^3}$

120. $\dfrac{(ab^{-2}c)^2}{(a^{-2}b)^{-3}}$

121. $\dfrac{(17x^5y^{-5}z)^{-3}}{(17x^{-5}y^3z^2)^{-4}}$

122. $\dfrac{16(x^{-2}yz)^{-2}}{(2x^{-3}z^0)^4}$

123. $\dfrac{x^{3n}}{x^{6n}}$

124. $(y^2)^{m+1}$

APPLICATIONS

125. **Present value** How much money must be invested at 7% to have $100,000 in 40 years?

126. **Present value** How much money must be invested at 8% to have $100,000 in 40 years?

127. **Present value** How much money must be invested at 9% to have $100,000 in 40 years?

128. **Present value** How much must be invested at 6% annual interest to have $1,000,000 in 60 years?

129. **Present value** How much must be invested at 8% to have $1,000,000 in 60 years?

130. **Biology** During bacterial reproduction, the time required for a population to double is called the **generation time.** If b bacteria are introduced into a medium, then after the generation time has elapsed, there will be $2b$ bacteria. After n generations, there will be $b \cdot 2^n$ bacteria. Give the meaning of this expression when $n = 0$.

WRITING ABOUT MATH

131. Explain how you would help a friend understand that 2^{-3} is not equal to -8.

132. Describe how you would verify on a calculator that

$$2^{-3} = \frac{1}{2^3}$$

SOMETHING TO THINK ABOUT

133. If a positive number x is raised to a negative power, is the result greater than, equal to, or less than x? Explore the possibilities.

134. We know that $x^{-n} = \frac{1}{x^n}$. Is it also true that $x^n = \frac{1}{x^{-n}}$? Explain.

SECTION
4.3

Scientific Notation

Objectives

1 Convert a number from standard notation to scientific notation.
2 Convert a number from scientific notation to standard notation.
3 Use scientific notation to simplify an expression.

Vocabulary

scientific notation   standard notation

Getting Ready

Evaluate each expression.

1. 10^2 **2.** 10^3 **3.** 10^1 **4.** 10^{-2}

5. $5(10^2)$ **6.** $8(10^3)$ **7.** $3(10^1)$ **8.** $7(10^{-2})$

We now use exponents to write very large and very small numbers in a compact form called *scientific notation.* In science, almost all large and small numbers are written in this form.

Convert a number from standard notation to scientific notation.

Scientists often deal with extremely large and extremely small numbers. For example,

- The distance from Earth to the Sun is approximately 150,000,000 kilometers.
- Ultraviolet light emitted from a mercury arc has a wavelength of approximately 0.000025 centimeter.

The large number of zeros in these numbers makes them difficult to read and hard to remember. Scientific notation provides a compact way of writing large and small numbers.

Scientific Notation

A number is written in **scientific notation** if it is written as the product of a number between 1 (including 1) and 10 and an integer power of 10.

Each of the following numbers is written in scientific notation.

$$3.67 \times 10^6 \qquad 2.24 \times 10^{-4} \qquad 9.875 \times 10^{22}$$

Every number that is written in scientific notation has the following form:

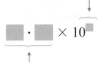

An integer exponent

A number between 1 and 10

EXAMPLE 1   Convert 150,000,000 to scientific notation.

Solution   We note that 1.5 lies between 1 and 10. To obtain 150,000,000, the decimal point in 1.5 must be moved eight places to the right. Because multiplying a number by 10 moves the decimal point one place to the right, we can accomplish this by multiplying 1.5 by 10 eight times.

1.5 0 0 0 0 0 0 0
8 places to the right

150,000,000 written in scientific notation is 1.5×10^8.

SELF CHECK 1   Convert 93,000,000 to scientific notation.

EXAMPLE 2   Convert 0.000025 to scientific notation.

Solution   We note that 2.5 is between 1 and 10. To obtain 0.000025, the decimal point in 2.5 must be moved five places to the left. We can accomplish this by dividing 2.5 by 10^5, which is equivalent to multiplying 2.5 by $\frac{1}{10^5}$ (or by 10^{-5}).

0 0 0 0 2.5
5 places to the left

In scientific notation, 0.000025 is written 2.5×10^{-5}.

SELF CHECK 2   Write 0.00125 in scientific notation.

EXAMPLE 3   Write **a.** 235,000   and   **b.** 0.00000235 in scientific notation.

Solution   **a.** $235,000 = 2.35 \times 10^5$, because $2.35 \times 10^5 = 235,000$ and 2.35 is between 1 and 10.

b. $0.00000235 = 2.35 \times 10^{-6}$, because $2.35 \times 10^{-6} = 0.00000235$ and 2.35 is between 1 and 10.

SELF CHECK 3   Write each number in scientific notation.
a. 17,500   **b.** 0.657

PERSPECTIVE   The Metric System

A common metric unit of length is the kilometer, which is 1,000 meters. Because 1,000 is 10^3, we can write 1 km = 10^3 m. Similarly, 1 centimeter is one-hundredth of a meter: 1 cm = 10^{-2} m. In the metric system, prefixes such as *kilo* and *centi* refer to powers of 10. Other prefixes are used in the metric system, as shown in the table.

To appreciate the magnitudes involved, consider these facts: Light, which travels 186,000 miles every second, will travel about one foot in one nanosecond. The distance to the nearest star (except for the Sun) is 43 petameters, and the diameter of an atom is about 10 nanometers. To measure some quantities, however, even these units are inadequate. The Sun, for example, radiates 5×10^{26} watts. That's a lot of light bulbs!

Prefix	Symbol	Meaning
peta	P	10^{15} = 1,000,000,000,000,000.
tera	T	10^{12} = 1,000,000,000,000.
giga	G	10^{9} = 1,000,000,000.
mega	M	10^{6} = 1,000,000.
kilo	k	10^{3} = 1,000.
deci	d	10^{-1} = 0.1
centi	c	10^{-2} = 0.01
milli	m	10^{-3} = 0.001
micro	μ	10^{-6} = 0.000 001
nano	n	10^{-9} = 0.000 000 001
pico	p	10^{-12} = 0.000 000 000 001
femto	f	10^{-15} = 0.000 000 000 000 001
atto	a	10^{-18} = 0.000 000 000 000 000 001

EXAMPLE 4   Write 432.0×10^5 in scientific notation.

Solution   The number 432.0×10^5 is not written in scientific notation, because 432.0 is not a number between 1 and 10. To write the number in scientific notation, we proceed as follows:

$$432.0 \times 10^5 = \mathbf{4.32} \times \mathbf{10^2} \times 10^5 \qquad \text{Write 432.0 in scientific notation.}$$
$$= 4.32 \times 10^7 \qquad 10^2 \times 10^5 = 10^7$$

⇨ **SELF CHECK 4**   Write 85×10^{-3} in scientific notation.

---

2   **Convert a number from scientific notation to standard notation.**

We can convert a number written in scientific notation to standard notation. For example, to write 9.3×10^7 in **standard notation,** we multiply 9.3 by 10^7.

$$9.3 \times 10^7 = 9.3 \times 10,000,000$$
$$= 93,000,000$$

EXAMPLE 5   Write   **a.** 3.4×10^5 and   **b.** 2.1×10^{-4} in standard notation.

Solution   **a.** $3.4 \times 10^5 = 3.4 \times 100,000$
$$= 340,000$$

b. $2.1 \times 10^{-4} = 2.1 \times \dfrac{1}{10^4}$

$= 2.1 \times \dfrac{1}{10,000}$

$= 0.00021$

⇨ **SELF CHECK 5**   Write each number in standard notation.
a. 4.76×10^5 **b.** 9.8×10^{-3}

Each of the following numbers is written in both scientific and standard notation. In each case, the exponent gives the number of places that the decimal point moves, and the sign of the exponent indicates the direction that it moves.

$5.32 \times 10^5 = 5\,3\,2\,0\,0\,0.$ 5 places to the right

$2.37 \times 10^6 = 2\,3\,7\,0\,0\,0\,0.$ 6 places to the right

$8.95 \times 10^{-4} = 0.0\,0\,0\,8\,9\,5$ 4 places to the left

$8.375 \times 10^{-3} = 0.0\,0\,8\,3\,7\,5$ 3 places to the left

$9.77 \times 10^0 = 9.77$ No movement of the decimal point

3   **Use scientific notation to simplify an expression.**

Another advantage of scientific notation becomes apparent when we simplify fractions such as

$$\dfrac{(0.0032)(25,000)}{0.00040}$$

that contain very large or very small numbers. Although we can simplify this fraction by using arithmetic, scientific notation provides an easier way. First, we write each number in scientific notation; then we do the arithmetic on the numbers and the exponential expressions separately. Finally, we write the result in standard form, if desired.

$$\dfrac{(0.0032)(25,000)}{0.00040} = \dfrac{(3.2 \times 10^{-3})(2.5 \times 10^4)}{4.0 \times 10^{-4}}$$

$$= \dfrac{(3.2)(2.5)}{4.0} \times \dfrac{10^{-3}10^4}{10^{-4}}$$

$$= \dfrac{8.0}{4.0} \times 10^{-3+4-(-4)}$$

$$= 2.0 \times 10^5$$

$$= 200,000$$

EXAMPLE 6   **SPEED OF LIGHT**   In a vacuum, light travels 1 meter in approximately 0.000000003 second. How long does it take for light to travel 500 kilometers?

Solution   Since 1 kilometer = 1,000 meters, the length of time for light to travel 500 kilometers (500 · 1,000 meters) is given by

$$(0.000000003)(500)(1,000) = (3 \times 10^{-9})(5 \times 10^2)(1 \times 10^3)$$
$$= 3(5) \times 10^{-9+2+3}$$
$$= \mathbf{15 \times 10^{-4}}$$
$$= \mathbf{1.5 \times 10^1 \times 10^{-4}}$$
$$= 1.5 \times 10^{-3}$$
$$= 0.0015$$

Light travels 500 kilometers in approximately 0.0015 second.

ACCENT ON TECHNOLOGY

Finding Powers of Decimals

To find the value of $(453.46)^5$, we can use a calculator and enter these numbers and press these keys:

453.46 $\boxed{y^x}$ 5 $\boxed{=}$ Using a calculator with a $\boxed{y^x}$ key

453.46 $\boxed{\wedge}$ 5 $\boxed{\textbf{ENTER}}$ Using a graphing calculator

Either way, we have $(453.46)^5 = 1.917321395 \times 10^{13}$. Since this number is too large to show on the display, the calculator gives the result as $\boxed{\textbf{1.917321395}\quad\textsc{E}\textbf{13}}$.

⇨ **SELF CHECK ANSWERS**   **1.** 9.3×10^7 **2.** 1.25×10^{-3} **3. a.** 1.75×10^4 **b.** 6.57×10^{-1} **4.** 8.5×10^{-2} **5. a.** 476,000   **b.** 0.0098

NOW TRY THIS

1. Write the result shown on the graphing calculator screen in
   a. scientific notation
   b. standard notation

> 56900000*2570000
> 0000
>   1.46233E18

2. Write the result shown on the graphing calculator screen in
   a. scientific notation
   b. standard notation

> .000000562*.0000
> 903
>   5.07486E⁻11

3. There are approximately 1.45728×10^7 inches of wiring in the space shuttle. How many miles of wiring is this?   (*Hint:* Recall that 5,280 feet = 1 mile.)

4.3 EXERCISES

WARM-UPS *Determine which number of each pair is the larger.*

1. 37.2 or 3.72×10^2

2. 37.2 or 3.72×10^{-1}

3. 3.72×10^3 or 4.72×10^3

4. 3.72×10^3 or 4.72×10^2

5. 3.72×10^{-1} or 4.72×10^{-2}

6. 3.72×10^{-3} or 2.72×10^{-2}

REVIEW

7. If $y = -1$, find the value of $-5y^{55}$.

8. Evaluate $\dfrac{3a^2 - 2b}{2a + 2b}$ if $a = 4$ and $b = 3$.

Determine which property of real numbers justifies each statement.

9. $5 + z = z + 5$

10. $7(u + 3) = 7u + 7 \cdot 3$

Solve each equation.

11. $3(x - 4) - 6 = 0$

12. $8(3x - 5) - 4(2x + 3) = 12$

VOCABULARY AND CONCEPTS   *Fill in the blanks.*

13. A number is written in _____ when it is written as the product of a number between 1 (including 1) and 10 and an integer power of 10.

14. The number 125,000 is written in _____ notation.

GUIDED PRACTICE

Write each number in scientific notation. **See Examples 1–3.**
(Objective 1)

15. 23,000

16. 4,750

17. 1,700,000

18. 290,000

19. 0.062

20. 0.00073

21. 0.00000275

22. 0.000000055

Write each number in scientific notation. **See Example 4.**
(Objective 1)

23. 42.5×10^2

24. 0.3×10^3

25. 0.25×10^{-2}

26. 25.2×10^{-3}

Write each number in standard notation. **See Example 5.**
(Objective 2)

27. 2.3×10^2

28. 3.75×10^4

29. 8.12×10^5

30. 1.2×10^3

31. 1.15×10^{-3}

32. 4.9×10^{-2}

33. 9.76×10^{-4}

34. 7.63×10^{-5}

Use scientific notation to simplify each expression. Give all answers in standard notation. **See Example 6.** (Objective 3)

35. $(3.4 \times 10^2)(2.1 \times 10^3)$

36. $(4.1 \times 10^{-3})(3.4 \times 10^4)$

37. $\dfrac{9.3 \times 10^2}{3.1 \times 10^{-2}}$

38. $\dfrac{7.2 \times 10^6}{1.2 \times 10^8}$

39. $\dfrac{96{,}000}{(12{,}000)(0.00004)}$

40. $\dfrac{(0.48)(14{,}400{,}000)}{96{,}000{,}000}$

41. $\dfrac{2{,}475}{(132{,}000{,}000)(0.25)}$

42. $\dfrac{147{,}000{,}000{,}000{,}000}{25(0.000049)}$

ADDITIONAL PRACTICE

Write each number in scientific notation.

43. 0.0000051

44. 0.04

45. 257,000,000

46. 365,000

47. $\dfrac{2.4 \times 10^2}{6 \times 10^{23}}$

48. $\dfrac{1.98 \times 10^2}{6 \times 10^{23}}$

Write each number in standard notation.

49. 25×10^6

50. 0.07×10^3

51. 0.51×10^{-3}

52. 617×10^{-2}

APPLICATIONS

53. Distance to Alpha Centauri   The distance from Earth to the nearest star outside our solar system is approximately 25,700,000,000,000 miles. Write this number in scientific notation.

54. Speed of sound   The speed of sound in air is 33,100 centimeters per second. Write this number in scientific notation.

55. Distance to Mars   The distance from Mars to the Sun is approximately 1.14×10^8. Write this number in standard notation.

56. Distance to Venus   The distance from Venus to the Sun is approximately 6.7×10^7. Write this number in standard notation.

57. Length of one meter   One meter is approximately 0.00622 mile. Write this number in scientific notation.

58. Angstroms One angstrom is 1×10^{-7} millimeter. Write this number in standard notation.

59. Distance between Mercury and the Sun The distance from Mercury to the Sun is approximately 3.6×10^{7} miles. Use scientific notation to express this distance in feet. (*Hint:* 5,280 feet = 1 mile.)

60. Mass of a proton The mass of one proton is approximately 1.7×10^{-24} gram. Use scientific notation to express the mass of 1 million protons.

61. Oil reserves Recently, Saudi Arabia was believed to have crude oil reserves of about 2.617×10^{11} barrels. A barrel contains 42 gallons of oil. Use scientific notation to express its oil reserves in gallons.

62. Interest At the beginning of the decade, the total insured deposits in U.S. banks and savings and loans was approximately 5.1×10^{12} dollars. If this money was invested at a rate of 5% simple annual interest, how much would it earn in 1 year? Use scientific notation to express the answer.

63. Speed of sound The speed of sound in air is approximately 3.3×10^{4} centimeters per second. Use scientific notation to express this speed in kilometers per second. (*Hint:* 100 centimeters = 1 meter and 1,000 meters = 1 kilometer.)

64. Light year One light year is approximately 5.87×10^{12} miles. Use scientific notation to express this distance in feet. (*Hint:* 5,280 feet = 1 mile.)

65. Wavelengths Some common types of electromagnetic waves are given in the table. List the wavelengths in order from shortest to longest.

Type	Use	Wavelength (m)
visible light	lighting	9.3×10^{-6}
infrared	photography	3.7×10^{-5}
x-rays	medical	2.3×10^{-11}

66. Wavelengths More common types of electromagnetic waves are given in the table. List the wavelengths in order from longest to shortest.

Type	Use	Wavelength (m)
radio waves	communication	3.0×10^{2}
microwaves	cooking	1.1×10^{-2}
ultraviolet	sun lamp	6.1×10^{-8}

The bulk of the surface area of the red blood cell shown in the illustration is contained on its top and bottom. That area is $2\pi r^{2}$, twice the area of one circle. If there are N discs, their total surface area T will be N times the surface area of a single disc: $T = 2N\pi r^{2}$.

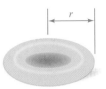

67. Red blood cells The red cells in human blood pick up oxygen in the lungs and carry it to all parts of the body. Each cell is a tiny circular disc with a radius of about 0.00015 in. Because the amount of oxygen carried depends on the surface area of the cells, and the cells are so tiny, a great number are needed—about 25 trillion in an average adult. Write these two numbers in scientific notation.

68. Red blood cells Find the total surface area of all the red blood cells in the body of an average adult. See Exercise 67.

WRITING ABOUT MATH

69. In what situations would scientific notation be more convenient than standard notation?

70. To multiply a number by a power of 10, we move the decimal point. Which way, and how far? Explain.

SOMETHING TO THINK ABOUT

71. Two positive numbers are written in scientific notation. How could you decide which is larger, without converting either to standard notation?

72. The product $1 \cdot 2 \cdot 3 \cdot 4 \cdot 5$, or 120, is called **5 factorial,** written 5!. Similarly, the number $6! = 6 \cdot 5 \cdot 4 \cdot 3 \cdot 2 \cdot 1 = 720$. Factorials get large very quickly. Calculate 30!, and write the number in standard notation. How large a factorial can you compute with a calculator?

SECTION 4.4 Polynomials and Polynomial Functions

Objectives

1 Determine whether an expression is a polynomial.
2 Classify a polynomial as a monomial, binomial, or trinomial, if applicable.
3 Find the degree of a polynomial.
4 Evaluate a polynomial for a specified value.
5 Define a function and evaluate it using function notation.
6 Graph a linear, quadratic, and cubic polynomial function.

Vocabulary

algebraic term	dependent variable	degree of a polynomial
polynomial	independent variable	polynomial function
monomial	squaring function	linear function
binomial	degree of a monomial	quadratic function
trinomial	descending powers of a	parabola
function	variable	cubing function
domain	ascending powers of a	
range	variable	

Getting Ready

Write each expression using exponents.

1. $2xxyyy$ **2.** $3xyyy$
3. $2xx + 3yy$ **4.** $xxx + yyy$
5. $(3xxy)(2xyy)$ **6.** $(5xyzzz)(xyz)$
7. $3(5xy)\left(\frac{1}{3}xy\right)$ **8.** $(xy)(xz)(yz)(xyz)$

In algebra, exponential expressions are combined to form **polynomials.** In this section, we will introduce the topic of polynomials and graph some basic polynomial functions.

1 **Determine whether an expression is a polynomial.**

Recall that expressions such as

$$3x \qquad 4y^2 \qquad -8x^2y^3 \qquad \text{and} \qquad 25$$

with constant and/or variable factors are called **algebraic terms.** The numerical coefficients of the first three of these terms are 3, 4, and −8, respectively. Because $25 = 25x^0$, 25 is considered to be the numerical coefficient of the term 25.

Polynomials

A **polynomial** is an algebraic expression that is a single term or the sum of several terms containing whole-number exponents on the variables.

Here are some examples of polynomials:

$$8xy^2t \qquad 3x + 2 \qquad 4y^2 - 2y + 3 \qquad \text{and} \qquad 3a - 4b - 4c + 8d$$

COMMENT The expression $2x^3 - 3y^{-2}$ is not a polynomial, because the second term contains a negative exponent on a variable base.

EXAMPLE 1   Determine whether each expression is a polynomial.

    a. $x^2 + 2x + 1$ A polynomial

    b. $3x^{-1} - 2x - 3$ No. The first term has a negative exponent on a variable base.

    c. $\dfrac{1}{2}x^3 - 2.3x + 5$ A polynomial

    d. $-2x + 3x^{1/2}$ No. The second term has a fractional exponent on a variable base.

SELF CHECK 1   Determine whether each expression is a polynomial:
    a. $3x^{-4} + 2x^2 - 3$ **b.** $7.5x^3 - 4x^2 - 3x$

2   **Classify a polynomial as a monomial, binomial, or trinomial, if applicable.**

A polynomial with one term is called a **monomial.** A polynomial with two terms is called a **binomial.** A polynomial with three terms is called a **trinomial.** Here are some examples.

Monomials	Binomials	Trinomials
$5x^2y$	$3u^3 - 4u^2$	$-5t^2 + 4t + 3$
$-6x$	$18a^2b + 4ab$	$27x^3 - 6x - 2$
29	$-29z^{17} - 1$	$-32r^6 + 7y^3 - z$

EXAMPLE 2   Classify each polynomial as a monomial, a binomial, or a trinomial, if applicable.

    a. $5x^4 + 3x$ Since the polynomial has two terms, it is a binomial.

    b. $7x^4 - 5x^3 - 2$ Since the polynomial has three terms, it is a trinomial.

    c. $-5x^2y^3$ Since the polynomial has one term, it is a monomial.

    d. $9x^5 - 5x^2 + 8x - 7$ Since the polynomial has four terms, it has no special name. It is none of these.

SELF CHECK 2   Classify each polynomial as a monomial, a binomial, or a trinomial, if applicable.
    a. $5x$ **b.** $-5x^2 + 2x - 5$
    c. $16x^2 - 9y^2$ **d.** $x^9 + 7x^4 - x^2 + 6x - 1$

3   **Find the degree of a polynomial.**

The monomial $7x^6$ is called a monomial of **sixth degree** or a monomial of **degree 6,** because the variable x occurs as a factor six times. The monomial $3x^3y^4$ is a monomial of the seventh degree, because the variables x and y occur as factors a total of seven times. Other examples are

    $-2x^3$ is a monomial of degree 3.

    $47x^2y^3$ is a monomial of degree 5.

$18x^4y^2z^8$ is a monomial of degree 14.

8 is a monomial of degree 0, because $8 = 8x^0$.

These examples illustrate the following definition.

Degree of a Monomial	If a is a nonzero coefficient, the **degree of the monomial ax^n is n.**
	The **degree of a monomial with several variables** is the sum of the exponents on those variables.

COMMENT   Note that the degree of ax^n is not defined when $a = 0$. Since $ax^n = 0$ when $a = 0$, the constant 0 has no defined degree.

Because each term of a polynomial is a monomial, we define the degree of a polynomial by considering the degree of each of its terms.

Degree of a Polynomial	The **degree of a polynomial** is the degree of its term with largest degree.

For example,

- $x^2 + 2x$ is a binomial of degree 2, because the degree of its first term is 2 and the degree of its other term is less than 2.
- $3x^3y^2 + 4x^4y^4 - 3x^3$ is a trinomial of degree 8, because the degree of its second term is 8 and the degree of each of its other terms is less than 8.
- $25x^4y^3z^7 - 15xy^8z^{10} - 32x^8y^8z^3 + 4$ is a polynomial of degree 19, because its second and third terms are of degree 19. Its other terms have degrees less than 19.

EXAMPLE 3   Find the degree of each polynomial.

a. $-4x^3 - 5x^2 + 3x$ 3, the degree of the first term because it has largest degree

b. $5x^4y^2 + 7xy^2 - 16x^3y^5$ 8, the degree of the last term

c. $-17a^2b^3c^4 + 12a^3b^4c$ 9, the degree of the first term

⇨ **SELF CHECK 3**   Find the degree of each polynomial.
a. $15p^3q^4 - 25p^4q^2$ **b.** $-14rs^3t^4 + 12r^3s^3t^3$

If the polynomial contains a single variable, we usually write it with its exponents in **descending order** where the term with the highest degree is listed first, followed by the term with the next highest degree, and so on. If we reverse the order, the polynomial is said to be written with its exponents in **ascending order.**

4   Evaluate a polynomial for a specified value.

When a number is substituted for the variable in a polynomial, the polynomial takes on a numerical value. Finding that value is called *evaluating the polynomial.*

EXAMPLE 4   Evaluate the polynomial $3x^2 + 2$ when
a. $x = 0$ **b.** $x = 2$ **c.** $x = -3$ **d.** $x = -\frac{1}{5}$.

Solution   **a.** $3x^2 + 2 = 3(0)^2 + 2$ **b.** $3x^2 + 2 = 3(2)^2 + 2$
$= 3(0) + 2$ $= 3(4) + 2$
$= 0 + 2$ $= 12 + 2$
$= 2$ $= 14$

c. $3x^2 + 2 = 3(-3)^2 + 2$ **d.** $3x^2 + 2 = 3\left(-\frac{1}{5}\right)^2 + 2$
$= 3(9) + 2$ $= 3\left(\frac{1}{25}\right) + 2$
$= 27 + 2$
$= 29$ $= \frac{3}{25} + \frac{50}{25}$

$= \frac{53}{25}$

▷ **SELF CHECK 4**   Evaluate $3x^2 + x - 2$ when   **a.** $x = 2$ **b.** $x = -1$.

When we evaluate a polynomial for several values of its variable, we often write the results in a table.

EXAMPLE 5   Evaluate the polynomial $x^3 + 1$ for the following values and write the results in a table.
a. $x = -2$ **b.** $x = -1$ **c.** $x = 0$ **d.** $x = 1$ **e.** $x = 2$

Solution

x	$x^3 + 1$	
a. -2	-7	$x^3 + 1 = (-2)^3 + 1 = -7$
b. -1	0	$x^3 + 1 = (-1)^3 + 1 = 0$
c. 0	1	$x^3 + 1 = (0)^3 + 1 = 1$
d. 1	2	$x^3 + 1 = (1)^3 + 1 = 2$
e. 2	9	$x^3 + 1 = (2)^3 + 1 = 9$

▷ **SELF CHECK 5**   Complete the following table.

x	$-x^3 + 1$
-2	
-1	
0	
1	
2	

5   **Define a function and evaluate it using function notation.**

The results of Examples 4 and 5 illustrate that for every input value x that we substitute into a polynomial containing the variable x, there is exactly one output value. Whenever we consider a polynomial equation such as $y = 3x^2 + 2$, where each input value x determines a single output value y, we say that y is a *function* of x.

Functions

Any equation in x and y where each value of x (the input) determines a single value of y (the output) is called a **function.** In this case, we say that y is a function of x.

The set of all input values x is called the **domain** of the function, and the set of all output values y is called the **range.**

Since each output value y depends on some input value x, we call y the **dependent variable** and x the **independent variable.** Here are some equations that define y to be a function of x.

1. $y = 2x - 3$ Note that each input value x determines a single output value y. For example, if $x = 4$, then $y = 5$. Since any real number can be substituted for x, the domain is the set of real numbers. We will soon show that the range is also the set of real numbers.

2. $y = x^2$ Note that each input value x determines a single output value y. For example, if $x = 3$, then $y = 9$. Since any real number can be substituted for x, the domain is the set of real numbers. Since the square of any real number is positive or 0, the range is the set of all numbers y such that $y \geq 0$.

3. $y = x^3$ Note that each input value x determines a single output value y. For example, if $x = -2$, then $y = -8$. Since any real number can be substituted for x, the domain is the set of real numbers. We will soon show that the range is also the set of real numbers.

There is a special notation for functions that uses the symbol $f(x)$, read as "f of x."

Function Notation

The notation $y = f(x)$ denotes that the variable y is a function of x.

COMMENT The notation $f(x)$ does not mean "f times x."

The notation $y = f(x)$ provides a way to denote the values of y in a function that correspond to individual values of x. For example, if $y = f(x)$, the value of y that is determined by $x = 3$ is denoted as $f(3)$. Similarly, $f(-1)$ represents the value of y that corresponds to $x = -1$.

EXAMPLE 6 Let $y = f(x) = 2x - 3$ and find: **a.** $f(3)$ **b.** $f(-1)$ **c.** $f(0)$ **d.** the value of x that will make $f(x) = -2.6$.

Solution **a.** We replace x with 3.

$$f(x) = 2x - 3$$
$$f(3) = 2(3) - 3$$
$$= 6 - 3$$
$$= 3$$

b. We replace x with -1.

$$f(x) = 2x - 3$$
$$f(-1) = 2(-1) - 3$$
$$= -2 - 3$$
$$= -5$$

c. We replace x with 0.

$$f(x) = 2x - 3$$
$$f(0) = 2(0) - 3$$
$$= 0 - 3$$
$$= -3$$

d. We replace $f(x)$ with -2.6 and solve for x.

$$f(x) = 2x - 3$$
$$-2.6 = 2x - 3$$
$$0.4 = 2x$$
$$0.2 = x$$

⇨ **SELF CHECK 6**   If $f(x) = 2x - 3$, find: **a.** $f(-2)$ **b.** $f\left(\frac{3}{2}\right)$
c. the value of x that will make $f(x) = 5$.

ACCENT ON TECHNOLOGY

Height of a Rocket

The height h (in feet) of a toy rocket launched straight up into the air with an initial velocity of 64 feet per second is given by the polynomial function

$$h = f(t) = -16t^2 + 64t$$

In this case, the height h is the dependent variable, and the time t is the independent variable. To find the height of the rocket 3.5 seconds after launch, we substitute 3.5 for t and evaluate h.

$$h = -16t^2 + 64t$$
$$h = -16(3.5)^2 + 64(3.5)$$

To evaluate h with a calculator, we enter these numbers and press these keys:

16 +/− × 3.5 x^2 + (64 × 3.5) =   Using a calculator with a +/− key

(−) 16 × 3.5 x^2 + 64 × 3.5 **ENTER**   Using a graphing calculator

Either way, the display reads 28. After 3.5 seconds, the rocket will be 28 feet above the ground.

---

6 **Graph a linear, quadratic, and cubic polynomial function.**

A function of the form $y = f(x)$, where $f(x)$ is a polynomial, is called a **polynomial function.** We can graph polynomial functions as we graphed equations in Section 3.2. We make a table of values, plot points, and draw the line or curve that passes through those points.

In the next example, we graph the polynomial function $f(x) = 2x - 3$. Since its graph is a line, it is a **linear function.**

COMMENT   The ordered pair (x, y) can be written as $(x, f(x))$.

EXAMPLE 7   Graph: $y = f(x) = 2x - 3$.

Solution   We substitute numbers for x, compute the corresponding values of $f(x)$, and list the results in a table, as in Figure 4-1 on the next page. We then plot the pairs (x, y) and draw a line through the points, as shown in the figure. From the graph, we can see that x can be any value. This confirms that the domain is the set of real numbers $\mathbb{R}$. We also can see that y can be any value. This confirms the range is also the set of real numbers $\mathbb{R}$.

$$y = f(x) = 2x - 3$$

x	$f(x)$	$(x, f(x))$
-3	-9	$(-3, -9)$
-2	-7	$(-2, -7)$
-1	-5	$(-1, -5)$
0	-3	$(0, -3)$
1	-1	$(1, -1)$
2	1	$(2, 1)$
3	3	$(3, 3)$

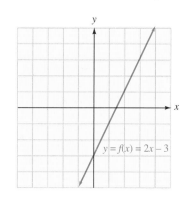

Figure 4-1

⇨ SELF CHECK 7   Graph $y = f(x) = \frac{1}{2}x + 3$ and determine whether it is a linear function.

In the next example, we graph the function $f(x) = x^2$, called the **squaring function.** Since the polynomial on the right side is of second degree, we also can call this function a **quadratic function.**

EXAMPLE 8   Graph: $f(x) = x^2$.

Solution   We substitute numbers for x, compute the corresponding values of $f(x)$, and list the results in a table, as in Figure 4-2. We then plot the pairs (x, y) and draw a smooth curve through the points, as shown in the figure. This curve is called a **parabola.** From the graph, we can see that x can be any value. This confirms that the domain is the set of real numbers $\mathbb{R}$. We can also see that y is always a positive number or 0. This confirms that the range is $\{y \mid y$ is a real number and $y \geq 0\}$. In interval notation, this is $[0, \infty)$.

**Amalie Noether
(1882–1935)**

Albert Einstein described Noether as the most creative female mathematical genius since the beginning of higher education for women. Her work was in the area of abstract algebra. Although she received a doctoral degree in mathematics, she was denied a mathematics position in Germany because she was a woman.

$$f(x) = x^2$$

x	$f(x)$	$(x, f(x))$
-3	9	$(-3, 9)$
-2	4	$(-2, 4)$
-1	1	$(-1, 1)$
0	0	$(0, 0)$
1	1	$(1, 1)$
2	4	$(2, 4)$
3	9	$(3, 9)$

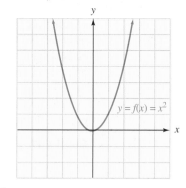

Figure 4-2

⇨ SELF CHECK 8   Graph $f(x) = x^2 - 3$ and compare the graph to the graph of $f(x) = x^2$ shown in Figure 4-2.

In the next example, we graph the function $f(x) = x^3$, called the **cubing function.** Since the polynomial on the right side is of third degree, we can also call this function a **cubic function.**

EXAMPLE 9   Graph: $f(x) = x^3$.

Solution   We substitute numbers for x, compute the corresponding values of $f(x)$, and list the results in a table, as in Figure 4-3. We then plot the pairs $(x, f(x))$ and draw a smooth curve through the points, as shown in the figure.

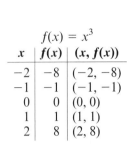

$$f(x) = x^3$$

x	$f(x)$	$(x, f(x))$
-2	-8	$(-2, -8)$
-1	-1	$(-1, -1)$
0	0	$(0, 0)$
1	1	$(1, 1)$
2	8	$(2, 8)$

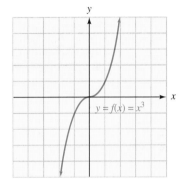

Figure 4-3

⇨ **SELF CHECK 9**   Graph $f(x) = x^3 + 3$ and compare the graph to the graph of $f(x) = x^3$ shown in Figure 4-3.

ACCENT ON TECHNOLOGY

Graphing Polynomial Functions

It is possible to use a graphing calculator to generate tables and graphs for polynomial functions. For example, Figure 4-4 shows calculator tables and the graphs of $f(x) = 2x - 3$, $f(x) = x^2$, and $f(x) = x^3$.

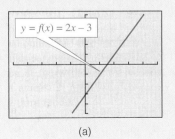

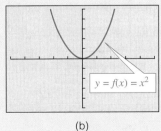

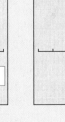

Figure 4-4

EXAMPLE 10   Graph: $f(x) = x^2 - 2x$.

Solution   We substitute numbers for x, compute the corresponding values of $f(x)$, and list the results in a table, as in Figure 4-5. We then plot the pairs $(x, f(x))$ and draw a smooth curve through the points, as shown in the figure.

$f(x) = x^2 - 2x$

x	$f(x)$	$(x, f(x))$
-2	8	$(-2, 8)$
-1	3	$(-1, 3)$
0	0	$(0, 0)$
1	-1	$(1, -1)$
2	0	$(2, 0)$
3	3	$(3, 3)$
4	8	$(4, 8)$

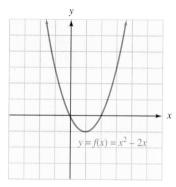

Figure 4-5

▷ **SELF CHECK 10**   Use a graphing calculator to graph $f(x) = x^2 - 2x$.

EVERYDAY CONNECTIONS   NBA Salaries

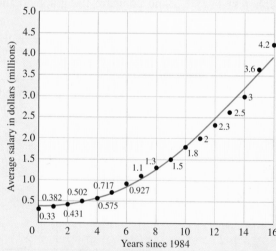

Source: http://blog.msumoney.com/2008/02/20/the-jason-kidd-trade-and-the-problem-with-the-nba-salary-cap.aspx

$$f(t) = 0.3169 + 0.0737t - 0.0076t^2 + 0.0022t^3 - 0.00007t^4$$

The polynomial function shown above models average player salary in the National Basketball Association during the time period 1984–2007, where t equals the number of years since 1984. The dots represent actual average salaries and points on the red graph represent predicted salaries. Use the graph to answer the following questions.

1. a. What was the actual average player salary in 1996?
 b. What was the average player salary predicted by the function $f(t)$ in 1996?
2. Does this function yield a realistic prediction of the average player salary in 2015?

⇨ **SELF CHECK ANSWERS**

1. a. no   **b.** yes   **2. a.** monomial   **b.** trinomial   **c.** binomial   **d.** none of these   **3. a.** 7
b. 9   **4. a.** 12   **b.** 0   **5.** 9, 2, 1, 0, −7   **6. a.** −7   **b.** 0   **c.** 4
7. a linear function   **8.** same shape but 3 units lower

9. same shape but 3 units higher   **10.**

NOW TRY THIS

1. Classify each polynomial and state its degree:
   a. $9x^2 - 6x^8$
   b. 1
2. If $f(x) = -3x^2 - 2x$,
   a. find $f(-4)$
   b. find $f(3p)$
3. Use a graphing calculator to graph $f(x) = \frac{1}{2}x^3 - x^2 + 3x + 1$.

4.4 EXERCISES

WARM-UPS   *Give an example of a polynomial that is . . .*

 1. a binomial
 3. a trinomial
 5. of degree 3
 7. of degree 0

 2. a monomial
 4. not a monomial, a binomial, or a trinomial
 6. of degree 1
 8. of no defined degree

REVIEW

Solve each equation.

 9. $5(u - 5) + 9 = 2(u + 4)$
10. $8(3a - 5) - 12 = 4(2a + 3)$

Solve each inequality and graph the solution set.

11. $-4(3y + 2) \le 28$ **12.** $-5 < 3t + 4 \le 13$

Write each expression without using parentheses or negative exponents. Assume no variable is zero.

13. $(x^2 x^4)^3$ **14.** $(a^2)^3(a^3)^2$
15. $\left(\dfrac{y^2 y^5}{y^4}\right)^3$ **16.** $\left(\dfrac{2t^3}{t}\right)^{-4}$

VOCABULARY AND CONCEPTS   *Fill in the blanks.*

17. An expression such as $3t^4$ with a constant and/or variable factor is called an _____ term.
18. A _____ is an algebraic expression that is the sum of one or more terms containing whole-number exponents on the variables.

19. A _____ is a polynomial with one term. A _____ is a polynomial with two terms. A _____ is a polynomial with three terms.

20. If $a \neq 0$, the _____ of ax^n is n.

21. The degree of a monomial with several variables is the ____ of the exponents on those variables.

22. A function of the form $y = f(x)$ where $f(x)$ is a polynomial is called a _____ function. Its _____ is the set of all input values x and its _____ is the set of all output values y.

23. In the function $y = f(x)$, x is called the _____ variable and y is called the _____ variable.

24. The graph of a _____ function is a line.

25. The function $f(x) = x^2$ is called the squaring or _____ function. The graph of a quadratic function is called a _____.

26. The function $f(x) = x^3$ is called the cubing or _____ function.

27. The polynomial $8x^5 - 3x^3 + 6x^2 - 1$ is written with its exponents in _____ order. Its degree is __.

28. The polynomial $-2x + x^2 - 5x^3 + 7x^4$ is written with its exponents in _____ order. Its degree is __.

29. Any equation in x and y where each input value x determines exactly one output value y is called a _____.

30. $f(x)$ is read as _____.

GUIDED PRACTICE

Determine whether each expression is a polynomial. See Example 1. (Objective 1)

31. $x^3 - 5x^2 - 2$ **32.** $x^{-4} - 5x$

33. $3x^{1/2} - 4$ **34.** $0.5x^5 - 0.25x^2$

Classify each polynomial as a monomial, a binomial, a trinomial, or none of these. See Example 2. (Objective 2)

35. $3x + 7$ **36.** $3y - 5$

37. $3y^2 + 4y + 3$ **38.** $3xy$

39. $3z^2$ **40.** $3x^4 - 2x^3 + 3x - 1$

41. $5t - 32$ **42.** $9x^2y^3z^4$

Give the degree of each polynomial. See Example 3. (Objective 3)

43. $3x^4$ **44.** $3x^5 - 4x^2$
45. $-2x^2 + 3x^3$ **46.** $-5x^5 + 3x^2 - 3x$
47. $3x^2y^3 + 5x^3y^5$ **48.** $-2x^2y^3 + 4x^3y^2z$
49. $-5r^2s^2t - 3r^3st^2 + 3$ **50.** $4r^2s^3t^3 - 5r^2s^8$

Evaluate $5x - 3$ for each value. See Example 4. (Objective 4)

51. $x = 2$ **52.** $x = 0$
53. $x = -1$ **54.** $x = -2$

Evaluate $-x^2 - 4$ for each value. See Example 4. (Objective 4)

55. $x = 0$ **56.** $x = 1$

57. $x = -1$ **58.** $x = -2$

Complete each table. See Example 5. (Objective 4)

59.

x	$x^2 - 3$
-2	
-1	
0	
1	
2	

60.

x	$-x^2 + 3$
-2	
-1	
0	
1	
2	

61.

x	$x^3 + 2$
-2	
-1	
0	
1	
2	

62.

x	$-x^3 + 2$
-2	
-1	
0	
1	
2	

If $f(x) = 5x + 1$, find each value. See Example 6. (Objective 5)

63. $f(0)$ **64.** $f(2)$

65. $f\left(-\dfrac{1}{2}\right)$ **66.** $f\left(\dfrac{2}{5}\right)$

67. the value of x that will make $f(x) = 26$
68. the value of x that will make $f(x) = -9$
69. the value of x that will make $f(x) = -21$
70. the value of x that will make $f(x) = 25.5$

Graph each polynomial function and give the domain and range. Check your work with a graphing calculator. See Examples 7–10. (Objective 6)

71. $f(x) = x^2 - 1$

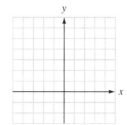

72. $f(x) = x^2 + 2$

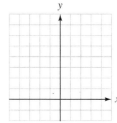

73. $f(x) = x^3 + 2$ **74.** $f(x) = x^3 - 2$

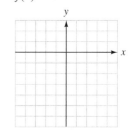

ADDITIONAL PRACTICE

Classify each polynomial as a monomial, a binomial, a trinomial, or none of these.

75. $s^2 - 23s + 31$ **76.** $12x^3 - 12x^2 + 36x - 3$

77. $3x^5 - 2x^4 - 3x^3 + 17$ **78.** x^3

79. $\frac{1}{2}x^3 + 3$ **80.** $x^3 - 1$

Give the degree of each polynomial.

81. $x^{12} + 3x^2y^3z^4$ **82.** 17^2x

83. 38 **84.** -25

If $f(x) = x^2 - 2x + 3$, find each value.

85. $f(0)$ **86.** $f(3)$

87. $f(-2)$ **88.** $f(-1)$

89. $f(0.5)$ **90.** $f(1.2)$

APPLICATIONS   *Use a calculator to help solve each problem.*

91. **Height of a rocket**   See the Accent on Technology section on page 273. Find the height of the rocket 2 seconds after launch.

92. **Height of a rocket**   Again referring to page 273, make a table of values to find the rocket's height at various times. For what values of t will the height of the rocket be 0?

93. **Computing revenue**   The revenue r (in dollars) that a manufacturer of desk chairs receives is given by the polynomial function

$$r = f(d) = -0.08d^2 + 100d$$

where d is the number of chairs manufactured. Find the revenue received when 815 chairs are manufactured.

94. **Falling balloons**   Some students threw balloons filled with water from a dormitory window. The height h (in feet) of the balloons t seconds after being thrown is given by the polynomial function

$$h = f(t) = -16t^2 + 12t + 20$$

How far above the ground is a balloon 1.5 seconds after being thrown?

95. **Stopping distance**   The number of feet that a car travels before stopping depends on the driver's reaction time and the braking distance. For one driver, the stopping distance d is given by the function $d = f(v) = 0.04v^2 + 0.9v$, where v is the velocity of the car. Find the stopping distance when the driver is traveling at 30 mph.

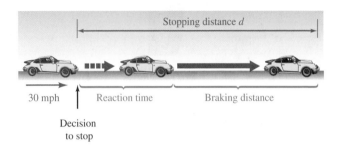

96. **Stopping distance**   Find the stopping distance of the car discussed in Exercise 95 when the driver is going 70 mph.

WRITING ABOUT MATH

97. Describe how to determine the degree of a polynomial.

98. Describe how to classify a polynomial as a monomial, a binomial, a trinomial, or none of these.

SOMETHING TO THINK ABOUT

99. Find a polynomial whose value will be 1 if you substitute $\frac{3}{2}$ for x.

100. Graph the function $f(x) = -x^2$. What do you discover?

SECTION 4.5   Adding and Subtracting Polynomials

Objectives

1 Add two or more monomials.

2 Subtract two monomials.

3 Add two polynomials.

4 Subtract two polynomials.

5 Simplify an expression using the order of operations and combining like terms.

6 Solve an application problem requiring operations with polynomials.

subtrahend   minuend

Getting Ready

Combine like terms and simplify, if possible.

1. $3x + 2x$ **2.** $5y - 3y$ **3.** $19x + 6x$ **4.** $8z - 3z$
5. $9r + 3r$ **6.** $4r - 3s$ **7.** $7r - 7r$ **8.** $17r - 17r^2$

In this section, we will discuss how to add and subtract polynomials.

1 **Add two or more monomials.**

Recall that like terms have the same variables with the same exponents. For example,

$3xyz^2$ and $-2xyz^2$ are like terms.

$\frac{1}{2}ab^2c$ and $\frac{1}{3}a^2bd^2$ are unlike terms.

Also recall that to combine like terms, we add (or subtract) their coefficients and keep the same variables with the same exponents. For example,

$$2y + 5y = (2 + 5)y \qquad -3x^2 + 7x^2 = (-3 + 7)x^2$$
$$= 7y \qquad\qquad\qquad = 4x^2$$

Likewise,

$$4x^3y^2 + 9x^3y^2 = 13x^3y^2 \qquad 4r^2s^3t^4 + 7r^2s^3t^4 = 11r^2s^3t^4$$

These examples suggest that to add like monomials, we simply combine like terms.

EXAMPLE 1 Perform the following additions.

a. $5xy^3 + 7xy^3 = 12xy^3$

b. $-7x^2y^2 + 6x^2y^2 + 3x^2y^2 = -x^2y^2 + 3x^2y^2$
$$= 2x^2y^2$$

c. $(2x^2)^2 + 81x^4 = 4x^4 + 81x^4 \quad (2x^2)^2 = (2x^2)(2x^2) = 4x^4$
$$= 85x^4$$

⇨ **SELF CHECK 1** Perform the following additions.   **a.** $6a^3b^2 + 5a^3b^2$
b. $-2pq^2 + 5pq^2 + 8pq^2$ **c.** $27x^6 + (2x^2)^3$

2 **Subtract two monomials.**

To subtract one monomial from another, we add the opposite of the monomial that is to be subtracted. In symbols, $x - y = x + (-y)$.

EXAMPLE 2   Find each difference.

a. $8x^2 - 3x^2 = 8x^2 + (-3x^2)$
$= 5x^2$

b. $6x^3y^2 - 9x^3y^2 = 6x^3y^2 + (-9x^3y^2)$
$= -3x^3y^2$

c. $-3r^2st^3 - 5r^2st^3 = -3r^2st^3 + (-5r^2st^3)$
$= -8r^2st^3$

➡ **SELF CHECK 2**   Find each difference: **a.** $12m^3 - 7m^3$ **b.** $-4p^3q^2 - 8p^3q^2$

3 **Add two polynomials.**

Because of the distributive property, we can remove parentheses enclosing several terms when the sign preceding the parentheses is $+$. We can simply drop the parentheses.

$$+(3x^2 + 3x - 2) = +1(3x^2 + 3x - 2)$$
$$= 1(3x^2) + 1(3x) + 1(-2)$$
$$= 3x^2 + 3x + (-2)$$
$$= 3x^2 + 3x - 2$$

We can add polynomials by removing parentheses, if necessary, and then combining any like terms that are contained within the polynomials.

EXAMPLE 3   Add: $(3x^2 - 3x + 2) + (2x^2 + 7x - 4)$.

Solution $(3x^2 - 3x + 2) + (2x^2 + 7x - 4)$
$$= 3x^2 - 3x + 2 + 2x^2 + 7x - 4$$
$$= 3x^2 + 2x^2 - 3x + 7x + 2 - 4$$
$$= 5x^2 + 4x - 2$$

➡ **SELF CHECK 3**   Add: $(2a^2 - a + 4) + (5a^2 + 6a - 5)$.

Additions such as Example 3 often are written with like terms aligned vertically. We then can add the polynomials column by column.

$$\begin{array}{r} 3x^2 - 3x + 2 \\ 2x^2 + 7x - 4 \\ \hline 5x^2 + 4x - 2 \end{array}$$

EXAMPLE 4   Add.

$$4x^2y + 8x^2y^2 - 3x^2y^3$$
$$\underline{3x^2y - 8x^2y^2 + 8x^2y^3}$$
$$7x^2y \qquad\quad + 5x^2y^3$$

SELF CHECK 4   Add.

$$4pq^2 + 6pq^3 - 7pq^4$$
$$\underline{2pq^2 - 8pq^3 + 9pq^4}$$

4 Subtract two polynomials.

Because of the distributive property, we can remove parentheses enclosing several terms when the sign preceding the parentheses is $-$. We can simply drop the negative sign and the parentheses, and *change the sign of every term within the parentheses.*

$$\begin{aligned}
-(3x^2 + 3x - 2) &= -1(3x^2 + 3x - 2) \\
&= -1(3x^2) + (-1)(3x) + (-1)(-2) \\
&= -3x^2 + (-3x) + 2 \\
&= -3x^2 - 3x + 2
\end{aligned}$$

This suggests that the way to subtract polynomials is to remove parentheses and combine like terms.

EXAMPLE 5   Subtract:

a. $\begin{aligned}(3x - 4) - (5x + 7) &= 3x - 4 - 5x - 7 \\ &= -2x - 11\end{aligned}$

b. $\begin{aligned}(3x^2 - 4x - 6) - (2x^2 - 6x + 12) &= 3x^2 - 4x - 6 - 2x^2 + 6x - 12 \\ &= x^2 + 2x - 18\end{aligned}$

c. $\begin{aligned}(-4rt^3 + 2r^2t^2) - (-3rt^3 + 2r^2t^2) &= -4rt^3 + 2r^2t^2 + 3rt^3 - 2r^2t^2 \\ &= -rt^3\end{aligned}$

SELF CHECK 5   Subtract: $-2a^2b + 5ab^2 - (-5a^2b - 7ab^2)$.

To subtract polynomials in vertical form, we add the negative of the **subtrahend** (the bottom polynomial) to the **minuend** (the top polynomial) to obtain the difference.

EXAMPLE 6   Subtract $(3x^2y - 2xy^2)$ from $(2x^2y + 4xy^2)$.

Solution   We write the subtraction in vertical form, change the signs of the terms of the subtrahend, and add:

$$\begin{array}{r} 2x^2y + 4xy^2 \\ - \underline{3x^2y - 2xy^2} \end{array} \quad \rightarrow \quad \begin{array}{r} 2x^2y + 4xy^2 \\ + \underline{-3x^2y + 2xy^2} \\ - x^2y + 6xy^2 \end{array}$$

In horizontal form, the solution is

$$2x^2y + 4xy^2 - (3x^2y - 2xy^2) = 2x^2y + 4xy^2 - 3x^2y + 2xy^2$$
$$= -x^2y + 6xy^2$$

⇨ SELF CHECK 6   Subtract. $5p^2q - 6pq + 7q$
  $-\quad \underline{2p^2q + 2pq - 8q}$

EXAMPLE 7   Subtract $(6xy^2 + 4x^2y^2 - x^3y^2)$ from $(-2xy^2 - 3x^3y^2)$.

Solution
$$
\begin{array}{l}
-2xy^2 \qquad\quad - 3x^3y^2 \\
-\ \underline{6xy^2 + 4x^2y^2 - x^3y^2}
\end{array}
\rightarrow
\begin{array}{l}
-2xy^2 \qquad\quad - 3x^3y^2 \\
+\ \underline{-6xy^2 - 4x^2y^2 + x^3y^2} \\
-8xy^2 - 4x^2y^2 - 2x^3y^2
\end{array}
$$

In horizontal form, the solution is

$$-2xy^2 - 3x^3y^2 - (6xy^2 + 4x^2y^2 - x^3y^2)$$
$$= -2xy^2 - 3x^3y^2 - 6xy^2 - 4x^2y^2 + x^3y^2$$
$$= -8xy^2 - 4x^2y^2 - 2x^3y^2$$

⇨ SELF CHECK 7   Subtract $(-2pq^2 - 2p^2q^2 + 3p^3q^2)$ from $(5pq^2 + 3p^2q^2 - p^3q^2)$.

---

5   **Simplify an expression using the order of operations and combining like terms.**

Because of the distributive property, we can remove parentheses enclosing several terms when a monomial precedes the parentheses. We multiply every term within the parentheses by that monomial. For example, to add $3(2x + 5)$ and $2(4x - 3)$, we proceed as follows:

$$3(2x + 5) + 2(4x - 3) = 6x + 15 + 8x - 6$$
$$= 6x + 8x + 15 - 6 \qquad \text{Use the commutative property of addition.}$$
$$= 14x + 9 \qquad\qquad\quad \text{Combine like terms.}$$

EXAMPLE 8   Simplify.

a. $3(x^2 + 4x) + 2(x^2 - 4) = 3x^2 + 12x + 2x^2 - 8$
$$= 5x^2 + 12x - 8$$

b. $8(y^2 - 2y + 3) - 4(2y^2 + y - 3) = 8y^2 - 16y + 24 - 8y^2 - 4y + 12$
$$= -20y + 36$$

c. $-4(x^2y^2 - x^2y + 3x) - (x^2y^2 - 2x) + 3(x^2y^2 + 2x^2y)$
$$= -4x^2y^2 + 4x^2y - 12x - x^2y^2 + 2x + 3x^2y^2 + 6x^2y$$
$$= -2x^2y^2 + 10x^2y - 10x$$

⇨ SELF CHECK 8   Simplify: **a.** $2(a^3 - 3a) + 5(a^3 + 2a)$
  b. $5(x^2y + 2x^2) - (x^2y - 3x^2)$

6 Solve an application problem requiring operations with polynomials.

EXAMPLE 9 **PROPERTY VALUES** A house purchased for $95,000 is expected to appreciate according to the formula $y = 2,500x + 95,000$, where y is the value of the house after x years. A second house purchased for $125,000 is expected to appreciate according to the formula $y = 4,500x + 125,000$. Find one formula that will give the value of both properties after x years.

Solution The value of the first house after x years is given by the polynomial $2,500x + 95,000$. The value of the second house after x years is given by the polynomial $4,500x + 125,000$. The value of both houses will be the sum of these two polynomials.

$$2,500x + 95,000 + 4,500x + 125,000 = 7,000x + 220,000$$

The total value y of the properties is given by $y = 7,000x + 220,000$.

⇨ **SELF CHECK ANSWERS**

1. a. $11a^3b^2$ **b.** $11pq^2$ **c.** $35x^6$ **2. a.** $5m^3$ **b.** $-12p^3q^2$ **3.** $7a^2 + 5a - 1$
4. $6pq^2 - 2pq^3 + 2pq^4$ **5.** $3a^2b + 12ab^2$ **6.** $3p^2q - 8pq + 15q$ **7.** $7pq^2 + 5p^2q^2 - 4p^3q^2$
8. a. $7a^3 + 4a$ **b.** $4x^2y + 13x^2$

NOW TRY THIS

1. If the lengths of the sides of a triangle represent consecutive even integers, find the perimeter of the triangle.

2. If the length of a rectangle is $(15x - 3)$ ft and the width is $(8x + 17)$ ft, find the perimeter.

3. If the length of one side of a rectangle is represented by the polynomial $(4x - 18)$ cm, and the perimeter is $(12x - 36)$ cm, find the width.

4.5 EXERCISES

WARM-UPS *Simplify.*

1. $x^3 + 3x^3$

2. $3xy + xy$

3. $(x + 3y) - (x + y)$

4. $5(1 - x) + 3(x - 1)$

5. $(2x - y^2) - (2x + y^2)$

6. $5(x^2 + y) + (x^2 - y)$

7. $3x^2 + 2y + x^2 - y$

8. $2x^2y + y - (2x^2y - y)$

REVIEW *Let $a = 3, b = -2, c = -1,$ and $d = 2$. Evaluate each expression.*

9. $ab + cd$

10. $ad + bc$

11. $a(b + c)$

12. $d(b + a)$

13. Solve the inequality $-4(2x - 9) \geq 12$ and graph the solution set.

14. The **kinetic energy** of a moving object is given by the formula

$$K = \frac{mv^2}{2}$$

Solve the formula for m.

VOCABULARY AND CONCEPTS

Fill in the blanks.

15. A _____ is a polynomial with one term.

16. If two polynomials are subtracted in vertical form, the bottom polynomial is called the _____, and the top polynomial is called the _____.

17. To add like monomials, add the numerical _____ and keep the _____.

18. $a - b = a + $ _____

19. To add two polynomials, combine any _____ contained in the polynomials.

20. To subtract polynomials, remove parentheses and combine _____.

Determine whether the terms are like or unlike terms. If they are like terms, add them.

21. $3y, 4y$ **22.** $3x^2, 5x^2$

23. $3x, 3y$ **24.** $3x^2, 6x$

25. $3x^3, 4x^3, 6x^3$ **26.** $-2y^4, -6y^4, 10y^4$

27. $-5x^3y^2, 13x^3y^2$ **28.** $23, 12x$

29. $-23t^6, 32t^6, 56t^6$

30. $32x^5y^3, -21x^5y^3, -11x^5y^3$

31. $-x^2y, xy, 3xy^2$

32. $4x^3y^2z, -6x^3y^2z, 2x^3y^2z$

GUIDED PRACTICE

Simplify each expression. See Example 1. (Objective 1)

33. $4y + 5y$ **34.** $3t + 6t$

35. $-2x + 3x$ **36.** $-5p + 8p$

37. $-8t^2 + 4t^2$ **38.** $-7m^3 + 2m^3$

39. $15x^2 + 10x^2$ **40.** $25r^4 + 15r^4$

Simplify each expression. See Example 2. (Objective 2)

41. $-18a - 3a$ **42.** $46x^2y - 64x^2y$

43. $32u^3 - 16u^3$ **44.** $25xy^2 - 7xy^2$

45. $18x^5y^2 - 11x^5y^2$ **46.** $17x^6y - 22x^6y$

47. $22ab^2 - 30ab^2$ **48.** $17m^2n - 20m^2n$

Perform each addition and simplify. See Example 3. (Objective 3)

49. $(3x + 7) + (4x - 3)$

50. $(2y - 3) + (4y + 7)$

51. $(2x + 3y + z) + (5x - 10y + z)$

52. $(3x^2 - 3x - 2) + (3x^2 + 4x - 3)$

Perform each addition. See Example 4. (Objective 3)

53. Add: $3x^2 + 4x + 5$
$\underline{2x^2 - 3x + 6}$

54. Add: $2x^3 + 2x^2 - 3x + 5$
$\underline{3x^3 - 4x^2 - x - 7}$

55. Add: $2x^3 - 3x^2 + 4x - 7$
$\underline{-9x^3 - 4x^2 - 5x + 6}$

56. Add: $-3x^3 + 4x^2 - 4x + 9$
$\underline{2x^3 + 9x - 3}$

Perform each subtraction and simplify. See Example 5. (Objective 4)

57. $(4a + 3) - (2a - 4)$

58. $(5b - 7) - (3b + 5)$

59. $(3a^2 - 2a + 4) - (a^2 - 3a + 7)$

60. $(2b^2 + 3b - 5) - (2b^2 - 4b - 9)$

Perform each subtraction. See Example 6. (Objective 4)

61. Subtract: $3x^2 + 4x - 5$
$\underline{-2x^2 - 2x + 3}$

62. Subtract: $3y^2 - 4y + 7$
$\underline{6y^2 - 6y - 13}$

63. Subtract: $4x^3 + 4x^2 - 3x + 10$
$\underline{5x^3 - 2x^2 - 4x - 4}$

64. Subtract: $3x^3 + 4x^2 + 7x + 12$
$\underline{-4x^3 + 6x^2 + 9x - 3}$

Perform each subtraction. See Example 7. (Objective 4)

65. Subtract $11x + y$ from $-8x - 3y$.

66. Subtract $2x + 5y$ from $5x - 8y$.

67. Subtract $4x^2 - 3x + 2$ from $2x^2 - 3x + 1$.

68. Subtract $-4a + b$ from $6a^2 + 5a - b$.

Simplify each expression. See Example 8. (Objective 5)

69. $2(x + 3) + 4(x - 2)$

70. $3(y - 4) - 5(y + 3)$

71. $-2(x^2 + 7x - 1) - 3(x^2 - 2x + 7)$

72. $-5(y^2 - 2y - 6) + 6(2y^2 + 2y - 5)$

73. $2(x^2 - 5x - 4) - 3(x^2 - 5x - 4) + 6(x^2 - 5x - 4)$

74. $7(x^2 + 3x + 1) + 9(x^2 + 3x + 1) - 5(x^2 + 3x + 1)$

75. $2(2y^2 - 2y + 2) - 4(3y^2 - 4y - 1) + 4(y^3 - y^2 - y)$

76. $-4(z^2 - 5z) - 5(4z^2 - 1) + 6(2z - 3)$

ADDITIONAL PRACTICE *Perform the operations and simplify when possible.*

77. $3rst + 4rst + 7rst$

78. $-2ab + 7ab - 3ab$

79. $-4a^2bc + 5a^2bc - 7a^2bc$

80. $(xy)^2 + 4x^2y^2 - 2x^2y^2$

81. $(3x)^2 - 4x^2 + 10x^2$

82. $(2x)^4 - (3x^2)^2$

83. $5x^2y^2 + 2(xy)^2 - (3x^2)y^2$

84. $-3x^3y^6 + 2(xy^2)^3 - (3x)^3y^6$

85. $(-3x^2y)^4 + (4x^4y^2)^2 - 2x^8y^4$

86. $5x^5y^{10} - (2xy^2)^5 + (3x)^5y^{10}$

87. $2(x + 3) + 3(x + 3)$

88. $5(x + y) + 7(x + y)$

89. $-8(x - y) + 11(x - y)$

90. $-4(a - b) - 5(a - b)$

91. $(4c^2 + 3c - 2) + (3c^2 + 4c + 2)$

92. $(-3z^2 - 4z + 7) + (2z^2 + 2z - 1) - (2z^2 - 3z + 7)$

93. Add: $-3x^2y + 4xy + 25y^2$
          $5x^2y - 3xy - 12y^2$

94. Add: $-6x^3z - 4x^2z^2 + 7z^3$
          $-7x^3z + 9x^2z^2 - 21z^3$

95. Subtract: $-2x^2y^2 - 4xy + 12y^2$
              $10x^2y^2 + 9xy - 24y^2$

96. Subtract: $25x^3 - 45x^2z + 31xz^2$
              $12x^3 + 27x^2z - 17xz^2$

97. $2(a^2b^2 - ab) - 3(ab + 2ab^2) + (b^2 - ab + a^2b^2)$

98. $3(xy^2 + y^2) - 2(xy^2 - 4y^2 + y^3) + 2(y^3 + y^2)$

99. $-4(x^2y^2 + xy^3 + xy^2z) - 2(x^2y^2 - 4xy^2z) - 2(8xy^3 - y)$

100. $-3(u^2v - uv^3 + uvw) + 4(uvw + w^2) - 3(w^2 + uvw)$

101. Find the sum when $x^2 + x - 3$ is added to the sum of $2x^2 - 3x + 4$ and $3x^2 - 2$.

102. Find the sum when $3y^2 - 5y + 7$ is added to the sum of $-3y^2 - 7y + 4$ and $5y^2 + 5y - 7$.

103. Find the difference when $t^3 - 2t^2 + 2$ is subtracted from the sum of $3t^3 + t^2$ and $-t^3 + 6t - 3$.

104. Find the difference when $-3z^3 - 4z + 7$ is subtracted from the sum of $-2z^2 + 3z - 7$ and $-4z^3 - 2z - 3$.

105. Find the sum when $3x^2 + 4x - 7$ is added to the sum of $-2x^2 - 7x + 1$ and $-4x^2 + 8x - 1$.

106. Find the difference when $32x^2 - 17x + 45$ is subtracted from the sum of $23x^2 - 12x - 7$ and $-11x^2 + 12x + 7$.

APPLICATIONS

Consider the following information: If a house was purchased for $105,000 and is expected to appreciate $900 per year, its value y after x years is given by the formula $y = 900x + 105,000$. See Example 9. (Objective 6)

107. Value of a house   Find the expected value of the house in 10 years.

108. Value of a house   A second house was purchased for $120,000 and was expected to appreciate $1,000 per year. Find a polynomial equation that will give the value of the house in x years.

109. Value of a house   Find the value of the house discussed in Exercise 108 after 12 years.

110. Value of a house   Find one polynomial equation that will give the combined value y of both houses after x years.

111. Value of two houses   Find the value of the two houses after 20 years by
  a. substituting 20 into the polynomial equations $y = 900x + 105,000$ and $y = 1,000x + 120,000$ and adding the results.
  b. substituting into the result of Exercise 110.

112. Value of two houses   Find the value of the two houses after 25 years by
  a. substituting 25 into the polynomial equations $y = 900x + 105,000$ and $y = 1,000x + 120,000$ and adding the results.
  b. substituting into the result of Exercise 110.

Consider the following information: A business bought two computers, one for $6,600 and the other for $9,200. The first computer is expected to depreciate $1,100 per year and the second $1,700 per year.

113. Value of a computer   Write a polynomial equation that will give the value of the first computer after x years.

114. Value of a computer   Write a polynomial equation that will give the value of the second computer after x years.

115. Value of two computers   Find one polynomial equation that will give the value of both computers after x years.

116. Value of two computers   In two ways, find the value of the computers after 3 years.

WRITING ABOUT MATH

117. How do you recognize like terms?

118. How do you add like terms?

SOMETHING TO THINK ABOUT

Let P(x) = 3x − 5. Find each value.

119. $P(x + h) + P(x)$

120. $P(x + h) − P(x)$

121. If $P(x) = x^{23} + 5x^2 + 73$ and $Q(x) = x^{23} + 4x^2 + 73$, find $P(7) − Q(7)$.

122. If two numbers written in scientific notation have the same power of 10, they can be added as similar terms:

$$2 \times 10^3 + 3 \times 10^3 = 5 \times 10^3$$

Without converting to standard form, how could you add

$$2 \times 10^3 + 3 \times 10^4$$

SECTION 4.6

Multiplying Polynomials

Objectives

1 Multiply two or more monomials.

2 Multiply a polynomial by a monomial.

3 Multiply a binomial by a binomial using the distributive property or FOIL method.

4 Multiply a polynomial by a binomial.

5 Solve an equation that simplifies to a linear equation.

6 Solve an application problem involving multiplication of polynomials.

Vocabulary

FOIL method   special products   conjugate binomials

Getting Ready

Simplify:

1. $(2x)(3)$ **2.** $(3xxx)(x)$ **3.** $5x^2 \cdot x$ **4.** $8x^2x^3$

Use the distributive property to remove parentheses.

5. $3(x + 5)$ **6.** $−2(x + 5)$ **7.** $4(y − 3)$ **8.** $−2(y^2 − 3)$

We now discuss how to multiply polynomials. After introducing general methods for multiplication, we will introduce a special method, called the *FOIL method,* used for multiplying binomials.

1 Multiply two or more monomials.

We have previously multiplied monomials by other monomials. For example, to multiply $4x^2$ by $−2x^3$, we use the commutative and associative properties of multiplication to group the numerical factors together and the variable factors together. Then we multiply the numerical factors and multiply the variable factors.

$$4x^2(-2x^3) = 4(-2)x^2x^3$$
$$= -8x^5$$

This example suggests the following rule.

Multiplying Monomials	To multiply two simplified monomials, multiply the numerical factors and then multiply the variable factors.

EXAMPLE 1 Multiply. **a.** $3x^5(2x^5)$ **b.** $-2a^2b^3(5ab^2)$ **c.** $-4y^5z^2(2y^3z^3)(3yz)$

Solution **a.** $3x^5(2x^5) = 3(2)x^5x^5$
$$= 6x^{10}$$

b. $-2a^2b^3(5ab^2) = -2(5)a^2ab^3b^2$
$$= -10a^3b^5$$

c. $-4y^5z^2(2y^3z^3)(3yz) = -4(2)(3)y^5y^3yz^2z^3z$
$$= -24y^9z^6$$

⇨ **SELF CHECK 1** Multiply.
a. $(5a^2b^3)(6a^3b^4)$
b. $(-15p^3q^2)(5p^3q^2)$

2 **Multiply a polynomial by a monomial.**

To find the product of a monomial and a polynomial with more than one term, we use the distributive property. To multiply $2x + 4$ by $5x$, for example, we proceed as follows:

$$5x(2x + 4) = 5x \cdot 2x + 5x \cdot 4 \quad \text{Use the distributive property.}$$
$$= 10x^2 + 20x \quad \text{Multiply the monomials } 5x \cdot 2x = 10x^2 \text{ and } 5x \cdot 4 = 20x.$$

This example suggests the following rule.

Multiplying Polynomials by Monomials	To multiply a polynomial with more than one term by a monomial, use the distributive property to remove parentheses and simplify.

EXAMPLE 2 Multiply. **a.** $3a^2(3a^2 - 5a)$ **b.** $-2xz^2(2x - 3z + 2z^2)$

Solution **a.** $3a^2(3a^2 - 5a) = 3a^2 \cdot 3a^2 - 3a^2 \cdot 5a \quad \text{Use the distributive property.}$
$$= 9a^4 - 15a^3 \quad \text{Multiply.}$$

b. $-2xz^2(2x - 3z + 2z^2)$
$= -2xz^2 \cdot 2x - (-2xz^2) \cdot 3z + (-2xz^2) \cdot 2z^2$ Use the distributive property.
$= -4x^2z^2 - (-6xz^3) + (-4xz^4)$ Multiply.
$= -4x^2z^2 + 6xz^3 - 4xz^4$

⇨ **SELF CHECK 2**   Multiply.
a. $2p^3(3p^2 - 5p)$
b. $-5a^2b(3a + 2b - 4ab)$

3 **Multiply a binomial by a binomial using the distributive property or FOIL method.**

To multiply two binomials, we must use the distributive property more than once. For example, to multiply $2a - 4$ by $3a + 5$, we proceed as follows.

$(2a - 4)(3a + 5) = (2a - 4) \cdot 3a + (2a - 4) \cdot 5$ Use the distributive property.
$= 3a(2a - 4) + 5(2a - 4)$ Use the commutative property of multiplication.
$= 3a \cdot 2a - 3a \cdot 4 + 5 \cdot 2a - 5 \cdot 4$ Use the distributive property.
$= 6a^2 - 12a + 10a - 20$ Do the multiplications.
$= 6a^2 - 2a - 20$ Combine like terms.

This example suggests the following rule.

Multiplying Two Binomials

To multiply two binomials, multiply each term of one binomial by each term of the other binomial and combine like terms.

To multiply binomials, we can apply the distributive property using a shortcut method, called the **FOIL method.** FOIL is an acronym for **F**irst terms, **O**uter terms, **I**nner terms, and **L**ast terms. To use this method to multiply $(2a - 4)$ by $(3a + 5)$, we

1. multiply the **F**irst terms $2a$ and $3a$ to obtain $6a^2$,
2. multiply the **O**uter terms $2a$ and 5 to obtain $10a$,
3. multiply the **I**nner terms -4 and $3a$ to obtain $-12a$, and
4. multiply the **L**ast terms -4 and 5 to obtain -20.

Then we simplify the resulting polynomial, if possible.

First terms   Last terms

$(2a - 4)(3a + 5) = 2a(3a) + 2a(5) + (-4)(3a) + (-4)(5)$
Inner terms $= 6a^2 + 10a - 12a - 20$ Simplify.
Outer terms $= 6a^2 - 2a - 20$ Combine like terms.

EXAMPLE 3 Find each product.

a. $(3x + 4)(2x - 3) = 3x(2x) + 3x(-3) + 4(2x) + 4(-3)$
$$= 6x^2 - 9x + 8x - 12$$
$$= 6x^2 - x - 12$$

b. $(2y - 7)(5y - 4) = 2y(5y) + 2y(-4) + (-7)(5y) + (-7)(-4)$
$$= 10y^2 - 8y - 35y + 28$$
$$= 10y^2 - 43y + 28$$

c. $(2r - 3s)(2r + t) = 2r(2r) + 2r(t) - 3s(2r) - 3s(t)$
$$= 4r^2 + 2rt - 6sr - 3st$$
$$= 4r^2 + 2rt - 6rs - 3st$$

⇨ **SELF CHECK 3** Find each product.
a. $(2a - 1)(3a + 2)$
b. $(5y - 2z)(2y + 3z)$

EXAMPLE 4 Simplify each expression.

a. $3(2x - 3)(x + 1)$

$= 3(2x^2 + 2x - 3x - 3)$ Multiply the binomials.
$= 3(2x^2 - x - 3)$ Combine like terms.
$= 6x^2 - 3x - 9$ Use the distributive property to remove parentheses.

b. $(x + 1)(x - 2) - 3x(x + 3)$

$= x^2 - 2x + x - 2 - 3x^2 - 9x$ Use the distributive property to remove parentheses.

$= -2x^2 - 10x - 2$ Combine like terms.

⇨ **SELF CHECK 4** Simplify: $(x + 3)(2x - 1) + 2x(x - 1)$.

The products discussed in Example 5 are called **special products.**

EXAMPLE 5   Find each product.

a. $(x + y)^2 = (x + y)(x + y)$

$$= x^2 + xy + xy + y^2$$
$$= x^2 + 2xy + y^2$$

The square of the sum of two quantities has three terms: *the square of the first quantity, plus twice the product of the quantities, plus the square of the second quantity.*

b. $(x - y)^2 = (x - y)(x - y)$

$$= x^2 - xy - xy + y^2$$
$$= x^2 - 2xy + y^2$$

The square of the difference of two quantities has three terms: *the square of the first quantity, minus twice the product of the quantities, plus the square of the second quantity.*

c. $(x + y)(x - y) = x^2 - xy + xy - y^2$

$$= x^2 - y^2$$

The product of the sum and the difference of two quantities is a binomial. *It is the product of the first quantities minus the product of the second quantities.*

Binomials that have the same terms, but with opposite signs between the terms, are called **conjugate binomials.**

⇨ **SELF CHECK 5**   Find each product.
a. $(p + 2)^2$
b. $(p - 2)^2$
c. $(p + 2q)(p - 2q)$

Because the products discussed in Example 5 occur so often, it is wise to learn their forms.

Special Products

$$(x + y)^2 = x^2 + 2xy + y^2$$
$$(x - y)^2 = x^2 - 2xy + y^2$$
$$(x + y)(x - y) = x^2 - y^2$$

4   **Multiply a polynomial by a binomial.**

We must use the distributive property more than once to multiply a polynomial by a binomial. For example, to multiply $3x^2 + 3x - 5$ by $2x + 3$, we proceed as follows:

COMMENT   Note that

$$(x + y)^2 \neq x^2 + y^2$$

and

$$(x - y)^2 \neq x^2 - y^2$$

$$(2x + 3)(3x^2 + 3x - 5) = (2x + 3)3x^2 + (2x + 3)3x - (2x + 3)5$$
$$= 3x^2(2x + 3) + 3x(2x + 3) - 5(2x + 3)$$
$$= 6x^3 + 9x^2 + 6x^2 + 9x - 10x - 15$$
$$= 6x^3 + 15x^2 - x - 15$$

This example suggests the following rule.

| **Multiplying Polynomials** | To multiply one polynomial by another, multiply each term of one polynomial by each term of the other polynomial and combine like terms. |

It is often convenient to organize the work vertically.

EXAMPLE 6   **a.** Multiply:

$$
\begin{array}{r}
3a^2 - 4a + 7 \\
2a + 5 \\
\hline
\end{array}
$$

$2a(3a^2 - 4a + 7) \longrightarrow \quad 6a^3 - 8a^2 + 14a$
$5(3a^2 - 4a + 7) \longrightarrow \quad \underline{+ 15a^2 - 20a + 35}$
$$6a^3 + 7a^2 - 6a + 35$$

b. Multiply:

$$
\begin{array}{r}
3y^2 - 5y + 4 \\
- 4y^2 - 3 \\
\hline
\end{array}
$$

$-4y^2(3y^2 - 5y + 4) \longrightarrow \quad -12y^4 + 20y^3 - 16y^2$
$-3(3y^2 - 5y + 4) \longrightarrow \quad \underline{\quad\quad\quad - 9y^2 + 15y - 12}$
$$-12y^4 + 20y^3 - 25y^2 + 15y - 12$$

⇨ **SELF CHECK 6**   Multiply:
a. $(3x + 2)(2x^2 - 4x + 5)$
b. $(-2x^2 + 3)(2x^2 - 4x - 1)$

COMMENT   An expression (without an = sign) can be simplified by combining its like terms. An equation (with an = sign) can be solved. Remember that

Expressions are to be simplified.

Equations are to be solved.

5   **Solve an equation that simplifies to a linear equation.**

To solve an equation such as $(x + 2)(x + 3) = x(x + 7)$, we can use the FOIL method to remove the parentheses on the left side, use the distributive property to remove parentheses on the right side, and proceed as follows:

$$(x + 2)(x + 3) = x(x + 7)$$
$$x^2 + 3x + 2x + 6 = x^2 + 7x$$
$$x^2 + 5x + 6 = x^2 + 7x \quad \text{Combine like terms.}$$

$$5x + 6 = 7x \qquad \text{Subtract } x^2 \text{ from both sides.}$$
$$6 = 2x \qquad \text{Subtract } 5x \text{ from both sides.}$$
$$3 = x \qquad \text{Divide both sides by 2.}$$

Check: $(x + 2)(x + 3) = x(x + 7)$
$$(3 + 2)(3 + 3) \overset{2}{=} 3(3 + 7) \qquad \text{Replace } x \text{ with 3.}$$
$$5(6) \overset{2}{=} 3(10) \qquad \text{Do the additions within parentheses.}$$
$$30 = 30$$

Since the answer checks, the solution is 3.

EXAMPLE 7   Solve: $(x + 5)(x + 4) = (x + 9)(x + 10)$.

Solution   We remove parentheses on both sides of the equation and proceed as follows:

$$(x + 5)(x + 4) = (x + 9)(x + 10)$$
$$x^2 + 4x + 5x + 20 = x^2 + 10x + 9x + 90$$
$$x^2 + 9x + 20 = x^2 + 19x + 90 \qquad \text{Combine like terms.}$$
$$9x + 20 = 19x + 90 \qquad \text{Subtract } x^2 \text{ from both sides.}$$
$$20 = 10x + 90 \qquad \text{Subtract } 9x \text{ from both sides.}$$
$$-70 = 10x \qquad \text{Subtract 90 from both sides.}$$
$$-7 = x \qquad \text{Divide both sides by 10.}$$

Check: $(x + 5)(x + 4) = (x + 9)(x + 10)$
$$(-7 + 5)(-7 + 4) \overset{2}{=} (-7 + 9)(-7 + 10) \qquad \text{Replace } x \text{ with } -7.$$
$$(-2)(-3) \overset{2}{=} (2)(3) \qquad \text{Do the additions within parentheses.}$$
$$6 = 6$$

Since the result checks, the solution is -7.

▷ **SELF CHECK 7**   Solve: $(x + 2)(x - 4) = (x + 6)(x - 3)$.

---

6   **Solve an application problem involving multiplication of polynomials.**

EXAMPLE 8   **DIMENSIONS OF A PAINTING**   A square painting is surrounded by a border 2 inches wide. If the area of the border is 96 square inches, find the dimensions of the painting.

Analyze the problem   Refer to Figure 4-6, which shows a square painting surrounded by a border 2 inches wide. We can let x represent the length of each side of the square painting. The outer rectangle is also a square, and its dimensions are $x + 4$ by $x + 4$ inches.

Figure 4-6
©Shutterstock.com/Olga Lyubkina

Form an equation   We know that the area of the border is 96 square inches, the area of the larger square is $(x + 4)(x + 4)$, and the area of the painting is $x \cdot x$. If we subtract the area of the painting from the area of the larger square, the difference is 96 (the area of the border).

	The area of the large square	minus	the area of the square painting	equals	the area of the border.
	$(x + 4)(x + 4)$	$-$	$x \cdot x$	$=$	96

Solve the equation

$$(x + 4)(x + 4) - x^2 = 96$$

$$x^2 + 8x + 16 - x^2 = 96 \quad \text{Use the distributive property.}$$

$$8x + 16 = 96 \quad \text{Combine like terms.}$$

$$8x = 80 \quad \text{Subtract 16 from both sides.}$$

$$x = 10 \quad \text{Divide both sides by 8.}$$

State the conclusion   The dimensions of the painting are 10 inches by 10 inches.

Check the result   Check the result.

⇨ SELF CHECK ANSWERS

1. a. $30a^5b^7$ **b.** $-75p^6q^4$ **2. a.** $6p^5 - 10p^4$ **b.** $-15a^3b - 10a^2b^2 + 20a^3b^2$ **3. a.** $6a^2 + a - 2$
b. $10y^2 + 11yz - 6z^2$ **4.** $4x^2 + 3x - 3$ **5. a.** $p^2 + 4p + 4$ **b.** $p^2 - 4p + 4$ **c.** $p^2 - 4q^2$
6. a. $6x^3 - 8x^2 + 7x + 10$ **b.** $-4x^4 + 8x^3 + 8x^2 - 12x - 3$ **7.** 2

NOW TRY THIS

Simplify or solve as appropriate:

1. $-\dfrac{1}{2}x(8x^2 - 16x + 2)$

2. $(2x - 3)(4x^2 + 6x + 9)$

3. $(x - 2)(x + 5) = (x - 1)(x + 8)$

4. Find the area of a square with one side represented by $(3x + 5)$ ft.

4.6 EXERCISES

WARM-UPS *Find each product.*

1. $2x^2(3x - 1)$

2. $5y(2y^2 - 3)$

3. $7xy(x + y)$

4. $-2y(2x - 3y)$

5. $(x + 3)(x + 2)$

6. $(x - 3)(x + 2)$

7. $(2x + 3)(x + 2)$

8. $(3x - 1)(3x + 1)$

9. $(x + 3)^2$

10. $(x - 5)^2$

REVIEW *Determine which property of real numbers justifies each statement.*

11. $3(x + 5) = 3x + 3 \cdot 5$

12. $(x + 3) + y = x + (3 + y)$

13. $3(ab) = (ab)3$

14. $a + 0 = a$

15. Solve: $\dfrac{5}{3}(5y + 6) - 10 = 0$.

16. Solve $F = \dfrac{GMm}{d^2}$ for m.

VOCABULARY AND CONCEPTS

Fill in the blanks.

17. A polynomial with one term is called a _____.

18. A binomial is a polynomial with ____ terms. The binomials $a + b$ and $a - b$ are called _____ binomials.

19. Products in the form $(a + b)^2$, $(a - b)^2$, or $(a + b)(a - b)$ are called _____.

20. In the acronym FOIL, F stands for _____, O stands for _____, I stands for _____, and L stands for _____.

Consider the product $(2x + 5)(3x - 4)$.

21. The product of the first terms is ____.

22. The product of the outer terms is _____.

23. The product of the inner terms is ____.

24. The product of the last terms is _____.

GUIDED PRACTICE

Find each product or power. See Example 1. (Objective 1)

25. $(3x^2)(4x^3)$ **26.** $(-2a^3)(3a^2)$

27. $(-5t^3)(2t^4)$ **28.** $(-6a^2)(-3a^5)$

29. $(2x^2y^3)(3x^3y^2)$ **30.** $(-x^3y^6z)(x^2y^2z^7)$

31. $(3b^2)(-2b)(4b^3)$ **32.** $(3y)(2y^2)(-y^4)$

33. $(a^2b^3c)^5$ **34.** $(x^3y^3z^2)^4$

35. $(a^3b^2c)(abc^3)^2$ **36.** $(xyz^3)(xy^2z^2)^3$

Find each product. See Example 2. (Objective 2)

37. $3(x + 4)$ **38.** $-3(a - 2)$

39. $-4(t + 7)$ **40.** $6(s^2 - 3)$

41. $3x(x - 2)$ **42.** $4y(y + 5)$

43. $-2x^2(3x^2 - x)$ **44.** $4b^3(2 - 2b)$

45. $3xy(x + y)$ **46.** $-4x^2(3x^2 - x)$

47. $2x^2(3x^2 + 4x - 7)$ **48.** $3y^3(2y^2 - 7y - 8)$

49. $\frac{1}{4}x^2(8x^5 - 4)$ **50.** $\frac{4}{3}a^2b(6a - 5b)$

51. $-\frac{2}{3}r^2t^2(9r - 3t)$ **52.** $-\frac{4}{5}p^2q(10p + 15q)$

Find each product. See Example 3. (Objective 3)

53. $(a + 4)(a + 5)$ **54.** $(y - 3)(y + 5)$

55. $(3x - 2)(x + 4)$ **56.** $(t + 4)(2t - 3)$

57. $(2a + 4)(3a - 5)$ **58.** $(2b - 1)(3b + 4)$

59. $(3x - 5)(2x + 1)$ **60.** $(2y - 5)(3y + 7)$

61. $(2s + 3t)(3s - t)$ **62.** $(3a - 2b)(4a + b)$

63. $(u + v)(u + 2t)$ **64.** $(x - 5y)(a + 2y)$

65. $(x + y)(x + z)$ **66.** $(a - b)(x + y)$

Find each product. See Example 4. (Objective 3)

67. $2(x - 4)(x + 1)$

68. $-3(2x + 3y)(3x - 4y)$

69. $3a(a + b)(a - b)$

70. $-2r(r + s)(r + s)$

71. $(3xy)(-2x^2y^3)(x + y)$

72. $(-2a^2b)(-3a^3b^2)(3a - 2b)$

73. $2t(t + 2) + 3t(t - 5)$

74. $3a(a - 2) + 2a(a + 4)$

Find each product. See Example 5. (Objective 3)

75. $(x + 5)^2$ **76.** $(y - 6)^2$

77. $(x - 4)^2$ **78.** $(a + 3)^2$

79. $(2s + 1)^2$ **80.** $(3t - 2)^2$

81. $(x - 2y)^2$ **82.** $(3a + 2b)^2$

83. $(r + 4)(r - 4)$ **84.** $(b + 2)(b - 2)$

85. $(4x + 5)(4x - 5)$ **86.** $(5z + 1)(5z - 1)$

Find each product. See Example 6. (Objective 4)

87. $(2x + 1)(x^2 + 3x - 1)$ **88.** $(3x - 2)(2x^2 - x + 2)$

89. $(4t + 3)(t^2 + 2t + 3)$

90. $(3x + y)(2x^2 - 3xy + y^2)$

91. $\begin{array}{r} 4x + 3 \\ \underline{x + 2} \end{array}$ **92.** $\begin{array}{r} 5r + 6 \\ \underline{2r - 1} \end{array}$

93. $\begin{array}{r} 4x - 2y \\ \underline{3x + 5y} \end{array}$ **94.** $\begin{array}{r} 5r + 6s \\ \underline{2r - s} \end{array}$

Solve each equation. See Example 7. (Objective 5)

95. $(s - 4)(s + 1) = s^2 + 5$

96. $(y - 5)(y - 2) = y^2 - 4$

97. $z(z + 2) = (z + 4)(z - 4)$

98. $(z + 3)(z - 3) = z(z - 3)$

99. $(x + 4)(x - 4) = (x - 2)(x + 6)$

100. $(y - 1)(y + 6) = (y - 3)(y - 2) + 8$
101. $(a - 3)^2 = (a + 3)^2$
102. $(b + 2)^2 = (b - 1)^2$

ADDITIONAL PRACTICE

Find each product or power and simplify the result.

103. $(x^2 y^3)^5$ **104.** $(a^3 b^2)^4$

105. $(x^5 y^2)^3$ **106.** $(m^3 n^4)^4$

107. $(x^2 y^5)(x^2 z^5)(-3y^2 z^3)$ **108.** $(-r^4 st^2)(2r^2 st)(rst)$

109. $(x + 3)(2x - 3)$ **110.** $(2x + 3)(2x - 5)$

111. $(t - 3)(t - 3)$ **112.** $(z - 5)(z - 5)$

113. $(3x - 5)(2x + 1)$ **114.** $(2y - 5)(3y + 7)$

115. $(-2r - 3s)(2r + 7s)$ **116.** $(-4a + 3)(-2a - 3)$

117. $(2a - 3b)^2$ **118.** $(2x + 5y)^2$

119. $(4x + 5y)(4x - 5y)$ **120.** $(6p + 5q)(6p - 5q)$

121. $x^2 + x + 1$ **122.** $4x^2 - 2x + 1$
$\underline{\qquad x - 1\qquad}$ $\underline{\qquad 2x + 1\qquad}$

123. $(-3x + y)(x^2 - 8xy + 16y^2)$

124. $(3x - y)(x^2 + 3xy - y^2)$
125. $(x - 2y)(x^2 + 2xy + 4y^2)$
126. $(2m + n)(4m^2 - 2mn + n^2)$

Simplify or solve as appropriate.

127. $3xy(x + y) - 2x(xy - x)$
128. $(a + b)(a - b) - (a + b)(a + b)$
129. $(x + y)(x - y) + x(x + y)$
130. $(2x - 1)(2x + 1) + x(2x + 1)$
131. $7s^2 + (s - 3)(2s + 1) = (3s - 1)^2$
132. $(x + 2)^2 - (x - 2)^2$
133. $(x - 3)^2 - (x + 3)^2$
134. $(2s - 3)(s + 2) + (3s + 1)(s - 3)$
135. $(3x + 4)(2x - 2) - (2x + 1)(x + 3)$
136. $4 + (2y - 3)^2 = (2y - 1)(2y + 3)$
137. $(b + 2)(b - 2) + 2b(b + 1)$
138. $3y(y + 2) + (y + 1)(y - 1)$

APPLICATIONS   See Example 8. (Objective 6)

139. Millstones   The radius of one millstone in the illustration is 3 meters greater than the radius of the other, and their areas differ by 15π square meters. Find the radius of the larger millstone.

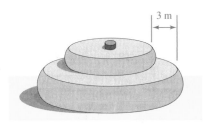

140. Bookbinding   Two square sheets of cardboard used for making book covers differ in area by 44 square inches. An edge of the larger square is 2 inches greater than an edge of the smaller square. Find the length of an edge of the smaller square.

141. Baseball   In major league baseball, the distance between bases is 30 feet greater than it is in softball. The bases in major league baseball mark the corners of a square that has an area 4,500 square feet greater than for softball. Find the distance between the bases in baseball.

142. Pulley designs   The radius of one pulley in the illustration is 1 inch greater than the radius of the second pulley, and their areas differ by 4π square inches. Find the radius of the smaller pulley.

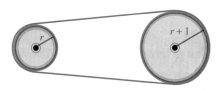

WRITING ABOUT MATH

143. Describe the steps involved in finding the product of a binomial and its conjugate.
144. Writing the expression $(x + y)^2$ as $x^2 + y^2$ illustrates a common error. Explain.

SOMETHING TO THINK ABOUT

145. The area of the square in the illustration is the total of the areas of the four smaller regions. The picture illustrates the product $(x + y)^2$. Explain.

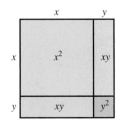

146. The illustration represents the product of two binomials. Explain.

SECTION 4.7

Dividing Polynomials by Monomials

Objectives

1 Divide a monomial by a monomial.
2 Divide a polynomial by a monomial.
3 Solve an application problem requiring division by a monomial.

Getting Ready

Simplify each fraction.

1. $\dfrac{4x^2y^3}{2xy}$ **2.** $\dfrac{9xyz}{9xz}$ **3.** $\dfrac{15x^2y}{10x}$ **4.** $\dfrac{6x^2y}{6xy^2}$

5. $\dfrac{(2x^2)(5y^2)}{10xy}$ **6.** $\dfrac{(5x^3y)(6xy^3)}{10x^4y^4}$

In this section, we will show how to divide polynomials by monomials. We will discuss how to divide polynomials by polynomials in the next section.

1 **Divide a monomial by a monomial.**

We have seen that dividing by a number is equivalent to multiplying by its reciprocal. For example, dividing the number 8 by 2 gives the same answer as multiplying 8 by $\frac{1}{2}$.

$$\frac{8}{2} = 4 \qquad \text{and} \qquad 8 \cdot \frac{1}{2} = 4$$

In general, the following is true.

Division

$$\frac{a}{b} = a \cdot \frac{1}{b} \quad (b \neq 0)$$

Recall that to simplify a fraction, we write both its numerator and its denominator as the product of several factors and then divide out all common factors. For example,

$$\frac{20}{25} = \frac{4 \cdot 5}{5 \cdot 5} \qquad \text{Factor:} \quad 20 = 4 \cdot 5 \text{ and } 25 = 5 \cdot 5.$$

$$= \frac{4 \cdot \overset{1}{\cancel{5}}}{\cancel{5} \cdot 5} \qquad \text{Divide out the common factor of 5.}$$
$$\phantom{=\frac{4 \cdot 5}{5}}_{1}$$

$$= \frac{4}{5} \qquad \frac{5}{5} = 1$$

We can use the same method to simplify algebraic fractions that contain variables. We must assume, however, that no variable is 0.

$$\frac{3p^2q}{6pq^3} = \frac{3 \cdot p \cdot p \cdot q}{2 \cdot 3 \cdot p \cdot q \cdot q \cdot q} \qquad \text{Factor: } p^2 = p \cdot p, 6 = 2 \cdot 3, \text{ and } q^3 = q \cdot q \cdot q.$$

$$= \frac{\overset{1}{\cancel{3}} \cdot \overset{1}{\cancel{p}} \cdot p \cdot \overset{1}{\cancel{q}}}{2 \cdot \underset{1}{\cancel{3}} \cdot \underset{1}{\cancel{p}} \cdot \underset{1}{\cancel{q}} \cdot q \cdot q} \qquad \text{Divide out the common factors of 3, } p, \text{ and } q.$$

$$= \frac{p}{2q^2} \qquad \frac{3}{3} = 1, \frac{p}{p} = 1, \text{ and } \frac{q}{q} = 1.$$

To divide monomials, we can either use the previous method used for simplifying arithmetic fractions or use the rules of exponents.

COMMENT In all examples and exercises, we will assume that no variables are 0.

EXAMPLE 1 Simplify. **a.** $\dfrac{x^2y}{xy^2}$ **b.** $\dfrac{-8a^3b^2}{4ab^3}$

Solution **_Using Fractions_**

a. $\dfrac{x^2y}{xy^2} = \dfrac{x \cdot x \cdot y}{x \cdot y \cdot y}$

$$= \frac{\overset{1}{\cancel{x}} \cdot x \cdot \overset{1}{\cancel{y}}}{\underset{1}{\cancel{x}} \cdot y \cdot \underset{1}{\cancel{y}}}$$

$$= \frac{x}{y}$$

Using the Rules of Exponents

$$\frac{x^2y}{xy^2} = x^{2-1}y^{1-2}$$

$$= x^1y^{-1}$$

$$= x \cdot \frac{1}{y}$$

$$= \frac{x}{y}$$

b. $\dfrac{-8a^3b^2}{4ab^3} = \dfrac{-2 \cdot 4 \cdot a \cdot a \cdot a \cdot b \cdot b}{4 \cdot a \cdot b \cdot b \cdot b}$

$$= \frac{-2 \cdot \overset{1}{\cancel{4}} \cdot \overset{1}{\cancel{a}} \cdot a \cdot a \cdot \overset{1}{\cancel{b}} \cdot \overset{1}{\cancel{b}}}{\underset{1}{\cancel{4}} \cdot \underset{1}{\cancel{a}} \cdot \underset{1}{\cancel{b}} \cdot \underset{1}{\cancel{b}} \cdot b}$$

$$= \frac{-2a^2}{b}$$

$$\frac{-8a^3b^2}{4ab^3} = \frac{(-1)2^3a^3b^2}{2^2ab^3}$$

$$= (-1)2^{3-2}a^{3-1}b^{2-3}$$

$$= (-1)2^1a^2b^{-1}$$

$$= -2a^2 \cdot \frac{1}{b}$$

$$= \frac{-2a^2}{b}$$

SELF CHECK 1 Simplify. $\dfrac{-5p^2q^3}{10pq^4}$

2 **Divide a polynomial by a monomial.**

In Chapter 1, we saw that

$$\frac{a}{d} + \frac{b}{d} = \frac{a+b}{d}$$

Since this is true, we also have

$$\frac{a + b}{d} = \frac{a}{d} + \frac{b}{d}$$

This suggests that, to divide a polynomial by a monomial, we can divide each term of the polynomial in the numerator by the monomial in the denominator.

EXAMPLE 2   Simplify. $\dfrac{9x + 6y}{3xy}$

Solution $\dfrac{9x + 6y}{3xy} = \dfrac{9x}{3xy} + \dfrac{6y}{3xy}$ Divide each term in the numerator by the monomial.

$$= \frac{3}{y} + \frac{2}{x}$$ Simplify each fraction.

⇨ **SELF CHECK 2**   Simplify. $\dfrac{4a - 8b}{4ab}$

EXAMPLE 3   Simplify. $\dfrac{6x^2y^2 + 4x^2y - 2xy}{2xy}$

Solution $\dfrac{6x^2y^2 + 4x^2y - 2xy}{2xy}$

COMMENT   Remember that any nonzero value divided by itself is 1.

$$= \frac{6x^2y^2}{2xy} + \frac{4x^2y}{2xy} - \frac{2xy}{2xy}$$ Divide each term in the numerator by the monomial.

$$= 3xy + 2x - 1$$ Simplify each fraction.

⇨ **SELF CHECK 3**   Simplify. $\dfrac{9a^2b - 6ab^2 + 3ab}{3ab}$

EXAMPLE 4   Simplify. $\dfrac{12a^3b^2 - 4a^2b + a}{6a^2b^2}$

Solution $\dfrac{12a^3b^2 - 4a^2b + a}{6a^2b^2}$

$$= \frac{12a^3b^2}{6a^2b^2} - \frac{4a^2b}{6a^2b^2} + \frac{a}{6a^2b^2}$$ Divide each term in the numerator by the monomial.

$$= 2a - \frac{2}{3b} + \frac{1}{6ab^2}$$ Simplify each fraction.

⇨ **SELF CHECK 4**   Simplify. $\dfrac{14p^3q + pq^2 - p}{7p^2q}$

EXAMPLE 5   Simplify. $\dfrac{(x - y)^2 - (x + y)^2}{xy}$

Solution $\dfrac{(x - y)^2 - (x + y)^2}{xy}$

$= \dfrac{x^2 - 2xy + y^2 - (x^2 + 2xy + y^2)}{xy}$ Square the binomials in the numerator.

$= \dfrac{x^2 - 2xy + y^2 - x^2 - 2xy - y^2}{xy}$ Remove parentheses.

$= \dfrac{-4xy}{xy}$ Combine like terms.

$= -4$ Divide out xy.

⇨ **SELF CHECK 5**   Simplify. $\dfrac{(x + y)^2 - (x - y)^2}{xy}$

---

3   **Solve an application problem requiring division by a monomial.**

The cross-sectional area of the trapezoidal drainage ditch shown in Figure 4-7 is given by the formula $A = \frac{1}{2}h(B + b)$, where B and b are its bases and h is its height. To solve the formula for b, we proceed as follows.

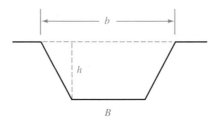

Figure 4-7

$A = \dfrac{1}{2}h(B + b)$

$2A = 2 \cdot \dfrac{1}{2}h(B + b)$ Multiply both sides by 2.

$2A = h(B + b)$ Simplify.

$2A = hB + hb$ Use the distributive property to remove parentheses.

$2A - hB = hB - hB + hb$ Subtract hB from both sides.

$2A - hB = hb$ Combine like terms: $hB - hB = 0$.

$\dfrac{2A - hB}{h} = \dfrac{hb}{h}$ Divide both sides by h.

$\dfrac{2A - hB}{h} = b$ $\frac{hb}{h} = b$

EXAMPLE 6 Another student worked the previous problem in a different way and got a result of $b = \frac{2A}{h} - B$. Is this also correct?

Solution To show that this result is correct, we must show that $\frac{2A - hB}{h} = \frac{2A}{h} - B$. We can do this by dividing $2A - hB$ by h.

$$\frac{2A - hB}{h} = \frac{2A}{h} - \frac{hB}{h}$$ Divide each term in the numerator by the monomial.

$$= \frac{2A}{h} - B$$ Simplify: $\frac{hB}{h} = B$.

The results are the same.

SELF CHECK 6 Suppose another student got $2A - B$. Is this result correct?

SELF CHECK ANSWERS   **1.** $-\frac{p}{2q}$ **2.** $\frac{1}{b} - \frac{2}{a}$ **3.** $3a - 2b + 1$ **4.** $2p + \frac{q}{7p} - \frac{1}{7pq}$ **5.** 4   **6.** no

---

NOW TRY THIS

Perform each division:

1. $\dfrac{6 - 2i}{3}$

2. a. $\dfrac{2x^{p+1}}{6x^{p-1}}$ **b.** $\dfrac{x^{m-1}}{x^{1-m}}$

3. $\dfrac{(x + 3)^4 - (x + 3)^2}{(x + 3)^2}$

4.7 EXERCISES

WARM-UPS   *Simplify each fraction. Assume that no variable is 0.*

1. $\dfrac{4x^3y}{2xy}$

2. $\dfrac{6x^3y^2}{3x^3y}$

3. $\dfrac{35ab^2c^3}{7abc}$

4. $\dfrac{-14p^2q^5}{7pq^4}$

5. $\dfrac{(x + y) + (x - y)}{2x}$

6. $\dfrac{(2x^2 - z) + (x^2 + z)}{x}$

REVIEW

Identify each polynomial as a monomial, a binomial, a trinomial, or none of these.

7. $5a^2b + 2ab^2$

8. $-3x^3y$

9. $-2x^3 + 3x^2 - 4x + 12$

10. $17t^2 - 15t + 27$

11. Find the degree of the trinomial $3x^2 - 2x + 4$.

12. What is the numerical coefficient of the second term of the trinomial $-7t^2 - 5t + 17$?

Simplify each fraction.

13. $\dfrac{5}{15}$

14. $\dfrac{64}{128}$

15. $\dfrac{-125}{75}$

16. $\dfrac{-98}{21}$

17. $\dfrac{120}{160}$

18. $\dfrac{70}{420}$

19. $\dfrac{-3,612}{-3,612}$

20. $\dfrac{-288}{-112}$

21. $\dfrac{-90}{360}$

22. $\dfrac{8,423}{-8,423}$

23. $\dfrac{5,880}{2,660}$

24. $\dfrac{-762}{366}$

VOCABULARY AND CONCEPTS *Fill in the blanks.*

25. A _____ is an algebraic expression in which the exponents on the variables are whole numbers.

26. A _____ is a polynomial with one algebraic term.

27. A binomial is a polynomial with ____ terms.

28. A trinomial is a polynomial with ____ terms.

29. $\dfrac{1}{b} \cdot a = $ ___

30. $\dfrac{15x - 6y}{6xy} = \dfrac{15x}{\rule{1cm}{0.4pt}} - \dfrac{6y}{6xy}$

GUIDED PRACTICE

In all fractions, assume that no denominators are 0. Perform each division by simplifying each fraction. Write all answers without using negative or zero exponents. See Example 1. (Objective 1)

31. $\dfrac{xy}{yz}$

32. $\dfrac{a^2 b}{ab^2}$

33. $\dfrac{r^3 s^2}{rs^3}$

34. $\dfrac{y^4 z^3}{y^2 z^2}$

35. $\dfrac{8x^3 y^2}{4xy^3}$

36. $\dfrac{-3y^3 z}{6yz^2}$

37. $\dfrac{12u^5 v}{-4u^2 v^3}$

38. $\dfrac{16rst^2}{-8rst^3}$

Simplify. See Example 2. (Objective 2)

39. $\dfrac{6x + 9y}{3xy}$

40. $\dfrac{8x + 12y}{4xy}$

41. $\dfrac{xy + 6}{3y}$

42. $\dfrac{ab + 10}{2b}$

43. $\dfrac{5x - 10y}{25xy}$

44. $\dfrac{2x - 32}{16x}$

45. $\dfrac{3x^2 + 6y^3}{3x^2 y^2}$

46. $\dfrac{4a^2 - 9b^2}{12ab}$

Simplify. See Examples 3–4. (Objective 2)

47. $\dfrac{4x - 2y + 8z}{4xy}$

48. $\dfrac{5a^2 + 10b^2 - 15ab}{5ab}$

49. $\dfrac{12x^3 y^2 - 8x^2 y - 4x}{4xy}$

50. $\dfrac{12a^2 b^2 - 8a^2 b - 4ab}{4ab}$

51. $\dfrac{-25x^2 y + 30xy^2 - 5xy}{-5xy}$

52. $\dfrac{-30a^2 b^2 - 15a^2 b - 10ab^2}{-10ab}$

53. $\dfrac{15a^3 b^2 - 10a^2 b^3}{5a^2 b^2}$

54. $\dfrac{9a^4 b^3 - 16a^3 b^4}{12a^2 b}$

Simplify each numerator and perform the division. See Example 5. (Objective 2)

55. $\dfrac{5x(4x - 2y)}{2y}$

56. $\dfrac{9y^2(x^2 - 3xy)}{3x^2}$

57. $\dfrac{(-2x)^3 + (3x^2)^2}{6x^2}$

58. $\dfrac{(-3x^2 y)^3 + (3xy^2)^3}{27x^3 y^4}$

59. $\dfrac{4x^2 y^2 - 2(x^2 y^2 + xy)}{2xy}$

60. $\dfrac{-5a^3 b - 5a(ab^2 - a^2 b)}{10a^2 b^2}$

61. $\dfrac{(a + b)^2 - (a - b)^2}{2ab}$

62. $\dfrac{(x - y)^2 + (x + y)^2}{2x^2 y^2}$

ADDITIONAL PRACTICE *In all fractions, assume that no denominators are 0. Simplify each expression.*

63. $\dfrac{-16r^3 y^2}{-4r^2 y^4}$

64. $\dfrac{35xyz^2}{-7x^2 yz}$

65. $\dfrac{-65rs^2 t}{15r^2 s^3 t}$

66. $\dfrac{112u^3 z^6}{-42u^3 z^6}$

67. $\dfrac{x^2 x^3}{xy^6}$

68. $\dfrac{(xy)^2}{x^2 y^3}$

69. $\dfrac{(a^3 b^4)^3}{ab^4}$

70. $\dfrac{(a^2 b^3)^3}{a^6 b^6}$

71. $\dfrac{15(r^2 s^3)^2}{-5(rs^5)^3}$

72. $\dfrac{-5(a^2 b)^3}{10(ab^2)^3}$

73. $\dfrac{-32(x^3 y)^3}{128(x^2 y^2)^3}$

74. $\dfrac{68(a^6 b^7)^2}{-96(abc^2)^3}$

75. $\dfrac{(5a^2 b)^3}{(2a^2 b^2)^3}$

76. $\dfrac{-(4x^3 y^3)^2}{(x^2 y^4)^8}$

77. $\dfrac{-(3x^3 y^4)^3}{-(9x^4 y^5)^2}$

78. $\dfrac{(2r^3 s^2 t)^2}{-(4r^2 s^2 t^2)^2}$

79. $\dfrac{(a^2a^3)^4}{(a^4)^3}$

80. $\dfrac{(b^3b^4)^5}{(bb^2)^2}$

81. $\dfrac{(z^3z^{-4})^3}{(z^{-3})^2}$

82. $\dfrac{(t^{-3}t^5)}{(t^2)^{-3}}$

83. $\dfrac{(a^2b)^3(ab^2)^2}{(3a^3b^2)^4}$

84. $\dfrac{(x^3y^2)^4(3x^2y^4)^3}{(6xy^3)^2(2x^4y)^3}$

85. $\dfrac{(3x - y)(2x - 3y)}{6xy}$

86. $\dfrac{(2m - n)(3m - 2n)}{-3m^2n^2}$

APPLICATIONS   See Example 6. (Objective 3)

87. Reconciling formulas   Are the following formulas the same?

$$l = \frac{P - 2w}{2} \quad \text{and} \quad l = \frac{P}{2} - w$$

88. Reconciling formulas   Are the formulas the same?

$$r = \frac{G + 2b}{2b} \quad \text{and} \quad r = \frac{G}{2b} + b$$

89. Phone bills   On a phone bill, the following formulas are given to compute the average cost per minute of x minutes of phone usage. Are they equivalent?

$$C = \frac{0.15x + 12}{x} \quad \text{and} \quad C = 0.15 + \frac{12}{x}$$

90. Electric bills   On an electric bill, the following formulas are given to compute the average cost of x kwh of electricity. Are they equivalent?

$$C = \frac{0.08x + 5}{x} \quad \text{and} \quad C = 0.08x + \frac{5}{x}$$

WRITING ABOUT MATH

91. Describe how you would simplify the fraction

$$\frac{4x^2y + 8xy^2}{4xy}$$

92. A student incorrectly attempts to simplify the fraction $\dfrac{3x + 5}{x + 5}$ as follows:

$$\frac{3x + 5}{x + 5} = \frac{3\cancel{x + 5}}{\cancel{x + 5}} = 3$$

How would you explain the error?

SOMETHING TO THINK ABOUT

93. If $x = 501$, evaluate $\dfrac{x^{500} - x^{499}}{x^{499}}$.

94. An exercise reads as follows:

$$\textit{Simplify:} \quad \frac{3x^3y + 6xy^2}{3xy^3}.$$

It contains a misprint: one mistyped letter or digit. The correct answer is $\dfrac{x^2}{y} + 2$. Fix the exercise.

SECTION 4.8

Dividing Polynomials by Polynomials

Objectives

1 Divide a polynomial by a binomial.

2 Divide a polynomial by a binomial by first writing exponents in descending order.

3 Divide a polynomial with one or more missing terms by a binomial.

Vocabulary

divisor   quotient   remainder
dividend

Getting Ready

Divide:

1. $12\overline{)156}$ **2.** $17\overline{)357}$ **3.** $13\overline{)247}$ **4.** $19\overline{)247}$

We now complete our work of operations on polynomials by considering how to divide one polynomial by another.

1   ## Divide a polynomial by a binomial.

To divide one polynomial by another, we use a method similar to long division in arithmetic. Recall that the parts of a division problem are defined as

$$divisor\overline{)dividend}^{\;quotient}$$

EXAMPLE 1   Divide $(x^2 + 5x + 6)$ by $(x + 2)$ $x \neq -2$.

Solution   Here the **divisor** is $x + 2$ and the **dividend** is $x^2 + 5x + 6$. We proceed as follows:

Step 1:
$$x + 2\overline{)x^2 + 5x + 6}^{\;\;x}$$
How many times does x divide x^2? $\frac{x^2}{x} = x$
Write x above the division symbol.

Step 2:
$$x + 2\overline{)x^2 + 5x + 6}^{\;\;x}$$
$$\underline{x^2 + 2x}$$
Multiply each item in the divisor by x.
Write the product under $x^2 + 5x$ and draw a line.

Step 3:
$$x + 2\overline{)x^2 + 5x + 6}^{\;\;x}$$
$$\underline{x^2 + 2x}$$
$$3x + 6$$
Subtract $x^2 + 2x$ from $x^2 + 5x$ by adding the negative of $x^2 + 2x$ to $x^2 + 5x$.

Bring down the 6.

Step 4:
$$x + 2\overline{)x^2 + 5x + 6}^{\;\;x + 3}$$
$$\underline{x^2 + 2x}$$
$$3x + 6$$
How many times does x divide $3x$? $\frac{3x}{x} = +3$
Write $+3$ above the division symbol.

Step 5:
$$x + 2\overline{)x^2 + 5x + 6}^{\;\;x + 3}$$
$$\underline{x^2 + 2x}$$
$$3x + 6$$
$$\underline{3x + 6}$$
Multiply each term in the divisor by 3.
Write the product under the $3x + 6$ and draw a line.

Step 6:
$$
\begin{array}{r}
x + 3 \\
x + 2 \overline{)\,x^2 + 5x + 6} \\
\underline{x^2 + 2x} \\
3x + 6 \\
\underline{3x + 6} \\
0
\end{array}
$$
Subtract $3x + 6$ from $3x + 6$ by adding the negative of $3x + 6$.

The **quotient** is $x + 3$, and the **remainder** is 0.

Step 7: Check by verifying that $x + 2$ times $x + 3$ is $x^2 + 5x + 6$.

$$(x + 2)(x + 3) = x^2 + 3x + 2x + 6$$
$$= x^2 + 5x + 6$$

⇨ **SELF CHECK 1** Divide $(x^2 + 7x + 12)$ by $(x + 3)$ $(x \neq -3)$.

EXAMPLE 2 Divide: $\dfrac{6x^2 - 7x - 2}{2x - 1}$ $\left(x \neq \dfrac{1}{2}\right)$.

Solution Here the divisor is $2x - 1$ and the dividend is $6x^2 - 7x - 2$.

Step 1:
$$
\begin{array}{r}
3x \\
2x - 1 \overline{)\,6x^2 - 7x - 2}
\end{array}
$$
How many times does $2x$ divide $6x^2$? $\dfrac{6x^2}{2x} = 3x$
Write $3x$ above the division symbol.

Step 2:
$$
\begin{array}{r}
3x \\
2x - 1 \overline{)\,6x^2 - 7x - 2} \\
6x^2 - 3x
\end{array}
$$
Multiply each term in the divisor by $3x$.
Write the product under $6x^2 - 7x$ and draw a line.

Step 3:
$$
\begin{array}{r}
3x \\
2x - 1 \overline{)\,6x^2 - 7x - 2} \\
\underline{6x^2 - 3x } \\
-4x - 2
\end{array}
$$
Subtract $6x^2 - 3x$ from $6x^2 - 7x$ by adding the negative of $6x^2 - 3x$ to $6x^2 - 7x$.
Bring down the -2.

Step 4:
$$
\begin{array}{r}
3x - 2 \\
2x - 1 \overline{)\,6x^2 - 7x - 2} \\
6x^2 - 3x \\
-4x - 2
\end{array}
$$
How many times does $2x$ divide $-4x$? $\dfrac{-4x}{2x} = -2$
Write -2 above the division symbol.

Step 5:
$$
\begin{array}{r}
3x - 2 \\
2x - 1 \overline{)\,6x^2 - 7x - 2} \\
6x^2 - 3x \\
-4x - 2 \\
-4x + 2
\end{array}
$$
Multiply each term in the divisor by -2.
Write the product under $-4x - 2$ and draw a line.

Step 6:
$$
\begin{array}{r}
3x - 2 \\
2x - 1 \overline{)\,6x^2 - 7x - 2} \\
\underline{6x^2 - 3x } \\
-4x - 2 \\
\underline{-4x + 2} \\
-4
\end{array}
$$
Subtract $-4x + 2$ from $-4x - 2$ by adding the negative of $-4x + 2$.

COMMENT The division process ends when the degree of the remainder is less than the degree of the divisor.

Here the quotient is $3x - 2$, and the remainder is -4. It is common to write the answer in quotient $+ \frac{\text{remainder}}{\text{divisor}}$ form:

$$3x - 2 + \frac{-4}{2x - 1}$$

where the fraction $\frac{-4}{2x - 1}$ is formed by dividing the remainder by the divisor.

Step 7: To check the answer, we multiply $3x - 2 + \frac{-4}{2x - 1}$ by $2x - 1$. The product should be the dividend.

$$(2x - 1)\left(3x - 2 + \frac{-4}{2x - 1}\right) = (2x - 1)(3x - 2) + (2x + 1)\left(\frac{-4}{2x - 1}\right)$$

$$= (2x - 1)(3x - 2) - 4$$

$$= 6x^2 - 4x - 3x + 2 - 4$$

$$= 6x^2 - 7x - 2$$

⇨ **SELF CHECK 2**   Divide. $\frac{8x^2 + 6x - 3}{2x + 3}$ $\left(x \neq -\frac{3}{2}\right)$

EXAMPLE 3   Divide: $\frac{6x^2 - xy - y^2}{3x + y}$. Assume no division by 0.

Solution   Here the divisor is $3x + y$ and the dividend is $6x^2 - xy - y^2$.

Step 1:

$$3x + y \overline{)6x^2 - xy - y^2} \quad \overset{2x}{}$$

How many times does $3x$ divide $6x^2$? $\frac{6x^2}{3x} = 2x$
Write $2x$ above the division symbol.

Step 2:

$$\begin{array}{r} 2x \\ 3x + y \overline{)6x^2 - xy - y^2} \\ 6x^2 + 2xy \end{array}$$

Multiply each term in the divisor by $2x$.
Write the product under $6x^2 - xy$ and draw a line.

Step 3:

$$\begin{array}{r} 2x \\ 3x + y \overline{)6x^2 - xy - y^2} \\ 6x^2 + 2xy \\ \hline -3xy - y^2 \end{array}$$

Subtract $6x^2 + 2xy$ from $6x^2 - xy$ by adding the negative of $6x^2 + 2xy$ to $6x^2 - xy$.

Bring down the $-y^2$.

Step 4:

$$\begin{array}{r} 2x - y \\ 3x + y \overline{)6x^2 - xy - y^2} \\ 6x^2 + 2xy \\ \hline -3xy - y^2 \end{array}$$

How many times does $3x$ divide $-3xy$? $\frac{-3xy}{3x} = -y$
Write $-y$ above the division symbol.

Step 5:

$$\begin{array}{r} 2x - y \\ 3x + y \overline{)6x^2 - xy - y^2} \\ 6x^2 + 2xy \\ \hline -3xy - y^2 \\ -3xy - y^2 \end{array}$$

Multiply each term in the divisor by $-y$.
Write the product under the $-3x - y^2$ and draw a line.

Step 6:

$$
\begin{array}{r}
2x - y \\
3x + y{\overline{\smash{\big)}\,6x^2 - xy - y^2}} \\
\underline{6x^2 + 2xy} \\
-3xy - y^2 \\
\underline{-3xy - y^2} \\
0
\end{array}
$$

Subtract $-3xy - y^2$ from $-3xy - y^2$ by adding the negative of $-3xy - y^2$.

The quotient is $2x - y$ and the remainder is 0.

SELF CHECK 3 Divide $(6x^2 - xy - y^2)$ by $(2x - y)$. Assume no division by 0.

2 ## Divide a polynomial by a binomial by first writing exponents in descending order.

The division method works best when exponents of the terms in the divisor and the dividend are written in descending order. This means that the term involving the highest power of x appears first, the term involving the second-highest power of x appears second, and so on. For example, the terms in

$$3x^3 + 2x^2 - 7x + 5 \qquad 5 = 5x^0$$

have their exponents written in descending order.

If the powers in the dividend or divisor are not in descending order, we can use the commutative property of addition to write them that way.

EXAMPLE 4 Divide: $\dfrac{4x^2 + 2x^3 + 12 - 2x}{x + 3}$ $(x \neq -3)$.

Solution We write the dividend so that the exponents are in descending order and divide.

$$
\begin{array}{r}
2x^2 - 2x + 4 \\
x + 3{\overline{\smash{\big)}\,2x^3 + 4x^2 - 2x + 12}} \\
\underline{2x^3 + 6x^2} \\
-2x^2 - 2x \\
\underline{-2x^2 - 6x} \\
+4x + 12 \\
\underline{+4x + 12} \\
0
\end{array}
$$

Check: $(x + 3)(2x^2 - 2x + 4) = 2x^3 - 2x^2 + 4x + 6x^2 - 6x + 12$
$$= 2x^3 + 4x^2 - 2x + 12$$

SELF CHECK 4 Divide: $\dfrac{x^2 - 10x + 6x^3 + 4}{2x - 1}$ $\left(x \neq \dfrac{1}{2}\right)$.

3 **Divide a polynomial with one or more missing terms by a binomial.**

When we write the terms of a dividend in descending powers of x, we may notice that some powers of x are missing. For example, in the dividend of

$$x + 1\overline{)3x^4 - 7x^2 - 3x + 15}$$

the term involving x^3 is missing. When this happens, we should either write the term with a coefficient of 0 or leave a blank space for it. In this case, we would write the dividend as

$$3x^4 + 0x^3 - 7x^2 - 3x + 15 \quad \text{or} \quad 3x^4 \quad -7x^2 - 3x + 15$$

EXAMPLE 5 Divide: $\dfrac{x^2 - 4}{x + 2}$ ($x \neq -2$).

Solution Since $x^2 - 4$ does not have a term involving x, we must either include the term $0x$ or leave a space for it.

$$
\begin{array}{r}
x - 2 \\
x + 2\overline{)x^2 + 0x - 4} \\
\underline{x^2 + 2x} \\
-2x - 4 \\
\underline{-2x - 4} \\
0
\end{array}
$$

Check: $(x + 2)(x - 2) = x^2 - 2x + 2x - 4$
$$= x^2 - 4$$

⇨ SELF CHECK 5 Divide: $\dfrac{x^2 - 9}{x - 3}$ ($x \neq 3$).

EXAMPLE 6 Divide: $\dfrac{x^3 + y^3}{x + y}$. Assume no division by 0.

Solution In $x^3 + y^3$, the exponents on x are written in descending order, and the exponents on y are written in ascending order. In this case, we can consider $x^3 + y^3$ to be the simplified form of

$$x^3 + 0x^2y + 0xy^2 + y^3$$

To do the division, we will write $x^3 + y^3$, leaving spaces for the missing terms, and proceed as follows.

$$
\begin{array}{r}
x^2 - xy + y^2 \\
x + y\overline{)x^3 \qquad\qquad + y^3} \\
\underline{x^3 + x^2y} \\
-x^2y \\
\underline{-x^2y - xy^2} \\
+xy^2 + y^3 \\
\underline{xy^2 + y^3} \\
0
\end{array}
$$

Check: $(x + y)(x^2 - xy + y^2) = x^3 - x^2y + xy^2 + x^2y - xy^2 + y^3$
$$= x^3 + y^3$$

⇨ **SELF CHECK 6** Divide: $(x^3 - y^3)$ by $(x - y)$. Assume no division by 0.

⇨ **SELF CHECK ANSWERS** **1.** $x + 4$ **2.** $4x - 3 + \frac{6}{2x + 3}$ **3.** $3x + y$ **4.** $3x^2 + 2x - 4$ **5.** $x + 3$ **6.** $x^2 + xy + y^2$

NOW TRY THIS

1. Identify the missing term(s): $8x^3 - 7x + 2x^5 - x^2$

2. Perform the division: $\dfrac{x^2 + 3x - 5}{x + 3}$ $(x \neq -3)$.

3. $(8x^2 - 2x + 3) \div (1 + 2x)$ $\left(x \neq -\dfrac{1}{2}\right)$

4. The area of a rectangle is represented by $(3x^2 + 17x - 6)$ m^2 and the width is represented by $(3x - 1)$ m. Find a polynomial representation of the length.

4.8 EXERCISES

WARM-UPS *Divide and give the answer in* quotient $+ \frac{\text{remainder}}{\text{divisor}}$
form. Assume no division by 0.

1. $x\overline{)2x + 3}$ **2.** $x\overline{)3x - 5}$

3. $x + 1\overline{)2x + 3}$ **4.** $x + 1\overline{)3x + 5}$

5. $x + 1\overline{)x^2 + x}$ **6.** $x + 2\overline{)x^2 + 2x}$

REVIEW

7. List the composite numbers between 20 and 30.

8. Graph the set of prime numbers between 10 and 20 on a number line.

   10 11 12 13 14 15 16 17 18 19 20

Let a $= -2$ *and b* $= 3$. *Evaluate each expression.*

9. $|a - b|$ **10.** $|a + b|$
11. $-|a^2 - b^2|$ **12.** $a - |-b|$

Simplify each expression.
13. $3(2x^2 - 4x + 5) + 2(x^2 + 3x - 7)$
14. $-2(y^3 + 2y^2 - y) - 3(3y^3 + y)$

VOCABULARY AND CONCEPTS

Fill in the blanks.

15. In the long division $x + 1\overline{)x^2 + 2x + 1}$, $x + 1$ is called the
_____, and $x^2 + 2x + 1$ is called the _____.

16. The answer to a division problem is called the _____.

17. If a division does not come out even, the leftover part is
called a _____.

18. The exponents in $2x^4 + 3x^3 + 4x^2 - 7x - 2$ are said to be
written in _____ order.

Write each polynomial with the powers in descending order.

19. $4x^3 + 7x - 2x^2 + 6$
20. $5x^2 + 7x^3 - 3x - 9$
21. $9x + 2x^2 - x^3 + 6x^4$
22. $7x^5 + x^3 - x^2 + 2x^4$

Identify the missing terms in each polynomial.

23. $5x^4 + 2x^2 - 1$
24. $-3x^5 - 2x^3 + 4x - 6$

GUIDED PRACTICE

Perform each division. Assume no division by 0. See Example 1.
(Objective 1)

25. Divide $(x^2 + 4x + 4)$ by $(x + 2)$.

26. Divide $(y^2 + 13y + 12)$ by $(y + 1)$.

27. $x + 5 \overline{)x^2 + 7x + 10}$

28. $x + 6 \overline{)x^2 + 5x - 6}$

29. $\dfrac{x^2 - 5x + 6}{x - 2}$

30. $\dfrac{z^2 - 7z + 12}{z - 3}$

31. $a - 4 \overline{)a^2 + a - 20}$

32. $t - 7 \overline{)t^2 - 8t + 7}$

Perform each division. Assume no division by 0. See Example 2.
(Objective 1)

33. $\dfrac{6a^2 + 5a - 6}{2a + 3}$

34. $\dfrac{8a^2 + 2a - 3}{2a - 1}$

35. $\dfrac{3b^2 + 11b + 6}{3b + 2}$

36. $\dfrac{3b^2 - 5b + 2}{3b - 2}$

37. $\dfrac{2x^2 + 5x + 2}{2x + 3}$

38. $\dfrac{3x^2 - 8x + 3}{3x - 2}$

39. $\dfrac{4x^2 + 6x - 1}{2x + 1}$

40. $\dfrac{6x^2 - 11x + 2}{3x - 1}$

Perform each division. Assume no division by 0. See Example 3.
(Objective 1)

41. Divide $(a^2 + 2ab + b^2)$ by $(a + b)$.

42. Divide $(a^2 - 2ab + b^2)$ by $(a - b)$.

43. $x + 2y \overline{)2x^2 + 3xy - 2y^2}$

44. $x + 3y \overline{)2x^2 + 5xy - 3y^2}$

45. $\dfrac{2x^2 - 7xy + 3y^2}{2x - y}$

46. $\dfrac{3x^2 + 5xy - 2y^2}{x + 2y}$

47. $\dfrac{a^2 + 3ab + 2b^2}{a + b}$

48. $\dfrac{2m^2 - mn - n^2}{m - n}$

Write the powers of x in descending order (if necessary) and perform each division. Assume no division by 0. See Example 4.
(Objective 2)

49. $5x + 3 \overline{)11x + 10x^2 + 3}$

50. $2x - 7 \overline{)-x - 21 + 2x^2}$

51. $4 + 2x \overline{)-10x - 28 + 2x^2}$

52. $1 + 3x \overline{)9x^2 + 1 + 6x}$

Perform each division. Assume no division by 0. See Example 5.
(Objective 3)

53. $\dfrac{x^2 - 1}{x - 1}$

54. $\dfrac{x^2 - 9}{x + 3}$

55. $\dfrac{4x^2 - 9}{2x + 3}$

56. $\dfrac{25x^2 - 16}{5x - 4}$

57. $\dfrac{x^2 - y^2}{x + y}$

58. $\dfrac{x^2 - y^2}{x - y}$

59. $\dfrac{x^3 - 8}{x - 2}$

60. $\dfrac{x^3 + 27}{x + 3}$

Perform each division. Assume no division by 0. See Example 6.
(Objective 3)

61. $\dfrac{x^3 - y^3}{x - y}$

62. $\dfrac{x^3 + y^3}{x + y}$

63. $\dfrac{a^3 + a}{a + 3}$

64. $\dfrac{y^3 - 50z^3}{y - 5z}$

ADDITIONAL PRACTICE

Perform each division. If there is a remainder, leave the answer in quotient $+ \frac{remainder}{divisor}$ *form. Assume no division by 0.*

65. $2x - y \overline{)xy - 2y^2 + 6x^2}$

66. $2x - 3y \overline{)2x^2 - 3y^2 - xy}$

67. $3x - 2y \overline{)-10y^2 + 13xy + 3x^2}$

68. $2x + 3y \overline{)-12y^2 + 10x^2 + 7xy}$

69. $4x + y \overline{)-19xy + 4x^2 - 5y^2}$

70. $x - 4y \overline{)5x^2 - 4y^2 - 19xy}$

71. $2x + 3 \overline{)2x^3 + 7x^2 + 4x - 3}$

72. $2x - 1 \overline{)2x^3 - 3x^2 + 5x - 2}$

73. $3x + 2 \overline{)6x^3 + 10x^2 + 7x + 2}$

74. $4x + 3 \overline{)4x^3 - 5x^2 - 2x + 3}$

75. $2x + y \overline{)2x^3 + 3x^2y + 3xy^2 + y^3}$

76. $3x - 2y \overline{)6x^3 - x^2y + 4xy^2 - 4y^3}$

77. $\dfrac{x^3 + 3x^2 + 3x + 1}{x + 1}$

78. $\dfrac{x^3 + 6x^2 + 12x + 8}{x + 2}$

79. $\dfrac{2x^3 + 7x^2 + 4x + 3}{2x + 3}$

80. $\dfrac{6x^3 + x^2 + 2x + 1}{3x - 1}$

81. $\dfrac{2x^3 + 4x^2 - 2x + 3}{x - 2}$

82. $3x - 4 \overline{)15x^3 - 23x^2 + 16x}$

83. $2y + 3 \overline{)21y^2 + 6y^3 - 20}$

84. $5t - 2u \overline{)10t^3 - 19t^2u + 11tu^2 - u^3}$

WRITING ABOUT MATH

85. Distinguish among *dividend, divisor, quotient,* and *remainder.*

86. How would you check the results of a division?

SOMETHING TO THINK ABOUT

87. Find the error in the following work.

$$
\begin{array}{r}
x + 1 \\
x - 2 \overline{) x^2 + 3x - 2} \\
\underline{x^2 - 2x} \\
x - 2 \\
\underline{x - 2} \\
0
\end{array}
$$

88. Find the error in the following work.

$$
x + 2 \overline{) \begin{array}{l} 3x \\ 3x^2 + 10x + 7 \\ \underline{3x^2 + 6x} \\ 4x + 7 \end{array}} = 3x + \frac{4x + 7}{x + 2}
$$

PROJECTS

Project 1

Let $f(x) = 3x^2 + 3x - 2$, $g(x) = 2x^2 - 5$, and $t(x) = x + 2$. Perform each operation.

a. $f(x) + g(x)$

b. $g(x) - t(x)$

c. $f(x) \cdot g(x)$

d. $\dfrac{f(x)}{t(x)}$

e. $f(x) + g(x) + t(x)$

f. $f(x) \cdot g(x) \cdot t(x)$

g. $\dfrac{f(x) - t(x) + g(x)}{t(x)}$

h. $\dfrac{[g(x)]^2}{t(x)}$

Project 2

To discover a pattern in the behavior of polynomials, consider the polynomial $2x^2 - 3x - 5$. First, evaluate the polynomial at $x = 1$ and $x = 3$. Then divide the polynomial by $x - 1$ and again by $x - 3$.

1. What do you notice about the remainders of these divisions?

2. Try others. For example, evaluate the polynomial at $x = 2$ and then divide by $x - 2$.

3. Can you make the pattern hold when you evaluate the polynomial at $x = -2$?

4. Does the pattern hold for other polynomials? Try some polynomials of your own, experiment, and report your conclusions.

Chapter 4 REVIEW

SECTION 4.1 Natural-Number Exponents

DEFINITIONS AND CONCEPTS	EXAMPLES
If n is a natural number, then $$x^n = \overbrace{x \cdot x \cdot x \cdot \cdots \cdot x}^{n \text{ factors of } x}$$	$$x^5 = \overbrace{x \cdot x \cdot x \cdot x \cdot x}^{5 \text{ factors of } x} \qquad x^7 = \overbrace{x \cdot x \cdot x \cdot x \cdot x \cdot x \cdot x}^{7 \text{ factors of } x}$$

If m and n are integers, then

$x^m x^n = x^{m+n}$	$x^2 \cdot x^7 = x^{2+7} = x^9$
$(x^m)^n = x^{m \cdot n}$	$(x^2)^7 = x^{2 \cdot 7} = x^{14}$
$(xy)^n = x^n y^n$	$(xy)^3 = x^3 y^3$
$\left(\dfrac{x}{y}\right)^n = \dfrac{x^n}{y^n} \quad (y \neq 0)$	$\left(\dfrac{x}{y}\right)^3 = \dfrac{x^3}{y^3} \quad (y \neq 0)$
$\dfrac{x^m}{x^n} = x^{m-n} \quad (x \neq 0)$	$\dfrac{x^7}{x^2} = x^{7-2} = x^5 \quad (x \neq 0)$

REVIEW EXERCISES

Write each expression without exponents.

1. $(-3x)^4$

2. $\left(\dfrac{1}{2}pq\right)^3$

Evaluate each expression.

3. 5^3 **4.** 3^5

5. $(-8)^2$ **6.** -8^2

7. $3^2 + 2^2$ **8.** $(3 + 2)^2$

Perform the operations and simplify.

9. $x^3 x^2$ **10.** $x^2 x^7$

11. $(y^7)^3$ **12.** $(x^{21})^2$

13. $(ab)^3$ **14.** $(3x)^4$

15. $b^3 b^4 b^5$ **16.** $-z^2(z^3 y^2)$

17. $(16s)^2 s$ **18.** $-3y(y^5)$

19. $(x^2 x^3)^3$ **20.** $(2x^2 y)^2$

21. $\dfrac{x^7}{x^3}$ **22.** $\left(\dfrac{x^2 y}{xy^2}\right)^2$

23. $\dfrac{8(y^2 x)^2}{4(yx^2)^2}$ **24.** $\dfrac{(5y^2 z^3)^3}{25(yz)^5}$

SECTION 4.2   Zero and Negative-Integer Exponents

DEFINITIONS AND CONCEPTS	EXAMPLES
$x^0 = 1 \quad (x \neq 0)$	$(2x)^0 = 1 \quad (x \neq 0)$
$x^{-n} = \dfrac{1}{x^n} \quad (x \neq 0)$	$x^{-3} = \dfrac{1}{x^3} \quad (x \neq 0)$
$\dfrac{1}{x^{-n}} = x^n \quad (x \neq 0)$	$\dfrac{1}{x^{-3}} = x^3 \quad (x \neq 0)$

REVIEW EXERCISES

Write each expression without negative exponents or parentheses.

25. x^0 **26.** $(3x^2 y^2)^0$

27. $(3x^0)^2$ **28.** $(3x^2 y^0)^2$

29. x^{-3} **30.** $x^{-2} x^3$

31. $y^4 y^{-3}$ **32.** $\dfrac{x^3}{x^{-7}}$

33. $(x^{-3} x^4)^{-2}$ **34.** $(a^{-2}b)^{-3}$

35. $\left(\dfrac{x^2}{x}\right)^{-5}$ **36.** $\left(\dfrac{15z^4}{5z^3}\right)^{-2}$

SECTION 4.3   Scientific Notation

DEFINITIONS AND CONCEPTS	EXAMPLES
A number is written in scientific notation if it is written as the product of a number between 1 (including 1) and 10 and an integer power of 10.	4,582,000,000 is written as 4.582×10^9 in scientific notation. 0.00035 is written as 3.5×10^{-4} in scientific notation.

REVIEW EXERCISES

Write each number in scientific notation.

37. 728   **38.** 9,370

39. 0.0136   **40.** 0.00942

41. 7.73   **42.** 753×10^3

43. 0.018×10^{-2} **44.** 600×10^2

Write each number in standard notation.

45. 7.26×10^5 **46.** 3.91×10^{-4}

47. 2.68×10^0 **48.** 5.76×10^1

49. 739×10^{-2} **50.** 0.437×10^{-3}

51. $\dfrac{(0.00012)(0.00004)}{0.00000016}$ **52.** $\dfrac{(4,800)(20,000)}{600,000}$

SECTION 4.4   Polynomials and Polynomial Functions

DEFINITIONS AND CONCEPTS	EXAMPLES
A **polynomial** is an algebraic expression that is one term or the sum of terms containing whole-number exponents on the variables.	**Polynomials:** $9xy$, $5x^2 + 9x - 1$, and $11x - 5y$ monomial trinomial binomial
If a is a nonzero coefficient, the degree of the monomial ax^n is n. The **degree of a polynomial** is the same as the degree of its term with largest degree.	Find the degree of each term and the degree of the polynomial $8x^2 - 5x + 3$. The degree of the first term is 2. The degree of the second term is 1. The degree of the third term is 0. The degree of the polynomial is 2.
When a number is substituted for the variable in a polynomial, the polynomial takes on a numerical value.	Evaluate $5x - 4$ when $x = -3$. $\quad 5x - 4 = 5(-3) - 4$ Substitute -3 for x. $\qquad\qquad = -15 - 4$ Simplify. $\qquad\qquad = -19$
Finding a function value for a polynomial uses the same process as evaluating a polynomial for a specified value.	If $f(x) = x^2 - 8x + 3$, find $f(-3)$. $\quad f(x) = x^2 - 8x + 3$ $\quad f(-3) = (-3)^2 - 8(-3) + 3$ Substitute -3 for x. $\qquad\quad = 9 + 24 + 3$ Simplify. $\qquad\quad = 36$ Since the result is 36, $f(-3) = 36$.
Any equation in x and y where each value of x determines a single value of y is a **function.** We say that y is a function of x. The set of input values x is called the **domain** of the function. The set of output values y is called the **range** of the function.	Graph the polynomial function $f(x) = x^2 - 8x + 3$ and determine its domain and range.

x	$f(x) = x^2 - 8x + 3$	$(x, f(x))$
-1	$f(-1) = (-1)^2 - 8(-1) + 3 = 12$	$(-1, 12)$
0	$f(0) = (0)^2 - 8(0) + 3 = 3$	$(0, 3)$
1	$f(1) = (1)^2 - 8(1) + 3 = -4$	$(1, -4)$
2	$f(2) = (2)^2 - 8(2) + 3 = -9$	$(2, -9)$
4	$f(4) = (4)^2 - 8(4) + 3 = -13$	$(4, -13)$
5	$f(5) = (5)^2 - 8(5) + 3 = -12$	$(5, -12)$

$f(x) = x^2 - 8x + 3$

D: $\mathbb{R}$; R: $[-13, \infty)$ |

REVIEW EXERCISES

Find the degree of each polynomial and classify it as a monomial, a binomial, or a trinomial.

53. $13x^7$

54. $5^3x + x^2$

55. $-3x^5 + x - 1$

56. $9xy + 21x^3y^2$

Evaluate $3x + 2$ for each value of x.

57. $x = 3$

58. $x = 0$

59. $x = -2$

60. $x = \dfrac{2}{3}$

Evaluate $5x^4 - x$ for each value of x.

61. $x = 3$

62. $x = 0$

63. $x = -2$

64. $x = -0.3$

If $y = f(x) = x^2 - 4$, find each value.

65. $f(0)$

66. $f(5)$

67. $f(-2)$

68. $f\left(\dfrac{1}{2}\right)$

Graph each polynomial function.

69. $y = f(x) = x^2 - 5$

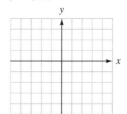

70. $y = f(x) = x^3 - 2$

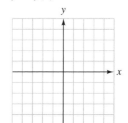

SECTION 4.5   Adding and Subtracting Polynomials

DEFINITIONS AND CONCEPTS	EXAMPLES	
We can add polynomials by removing parentheses, if necessary, and then combining any like terms that are contained within the polynomials.	$(8x^3 - 6x + 13) + (9x - 7)$ $= 8x^3 - 6x + 13 + 9x - 7$ $= 8x^3 + 3x + 6$	Remove parentheses. Combine like terms.
We can subtract polynomials by dropping the negative sign and the parentheses, and *changing the sign of every term within the second set of parentheses.*	$(8x^3 - 6x + 13) - (9x - 7)$ $= 8x^3 - 6x + 13 - 9x + 7$ $= 8x^3 - 15x + 20$	Change the sign of each term in the second set of parentheses. Combine like terms.

REVIEW EXERCISES

Simplify each expression, if possible.

71. $3x + 5x - x$

72. $3x + 2y$

73. $(xy)^2 + 3x^2y^2$

74. $-2x^2yz + 3yx^2z$

75. $(3x^2 + 2x) + (5x^2 - 8x)$

76. $(7a^2 + 2a - 5) - (3a^2 - 2a + 1)$

77. $3(9x^2 + 3x + 7) - 2(11x^2 - 5x + 9)$

78. $4(4x^3 + 2x^2 - 3x - 8) - 5(2x^3 - 3x + 8)$

SECTION 4.6   Multiplying Polynomials

DEFINITIONS AND CONCEPTS	EXAMPLES	
To multiply two monomials, first multiply the numerical factors and then multiply the variable factors using the properties of exponents.	$(5x^2y^3)(4xy^2)$ $= 5(4)x^2xy^3y^2$ $= 20x^3y^5$	Use the commutative property of multiplication. Use multiplication and the properties of exponents.
To multiply a polynomial with more than one term by a monomial, multiply each term of the polynomial by the monomial and simplify.	$4x(3x^2 + 2x)$ $= 4x \cdot 3x^2 + 4x \cdot 2x$ $= 12x^3 + 8x^2$	Use the distributive property. Multiply.

To multiply two binomials, use the distributive property or FOIL method.	$(2x - 5)(x + 3)$
	$= 2x(x) + 2x(3) + (-5)(x) + (-5)(3)$
	$= 2x^2 + 6x - 5x - 15$
	$= 2x^2 + x - 15$

Special products:

$(x + y)^2 = x^2 + 2xy + y^2$

$(x - y)^2 = x^2 - 2xy + y^2$

$(x + y)(x - y) = x^2 - y^2$

$(x + 7)^2 = x^2 + 2(x)(7) + 7^2$
$\qquad = x^2 + 14x + 49$

$(x - 7)^2 = x^2 - 2(x)(7) + 7^2$
$\qquad = x^2 - 14x + 49$

$(2x + 3)(2x - 3) = (2x)^2 - (3)^2$
$\qquad\qquad\qquad = 4x^2 - 9$

To multiply one polynomial by another, multiply each term of one polynomial by each term of the other polynomial, and simplify.

$$\begin{array}{r} 4x^2 - x + 3 \\ x + 2 \\ \hline 4x^3 - x^2 + 3x \\ 8x^2 - 2x + 6 \\ \hline 4x^3 + 7x^2 + x + 6 \end{array}$$

REVIEW EXERCISES

Find each product.

79. $(2x^2y^3)(5xy^2)$ **80.** $(xyz^3)(x^3z)^2$

Find each product.

81. $5(x + 3)$ **82.** $3(2x + 4)$

83. $x^2(3x^2 - 5)$ **84.** $2y^2(y^2 + 5y)$

85. $-x^2y(y^2 - xy)$ **86.** $-3xy(xy - x)$

Find each product.

87. $(x + 3)(x + 2)$ **88.** $(2x + 1)(x - 1)$

89. $(3a - 3)(2a + 2)$ **90.** $6(a - 1)(a + 1)$

91. $(a - b)(2a + b)$ **92.** $(3x - y)(2x + y)$

Find each product.

93. $(x + 3)(x + 3)$ **94.** $(x + 5)(x - 5)$

95. $(y - 2)(y + 2)$ **96.** $(x + 4)^2$

97. $(x - 3)^2$ **98.** $(y - 1)^2$

99. $(2y + 1)^2$ **100.** $(y^2 + 1)(y^2 - 1)$

Find each product.

101. $(3x + 1)(x^2 + 2x + 1)$

102. $(2a - 3)(4a^2 + 6a + 9)$

Solve each equation.

103. $x^2 + 3 = x(x + 3)$

104. $x^2 + x = (x + 1)(x + 2)$

105. $(x + 2)(x - 5) = (x - 4)(x - 1)$

106. $(x - 1)(x - 2) = (x - 3)(x + 1)$

107. $x^2 + x(x + 2) = x(2x + 1) + 1$

108. $(x + 5)(3x + 1) = x^2 + (2x - 1)(x - 5)$

SECTION 4.7 Dividing Polynomials by Monomials

DEFINITIONS AND CONCEPTS	EXAMPLES
To divide a polynomial by a monomial, divide each term in the numerator by the monomial in the denominator.	Divide: $\dfrac{12x^6 - 8x^4 + 2x}{2x}$ $(x \neq 0)$ $\dfrac{12x^6 - 8x^4 + 2x}{2x}$ $= \dfrac{12x^6}{2x} - \dfrac{8x^4}{2x} + \dfrac{2x}{2x}$ Divide each term in the numerator by the monomial in the denominator. $= 6x^5 - 4x^3 + 1$

REVIEW EXERCISES
Perform each division. Assume no variable is 0.

109. $\dfrac{3x + 6y}{2xy}$

110. $\dfrac{14xy - 21x}{7xy}$

111. $\dfrac{15a^2bc + 20ab^2c - 25abc^2}{-5abc}$

112. $\dfrac{(x + y)^2 + (x - y)^2}{-2xy}$

SECTION 4.8 Dividing Polynomials by Polynomials

DEFINITIONS AND CONCEPTS	EXAMPLES
Use long division to divide one polynomial by another. Answers are written in $quotient + \frac{remainder}{divisor}$ form.	Divide: $\dfrac{6x^2 - 3x + 5}{x - 3}$ $(x \neq 3)$ $\begin{array}{r} 6x + 15 \\ x - 3\overline{)6x^2 - 3x + 5} \\ \underline{6x^2 - 18x} \\ 15x + 5 \\ \underline{15x - 45} \\ 50 \end{array}$ The result is $6x + 15 + \dfrac{50}{x - 3}$.

REVIEW EXERCISES
Perform each division. Assume no division by 0.

113. $x + 2\overline{)x^2 + 3x + 5}$

114. $x - 1\overline{)x^2 - 6x + 5}$

115. $x + 3\overline{)2x^2 + 7x + 3}$

116. $3x - 1\overline{)3x^2 + 14x - 2}$

117. $2x - 1\overline{)6x^3 + x^2 + 1}$

118. $3x + 1\overline{)-13x - 4 + 9x^3}$

Chapter 4 TEST

1. Use exponents to rewrite $2xxxyyy$.

2. Evaluate: $3^2 + 5^3$.

Write each expression as an expression containing only one exponent.

3. $y^2(yy^3)$

4. $(-3b^2)(2b^3)(-b^2)$

5. $(2x^3)^5(x^2)^3$

6. $(2rr^2r^3)^3$

Simplify each expression. Write answers without using parentheses or negative exponents. Assume no variable is 0.

7. $3x^0$

8. $2y^{-5}y^2$

9. $\dfrac{y^2}{yy^{-2}}$

10. $\left(\dfrac{a^2b^{-1}}{4a^3b^{-2}}\right)^{-3}$

11. Write 28,000 in scientific notation.

12. Write 0.0025 in scientific notation.

13. Write 7.4×10^3 in standard notation.

14. Write 9.3×10^{-5} in standard notation.

15. Classify $3x^2 + 2$ as a monomial, a binomial, or a trinomial.

16. Find the degree of the polynomial $3x^2y^3z^4 + 2x^3y^2z - 5x^2y^3z^5$.

17. Evaluate $x^2 + x - 2$ when $x = -2$.

18. Graph the polynomial function $f(x) = x^2 + 2$ and determine the domain and range.

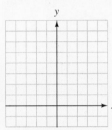

19. Simplify: $-6(x - y) + 2(x + y) - 3(x + 2y)$.

20. Simplify: $-2(x^2 + 3x - 1) - 3(x^2 - x + 2) + 5(x^2 + 2)$.

21. Add: $3x^3 + 4x^2 - x - 7$
$\underline{2x^3 - 2x^2 + 3x + 2}$

22. Subtract: $2x^2 - 7x + 3$
$\underline{3x^2 - 2x - 1}$

Find each product.

23. $(-2x^3)(2x^2y)$

24. $3y^2(y^2 - 2y + 3)$

25. $(2x - 5)(3x + 4)$

26. $(2x - 3)(x^2 - 2x + 4)$

Simplify each expression. Assume no division by 0.

27. Simplify: $\dfrac{8x^2y^3z^4}{16x^3y^2z^4}$.

28. Simplify: $\dfrac{6a^2 - 12b^2}{24ab}$.

29. Divide: $2x + 3)\overline{2x^2 - x - 6}$.

30. Solve: $(a + 2)^2 = (a - 3)^2$.

Cumulative Review Exercises

Evaluate each expression. Let x = 2 and y = −5.

1. $5 + 3 \cdot 2$

2. $3 \cdot 5^2 - 4$

3. $\dfrac{3x - y}{xy}$

4. $\dfrac{x^2 - y^2}{x + y}$

Solve each equation.

5. $\dfrac{4}{5}x + 6 = 18$

6. $x - 2 = \dfrac{x + 2}{3}$

7. $2(5x + 2) = 3(3x - 2)$

8. $4(y + 1) = -2(4 - y)$

Graph the solution of each inequality.

9. $5x - 3 > 7$

10. $7x - 9 < 5$

11. $-2 < -x + 3 < 5$

12. $0 \le \dfrac{4 - x}{3} \le 2$

Solve each formula for the indicated variable.

13. $A = p + prt$, for r

14. $A = \dfrac{1}{2}bh$, for h

Graph each equation.

15. $3x - 4y = 12$

16. $y - 2 = \dfrac{1}{2}(x - 4)$

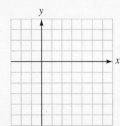

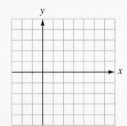

Let f(x) = 5x − 2 and find each value.

17. $f(0)$

18. $f(3)$

19. $f(-2)$

20. $f\left(\dfrac{1}{5}\right)$

Write each expression as an expression using only one exponent. Assume no division by 0.

21. $(y^3y^5)y^6$

22. $\dfrac{x^3y^4}{x^2y^3}$

23. $\dfrac{a^4b^{-3}}{a^{-3}b^3}$

24. $\left(\dfrac{-x^{-2}y^3}{x^{-3}y^2}\right)^2$

Perform each operation.

25. $(3x^2 + 2x - 7) - (2x^2 - 2x + 7)$

26. $(3x - 7)(2x + 8)$

27. $(x - 2)(x^2 + 2x + 4)$

28. $x - 3\overline{)2x^2 - 5x - 3}$ $(x \neq 3)$

29. Astronomy The **parsec**, a unit of distance used in astronomy, is 3×10^{16} meters. The distance from Earth to Betelgeuse, a star in the constellation Orion, is 1.6×10^2 parsecs. Use scientific notation to express this distance in meters.

30. Surface area The total surface area A of a box with dimensions l, w, and d is given by the formula

$$A = 2lw + 2wd + 2ld$$

If $A = 202$, $l = 9$, and $w = 5$, find d.

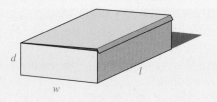

31. Concentric circles The area of the ring between the two concentric circles of radius r and R is given by the formula

$$A = \pi(R + r)(R - r)$$

If $r = 3$ and $R = 17$, find A to the nearest tenth.

32. Employee discounts Employees at an appliance store can purchase merchandise at 25% less than the regular price. An employee buys a TV set for $414.72, including 8% sales tax. Find the regular price of the TV.

Factoring Polynomials

In this chapter ▶

In this chapter, we will reverse the operation of multiplying polynomials and show which polynomials were used to find a given product. We will use this skill to solve many equations and, in the next chapter, to simplify rational expressions.

©Shutterstock.com/Pete Saloutos

Careers and Mathematics

ATHLETES, COACHES, AND RELATED WORKERS

We are a nation of sports fans and sports players. Some of those who participate in amateur sports dream of becoming paid professional athletes, coaches, or sports officials, but very few beat the long odds of making a full-time living from professional sports. In 2006, coaches and scouts held 217,000 jobs, while athletes held 18,000 jobs. Nearly 42% of athletes and coaches worked part time. Education and training for coaches and athletes vary greatly by the level and type of sport.

Job Outlook:
People who are state-certified to teach academic subjects in addition to physical education will have the best prospects for obtaining coaching and instructor jobs. Employment of athletes, coaches, and related workers is expected to increase faster than average for all occupations through 2016.

Annual Earnings:
Athletes: $41,060.
Coaches and scouts: $26,950.

For More Information:
http://www.bls.gov/oco/ocos251.htm

For a Sample Application:
See Problem 40 in Section 5.8.

Factoring Out the Greatest Common Factor; Factoring by Grouping

Objectives

1. Find the prime factorization of a natural number.
2. Factor a polynomial using the greatest common factor.
3. Factor a polynomial with a negative greatest common factor.
4. Factor a polynomial with a binomial greatest common factor.
5. Factor a four-term polynomial using grouping.

Vocabulary

prime-factored form
factoring tree

fundamental theorem
of arithmetic

greatest common factor (GCF)
factoring by grouping

Getting Ready

Simplify each expression by removing parentheses.

1. $5(x + 3)$ **2.** $7(y - 8)$ **3.** $x(3x - 2)$ **4.** $y(5y + 9)$

5. $3(x + y) + a(x + y)$ **6.** $x(y + 1) + 5(y + 1)$

7. $5(x + 1) - y(x + 1)$ **8.** $x(x + 2) - y(x + 2)$

In this chapter, we shall reverse the operation of multiplication and show how to find the factors of a known product. The process of finding the individual factors of a product is called *factoring*.

1 Find the prime factorization of a natural number.

Because 4 divides 12 exactly, 4 is called a *factor* of 12. The numbers 1, 2, 3, 4, 6, and 12 are the natural-number factors of 12, because each one divides 12 exactly. Recall that a natural number greater than 1 whose only factors are 1 and the number itself is called a **prime number.** For example, 19 is a prime number, because

1. 19 is a natural number greater than 1, and

2. the only two natural-number factors of 19 are 1 and 19.

The prime numbers less than 50 are

2, 3, 5, 7, 11, 13, 17, 19, 23, 29, 31, 37, 41, 43, and 47

A natural number is said to be in **prime-factored form** if it is written as the product of factors that are prime numbers.

To find the prime-factored form of a natural number, we can use a **factoring tree.** For example, to find the prime-factored form of 60, we proceed as follows:

Solution 1

1. Start with 60.

2. Factor 60 as $6 \cdot 10$.

3. Factor 6 and 10.

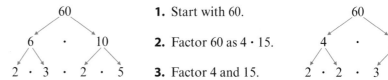

Solution 2

1. Start with 60.

2. Factor 60 as $4 \cdot 15$.

3. Factor 4 and 15.

We stop when only prime numbers appear. In either case, the prime factors of 60 are $2 \cdot 2 \cdot 3 \cdot 5$. Thus, the prime-factored form of 60 is $2^2 \cdot 3 \cdot 5$. This illustrates the **fundamental theorem of arithmetic,** which states that there is exactly one prime factorization for any natural number greater than 1.

The right sides of the equations

$$42 = 2 \cdot 3 \cdot 7$$
$$60 = 2^2 \cdot 3 \cdot 5$$
$$90 = 2 \cdot 3^2 \cdot 5$$

show the prime-factored forms (or *prime factorizations*) of 42, 60, and 90. The largest natural number that divides each of these numbers is called their **greatest common factor (GCF).** The GCF of 42, 60, and 90 is 6, because 6 is the largest natural number that divides each of these numbers:

$$\frac{42}{6} = 7 \qquad \frac{60}{6} = 10 \qquad \text{and} \qquad \frac{90}{6} = 15$$

2 **Factor a polynomial using the greatest common factor.**

Algebraic monomials also can have a greatest common factor. The right sides of the equations show the prime factorizations of $6a^2b^3$, $4a^3b^2$, and $18a^2b$.

$$6a^2b^3 = 2 \cdot 3 \cdot a \cdot a \cdot b \cdot b \cdot b$$
$$4a^3b^2 = 2 \cdot 2 \cdot a \cdot a \cdot a \cdot b \cdot b$$
$$18a^2b = 2 \cdot 3 \cdot 3 \cdot a \cdot a \cdot b$$

Since all three of these monomials have one factor of 2, two factors of a, and one factor of b, the GCF is

$$2 \cdot a \cdot a \cdot b \qquad \text{or} \qquad 2a^2b$$

To find the GCF of several monomials, we follow these steps.

Finding the Greatest Common Factor (GCF)

1. Identify the number of terms.

2. Find the prime factorization of each term.

3. List each common factor the least number of times it appears in any one monomial.

4. Find the product of the factors found in the list to obtain the GCF.

PERSPECTIVE

Much of the mathematics that we have inherited from earlier times is the result of teamwork. In a battle early in the 12th century, control of the Spanish city of Toledo was taken from the Mohammedans, who had ruled there for four centuries. Libraries in this great city contained many books written in Arabic, full of knowledge that was unknown in Europe.

The Archbishop of Toledo wanted to share this knowledge with the rest of the world. He knew that these books should be translated into Latin, the universal language of scholarship. But what European scholar could read Arabic? The citizens of Toledo knew both Arabic and Spanish, and most scholars of Europe could read Spanish.

Teamwork saved the day. A citizen of Toledo read the Arabic text aloud, in Spanish. The scholars listened to the Spanish version and wrote it down in Latin. One of these scholars was an Englishman, Robert of Chester. It was he who translated al-Khowarazmi's book, Ihm al-jabr wa'l muqabalah, the beginning of the subject we now know as algebra.

EXAMPLE 1   Find the GCF of $10x^3y^2$, $60x^2y$, and $30xy^2$.

Solution   **1.** We want to find the prime factorization of three monomials.

2. Find the prime factorization of each monomial.

$$10x^3y^2 = 2 \cdot 5 \cdot x \cdot x \cdot x \cdot y \cdot y$$
$$60x^2y = 2 \cdot 2 \cdot 3 \cdot 5 \cdot x \cdot x \cdot y$$
$$30xy^2 = 2 \cdot 3 \cdot 5 \cdot x \cdot y \cdot y$$

3. List each common factor the least number of times it appears in any one monomial: 2, 5, x, and y.

4. Find the product of the factors in the list:

$$2 \cdot 5 \cdot x \cdot y = 10xy$$

▷ **SELF CHECK 1**   Find the GCF of $20a^2b^3$, $12ab^4$, and $8a^3b^2$.

Recall that the distributive property provides a way to multiply a polynomial by a monomial. For example,

$$3x^2(2x - 3y) = 3x^2 \cdot 2x - 3x^2 \cdot 3y$$
$$= 6x^3 - 9x^2y$$

To reverse this process and factor the product $6x^3 - 9x^2y$, we can find the GCF of each term (which is $3x^2$) and then use the distributive property.

$$6x^3 - 9x^2y = 3x^2 \cdot 2x - 3x^2 \cdot 3y$$
$$= 3x^2(2x - 3y)$$

This process is called **factoring out the greatest common factor.**

EXAMPLE 2   Factor: $12y^2 + 20y$.

Solution   To find the GCF, we find the prime factorization of $12y^2$ and $20y$.

$$\left.\begin{array}{l} 12y^2 = 2 \cdot 2 \cdot 3 \cdot y \cdot y \\ 20y = 2 \cdot 2 \cdot 5 \cdot y \end{array}\right\} \quad \text{GCF} = 4y$$

We can use the distributive property to factor out the GCF of $4y$.

$$\begin{aligned} 12y^2 + 20y &= 4y \cdot 3y + 4y \cdot 5 \\ &= 4y(3y + 5) \end{aligned}$$

Check by verifying that $4y(3y + 5) = 12y^2 + 20y$.

➡ **SELF CHECK 2**   Factor: $15x^3 - 20x^2$.

EXAMPLE 3   Factor: $35a^3b^2 - 14a^2b^3$.

Solution   To find the GCF, we find the prime factorization of $35a^3b^2$ and $-14a^2b^3$.

$$\left.\begin{array}{l} 35a^3b^2 = 5 \cdot 7 \cdot a \cdot a \cdot a \cdot b \cdot b \\ -14a^2b^3 = -2 \cdot 7 \cdot a \cdot a \cdot b \cdot b \cdot b \end{array}\right\} \quad \text{GCF} = 7a^2b^2$$

We factor out the GCF of $7a^2b^2$.

$$\begin{aligned} 35a^3b^2 - 14a^2b^3 &= 7a^2b^2 \cdot 5a - 7a^2b^2 \cdot 2b \\ &= 7a^2b^2(5a - 2b) \end{aligned}$$

Check: $7a^2b^2(5a - 2b) = 35a^3b^2 - 14a^2b^3$

➡ **SELF CHECK 3**   Factor: $40x^2y^3 + 15x^3y^2$.

EXAMPLE 4   Factor: $a^2b^2 - ab$.

Solution   We factor out the GCF, which is ab.

COMMENT   The last term of $a^2b^2 - ab$ has an implied coefficient of -1. When ab is factored out, we must write the coefficient of -1.

$$\begin{aligned} a^2b^2 - ab &= ab \cdot ab - ab \cdot 1 \\ &= ab(ab - 1) \end{aligned}$$

Check: $ab(ab - 1) = a^2b^2 - ab$

➡ **SELF CHECK 4**   Factor: $x^3y^5 + x^2y^3$.

EXAMPLE 5   Factor: $12x^3y^2z + 6x^2yz - 3xz$.

Solution   We factor out the GCF, which is $3xz$.

$$\begin{aligned} 12x^3y^2z + 6x^2yz - 3xz &= 3xz \cdot 4x^2y^2 + 3xz \cdot 2xy - 3xz \cdot 1 \\ &= 3xz(4x^2y^2 + 2xy - 1) \end{aligned}$$

Check: $3xz(4x^2y^2 + 2xy - 1) = 12x^3y^2z + 6x^2yz - 3xz$

⇨ **SELF CHECK 5** Factor: $6ab^2c - 12a^2bc + 3ab$.

3 **Factor a polynomial with a negative greatest common factor.**

It is often useful to factor -1 out of a polynomial, especially if the leading coefficient is negative.

EXAMPLE 6 Factor -1 out of $-a^3 + 2a^2 - 4$.

Solution $-a^3 + 2a^2 - 4$
$= (-1)a^3 + (-1)(-2a^2) + (-1)4$ $(-1)(-2a^2) = +2a^2$
$= -1(a^3 - 2a^2 + 4)$ Factor out -1.
$= -(a^3 - 2a^2 + 4)$ The coefficient of 1 need not be written.

Check: $-(a^3 - 2a^2 + 4) = -a^3 + 2a^2 - 4$

⇨ **SELF CHECK 6** Factor -1 out of $-b^4 - 3b^2 + 2$.

EXAMPLE 7 Factor out the negative of the GCF: $-18a^2b + 6ab^2 - 12a^2b^2$.

Solution The GCF is $6ab$. To factor out its negative, we factor out $-6ab$.
$$-18a^2b + 6ab^2 - 12a^2b^2 = (-6ab)3a + (-6ab)(-b) + (-6ab)2ab$$
$$= -6ab(3a - b + 2ab)$$

Check: $-6ab(3a - b + 2ab) = -18a^2b + 6ab^2 - 12a^2b^2$

⇨ **SELF CHECK 7** Factor out the negative of the GCF: $-25xy^2 - 15x^2y + 30x^2y^2$.

4 **Factor a polynomial with a binomial greatest common factor.**

If the GCF of several terms is a polynomial, we can factor out the common polynomial factor. For example, since $a + b$ is a common factor of $(a + b)x$ and $(a + b)y$, we can factor out the $a + b$.

$$(a + b)x + (a + b)y = (a + b)(x + y)$$

We can check by verifying that $(a + b)(x + y) = (a + b)x + (a + b)y$.

EXAMPLE 8   Factor $a + 3$ out of $(a + 3) + (a + 3)^2$.

Solution   Recall that $a + 3$ is equal to $(a + 3)^1$ and that $(a + 3)^2$ is equal to $(a + 3)(a + 3)$. We can factor out $a + 3$ and simplify.

$$(a + 3) + (a + 3)^2 = (a + 3)1 + (a + 3)(a + 3)$$
$$= (a + 3)[1 + (a + 3)]$$
$$= (a + 3)(a + 4)$$

SELF CHECK 8   Factor out $y + 2$: $(y + 2)^2 - 3(y + 2)$.

EXAMPLE 9   Factor: $6a^2b^2(x + 2y) - 9ab(x + 2y)$.

Solution   The GCF of $6a^2b^2$ and $9ab$ is $3ab$. We can factor out this GCF as well as $(x + 2y)$.

$$6a^2b^2(x + 2y) - 9ab(x + 2y)$$
$$= 3ab \cdot 2ab(x + 2y) - 3ab \cdot 3(x + 2y)$$
$$= 3ab(x + 2y)(2ab - 3) \qquad \text{Factor out } 3ab(x + 2y).$$

SELF CHECK 9   Factor: $4p^3q^2(2a + b) + 8p^2q^3(2a + b)$.

5 **Factor a four-term polynomial using grouping.**

Suppose we want to factor

$$ax + ay + cx + cy$$

Although no factor is common to all four terms, there is a common factor of a in $ax + ay$ and a common factor of c in $cx + cy$. We can factor out the a and the c to obtain

$$ax + ay + cx + cy = a(x + y) + c(x + y)$$
$$= (x + y)(a + c) \qquad \text{Factor out } x + y.$$

We can check the result by multiplication.

$$(x + y)(a + c) = ax + cx + ay + cy$$
$$= ax + ay + cx + cy$$

Thus, $ax + ay + cx + cy$ factors as $(x + y)(a + c)$. This type of factoring is called **factoring by grouping.**

EXAMPLE 10   Factor: $2c + 2d - cd - d^2$.

Solution $$2c + 2d - cd - d^2 = 2(c + d) - d(c + d) \qquad \text{Factor out 2 from } 2c + 2d \text{ and } -d$$
$$\text{from } -cd - d^2.$$

$$= (c + d)(2 - d) \qquad \text{Factor out } c + d.$$

Check: $(c + d)(2 - d) = 2c - cd + 2d - d^2$

$$= 2c + 2d - cd - d^2$$

⇨ **SELF CHECK 10**   Factor: $3a + 3b - ac - bc$.

EXAMPLE 11   Factor: $x^2y - ax - xy + a$.

Solution $x^2y - ax - xy + a = x(xy - a) - 1(xy - a)$ Factor out x from $x^2y - ax$ and -1 from $-xy + a$.

$$= (xy - a)(x - 1)$$ Factor out $xy - a$.

Check by multiplication.

⇨ **SELF CHECK 11**   Factor: $pq^2 + tq + 2pq + 2t$.

COMMENT   When factoring expressions, the final result must be a product. Expressions such as $2(c + d) - d(c + d)$ and $x(xy - a) - 1(xy - a)$ are not in factored form.

EXAMPLE 12   Factor: **a.** $a(c - d) + b(d - c)$ **b.** $ac + bd - ad - bc$.

Solution   **a.** $a(c - d) + b(d - c) = a(c - d) - b(-d + c)$ Factor -1 from $d - c$.

$$= a(c - d) - b(c - d)$$ $-d + c = c - d$

$$= (c - d)(a - b)$$ Factor out $c - d$.

b. In this example, we cannot factor anything from the first two terms or the last two terms. However, if we rearrange the terms, we can factor by grouping.

$$ac + bd - ad - bc = ac - ad + bd - bc$$ $bd - ad = -ad + bd$

$$= a(c - d) + b(d - c)$$ Factor a from $ac - ad$ and b from $bd - bc$.

$$= (c - d)(a - b)$$ Factor out $c - d$.

⇨ **SELF CHECK 12**   Factor: $ax - by - ay + bx$.

COMMENT   In Example 12(b) above, we also could have factored the polynomial if we rearranged the terms as $ac - bc - ad + bd$.

⇨ **SELF CHECK ANSWERS**   **1.** $4ab^2$ **2.** $5x^2(3x - 4)$ **3.** $5x^2y^2(8y + 3x)$ **4.** $x^2y^3(xy^2 + 1)$ **5.** $3ab(2bc - 4ac + 1)$
6. $-(b^4 + 3b^2 - 2)$ **7.** $-5xy(5y + 3x - 6xy)$ **8.** $(y + 2)(y - 1)$ **9.** $4p^2q^2(2a + b)(p + 2q)$
10. $(a + b)(3 - c)$ **11.** $(pq + t)(q + 2)$ **12.** $(a + b)(x - y)$

NOW TRY THIS

Factor:

1. $(x + y)(x^2 - 3) + (x + y)$

2. a. $x^{2n} + x^n$

    b. $x^3 + x^{-1}$

3. Which of the following is equivalent to $\frac{3 - x}{x + 2}$? There may be more than one answer.

    a. $\dfrac{-(x - 3)}{x + 2}$ **b.** $\dfrac{x - 3}{x + 2}$ **c.** $\dfrac{-x + 3}{x + 2}$ **d.** $-\dfrac{x - 3}{x + 2}$

5.1 EXERCISES

WARM-UPS

Find the prime factorization of each number.

  1. 36   **2.** 27

  3. 81   **4.** 45

Find the greatest common factor:

  5. 3, 6, and 9   **6.** $3a^2b$, $6ab$, and $9ab^2$

  7. $a(x + 3)$ and $3(x + 3)$ **8.** $5(a - 1)$ and $xy(a - 1)$

Factor out the greatest common factor:

  9. $15xy + 10$ **10.** $15xy + 10xy^2$

 11. $a(x + 3) - 3(x + 3)$ **12.** $b(x - 2) + (x - 2)$

REVIEW   *Solve each equation and check all solutions.*

 13. $3x - 2(x + 1) = 5$ **14.** $5(y - 1) + 1 = y$

 15. $\dfrac{2x - 7}{5} = 3$ **16.** $2x - \dfrac{x}{2} = 5x$

VOCABULARY AND CONCEPTS   *Fill in the blanks.*

 17. If a natural number is written as the product of prime numbers, it is written in _____ form.

 18. The _____ states that each natural number greater than 1 has exactly one prime factorization.

 19. The GCF of several natural numbers is the _____ number that divides each of the numbers.

 20. In order to find the prime factorization of a natural number, you can use a _____.

 21. To factor a four-term polynomial, it is often necessary to factor by _____.

 22. Check the results of a factoring problem by _____.

GUIDED PRACTICE

Find the prime factorization of each number. (See Objective 1)

 23. 12   **24.** 24

 25. 15   **26.** 20

 27. 40   **28.** 62

 29. 98   **30.** 112

 31. 225   **32.** 144

 33. 288   **34.** 968

Find the GCF of the given monomials. See Example 1.

 35. $5xy^2$, $10xy$

 36. $7a^2b$, $14ab^2$

 37. $6x^2y^2$, $12xyz$, $18xy^2z^3$

 38. $4a^3b^2c$, $12ab^2c^2$, $20ab^2c^2$

Complete each factorization. See Example 2. (Objective 2)

 39. $4a + 12 = \blacksquare(a + 3)$ **40.** $3t - 27 = 3(t - \blacksquare)$

 41. $r^4 + r^2 = r^2(\blacksquare + 1)$ **42.** $a^3 - a^2 = \blacksquare(a - 1)$

Factor each polynomial by factoring out the GCF. See Example 2. (Objective 2)

 43. $3x + 6$ **44.** $2y - 10$

 45. $4x - 8$ **46.** $4t + 12$

Factor each polynomial by factoring out the GCF. See Example 3. (Objective 2)

 47. $xy - xz$ **48.** $uv + ut$

 49. $t^3 + 2t^2$ **50.** $b^3 - 3b^2$

Factor each polynomial by factoring out the GCF. **See Example 4. (Objective 2)**

51. $a^3b^3z^3 - a^2b^3z^2$

52. $r^3s^6t^9 + r^2s^2t^2$

53. $24x^2y^3z^4 + 8xy^2z^3$

54. $3x^2y^3 - 9x^4y^3z$

Factor each polynomial by factoring out the GCF. **See Example 5. (Objective 2)**

55. $3x + 3y - 6z$

56. $2x - 4y + 8z$

57. $ab + ac - ad$

58. $rs - rt + ru$

59. $4y^2 + 8y - 2xy$

60. $3x^2 - 6xy + 9xy^2$

61. $12r^2 - 3rs + 9r^2s^2$

62. $6a^2 - 12a^3b + 36ab$

63. $abx - ab^2x + abx^2$

64. $a^2b^2x^2 + a^3b^2x^2 - a^3b^3x^3$

65. $4x^2y^2z^2 - 6xy^2z^2 + 12xyz^2$

66. $32xyz + 48x^2yz + 36xy^2z$

Factor out −1 from each polynomial. **See Example 6. (Objective 3)**

67. $-x - 2$

68. $-y + 3$

69. $-a - b$

70. $-x - 2y$

71. $-2x + 5y$

72. $-3x + 8z$

73. $-2a + 3b$

74. $-2x + 5y$

75. $-3xy + 2z + 5w$

76. $-4ab + 3c - 5d$

77. $-3ab - 5ac + 9bc$

78. $-6yz + 12xz - 5xy$

Factor out the negative of the GCF. **See Example 7. (Objective 3)**

79. $-3x^2y - 6xy^2$

80. $-4a^2b^2 + 6ab^2$

81. $-4a^2b^3 + 12a^3b^2$

82. $-25x^4y^3z^2 + 30x^2y^3z^4$

83. $-8a^5b^2 - 8a^3b^4$

84. $-14p^3q^5 + 21p^4q^4$

85. $-4a^2b^2c^2 + 14a^2b^2c - 10ab^2c^2$

86. $-10x^4y^3z^2 + 8x^3y^2z - 20x^2y$

Complete each factorization. **See Examples 8–9. (Objective 4)**

87. $a(x + y) + b(x + y) = (x + y)$ ▓

88. $x(a + b) + p(a + b) = $ ▓ $(x + p)$

89. $p(m - n) - q(m - n) = $ ▓ $(p - q)$

90. $(r - s)p - (r - s)q = (r - s)$ ▓

Factor each expression. **See Example 8. (Objective 4)**

91. $(x + y)2 + (x + y)b$

92. $(a - b)c + (a - b)d$

93. $(x - 3)^2 + (x - 3)$

94. $2x(a^2 + b) + 2y(a^2 + b)$

Factor each expression. **See Example 9. (Objective 4)**

95. $x(y + 1) - 5(y + 1)$

96. $3(x + y) - a(x + y)$

97. $(3t + 5)^2 - (3t + 5)$

98. $9a^2b^2(3x - 2y) - 6ab(3x - 2y)$

Factor each polynomial by grouping. **See Examples 10–12. (Objective 5)**

99. $2x + 2y + ax + ay$

100. $bx + bz + 5x + 5z$

101. $9p - 9q + mp - mq$

102. $7r + 7s - kr - ks$

103. $ax + bx - a - b$

104. $mp - np - m + n$

105. $x(a - b) + y(b - a)$

106. $p(m - n) - q(n - m)$

ADDITIONAL PRACTICE

Complete the factorization.

107. $4y^2 + 8y - 2xy = 2y\left(2y + \text{▓} - \text{▓}\right)$

108. $3x^2 - 6xy + 9xy^2 = \text{▓}\left(\text{▓} - 2y + 3y^2\right)$

Factor each expression completely.

109. $r^4 + r^2$

110. $a^3 + a^2$

111. $12uvw^3 - 18uv^2w^2$

112. $14xyz - 16x^2y^2z$

113. $70a^3b^2c^2 + 49a^2b^3c^3 - 21a^2b^2c^2$

114. $8a^2b^2 - 24ab^2c + 9b^2c^2$

115. $-3m - 4n + 1$

116. $-3r + 2s - 3$

117. $-14a^6b^6 + 49a^2b^3 - 21ab$

118. $-35r^9s^9t^9 + 25r^6s^6t^6 + 75r^3s^3t^3$

119. $-5a^2b^3c + 15a^3b^4c^2 - 25a^4b^3c$

120. $-7x^5y^4z^3 + 49x^5y^5z^4 - 21x^6y^4z^3$

121. $3(r - 2s) - x(r - 2s)$

122. $x(a + 2b) + y(a + 2b)$

123. $3x(a + b + c) - 2y(a + b + c)$

124. $2m(a - 2b + 3c) - 21xy(a - 2b + 3c)$

125. $14x^2y(r + 2s - t) - 21xy(r + 2s - t)$

126. $15xy^3(2x - y + 3z) + 25xy^2(2x - y + 3z)$

127. $(x + 3)(x + 1) - y(x + 1)$

128. $x(x^2 + 2) - y(x^2 + 2)$
129. $(3x - y)(x^2 - 2) + (x^2 - 2)$
130. $(x - 5y)(a + 2) - (x - 5y)$
131. $3x(c - 3d) + 6y(c - 3d)$
132. $3x^2(r + 3s) - 6y^2(r + 3s)$
133. $xr + xs + yr + ys$
134. $pm - pn + qm - qn$
135. $2ax + 2bx + 3a + 3b$
136. $3xy + 3xz - 5y - 5z$
137. $2ab + 2ac + 3b + 3c$
138. $3ac + a + 3bc + b$
139. $3tv - 9tw + uv - 3uw$
140. $ce - 2cf + 3de - 6df$
141. $9mp + 3mq - 3np - nq$
142. $6x^2u - 3x^2v + 2yu - yv$
143. $ax^3 + bx^3 + 2ax^2y + 2bx^2y$
144. $x^3y^2 - 2x^2y^2 + 3xy^2 - 6y^2$
145. $4a^2b + 12a^2 - 8ab - 24a$
146. $-4abc - 4ac^2 + 2bc + 2c^2$
147. $2x^2 + 2xy - 3x - 3y$
148. $3ab + 9a - 2b - 6$
149. $x^3 + 2x^2 + x + 2$
150. $y^3 - 3y^2 - 5y + 15$
151. $x^3y - x^2y - xy^2 + y^2$
152. $2x^3z - 4x^2z + 32xz - 64z$

Factor each expression completely. You may have to rearrange terms first.

153. $2r - bs - 2s + br$
154. $5x + ry + rx + 5y$
155. $ax + by + bx + ay$

156. $mr + ns + ms + nr$
157. $ac + bd - ad - bc$
158. $sx - ry + rx - sy$
159. $ar^2 - brs + ars - br^2$
160. $a^2bc + a^2c + abc + ac$
161. $ba + 3 + a + 3b$
162. $xy + 7 + y + 7x$
163. $pr + qs - ps - qr$
164. $ac - bd - ad + bc$

WRITING ABOUT MATH

165. When we add $5x$ and $7x$, we combine like terms: $5x + 7x = 12x$. Explain how this is related to factoring out a common factor.
166. Explain how you would factor $x(a - b) + y(b - a)$.

SOMETHING TO THINK ABOUT

167. Think of two positive integers. Divide their product by their greatest common factor. Why do you think the result is called the lowest common multiple of the two integers? (*Hint:* The multiples of an integer such as 5 are 5, 10, 15, 20, 25, 30, and so on.)
168. Two integers are called **relatively prime** if their greatest common factor is 1. For example, 6 and 25 are relatively prime, but 6 and 15 are not. If the greatest common factor of three integers is 1, must any two of them be relatively prime? Explain.
169. Factor $ax + ay + bx + by$ by grouping the first two terms and the last two terms. Then rearrange the terms as $ax + bx + ay + by$, and factor again by grouping the first two and the last two. Do the results agree?
170. Factor $2xy + 2xz - 3y - 3z$ by grouping in two different ways.

SECTION 5.2
Factoring the Difference of Two Squares

Objectives

1 Factor the difference of two squares.
2 Completely factor a polynomial.

Vocabulary

difference of two squares   sum of two squares   prime polynomial

Getting Ready

Multiply the binomials.

1. $(a + b)(a - b)$ **2.** $(2r + s)(2r - s)$

3. $(3x + 2y)(3x - 2y)$ **4.** $(4x^2 + 3)(4x^2 - 3)$

Whenever we multiply a binomial of the form $x + y$ by a binomial of the form $x - y$, we obtain a binomial of the form $x^2 - y^2$.

$$(x + y)(x - y) = x^2 - xy + xy - y^2$$
$$= x^2 - y^2$$

In this section, we will show how to reverse the multiplication process and factor binomials such as $x^2 - y^2$.

1 **Factor the difference of two squares.**

The binomial $x^2 - y^2$ is called the **difference of two squares,** because x^2 is the square of x and y^2 is the square of y. The **difference** of the squares of two quantities always factors into the **sum** of those two quantities multiplied by the **difference** of those two quantities.

Factoring the Difference of Two Squares

$$x^2 - y^2 = (x + y)(x - y)$$

COMMENT The factorization of $x^2 - y^2$ also can be expressed as $(x - y)(x + y)$.

If we think of the difference of two squares as the square of a **First** quantity minus the square of a **Last** quantity, we have the formula

$$F^2 - L^2 = (F + L)(F - L)$$

and we say, *To factor the square of a First quantity minus the square of a Last quantity, we multiply the First plus the Last by the First minus the Last.*

To factor $x^2 - 9$, we note that it can be written in the form $x^2 - 3^2$ and use the formula for factoring the difference of two squares:

$$F^2 - L^2 = (F + L)(F - L)$$
$$x^2 - 3^2 = (x + 3)(x - 3)$$

We can check by verifying that $(x + 3)(x - 3) = x^2 - 9$.

To factor the difference of two squares, it is helpful to know the integers that are perfect squares. The number 400, for example, is a perfect square, because $20^2 = 400$. The perfect integer squares less than 400 are

1, 4, 9, 16, 25, 36, 49, 64, 81, 100, 121, 144, 169, 196, 225, 256, 289, 324, 361

Expressions containing variables such as x^4y^2 are also perfect squares, because they can be written as the square of a quantity:

$$x^4y^2 = (x^2y)^2$$

EXAMPLE 1   Factor: $25x^2 - 49$.

Solution   We can write $25x^2 - 49$ in the form $(5x)^2 - 7^2$ and use the formula for factoring the difference of two squares:

$$\text{F}^2 - \text{L}^2 = (\text{F} + \text{L})(\text{F} - \text{L})$$
$$(5x)^2 - 7^2 = (5x + 7)(5x - 7)$$

Substitute $5x$ for F and 7 for L.

We can check by multiplying $5x + 7$ and $5x - 7$.

$$(5x + 7)(5x - 7) = 25x^2 - 35x + 35x - 49$$
$$= 25x^2 - 49$$

SELF CHECK 1   Factor: $16a^2 - 81$.

EXAMPLE 2   Factor: $4y^4 - 25z^2$.

Solution   We can write $4y^4 - 25z^2$ in the form $(2y^2)^2 - (5z)^2$ and use the formula for factoring the difference of two squares:

$$\text{F}^2 - \text{L}^2 = (\text{F} + \text{L})(\text{F} - \text{L})$$
$$(2y^2)^2 - (5z)^2 = (2y^2 + 5z)(2y^2 - 5z)$$

Check by multiplication.

SELF CHECK 2   Factor: $9m^2 - 64n^4$.

2   **Completely factor a polynomial.**

We often can factor out a greatest common factor before factoring the difference of two squares. To factor $8x^2 - 32$, for example, we factor out the GCF of 8 and then factor the resulting difference of two squares.

$$8x^2 - 32 = 8(x^2 - 4) \qquad \text{Factor out 8.}$$
$$= 8(x^2 - 2^2) \qquad \text{Write 4 as } 2^2.$$
$$= 8(x + 2)(x - 2) \qquad \text{Factor the difference of two squares.}$$

We can check by multiplication:

$$8(x + 2)(x - 2) = 8(x^2 - 4)$$
$$= 8x^2 - 32$$

EXAMPLE 3   Factor: $2a^2x^3y - 8b^2xy$.

Solution   We factor out the GCF of $2xy$ and then factor the resulting difference of two squares.

$$2a^2x^3y - 8b^2xy$$
$$= \mathbf{2xy} \cdot a^2x^2 - \mathbf{2xy} \cdot 4b^2 \qquad \text{The GCF is } 2xy.$$
$$= \mathbf{2xy}(a^2x^2 - 4b^2) \qquad \text{Factor out } 2xy.$$
$$= 2xy[(ax)^2 - (2b)^2] \qquad \text{Write } a^2x^2 \text{ as } (ax)^2 \text{ and } 4b^2 \text{ as } (2b)^2.$$
$$= 2xy(ax + 2b)(ax - 2b) \qquad \text{Factor the difference of two squares.}$$

Check by multiplication.

➯ **SELF CHECK 3**   Factor: $2p^2q^2s - 18r^2s$.

Sometimes we must factor a difference of two squares more than once to completely factor a polynomial. For example, the binomial $625a^4 - 81b^4$ can be written in the form $(25a^2)^2 - (9b^2)^2$, which factors as

$$625a^4 - 81b^4 = (25a^2)^2 - (9b^2)^2$$
$$= (25a^2 + 9b^2)\mathbf{(25a^2 - 9b^2)}$$

Since the factor $25a^2 - 9b^2$ can be written in the form $(5a)^2 - (3b)^2$, it is the difference of two squares and can be factored as $(5a + 3b)(5a - 3b)$. Thus,

$$625a^4 - 81b^4 = (25a^2 + 9b^2)(5a + 3b)(5a - 3b)$$

COMMENT   The binomial $25a^2 + 9b^2$ is the **sum of two squares,** because it can be written in the form $(5a)^2 + (3b)^2$. If we are limited to rational coefficients, binomials that are the sum of two squares cannot be factored unless they contain a GCF. Polynomials that do not factor are called **prime polynomials.**

EXAMPLE 4   Factor: $2x^4y - 32y$.

Solution
$$2x^4y - 32y = \mathbf{2y} \cdot x^4 - \mathbf{2y} \cdot 16$$
$$= \mathbf{2y}(x^4 - 16) \qquad \text{Factor out the GCF of } 2y.$$
$$= 2y(x^2 + 4)(x^2 - 4) \qquad \text{Factor } x^4 - 16.$$
$$= 2y(x^2 + 4)(x + 2)(x - 2) \qquad \text{Factor } x^2 - 4. \text{ Note that } x^2 + 4 \text{ does not}$$
$$\text{factor using rational coefficients.}$$

Check by multiplication.

➯ **SELF CHECK 4**   Factor: $48a^5 - 3ab^4$.

Example 5 requires the techniques of factoring out a common factor, factoring by grouping, and factoring the difference of two squares.

EXAMPLE 5   Factor: $2x^3 - 8x + 2yx^2 - 8y$.

Solution

$$
\begin{aligned}
2x^3 - 8x + 2yx^2 - 8y &= 2(x^3 - 4x + yx^2 - 4y) &&\text{Factor out 2.}\\
&= 2[x(x^2 - 4) + y(x^2 - 4)] &&\text{Factor out } x \text{ from } x^3 - 4x\\
&&&\text{and } y \text{ from } yx^2 - 4y.\\
&= 2[(x^2 - 4)(x + y)] &&\text{Factor out } x^2 - 4.\\
&= 2(x + 2)(x - 2)(x + y) &&\text{Factor } x^2 - 4.
\end{aligned}
$$

COMMENT   To *factor* an expression means to factor the expression *completely*.

Check by multiplication.

⇨ **SELF CHECK 5**   Factor: $3a^3 - 12a + 3a^2b - 12b$.

⇨ **SELF CHECK ANSWERS**   **1.** $(4a + 9)(4a - 9)$ **2.** $(3m + 8n^2)(3m - 8n^2)$ **3.** $2s(pq + 3r)(pq - 3r)$ **4.** $3a(4a^2 + b^2)(2a + b)(2a - b)$ **5.** $3(a + 2)(a - 2)(a + b)$

NOW TRY THIS

Factor completely:

1. a. $x^2 - \dfrac{1}{9}$
   b. $2x^2 - 0.72$
   c. $16 - x^2$

2. $(x + y)^2 - 25$

3. $x^{2n} - 9$

5.2 EXERCISES

WARM-UPS   *Factor each binomial.*

1. $x^2 - 9$
3. $z^2 - 4$
5. $25 - t^2$
7. $100 - y^2$

2. $y^2 - 36$
4. $p^2 - q^2$
6. $36 - r^2$
8. $100 - y^4$

REVIEW

9. In the study of the flow of fluids, Bernoulli's law is given by the following equation. Solve it for p.

$$\frac{p}{w} + \frac{v^2}{2g} + h = k$$

10. Solve Bernoulli's law for h. (See Exercise 9.)

VOCABULARY AND CONCEPTS   *Fill in the blanks.*

11. A binomial of the form $a^2 - b^2$ is called the

_____.

12. A binomial of the form $a^2 + b^2$ is called the

_____.

13. A polynomial that cannot be factored over the rational numbers is said to be a _____ polynomial.

14. The _____ of two squares cannot be factored unless it has a GCF.

GUIDED PRACTICE

Complete each factorization. **See Examples 1–2. (Objective 1)**

15. $x^2 - 9 = (x + 3)$_____

16. $p^2 - q^2 =$ _____$(p - q)$

17. $4m^2 - 9n^2 = (2m + 3n)$_____

18. $16p^2 - 25q^2 =$ _____$(4p - 5q)$

Factor each polynomial. **See Examples 1–2. (Objective 1)**

19. $x^2 - 16$ **20.** $x^2 - 25$

21. $y^2 - 49$ **22.** $y^2 - 81$

23. $4y^2 - 49$ **24.** $9z^2 - 4$

25. $9x^2 - y^2$ **26.** $4x^2 - z^2$

27. $25t^2 - 36u^2$ **28.** $49u^2 - 64v^2$

29. $16a^2 - 25b^2$ **30.** $36a^2 - 121b^2$

Factor each polynomial. **See Example 3. (Objective 2)**

31. $8x^2 - 32y^2$ **32.** $2a^2 - 200b^2$

33. $2a^2 - 8y^2$ **34.** $32x^2 - 8y^2$

35. $3r^2 - 12s^2$ **36.** $45u^2 - 20v^2$

37. $x^3 - xy^2$ **38.** $a^2b - b^3$

Factor each polynomial. **See Example 4. (Objective 2)**

39. $a^4 - 16$

40. $b^4 - 256$

41. $a^4 - b^4$

42. $m^4 - 16n^4$

43. $2x^4 - 2y^4$

44. $a^5 - ab^4$

45. $a^4b - b^5$

46. $m^5 - 16mn^4$

47. $2x^4y - 512y^5$

48. $2x^8y^2 - 32y^6$

49. $a^3 - 9a + 3a^2 - 27$

50. $2x^3 - 18x - 6x^2 + 54$

ADDITIONAL PRACTICE   *Factor each polynomial completely, if possible. If a polynomial is prime, so indicate.*

51. $a^4 - 4b^2$ **52.** $121a^2 - 144b^2$

53. $a^2 + b^2$ **54.** $9y^2 + 16z^2$

55. $49y^2 - 225z^4$ **56.** $25x^2 + 36y^2$

57. $196x^4 - 169y^2$ **58.** $144a^4 + 169b^4$

59. $4a^2x - 9b^2x$ **60.** $4b^2y - 16c^2y$

61. $3m^3 - 3mn^2$ **62.** $2p^2q - 2q^3$

63. $4x^4 - x^2y^2$ **64.** $9xy^2 - 4xy^4$

65. $2a^3b - 242ab^3$ **66.** $50c^4d^2 - 8c^2d^4$

67. $x^4 - 81$ **68.** $y^4 - 625$

69. $81r^4 - 256s^4$

70. $x^8 - y^4$

71. $a^4 - b^8$

72. $16y^8 - 81z^4$

73. $x^8 - y^8$

74. $x^8y^8 - 1$

75. $48m^4n - 243n^5$

76. $3a^5y + 6ay^5$

77. $2p^{10}q - 32p^2q^5$

78. $3a^{10} - 3a^2b^4$

79. $2x^9y + 2xy^9$

80. $3a^8 - 243a^4b^8$

81. $a^6b^2 - a^2b^6c^4$

82. $a^2b^3c^4 - a^2b^3d^4$

83. $a^2b^7 - 625a^2b^3$

84. $16x^3y^4z - 81x^3y^4z^5$

85. $243r^5s - 48rs^5$

86. $1{,}024m^5n - 324mn^5$

87. $16(x - y)^2 - 9$

88. $9(x + 1)^2 - y^2$

89. $b^3 - 25b - 2b^2 + 50$

90. $y^3 - 16y - 3y^2 + 48$

91. $a^3 - 49a + 2a^2 - 98$

92. $3x^3 - 12x + 3x^2 - 12$

93. $3m^3 - 3mn^2 + 3am^2 - 3an^2$

94. $ax^3 - axy^2 - bx^3 + bxy^2$

95. $2m^3n^2 - 32mn^2 + 8m^2 - 128$

96. $2x^3y + 4x^2y - 98xy - 196y$

WRITING ABOUT MATH

97. Explain how to factor the difference of two squares.

98. Explain why $x^4 - y^4$ is not completely factored as $(x^2 + y^2)(x^2 - y^2)$.

SOMETHING TO THINK ABOUT

99. It is easy to multiply 399 by 401 without a calculator: The product is $400^2 - 1$, or 159,999. Explain.

100. Use the method in the previous exercise to find $498 \cdot 502$ without a calculator.

SECTION 5.3

Factoring Trinomials with a Leading Coefficient of 1

Objectives

1. Factor a trinomial of the form $x^2 + bx + c$ by trial and error.
2. Factor a trinomial with a negative greatest common factor.
3. Identify a prime trinomial.
4. Factor a polynomial completely.
5. Factor a trinomial of the form $x^2 + bx + c$ by grouping (*ac* method).
6. Factor a perfect-square trinomial.

Vocabulary

perfect-square trinomial

Getting Ready

Multiply the binomials.

1. $(x + 6)(x + 6)$ **2.** $(y - 7)(y - 7)$ **3.** $(a - 3)(a - 3)$

4. $(x + 4)(x + 5)$ **5.** $(r - 2)(r - 5)$ **6.** $(m + 3)(m - 7)$

7. $(a - 3b)(a + 4b)$ **8.** $(u - 3v)(u - 5v)$ **9.** $(x + 4y)(x - 6y)$

We now discuss how to factor trinomials of the form $x^2 + bx + c$, where the coefficient of x^2 is 1 and there are no common factors.

1 Factor a trinomial of the form $x^2 + bx + c$ by trial and error.

The product of two binomials is often a trinomial. For example,

$$(x + 3)(x + 3) = x^2 + 6x + 9 \quad \text{and} \quad (x - 4y)(x - 4y) = x^2 - 8xy + 16y^2$$

For this reason, we should not be surprised that many trinomials factor into the product of two binomials. To develop a method for factoring trinomials, we multiply $(x + a)$ and $(x + b)$.

$$(x + a)(x + b) = x^2 + bx + ax + ab \qquad \text{Use the FOIL method.}$$
$$= x^2 + ax + bx + ab \qquad \text{Write } bx + ax \text{ as } ax + bx.$$
$$= x^2 + (a + b)x + ab \qquad \text{Factor } x \text{ out of } ax + bx.$$

From the result, we can see that

- the coefficient of the middle term is the sum of a and b, and
- the last term is the product of a and b.

We can use these facts to factor trinomials with leading coefficients of 1.

EXAMPLE 1 Factor: $x^2 + 5x + 6$.

Solution To factor this trinomial, we will write it as the product of two binomials. Since the first term of the trinomial is x^2, the first term of each binomial factor must be x because $x \cdot x = x^2$. To fill in the following blanks, we must find two integers whose product is $+6$ and whose sum is $+5$.

$$x^2 + 5x + 6 = \left(x \quad \right)\left(x \quad \right)$$

The positive factorizations of 6 and the sums of the factors are shown in the following table.

Product of the factors	Sum of the factors
$1(6) = 6$	$1 + 6 = 7$
$2(3) = 6$	$2 + 3 = 5$

The last row contains the integers $+2$ and $+3$, whose product is $+6$ and whose sum is $+5$. So we can fill in the blanks with $+2$ and $+3$.

$$x^2 + 5x + 6 = (x + 2)(x + 3)$$

To check the result, we verify that $(x + 2)$ times $(x + 3)$ is $x^2 + 5x + 6$.

$$(x + 2)(x + 3) = x^2 + 3x + 2x + 2 \cdot 3$$
$$= x^2 + 5x + 6$$

⇨ SELF CHECK 1 Factor: $y^2 + 5y + 4$.

COMMENT In Example 1, the factors can be written in either order. An equivalent factorization is $x^2 + 5x + 6 = (x + 3)(x + 2)$.

EXAMPLE 2 Factor: $y^2 - 7y + 12$.

Solution Since the first term of the trinomial is y^2, the first term of each binomial factor must be y. To fill in the following blanks, we must find two integers whose product is $+12$ and whose sum is -7.

$$y^2 - 7y + 12 = \left(y \quad \right)\left(y \quad \right)$$

The factorizations of 12 and the sums of the factors are shown in the table.

Product of the factors	Sum of the factors
$1(12) = 12$	$1 + 12 = 13$
$2(6) = 12$	$2 + 6 = 8$
$3(4) = 12$	$3 + 4 = 7$
$-1(-12) = 12$	$-1 + (-12) = -13$
$-2(-6) = 12$	$-2 + (-6) = -8$
$-3(-4) = 12$	$-3 + (-4) = -7$

The last row contains the integers -3 and -4, whose product is $+12$ and whose sum is -7. So we can fill in the blanks with -3 and -4.

$$y^2 - 7y + 12 = (y - 3)(y - 4)$$

To check the result, we verify that $(y - 3)$ times $(y - 4)$ is $y^2 - 7y + 12$.

$$(y - 3)(y - 4) = y^2 - 3y - 4y + 12$$
$$= y^2 - 7y + 12$$

⇨ **SELF CHECK 2**   Factor: $p^2 - 5p + 6$.

EXAMPLE 3   Factor: $a^2 + 2a - 15$.

Solution   Since the first term is a^2, the first term of each binomial factor must be a. To fill in the blanks, we must find two integers whose product is -15 and whose sum is $+2$.

$$a^2 + 2a - 15 = \left(a \quad\right)\left(a \quad\right)$$

The factorizations of -15 and the sums of the factors are shown in the table.

Product of the factors	Sum of the factors
$1(-15) = -15$	$1 + (-15) = -14$
$3(-5) = -15$	$3 + (-5) = -2$
$5(-3) = -15$	$5 + (-3) = 2$
$15(-1) = -15$	$15 + (-1) = 14$

The third row contains the integers $+5$ and -3, whose product is -15 and whose sum is $+2$. So we can fill in the blanks with $+5$ and -3.

$$a^2 + 2a - 15 = (a + 5)(a - 3)$$

Check: $(a + 5)(a - 3) = a^2 - 3a + 5a - 15$
$$= a^2 + 2a - 15$$

⇨ **SELF CHECK 3**   Factor: $p^2 + 3p - 18$.

EXAMPLE 4   Factor: $z^2 - 4z - 21$.

Solution   Since the first term is z^2, the first term of each binomial factor must be z. To fill in the blanks, we must find two integers whose product is -21 and whose sum is -4.

$$z^2 - 4z - 21 = \left(z \right)\left(z \right)$$

The factorizations of -21 and the sums of the factors are shown in the table.

Product of the factors	Sum of the factors
$1(-21) = -21$	$1 + (-21) = -20$
$3(-7) = -21$	$3 + (-7) = -4$
$7(-3) = -21$	$7 + (-3) = 4$
$21(-1) = -21$	$21 + (-1) = 20$

The second row contains the integers $+3$ and -7, whose product is -21 and whose sum is -4. So we can fill in the blanks with $+3$ and -7.

$$z^2 - 4z - 21 = (z + 3)(z - 7)$$

Check: $(z + 3)(z - 7) = z^2 - 7z + 3z - 21$
$$= z^2 - 4z - 21$$

▷ **SELF CHECK 4** Factor: $q^2 - 2q - 24$.

The next example has two variables.

EXAMPLE 5 Factor: $x^2 + xy - 6y^2$.

Solution Since the first term is x^2, the first term of each binomial factor must be x. Since the last term is $-6y^2$, the second term of each binomial factor has a factor of y. To fill in the blanks, we must find coefficients whose product is -6 that will give a middle coefficient of 1.

$$x^2 + xy - 6y^2 = \left(x y\right)\left(x y\right)$$

The factorizations of -6 and the sums of the factors are shown in the table.

Product of the factors	Sum of the factors
$1(-6) = -6$	$1 + (-6) = -5$
$2(-3) = -6$	$2 + (-3) = -1$
$3(-2) = -6$	$3 + (-2) = 1$
$6(-1) = -6$	$6 + (-1) = 5$

The third row contains the integers 3 and -2. These are the only integers whose product is -6 and will give the correct middle coefficient of 1. So we can fill in the blanks with 3 and -2.

$$x^2 + xy - 6y^2 = (x + 3y)(x - 2y)$$

Check: $(x + 3y)(x - 2y) = x^2 - 2xy + 3xy - 6y^2$
$$= x^2 + xy - 6y^2$$

Carl Friedrich Gauss (1777–1855)

Many people consider Gauss to be the greatest mathematician of all time. He made contributions in the areas of number theory, solutions of equations, geometry of curved surfaces, and statistics. For his efforts, he has earned the title "Prince of the Mathematicians."

▷ **SELF CHECK 5** Factor: $a^2 + ab - 12b^2$.

2 **Factor a trinomial with a negative greatest common factor.**

When the coefficient of the first term is -1, we begin by factoring out -1.

EXAMPLE 6 Factor: $-x^2 + 2x + 15$.

Solution We factor out -1 and then factor the trinomial.

$$-x^2 + 2x + 15 = -(x^2 - 2x - 15) \quad \text{Factor out } -1.$$
$$= -(x - 5)(x + 3) \quad \text{Factor } x^2 - 2x - 15.$$

Check: $-(x - 5)(x + 3) = -(x^2 + 3x - 5x - 15)$
$$= -(x^2 - 2x - 15)$$
$$= -x^2 + 2x + 15$$

COMMENT In Example 6, it is not necessary to factor out the -1, but by doing so, it usually will be easier to factor the remaining trinomial.

SELF CHECK 6 Factor: $-x^2 + 11x - 18$.

---

3 **Identify a prime trinomial.**

If a trinomial cannot be factored using only rational coefficients, it is called a **prime polynomial** over the set of rational numbers.

EXAMPLE 7 Factor: $x^2 + 2x + 3$, if possible.

Solution To factor the trinomial, we must find two integers whose product is $+3$ and whose sum is 2. The possible factorizations of 3 and the sums of the factors are shown in the table.

Product of the factors	Sum of the factors
$1(3) = 3$	$1 + 3 = 4$
$-1(-3) = 3$	$-1 + (-3) = -4$

Since two integers whose product is $+3$ and whose sum is $+2$ do not exist, $x^2 + 2x + 3$ cannot be factored. It is a prime trinomial.

SELF CHECK 7 Factor: $x^2 - 4x + 6$, if possible.

---

4 **Factor a polynomial completely.**

The following examples require more than one type of factoring.

EXAMPLE 8 Factor: $-3ax^2 + 9a - 6ax$.

Solution We write the trinomial in descending powers of x and factor out the common factor of $-3a$.

$$-3ax^2 + 9a - 6ax = -3ax^2 - 6ax + 9a$$
$$= -3a(x^2 + 2x - 3)$$

Finally, we factor the trinomial $x^2 + 2x - 3$.

$$-3ax^2 + 9a - 6ax = -3a(x + 3)(x - 1)$$

Check: $-3a(x + 3)(x - 1) = -3a(x^2 + 2x - 3)$
$$= -3ax^2 - 6ax + 9a$$
$$= -3ax^2 + 9a - 6ax$$

⇨ **SELF CHECK 8** Factor: $-2pq^2 + 6p - 4pq$.

EXAMPLE 9 Factor: $m^2 - 2mn + n^2 - 64a^2$.

Solution We group the first three terms together and factor the resulting trinomial.

$$m^2 - 2mn + n^2 - 64a^2 = (m - n)(m - n) - 64a^2$$
$$= (m - n)^2 - (8a)^2$$

Then we factor the resulting difference of two squares:

$$m^2 - 2mn + n^2 - 64a^2 = (m - n)^2 - (8a)^2$$
$$= (m - n + 8a)(m - n - 8a)$$

⇨ **SELF CHECK 9** Factor: $p^2 + 4pq + 4q^2 - 25y^2$.

5 **Factor a trinomial of the form $x^2 + bx + c$ by grouping (*ac* method).**

An alternate way of factoring trinomials of the form $x^2 + bx + c$ uses the technique of factoring by grouping, sometimes referred to as the *ac method*. For example, to factor $x^2 + x - 12$ by grouping, we proceed as follows:

1. Determine the values of a and c ($a = 1$ and $c = -12$) and find ac:

$$(1)(-12) = -12$$

This number is called the **key number.**

2. Find two factors of the key number -12 whose sum is $b = 1$. Two such factors are $+4$ and -3.

$$+4(-3) = -12 \quad \text{and} \quad +4 + (-3) = 1$$

3. Use the factors $+4$ and -3 as the coefficients of two terms to be placed between x^2 and -12 to replace x.

$$x^2 + x - 12 = x^2 + 4x - 3x - 12 \quad x = +4x - 3x$$

4. Factor the right side of the previous equation by grouping.

$$x^2 + 4x - 3x - 12 = x(x + 4) - 3(x + 4) \quad \text{Factor } x \text{ out of } x^2 + 4x \text{ and } -3 \text{ out of } -3x - 12.$$

$$= (x + 4)(x - 3) \quad \text{Factor out } x + 4.$$

We can check this factorization by multiplication.

EXAMPLE 10   Factor $y^2 + 7y + 10$ by grouping.

Solution   We note that this equation is in the form $y^2 + by + c$, with $a = 1$, $b = 7$, and $c = 10$. First, we determine the key number ac:

$$ac = 1(10) = 10$$

Then, we find two factors of 10 whose sum is $b = 7$. Two such factors are $+2$ and $+5$. We use these factors as the coefficients of two terms to be placed between y^2 and 10 to replace $7y$.

$$y^2 + 7y + 10 = y^2 + 2y + 5y + 10 \qquad 7y = +2y + 5y$$

Finally, we factor the right side of the previous equation by grouping.

$$y^2 + 2y + 5y + 10 = y(y + 2) + 5(y + 2) \qquad \text{Factor out } y \text{ from } y^2 + 2y \text{ and factor out 5 from } 5y + 10.$$

$$= (y + 2)(y + 5) \qquad \text{Factor out } y + 2.$$

➡ **SELF CHECK 10**   Use grouping to factor $p^2 - 7p + 12$.

EXAMPLE 11   Factor: $z^2 - 4z - 21$.

Solution   This is the trinomial of Example 4. To factor it by grouping, we note that the trinomial is in the form $z^2 + bz + c$, with $a = 1$, $b = -4$, and $c = -21$. First, we determine the key number ac:

$$ac = 1(-21) = -21$$

Then, we find two factors of -21 whose sum is $b = -4$. Two such factors are $+3$ and -7. We use these factors as the coefficients of two terms to be placed between z^2 and -21 to replace $-4z$.

$$z^2 - 4z - 21 = z^2 + 3z - 7z - 21 \qquad -4z = +3z - 7z$$

Finally, we factor the right side of the previous equation by grouping.

$$z^2 + 3z - 7z - 21 = z(z + 3) - 7(z + 3) \qquad \text{Factor out } z \text{ from } z^2 + 3z \text{ and factor out } -7 \text{ from } -7z - 21.$$

$$= (z + 3)(z - 7) \qquad \text{Factor out } z + 3.$$

➡ **SELF CHECK 11**   Use grouping to factor $a^2 + 2a - 15$. This is the trinomial of Example 3.

6   **Factor a perfect-square trinomial.**

We have discussed the following special-product formulas used to square binomials.

1. $(x + y)^2 = x^2 + 2xy + y^2$
2. $(x - y)^2 = x^2 - 2xy + y^2$

These formulas can be used in reverse order to factor special trinomials called **perfect-square trinomials.**

| Perfect-Square Trinomials | **1.** $x^2 + 2xy + y^2 = (x + y)^2$ |
| | **2.** $x^2 - 2xy + y^2 = (x - y)^2$ |

In words, Formula 1 states that *if a trinomial is the square of one quantity, plus twice the product of two quantities, plus the square of the second quantity, it factors into the square of the sum of the quantities.*

Formula 2 states that *if a trinomial is the square of one quantity, minus twice the product of two quantities, plus the square of the second quantity, it factors into the square of the difference of the quantities.*

The trinomials on the left sides of the previous equations are perfect-square trinomials, because they are the results of squaring a binomial. Although we can factor perfect-square trinomials by using the techniques discussed earlier in this section, we usually can factor them by inspecting their terms. For example, $x^2 + 8x + 16$ is a perfect-square trinomial, because

- The first term x^2 is the square of x.
- The last term 16 is the square of 4.
- The middle term $8x$ is twice the product of x and 4.

Thus,

$$x^2 + 8x + 16 = x^2 + 2(x)(4) + 4^2$$
$$= (x + 4)^2$$

EXAMPLE 12   Factor: $x^2 - 10x + 25$.

Solution $x^2 - 10x + 25$ is a perfect-square trinomial, because

- The first term x^2 is the square of x.
- The last term 25 is the square of 5.
- The middle term $-10x$ is the negative of twice the product of x and 5.

Thus,

$$x^2 - 10x + 25 = x^2 - 2(x)(5) + 5^2$$
$$= (x - 5)^2$$

⇨ **SELF CHECK 12**   Factor: $x^2 + 10x + 25$.

⇨ **SELF CHECK ANSWERS**   **1.** $(y + 1)(y + 4)$ **2.** $(p - 3)(p - 2)$ **3.** $(p + 6)(p - 3)$ **4.** $(q + 4)(q - 6)$ **5.** $(a - 3b)(a + 4b)$ **6.** $-(x - 9)(x - 2)$ **7.** It is prime.   **8.** $-2p(q + 3)(q - 1)$ **9.** $(p + 2q + 5y)(p + 2q - 5y)$ **10.** $(p - 4)(p - 3)$ **11.** $(a + 5)(a - 3)$ **12.** $(x + 5)^2$

NOW TRY THIS

Factor completely:

1. $18 + 3x - x^2$

2. $x^2 + \dfrac{2}{5}x + \dfrac{1}{25}$

3. $x^{2n} + x^n - 2$

5.3 EXERCISES

WARM-UPS   *Finish factoring each problem.*

1. $x^2 + 5x + 4 = (x + 1)(x + \blacksquare)$

2. $x^2 - 5x + 6 = (x \ \blacksquare \ 2)(x \ \blacksquare \ 3)$

3. $x^2 + x - 6 = (x \ \blacksquare \ 2)(x + \blacksquare)$

4. $x^2 - x - 6 = (x \ \blacksquare \ 3)(x + \blacksquare)$

5. $x^2 + 5x - 6 = (x + \blacksquare)(x - \blacksquare)$

6. $x^2 - 7x + 6 = (x - \blacksquare)(x - \blacksquare)$

REVIEW   *Graph the solution of each inequality on a number line.*

7. $x - 3 > 5$

8. $x + 4 \le 3$

9. $-3x - 5 \ge 4$

10. $2x - 3 < 7$

11. $\dfrac{3(x - 1)}{4} < 12$

12. $\dfrac{-2(x + 3)}{3} \ge 9$

13. $-2 < x \le 4$

14. $-5 \le x + 1 < 5$

VOCABULARY AND CONCEPTS

Complete each formula for a perfect-square trinomial.

15. $x^2 + 2xy + y^2 =$ _____

16. $x^2 - 2xy + y^2 =$ _____

Complete each factorization.

17. $y^2 + 6y + 8 = (y + \blacksquare)(y + \blacksquare)$

18. $z^2 - 3z - 10 = (z + \blacksquare)(z - \blacksquare)$

19. $x^2 - xy - 2y^2 = (x + \blacksquare)(x - \blacksquare)$

20. $a^2 + ab - 6b^2 = (a + \blacksquare)(a - \blacksquare)$

GUIDED PRACTICE

Factor each trinomial and check each result. See Example 1. (Objective 1)

21. $x^2 + 3x + 2$

22. $y^2 + 4y + 3$

23. $z^2 + 12z + 11$

24. $x^2 + 7x + 10$

Factor each trinomial and check each result. See Example 2. (Objective 1)

25. $t^2 - 9t + 14$

26. $c^2 - 9c + 8$

27. $p^2 - 6p + 5$

28. $q^2 - 6q + 8$

Factor each trinomial and check each result. See Examples 3–4. (Objective 1)

29. $a^2 + 6a - 16$

30. $x^2 + 5x - 24$

31. $s^2 + 11s - 26$

32. $b^2 + 6b - 7$

33. $c^2 + 4c - 5$

34. $b^2 - 5b - 6$

35. $t^2 - 5t - 50$

36. $a^2 - 10a - 39$

37. $a^2 - 4a - 5$

38. $m^2 - 3m - 10$

39. $y^2 - y - 30$

40. $x^2 - 3x - 40$

Factor each trinomial and check each result. **See Example 5.** (Objective 1)

41. $m^2 + 3mn - 10n^2$ **42.** $m^2 - mn - 12n^2$

43. $a^2 - 4ab - 12b^2$ **44.** $p^2 + pq - 6q^2$

45. $a^2 + 10ab + 9b^2$ **46.** $u^2 + 2uv - 15v^2$

47. $m^2 - 11mn + 10n^2$ **48.** $x^2 + 6xy + 9y^2$

Factor each trinomial. Factor out -1 *first.* **See Example 6.** (Objective 2)

49. $-x^2 - 7x - 10$ **50.** $-x^2 + 9x - 20$

51. $-y^2 - 2y + 15$ **52.** $-y^2 - 3y + 18$

53. $-t^2 - 15t + 34$ **54.** $-t^2 - t + 30$

55. $-r^2 + 14r - 40$ **56.** $-r^2 + 14r - 45$

Factor each trinomial, if possible. **See Example 7.** (Objective 3)

57. $u^2 + 10u + 15$ **58.** $v^2 + 9v + 15$

59. $r^2 - 9r - 12$ **60.** $b^2 + 6b - 18$

Factor each trinomial completely, if possible. **See Example 8.** (Objective 4)

61. $2x^2 + 10x + 12$ **62.** $-2b^2 + 20b - 18$

63. $3y^3 - 21y^2 + 18y$ **64.** $-5a^3 + 25a^2 - 30a$

65. $3z^2 - 15tz + 12t^2$ **66.** $5m^2 + 45mn - 50n^2$

67. $-4x^2y - 4x^3 + 24xy^2$ **68.** $3x^2y^3 + 3x^3y^2 - 6xy^4$

Completely factor each expression. **See Example 9.** (Objective 4)

69. $x^2 + 4x + 4 - y^2$
70. $p^2 - 2p + 1 - q^2$
71. $b^2 - 6b + 9 - c^2$
72. $m^2 + 8m + 16 - n^2$

Use grouping to factor each expression. **See Examples 10–11.** (Objective 5)

73. $x^2 + 3x + 2$ **74.** $y^2 + 4y + 3$

75. $t^2 - 9t + 14$ **76.** $c^2 - 9c + 8$

77. $a^2 + 6a - 16$ **78.** $x^2 + 5x - 24$

79. $y^2 - y - 30$ **80.** $x^2 - 3x - 40$

Factor each expression. **See Example 12.** (Objective 6)

81. $x^2 + 6x + 9$ **82.** $x^2 + 10x + 25$

83. $y^2 - 8y + 16$ **84.** $z^2 - 2z + 1$

85. $u^2 - 18u + 81$ **86.** $v^2 - 14v + 49$

87. $x^2 + 4xy + 4y^2$ **88.** $a^2 + 6ab + 9b^2$

ADDITIONAL PRACTICE *Completely factor each expression. Write each trinomial in descending powers of one variable, if necessary.*

89. $4 - 5x + x^2$ **90.** $y^2 + 5 + 6y$

91. $10y + 9 + y^2$ **92.** $x^2 - 13 - 12x$

93. $-r^2 + 2s^2 + rs$ **94.** $u^2 - 3v^2 + 2uv$

95. $4rx + r^2 + 3x^2$ **96.** $-a^2 + 5b^2 + 4ab$

97. $-3ab + a^2 + 2b^2$ **98.** $-13yz + y^2 - 14z^2$

99. $-a^2 - 4ab - 3b^2$ **100.** $-a^2 - 6ab - 5b^2$

101. $-x^2 + 6xy + 7y^2$ **102.** $-x^2 - 10xy + 11y^2$

103. $3y^3 + 6y^2 + 3y$ **104.** $4x^4 + 16x^3 + 16x^2$

105. $12xy + 4x^2y - 72y$ **106.** $48xy + 6xy^2 + 96x$

107. $y^2 + 2yz + z^2$ **108.** $r^2 - 2rs + 4s^2$

109. $t^2 + 20t + 100$ **110.** $r^2 + 24r + 144$

111. $r^2 - 10rs + 25s^2$ **112.** $m^2 - 12mn + 36n^2$

113. $a^2 + 2ab + b^2 - 4$
114. $a^2 + 6a + 9 - b^2$
115. $b^2 - y^2 - 4y - 4$
116. $c^2 - a^2 + 8a - 16$

WRITING ABOUT MATH

117. Explain how you would write a trinomial in descending order.

118. Explain how to use the FOIL method to check the factoring of a trinomial.

SOMETHING TO THINK ABOUT

119. Two students factor $2x^2 + 20x + 42$ and get two different answers: $(2x + 6)(x + 7)$ and $(x + 3)(2x + 14)$. Do both answers check? Why don't they agree? Is either completely correct?

120. Find the error:

$$x = y$$
$$x^2 = xy \qquad \text{Multiply both sides by } x.$$
$$x^2 - y^2 = xy - y^2 \qquad \text{Subtract } y^2 \text{ from both sides.}$$
$$(x + y)(x - y) = y(x - y) \qquad \text{Factor.}$$
$$x + y = y \qquad \text{Divide both sides by } (x - y).$$
$$y + y = y \qquad \text{Substitute } y \text{ for its equal, } x.$$
$$2y = y \qquad \text{Combine like terms.}$$
$$2 = 1 \qquad \text{Divide both sides by } y.$$

SECTION 5.4   Factoring General Trinomials

Objectives

1 Factor a trinomial of the form $ax^2 + bx + c$ using trial and error.

2 Completely factor a trinomial of the form $ax^2 + bx + c$ by grouping (*ac* method).

3 Completely factor a polynomial involving a perfect-square trinomial.

Getting Ready

Multiply and combine like terms.

1. $(2x + 1)(3x + 2)$ 2. $(3y - 2)(2y - 5)$ 3. $(4t - 3)(2t + 3)$

4. $(2r + 5)(2r - 3)$ 5. $(2m - 3)(3m - 2)$ 6. $(4a + 3)(4a + 1)$

In the previous section, we saw how to factor trinomials whose leading coefficients are 1. We now show how to factor trinomials whose leading coefficients are other than 1.

1   **Factor a trinomial of the form $ax^2 + bx + c$ using trial and error.**

We must consider more combinations of factors when we factor trinomials with leading coefficients other than 1.

EXAMPLE 1   Factor: $2x^2 + 5x + 3$.

Solution   Since the first term is $2x^2$, the first terms of the binomial factors must be $2x$ and x. To fill in the blanks, we must find two factors of $+3$ that will give a middle term of $+5x$.

$$\left(2x \quad \right)\left(x \quad \right)$$

Since the sign of each term of the trinomial is $+$, we need to consider only positive factors of the last term (3). Since the positive factors of 3 are 1 and 3, there are two possible factorizations.

$$(2x + 1)(x + 3) \qquad \text{or} \qquad (2x + 3)(x + 1)$$

The first possibility is incorrect, because it gives a middle term of $7x$. The second possibility is correct, because it gives a middle term of $5x$. Thus,

$$2x^2 + 5x + 3 = (2x + 3)(x + 1)$$

Check by multiplication.

⇨ **SELF CHECK 1**   Factor: $3x^2 + 7x + 2$.

EXAMPLE 2   Factor: $6x^2 - 17x + 5$.

Solution   Since the first term is $6x^2$, the first terms of the binomial factors must be $6x$ and x or $3x$ and $2x$. To fill in the blanks, we must find two factors of $+5$ that will give a middle term of $-17x$.

$$\left(6x \quad\right)\left(x \quad\right) \qquad \text{or} \qquad \left(3x \quad\right)\left(2x \quad\right)$$

Since the sign of the third term is $+$ and the sign of the middle term is $-$, we need to consider only negative factors of the last term (5). Since the negative factors of 5 are -1 and -5, there are four possible factorizations.

$(6x - 1)(x - 5)$	$(6x - 5)(x - 1)$
The one to choose → $(3x - 1)(2x - 5)$	$(3x - 5)(2x - 1)$

Only the possibility printed in red gives the correct middle term of $-17x$. Thus,

$$6x^2 - 17x + 5 = (3x - 1)(2x - 5)$$

Check by multiplication.

⇨ **SELF CHECK 2**   Factor: $6x^2 - 7x + 2$.

EXAMPLE 3   Factor: $3y^2 - 5y - 12$.

Solution   Since the sign of the third term of $3y^2 - 5y - 12$ is $-$, the signs between the binomial factors will be opposite. Because the first term is $3y^2$, the first terms of the binomial factors must be $3y$ and y.

Since $1(-12)$, $2(-6)$, $3(-4)$, $12(-1)$, $6(-2)$, and $4(-3)$ all give a product of -12, there are 12 possible combinations to consider.

$(3y + 1)(y - 12)$	$(3y - 12)(y + 1)$
$(3y + 2)(y - 6)$	$(3y - 6)(y + 2)$
$(3y + 3)(y - 4)$	$(3y - 4)(y + 3)$
$(3y + 12)(y - 1)$	$(3y - 1)(y + 12)$
$(3y + 6)(y - 2)$	$(3y - 2)(y + 6)$
The one to choose → $(3y + 4)(y - 3)$	$(3y - 3)(y + 4)$

The combinations printed in blue cannot work, because one of the factors has a common factor. This implies that $3y^2 - 5y - 12$ would have a common factor, which it doesn't.

After mentally trying the remaining factors, we see that only $(3y + 4)(y - 3)$ gives the correct middle term of $-5x$. Thus,

$$3y^2 - 5y - 12 = (3y + 4)(y - 3)$$

Check by multiplication.

⇨ **SELF CHECK 3**   Factor: $5a^2 - 7a - 6$.

EXAMPLE 4   Factor: $6b^2 + 7b - 20$.

Solution   Since the first term is $6b^2$, the first terms of the binomial factors must be $6b$ and b or $3b$ and $2b$. To fill in the blanks, we must find two factors of -20 that will give a middle term of $+7b$.

$$\left(6b \ \boxed{}\right)\left(b \ \boxed{}\right) \quad \text{or} \quad \left(3b \ \boxed{}\right)\left(2b \ \boxed{}\right)$$

Since the sign of the third term is $-$, the signs inside the binomial factors will be different. Because the factors of the last term (20) are 1, 2, 4, 5, 10, and 20, there are many possible combinations for the last terms. We must try to find a combination that will give a last term of -20 and a sum of the products of the outer terms and inner terms of $+7b$.

If we choose factors of $6b$ and b for the first terms and -5 and 4 for the last terms, we have

$$(6b - 5)(b + 4)$$

$$\begin{array}{r} -5b \\ 24b \\ \hline 19b \end{array}$$

which gives an incorrect middle term of $19b$.

If we choose factors of $3b$ and $2b$ for the first terms and -4 and $+5$ for the last terms, we have

$$(3b - 4)(2b + 5)$$

$$\begin{array}{r} -8b \\ 15b \\ \hline 7b \end{array}$$

which gives the correct middle term of $+7b$ and the correct last term of -20. Thus,

$$6b^2 + 7b - 20 = (3b - 4)(2b + 5)$$

Check by multiplication.

⇨ **SELF CHECK 4**   Factor: $4x^2 + 4x - 3$.

The next example has two variables.

EXAMPLE 5   Factor: $2x^2 + 7xy + 6y^2$.

Solution   Since the first term is $2x^2$, the first terms of the binomial factors must be $2x$ and x. To fill in the blanks, we must find two factors of $6y^2$ that will give a middle term of $+7xy$.

$$\left(2x \quad \rule{1cm}{0.4pt}\ \right)\left(x \quad \rule{1cm}{0.4pt}\ \right)$$

Since the sign of each term is $+$, the signs inside the binomial factors will be $+$. The possible factors of the last term $6y^2$ are

$$y \text{ and } 6y \qquad \text{or} \qquad 3y \text{ and } 2y$$

We must try to find a combination that will give a last term of $+6y^2$ and a middle term of $+7xy$.

If we choose y and $6y$ to be the factors of the last term, we have

$$(2x + y)(x + 6y)$$

$$\begin{array}{r} xy \\ 12xy \\ \hline 13xy \end{array}$$

which gives an incorrect middle term of $13xy$.

If we choose $3y$ and $2y$ to be the factors of the last term, we have

$$(2x + 3y)(x + 2y)$$

$$\begin{array}{r} 3xy \\ 4xy \\ \hline 7xy \end{array}$$

which gives a correct middle term of $7xy$. Thus,

$$2x^2 + 7xy + 6y^2 = (2x + 3y)(x + 2y)$$

Check by multiplication.

➡️ **SELF CHECK 5**   Factor: $4x^2 + 8xy + 3y^2$.

Because some guesswork is often necessary, it is difficult to give specific rules for factoring trinomials. However, the following hints are often helpful.

Factoring General Trinomials Using Trial and Error	**1.** Write the trinomial in descending powers of one variable.
	2. Factor out any GCF (including -1 if that is necessary to make the coefficient of the first term positive).
	3. If the sign of the third term is $+$, the signs between the terms of the binomial factors are the same as the sign of the middle term. If the sign of the third term is $-$, the signs between the terms of the binomial factors are opposite.
	4. Try combinations of first terms and last terms until you find one that works, or until you exhaust all the possibilities. If no combination works, the trinomial is prime.
	5. Check the factorization by multiplication.

EXAMPLE 6   Factor: $2x^2y - 8x^3 + 3xy^2$.

Solution   **Step 1:**   Write the trinomial in descending powers of x.

$$-8x^3 + 2x^2y + 3xy^2$$

Step 2:   Factor out the negative of the GCF, which is $-x$.

$$-8x^3 + 2x^2y + 3xy^2 = -x(8x^2 - 2xy - 3y^2)$$

Step 3:   Because the sign of the third term of the trinomial factor is $-$, the signs within its binomial factors will be opposites.

Step 4:   Find the binomial factors of the trinomial.

$$-8x^3 + 2x^2y + 3xy^2 = -x(8x^2 - 2xy - 3y^2)$$
$$= -x(2x + y)(4x - 3y)$$

Step 5:   Check by multiplication.

$$-x(2x + y)(4x - 3y) = -x(8x^2 - 6xy + 4xy - 3y^2)$$
$$= -x(8x^2 - 2xy - 3y^2)$$
$$= -8x^3 + 2x^2y + 3xy^2$$
$$= 2x^2y - 8x^3 + 3xy^2$$

SELF CHECK 6   Factor: $12y - 2y^3 - 2y^2$.

2 Completely factor a trinomial of the form $ax^2 + bx + c$ by grouping (*ac* method).

Another way to factor trinomials of the form $ax^2 + bx + c$ uses the grouping (*ac* method), first discussed in the previous section. For example, to factor $6x^2 - 17x + 5$ (Example 2) by grouping, we note that $a = 6$, $b = -17$, and $c = 5$ and proceed as follows:

1. Determine the product ac: $6(+5) = 30$. This is the *key number*.

2. Find two factors of the key number 30 whose sum is -17. Two such factors are -15 and -2.

$$-15(-2) = 30 \quad \text{and} \quad -15 + (-2) = -17$$

3. Use -15 and -2 as coefficients of two terms to be placed between $6x^2$ and 5 to replace $-17x$.

$$6x^2 - 17x + 5 = 6x^2 - 15x - 2x + 5$$

4. Factor the right side of the previous equation by grouping.

$$6x^2 - 15x - 2x + 5 = 3x(2x - 5) - 1(2x - 5) \qquad \text{Factor out } 3x \text{ from } 6x^2 - 15x$$
$$\text{and } -1 \text{ from } -2x + 5.$$
$$= (2x - 5)(3x - 1) \qquad \text{Factor out } 2x - 5.$$

We can verify this factorization by multiplication.

EXAMPLE 7 Factor $4y^2 + 12y + 5$ by grouping.

Solution To factor this trinomial by grouping, we note that it is written in the form $ay^2 + by + c$, with $a = 4$, $b = 12$, and $c = 5$. Since $a = 4$ and $c = 5$, we have $ac = 20$.

We now find two factors of 20 whose sum is 12. Two such factors are 10 and 2. We use these factors as coefficients of two terms to be placed between $4y^2$ and 5 to replace $+12y$.

$$4y^2 + 12y + 5 = 4y^2 + 10y + 2y + 5$$

Finally, we factor the right side of the previous equation by grouping.

$$
\begin{aligned}
4y^2 + 10y + 2y + 5 &= 2y(2y + 5) + (2y + 5) && \text{Factor out } 2y \text{ from } 4y^2 + 10y. \\
&= 2y(2y + 5) + 1 \cdot (2y + 5) && (2y + 5) = 1 \cdot (2y + 5) \\
&= (2y + 5)(2y + 1) && \text{Factor out } 2y + 5.
\end{aligned}
$$

Check by multiplication.

⇨ **SELF CHECK 7** Use grouping to factor $2p^2 - 7p + 3$.

EXAMPLE 8 Factor: $6b^2 + 7b - 20$.

Solution This is the trinomial of Example 4. Since $a = 6$ and $c = -20$ in the trinomial, $ac = -120$. We now find two factors of -120 whose sum is $+7$. Two such factors are 15 and -8. We use these factors as coefficients of two terms to be placed between $6b^2$ and -20 to replace $+7b$.

$$6b^2 + 7b - 20 = 6b^2 + 15b - 8b - 20$$

Finally, we factor the right side of the previous equation by grouping.

COMMENT When using the grouping method, if no pair of factors of ac produces the desired value b, the trinomial is prime over the rationals.

$$
\begin{aligned}
6b^2 + 15b - 8b - 20 &= 3b(2b + 5) - 4(2b + 5) && \text{Factor out } 3b \text{ from } 6b^2 + 15b \\
& && \text{and } -4 \text{ from } -8b - 20. \\
&= (2b + 5)(3b - 4) && \text{Factor out } 2b + 5.
\end{aligned}
$$

Check by multiplication.

⇨ **SELF CHECK 8** Factor: $3y^2 - 4y - 4$.

3 **Completely factor a polynomial involving a perfect-square trinomial.**

As before, we can factor perfect-square trinomials by inspection.

EXAMPLE 9 Factor: $4x^2 - 20x + 25$.

Solution $4x^2 - 20x + 25$ is a perfect-square trinomial, because

- The first term $4x^2$ is the square of $2x$: $(2x)^2 = 4x^2$.
- The last term 25 is the square of 5: $5^2 = 25$.
- The middle term $-20x$ is the negative of twice the product of $2x$ and 5.

Thus,

$$4x^2 - 20x + 25 = (2x)^2 - 2(2x)(5) + 5^2$$
$$= (2x - 5)^2$$

Check by multiplication.

➡ **SELF CHECK 9**   Factor: $9x^2 - 12x + 4$.

The next examples combine several factoring techniques.

EXAMPLE 10   Factor: $4x^2 - 4xy + y^2 - 9$.

Solution $4x^2 - 4xy + y^2 - 9$
$= (4x^2 - 4xy + y^2) - 9$ Group the first three terms.
$= (2x - y)^2 - 9$ Factor the perfect-square trinomial.
$= [(2x - y) + 3][(2x - y) - 3]$ Factor the difference of two squares.
$= (2x - y + 3)(2x - y - 3)$ Remove the inner parentheses.

Check by multiplication.

➡ **SELF CHECK 10**   Factor: $x^2 + 4x + 4 - y^2$.

EXAMPLE 11   Factor: $9 - 4x^2 - 4xy - y^2$.

Solution $9 - 4x^2 - 4xy - y^2 = 9 - (4x^2 + 4xy + y^2)$ Factor -1 from the last three terms.

$= 9 - (2x + y)(2x + y)$ Factor the perfect-square trinomial.

$= 9 - (2x + y)^2$ $(2x + y)(2x + y) = (2x + y)^2$

$= [3 + (2x + y)][3 - (2x + y)]$ Factor the difference of two squares.

$= (3 + 2x + y)(3 - 2x - y)$ Simplify.

Check by multiplication.

➡ **SELF CHECK 11**   Factor: $16 - a^2 - 2ab - b^2$.

➡ **SELF CHECK ANSWERS**   **1.** $(3x + 1)(x + 2)$ **2.** $(3x - 2)(2x - 1)$ **3.** $(5a + 3)(a - 2)$ **4.** $(2x + 3)(2x - 1)$
5. $(2x + 3y)(2x + y)$ **6.** $-2y(y + 3)(y - 2)$ **7.** $(2p - 1)(p - 3)$ **8.** $(3y + 2)(y - 2)$
9. $(3x - 2)^2$ **10.** $(x + 2 + y)(x + 2 - y)$ **11.** $(4 + a + b)(4 - a - b)$

NOW TRY THIS

1. If the area of a rectangle can be expressed by the polynomial $(35x^2 - 31x + 6)$ cm^2, factor this to find expressions for the length and width.

2. Factor completely, if possible:
   a. $-8x^2 - 15 + 22x$

   b. $15x^2 - 28x - 12$

5.4 EXERCISES

WARM-UPS   *Finish factoring each problem.*

1. $2x^2 + 5x + 3 = (\boxed{}x + \boxed{})(x + 1)$

2. $6x^2 + 5x + 1 = (\boxed{}x + 1)(3x + 1)$

3. $6x^2 + 5x - 1 = (x\ \boxed{}\ 1)(6x\ \boxed{}\ 1)$

4. $6x^2 + x - 1 = (2x\ \boxed{}\ 1)(3x\ \boxed{}\ 1)$

5. $4x^2 + 4x - 3 = (2x + \boxed{})(2x - \boxed{})$

6. $4x^2 - x - 3 = (4x + \boxed{})(x - \boxed{})$

REVIEW

7. The nth term l of an arithmetic sequence is

$$l = f + (n - 1)d$$

where f is the first term and d is the common difference. Remove the parentheses and solve for n.

8. The sum S of n consecutive terms of an arithmetic sequence is

$$S = \frac{n}{2}(f + l)$$

where f is the first term and l is the nth term. Solve for f.

VOCABULARY AND CONCEPTS

Fill in the blanks.

9. To factor a general trinomial, first write the trinomial in _____ powers of one variable.

10. If the sign of the first and third terms of a trinomial are +, the signs within the binomial factors are _____ the sign of the middle term.

11. If the sign of the first term of a trinomial is + and the sign of the third term is −, the signs within the binomial factors are _____.

12. Always check factorizations by _____.

Complete each factorization.

13. $6x^2 + 7x + 2 = (2x + 1)(3x + \boxed{})$

14. $3t^2 + t - 2 = (3t - \boxed{})(t + 1)$

15. $6x^2 + x - 2 = (3x + \boxed{})(2x - \boxed{})$

16. $15x^2 - 7x - 4 = (5x - \boxed{})(3x + \boxed{})$

17. $12x^2 - 7xy + y^2 = (3x - \boxed{})(4x - \boxed{})$

18. $6x^2 + 5xy - 6y^2 = (2x + \boxed{})(3x - \boxed{})$

GUIDED PRACTICE

Factor each trinomial. **See Examples 1–2. (Objective 1)**

19. $3a^2 + 10a + 3$

20. $6y^2 + 7y + 2$

21. $3a^2 + 13a + 4$

22. $2b^2 + 7b + 6$

23. $6b^2 - 5b + 1$

24. $2x^2 - 3x + 1$

25. $2y^2 - 7y + 3$

26. $4z^2 - 9z + 2$

27. $5t^2 + 13t + 6$

28. $16y^2 + 10y + 1$

29. $16m^2 - 14m + 3$

30. $16x^2 + 16x + 3$

Factor each trinomial. **See Examples 3–4. (Objective 1)**

31. $3a^2 - 4a - 4$

32. $8q^2 + 10q - 3$

33. $2x^2 - 3x - 2$

34. $12y^2 - y - 1$

35. $2m^2 + 5m - 12$ **36.** $10x^2 + 21x - 10$

37. $6y^2 + y - 2$ **38.** $8u^2 - 2u - 15$

Factor each trinomial. See Example 5. (Objective 1)

39. $2x^2 + 3xy + y^2$ **40.** $3m^2 + 5mn + 2n^2$

41. $3x^2 - 4xy + y^2$ **42.** $2b^2 - 5bc + 2c^2$

43. $2u^2 + uv - 3v^2$ **44.** $2u^2 + 3uv - 2v^2$

45. $6p^2 - pq - 2q^2$ **46.** $8r^2 - 10rs - 25s^2$

Write the terms of each trinomial in descending powers of one variable. Then factor the trinomial completely. See Example 6. (Objective 1)

47. $-26x + 6x^2 - 20$ **48.** $-42 + 9a^2 - 3a$

49. $15 + 8a^2 - 26a$ **50.** $16 - 40a + 25a^2$

51. $12x^2 + 10y^2 - 23xy$ **52.** $5ab + 25a^2 - 2b^2$

53. $-21mn - 10n^2 + 10m^2$ **54.** $-6d^2 + 6c^2 + 35cd$

Use grouping to factor each polynomial. See Examples 7–8. (Objective 2)

55. $4z^2 + 13z + 3$ **56.** $4t^2 - 4t + 1$

57. $4x^2 + 8x + 3$ **58.** $6x^2 - 7x + 2$

59. $10u^2 - 13u - 3$ **60.** $12y^2 - 5y - 2$

61. $10y^2 - 3y - 1$ **62.** $6m^2 + 19m + 3$

Factor each perfect-square trinomial. See Example 9. (Objective 3)

63. $9x^2 - 12x + 4$ **64.** $9x^2 + 6x + 1$

65. $25x^2 + 30x + 9$ **66.** $16y^2 - 24y + 9$

67. $4x^2 + 12x + 9$ **68.** $4x^2 - 4x + 1$

69. $9x^2 + 12x + 4$ **70.** $4x^2 - 20x + 25$

Factor each polynomial, if possible. See Examples 10–11. (Objective 3)

71. $4x^2 + 4xy + y^2 - 16$
72. $9x^2 - 6x + 1 - d^2$
73. $9 - a^2 - 4ab - 4b^2$
74. $25 - 9a^2 + 6ac - c^2$

ADDITIONAL PRACTICE   *Factor each polynomial completely. If the polynomial cannot be factored, state prime.*

75. $4a^2 - 15ab + 9b^2$ **76.** $12x^2 + 5xy - 3y^2$

77. $2a^2 + 3b^2 + 5ab$ **78.** $11uv + 3u^2 + 6v^2$

79. $pq + 6p^2 - q^2$ **80.** $-11mn + 12m^2 + 2n^2$

81. $b^2 + 4a^2 + 16ab$ **82.** $3b^2 + 3a^2 - ab$

83. $-12y^2 - 12 + 25y$ **84.** $-12t^2 + 1 + 4t$

85. $3x^2 + 6 + x$ **86.** $25 + 2u^2 + 3u$

87. $16x^2 - 8xy + y^2$ **88.** $25x^2 + 20xy + 4y^2$

89. $4x^2 + 8xy + 3y^2$ **90.** $4b^2 + 15bc - 4c^2$

91. $4x^2 + 10x - 6$ **92.** $9x^2 + 21x - 18$

93. $y^3 + 13y^2 + 12y$ **94.** $2xy^2 + 8xy - 24x$

95. $6x^3 - 15x^2 - 9x$ **96.** $9y^3 + 3y^2 - 6y$

97. $30r^5 + 63r^4 - 30r^3$ **98.** $6s^5 - 26s^4 - 20s^3$

99. $4a^2 - 4ab - 8b^2$ **100.** $6x^2 + 3xy - 18y^2$

101. $8x^2 - 12xy - 8y^2$ **102.** $24a^2 + 14ab + 2b^2$

103. $4a^2 - 4ab + b^2$
104. $6r^2 + rs - 2s^2$
105. $-16m^3n - 20m^2n^2 - 6mn^3$
106. $-84x^4 - 100x^3y - 24x^2y^2$
107. $-28u^3v^3 + 26u^2v^4 - 6uv^5$
108. $-16x^4y^3 + 30x^3y^4 + 4x^2y^5$
109. $9p^2 + 1 + 6p - q^2$
110. $16m^2 - 24m - n^2 + 9$

WRITING ABOUT MATH

111. Describe an organized approach to finding all of the possibilities when you attempt to factor $12x^2 - 4x + 9$.

112. Explain how to determine whether a trinomial is prime.

SOMETHING TO THINK ABOUT

113. For what values of b will the trinomial $6x^2 + bx + 6$ be factorable?

114. For what values of b will the trinomial $5y^2 - by - 3$ be factorable?

SECTION 5.5   Factoring the Sum and Difference of Two Cubes

Objectives

1. Factor the sum of two cubes.
2. Factor the difference of two cubes.
3. Completely factor a polynomial involving the sum or difference of two cubes.

Vocabulary

sum of two cubes   difference of two cubes

Getting Ready

Find each product.

1. $(x - 3)(x^2 + 3x + 9)$
2. $(x + 2)(x^2 - 2x + 4)$
3. $(y + 4)(y^2 - 4y + 16)$
4. $(r - 5)(r^2 + 5r + 25)$
5. $(a - b)(a^2 + ab + b^2)$
6. $(a + b)(a^2 - ab + b^2)$

Recall that the difference of the squares of two quantities factors into the product of two binomials. One binomial is the sum of the quantities, and the other is the difference of the quantities.

$$x^2 - y^2 = (x + y)(x - y) \quad \text{or} \quad F^2 - L^2 = (F + L)(F - L)$$

In this section, we will discuss formulas for factoring the *sum of two cubes* and the *difference of two cubes.*

1   Factor the sum of two cubes.

To discover the formula for factoring the sum of two cubes, we find the following product:

$$(x + y)(x^2 - xy + y^2) = (x + y)x^2 - (x + y)xy + (x + y)y^2 \quad \text{Use the distributive property.}$$

$$= x^3 + x^2y - x^2y - xy^2 + xy^2 + y^3$$
$$= x^3 + y^3$$

This result justifies the formula for factoring the **sum of two cubes.**

Factoring the Sum of Two Cubes

$$x^3 + y^3 = (x + y)(x^2 - xy + y^2)$$

If we think of the sum of two cubes as the cube of a **F**irst quantity plus the cube of a **L**ast quantity, we have the formula

$$F^3 + L^3 = (F + L)(F^2 - FL + L^2)$$

In words, we say, *To factor the cube of a **F**irst quantity plus the cube of a **L**ast quantity, we multiply the **F**irst plus the **L**ast by*

- *the **F**irst squared*
- *minus the **F**irst times the **L**ast*
- *plus the **L**ast squared.*

To factor the sum of two cubes, it is helpful to know the cubes of the numbers from 1 to 10:

$$1, 8, 27, 64, 125, 216, 343, 512, 729, 1{,}000$$

Expressions containing variables such as x^6y^3 are also perfect cubes, because they can be written as the cube of a quantity:

$$x^6y^3 = (x^2y)^3$$

EXAMPLE 1   Factor: $x^3 + 8$.

Solution   The binomial $x^3 + 8$ is the sum of two cubes, because

$$x^3 + 8 = x^3 + 2^3$$

Thus, $x^3 + 8$ factors as $(x + 2)$ times the trinomial $x^2 - 2x + 2^2$.

$$F^3 + L^3 = (F + L)(F^2 - F\ L + L^2)$$
$$\downarrow \quad \downarrow \quad \quad \downarrow \quad \downarrow \ \downarrow \quad \ \downarrow \ \downarrow \quad \ \downarrow$$
$$x^3 + 2^3 = (x + 2)(x^2 - x \cdot 2 + 2^2)$$
$$= (x + 2)(x^2 - 2x + 4)$$

We can use the distributive property and check by multiplication.

$$(x + 2)(x^2 - 2x + 4) = (x + 2)x^2 - (x + 2)2x + (x + 2)4$$
$$= x^3 + 2x^2 - 2x^2 - 4x + 4x + 8$$
$$= x^3 - 8$$

SELF CHECK 1   Factor: $p^3 + 64$.

EXAMPLE 2   Factor: $8b^3 + 27c^3$.

Solution   The binomial $8b^3 + 27c^3$ is the sum of two cubes, because

$$8b^3 + 27c^3 = (2b)^3 + (3c)^3$$

Thus, the binomial $8b^3 + 27c^3$ factors as $(2b + 3c)$ times the trinomial $(2b)^2 - (2b)(3c) + (3c)^2$.

$$F^3 + L^3 = (F + L)(F^2 - F\ L + L^2)$$
$$\downarrow \quad \ \downarrow \quad \quad \downarrow \quad \downarrow \quad \quad \ \downarrow \ \downarrow \quad \ \downarrow$$
$$(2b)^3 + (3c)^3 = (2b + 3c)[(2b)^2 - (2b)(3c) + (3c)^2]$$
$$= (2b + 3c)(4b^2 - 6bc + 9c^2)$$

We can use the distributive property and check by multiplication.

$$(2b + 3c)(4b^2 - 6bc + 9c^2)$$
$$= (2b + 3c)4b^2 - (2b + 3c)6bc + (2b + 3c)9c^2$$
$$= 8b^3 + 12b^2c - 12b^2c - 18bc^2 + 18bc^2 + 27c^3$$
$$= 8b^3 + 27c^3$$

⇨ **SELF CHECK 2**   Factor: $1,000p^3 + q^3$.

---

2   **Factor the difference of two cubes.**

To discover the formula for factoring the difference of two cubes, we find the following product:

$$(x - y)(x^2 + xy + y^2) = (x - y)x^2 + (x - y)xy + (x - y)y^2 \quad \text{Use the distributive property.}$$
$$= x^3 - x^2y + x^2y - xy^2 + xy^2 - y^3$$
$$= x^3 - y^3$$

This result justifies the formula for factoring the **difference of two cubes.**

Factoring the Difference of Two Cubes	$x^3 - y^3 = (x - y)(x^2 + xy + y^2)$

If we think of the difference of two cubes as the cube of a **F**irst quantity minus the cube of a **L**ast quantity, we have the formula

$$F^3 - L^3 = (F - L)(F^2 + FL + L^2)$$

In words, we say, *To factor the cube of a **F**irst quantity minus the cube of a **L**ast quantity, we multiply the **F**irst minus the **L**ast by*

- *the **F**irst squared*
- *plus the **F**irst times the **L**ast*
- *plus the **L**ast squared.*

EXAMPLE 3   Factor: $a^3 - 64b^3$.

Solution   The binomial $a^3 - 64b^3$ is the difference of two cubes.

$$a^3 - 64b^3 = a^3 - (4b)^3$$

Thus, its factors are the difference $a - 4b$ and the trinomial $a^2 + a(4b) + (4b)^2$.

$$F^3 - L^3 = (F - L)(F^2 + F L + L^2)$$
$$\downarrow \quad \downarrow \qquad \downarrow \quad \downarrow \quad \downarrow \quad \downarrow \quad \downarrow$$
$$a^3 - (4b)^3 = (a - 4b)[a^2 + a(4b) + (4b)^2]$$
$$= (a - 4b)(a^2 + 4ab + 16b^2)$$

We can use the distributive property and check by multiplication.

$$(a - 4b)(a^2 + 4ab + 16b^2)$$
$$= (a - 4b)a^2 + (a - 4b)4ab + (a - 4b)16b^2$$
$$= a^3 - 4a^2b + 4a^2b - 16ab^2 + 16ab^2 - 64b^3$$
$$= a^3 - 64b^3$$

⇨ **SELF CHECK 3**   Factor: $27p^3 - 8$.

3 **Completely factor a polynomial involving the sum or difference of two cubes.**

Sometimes we must factor out a greatest common factor before factoring a sum or difference of two cubes.

EXAMPLE 4   Factor: $-2t^5 + 128t^2$.

Solution
$$-2t^5 + 128t^2 = -2t^2(t^3 - 64) \qquad \text{Factor out } -2t^2.$$
$$= -2t^2(t - 4)(t^2 + 4t + 16) \quad \text{Factor } t^3 - 64.$$

We can check by multiplication.

⇨ **SELF CHECK 4**   Factor: $-3p^4 + 81p$.

EXAMPLE 5   Factor: $x^6 - 64$.

Solution   The binomial $x^6 - 64$ is both the difference of two squares and the difference of two cubes. To completely factor the polynomial using the formulas we have discussed, we will factor the difference of two squares first.

If we consider the polynomial to be the difference of two squares, we can factor it as follows:

$$x^6 - 64 = (x^3)^2 - 8^2$$
$$= (x^3 + 8)(x^3 - 8)$$

Because $x^3 + 8$ is the sum of two cubes and $x^3 - 8$ is the difference of two cubes, each of these binomials can be factored.

$$x^6 - 64 = (x^3 + 8)(x^3 - 8)$$
$$= (x + 2)(x^2 - 2x + 4)(x - 2)(x^2 + 2x + 4)$$

We can check by multiplication.

⇨ **SELF CHECK 5**   Factor: $a^6 - 1$.

⇨ **SELF CHECK ANSWERS**   **1.** $(p + 4)(p^2 - 4p + 16)$ **2.** $(10p + q)(100p^2 - 10pq + q^2)$ **3.** $(3p - 2)(9p^2 + 6p + 4)$
4. $-3p(p - 3)(p^2 + 3p + 9)$ **5.** $(a + 1)(a^2 - a + 1)(a - 1)(a^2 + a + 1)$

NOW TRY THIS

Factor completely:

1. $x^3 - \dfrac{1}{8}$

2. $x^3 - y^{12}$

3. $64x^3 - 8$

4. $x^3(x^2 - 9) - 8(x^2 - 9)$

5.5 EXERCISES

WARM-UPS   *Factor each sum or difference of two cubes.*

1. $x^3 - y^3$

2. $x^3 + y^3$

3. $a^3 + 8$

4. $b^3 - 27$

5. $1 + 8x^3$

6. $8 - r^3$

7. $x^3y^3 + 1$

8. $125 - 8t^3$

REVIEW

9. The length of one fermi is 1×10^{-13} centimeter, approximately the radius of a proton. Express this number in standard notation.

10. In the 14th century, the Black Plague killed about 25,000,000 people, which was 25% of the population of Europe. Find the population at that time, expressed in scientific notation.

VOCABULARY AND CONCEPTS

Fill in the blanks.

11. A polynomial in the form of $a^3 + b^3$ is called a _____.

12. A polynomial in the form of $a^3 - b^3$ is called a _____.

Complete each formula.

13. $x^3 + y^3 = (x + y)$_____

14. $x^3 - y^3 = (x - y)$_____

GUIDED PRACTICE

Factor each polynomial. **See Example 1. (Objective 1)**

15. $y^3 + 1$

16. $b^3 + 125$

17. $8 + x^3$

18. $z^3 + 64$

Factor each polynomial. **See Example 2. (Objective 1)**

19. $m^3 + n^3$

20. $27x^3 + y^3$

21. $8u^3 + w^3$

22. $a^3 + 8b^3$

Factor each polynomial. **See Example 3. (Objective 2)**

23. $x^3 - 8$

24. $a^3 - 27$

25. $s^3 - t^3$

26. $27 - y^3$

27. $125p^3 - q^3$

28. $x^3 - 27y^3$

29. $27a^3 - b^3$

30. $64x^3 - 27$

Factor each polynomial completely. Factor out any greatest common factors first, including -1. **See Example 4. (Objective 3)**

31. $2x^3 + 54$

32. $2x^3 - 2$

33. $-x^3 + 216$

34. $-x^3 - 125$

35. $64m^3x - 8n^3x$

36. $16r^4 + 128rs^3$

37. $x^4y + 216xy^4$

38. $16a^5 - 54a^2b^3$

Factor each polynomial completely. Factor a difference of two squares first. See Example 5. (Objective 3)

39. $x^6 - 1$
40. $x^6 - y^6$
41. $x^{12} - y^6$
42. $a^{12} - 64$

ADDITIONAL PRACTICE *Factor each polynomial completely.*

43. $125 + b^3$
44. $64 - z^3$
45. $27x^3 + 125$
46. $27x^3 - 125y^3$
47. $64x^3 + 27y^3$
48. $a^6 - b^3$
49. $a^3 + b^6$
50. $x^9 + y^6$
51. $x^3 - y^9$
52. $81r^4s^2 - 24rs^5$
53. $4m^5n + 500m^2n^4$
54. $125a^6b^2 + 64a^3b^5$
55. $216a^4b^4 - 1,000ab^7$
56. $y^7z - yz^4$
57. $x^{10}y^2 - xy^5$
58. $2mp^4 + 16mpq^3$
59. $24m^5n - 3m^2n^4$
60. $3(x^3 + y^3) - z(x^3 + y^3)$

61. $x(8a^3 - b^3) + 4(8a^3 - b^3)$
62. $(m^3 + 8n^3) + (m^3x + 8n^3x)$
63. $(a^3x + b^3x) - (a^3y + b^3y)$
64. $(a^4 + 27a) - (a^3b + 27b)$
65. $(x^4 + xy^3) - (x^3y + y^4)$
66. $y^3(y^2 - 1) - 27(y^2 - 1)$
67. $z^3(y^2 - 4) + 8(y^2 - 4)$
68. $a^2(b^3 + 8) - b^2(b^3 + 8)$

WRITING ABOUT MATH

69. Explain how to factor $a^3 + b^3$.
70. Explain the difference between $x^3 - y^3$ and $(x - y)^3$.

SOMETHING TO THINK ABOUT

71. Let $a = 11$ and $b = 7$. Use a calculator to verify that
$$a^3 - b^3 = (a - b)(a^2 + ab + b^2)$$

72. Let $p = 5$ and $q = -2$. Use a calculator to verify that
$$p^3 + q^3 = (p + q)(p^2 - pq + q^2)$$

SECTION 5.6 Summary of Factoring Techniques

Objectives

1 Completely factor a polynomial by applying the appropriate technique(s).

Getting Ready

Factor each polynomial.

1. $3ax^2 + 3a^2x$
2. $x^2 - 9y^2$
3. $x^3 - 8$
4. $2x^2 - 8$
5. $x^2 - 3x - 10$
6. $6x^2 - 13x + 6$
7. $6x^2 - 14x + 4$
8. $ax^2 + bx^2 - ay^2 - by^2$

In this section, we will discuss ways to approach a randomly chosen factoring problem.

1 Completely factor a polynomial by applying the appropriate technique(s).

Suppose we want to factor the trinomial

$$x^4y + 7x^3y - 18x^2y$$

We begin by attempting to identify the problem type. The first type we look for is one that **contains a common factor.** Because the trinomial has a common factor of x^2y, we factor it out first:

$$x^4y + 7x^3y - 18x^2y = x^2y(x^2 + 7x - 18)$$

We can factor the remaining trinomial $x^2 + 7x - 18$ as $(x + 9)(x - 2)$. Thus,

$$x^4y + 7x^3y - 18x^2y = x^2y(x^2 + 7x - 18)$$
$$= x^2y(x + 9)(x - 2)$$

To identify the type of factoring problem, we follow these steps.

Factoring a Polynomial

1. Factor out all common factors.
2. If an expression has two terms, check to see if the problem type is
   a. the **difference of two squares:** $x^2 - y^2 = (x + y)(x - y)$
   b. the **sum of two cubes:** $x^3 + y^3 = (x + y)(x^2 - xy + y^2)$
   c. the **difference of two cubes:** $x^3 - y^3 = (x - y)(x^2 + xy + y^2)$
3. If an expression has three terms, check to see if it is a **perfect-square trinomial:**

   $$x^2 + 2xy + y^2 = (x + y)(x + y)$$
   $$x^2 - 2xy + y^2 = (x - y)(x - y)$$

   If the trinomial is not a perfect trinomial square, attempt to factor the trinomial as a **general trinomial.**
4. If an expression has four terms, try to factor the expression by **grouping.** It may be necessary to rearrange the terms.
5. Continue factoring until each nonmonomial factor is prime.
6. If the polynomial does not factor, the polynomial is *prime* over the set of rational numbers.
7. Check the results by multiplying.

EXAMPLE 1   Factor: $x^5y^2 - xy^6$.

Solution   We begin by factoring out the common factor of xy^2.

$$x^5y^2 - xy^6 = xy^2(x^4 - y^4)$$

Since the expression $x^4 - y^4$ has two terms, we check to see whether it is the difference of two squares, which it is. As the difference of two squares, it factors as $(x^2 + y^2)(x^2 - y^2)$.

$$x^5y^2 - xy^6 = xy^2(x^4 - y^4)$$
$$= xy^2(x^2 + y^2)(x^2 - y^2)$$

The binomial $x^2 + y^2$ is the sum of two squares and cannot be factored. However, $x^2 - y^2$ is the difference of two squares and factors as $(x + y)(x - y)$.

$$\begin{aligned} x^5y^2 - xy^6 &= xy^2(x^4 - y^4) \\ &= xy^2(x^2 + y^2)(x^2 - y^2) \\ &= xy^2(x^2 + y^2)(x + y)(x - y) \end{aligned}$$

Since each individual factor is prime, the given expression is in completely factored form.

SELF CHECK 1   Factor: $-a^5b + ab^5$.

EXAMPLE 2   Factor: $x^6 - x^4y^2 - x^3y^3 + xy^5$.

Solution   We begin by factoring out the common factor of x.

$$x^6 - x^4y^2 - x^3y^3 + xy^5 = x(x^5 - x^3y^2 - x^2y^3 + y^5)$$

Since $x^5 - x^3y^2 - x^2y^3 + y^5$ has four terms, we try factoring it by grouping:

$$\begin{aligned} x^6 - x^4y^2 - x^3y^3 + xy^5 &= x(x^5 - x^3y^2 - x^2y^3 + y^5) \\ &= x[x^3(x^2 - y^2) - y^3(x^2 - y^2)] \\ &= x(x^2 - y^2)(x^3 - y^3) \qquad \text{Factor out } x^2 - y^2. \end{aligned}$$

Finally, we factor the difference of two squares and the difference of two cubes:

$$x^6 - x^4y^2 - x^3y^3 + xy^5 = x(x + y)(x - y)(x - y)(x^2 + xy + y^2)$$

Since each factor is prime, the given expression is in completely factored form.

SELF CHECK 2   Factor: $2a^5 - 2a^2b^3 - 8a^3 + 8b^3$.

SELF CHECK ANSWERS   **1.** $-ab(a^2 + b^2)(a + b)(a - b)$ **2.** $2(a + 2)(a - 2)(a - b)(a^2 + ab + b^2)$

NOW TRY THIS

Factor completely.

1. $4x^2 + 16$

2. $ax^2 + bx^2 - 36a - 36b$

3. $9x^2 - 9x$

4. $64 - x^6$

5.6 EXERCISES

WARM-UPS *Indicate which factoring technique you would use first, if any.*

1. $2x^2 - 4x$

2. $16 - 25y^2$

3. $125 + r^3 s^3$

4. $ax + ay - x - y$

5. $x^2 + 4$

6. $8x^2 - 50$

7. $25r^2 - s^4$

8. $8a^3 - 27b^3$

REVIEW *Solve each equation, if possible.*

9. $2(t - 5) + t = 3(2 - t)$

10. $5 + 3(2x - 1) = 2(4 + 3x) - 24$

11. $5 - 3(t + 1) = t + 2$

12. $4m - 3 = -2(m + 1) - 3$

VOCABULARY AND CONCEPTS   *Fill in the blanks.*

13. The first step in any factoring problem is to factor out all common _____, if possible.

14. If a polynomial has two terms, check to see if it is the _____, the sum of two cubes, or the _____ of two cubes.

15. If a polynomial has three terms, try to factor it as the product of two _____.

16. If a polynomial has four or more terms, try factoring by _____.

RANDOM PRACTICE   *Factor each polynomial completely.*

17. $6x + 3$

18. $x^2 - 9$

19. $x^2 - 6x - 7$

20. $a^3 - 8$

21. $6t^2 + 7t - 3$

22. $4x^2 - 25$

23. $t^2 - 2t + 1$

24. $6p^2 - 3p - 2$

25. $2x^2 - 32$

26. $t^4 - 16$

27. $x^2 + 7x + 1$

28. $10r^2 - 13r - 4$

29. $-2x^5 + 128x^2$

30. $16 - 40z + 25z^2$

31. $14t^3 - 40t^2 + 6t^4$

32. $6x^2 + 7x - 20$

33. $6x^2 - x - 16$

34. $30a^4 + 5a^3 - 200a^2$

35. $6a^3 + 35a^2 - 6a$

36. $21t^3 - 10t^2 + t$

37. $16x^2 - 40x^3 + 25x^4$

38. $25a^2 - 60a + 36$

39. $-84x^2 - 147x - 12x^3$

40. $x^3 - 5x^2 - 25x + 125$

41. $8x^6 - 8$

42. $16x^2 + 64$

43. $5x^3 - 5x^5 + 25x^2$

44. $18y^3 - 8y$

45. $9x^2 + 12x + 16$

46. $70p^4 q^3 - 35p^4 q^2 + 49p^5 q^2$

47. $2ab^2 + 8ab - 24a$

48. $3rs^2 - 6r^2 st$

49. $-8p^3 q^7 - 4p^2 q^3$

50. $8m^2 n^3 - 24mn^4$

51. $4a^2 - 4ab + b^2 - 9$

52. $3rs + 6r^2 - 18s^2$

53. $a^3 + b^3$

54. $ac + ad + bc + bd$

55. $x^2 y^2 - 2x^2 - y^2 + 2$

56. $a^2 c + a^2 d^2 + bc + bd^2$

57. $a^2 + 2ab + b^2 - y^2$

58. $3a^3 + 24b^3$

59. $a^2(x - a) - b^2(x - a)$

60. $5x^3 y^3 z^4 + 25x^2 y^3 z^2 - 35x^3 y^2 z^5$

61. $8p^6 - 27q^6$

62. $2c^2 - 5cd - 3d^2$

63. $125p^3 - 64y^3$

64. $8a^2 x^3 y - 2b^2 xy$

65. $-16x^4 y^2 z + 24x^5 y^3 z^4 - 15x^2 y^3 z^7$

66. $2ac + 4ad + bc + 2bd$

67. $81p^4 - 16q^4$

68. $4x^2 + 9y^2$

69. $54x^3 + 250y^6$

70. $4x^2 + 4x + 1 - y^2$

71. $x^5 - x^3 y^2 + x^2 y^3 - y^5$

72. $a^3 x^3 - a^3 y^3 + b^3 x^3 - b^3 y^3$

73. $2a^2 c - 2b^2 c + 4a^2 d - 4b^2 d$

74. $3a^2 x^2 + 6a^2 x + 3a^2 - 3b^2$

WRITING ABOUT MATH

75. Explain how to identify the type of factoring required to factor a polynomial.

76. Which factoring technique do you find most difficult? Why?

SOMETHING TO THINK ABOUT

77. Write $x^6 - y^6$ as $(x^3)^2 - (y^3)^2$, factor it as the difference of two squares, and show that you get

$$(x + y)(x^2 - xy + y^2)(x - y)(x^2 + xy + y^2)$$

Write $x^6 - y^6$ as $(x^2)^3 - (y^2)^3$, factor it as the difference of two cubes, and show that you get

$$(x + y)(x - y)(x^4 + x^2y^2 + y^4)$$

78. Verify that the results of Exercise 77 agree by showing the parts in color agree. Which do you think is completely factored?

SECTION 5.7 Solving Equations by Factoring

Objectives

1 Solve a quadratic equation in one variable using the zero-factor property.

2 Solve a higher-order polynomial equation in one variable.

Vocabulary

quadratic equation   zero-factor property

Getting Ready

Solve each equation.

1. $x + 3 = 4$ **2.** $y - 8 = 5$ **3.** $3x - 2 = 7$ **4.** $5y + 9 = 19$

In this section, we will learn how to use factoring to solve many equations that contain second-degree polynomials in one variable. These equations are called *quadratic equations*.

Equations such as

$$3x + 2 = 0 \quad \text{and} \quad 9x - 6 = 0$$

that contain first-degree polynomials are *linear equations*. Equations such as

$$9x^2 - 6x = 0 \quad \text{and} \quad 3x^2 + 4x - 7 = 0$$

that contain second-degree polynomials are called **quadratic equations.**

Quadratic Equations	A **quadratic equation** in one variable is an equation of the form

$$ax^2 + bx + c = 0 \quad \text{(This is called } quadratic\ form.)$$

where a, b, and c are real numbers, and $a \neq 0$.

1 **Solve a quadratic equation in one variable using the zero-factor property.**

Many quadratic equations can be solved by factoring. For example, to solve the quadratic equation

$$x^2 + 5x - 6 = 0$$

we begin by factoring the trinomial and writing the equation as

$$(1) \qquad (x + 6)(x - 1) = 0$$

This equation indicates that the product of two quantities is 0. However, if the product of two quantities is 0, then at least one of those quantities must be 0. This fact is called the **zero-factor property.**

Zero-Factor Property	Suppose a and b represent two real numbers.

If $ab = 0$, then $a = 0$ or $b = 0$.

By applying the zero-factor property to Equation 1, we have

$$x + 6 = 0 \qquad \text{or} \qquad x - 1 = 0$$

We can solve each of these linear equations to get

$$x = -6 \qquad \text{or} \qquad x = 1$$

To check, we substitute -6 for x, and then 1 for x in the original equation and simplify.

For $x = -6$	*For $x = 1$*
$x^2 + 5x - 6 = 0$	$x^2 + 5x - 6 = 0$
$(-6)^2 + 5(-6) - 6 \stackrel{?}{=} 0$	$(1)^2 + 5(1) - 6 \stackrel{?}{=} 0$
$36 - 30 - 6 \stackrel{?}{=} 0$	$1 + 5 - 6 \stackrel{?}{=} 0$
$6 - 6 \stackrel{?}{=} 0$	$6 - 6 \stackrel{?}{=} 0$
$0 = 0$	$0 = 0$

Both solutions check.

The quadratic equations $9x^2 - 6x = 0$ and $4x^2 - 36 = 0$ are each missing a term. The first equation is missing the constant term, and the second equation is missing the term involving x. These types of equations often can be solved by factoring.

EXAMPLE 1 Solve: $9x^2 - 6x = 0$.

Solution We begin by factoring the left side of the equation.

$$9x^2 - 6x = 0$$

$$3x(3x - 2) = 0 \qquad \text{Factor out the common factor of } 3x.$$

By the zero-factor property, we have

$$3x = 0 \quad \text{or} \quad 3x - 2 = 0$$

We can solve each of these equations to get

$$x = 0 \quad \text{or} \quad x = \frac{2}{3}$$

Check: We substitute these results for x in the original equation and simplify.

For $x = 0$	*For $x = \frac{2}{3}$*
$9x^2 - 6x = 0$	$9x^2 - 6x = 0$
$9(0)^2 - 6(0) \stackrel{?}{=} 0$	$9\left(\frac{2}{3}\right)^2 - 6\left(\frac{2}{3}\right) \stackrel{?}{=} 0$
$0 - 0 \stackrel{?}{=} 0$	$9\left(\frac{4}{9}\right) - 6\left(\frac{2}{3}\right) \stackrel{?}{=} 0$
$0 = 0$	$4 - 4 \stackrel{?}{=} 0$
	$0 = 0$

Both solutions check.

⇨ **SELF CHECK 1**   Solve: $5y^2 + 10y = 0$.

EXAMPLE 2   Solve: $4x^2 - 36 = 0$.

Solution   To make the numbers smaller, we divide both sides of the equation by 4. Then we proceed as follows:

$$4x^2 - 36 = 0$$
$$x^2 - 9 = 0 \qquad \text{Divide both sides by 4.}$$
$$(x + 3)(x - 3) = 0 \qquad \text{Factor } x^2 - 9.$$
$$x + 3 = 0 \quad \text{or} \quad x - 3 = 0 \qquad \text{Set each factor equal to 0.}$$
$$x = -3 \qquad \qquad x = 3 \qquad \text{Solve each linear equation.}$$

Check each solution.

For $x = -3$	*For $x = 3$*
$4x^2 - 36 = 0$	$4x^2 - 36 = 0$
$4(-3)^2 - 36 \stackrel{?}{=} 0$	$4(3)^2 - 36 \stackrel{?}{=} 0$
$4(9)^2 - 36 \stackrel{?}{=} 0$	$4(9) - 36 \stackrel{?}{=} 0$
$0 = 0$	$0 = 0$

Both solutions check.

⇨ **SELF CHECK 2**   Solve: $9p^2 - 64 = 0$.

In the next example, we solve an equation whose polynomial is a trinomial.

EXAMPLE 3 Solve: $x^2 - 3x - 18 = 0$.

Solution

$$x^2 - 3x - 18 = 0$$
$$(x + 3)(x - 6) = 0 \qquad \text{Factor } x^2 - 3x - 18.$$
$$x + 3 = 0 \quad \text{or} \quad x - 6 = 0 \quad \text{Set each factor equal to 0.}$$
$$x = -3 \qquad \qquad x = 6 \quad \text{Solve each linear equation.}$$

Check each solution.

⇨ **SELF CHECK 3** Solve: $x^2 + 3x - 18 = 0$.

EXAMPLE 4 Solve: $2x^2 + 3x = 2$.

Solution We write the equation in the form $ax^2 + bx + c = 0$ and solve for x.

$$2x^2 + 3x = 2$$
$$2x^2 + 3x - 2 = 0 \qquad \text{Subtract 2 from both sides.}$$
$$(2x - 1)(x + 2) = 0 \qquad \text{Factor } 2x^2 + 3x - 2.$$
$$2x - 1 = 0 \quad \text{or} \quad x + 2 = 0 \quad \text{Set each factor equal to 0.}$$
$$2x = 1 \qquad \qquad x = -2 \quad \text{Solve each linear equation.}$$
$$x = \frac{1}{2}$$

Check each solution.

⇨ **SELF CHECK 4** Solve: $3x^2 - 5x = 2$.

EXAMPLE 5 Solve: $(x - 2)(x^2 - 7x + 6) = 0$.

Solution We begin by factoring the quadratic trinomial.

$$(x - 2)(x^2 - 7x + 6) = 0$$
$$(x - 2)(x - 6)(x - 1) = 0 \qquad \text{Factor } x^2 - 7x + 6.$$

If the product of these three quantities is 0, then at least one of the quantities must be 0.

$$x - 2 = 0 \quad \text{or} \quad x - 6 = 0 \quad \text{or} \quad x - 1 = 0$$
$$x = 2 \qquad \qquad x = 6 \qquad \qquad x = 1$$

Check each solution.

⇨ **SELF CHECK 5** Solve: $(x + 3)(x^2 + 7x - 8) = 0$.

2 **Solve a higher-order polynomial equation in one variable.**

A *higher-order polynomial equation* is any equation in one variable with a degree of 3 or larger.

EXAMPLE 6 Solve: $x^3 - 2x^2 - 63x = 0$.

Solution We begin by completely factoring the left side.

$$x^3 - 2x^2 - 63x = 0$$
$$x(x^2 - 2x - 63) = 0 \qquad \text{Factor out } x, \text{ the GCF.}$$
$$x(x + 7)(x - 9) = 0 \qquad \text{Factor the trinomial.}$$

$x = 0$ or $x + 7 = 0$ or $x - 9 = 0$ Set each factor equal to 0.

$\qquad\qquad\qquad x = -7 \qquad\qquad\quad x = 9$ Solve each linear equation.

Check each solution.

SELF CHECK 6 Solve: $x^3 - x^2 - 2x = 0$.

EXAMPLE 7 Solve: $6x^3 + 12x = 17x^2$.

Solution To get all of the terms on the left side, we subtract $17x^2$ from both sides. Then we proceed as follows:

$$6x^3 + 12x = 17x^2$$
$$6x^3 - 17x^2 + 12x = 0 \qquad \text{Subtract } 17x^2 \text{ from both sides.}$$
$$x(6x^2 - 17x + 12) = 0 \qquad \text{Factor out } x, \text{ the GCF.}$$
$$x(2x - 3)(3x - 4) = 0 \qquad \text{Factor } 6x^2 - 17x + 12.$$

$x = 0$ or $2x - 3 = 0$ or $3x - 4 = 0$ Set each factor equal to 0.

$\qquad\qquad\quad 2x = 3 \qquad\qquad 3x = 4$ Solve the linear equations.

$\qquad\qquad\quad x = \dfrac{3}{2} \qquad\qquad x = \dfrac{4}{3}$

Check each solution.

SELF CHECK 7 Solve: $6x^3 + 7x^2 = 5x$.

EVERYDAY CONNECTIONS   Selling Calendars

A bookshop is selling calendars at a price of \$4 each. At this price, the store can sell 12 calendars per day. The manager estimates that for each \$1 increase in the selling price, the store will sell 3 fewer calendars per day. Each calendar costs the store \$2. We can rep-resent the store's total daily profit from calendar sales by the function $p(x) = -3x^2 + 30x - 48$, where x represents the selling price, in dollars, of a calendar. Find the selling price at which the profit $p(x)$ equals zero.

NOW TRY THIS

Solve each equation:

1. $8x^2 - 8 = 0$

2. $x^2 = 3x$

3. $x(x + 10) = -25$

5.7 EXERCISES

WARM-UPS   *Solve each equation.*

1. $(x - 8)(x - 7) = 0$ **2.** $(x + 9)(x - 2) = 0$

3. $x^2 + 7x = 0$ **4.** $x^2 - 12x = 0$

5. $x^2 - 2x + 1 = 0$ **6.** $x^2 + x - 20 = 0$

REVIEW   *Simplify each expression and write all results without using negative exponents.*

7. $u^3 u^2 u^4$ **8.** $\dfrac{y^6}{y^8}$

9. $\dfrac{a^3 b^4}{a^2 b^5}$ **10.** $(3x^5)^0$

VOCABULARY AND CONCEPTS   *Fill in the blanks.*

11. An equation of the form $ax^2 + bx + c = 0$, where $a \neq 0$, is called a _____ equation.

12. The property "If $ab = 0$, then $a =$ __ or $b =$ __" is called the _____ property.

13. A quadratic equation contains a _____-degree polynomial in one variable.

14. If the product of three factors is 0, then at least one of the numbers must be __.

GUIDED PRACTICE

Solve each equation. (Objective 1)

15. $(x - 2)(x + 3) = 0$ **16.** $(x - 3)(x - 2) = 0$

17. $(x - 4)(x + 1) = 0$ **18.** $(x + 5)(x + 2) = 0$

19. $(2x - 5)(3x + 6) = 0$ **20.** $(3x - 4)(x + 1) = 0$

21. $(x - 1)(x + 2)(x - 3) = 0$
22. $(x + 2)(x + 3)(x - 4) = 0$

Solve each equation. See Example 1. (Objective 1)

23. $x^2 - 3x = 0$ **24.** $x^2 + 5x = 0$
25. $5x^2 + 7x = 0$ **26.** $2x^2 - 5x = 0$
27. $x^2 - 7x = 0$ **28.** $2x^2 + 10x = 0$
29. $3x^2 + 8x = 0$ **30.** $5x^2 - x = 0$

Solve each equation. See Example 2. (Objective 1)

31. $x^2 - 25 = 0$ **32.** $x^2 - 36 = 0$
33. $9y^2 - 4 = 0$ **34.** $16z^2 - 25 = 0$
35. $x^2 = 49$ **36.** $z^2 = 25$
37. $4x^2 = 81$ **38.** $9y^2 = 64$

Solve each equation. See Example 3. (Objective 1)

39. $x^2 - 13x + 12 = 0$ **40.** $x^2 + 7x + 6 = 0$

41. $x^2 - 2x - 15 = 0$ **42.** $x^2 - x - 20 = 0$

Solve each equation. See Example 4. (Objective 1)

43. $6x^2 + x = 2$ **44.** $12x^2 + 5x = 3$
45. $2x^2 - 5x = -2$ **46.** $5p^2 - 6p = -1$

Solve each equation. See Example 5. (Objective 1)

47. $(x - 1)(x^2 + 5x + 6) = 0$

48. $(x - 2)(x^2 - 8x + 7) = 0$
49. $(x + 3)(x^2 + 2x - 15) = 0$
50. $(x + 4)(x^2 - 2x - 15)$

Solve each equation. **See Example 6. (Objective 2)**

51. $x^3 + 3x^2 + 2x = 0$
52. $x^3 - 7x^2 + 10x = 0$

53. $x^3 - 27x - 6x^2 = 0$
54. $x^3 - 22x - 9x^2 = 0$

Solve each equation. **See Example 7. (Objective 2)**

55. $6x^3 + 20x^2 = -6x$
56. $2x^3 - 2x^2 = 4x$

57. $x^3 + 7x^2 = x^2 - 9x$
58. $x^3 + 10x^2 = 2x^2 - 16x$

ADDITIONAL PRACTICE   *Solve each equation.*

59. $8x^2 - 16x = 0$
60. $15x^2 - 20x = 0$
61. $10x^2 + 2x = 0$
62. $5x^2 + x = 0$
63. $y^2 - 49 = 0$
64. $x^2 - 121 = 0$
65. $4x^2 - 1 = 0$
66. $9y^2 - 1 = 0$
67. $x^2 - 4x - 21 = 0$
68. $x^2 + 2x - 15 = 0$

69. $x^2 + 8 - 9x = 0$
70. $45 + x^2 - 14x = 0$

71. $a^2 + 8a = -15$
72. $a^2 - a = 56$

73. $2y - 8 = -y^2$
74. $-3y + 18 = y^2$

75. $2x^2 + x - 3 = 0$
76. $6q^2 - 5q + 1 = 0$

77. $14m^2 + 23m + 3 = 0$
78. $35n^2 - 34n + 8 = 0$

79. $(x - 5)(2x^2 + x - 3) = 0$
80. $(a + 1)(6a^2 + a - 2) = 0$

81. $(p^2 - 81)(p + 2) = 0$
82. $(4q^2 - 49)(q - 7) = 0$

83. $3x^2 - 8x = 3$
84. $2x^2 - 11x = 21$

85. $15x^2 - 2 = 7x$
86. $8x^2 + 10x = 3$

87. $x(6x + 5) = 6$
88. $x(2x - 3) = 14$

89. $(x + 1)(8x + 1) = 18x$
90. $4x(3x + 2) = x + 12$

91. $x^3 + 1.3x^2 - 0.3x = 0$
92. $2.4x^3 - x^2 - 0.4x = 0$

WRITING ABOUT MATH

93. If the product of several numbers is 0, at least one of the numbers is 0. Explain why.
94. Explain the error in this solution.

$$5x^2 + 2x = 10$$
$$x(5x + 2) = 10$$
$$x = 10 \quad \text{or} \quad 5x + 2 = 10$$
$$5x = 8$$
$$x = \frac{8}{5}$$

SOMETHING TO THINK ABOUT

95. Explain how you would factor

$$3a + 3b + 3c - ax - bx - cx$$

96. Explain how you would factor

$$9 - a^2 - 4ab - 4b^2$$

97. Solve in two ways: $3a^2 + 9a - 2a - 6 = 0$.
98. Solve in two ways: $p^2 - 2p + p - 2 = 0$.

SECTION
5.8   Problem Solving

Objectives

1 Solve an integer application problem using a quadratic equation.
2 Solve a motion application problem using a quadratic equation.
3 Solve a geometric application problem using a quadratic equation.

Getting Ready

1. One side of a square is s inches long. Find an expression that represents its area.

2. The length of a rectangle is 4 centimeters more than twice the width. If w represents the width, find an expression that represents the length.

3. If x represents the smaller of two consecutive integers, find an expression that represents their product.

4. The length of a rectangle is 3 inches greater than the width. If w represents the width of the rectangle, find an expression that represents the area.

Finally, we can use the methods for solving quadratic equations discussed in the previous section to solve problems.

1 **Solve an integer application problem using a quadratic equation.**

EXAMPLE 1 One integer is 5 less than another and their product is 84. Find the integers.

Analyze the problem We are asked to find two integers. Let x represent the larger number. Then $x - 5$ represents the smaller number.

Form an equation We know that the product of the integers is 84. Since a product refers to a multiplication problem, we can form the equation $x(x - 5) = 84$.

Solve the equation To solve the equation, we proceed as follows.

$$
\begin{aligned}
x(x - 5) &= 84 \\
x^2 - 5x &= 84 \qquad &\text{Remove parentheses.} \\
x^2 - 5x - 84 &= 0 \qquad &\text{Subtract 84 from both sides.} \\
(x - 12)(x + 7) &= 0 \qquad &\text{Factor.}
\end{aligned}
$$

$x - 12 = 0 \quad$ or $\quad x + 7 = 0 \qquad$ Set each factor equal to 0.

$\qquad x = 12 \qquad\qquad x = -7 \qquad$ Solve each linear equation.

State the conclusion We have two different values for the first integer.

$$x = 12 \quad \text{or} \quad x = -7$$

and two different values for the second integer

$$x - 5 = 7 \quad \text{or} \quad x - 5 = -12$$

There are two pairs of integers: 12 and 7, and -7 and -12.

Check the result The number 7 is five less than 12 and $12 \cdot 7 = 84$. The number -12 is five less than -7 and $-7 \cdot -12 = 84$. Both pairs of integers check.

COMMENT In this problem, we could have let x represent the smaller number, in which case the larger number would be described as $x + 5$. The results would be the same.

2 **Solve a motion application problem using a quadratic equation.**

EXAMPLE 2 **FLYING OBJECTS** If an object is thrown straight up into the air with an initial velocity of 112 feet per second, its height after t seconds is given by the formula

$$h = 112t - 16t^2$$

where h represents the height of the object in feet. After this object has been thrown, in how many seconds will it hit the ground?

Analyze the problem
We are asked to find the number of seconds it will take for an object to hit the ground. When the object is thrown, it will go up and then come down. When it hits the ground, its height will be 0. So, we let $h = 0$.

Form an equation
If we substitute 0 for h in the formula $h = 112t - 16t^2$, the new equation will be $0 = 112t - 16t^2$ and we will solve for t.

$$h = 112t - 16t^2$$
$$0 = 112t - 16t^2$$

Solve the equation
We solve the equation as follows.

$$0 = 112t - 16t^2$$
$$0 = 16t(7 - t) \qquad \text{Factor out 16.}$$
$$16t = 0 \quad \text{or} \quad 7 - t = 0 \qquad \text{Set each factor equal to 0.}$$
$$t = 0 \quad | \quad t = 7 \qquad \text{Solve each linear equation.}$$

State the conclusion
When $t = 0$, the object's height above the ground is 0 feet, because it has not been released. When $t = 7$, the height is again 0 feet. The object has hit the ground. The solution is 7 seconds.

Check the result
When $t = 7$,

$$h = 112(7) - 16(7)^2$$
$$= 184 - 16(49)$$
$$= 0$$

Since the height is 0 feet, the object has hit the ground after 7 seconds.

3 ## Solve a geometric application problem using a quadratic equation.

Recall that the area of a rectangle is given by the formula

$$A = lw$$

where A represents the area, l the length, and w the width of the rectangle. The perimeter of a rectangle is given by the formula

$$P = 2l + 2w$$

where P represents the perimeter of the rectangle, l the length, and w the width.

EXAMPLE 3 **RECTANGLES** Assume that the rectangle in Figure 5-1 has an area of 52 square centimeters and that its length is 1 centimeter more than 3 times its width. Find the perimeter of the rectangle.

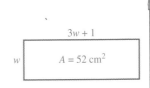

Figure 5-1

Analyze the problem
We are asked to find the perimeter of the rectangle. To do so, we must know both the length and the width. If we let w represent the width of the rectangle, then $3w + 1$ represents its length.

Form and solve an equation

We are given that the area of the rectangle is 52 square centimeters. We can use this fact to find the values of the width and length and then find the perimeter. To find the width, we can substitute 52 for A and $3w + 1$ for l in the formula $A = lw$ and solve for w.

$$A = lw$$
$$52 = (3w + 1)w$$
$$52 = 3w^2 + w \qquad \text{Remove parentheses.}$$
$$0 = 3w^2 + w - 52 \qquad \text{Subtract 52 from both sides.}$$
$$0 = (3w + 13)(w - 4) \qquad \text{Factor.}$$

$3w + 13 = 0$	or $\quad w - 4 = 0$	Set each factor equal to 0.
$3w = -13$	$w = 4$	Solve each linear equation.
$w = -\dfrac{13}{3}$		

Because the width of a rectangle cannot be negative, we discard the result $w = -\frac{13}{3}$. Thus, the width of the rectangle is 4, and the length is given by

$$3w + 1 = 3(4) + 1$$
$$= 12 + 1$$
$$= 13$$

The dimensions of the rectangle are 4 centimeters by 13 centimeters. We find the perimeter by substituting 13 for l and 4 for w in the formula for the perimeter.

$$P = 2l + 2w$$
$$= 2(13) + 2(4)$$
$$= 26 + 8$$
$$= 34$$

State the conclusion

The perimeter of the rectangle is 34 centimeters.

Check the result

A rectangle with dimensions of 13 centimeters by 4 centimeters does have an area of 52 square centimeters, and the length is 1 centimeter more than 3 times the width. A rectangle with these dimensions has a perimeter of 34 centimeters.

EXAMPLE 4 **TRIANGLES** The triangle in Figure 5-2 has an area of 10 square centimeters and a height that is 3 centimeters less than twice the length of its base. Find the length of the base and the height of the triangle.

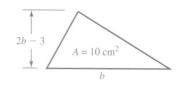

Figure 5-2

Analyze the problem

We are asked to find the length of the base and the height of the triangle, so we will let b represent the length of the base of the triangle. Then $2b - 3$ represents the height.

Form and solve an equation

Because the area is 10 square centimeters, we can substitute 10 for A and $2b - 3$ for h in the formula $A = \frac{1}{2}bh$ and solve for b.

$$A = \frac{1}{2}bh$$

$$10 = \frac{1}{2}b(2b - 3)$$

$$20 = b(2b - 3) \qquad \text{Multiply both sides by 2.}$$
$$20 = 2b^2 - 3b \qquad \text{Remove parentheses.}$$
$$0 = 2b^2 - 3b - 20 \qquad \text{Subtract 20 from both sides.}$$
$$0 = (2b + 5)(b - 4) \qquad \text{Factor.}$$

$2b + 5 = 0$	or $\quad b - 4 = 0$	Set both factors equal to 0.
$2b = -5$	$b = 4$	Solve each linear equation.
$b = -\dfrac{5}{2}$		

State the conclusion   Because a triangle cannot have a negative number for the length of its base, we discard the result $b = -\frac{5}{2}$. The length of the base of the triangle is 4 centimeters. Its height is $2(4) - 3$, or 5 centimeters.

Check the result   If the base of the triangle has a length of 4 centimeters and the height of the triangle is 5 centimeters, its height is 3 centimeters less than twice the length of its base. Its area is 10 centimeters.

$$A = \frac{1}{2}bh = \frac{1}{2}(4)(5) = 2(5) = 10$$

NOW TRY THIS

1. A phone is shaped like a rectangle and its longer edge is one inch longer than twice its shorter edge. If the area of the phone is 6 in.^{2}, find the dimensions of the phone.

5.8 EXERCISES

WARM-UPS   *Give the formula for . . .*

1. the area of a rectangle
2. the area of a triangle
3. the area of a square
4. the volume of a rectangular solid
5. the perimeter of a rectangle
6. the perimeter of a square

REVIEW   *Solve each equation.*

7. $-2(5x + 2) = 3(2 - 3x)$
8. $3(2a - 1) - 9 = 2a$
9. **Rectangles**   A rectangle is 3 times as long as it is wide, and its perimeter is 120 centimeters. Find its area.
10. **Investing**   A woman invested $15,000, part at 7% simple annual interest and part at 8% annual interest. If she receives $1,100 interest per year, how much did she invest at 7%?

VOCABULARY AND CONCEPTS   *Fill in the blanks.*

11. The first step in the problem-solving process is to _____ the problem.
12. The last step in the problem-solving process is to _____.

APPLICATIONS

13. **Integer problem**   One integer is 2 more than another. Their product is 35. Find the integers.
14. **Integer problem**   One integer is 5 less than 4 times another. Their product is 21. Find the integers.
15. **Integer problem**   If 4 is added to the square of an integer, the result is 5 less than 10 times that integer. Find the integer(s).
16. **Integer problem**   If 3 times the square of a number is added to the number itself, the result is 14. Find the number.

An object has been thrown straight up into the air. The formula
h = vt − 16t² gives the height h of the object above the ground
after t seconds when it is thrown upward with an initial velocity v.

17. **Time of flight** After how many seconds will an object hit the ground if it was thrown with a velocity of 144 feet per second?

18. **Time of flight** After how many seconds will an object hit the ground if it was thrown with a velocity of 160 feet per second?

19. **Ballistics** If a cannonball is fired with an upward velocity of 220 feet per second, at what times will it be at a height of 600 feet?

20. **Ballistics** A cannonball's initial upward velocity is 128 feet per second. At what times will it be 192 feet above the ground?

21. **Exhibition diving** At a resort, tourists watch swimmers dive from a cliff to the water 64 feet below. A diver's height *h* above the water *t* seconds after diving is given by $h = -16t^2 + 64$. How long does a dive last?

22. **Forensic medicine** The kinetic energy *E* of a moving object is given by $E = \frac{1}{2}mv^2$, where *m* is the mass of the object (in kilograms) and *v* is the object's velocity (in meters per second). Kinetic energy is measured in joules. By the damage done to a victim, a police pathologist determines that the energy of a 3-kilogram mass at impact was 54 joules. Find the velocity at impact.

In Exercises 23–24, note that in the triangle $y^2 = h^2 + x^2$.

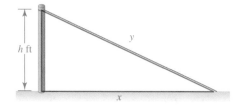

23. **Ropes courses** A camper slides down the cable of a high-adventure ropes course to the ground as shown in the illustration. At what height did the camper start his slide?

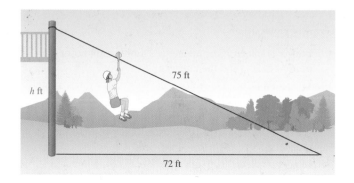

75 ft

h ft

72 ft

24. **Ropes courses** If the pole and the landing area discussed in Exercise 23 are 24 feet apart and the high end of the cable is 7 feet, how long is the cable?

25. **Insulation** The area of the rectangular slab of foam insulation is 36 square meters. Find the dimensions of the slab.

w m

(2*w* + 1) m

26. **Shipping pallets** The length of a rectangular shipping pallet is 2 feet less than 3 times its width. Its area is 21 square feet. Find the dimensions of the pallet.

27. **Carpentry** A rectangular room containing 143 square feet is 2 feet longer than it is wide. How long a crown molding is needed to trim the perimeter of the ceiling?

28. **Designing tents** The length of the base of the triangular sheet of canvas above the door of the tent shown below is 2 feet more than twice its height. The area is 30 square feet. Find the height and the length of the base of the triangle.

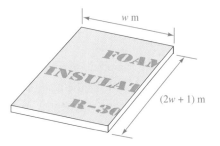

h

29. **Dimensions of a triangle** The height of a triangle is 2 inches less than 5 times the length of its base. The area is 36 square inches. Find the length of the base and the height of the triangle.

30. **Area of a triangle** The base of a triangle is numerically 3 less than its area, and the height is numerically 6 less than its area. Find the area of the triangle.

31. **Area of a triangle** The length of the base and the height of a triangle are numerically equal. Their sum is 6 less than the number of units in the area of the triangle. Find the area of the triangle.

32. Dimensions of a parallelogram The formula for the area of a parallelogram is $A = bh$. The area of the parallelogram in the illustration is 200 square centimeters. If its base is twice its height, how long is the base?

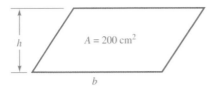

$A = 200 \text{ cm}^2$

33. Swimming pool borders The owners of the rectangular swimming pool want to surround the pool with a crushed-stone border of uniform width. They have enough stone to cover 74 square meters. How wide should they make the border? (*Hint:* The area of the larger rectangle minus the area of the smaller is the area of the border.)

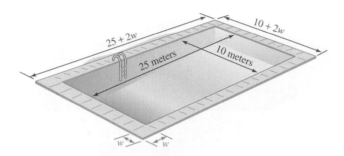

$25 + 2w$
$10 + 2w$
25 meters
10 meters
w w

34. House construction The formula for the area of a trapezoid is $A = \frac{h(B + b)}{2}$. The area of the trapezoidal truss in the illustration is 24 square meters. Find the height of the trapezoid if one base is 8 meters and the other base is the same as the height.

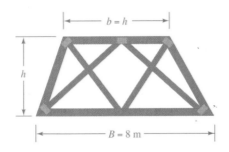

$b = h$
h
$B = 8 \text{ m}$

35. Volume of a solid The volume of a rectangular solid is given by the formula $V = lwh$, where l is the length, w is the width, and h is the height. The volume of the rectangular solid in the illustration is 210 cubic centimeters. Find the width of the rectangular solid if its length is 10 centimeters and its height is 1 centimeter longer than twice its width.

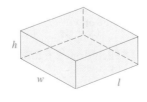

h w l

36. Volume of a pyramid The volume of a pyramid is given by the formula $V = \frac{Bh}{3}$, where B is the area of its base and h is its height. The volume of the pyramid in the illustration is 192 cubic centimeters. Find the dimensions of its rectangular base if one edge of the base is 2 centimeters longer than the other, and the height of the pyramid is 12 centimeters.

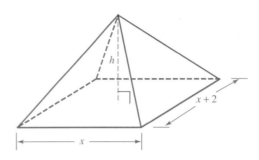

h
$x + 2$
x

37. Volume of a pyramid The volume of a pyramid is 84 cubic centimeters. Its height is 9 centimeters, and one side of its rectangular base is 3 centimeters shorter than the other. Find the dimensions of its base. (See Exercise 36.)

38. Volume of a solid The volume of a rectangular solid is 72 cubic centimeters. Its height is 4 centimeters, and its width is 3 centimeters shorter than its length. Find the sum of its length and width. (See Exercise 35.)

39. Telephone connections The number of connections C that can be made among n telephones is given by the formula

$$C = \frac{1}{2}(n^2 - n)$$

How many telephones are needed to make 66 connections?

40. Football schedules If each of t teams in a high school football league plays every other team in the league once, the total number T of games played is given by the formula

$$T = \frac{t(t - 1)}{2}$$

If the season includes a total of 10 games, how many teams are in the league?

41. Sewage treatment In one step in waste treatment, sewage is exposed to air by placing it in circular aeration pools. One sewage processing plant has two such pools, with diameters of 40 and 42 meters. Find the combined area of the pools.

42. Sewage treatment To meet new clean-water standards, the plant in Exercise 41 must double its capacity by building another pool. Find the radius of the circular pool that the engineering department should specify to double the plant's capacity.

In Exercises 43–44, $a^2 + b^2 = c^2$.

43. Tornado damage   The tree shown below was blown down in a tornado. Find x and the height of the tree when it was standing.

44. Car repairs   To work under a car, a mechanic drives it up steel ramps like the ones shown below. Find the length of each side of the ramp.

WRITING ABOUT MATH

45. Explain the steps you would use to set up and solve an application problem.

46. Explain how you should check the solution to an application problem.

SOMETHING TO THINK ABOUT

47. Here is an easy-sounding problem:

> *The length of a rectangle is 2 feet greater than the width, and the area is 18 square feet. Find the width of the rectangle.*

Set up the equation. Can you solve it? Why not?

48. Does the equation in Exercise 47 have a solution, even if you can't find it? If it does, find an estimate of the solution.

PROJECTS

Because the length of each side of the largest square in Figure 5-3 is $x + y$, its area is $(x + y)^2$. This area is also the sum of four smaller areas, which illustrates the factorization

$$x^2 + 2xy + y^2 = (x + y)^2$$

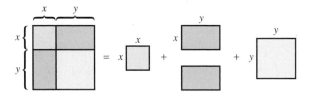

Figure 5-3

What factorization is illustrated by each of the following figures?

1.
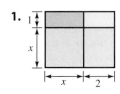

2.
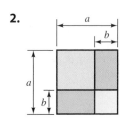

3.
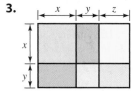

4.
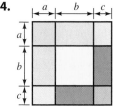

5. Factor the expression

$$a^2 + ac + 2a + ab + bc + 2b$$

and draw a figure that illustrates the factorization.

6. Verify the factorization

$$x^3 + 3x^2y + 3xy^2 + y^3 = (x + y)^3$$

Hint: Expand the right side:

$$(x + y)^3 = (x + y)(x + y)(x + y)$$

Then draw a figure that illustrates the factorization.

Chapter 5   REVIEW

SECTION 5.1   Factoring Out the Greatest Common Factor; Factoring by Grouping

DEFINITIONS AND CONCEPTS	EXAMPLES
A natural number is in **prime-factored form** if it is written as the product of prime-number factors.	$42 = 6 \cdot 7 = 2 \cdot 3 \cdot 7$ $56 = 8 \cdot 7 = 2 \cdot 4 \cdot 7 = 2 \cdot 2 \cdot 2 \cdot 7 = 2^3 \cdot 7$
The **greatest common factor (GCF)** of several monomials is found by taking each common prime factor the fewest number of times it appears in any one monomial.	Find the GCF of $12x^3y$, $42x^2y^2$, and $32x^2y^3$. $\left.\begin{array}{l} 12x^3y = 2 \cdot 2 \cdot 3 \cdot x \cdot x \cdot x \cdot y \\ 42x^2y^2 = 2 \cdot 3 \cdot 7 \cdot x \cdot x \cdot y \cdot y \\ 32x^2y^3 = 2 \cdot 2 \cdot 2 \cdot 2 \cdot 2 \cdot x \cdot x \cdot y \cdot y \cdot y \end{array}\right\}$ GCF $= 2x^2y$
If the leading coefficient of a polynomial is negative, it is often useful to factor out -1.	Factor completely: $-x^3 + 3x^2 - 5$. $\quad -x^3 + 3x^2 - 5$ $\quad = (-1)x^3 + (-1)(-3x^2) + (-1)5$ $\quad = -1(x^3 - 3x^2 + 5)$ Factor out -1. $\quad = -(x^3 - 3x^2 + 5)$ The coefficient of 1 need not be written.
If a polynomial has four terms, consider factoring it by grouping.	Factor completely: $x^2 + xy + 3x + 3y$. Factor x from $x^2 + xy$ and 3 from $3x + 3y$ and proceed as follows: $\quad x^2 + xy + 3x + 3y = x(x + y) + 3(x + y)$ $\qquad\qquad\qquad\qquad\quad = (x + y)(x + 3)$ Factor out $(x + y)$.

REVIEW EXERCISES

Find the prime factorization of each number.

1. 35

2. 45

3. 96

4. 102

5. 87

6. 99

7. 2,050

8. 4,096

Completely factor each expression.

9. $3x + 9y$

10. $5ax^2 + 15a$

11. $7x^2 + 14x$

12. $3x^2 - 3x$

13. $2x^3 + 4x^2 - 8x$

14. $ax + ay - az$

15. $ax + ay - a$

16. $x^2yz + xy^2z$

Completely factor each polynomial.

17. $(x + y)a + (x + y)b$

18. $(x + y)^2 + (x + y)$

19. $2x^2(x + 2) + 6x(x + 2)$

20. $3x(y + z) - 9x(y + z)^2$

21. $3p + 9q + ap + 3aq$

22. $ar - 2as + 7r - 14s$

23. $x^2 + ax + bx + ab$

24. $xy + 2x - 2y - 4$

25. $xa + yb + ya + xb$

26. $x^3 - 4x^2 + 3x - 12$

SECTION 5.2   Factoring the Difference of Two Squares

DEFINITIONS AND CONCEPTS	EXAMPLES
To factor the difference of two squares, use the pattern $$x^2 - y^2 = (x + y)(x - y)$$	$x^2 - 36 = x^2 - 6^2 = (x + 6)(x - 6)$
Binomials that are the sum of two squares cannot be factored over the real numbers unless they contain a GCF.	$9x^2 + 36 = 9(x^2 + 4)$ Factor out 9, the GCF. $(x^2 + 4)$ does not factor.

REVIEW EXERCISES
Completely factor each expression.

27. $x^2 - 9$

28. $x^2y^2 - 16$

29. $(x + 2)^2 - y^2$

30. $z^2 - (x + y)^2$

31. $6x^2y - 24y^3$

32. $(x + y)^2 - z^2$

SECTIONS 5.3–5.4   Factoring Trinomials

DEFINITIONS AND CONCEPTS	EXAMPLES
Factor trinomials using these steps (trial and error): **1.** Write the trinomial with the exponents of one variable in descending order. **2.** Factor out any greatest common factor (including -1 if that is necessary to make the coefficient of the first term positive). **3.** If the sign of the third term is $+$, the signs between the terms of the binomial factors are the same as the sign of the trinomial's second term. If the sign of the third term is $-$, the signs between the terms of the binomials are opposite. **4.** Try various combinations of first terms and last terms until you find the one that works. If none work, the trinomial is prime. **5.** Check by multiplication.	Factor completely: $12 - x^2 - x$. **1.** We will begin by writing the exponents of x in descending order. $$12 - x^2 - x = -x^2 - x + 12$$ **2.** Factor out -1 to get $$= -(x^2 + x - 12)$$ **3.** Since the sign of the third term is $-$, the signs between the binomials are opposite. **4.** We find the combination that works. $$= -(x + 4)(x - 3)$$ **5.** Since $-(x + 4)(x - 3) = 12 - x^2 - x$, the factorization is correct.
Factor trinomials by grouping (*ac* method).	$2x^2 - x - 10$ $\quad = 2x^2 - 5x + 4x - 10$ $a = 2, c = 10$. The two factors whose product is 20 and difference is -1 are -5 and 4. Replace $-x$ with $-5x + 4x$. Factor by grouping. $\quad = x(2x - 5) + 2(2x - 5)$ $\quad = (2x - 5)(x + 2)$

REVIEW EXERCISES
Completely factor each polynomial.

33. $x^2 + 10x + 21$

34. $x^2 + 4x - 21$

35. $x^2 + 2x - 24$

36. $x^2 - 4x - 12$

Completely factor each polynomial.

37. $2x^2 - 5x - 3$

38. $3x^2 - 14x - 5$

39. $6x^2 + 7x - 3$

40. $6x^2 + 3x - 3$

41. $6x^3 + 17x^2 - 3x$ **42.** $4x^3 - 5x^2 - 6x$ **43.** $12x - 4x^3 - 2x^2$ **44.** $-4a^3 + 4a^2b + 24ab^2$

SECTION 5.5   Factoring the Sum and Difference of Two Cubes

DEFINITIONS AND CONCEPTS	EXAMPLES
The sum and difference of two cubes factor according to the patterns $$x^3 + y^3 = (x + y)(x^2 - xy + y^2)$$ $$x^3 - y^3 = (x - y)(x^2 + xy + y^2)$$	$$x^3 + 64 = x^3 + 4^3 = (x + 4)(x^2 - x \cdot 4 + 4^2)$$ $$= (x + 4)(x^2 - 4x + 16)$$ $$x^3 - 64 = x^3 - 4^3 = (x - 4)(x^2 - x(-4) + (-4)^2)$$ $$= (x - 4)(x^2 + 4x + 16)$$

REVIEW EXERCISES
Factor each polynomial completely.

45. $c^3 - 27$ **47.** $2x^3 + 54$

46. $d^3 + 8$ **48.** $2ab^4 - 2ab$

SECTION 5.6   Summary of Factoring Techniques

DEFINITIONS AND CONCEPTS	EXAMPLES
Factoring polynomials: **1.** Factor out all common factors.	Factor: $-2x^6 + 2y^6$. **1.** Factor out the common factor of -2. $$-2x^6 + 2y^6 = -2 \cdot x^6 - (-2)y^6 = -2(x^6 - y^6)$$
2. If an expression has two terms, check to see if it is **a.** the **difference of two squares:** $$a^2 - b^2 = (a + b)(a - b)$$ **b.** the **sum of two cubes:** $$a^3 + b^3 = (a + b)(a^2 - ab + b^2)$$ **c.** the **difference of two cubes:** $$a^3 - b^3 = (a - b)(a^2 + ab + b^2)$$	**2.** Identify $x^6 - y^6$ as the difference of two squares and factor it: $$-2(x^6 - y^6) = -2(x^3 + y^3)(x^3 - y^3)$$ Then identify $x^3 + y^3$ as the sum of two cubes and $x^3 - y^3$ as the difference of two cubes and factor each binomial: $$-2(x^6 - y^6) = -2(x^3 + y^3)(x^3 - y^3)$$ $$= -2(x + y)(x^2 - xy + y^2)(x - y)(x^2 + xy + y^2)$$
3. If an expression has three terms, check to see if it is a **perfect-square trinomial square:** $$a^2 + 2ab + b^2 = (a + b)(a + b)$$ $$a^2 - 2ab + b^2 = (a - b)(a - b)$$ If the trinomial is not a perfect-square trinomial, attempt to factor it as a **general trinomial.**	**3.** Factor: $4x^2 - 12x + 9$. This is a perfect-square trinomial because it has the form $(2x)^2 - 2(2x)(3) + (3)^2$. It factors as $(2x - 3)^2$.
4. If an expression has four or more terms, factor it by **grouping.** **5.** Continue factoring until each individual factor is prime, except possibly a monomial factor. **6.** If the polynomial does not factor, the polynomial is *prime* over the set of rational numbers. **7.** Check the results by multiplying.	**4.** Factor: $ax - bx + ay - by$. Since the expression has four terms, use factoring by grouping: $$ax - bx + ay - by = x(a - b) + y(a - b)$$ $$= (a - b)(x + y)$$

REVIEW EXERCISES

Factor each polynomial.

49. $3x^2y - xy^2 - 6xy + 2y^2$

50. $5x^2 + 10x - 15xy - 30y$

51. $2a^2x + 2abx + a^3 + a^2b$

52. $x^2 + 2ax + a^2 - y^2$

53. $x^2 - 4 + bx + 2b$

54. $ax^6 - ay^6$

SECTION 5.7   Solving Equations by Factoring

DEFINITIONS AND CONCEPTS	EXAMPLES
A **quadratic equation** is an equation of the form $ax^2 + bx + c = 0$, where a, b, and c are real numbers and $a \neq 0$.	$2x^2 + 5x = 8$ and $x^2 - 5x = 0$ are quadratic equations.
Zero-factor property: If a and b represent two real numbers and if $ab = 0$, then $a = 0$ or $b = 0$.	To solve the quadratic equation $x^2 - 3x = 4$, proceed as follows: $x^2 - 3x = 4$ $x^2 - 3x - 4 = 0$　　Subtract 4 from both sides. $(x + 1)(x - 4) = 0$　　Factor $x^2 - 3x - 4$. $x + 1 = 0$　or　$x - 4 = 0$　　Set each factor equal to 0. $x = -1$　|　$x = 4$　　Solve each linear equation.

REVIEW EXERCISES

Solve each equation.

55. $x^2 + 2x = 0$

56. $2x^2 - 6x = 0$

57. $3x^2 = 2x$

58. $5x^2 + 25x = 0$

59. $x^2 - 9 = 0$

60. $x^2 - 25 = 0$

61. $a^2 - 7a + 12 = 0$

62. $x^2 - 2x - 15 = 0$

63. $2x - x^2 + 24 = 0$

64. $16 + x^2 - 10x = 0$

65. $2x^2 - 5x - 3 = 0$

66. $2x^2 + x - 3 = 0$

67. $4x^2 = 1$

68. $9x^2 = 4$

69. $x^3 - 7x^2 + 12x = 0$

70. $x^3 + 5x^2 + 6x = 0$

71. $2x^3 + 5x^2 = 3x$

72. $3x^3 - 2x = x^2$

SECTION 5.8   Problem Solving

DEFINITIONS AND CONCEPTS	EXAMPLES
Use the methods for solving quadratic equations discussed in Section 5.7 to solve application problems.	Assume that the area of a rectangle is 240 square inches and that its length is 4 inches less than twice its width. Find the perimeter of the rectangle. Let w represent the width of the rectangle. Then $2w - 4$ represents its length. We can find the length and width by substituting into the formula for the area: $A = l \cdot w$. $240 = (2w - 4)w$ $240 = 2w^2 - 4w$　　Remove parentheses. $0 = 2w^2 - 4w - 240$　　Subtract 240 from both sides. $0 = w^2 - 2w - 120$　　Divide each side by 2. $0 = (w - 12)(w + 10)$　　Factor. $w - 12 = 0$　or　$w + 10 = 0$　　Set each factor equal to 0. $w = 12$　|　$w = -10$　　Solve each linear equation.

Because the width cannot be negative, we discard the result $w = -10$. Thus, the width of the rectangle is 12, and the length is given by

$$2w - 4 = 2(12) - 4$$
$$= 24 - 4$$
$$= 20$$

The dimensions of the rectangle are 12 in. by 20 in. We find the perimeter by substituting 20 for l and 12 for w in the formula for perimeter.

$$P = 2l + 2w = 2(20) + 2(12) = 40 + 24 = 64$$

The perimeter of the rectangle is 64 inches.

REVIEW EXERCISES

73. Number problem   The sum of two numbers is 12, and their product is 35. Find the numbers.

74. Number problem   If 3 times the square of a positive number is added to 5 times the number, the result is 2. Find the number.

75. Dimensions of a rectangle   A rectangle is 2 feet longer than it is wide, and its area is 48 square feet. Find its dimensions.

76. Gardening   A rectangular flower bed is 3 feet longer than twice its width, and its area is 27 square feet. Find its dimensions.

77. Geometry   A rectangle is 3 feet longer than it is wide. Its area is numerically equal to its perimeter. Find its dimensions.

78. Geometry   A triangle has a height 1 foot longer than its base. If its area is 21 square feet, find its height.

Chapter 5   TEST

1. Find the prime factorization of 196.

2. Find the prime factorization of 111.

Factor out the greatest common factor.

3. $60ab^2c^3 + 30a^3b^2c - 25a$

4. $3x^2(a + b) - 6xy(a + b)$

Factor each expression completely.

5. $ax + ay + bx + by$

6. $x^2 - 25$

7. $3a^2 - 27b^2$

8. $16x^4 - 81y^4$

9. $x^2 + 4x + 3$

10. $x^2 - 9x - 22$

11. $x^2 + 10xy + 9y^2$

12. $6x^2 - 30xy + 24y^2$

13. $3x^2 + 13x + 4$

14. $2a^2 + 5a - 12$

15. $2x^2 + 3xy - 2y^2$

16. $12 - 25x + 12x^2$

17. $12a^2 + 6ab - 36b^2$

18. $x^3 - 64$

19. $216 + 8a^3$

20. $x^9z^3 - y^3z^6$

Solve each equation.

21. $x^2 + 3x = 0$

22. $2x^2 + 5x + 3 = 0$

23. $9y^2 - 81 = 0$

24. $-3(y - 6) + 2 = y^2 + 2$

25. $10x^2 - 13x = 9$

26. $10x^2 - x = 9$

27. $10x^2 + 43x = 9$

28. $10x^2 - 89x = 9$

29. **Cannon fire**   A cannonball is fired straight up into the air with a velocity of 192 feet per second. In how many seconds will it hit the ground? (Its height above the ground is given by the formula $h = vt - 16t^2$, where v is the velocity and t is the time in seconds.)

30. **Base of a triangle**   The base of a triangle with an area of 40 square meters is 2 meters longer than it is high. Find the base of the triangle.

Rational Expressions and Equations; Ratio and Proportion

©Shutterstock.co/Concettina D'Agnese

Careers and Mathematics

FOOD-PROCESSING OCCUPATIONS; BAKER

Bakers mix and bake ingredients in accordance to recipes to produce varying quantities of breads, pastries, and other baked goods. Bakers commonly are employed in grocery stores and specialty shops that produce small quantities of baked goods. In manufacturing, bakers produce goods in large quantities. Food-processing workers held about 705,000 jobs in 2006, of which about 149,000 were bakers. Training varies widely among the food-processing occupations. Bakers often start as apprentices or as trainees.

Job Outlook:

Overall employment in the food-processing occupations is projected to increase by 8 percent throughout the 2006–2016 decade. This is about as fast as the average for all occupations.

Annual Earnings:

$22,030–$30,000

For More Information:

http://www.bls.gov/oco/ocos219.htm

For a Sample Application:

See Problem 59 in Section 6.8.

In this chapter ▶

In Chapter 6, we will discuss rational expressions, the fractions of algebra. After learning how to simplify, add, subtract, multiply, and divide them, we will solve equations and application problems that involve rational expressions. We then will conclude by discussing ratio and proportion.

Objectives

1 Find all values of a variable for which a rational expression is undefined.

2 Write a rational expression in simplest form.

3 Simplify a rational expression containing factors that are negatives.

Vocabulary

rational expression   simplest form

Getting Ready

Simplify.

1. $\dfrac{12}{16}$ **2.** $\dfrac{16}{8}$ **3.** $\dfrac{25}{55}$ **4.** $\dfrac{36}{72}$

Fractions such as $\frac{1}{2}$ and $\frac{3}{4}$ that are the quotient of two integers are *rational numbers*. Expressions such as

$$\frac{a}{a + 2} \quad \text{and} \quad \frac{5x^2 + 3}{x^2 + x - 12}$$

where the numerators and denominators are polynomials, are called **rational expressions.** Since rational expressions indicate division, we must exclude any values of the variable that will make the denominator equal to 0. For example, a cannot be -2 in the rational expression

$$\frac{a}{a + 2}$$

because the denominator will be 0:

$$\frac{a}{a + 2} = \frac{-2}{-2 + 2} = \frac{-2}{0}$$

When the denominator of a rational expression is 0, we say that the expression is undefined.

1 Find all values of a variable for which a rational expression is undefined.

EXAMPLE 1 Find all values of x such that the following rational expression is undefined.

$$\frac{5x^2 + 3}{x^2 + x - 12}$$

Solution To find the values of x that make the rational expression undefined, we set its denominator equal to 0 and solve for x.

$$x^2 + x - 12 = 0$$
$$(x + 4)(x - 3) = 0 \qquad \text{Factor the trinomial.}$$
$$x + 4 = 0 \quad \text{or} \quad x - 3 = 0 \quad \text{Set each factor equal to 0.}$$
$$x = -4 \qquad\qquad x = 3 \quad \text{Solve each equation.}$$

We can check by substituting 3 and -4 for x and verifying that these values make the denominator of the rational expression equal to 0.

$$\textbf{\textit{For }} x = 3$$
$$\frac{5x^2 + 3}{x^2 + x - 12} = \frac{5(3)^2 + 3}{3^2 + 3 - 12}$$
$$= \frac{5(9) + 3}{9 + 3 - 12}$$
$$= \frac{45 + 3}{12 - 12}$$
$$= \frac{48}{0}$$

$$\textbf{\textit{For }} x = -4$$
$$\frac{5x^2 + 3}{x^2 + x - 12} = \frac{5(-4)^2 + 3}{(-4)^2 + (-4) - 12}$$
$$= \frac{5(16) + 3}{16 - 4 - 12}$$
$$= \frac{80 + 3}{12 - 12}$$
$$= \frac{83}{0}$$

Since the denominator is 0 when $x = 3$ or $x = -4$, the rational expression $\frac{5x^2 + 3}{x^2 + x - 12}$ is undefined at these values.

SELF CHECK 1 Find all values of x such that the following rational expression is undefined.

$$\frac{3x^2 - 2}{x^2 - 2x - 3}$$

2 Write a rational expression in simplest form.

We have seen that a fraction can be simplified by dividing out common factors shared by its numerator and denominator. For example,

$$\frac{18}{30} = \frac{3 \cdot 6}{5 \cdot 6} = \frac{3 \cdot \overset{1}{\cancel{6}}}{5 \cdot \cancel{6}} = \frac{3}{5} \qquad\qquad -\frac{6}{15} = -\frac{3 \cdot 2}{3 \cdot 5} = -\frac{\overset{1}{\cancel{3}} \cdot 2}{\cancel{3} \cdot 5} = -\frac{2}{5}$$

These examples illustrate the *fundamental property of fractions,* first discussed in Chapter 1.

EVERYDAY CONNECTIONS   U.S. Renewable Energy Consumption

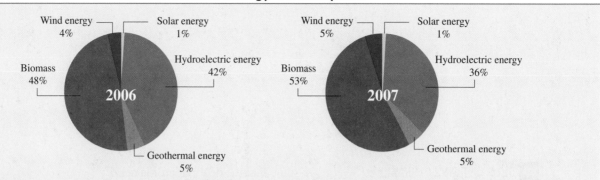

Source: http://www.eia.doe.gov/cneaf/solar.renewables/page/prelim_trends/rea_prereport.html

The pie charts compare the variety of renewable energy resources used by Americans in 2006 and 2007.

1. Suppose 3.285 quadrillion Btu (British thermal units) came from biomass resources in 2006. What was the total renewable energy consumption in 2006?

2. The total renewable energy consumption in 2007 was 6.83 quadrillion Btu. How many Btu came from geothermal energy resources?

The Fundamental Property of Fractions	If a, b, and x are real numbers, then $$\frac{a \cdot x}{b \cdot x} = \frac{a}{b} \quad (b \neq 0 \text{ and } x \neq 0)$$

Since rational expressions are fractions, we can use the fundamental property of fractions to simplify rational expressions. We factor the numerator and denominator of the rational expression and divide out all common factors. When all common factors have been divided out, we say that the rational expression has been written in **simplest form.**

EXAMPLE 2   Simplify: $\dfrac{21x^2y}{14xy^2}$. Assume that the denominator is not 0.

Solution   We will factor the numerator and the denominator and then divide out any common factors, if possible.

$$\frac{21x^2y}{14xy^2} = \frac{3 \cdot 7 \cdot x \cdot x \cdot y}{2 \cdot 7 \cdot x \cdot y \cdot y} \qquad \text{Factor the numerator and denominator.}$$

$$= \frac{3 \cdot \overset{1}{\cancel{7}} \cdot \overset{1}{\cancel{x}} \cdot x \cdot \overset{1}{\cancel{y}}}{2 \cdot \underset{1}{\cancel{7}} \cdot \underset{1}{\cancel{x}} \cdot y \cdot \underset{1}{\cancel{y}}} \qquad \text{Divide out the common factors of 7, } x \text{, and } y.$$

$$= \frac{3x}{2y}$$

This rational expression also can be simplified by using the rules of exponents.

$$\frac{21x^2y}{14xy^2} = \frac{3 \cdot 7}{2 \cdot 7}x^{2-1}y^{1-2} \qquad \frac{x^2}{x} = x^{2-1}; \frac{y}{y^2} = y^{1-2}$$

$$= \frac{3}{2}xy^{-1} \qquad\qquad 2 - 1 = 1; 1 - 2 = -1$$

$$= \frac{3}{2} \cdot \frac{x}{y} \qquad\qquad y^{-1} = \frac{1}{y}$$

$$= \frac{3x}{2y} \qquad\qquad \text{Multiply.}$$

⇨ **SELF CHECK 2**   Simplify: $\dfrac{32a^3b^2}{24ab^4}$. Assume that the denominator is not 0.

EXAMPLE 3   Simplify: $\dfrac{x^2 + 3x}{3x + 9}$. Assume that the denominator is not 0.

Solution   We will factor the numerator and the denominator and then divide out any common factors, if possible.

$$\frac{x^2 + 3x}{3x + 9} = \frac{x(x + 3)}{3(x + 3)} \qquad \text{Factor the numerator and the denominator.}$$

$$= \frac{\overset{1}{x(\cancel{x + 3})}}{\underset{1}{3(\cancel{x + 3})}} \qquad \text{Divide out the common factor of } x + 3.$$

$$= \frac{x}{3}$$

⇨ **SELF CHECK 3**   Simplify: $\dfrac{x^2 - 5x}{5x - 25}$. Assume that the denominator is not 0.

Any number divided by 1 remains unchanged. For example,

$$\frac{37}{1} = 37, \qquad \frac{5x}{1} = 5x, \qquad \text{and} \qquad \frac{3x + y}{1} = 3x + y$$

PERSPECTIVE

The fraction $\frac{8}{4}$ is equal to 2, because $4 \cdot 2 = 8$. The expression $\frac{8}{0}$ is undefined, because there is no number x for which $0 \cdot x = 8$. The expression $\frac{0}{0}$ presents a different problem, however, because $\frac{0}{0}$ seems to equal any number. For example, $\frac{0}{0} = 17$, because $0 \cdot 17 = 0$. Similarly, $\frac{0}{0} = \pi$, because $0 \cdot \pi = 0$. Since "no answer" and "any answer" are both unacceptable, division by 0 is not allowed.

Although $\frac{0}{0}$ represents many numbers, there is often one best answer. In the 17th century, mathematicians such as Sir Isaac Newton (1642–1727) and Gottfried Wilhelm von Leibniz (1646–1716) began to look more closely at expressions related to the fraction $\frac{0}{0}$. One of these expressions, called a **derivative,** is the foundation of **calculus,** an important area of mathematics discovered independently by both Newton and Leibniz. They discovered that under certain conditions, there was one best answer. Expressions related to $\frac{0}{0}$ are called **indeterminate forms.**

In general, for any real number a, the following is true.

Division by 1	$\dfrac{a}{1} = a$

EXAMPLE 4 Simplify: $\dfrac{x^3 + x^2}{1 + x}$. Assume that the denominator is not 0.

Solution We will factor the numerator and then divide out any common factors, if possible.

$$\frac{x^3 + x^2}{1 + x} = \frac{x^2(x + 1)}{1 + x} \qquad \text{Factor the numerator.}$$

$$= \frac{x^2 \overset{1}{\cancel{(x + 1)}}}{\underset{1}{\cancel{1 + x}}} \qquad \text{Divide out the common factor of } x + 1.$$

$$= \frac{x^2}{1}$$

$$= x^2 \qquad \text{Denominators of 1 need not be written.}$$

SELF CHECK 4 Simplify: $\dfrac{x^2 - x}{x - 1}$. Assume that the denominator is not 0.

EXAMPLE 5 Simplify: $\dfrac{x^2 + 13x + 12}{x^2 - 144}$. Assume that no denominators are 0.

Solution We will factor the numerator and the denominator and then divide out any common factors, if possible.

$$\frac{x^2 + 13x + 12}{x^2 - 144} = \frac{(x + 1)(x + 12)}{(x + 12)(x - 12)} \qquad \text{Factor the numerator and denominator.}$$

$$= \frac{(x + 1)\overset{1}{\cancel{(x + 12)}}}{\underset{1}{\cancel{(x + 12)}}(x - 12)} \qquad \text{Divide out the common factor of } x + 12.$$

$$= \frac{x + 1}{x - 12}$$

SELF CHECK 5 Simplify: $\dfrac{x^2 - 9}{x^3 - 3x^2}$. Assume that no denominators are 0.

COMMENT Remember that only *factors* common to the *entire numerator* and *entire denominator* can be divided out. *Terms* that are common to the numerator and denominator *cannot* be divided out. For example, consider the correct simplification

$$\frac{5 + 8}{5} = \frac{13}{5}$$

It would be incorrect to divide out the common *term* of 5 on the left side in the previous simplification. Doing so gives an incorrect answer.

$$\frac{5+8}{5} = \frac{\overset{1}{\cancel{5}}+8}{\underset{1}{\cancel{5}}} = \frac{1+8}{1} = 9$$

EXAMPLE 6   Simplify: $\dfrac{5(x+3)-5}{7(x+3)-7}$. Assume that the denominator is not 0.

Solution   We cannot divide out $x+3$, because it is not a factor of the entire numerator, nor is it a factor of the entire denominator. Instead, we simplify the numerator and denominator, factor them, and divide out all common factors, if any.

$$\frac{5(x+3)-5}{7(x+3)-7} = \frac{5x+15-5}{7x+21-7} \qquad \text{Remove parentheses.}$$

$$= \frac{5x+10}{7x+14} \qquad \text{Combine like terms.}$$

$$= \frac{5(x+2)}{7(x+2)} \qquad \text{Factor the numerator and denominator.}$$

$$= \frac{5\overset{1}{\cancel{(x+2)}}}{7\underset{1}{\cancel{(x+2)}}} \qquad \text{Divide out the common factor of } x+2.$$

$$= \frac{5}{7}$$

⇨ **SELF CHECK 6**   Simplify: $\dfrac{4(x-2)+4}{3(x-2)+3}$. Assume that the denominator is not 0.

EXAMPLE 7   Simplify: $\dfrac{x(x+3)-3(x-1)}{x^2+3}$.

Solution   Since the denominator x^2+3 is always positive, there are no restrictions on x. To simplify the fraction, we will simplify the numerator and then divide out any common factors, if possible.

$$\frac{x(x+3)-3(x-1)}{x^2+3} = \frac{x^2+3x-3x+3}{x^2+3} \qquad \text{Remove parentheses in the numerator.}$$

$$= \frac{x^2+3}{x^2+3} \qquad \text{Combine like terms in the numerator.}$$

$$= \frac{\overset{1}{\cancel{(x^2+3)}}}{\underset{1}{\cancel{(x^2+3)}}} \qquad \text{Divide out the common factor of } x^2+3.$$

$$= 1$$

⇨ **SELF CHECK 7**   Simplify: $\dfrac{a(a+2)-2(a-1)}{a^2+2}$.

Sometimes rational expressions do not simplify. For example, to attempt to simplify

$$\frac{x^2 + x - 2}{x^2 + x}$$

we factor the numerator and denominator.

$$\frac{x^2 + x - 2}{x^2 + x} = \frac{(x + 2)(x - 1)}{x(x + 1)}$$

Because there are no factors common to the numerator and denominator, this rational expression is already in simplest form.

EXAMPLE 8   Simplify: $\dfrac{x^3 + 8}{x^2 + ax + 2x + 2a}$. Assume that no denominators are 0.

Solution   We will factor the numerator and the denominator and then divide out any common factors, if possible.

$$\frac{x^3 + 8}{x^2 + ax + 2x + 2a} = \frac{(x + 2)(x^2 - 2x + 4)}{x(x + a) + 2(x + a)} \quad \text{Factor the numerator and begin to factor the denominator.}$$

$$= \frac{(x + 2)(x^2 - 2x + 4)}{(x + a)(x + 2)} \quad \text{Finish factoring the denominator.}$$

$$= \frac{\overset{1}{\cancel{(x + 2)}}(x^2 - 2x + 4)}{(x + a)\underset{1}{\cancel{(x + 2)}}} \quad \text{Divide out the common factor of } x + 2.$$

$$= \frac{x^2 - 2x + 4}{x + a}$$

SELF CHECK 8   Simplify: $\dfrac{ab + 3a - 2b - 6}{a^3 - 8}$. Assume that no denominators are 0.

---

3   **Simplify a rational expression containing factors that are negatives.**

If the terms of two polynomials are the same, except for signs, the polynomials are called *negatives* of each other. For example,

$x - y$ and $-x + y$ are negatives,
$2a - 1$ and $-2a + 1$ are negatives, and
$3x^2 - 2x + 5$ and $-3x^2 + 2x - 5$ are negatives.

Example 9 shows why the quotient of two polynomials that are negatives is always -1.

EXAMPLE 9   Simplify: **a.** $\dfrac{x - y}{y - x}$ **b.** $\dfrac{2a - 1}{1 - 2a}$. Assume that no denominators are 0.

Solution   We can rearrange terms in each numerator, factor out -1, and proceed as follows:

a. $\dfrac{x - y}{y - x} = \dfrac{-y + x}{y - x}$

$= \dfrac{-(y - x)}{y - x}$

$= \dfrac{\overset{1}{-(y - x)}}{\underset{1}{y - x}}$

$= -1$

b. $\dfrac{2a - 1}{1 - 2a} = \dfrac{-1 + 2a}{1 - 2a}$

$= \dfrac{-(1 - 2a)}{1 - 2a}$

$= \dfrac{\overset{1}{-(1 - 2a)}}{\underset{1}{1 - 2a}}$

$= -1$

➡ **SELF CHECK 9**   Simplify: $\dfrac{3p - 2q}{2q - 3p}$. Assume that the denominator is not 0.

The previous example suggests this important result.

Division of Negatives   The quotient of any nonzero expression and its negative is -1. In symbols, we have

If $a \neq b$, then $\dfrac{a - b}{b - a} = -1$.

➡ **SELF CHECK ANSWERS**   **1.** $3, -1$ **2.** $\dfrac{4a^2}{3b^2}$ **3.** $\dfrac{x}{5}$ **4.** x **5.** $\dfrac{x + 3}{x^2}$ **6.** $\dfrac{4}{3}$ **7.** 1 **8.** $\dfrac{b + 3}{a^2 + 2a + 4}$ **9.** -1

NOW TRY THIS

1. Evaluate $\dfrac{x - 3}{x + 4}$ for

    a. $x = 3$ **b.** $x = 0$ **c.** $x = -4$

2. Simplify: $\dfrac{4x + 20}{4x - 12}$. Assume $x \neq 3$.

3. Find all value(s) of x for which $\dfrac{x + 1}{9x^2 - x}$ is undefined.

6.1 EXERCISES

WARM-UPS   *Simplify each rational expression. Assume no denominators are zero.*

1. $\dfrac{14}{21}$

2. $\dfrac{34}{17}$

3. $\dfrac{xyz}{wxy}$

4. $\dfrac{8x^2}{4x}$

5. $\dfrac{6x^2y}{6xy^2}$

6. $\dfrac{x^2y^3}{x^2y^4}$

7. $\dfrac{x + y}{y + x}$

8. $\dfrac{x - y}{y - x}$

REVIEW

9. State the associative property of addition.

10. State the distributive property.

11. What is the additive identity?

12. What is the multiplicative identity?

13. Find the additive inverse of $-\frac{5}{3}$.

14. Find the multiplicative inverse of $-\frac{5}{3}$.

VOCABULARY AND CONCEPTS   *Fill in the blanks.*

15. In a fraction, the part above the fraction bar is called the _____.

16. In a fraction, the part below the fraction bar is called the _____.

17. The denominator of a fraction cannot be __.

18. A fraction that has polynomials in its numerator and denominator is called a _____ expression.

19. $x - 2$ and $2 - x$ are called _____ of each other.

20. To *simplify* a rational expression means to write it in _____ terms.

21. The fundamental property of fractions states that $\frac{ac}{bc}$ = __.

22. Any number x divided by 1 is __.

23. To simplify a rational expression, we _____ the numerator and denominator and divide out _____ factors.

24. A rational expression cannot be simplified when it is written in _____.

GUIDED PRACTICE

Find all values of the variable for which the following rational expressions are undefined. See Example 1. (Objective 1)

25. $\dfrac{2y + 1}{y - 2}$

26. $\dfrac{3x - 8}{x + 6}$

27. $\dfrac{3a^2 + 5a}{3a - 2}$

28. $\dfrac{12x - 7}{6x + 5}$

29. $\dfrac{3x - 13}{x^2 - x - 2}$

30. $\dfrac{2p^2 + 5p}{6p^2 - p - 1}$

31. $\dfrac{2m^2 + 5m}{2m^2 - m - 3}$

32. $\dfrac{5q^2 - 3}{6q^2 - q - 2}$

Write each expression in simplest form. If it is already in simplest form, so indicate. Assume that no denominators are 0. See Example 2. (Objective 2)

33. $\dfrac{28}{35}$

34. $\dfrac{-18}{54}$

35. $\dfrac{4x}{2}$

36. $\dfrac{2x}{4}$

37. $\dfrac{-6x}{18}$

38. $\dfrac{-25y}{5}$

39. $\dfrac{2x^2}{3y}$

40. $\dfrac{5y^2}{2x^2}$

Write each expression in simplest form. If it is already in simplest form, so indicate. Assume that no denominators are 0. See Examples 3–4. (Objective 2)

41. $\dfrac{(3 + 4)a}{24 - 3}$

42. $\dfrac{(3 - 18)k}{25}$

43. $\dfrac{x + 3}{3(x + 3)}$

44. $\dfrac{x - 9}{3x - 27}$

45. $\dfrac{2(x + 7)}{x + 7}$

46. $\dfrac{5x + 35}{x + 7}$

47. $\dfrac{x^2 + 3x}{2x + 6}$

48. $\dfrac{x + x}{2}$

Write each expression in simplest form. If it is already in simplest form, so indicate. Assume that no denominators are 0. See Example 5. (Objective 2)

49. $\dfrac{x^2 + 3x + 2}{x^2 + x - 2}$

50. $\dfrac{x^2 + x - 6}{x^2 - x - 2}$

51. $\dfrac{x^2 - 8x + 15}{x^2 - x - 6}$

52. $\dfrac{x^2 - 6x - 7}{x^2 + 8x + 7}$

53. $\dfrac{2x^2 - 8x}{x^2 - 6x + 8}$

54. $\dfrac{3y^2 - 15y}{y^2 - 3y - 10}$

55. $\dfrac{2a^3 - 16}{2a^2 + 4a + 8}$

56. $\dfrac{3y^3 + 81}{y^2 - 3y + 9}$

Write each expression in simplest form. If it is already in simplest form, so indicate. Assume that no denominators are 0. See Examples 6–7. (Objective 2)

57. $\dfrac{4(x + 3) + 4}{3(x + 2) + 6}$

58. $\dfrac{x^2 - 3(2x - 3)}{x^2 - 9}$

59. $\dfrac{x^2 + 5x + 4}{2(x + 3) - (x + 2)}$

60. $\dfrac{x^2 - 9}{(2x + 3) - (x + 6)}$

Write each expression in simplest form. If it is already in simplest form, so indicate. Assume that no denominators are 0. See Example 8. (Objective 2)

61. $\dfrac{x^3 + 1}{ax + a + x + 1}$

62. $\dfrac{x^3 - 8}{ax + x - 2a - 2}$

63. $\dfrac{ab + b + 2a + 2}{ab + a + b + 1}$

64. $\dfrac{xy + 2y + 3x + 6}{x^2 + 5x + 6}$

Write each expression in simplest form. If it is already in simplest form, so indicate. Assume that no denominators are 0. See Example 9. (Objective 3)

65. $\dfrac{x - 7}{7 - x}$

66. $\dfrac{d - c}{c - d}$

67. $\dfrac{6x - 3y}{3y - 6x}$

68. $\dfrac{3c - 4d}{4c - 3d}$

ADDITIONAL PRACTICE   *Write each expression in simplest form. If it is already in simplest form, so indicate. Assume that no denominators are 0.*

69. $\dfrac{45}{9a}$

70. $\dfrac{48}{16y}$

71. $\dfrac{7 + 3}{5z}$

72. $\dfrac{28x}{32y}$

73. $\dfrac{15x^2y}{5xy^2}$

74. $\dfrac{12xz}{4xz^2}$

75. $\dfrac{x^2 + 3x + 2}{x^3 + x^2}$

76. $\dfrac{6x^2 - 13x + 6}{3x^2 + x - 2}$

77. $\dfrac{14xz^2}{7x^2z^2}$

78. $\dfrac{xz - 2x}{yz - 2y}$

79. $\dfrac{3x + 15}{x^2 - 25}$

80. $\dfrac{x^2 - 8x + 16}{x^2 - 16}$

81. $\dfrac{a + b - c}{c - a - b}$

82. $\dfrac{x - y - z}{z + y - x}$

83. $\dfrac{6a - 6b + 6c}{9a - 9b + 9c}$

84. $\dfrac{3a - 3b - 6}{2a - 2b - 4}$

85. $\dfrac{3x + 3y}{x^2 + xy}$

86. $\dfrac{xy + 2x^2}{2xy + y^2}$

87. $\dfrac{2x^2 - 8}{x^2 - 3x + 2}$

88. $\dfrac{3x^2 - 27}{x^2 + 3x - 18}$

89. $\dfrac{x^2 - 2x - 15}{x^2 + 2x - 15}$

90. $\dfrac{x^2 + 4x - 77}{x^2 - 4x - 21}$

91. $\dfrac{15x - 3x^2}{25y - 5xy}$

92. $\dfrac{3y + xy}{3x + xy}$

93. $\dfrac{4 + 2(x - 5)}{3x - 5(x - 2)}$

94. $\dfrac{x^2 - 10x + 25}{25 - x^2}$

95. $\dfrac{x^3 + 1}{x^2 - x + 1}$

96. $\dfrac{x^3 - 1}{x^2 + x + 1}$

97. $\dfrac{xy + 3y + 3x + 9}{x^2 - 9}$

98. $\dfrac{ab + b^2 + 2a + 2b}{a^2 + 2a + ab + 2b}$

WRITING ABOUT MATH

99. Explain why $\dfrac{x - 7}{7 - x} = -1$.

100. Explain why $\dfrac{x + 7}{7 + x} = 1$.

SOMETHING TO THINK ABOUT

101. Exercise 93 has two possible answers: $\dfrac{x - 3}{5 - x}$ and $-\dfrac{x - 3}{x - 5}$.

Why is either answer correct?

102. Find two different-looking but correct answers for the following problem.

Simplify: $\dfrac{y^2 + 5(2y + 5)}{25 - y^2}$.

SECTION 6.2

Multiplying and Dividing Rational Expressions

Objectives

1. Multiply two rational expressions and write the result in simplest form.
2. Multiply a rational expression by a polynomial and write the result in simplest form.
3. Divide two rational expressions and write the result in simplest form.
4. Divide a rational expression by a polynomial and write the result in simplest form.
5. Perform combined operations on three or more rational expressions.

Getting Ready

Multiply or divide the fractions and simplify.

1. $\dfrac{3}{7} \cdot \dfrac{14}{9}$

2. $\dfrac{21}{15} \cdot \dfrac{10}{3}$

3. $\dfrac{19}{38} \cdot 6$

4. $42 \cdot \dfrac{3}{21}$

5. $\dfrac{4}{9} \div \dfrac{8}{45}$

6. $\dfrac{11}{7} \div \dfrac{22}{14}$

7. $\dfrac{75}{12} \div \dfrac{50}{6}$

8. $\dfrac{13}{5} \div \dfrac{26}{20}$

Just like arithmetic fractions, rational expressions can be multiplied, divided, added, and subtracted. In this section, we will show how to multiply and divide rational expressions, the *fractions* of algebra.

1 **Multiply two rational expressions and write the result in simplest form.**

Recall that to multiply fractions, we multiply their numerators and multiply their denominators. For example, to find the product of $\frac{4}{7}$ and $\frac{3}{5}$, we proceed as follows.

$$\frac{4}{7} \cdot \frac{3}{5} = \frac{4 \cdot 3}{7 \cdot 5} \quad \text{Multiply the numerators and multiply the denominators.}$$

$$= \frac{12}{35} \quad 4 \cdot 3 = 12 \text{ and } 7 \cdot 5 = 35.$$

This suggests the rule for multiplying rational expressions.

Multiplying Rational Expressions	If a, b, c, and d are real numbers and $b \neq 0$ and $d \neq 0$, then $$\frac{a}{b} \cdot \frac{c}{d} = \frac{ac}{bd}$$

EXAMPLE 1   Multiply. Assume that no denominators are 0.

a. $\dfrac{1}{3} \cdot \dfrac{2}{5}$ **b.** $\dfrac{7}{9} \cdot \dfrac{-5}{3x}$ **c.** $\dfrac{x^2}{2} \cdot \dfrac{3}{y^2}$ **d.** $\dfrac{t+1}{t} \cdot \dfrac{t-1}{t-2}$

Solution   We will multiply the numerators, multiply the denominators, and then simplify, if possible.

a. $\dfrac{1}{3} \cdot \dfrac{2}{5} = \dfrac{1 \cdot 2}{3 \cdot 5}$ **b.** $\dfrac{7}{9} \cdot \dfrac{-5}{3x} = \dfrac{7(-5)}{9 \cdot 3x}$

$= \dfrac{2}{15}$ $= \dfrac{-35}{27x}$

c. $\dfrac{x^2}{2} \cdot \dfrac{3}{y^2} = \dfrac{x^2 \cdot 3}{2 \cdot y^2}$ **d.** $\dfrac{t+1}{t} \cdot \dfrac{t-1}{t-2} = \dfrac{(t+1)(t-1)}{t(t-2)}$

$= \dfrac{3x^2}{2y^2}$

⇨ **SELF CHECK 1**   Multiply: $\dfrac{3x}{4} \cdot \dfrac{p-3}{y}$. Assume that no denominators are 0.

EXAMPLE 2   Multiply: $\dfrac{35x^2y}{7y^2z} \cdot \dfrac{z}{5xy}$. Assume that no denominators are 0.

Solution   We will multiply the numerators, multiply the denominators, and then simplify, if possible.

$$\frac{35x^2y}{7y^2z} \cdot \frac{z}{5xy} = \frac{35x^2y \cdot z}{7y^2z \cdot 5xy}$$

Multiply the numerators and multiply the denominators.

$$= \frac{5 \cdot 7 \cdot x \cdot x \cdot y \cdot z}{7 \cdot y \cdot y \cdot z \cdot 5 \cdot x \cdot y}$$

Factor.

$$= \frac{\overset{1}{\cancel{5}} \cdot \overset{1}{\cancel{7}} \cdot x \cdot x \cdot \overset{1}{\cancel{y}} \cdot \overset{1}{\cancel{z}}}{\underset{1}{\cancel{7}} \cdot \underset{1}{\cancel{y}} \cdot y \cdot \underset{1}{\cancel{z}} \cdot \underset{1}{\cancel{5}} \cdot \underset{1}{\cancel{x}} \cdot y}$$

Divide out common factors.

$$= \frac{x}{y^2}$$

⇨ **SELF CHECK 2** Multiply: $\dfrac{a^2b^2}{2a} \cdot \dfrac{9a^3}{3b^3}$. Assume that no denominators are 0.

EXAMPLE 3 Multiply: $\dfrac{x^2 - x}{2x + 4} \cdot \dfrac{x + 2}{x}$. Assume that no denominators are 0.

Solution We will multiply the numerators, multiply the denominators, and then simplify.

$$\frac{x^2 - x}{2x + 4} \cdot \frac{x + 2}{x} = \frac{(x^2 - x)(x + 2)}{(2x + 4)(x)}$$

Multiply the numerators and multiply the denominators.

$$= \frac{x(x - 1)(x + 2)}{2(x + 2)x}$$

Factor.

$$= \frac{\overset{1}{\cancel{x}}(x - 1)\overset{1}{\cancel{(x + 2)}}}{2\underset{1}{\cancel{(x + 2)}}\underset{1}{\cancel{x}}}$$

Divide out common factors.

$$= \frac{x - 1}{2}$$

⇨ **SELF CHECK 3** Multiply: $\dfrac{x^2 + x}{3x + 6} \cdot \dfrac{x + 2}{x + 1}$. Assume that no denominators are 0.

EXAMPLE 4 Multiply: $\dfrac{x^2 - 3x}{x^2 - x - 6}$ and $\dfrac{x^2 + x - 2}{x^2 - x}$. Assume that no denominators are 0.

Solution We will multiply the numerators, multiply the denominators, and then simplify.

$$\frac{x^2 - 3x}{x^2 - x - 6} \cdot \frac{x^2 + x - 2}{x^2 - x}$$

$$= \frac{(x^2 - 3x)(x^2 + x - 2)}{(x^2 - x - 6)(x^2 - x)}$$

Multiply the numerators and multiply the denominators.

$$= \frac{x(x - 3)(x + 2)(x - 1)}{(x + 2)(x - 3)x(x - 1)}$$

Factor.

$$= \frac{\overset{1}{\cancel{x}}(\overset{1}{\cancel{x-3}})(\overset{1}{\cancel{x+2}})(\overset{1}{\cancel{x-1}})}{(\cancel{x+2})(\cancel{x-3})\cancel{x}(\cancel{x-1})}$$ Divide out common factors.

$$= 1$$

SELF CHECK 4   Multiply: $\dfrac{a^2 + a}{a^2 - 4} \cdot \dfrac{a^2 - a - 2}{a^2 + 2a + 1}$. Assume that no denominators are 0.

2   **Multiply a rational expression by a polynomial and write the result in simplest form.**

Since any number divided by 1 remains unchanged, we can write any polynomial as a rational expression by inserting a denominator of 1.

EXAMPLE 5   Multiply: $\dfrac{x^2 + x}{x^2 + 8x + 7} \cdot (x + 7)$. Assume that no denominators are 0.

Solution   We will write $x + 7$ as $\frac{x + 7}{1}$, multiply the numerators, multiply the denominators, and then simplify.

$$\frac{x^2 + x}{x^2 + 8x + 7} \cdot (x + 7) = \frac{x^2 + x}{x^2 + 8x + 7} \cdot \frac{x + 7}{1}$$ Write $x + 7$ as a fraction with a denominator of 1.

$$= \frac{x(x + 1)(x + 7)}{(x + 1)(x + 7)1}$$ Multiply the fractions and factor where possible.

$$= \frac{x(\overset{1}{\cancel{x + 1}})(\overset{1}{\cancel{x + 7}})}{1(\cancel{x + 1})(\cancel{x + 7})}$$ Divide out all common factors.

$$= x$$

SELF CHECK 5   Multiply: $(a - 7) \cdot \dfrac{a^2 - a}{a^2 - 8a + 7}$. Assume that no denominators are 0.

3   **Divide two rational expressions and write the result in simplest form.**

Recall that division by a nonzero number is equivalent to multiplying by the reciprocal of that number. Thus, to divide two fractions, we can invert the *divisor* (the fraction following the ÷ sign) and multiply. For example, to divide $\frac{4}{7}$ by $\frac{3}{5}$, we proceed as follows:

$$\frac{4}{7} \div \frac{3}{5} = \frac{4}{7} \cdot \frac{5}{3}$$ Invert $\frac{3}{5}$ and change the division to a multiplication.

$$= \frac{20}{21}$$ Multiply the numerators and multiply the denominators.

This suggests the rule for dividing rational expressions.

Dividing Rational Expressions

If a is a real number and b, c, and d are nonzero real numbers, then

$$\frac{a}{b} \div \frac{c}{d} = \frac{a}{b} \cdot \frac{d}{c} = \frac{ad}{bc}$$

EXAMPLE 6 Divide, assuming that no denominators are 0:

a. $\dfrac{7}{13} \div \dfrac{21}{26}$ **b.** $\dfrac{-9x}{35y} \div \dfrac{15x^2}{14}$

Solution We will change each division to a multiplication and then multiply the resulting rational expressions.

a. $\dfrac{7}{13} \div \dfrac{21}{26} = \dfrac{7}{13} \cdot \dfrac{26}{21}$ Invert the divisor and multiply.

$= \dfrac{7 \cdot 2 \cdot 13}{13 \cdot 3 \cdot 7}$ Multiply the fractions and factor where possible.

$= \dfrac{\overset{1}{\cancel{7}} \cdot 2 \cdot \overset{1}{\cancel{13}}}{\underset{1}{\cancel{13}} \cdot 3 \cdot \underset{1}{\cancel{7}}}$ Divide out common factors.

$= \dfrac{2}{3}$

b. $\dfrac{-9x}{35y} \div \dfrac{15x^2}{14} = \dfrac{-9x}{35y} \cdot \dfrac{14}{15x^2}$ Invert the divisor and multiply.

$= \dfrac{-3 \cdot 3 \cdot x \cdot 2 \cdot 7}{5 \cdot 7 \cdot y \cdot 3 \cdot 5 \cdot x \cdot x}$ Multiply the fractions and factor where possible.

$= \dfrac{-3 \cdot \overset{1}{\cancel{3}} \cdot \overset{1}{\cancel{x}} \cdot 2 \cdot \overset{1}{\cancel{7}}}{5 \cdot \underset{1}{\cancel{7}} \cdot y \cdot \underset{1}{\cancel{3}} \cdot 5 \cdot \underset{1}{\cancel{x}} \cdot x}$ Divide out common factors.

$= -\dfrac{6}{25xy}$ Multiply the remaining factors.

 **SELF CHECK 6** Divide: $\dfrac{-8a}{3b} \div \dfrac{16a^2}{9b^2}$. Assume that no denominators are 0.

EXAMPLE 7 Divide: $\dfrac{x^2 + x}{3x - 15} \div \dfrac{x^2 + 2x + 1}{6x - 30}$. Assume that no denominators are 0.

Solution We will change the division to a multiplication and then multiply the resulting rational expressions.

$\dfrac{x^2 + x}{3x - 15} \div \dfrac{x^2 + 2x + 1}{6x - 30}$

$= \dfrac{x^2 + x}{3x - 15} \cdot \dfrac{6x - 30}{x^2 + 2x + 1}$ Invert the divisor and multiply.

$$= \frac{x(x+1) \cdot 2 \cdot 3(x-5)}{3(x-5)(x+1)(x+1)} \qquad \text{Multiply the fractions and factor.}$$

$$= \frac{x\cancel{(x+1)} \cdot 2 \cdot \cancel{3}\cancel{(x-5)}}{\cancel{3}\cancel{(x-5)}\cancel{(x+1)}(x+1)} \qquad \text{Divide out all common factors.}$$

$$= \frac{2x}{x+1}$$

⇨ **SELF CHECK 7**   Divide: $\dfrac{a^2-1}{a^2+4a+3} \div \dfrac{a-1}{a^2+2a-3}$. Assume that no denominators are 0.

4 ## Divide a rational expression by a polynomial and write the result in simplest form.

To divide a rational expression by a polynomial, we write the polynomial as a rational expression by inserting a denominator of 1 and then divide the expressions.

EXAMPLE 8   Divide: $\dfrac{2x^2-3x-2}{2x+1} \div (4-x^2)$. Assume that no denominators are 0.

Solution   We will write $4-x^2$ as $\frac{4-x^2}{1}$, change the division to a multiplication, and then multiply the resulting rational expressions.

$$\frac{2x^2-3x-2}{2x+1} \div (4-x^2)$$

$$= \frac{2x^2-3x-2}{2x+1} \div \frac{4-x^2}{1} \qquad \text{Write } 4-x^2 \text{ as a fraction with a denominator of 1.}$$

$$= \frac{2x^2-3x-2}{2x+1} \cdot \frac{1}{4-x^2} \qquad \text{Invert the divisor and multiply.}$$

$$= \frac{(2x+1)(x-2) \cdot 1}{(2x+1)(2+x)(2-x)} \qquad \text{Multiply the fractions and factor where possible.}$$

$$= \frac{\cancel{(2x+1)}\cancel{(x-2)} \cdot 1}{\cancel{(2x+1)}(2+x)\cancel{(2-x)}} \qquad \text{Divide out common factors: } \frac{x-2}{2-x} = -1.$$

$$= \frac{-1}{2+x}$$

$$= -\frac{1}{2+x} \qquad\qquad\qquad \frac{-a}{b} = -\frac{a}{b}$$

⇨ **SELF CHECK 8**   Divide: $(b-a) \div \dfrac{a^2-b^2}{a^2+ab}$. Assume that no denominators are 0.

5 **Perform combined operations on three or more rational expressions.**

Unless parentheses indicate otherwise, we will follow the order of operations rule and perform multiplications and divisions in order from left to right.

EXAMPLE 9 Simplify: $\dfrac{x^2 - x - 6}{x - 2} \div \dfrac{x^2 - 4x}{x^2 - x - 2} \cdot \dfrac{x - 4}{x^2 + x}$. Assume that no denominators are 0.

Solution Since there are no parentheses to indicate otherwise, we perform the division first.

$$\frac{x^2 - x - 6}{x - 2} \div \frac{x^2 - 4x}{x^2 - x - 2} \cdot \frac{x - 4}{x^2 + x}$$

$$= \frac{x^2 - x - 6}{x - 2} \cdot \frac{x^2 - x - 2}{x^2 - 4x} \cdot \frac{x - 4}{x^2 + x} \qquad \text{Invert the divisor and multiply.}$$

$$= \frac{(x + 2)(x - 3)(x + 1)(x - 2)(x - 4)}{(x - 2)x(x - 4)x(x + 1)} \qquad \text{Multiply the fractions and factor.}$$

$$= \frac{(x + 2)(x - 3)\overset{1}{\cancel{(x + 1)}}\overset{1}{\cancel{(x - 2)}}\overset{1}{\cancel{(x - 4)}}}{\cancel{(x - 2)}x\cancel{(x - 4)}x\cancel{(x + 1)}} \qquad \text{Divide out all common factors.}$$

$$= \frac{(x + 2)(x - 3)}{x^2}$$

⇨ **SELF CHECK 9** Simplify: $\dfrac{a^2 + ab}{ab - b^2} \cdot \dfrac{a^2 - b^2}{a^2 + ab} \div \dfrac{a + b}{b}$. Assume that no denominators are 0.

EXAMPLE 10 Simplify: $\dfrac{x^2 + 6x + 9}{x^2 - 2x}\left(\dfrac{x^2 - 4}{x^2 + 3x} \div \dfrac{x + 2}{x}\right)$. Assume that no denominators are 0.

Solution We perform the division within the parentheses first.

$$\frac{x^2 + 6x + 9}{x^2 - 2x}\left(\frac{x^2 - 4}{x^2 + 3x} \div \frac{x + 2}{x}\right)$$

$$= \frac{x^2 + 6x + 9}{x^2 - 2x}\left(\frac{x^2 - 4}{x^2 + 3x} \cdot \frac{x}{x + 2}\right) \qquad \text{Invert the divisor and multiply.}$$

$$= \frac{(x + 3)(x + 3)(x + 2)(x - 2)x}{x(x - 2)x(x + 3)(x + 2)} \qquad \text{Multiply the fractions and factor where possible.}$$

$$= \frac{\overset{1}{\cancel{(x + 3)}}(x + 3)\overset{1}{\cancel{(x + 2)}}\overset{1}{\cancel{(x - 2)}}\overset{1}{\cancel{x}}}{\cancel{x}\cancel{(x - 2)}x\cancel{(x + 3)}\cancel{(x + 2)}} \qquad \text{Divide out all common factors.}$$

$$= \frac{x + 3}{x}$$

⇨ **SELF CHECK 10** Simplify: $\dfrac{x^2 - 2x}{x^2 + 6x + 9} \div \left(\dfrac{x^2 - 4}{x^2 + 3x} \cdot \dfrac{x}{x + 2}\right)$. Assume that no denominators are 0.

 **SELF CHECK ANSWERS**   **1.** $\frac{3x(p-3)}{4y}$ **2.** $\frac{3a^4}{2b}$ **3.** $\frac{x}{3}$ **4.** $\frac{a}{a+2}$ **5.** a **6.** $-\frac{3b}{2a}$ **7.** $a-1$ **8.** $-a$ **9.** 1 **10.** $\frac{x}{x+3}$

NOW TRY THIS

Simplify. Assume no division by zero.

1. $(x^2 - 4x - 12) \cdot \dfrac{(x+6)^2}{x^2 - 36}$

2. $\dfrac{x^2 - 9}{x - 2} \div \dfrac{9 - x^2}{3x - 6}$

3. $\dfrac{\dfrac{1}{2}}{\dfrac{3}{4}}$

4. $\dfrac{\dfrac{3}{5} - \dfrac{2}{3}}{\dfrac{7}{3} + \dfrac{2}{5}}$

6.2 EXERCISES

WARM-UPS   *Perform the operations and simplify. Assume no denominator is zero.*

1. $\dfrac{x}{2} \cdot \dfrac{3}{x}$

2. $\dfrac{x+1}{5} \cdot \dfrac{7}{x+1}$

3. $\dfrac{5}{x+7} \cdot (x+7)$

4. $\dfrac{3}{7} \div \dfrac{3}{7}$

5. $\dfrac{3}{4} \div 3$

6. $(x+1) \div \dfrac{x+1}{x}$

REVIEW
Simplify each expression. Write all answers without using negative exponents. Assume that no denominators are 0.

7. $2x^3y^2(-3x^2y^4z)$

8. $\dfrac{8x^4y^5}{-2x^3y^2}$

9. $(3y)^{-4}$

10. $(a^{-2}a)^{-3}$

11. $\dfrac{x^{3m}}{x^{4m}}$

12. $(3x^2y^3)^0$

Perform the operations and simplify.

13. $-4(y^3 - 4y^2 + 3y - 2) + 6(-2y^2 + 4) - 4(-2y^3 - y)$

14. $y - 5\overline{)5y^3 - 3y^2 + 4y - 1}$ $(y \neq 5)$

VOCABULARY AND CONCEPTS   *Fill in the blanks.*

15. In a fraction, the part above the fraction bar is called the _____.

16. In a fraction, the part below the fraction bar is called the _____.

17. To multiply fractions, we multiply their _____ and multiply their _____.

18. $\dfrac{a}{b} \cdot \dfrac{c}{d} = $ ____

19. To write a polynomial in fractional form, we insert a denominator of __.

20. $\dfrac{a}{b} \div \dfrac{c}{d} = \dfrac{a}{b} \cdot$ ____

21. To divide two fractions, invert the _____ and _____.

22. Unless parentheses indicate otherwise, do multiplications and divisions in order from ____ to ____.

GUIDED PRACTICE

Perform the multiplication. Assume that no denominators are 0. Simplify the answers, if possible. See Examples 1–2. (Objective 1)

23. $\dfrac{5}{7} \cdot \dfrac{9}{13}$

24. $\dfrac{2}{7} \cdot \dfrac{5}{11}$

25. $\dfrac{2y}{z} \cdot \dfrac{z}{3}$

26. $\dfrac{3x}{y} \cdot \dfrac{y}{2}$

27. $\dfrac{4x}{3y} \cdot \dfrac{3y}{7x}$

28. $\dfrac{5y}{7} \cdot \dfrac{7x}{5z}$

29. $\dfrac{-2xy}{x^2} \cdot \dfrac{3xy}{2}$

30. $\dfrac{-3x}{x^2} \cdot \dfrac{2xz}{3}$

31. $\dfrac{ab^2}{a^2b} \cdot \dfrac{b^2c^2}{abc} \cdot \dfrac{abc^2}{a^3c^2}$

32. $\dfrac{x^3y}{z} \cdot \dfrac{xz^3}{x^2y^2} \cdot \dfrac{yz}{xyz}$

33. $\dfrac{z+7}{7} \cdot \dfrac{z+2}{z}$

34. $\dfrac{a-3}{a} \cdot \dfrac{a+3}{5}$

Perform the multiplication. Assume that no denominators are 0. Simplify the answers, if possible. See Example 3. (Objective 1)

35. $\dfrac{(x+1)^2}{x+1} \cdot \dfrac{x+2}{x+1}$

36. $\dfrac{(y-3)^2}{y-3} \cdot \dfrac{y-3}{y-3}$

37. $\dfrac{3y-9}{y-3} \cdot \dfrac{y}{3y^2}$

38. $\dfrac{x-5}{3x+9} \cdot \dfrac{x+3}{x^2-25}$

39. $\dfrac{7y-14}{y-2} \cdot \dfrac{x^2}{7x}$

40. $\dfrac{y^2+3y}{9} \cdot \dfrac{3x}{y+3}$

41. $\dfrac{abc^2}{a+1} \cdot \dfrac{c}{a^2b^2} \cdot \dfrac{a^2+a}{ac}$

42. $\dfrac{x^3yz^2}{4x+8} \cdot \dfrac{x^2-4}{2x^2y^2z^2} \cdot \dfrac{8yz}{x-2}$

Perform the multiplication. Assume that no denominators are 0. Simplify the answers, if possible. See Example 4. (Objective 1)

43. $\dfrac{5z-10}{z+2} \cdot \dfrac{3}{3z-6}$

44. $\dfrac{x^2-x}{x} \cdot \dfrac{3x-6}{3x-3}$

45. $\dfrac{z^2+4z-5}{5z-5} \cdot \dfrac{5z}{z+5}$

46. $\dfrac{x^2+x-6}{5x} \cdot \dfrac{5x-10}{x+3}$

47. $\dfrac{3x^2+5x+2}{x^2-9} \cdot \dfrac{x-3}{x^2-4} \cdot \dfrac{x^2+5x+6}{6x+4}$

48. $\dfrac{x^2-25}{3x+6} \cdot \dfrac{x^2+x-2}{2x+10} \cdot \dfrac{6x}{3x^2-18x+15}$

49. $\dfrac{a^2-ab+b^2}{a^3+b^3} \cdot \dfrac{ac+ad+bc+bd}{c^2-d^2}$

50. $\dfrac{ax+bx+ay+by}{x^3-y^3} \cdot \dfrac{x^2+xy+y^2}{ax+bx}$

Perform each division. Assume that no denominators are 0. Simplify answers when possible. See Example 6. (Objective 3)

51. $\dfrac{1}{3} \div \dfrac{1}{2}$

52. $\dfrac{3}{4} \div \dfrac{1}{3}$

53. $\dfrac{21}{14} \div \dfrac{5}{2}$

54. $\dfrac{14}{3} \div \dfrac{10}{3}$

55. $\dfrac{x^2y}{3xy} \div \dfrac{xy^2}{6y}$

56. $\dfrac{2xz}{z} \div \dfrac{4x^2}{z^2}$

57. $\dfrac{x+2}{3x} \div \dfrac{x+2}{2}$

58. $\dfrac{z-3}{3z} \div \dfrac{z+3}{z}$

Perform each division. Assume that no denominators are 0. Simplify answers when possible. See Example 7. (Objective 3)

59. $\dfrac{x^2-4}{3x+6} \div \dfrac{x-2}{x+2}$

60. $\dfrac{x^2-9}{5x+15} \div \dfrac{x-3}{x+3}$

61. $\dfrac{y(y+2)}{y^2(y-3)} \div \dfrac{y^2(y+2)}{(y-3)^2}$

62. $\dfrac{(z-2)^2}{3z^2} \div \dfrac{z-2}{6z}$

63. $\dfrac{5x^2+13x-6}{x+3} \div \dfrac{5x^2-17x+6}{x-2}$

64. $\dfrac{x^2-x-6}{2x^2+9x+10} \div \dfrac{x^2-25}{2x^2+15x+25}$

65. $\dfrac{ab+4a+2b+8}{b^2+4b+16} \div \dfrac{b^2-16}{b^3-64}$

66. $\dfrac{r^3-s^3}{r^2-s^2} \div \dfrac{r^2+rs+s^2}{mr+ms+nr+ns}$

Perform the operations. Assume that no denominators are 0. Simplify answers when possible. See Examples 5 and 8. (Objectives 2 and 4)

67. $\dfrac{x-5}{2x-8} \cdot (x-4)$

68. $(6x-8) \cdot \dfrac{x-2}{9x-12}$

69. $\dfrac{3x+9}{x+1} \div (x+3)$

70. $(3x+9) \div \dfrac{x^2-9}{6x}$

Perform the operations. Assume that no denominators are 0. Simplify answers when possible. See Examples 9–10. (Objective 5)

71. $\dfrac{x}{3} \cdot \dfrac{9}{4} \div \dfrac{x^2}{6}$

72. $\dfrac{y^2}{2} \div \dfrac{4}{y} \cdot \dfrac{y^2}{8}$

73. $\dfrac{x^2}{18} \div \dfrac{x^3}{6} \div \dfrac{12}{x^2}$

74. $\dfrac{y^3}{3y} \cdot \dfrac{3y^2}{4} \div \dfrac{15}{20}$

75. $\dfrac{2}{3x-3} \div \dfrac{2x+2}{x-1} \cdot \dfrac{5}{x+1}$

76. $\dfrac{x^2-4}{2x+6} \div \dfrac{x+2}{4} \cdot \dfrac{x+3}{x-2}$

77. $\dfrac{x^2+x-6}{x^2-4} \cdot \dfrac{x^2+2x}{x-2} \div \dfrac{x^2+3x}{x+2}$

78. $\dfrac{x^2-x-6}{x^2+6x-7} \cdot \dfrac{x^2+x-2}{x^2+2x} \div \dfrac{x^2+7x}{x^2-3x}$

ADDITIONAL PRACTICE *Perform the indicated operation(s). Assume that no denominators are 0. Simplify answers when possible.*

79. $\dfrac{25}{35} \cdot \dfrac{-21}{55}$

80. $-\dfrac{27}{24} \cdot \left(-\dfrac{56}{35}\right)$

81. $\dfrac{2}{3} \cdot \dfrac{15}{2} \cdot \dfrac{1}{7}$

82. $\dfrac{2}{5} \cdot \dfrac{10}{9} \cdot \dfrac{3}{2}$

83. $\dfrac{2}{y} \div \dfrac{4}{3}$

84. $\dfrac{3}{a} \div \dfrac{a}{9}$

85. $\dfrac{3x}{2} \div \dfrac{x}{2}$

86. $\dfrac{y}{6} \div \dfrac{2}{3y}$

87. $\dfrac{7z}{9z} \cdot \dfrac{4z}{2z}$

88. $\dfrac{8z}{2x} \cdot \dfrac{16x}{3x}$

89. $\dfrac{2x^2y}{3xy} \cdot \dfrac{3xy^2}{2}$

90. $\dfrac{2x^2z}{z} \cdot \dfrac{5x}{z}$

91. $\dfrac{8x^2y^2}{4x^2} \cdot \dfrac{2xy}{2y}$

92. $\dfrac{9x^2y}{3x} \cdot \dfrac{3xy}{3y}$

93. $\dfrac{10r^2st^3}{6rs^2} \cdot \dfrac{3r^3t}{2rst} \cdot \dfrac{2s^3t^4}{5s^2t^3}$

94. $\dfrac{3a^3b}{25cd^3} \cdot \dfrac{-5cd^2}{6ab} \cdot \dfrac{10abc^2}{2bc^2d}$

95. $\dfrac{3x}{y} \div \dfrac{2x}{4}$

96. $\dfrac{3y}{8} \div \dfrac{2y}{4y}$

97. $\dfrac{4x}{3x} \div \dfrac{2y}{9y}$

98. $\dfrac{14}{7y} \div \dfrac{10}{5z}$

99. $\dfrac{x^2}{3} \div \dfrac{2x}{4}$

100. $\dfrac{z^2}{z} \div \dfrac{z}{3z}$

101. $\dfrac{x-2}{2} \cdot \dfrac{2x}{x-2}$

102. $\dfrac{y+3}{y} \cdot \dfrac{3y}{y+3}$

103. $\dfrac{x+5}{5} \cdot \dfrac{x}{x+5}$

104. $\dfrac{y-9}{y+9} \cdot \dfrac{y}{9}$

105. $\dfrac{(z-2)^2}{3z^2} \div \dfrac{z-2}{6z}$

106. $\dfrac{(x+7)^2}{x+7} \div \dfrac{(x-3)^2}{x+7}$

107. $\dfrac{m^2 - 2m - 3}{2m + 4} \cdot \dfrac{m^2 - 4}{m^2 + 3m + 2}$

108. $\dfrac{p^2 - p - 6}{3p - 9} \cdot \dfrac{p^2 - 9}{p^2 + 6p + 9}$

109. $\dfrac{x^2 - y^2}{y^2 - xy} \cdot \dfrac{yx^3 - y^4}{ax + ay + bx + by}$

110. $\dfrac{xw - xz + wy - yz}{x^2 + 2xy + y^2} \cdot \dfrac{x^3 - y^3}{z^2 - w^2}$

111. $\dfrac{x^2 - 1}{3x - 3} \div \dfrac{x + 1}{3}$

112. $\dfrac{x^2 - 16}{x - 4} \div \dfrac{3x + 12}{x}$

113. $\dfrac{2x^2 + 8x - 42}{x - 3} \div \dfrac{2x^2 + 14x}{x^2 + 5x}$

114. $\dfrac{x^2 - 2x - 35}{3x^2 + 27x} \div \dfrac{x^2 + 7x + 10}{6x^2 + 12x}$

115. $\dfrac{x^2 + 7xy + 12y^2}{x^2 + 2xy - 8y^2} \cdot \dfrac{x^2 - xy - 2y^2}{x^2 + 4xy + 3y^2}$

116. $\dfrac{m^2 + 9mn + 20n^2}{m^2 - 25n^2} \cdot \dfrac{m^2 - 9mn + 20n^2}{m^2 - 16n^2}$

117. $\dfrac{p^3 - p^2q + pq^2}{mp - mq + np - nq} \div \dfrac{q^3 + p^3}{q^2 - p^2}$

118. $\dfrac{s^3 - r^3}{r^2 + rs + s^2} \div \dfrac{pr - ps - qr + qs}{q^2 - p^2}$

119. $\dfrac{x^2 - 1}{x^2 - 9} \cdot \dfrac{x + 3}{x + 2} \div \dfrac{5}{x + 2}$

120. $\dfrac{x^2 - 5x}{x + 1} \cdot \dfrac{x + 1}{x^2 + 3x} \div \dfrac{x - 5}{x - 3}$

121. $\dfrac{x - x^2}{x^2 - 4}\left(\dfrac{2x + 4}{x + 2} \div \dfrac{5}{x + 2}\right)$

122. $\dfrac{2}{3x - 3} \div \left(\dfrac{2x + 2}{x - 1} \cdot \dfrac{5}{x + 1}\right)$

123. $\dfrac{y^2}{x + 1} \cdot \dfrac{x^2 + 2x + 1}{x^2 - 1} \div \dfrac{3y}{xy - y}$

124. $\dfrac{x^2 - y^2}{x^4 - x^3} \div \dfrac{x - y}{x^2} \div \dfrac{x^2 + 2xy + y^2}{x + y}$

WRITING ABOUT MATH

125. Explain how to multiply two fractions and how to simplify the result.

126. Explain why any mathematical expression can be written as a fraction.

127. To divide fractions, you must first know how to multiply fractions. Explain.

128. Explain how to do the division $\dfrac{a}{b} \div \dfrac{c}{d} \div \dfrac{e}{f}$.

SOMETHING TO THINK ABOUT

129. Let x equal a number of your choosing. Without simplifying first, use a calculator to evaluate

$$\dfrac{x^2 + x - 6}{x^2 + 3x} \cdot \dfrac{x^2}{x - 2}$$

Try again, with a different value of x. If you were to simplify the expression, what do you think you would get?

130. Simplify the expression in Exercise 129 to determine whether your answer was correct.

Adding and Subtracting Rational Expressions

Objectives

1 Add two rational expressions with like denominators and write the answer in simplest form.

2 Subtract two rational expressions with like denominators and write the answer in simplest form.

3 Find the least common denominator (LCD) of two or more polynomials.

4 Add two rational expressions with unlike denominators and write the answer in simplest form.

5 Subtract two rational expressions with unlike denominators and write the answer in simplest form.

Vocabulary

least common denominator
(LCD)

Getting Ready

Add or subtract the fractions and simplify.

1. $\dfrac{1}{5} + \dfrac{3}{5}$ **2.** $\dfrac{3}{7} + \dfrac{4}{7}$ **3.** $\dfrac{3}{8} + \dfrac{4}{8}$ **4.** $\dfrac{18}{19} + \dfrac{20}{19}$

5. $\dfrac{5}{9} - \dfrac{4}{9}$ **6.** $\dfrac{7}{12} - \dfrac{1}{12}$ **7.** $\dfrac{7}{13} - \dfrac{9}{13}$ **8.** $\dfrac{20}{10} - \dfrac{7}{10}$

We now discuss how to add and subtract rational expressions.

1 **Add two rational expressions with like denominators and write the answer in simplest form.**

To add rational expressions with a common denominator, we follow the same process we use to add fractions; add their numerators and keep the common denominator. For example,

$$\frac{2x}{7} + \frac{3x}{7} = \frac{2x + 3x}{7} \qquad \text{Add the numerators and keep the common denominator.}$$

$$= \frac{5x}{7} \qquad 2x + 3x = 5x$$

In general, we have the following result.

Adding Rational Expressions with Like Denominators	If a, b, and d represent real numbers, then $$\frac{a}{d} + \frac{b}{d} = \frac{a+b}{d} \quad (d \neq 0)$$

EXAMPLE 1   Perform each addition. Assume that no denominators are 0.

a. In each part, we will add the numerators and keep the common denominator.

$$\frac{xy}{8z} + \frac{3xy}{8z} = \frac{xy + 3xy}{8z} \qquad \text{Add the numerators and keep the common denominator.}$$

$$= \frac{4xy}{8z} \qquad \text{Combine like terms.}$$

$$= \frac{xy}{2z} \qquad \frac{4xy}{8z} = \frac{4 \cdot xy}{4 \cdot 2z} = \frac{xy}{2z}, \text{ because } \frac{4}{4} = 1.$$

b. $\dfrac{3x + y}{5x} + \dfrac{x + y}{5x} = \dfrac{3x + y + x + y}{5x}$ Add the numerators and keep the common denominator.

$$= \frac{4x + 2y}{5x} \qquad \text{Combine like terms.}$$

COMMENT   After adding two fractions, simplify the result if possible.

 **SELF CHECK 1**   Perform each addition. Assume no denominators are 0.

a. $\dfrac{x}{7} + \dfrac{y}{7}$ **b.** $\dfrac{3x}{7y} + \dfrac{4x}{7y}$

EXAMPLE 2   Add: $\dfrac{3x + 21}{5x + 10} + \dfrac{8x + 1}{5x + 10} \quad (x \neq -2).$

Solution   Since the rational expressions have the same denominator, we add their numerators and keep the common denominator.

$$\frac{3x + 21}{5x + 10} + \frac{8x + 1}{5x + 10} = \frac{3x + 21 + 8x + 1}{5x + 10} \qquad \text{Add the fractions.}$$

$$= \frac{11x + 22}{5x + 10} \qquad \text{Combine like terms.}$$

$$= \frac{11\overset{1}{\cancel{(x + 2)}}}{5\underset{1}{\cancel{(x + 2)}}} \qquad \begin{array}{l}\text{Factor and divide out the common}\\\text{factor of } x + 2.\end{array}$$

$$= \frac{11}{5}$$

SELF CHECK 2   Add: $\dfrac{x + 4}{6x - 12} + \dfrac{x - 8}{6x - 12} \quad (x \neq 2).$

2 **Subtract two rational expressions with like denominators and write the answer in simplest form.**

To subtract rational expressions with a common denominator, we subtract their numerators and keep the common denominator.

Subtracting Rational Expressions with Like Denominators	If a, b, and d represent real numbers, then
	$$\frac{a}{d} - \frac{b}{d} = \frac{a - b}{d} \quad (d \neq 0)$$

EXAMPLE 3 Subtract, assuming no divisions by zero.

a. $\dfrac{5x}{3} - \dfrac{2x}{3}$ **b.** $\dfrac{5x + 1}{x - 3} - \dfrac{4x - 2}{x - 3}$

Solution In each part, the rational expressions have the same denominator. To subtract them, we subtract their numerators and keep the common denominator.

a. $\dfrac{5x}{3} - \dfrac{2x}{3} = \dfrac{5x - 2x}{3}$ Subtract the numerators and keep the common denominator.

$= \dfrac{3x}{3}$ Combine like terms.

$= \dfrac{x}{1}$ $\frac{3}{3} = 1$

$= x$ Denominators of 1 need not be written.

b. $\dfrac{5x + 1}{x - 3} - \dfrac{4x - 2}{x - 3} = \dfrac{(5x + 1) - (4x - 2)}{x - 3}$ Subtract the numerators and keep the common denominator.

$= \dfrac{5x + 1 - 4x + 2}{x - 3}$ Remove parentheses.

$= \dfrac{x + 3}{x - 3}$ Combine like terms.

⇨ **SELF CHECK 3** Subtract: $\dfrac{2y + 1}{y + 5} - \dfrac{y - 4}{y + 5}$ $(y \neq -5)$.

To add and/or subtract three or more rational expressions, we follow the rules for order of operations.

EXAMPLE 4 Simplify: $\dfrac{3x + 1}{x - 7} - \dfrac{5x + 2}{x - 7} + \dfrac{2x + 1}{x - 7}$ $(x \neq 7)$.

Solution This example involves both addition and subtraction of rational expressions. Unless parentheses indicate otherwise, we do additions and subtractions from left to right.

$$\frac{3x + 1}{x - 7} - \frac{5x + 2}{x - 7} + \frac{2x + 1}{x - 7}$$

$$= \frac{(3x + 1) - (5x + 2) + (2x + 1)}{x - 7}$$ Combine the numerators and keep the common denominator.

$$= \frac{3x + 1 - 5x - 2 + 2x + 1}{x - 7}$$ Remove parentheses.

$$= \frac{0}{x - 7}$$ Combine like terms.

$$= 0$$ Simplify.

⇨ **SELF CHECK 4**   Simplify: $\frac{2a - 3}{a - 5} + \frac{3a + 2}{a - 5} - \frac{24}{a - 5}$ $(a \neq 5)$.

Example 4 illustrates that if the numerator of a rational expression is 0 and the denominator is not, the value of the expression is 0.

3 **Find the least common denominator (LCD) of two or more polynomials.**

Since the denominators of the fractions in the addition $\frac{4}{7} + \frac{3}{5}$ are different, we cannot add the fractions in their present form.

four-sevenths   +   three-fifths
└─────── Different denominators ───────┘

To add these fractions, we need to find a common denominator. The smallest common denominator (called the **least** or **lowest common denominator**) is the easiest one to use.

Least Common Denominator	The least common denominator (LCD) for a set of fractions is the smallest number that each denominator will divide exactly.

In the addition $\frac{4}{7} + \frac{3}{5}$, the denominators are 7 and 5. The smallest number that 7 and 5 will divide exactly is 35. This is the LCD. We now build each fraction into a fraction with a denominator of 35.

$$\frac{4}{7} + \frac{3}{5} = \frac{4 \cdot 5}{7 \cdot 5} + \frac{3 \cdot 7}{5 \cdot 7}$$ Multiply numerator and denominator of $\frac{4}{7}$ by 5, and multiply numerator and denominator of $\frac{3}{5}$ by 7.

$$= \frac{20}{35} + \frac{21}{35}$$ Do the multiplications.

Now that the fractions have a common denominator, we can add them.

$$\frac{20}{35} + \frac{21}{35} = \frac{20 + 21}{35} = \frac{41}{35}$$

EXAMPLE 5   Write each rational expression as a rational expression with a denominator of $30y$ $(y \neq 0)$.

a. $\dfrac{1}{2y}$ **b.** $\dfrac{3y}{5}$ **c.** $\dfrac{7x}{10y}$

Solution   To build each rational expression into an expression with a denominator of $30y$, we multiply the numerator and denominator by what it takes to make the denominator $30y$.

a. $\dfrac{1}{2y} = \dfrac{1 \cdot 15}{2y \cdot 15} = \dfrac{15}{30y}$

b. $\dfrac{3y}{5} = \dfrac{3y \cdot 6y}{5 \cdot 6y} = \dfrac{18y^2}{30y}$

c. $\dfrac{7x}{10y} = \dfrac{7x \cdot 3}{10y \cdot 3} = \dfrac{21x}{30y}$

▷ **SELF CHECK 5**   Write $\frac{5a}{6b}$ as a rational expression with a denominator of $30ab$ $(a, b \neq 0)$.

There is a process that we can use to find the least common denominator of several rational expressions.

Finding the Least Common Denominator (LCD)

1. List the different denominators that appear in the rational expressions.
2. Completely factor each denominator.
3. Form a product using each different factor obtained in Step 2. Use each different factor the *greatest* number of times it appears in any *one* factorization. The product formed by multiplying these factors is the LCD.

EXAMPLE 6   Find the LCD of $\dfrac{5a}{24b}$, $\dfrac{11a}{18b}$, and $\dfrac{35a}{36b}$ $(b \neq 0)$.

Solution   We list and factor each denominator into the product of prime numbers.

$$24b = 2 \cdot 2 \cdot 2 \cdot 3 \cdot b = 2^3 \cdot 3 \cdot b$$
$$18b = 2 \cdot 3 \cdot 3 \cdot b = 2 \cdot 3^2 \cdot b$$
$$36b = 2 \cdot 2 \cdot 3 \cdot 3 \cdot b = 2^2 \cdot 3^2 \cdot b$$

We then form a product with factors of 2, 3, and b. To find the LCD, we use each of these factors the *greatest* number of times it appears in any one factorization. We use 2 three times, because it appears three times as a factor of 24. We use 3 twice, because it occurs twice as a factor of 18 and 36. We use b once because it occurs once in each factor of $24b$, $18b$, and $36b$.

$$\text{LCD} = 2 \cdot 2 \cdot 2 \cdot 3 \cdot 3 \cdot b$$
$$= 8 \cdot 9 \cdot b$$
$$= 72b$$

▷ **SELF CHECK 6**   Find the LCD of $\frac{3y}{28z}$ and $\frac{5x}{21z}$ $(z \neq 0)$.

④ **Add two rational expressions with unlike denominators and write the answer in simplest form.**

The process for adding and subtracting rational expressions with different denominators is the same as the process for adding and subtracting expressions with different numerical denominators.

For example, to add $\frac{4x}{7}$ and $\frac{3x}{5}$, we first find the LCD, which is 35. We then build the rational expressions so that each one has a denominator of 35. Finally, we add the results.

$$\frac{4x}{7} + \frac{3x}{5} = \frac{4x \cdot 5}{7 \cdot 5} + \frac{3x \cdot 7}{5 \cdot 7} \qquad \text{Multiply numerator and denominator of } \tfrac{4x}{7} \text{ by 5 and numerator and denominator of } \tfrac{3x}{5} \text{ by 7.}$$

$$= \frac{20x}{35} + \frac{21x}{35} \qquad \text{Do the multiplications.}$$

$$= \frac{41x}{35} \qquad \text{Add the numerators and keep the common denominator.}$$

The following steps summarize how to add rational expressions that have unlike denominators.

Adding Rational Expressions with Unlike Denominators

To add rational expressions with unlike denominators:

1. Find the LCD.
2. Write each fraction as a fraction with a denominator that is the LCD.
3. Add the resulting fractions and simplify the result, if possible.

EXAMPLE 7   Add: $\dfrac{5a}{24b}, \dfrac{11a}{18b},$ and $\dfrac{35a}{36b}$ $(b \neq 0)$.

Solution   In Example 6, we saw that the LCD of these rational expressions is $2 \cdot 2 \cdot 2 \cdot 3 \cdot 3 \cdot b = 72b$. To add the rational expressions, we first factor each denominator:

$$\frac{5a}{24b} + \frac{11a}{18b} + \frac{35a}{36b} = \frac{5a}{2 \cdot 2 \cdot 2 \cdot 3 \cdot b} + \frac{11a}{2 \cdot 3 \cdot 3 \cdot b} + \frac{35a}{2 \cdot 2 \cdot 3 \cdot 3 \cdot b}$$

In each resulting expression, we multiply the numerator and the denominator by whatever it takes to build the denominator to the lowest common denominator of $2 \cdot 2 \cdot 2 \cdot 3 \cdot 3 \cdot b$.

$$= \frac{5a \cdot 3}{2 \cdot 2 \cdot 2 \cdot 3 \cdot b \cdot 3} + \frac{11a \cdot 2 \cdot 2}{2 \cdot 3 \cdot 3 \cdot b \cdot 2 \cdot 2} + \frac{35a \cdot 2}{2 \cdot 2 \cdot 3 \cdot 3 \cdot b \cdot 2}$$

$$= \frac{15a + 44a + 70a}{72b} \qquad \text{Do the multiplications.}$$

$$= \frac{129a}{72b} \qquad \text{Add the fractions.}$$

$$= \frac{43a}{24b} \qquad \text{Simplify.}$$

⇨ SELF CHECK 7   Add: $\frac{3y}{28z} + \frac{5x}{21z}$ $(z \neq 0)$.

EXAMPLE 8 Add: $\dfrac{5y}{14x} + \dfrac{2y}{21x}$ $(x \neq 0)$.

Solution We first find the LCD

$$\left.\begin{array}{l} 14x = 2 \cdot 7 \cdot x \\ 21x = 3 \cdot 7 \cdot x \end{array}\right\} \quad \text{LCD} = 2 \cdot 3 \cdot 7 \cdot x = 42x$$

and then build the rational expressions so that each one has a denominator of $42x$.

$$\begin{aligned} \dfrac{5y}{14x} + \dfrac{2y}{21x} &= \dfrac{5y \cdot 3}{14x \cdot 3} + \dfrac{2y \cdot 2}{21x \cdot 2} && \text{Multiply the numerator and denominator of } \tfrac{5y}{14x} \text{ by} \\ && \text{3 and those of } \tfrac{2y}{21x} \text{ by 2.} \\ &= \dfrac{15y}{42x} + \dfrac{4y}{42x} && \text{Do the multiplications.} \\ &= \dfrac{19y}{42x} && \text{Add the fractions.} \end{aligned}$$

⇨ **SELF CHECK 8** Add: $\dfrac{3y}{4x} + \dfrac{2y}{3x}$ $(x \neq 0)$.

EXAMPLE 9 Add: $\dfrac{1}{x} + \dfrac{x}{y}$ $(x, y \neq 0)$.

Solution By inspection, the LCD is xy.

$$\begin{aligned} \dfrac{1}{x} + \dfrac{x}{y} &= \dfrac{1(y)}{x(y)} + \dfrac{(x)x}{(x)y} && \text{Build the fractions to get the common denominator of } xy. \\ &= \dfrac{y}{xy} + \dfrac{x^2}{xy} && \text{Do the multiplications.} \\ &= \dfrac{y + x^2}{xy} && \text{Add the fractions.} \end{aligned}$$

⇨ **SELF CHECK 9** Add: $\dfrac{a}{b} + \dfrac{3}{a}$ $(a, b \neq 0)$.

5 **Subtract two rational expressions with unlike denominators and write the answer in simplest form.**

To subtract rational expressions with unlike denominators, we first write them as expressions with the same denominator and then subtract the numerators.

EXAMPLE 10 Subtract: $\dfrac{x}{x + 1} - \dfrac{3}{x}$ $(x \neq 0, -1)$.

Solution Because x and $x + 1$ represent different values and have no common factors, the least common denominator (LCD) is their product, $(x + 1)x$.

$$\dfrac{x}{x + 1} - \dfrac{3}{x} = \dfrac{x(x)}{(x + 1)x} - \dfrac{3(x + 1)}{x(x + 1)} \qquad \text{Build the fractions to get the common denominator.}$$

$$= \frac{x(x) - 3(x + 1)}{(x + 1)x}$$

Subtract the numerators and keep the common denominator.

$$= \frac{x^2 - 3x - 3}{(x + 1)x}$$

Do the multiplication in the numerator.

⇨ **SELF CHECK 10** Subtract: $\dfrac{a}{a - 1} - \dfrac{5}{b}$ ($a \neq 1, b \neq 0$).

EXAMPLE 11 Subtract: $\dfrac{a}{a - 1} - \dfrac{2}{a^2 - 1}$ ($a \neq 1, -1$).

Solution To find the LCD, we factor both denominators.

$$\left. \begin{array}{l} a - 1 = a - 1 \\ a^2 - 1 = (a + 1)(a - 1) \end{array} \right\} \quad \text{LCD} = (a + 1)(a - 1)$$

After finding the LCD, we proceed as follows:

$$\frac{a}{a - 1} - \frac{2}{a^2 - 1}$$

$$= \frac{a}{(a - 1)} - \frac{2}{(a + 1)(a - 1)}$$

Factor the denominator.

$$= \frac{a(a + 1)}{(a - 1)(a + 1)} - \frac{2}{(a + 1)(a - 1)}$$

Build the first fraction.

$$= \frac{a(a + 1) - 2}{(a - 1)(a + 1)}$$

Subtract the numerators and keep the common denominator.

$$= \frac{a^2 + a - 2}{(a - 1)(a + 1)}$$

Remove parentheses.

$$= \frac{\overset{1}{(a + 2)(\cancel{a - 1})}}{\underset{1}{(\cancel{a - 1})(a + 1)}}$$

Factor and divide out the common factor of $a - 1$.

$$= \frac{a + 2}{a + 1}$$

Simplify.

⇨ **SELF CHECK 11** Subtract: $\dfrac{b}{b + 1} - \dfrac{3}{b^2 - 1}$ ($b \neq 1, -1$).

EXAMPLE 12 Subtract: $\dfrac{3}{x - y} - \dfrac{x}{y - x}$ ($x \neq y$).

Solution We note that the second denominator is the negative of the first, so we can multiply the numerator and denominator of the second fraction by -1 to get

$$\frac{3}{x - y} - \frac{x}{y - x} = \frac{3}{x - y} - \frac{-1x}{-1(y - x)}$$

Multiply numerator and denominator by -1.

$$= \frac{3}{x - y} - \frac{-x}{-y + x}$$

Remove parentheses.

$$= \frac{3}{x - y} - \frac{-x}{x - y}$$

$-y + x = x - y$

$$= \frac{3 - (-x)}{x - y}$$ Subtract the numerators and keep the common denominator.

$$= \frac{3 + x}{x - y}$$ $-(-x) = x$

⇨ **SELF CHECK 12** Subtract: $\dfrac{5}{a - b} - \dfrac{2}{b - a}$ $(a \ne b)$.

To add and/or subtract three or more rational expressions, we follow the rules for the order of operations.

EXAMPLE 13 Perform the operations: $\dfrac{3}{x^2 y} + \dfrac{2}{xy} - \dfrac{1}{xy^2}$ $(x \ne 0, y \ne 0)$.

Solution Find the least common denominator.

$$\left. \begin{array}{l} x^2 y = x \cdot x \cdot y \\ xy = x \cdot y \\ xy^2 = x \cdot y \cdot y \end{array} \right\}$$ Factor each denominator.

In any one of these denominators, the factor x occurs at most twice, and the factor y occurs at most twice. Thus,

$$\begin{aligned} \text{LCD} &= x \cdot x \cdot y \cdot y \\ &= x^2 y^2 \end{aligned}$$

We build each rational expression into an expression with a denominator of $x^2 y^2$.

$$\frac{3}{x^2 y} + \frac{2}{xy} - \frac{1}{xy^2}$$

$$= \frac{3 \cdot y}{x \cdot x \cdot y \cdot y} + \frac{2 \cdot x \cdot y}{x \cdot y \cdot x \cdot y} - \frac{1 \cdot x}{x \cdot y \cdot y \cdot x}$$ Factor each denominator and build each fraction.

$$= \frac{3y + 2xy - x}{x^2 y^2}$$ Do the multiplications and combine the numerators.

⇨ **SELF CHECK 13** Combine: $\dfrac{5}{ab^2} - \dfrac{b}{a} + \dfrac{a}{b}$ $(a, b \ne 0)$.

EXAMPLE 14 Perform the operations: $\dfrac{3}{x^2 - y^2} + \dfrac{2}{x - y} - \dfrac{1}{x + y}$. Assume that no denominator is 0.

Solution Find the least common denominator.

$$\left. \begin{array}{l} x^2 - y^2 = (x - y)(x + y) \\ x - y = x - y \\ x + y = x + y \end{array} \right\}$$ Factor each denominator, where possible.

Since the least common denominator is $(x - y)(x + y)$, we build each fraction into a new fraction with that common denominator.

$$\frac{3}{x^2 - y^2} + \frac{2}{x - y} - \frac{1}{x + y}$$

$$= \frac{3}{(x - y)(x + y)} + \frac{2}{x - y} - \frac{1}{x + y}$$ Factor.

$$= \frac{3}{(x - y)(x + y)} + \frac{2(x + y)}{(x - y)(x + y)} - \frac{1(x - y)}{(x + y)(x - y)}$$ Build each fraction to get a common denominator.

$$= \frac{3 + 2(x + y) - 1(x - y)}{(x - y)(x + y)}$$ Combine the numerators and keep the common denominator.

$$= \frac{3 + 2x + 2y - x + y}{(x - y)(x + y)}$$ Remove parentheses.

$$= \frac{3 + x + 3y}{(x - y)(x + y)}$$ Combine like terms.

⇨ **SELF CHECK 14** Perform the operations: $\frac{5}{a^2 - b^2} - \frac{3}{a + b} + \frac{4}{a - b}$ $(a \neq b, a \neq -b)$.

⇨ **SELF CHECK ANSWERS**
1. a. $\frac{x + y}{7}$ **b.** $\frac{x}{y}$ **2.** $\frac{1}{3}$ **3.** 1 **4.** 5 **5.** $\frac{25a^2}{30ab}$ **6.** $84z$ **7.** $\frac{9y + 20x}{84z}$ **8.** $\frac{17y}{12x}$ **9.** $\frac{a^2 + 3b}{ab}$
10. $\frac{ab - 5a + 5}{(a - 1)b}$ **11.** $\frac{b^2 - b - 3}{(b + 1)(b - 1)}$ **12.** $\frac{7}{a - b}$ **13.** $\frac{5 - b^3 + a^2b}{ab^2}$ **14.** $\frac{a + 7b + 5}{(a + b)(a - b)}$

NOW TRY THIS

Simplify:

1. $\dfrac{5}{x + 3} - \dfrac{2}{x - 3}$

2. $\left(\dfrac{2}{3x} - 1\right) \div \left(\dfrac{4}{9x} - x\right)$

3. $x^{-1} + x^{-2}$

6.3 EXERCISES

WARM-UPS *Determine whether the expressions are equal.*

1. $\dfrac{1}{2}, \dfrac{6}{12}$

2. $\dfrac{3}{8}, \dfrac{15}{40}$

3. $\dfrac{7}{9}, \dfrac{14}{27}$

4. $\dfrac{5}{10}, \dfrac{15}{30}$

5. $\dfrac{x}{3}, \dfrac{3x}{9}$

6. $\dfrac{5}{3}, \dfrac{5x}{3y}$ $(y \neq 0)$

7. $\dfrac{5}{3}, \dfrac{5x}{3x}$ $(x \neq 0)$

8. $\dfrac{5y}{10}, \dfrac{y}{2}$

REVIEW *Write each number in prime-factored form.*

9. 49 **10.** 64

11. 136 **12.** 242

13. 102   **14.** 315

15. 144   **16.** 145

VOCABULARY AND CONCEPTS   *Fill in the blanks.*

17. The _____ for a set of rational expressions is the smallest number that each denominator divides exactly.

18. When we multiply the numerator and denominator of a rational expressions by some number to get a common denominator, we say that we are _____ the fraction.

19. To add two rational expressions with like denominators, we add their _____ and keep the _____.

20. To subtract two rational expressions with _____ denominators, we need to find a common denominator.

GUIDED PRACTICE

Perform the operations. Simplify answers, if possible. Assume that no denominators are 0. See Examples 1–2. (Objective 1)

21. $\dfrac{1}{3} + \dfrac{1}{3}$ **22.** $\dfrac{3}{4} + \dfrac{3}{4}$

23. $\dfrac{2}{9} + \dfrac{1}{9}$ **24.** $\dfrac{5}{7} + \dfrac{9}{7}$

25. $\dfrac{2x}{y} + \dfrac{2x}{y}$ **26.** $\dfrac{4y}{3x} + \dfrac{2y}{3x}$

27. $\dfrac{3x-5}{x-2} + \dfrac{6x-13}{x-2}$ **28.** $\dfrac{8x-7}{x+3} + \dfrac{2x+37}{x+3}$

Perform the operations. Simplify answers, if possible. Assume that no denominators are 0. See Example 3. (Objective 2)

29. $\dfrac{35}{72} - \dfrac{44}{72}$ **30.** $\dfrac{35}{99} - \dfrac{13}{99}$

31. $\dfrac{2x}{y} - \dfrac{x}{y}$ **32.** $\dfrac{7y}{5} - \dfrac{4y}{5}$

33. $\dfrac{6x-5}{3xy} - \dfrac{3x-5}{3xy}$ **34.** $\dfrac{7x+7}{5y} - \dfrac{2x+7}{5y}$

35. $\dfrac{3y-2}{y+3} - \dfrac{2y-5}{y+3}$ **36.** $\dfrac{5x+8}{x+5} - \dfrac{3x-2}{x+5}$

Perform the operations. Simplify answers, if possible. Assume that no denominators are 0. See Example 4. (Objectives 1–2)

37. $\dfrac{13x}{15} + \dfrac{12x}{15} - \dfrac{5x}{15}$ **38.** $\dfrac{13y}{32} + \dfrac{13y}{32} - \dfrac{10y}{32}$

39. $\dfrac{x+1}{x-2} - \dfrac{2(x-3)}{x-2} + \dfrac{3(x+1)}{x-2}$

40. $\dfrac{3xy}{x-y} - \dfrac{x(3y-x)}{x-y} - \dfrac{x(x-y)}{x-y}$

Build each fraction into an equivalent fraction with the indicated denominator. Assume that no denominators are 0. See Example 5. (Objective 3)

41. $\dfrac{25}{4}$; 20   **42.** $\dfrac{5}{y}$; xy

43. $\dfrac{8}{x}$; x^2y **44.** $\dfrac{7}{y}$; xy^2

45. $\dfrac{3x}{x+1}$; $(x+1)^2$ **46.** $\dfrac{5y}{y-2}$; $(y-2)^2$

47. $\dfrac{2y}{x}$; x^2+x **48.** $\dfrac{3x}{y}$; y^2-y

49. $\dfrac{z}{z-1}$; z^2-1 **50.** $\dfrac{y}{y+2}$; y^2-4

51. $\dfrac{2}{x+1}$; x^2+3x+2 **52.** $\dfrac{3}{x-1}$; x^2+x-2

Several denominators are given. Find the LCD. See Example 6. (Objective 3)

53. $2x$, $6x$ **54.** $3y$, $9y$

55. $3x$, $6y$, $9xy$ **56.** $2x^2$, $6y$, $3xy$

57. x^2-1, $x+1$ **58.** y^2-9, $y-3$

59. x^2+6x, $x+6$, x **60.** xy^2-xy, xy, $y-1$

Perform the operations. Simplify answers, if possible. Assume that no denominators are 0. See Examples 7–9. (Objective 4)

61. $\dfrac{1}{2} + \dfrac{2}{3}$ **62.** $\dfrac{4x}{3} + \dfrac{2x}{y}$

63. $\dfrac{2y}{9} + \dfrac{y}{3}$ **64.** $\dfrac{7y}{6} + \dfrac{10y}{9}$

65. $\dfrac{x-1}{x} + \dfrac{y+1}{y}$ **66.** $\dfrac{a+2}{b} + \dfrac{b-2}{a}$

67. $\dfrac{x+1}{x-1} + \dfrac{x-1}{x+1}$ **68.** $\dfrac{2x}{x+2} + \dfrac{x+1}{x-3}$

69. $\dfrac{x+3}{x^2} + \dfrac{x+5}{2x}$ **70.** $\dfrac{y+2}{5y} + \dfrac{y+4}{15y}$

71. $\dfrac{x}{x+1} + \dfrac{x-1}{x}$ **72.** $\dfrac{3x}{xy} + \dfrac{x+1}{y-1}$

Perform the operations. Simplify answers, if possible. Assume that no denominators are 0. See Examples 10–12. (Objective 5)

73. $\dfrac{2}{3} - \dfrac{5}{6}$ **74.** $\dfrac{8a}{15} - \dfrac{5a}{12}$

75. $\dfrac{21x}{14} - \dfrac{5x}{21}$

76. $\dfrac{2y}{5x} - \dfrac{y}{2}$

77. $\dfrac{x+5}{xy} - \dfrac{x-1}{x^2 y}$

78. $\dfrac{y-7}{y^2} - \dfrac{y+7}{2y}$

79. $\dfrac{x}{x-2} + \dfrac{4+2x}{x^2-4}$

80. $\dfrac{y}{y+3} - \dfrac{2y-6}{y^2-9}$

81. $\dfrac{x+1}{x+2} - \dfrac{x^2+1}{x^2-x-6}$

82. $\dfrac{x+1}{2x+4} - \dfrac{x^2}{2x^2-8}$

83. $\dfrac{y+3}{y-1} - \dfrac{y+4}{1-y}$

84. $\dfrac{2x+2}{x-2} - \dfrac{2x}{2-x}$

Perform the operations. Simplify answers, if possible. Assume that no denominators are 0. See Examples 13–14. (Objectives 4–5)

85. $\dfrac{2x}{x^2-3x+2} + \dfrac{2x}{x-1} - \dfrac{x}{x-2}$

86. $\dfrac{4a}{a-2} - \dfrac{3a}{a-3} + \dfrac{4a}{a^2-5a+6}$

87. $\dfrac{a}{a-1} - \dfrac{2}{a+2} + \dfrac{3(a-2)}{a^2+a-2}$

88. $\dfrac{2x}{x-1} + \dfrac{3x}{x+1} - \dfrac{x+3}{x^2-1}$

ADDITIONAL PRACTICE

Several denominators are given. Find the LCD.

89. $x^2 - x - 6,\ x^2 - 9$

90. $x^2 - 4x - 5,\ x^2 - 25$

Perform the operations. Assume that no denominators are 0.

91. $\dfrac{4}{7y} + \dfrac{10}{7y}$

92. $\dfrac{x^2}{4y} + \dfrac{x^2}{4y}$

93. $\dfrac{y+2}{5z} + \dfrac{y+4}{5z}$

94. $\dfrac{x+3}{x^2} + \dfrac{x+5}{x^2}$

95. $\dfrac{9y}{3x} - \dfrac{6y}{3x}$

96. $\dfrac{5r^2}{2r} - \dfrac{r^2}{2r}$

97. $\dfrac{x}{3y} + \dfrac{2x}{3y} - \dfrac{x}{3y}$

98. $\dfrac{5y}{8x} + \dfrac{4y}{8x} - \dfrac{y}{8x}$

99. $14 + \dfrac{10}{y^2}$

100. $\dfrac{2}{x} - 3x$

101. $\dfrac{3x}{y+2} - \dfrac{3y}{y+2} + \dfrac{x+y}{y+2}$

102. $\dfrac{3y}{x-5} + \dfrac{x}{x-5} - \dfrac{y-x}{x-5}$

103. $\dfrac{-a}{3a^2-27} + \dfrac{1}{3a+9}$

104. $\dfrac{d}{d^2+6d+5} - \dfrac{d}{d^2+5d+4}$

WRITING ABOUT MATH

105. Explain how to add rational expressions with the same denominator.

106. Explain how to subtract rational expressions with the same denominator.

107. Explain how to find a lowest common denominator.

108. Explain how to add two rational expressions with different denominators.

SOMETHING TO THINK ABOUT

109. Find the error:

$$\dfrac{2x+3}{x+5} - \dfrac{x+2}{x+5} = \dfrac{2x+3-x+2}{x+5}$$
$$= \dfrac{x+5}{x+5}$$
$$= 1$$

110. Find the error:

$$\dfrac{5x-4}{y} + \dfrac{x}{y} = \dfrac{5x-4+x}{y+y}$$
$$= \dfrac{6x-4}{2y}$$
$$= \dfrac{3x-2}{y}$$

Show that each formula is true.

111. $\dfrac{a}{b} + \dfrac{c}{d} = \dfrac{ad+bc}{bd}$

112. $\dfrac{a}{b} - \dfrac{c}{d} = \dfrac{ad-bc}{bd}$

SECTION 6.4 Simplifying Complex Fractions

Objectives

1. Simplify a complex fraction.
2. Simplify a fraction containing terms with negative exponents.

Vocabulary

complex fraction

Getting Ready

Use the distributive property to remove parentheses, and simplify.

1. $3\left(1 + \dfrac{1}{3}\right)$ **2.** $10\left(\dfrac{1}{5} - 2\right)$ **3.** $4\left(\dfrac{3}{2} + \dfrac{1}{4}\right)$ **4.** $14\left(\dfrac{3}{7} - 1\right)$

5. $x\left(\dfrac{3}{x} + 3\right)$ **6.** $y\left(\dfrac{2}{y} - 1\right)$ **7.** $4x\left(3 - \dfrac{1}{2x}\right)$ **8.** $6xy\left(\dfrac{1}{2x} + \dfrac{1}{3y}\right)$

In this section, we consider fractions that contain fractions. These complicated fractions are called *complex fractions*.

1 Simplify a complex fraction.

Fractions such as

$$\dfrac{\dfrac{1}{3}}{4}, \qquad \dfrac{\dfrac{5}{3}}{\dfrac{2}{9}}, \qquad \dfrac{x + \dfrac{1}{2}}{3 - x}, \qquad \text{and} \qquad \dfrac{\dfrac{x + 1}{2}}{x + \dfrac{1}{x}}$$

that contain fractions in their numerators and/or denominators are called **complex fractions.** Complex fractions should be simplified. For example, we can simplify

$$\dfrac{\dfrac{5x}{3}}{\dfrac{2y}{9}}$$

by doing the division:

$$\frac{\dfrac{5x}{3}}{\dfrac{2y}{9}} = \frac{5x}{3} \div \frac{2y}{9} = \frac{5x}{3} \cdot \frac{9}{2y} = \frac{5x \cdot 3 \cdot \overset{1}{\cancel{3}}}{\underset{1}{\cancel{3}} \cdot 2y} = \frac{15x}{2y}$$

There are two methods that we can use to simplify complex fractions.

Simplifying Complex Fractions

Method 1
Write the numerator and the denominator of the complex fraction as single fractions. Then divide the fractions and simplify.

Method 2
Multiply the numerator and denominator of the complex fraction by the LCD of the fractions in its numerator and denominator. Then simplify the results, if possible.

Hypatia
(370 A.D.–415 A.D.)
Hypatia is the earliest known woman in the history of mathematics. She was a professor at the University of Alexandria. Because of her scientific beliefs, she was considered to be a heretic. At the age of 45, she was attacked by a mob and murdered for her beliefs.

To simplify $\dfrac{\dfrac{3x}{5} + 1}{2 - \dfrac{x}{5}}$ (assuming no division by 0) using Method 1, we proceed as follows:

$$\frac{\dfrac{3x}{5} + 1}{2 - \dfrac{x}{5}} = \frac{\dfrac{3x}{5} + \dfrac{5}{5}}{\dfrac{10}{5} - \dfrac{x}{5}}$$ Write 1 as $\frac{5}{5}$ and 2 as $\frac{10}{5}$.

$$= \frac{\dfrac{3x + 5}{5}}{\dfrac{10 - x}{5}}$$ Add the fractions in the numerator and subtract the fractions in the denominator.

$$= \frac{3x + 5}{5} \div \frac{10 - x}{5}$$ Write the complex fraction as an equivalent division problem.

$$= \frac{3x + 5}{5} \cdot \frac{5}{10 - x}$$ Invert the divisor and multiply.

$$= \frac{(3x + 5)5}{5(10 - x)}$$ Multiply the fractions.

$$= \frac{3x + 5}{10 - x}$$ Divide out the common factor of 5: $\frac{5}{5} = 1$.

To use Method 2, we first determine that the LCD of the fractions in the numerator and denominator is 5. We then multiply both the numerator and denominator by 5.

$$\frac{\dfrac{3x}{5} + 1}{2 - \dfrac{x}{5}} = \frac{5\left(\dfrac{3x}{5} + 1\right)}{5\left(2 - \dfrac{x}{5}\right)}$$ Multiply both numerator and denominator by 5.

$$= \frac{5 \cdot \dfrac{3x}{5} + 5 \cdot 1}{5 \cdot 2 - 5 \cdot \dfrac{x}{5}}$$ Remove parentheses.

$$= \frac{3x + 5}{10 - x} \qquad \text{Do the multiplications.}$$

With practice, you will be able to see which method is easier to understand in any given situation.

EXAMPLE 1 Simplify: $\dfrac{\frac{x}{3}}{\frac{y}{3}}$. Assume that no denominators are 0.

Solution We will simplify the complex fraction using both methods.

Method 1

$$\frac{\frac{x}{3}}{\frac{y}{3}} = \frac{x}{3} \div \frac{y}{3}$$

$$= \frac{x}{3} \cdot \frac{3}{y}$$

$$= \frac{3x}{3y}$$

$$= \frac{x}{y}$$

Method 2

$$\frac{\frac{x}{3}}{\frac{y}{3}} = \frac{3\left(\frac{x}{3}\right)}{3\left(\frac{y}{3}\right)}$$

$$= \frac{\frac{x}{1}}{\frac{y}{1}}$$

$$= \frac{x}{y}$$

⇨ **SELF CHECK 1** Simplify: $\dfrac{\frac{a}{4}}{\frac{5}{b}}$. Assume no denominator is 0.

EXAMPLE 2 Simplify: $\dfrac{\frac{x}{x + 1}}{\frac{y}{x}}$. Assume no denominator is 0.

Solution We will simplify the complex fraction using both methods.

Method 1

$$\frac{\frac{x}{x + 1}}{\frac{y}{x}} = \frac{x}{x + 1} \div \frac{y}{x}$$

$$= \frac{x}{x + 1} \cdot \frac{x}{y}$$

$$= \frac{x^2}{y(x + 1)}$$

Method 2

$$\frac{\frac{x}{x + 1}}{\frac{y}{x}} = \frac{x(x + 1)\left(\frac{x}{x + 1}\right)}{x(x + 1)\left(\frac{y}{x}\right)}$$

$$= \frac{\frac{x^2}{1}}{\frac{y(x + 1)}{1}}$$

$$= \frac{x^2}{y(x + 1)}$$

⇨ **SELF CHECK 2** Simplify: $\dfrac{\dfrac{x}{y}}{\dfrac{x}{y+1}}$. Assume no denominator is 0.

EXAMPLE 3 Simplify: $\dfrac{1 + \dfrac{1}{x}}{1 - \dfrac{1}{x}}$. Assume no denominator is 0.

Solution We will simplify the complex fraction using both methods.

$$\textit{Method 1}$$

$$\frac{1 + \dfrac{1}{x}}{1 - \dfrac{1}{x}} = \frac{\dfrac{x}{x} + \dfrac{1}{x}}{\dfrac{x}{x} - \dfrac{1}{x}}$$

$$= \frac{\dfrac{x+1}{x}}{\dfrac{x-1}{x}}$$

$$= \frac{x+1}{x} \div \frac{x-1}{x}$$

$$= \frac{x+1}{x} \cdot \frac{x}{x-1}$$

$$= \frac{(x+1)x}{x(x-1)}$$

$$= \frac{x+1}{x-1}$$

$$\textit{Method 2}$$

$$\frac{1 + \dfrac{1}{x}}{1 - \dfrac{1}{x}} = \frac{x\left(1 + \dfrac{1}{x}\right)}{x\left(1 - \dfrac{1}{x}\right)}$$

$$= \frac{x+1}{x-1}$$

⇨ **SELF CHECK 3** Simplify: $\dfrac{\dfrac{1}{x} + 1}{\dfrac{1}{x} - 1}$. Assume no denominator is 0.

EXAMPLE 4 Simplify: $\dfrac{1}{1 + \dfrac{1}{x+1}}$. Assume no denominator is 0.

Solution We will simplify this complex fraction by using Method 2 only.

$$\frac{1}{1 + \dfrac{1}{x+1}} = \frac{(x+1) \cdot 1}{(x+1)\left(1 + \dfrac{1}{x+1}\right)} \qquad \text{Multiply numerator and denominator by } x+1.$$

$$= \frac{x+1}{(x+1)1 + 1} \qquad \text{Simplify.}$$

$$= \frac{x+1}{x+2} \qquad \text{Simplify.}$$

⇨ **SELF CHECK 4** Simplify: $\dfrac{2}{\dfrac{1}{x+2}-2}$. Assume no denominator is 0.

2 **Simplify a fraction containing terms with negative exponents.**

Many fractions with terms containing negative exponents are complex fractions in disguise.

EXAMPLE 5 Simplify: $\dfrac{x^{-1}+y^{-2}}{x^{-2}-y^{-1}}$. Assume no denominator is 0.

Solution We will write the fraction as a complex fraction and simplify:

$$\frac{x^{-1}+y^{-2}}{x^{-2}-y^{-1}}=\frac{\dfrac{1}{x}+\dfrac{1}{y^2}}{\dfrac{1}{x^2}-\dfrac{1}{y}}$$

$$=\frac{x^2y^2\left(\dfrac{1}{x}+\dfrac{1}{y^2}\right)}{x^2y^2\left(\dfrac{1}{x^2}-\dfrac{1}{y}\right)} \qquad \text{Multiply numerator and denominator by } x^2y^2.$$

$$=\frac{xy^2+x^2}{y^2-x^2y} \qquad \text{Remove parentheses.}$$

$$=\frac{x(y^2+x)}{y(y-x^2)} \qquad \begin{array}{l}\text{Attempt to simplify the fraction by factoring the}\\\text{numerator and denominator.}\end{array}$$

The result cannot be simplified.

⇨ **SELF CHECK 5** Simplify: $\dfrac{x^{-2}-y^{-1}}{x^{-1}+y^{-2}}$. Assume no denominator is 0.

⇨ **SELF CHECK ANSWERS** 1. $\dfrac{ab}{20}$ 2. $\dfrac{y+1}{y}$ 3. $\dfrac{1+x}{1-x}$ 4. $\dfrac{2(x+2)}{-2x-3}$ 5. $\dfrac{y(y-x^2)}{x(y^2+x)}$

NOW TRY THIS

Simplify:

1. $\dfrac{\dfrac{a}{y^2}}{\dfrac{b}{x^3}}$

2. $\dfrac{\dfrac{x}{x+2}+\dfrac{5}{x}}{\dfrac{1}{3x}+\dfrac{x}{2x+4}}$

6.4 EXERCISES

WARM-UPS   *Simplify each complex fraction.*

1. $\dfrac{\frac{2}{3}}{\frac{1}{2}}$

2. $\dfrac{2}{\frac{1}{2}}$

3. $\dfrac{\frac{1}{2}}{2}$

4. $\dfrac{1+\frac{1}{2}}{\frac{1}{2}}$

REVIEW

Write each expression as an expression involving only one exponent. Assume no variable is zero.

5. $t^3 t^4 t^2$

6. $(a^0 a^2)^3$

7. $-2r(r^3)^2$

8. $(s^3)^2(s^4)^0$

Write each expression without parentheses or negative exponents.

9. $\left(\dfrac{3r}{4r^3}\right)^4$

10. $\left(\dfrac{12y^{-3}}{3y^2}\right)^{-2}$

11. $\left(\dfrac{6r^{-2}}{2r^3}\right)^{-2}$

12. $\left(\dfrac{4x^3}{5x^{-3}}\right)^{-2}$

VOCABULARY AND CONCEPTS   *Fill in the blanks.*

13. If a fraction has a fraction in its numerator or denominator, it is called a _____.

14. The denominator of the complex fraction

$$\dfrac{\frac{3}{x}+\frac{x}{y}}{\frac{1}{x}+2}\text{ is }\underline{\quad}.$$

15. In Method 1, we write the numerator and denominator of a complex fraction as _____ fractions and then _____.

16. In Method 2, we multiply the numerator and denominator of the complex fraction by the _____ of the fractions in its numerator and denominator.

GUIDED PRACTICE

Simplify each complex fraction. Assume no division by 0. See Examples 1–2 (Objective 1)

17. $\dfrac{\frac{2}{3}}{\frac{3}{4}}$

18. $\dfrac{\frac{3}{5}}{\frac{2}{7}}$

19. $\dfrac{\frac{4}{5}}{\frac{32}{15}}$

20. $\dfrac{\frac{7}{8}}{\frac{49}{4}}$

21. $\dfrac{\frac{x}{y}}{\frac{1}{x}}$

22. $\dfrac{\frac{y}{x}}{\frac{x}{xy}}$

23. $\dfrac{\frac{5t^2}{9x^2}}{\frac{3t}{x^2 t}}$

24. $\dfrac{\frac{5w^2}{4tz}}{\frac{15wt}{z^2}}$

Simplify each complex fraction. Assume no division by 0. See Example 3. (Objective 1)

25. $\dfrac{\frac{2}{3}+1}{\frac{1}{3}+1}$

26. $\dfrac{\frac{3}{5}-2}{\frac{2}{5}-2}$

27. $\dfrac{\frac{1}{2}+\frac{3}{4}}{\frac{3}{2}+\frac{1}{4}}$

28. $\dfrac{\frac{2}{3}-\frac{5}{2}}{\frac{2}{3}-\frac{3}{2}}$

29. $\dfrac{\frac{1}{y}+3}{\frac{3}{y}-2}$

30. $\dfrac{\frac{1}{x}-3}{\frac{5}{x}+2}$

31. $\dfrac{\frac{2}{x}+2}{\frac{4}{x}+2}$

32. $\dfrac{\frac{3}{x}-3}{\frac{9}{x}-3}$

33. $\dfrac{\frac{3y}{x}-y}{y-\frac{y}{x}}$

34. $\dfrac{\frac{y}{x}+3y}{y+\frac{2y}{x}}$

35. $\dfrac{\frac{2}{a+2}+1}{\frac{3}{a+2}}$

36. $\dfrac{3-\frac{2}{m-3}}{\frac{4}{m-3}}$

37. $\dfrac{\frac{1}{x+1}}{1+\frac{1}{x+1}}$

38. $\dfrac{\frac{1}{x-1}}{1-\frac{1}{x-1}}$

39. $\dfrac{\frac{x}{x+2}}{\frac{x}{x+2}+x}$

40. $\dfrac{3-\frac{2}{x-2}}{\frac{2}{x-2}-1}$

Simplify each complex fraction. Assume no division by 0. See Example 4. (Objective 1)

41. $\dfrac{1}{\dfrac{1}{x} + \dfrac{1}{y}}$

42. $\dfrac{1}{\dfrac{b}{a} - \dfrac{a}{b}}$

43. $\dfrac{\dfrac{2}{x}}{\dfrac{2}{y} - \dfrac{4}{x}}$

44. $\dfrac{\dfrac{2y}{3}}{\dfrac{2y}{3} - \dfrac{8}{y}}$

45. $\dfrac{\dfrac{3}{x} + \dfrac{2x}{y}}{\dfrac{4}{x}}$

46. $\dfrac{\dfrac{4}{a} - \dfrac{a}{b}}{\dfrac{b}{a}}$

47. $\dfrac{3 + \dfrac{3}{x-1}}{3 - \dfrac{3}{x}}$

48. $\dfrac{2 - \dfrac{2}{x+1}}{2 + \dfrac{2}{x}}$

Simplify each complex fraction. Assume no division by 0. See Example 5. (Objective 2)

49. $\dfrac{x^{-2}}{y^{-1}}$

50. $\dfrac{a^{-4}}{b^{-2}}$

51. $\dfrac{y^{-2} + 1}{y^{-2} - 1}$

52. $\dfrac{1 + x^{-1}}{x^{-1} - 1}$

53. $\dfrac{a^{-2} + a}{a + 1}$

54. $\dfrac{t - t^{-2}}{1 - t^{-1}}$

55. $\dfrac{2x^{-1} + 4x^{-2}}{2x^{-2} + x^{-1}}$

56. $\dfrac{x^{-2} - 3x^{-3}}{3x^{-2} - 9x^{-3}}$

ADDITIONAL PRACTICE *Simplify each complex fraction. Assume no division by 0.*

57. $\dfrac{\dfrac{y}{x-1}}{\dfrac{y}{x}}$

58. $\dfrac{\dfrac{a}{b}}{\dfrac{a-1}{b}}$

59. $\dfrac{\dfrac{3}{x} + \dfrac{4}{x+1}}{\dfrac{2}{x+1} - \dfrac{3}{x}}$

60. $\dfrac{\dfrac{5}{y-3} - \dfrac{2}{y}}{\dfrac{1}{y} + \dfrac{2}{y-3}}$

61. $\dfrac{\dfrac{2}{x} - \dfrac{3}{x+1}}{\dfrac{2}{x+1} - \dfrac{3}{x}}$

62. $\dfrac{\dfrac{5}{y} + \dfrac{4}{y+1}}{\dfrac{4}{y} - \dfrac{5}{y+1}}$

63. $\dfrac{\dfrac{m}{m+2} - \dfrac{2}{m-1}}{\dfrac{3}{m+2} + \dfrac{m}{m-1}}$

64. $\dfrac{\dfrac{2a}{a-3} + \dfrac{1}{a-2}}{\dfrac{a}{a-2} - \dfrac{3}{a-3}}$

65. $\dfrac{\dfrac{2}{x+2}}{\dfrac{3}{x-3} + \dfrac{1}{x}}$

66. $\dfrac{\dfrac{1}{x-1} - \dfrac{4}{x}}{\dfrac{3}{x+1}}$

67. $\dfrac{\dfrac{1}{x} + \dfrac{2}{x+1}}{\dfrac{2}{x-1} - \dfrac{1}{x}}$

68. $\dfrac{\dfrac{3}{x+1} - \dfrac{2}{x-1}}{\dfrac{1}{x+2} + \dfrac{2}{x-1}}$

69. $\dfrac{\dfrac{1}{y^2+y} - \dfrac{1}{xy+x}}{\dfrac{1}{xy+x} - \dfrac{1}{y^2+y}}$

70. $\dfrac{\dfrac{2}{b^2-1} - \dfrac{3}{ab-a}}{\dfrac{3}{ab-a} - \dfrac{2}{b^2-1}}$

71. $\dfrac{1 - 25y^{-2}}{1 + 10y^{-1} + 25y^{-2}}$

72. $\dfrac{1 - 9x^{-2}}{1 - 6x^{-1} + 9x^{-2}}$

WRITING ABOUT MATH

73. Explain how to use Method 1 to simplify

$$\dfrac{1 + \dfrac{1}{x}}{3 - \dfrac{1}{x}}$$

74. Explain how to use Method 2 to simplify the expression in Exercise 73.

SOMETHING TO THINK ABOUT

75. Simplify each complex fraction:

$$\dfrac{1}{1+1}, \quad \dfrac{1}{1 + \dfrac{1}{2}}, \quad \dfrac{1}{1 + \dfrac{1}{1 + \dfrac{1}{2}}}, \quad \dfrac{1}{1 + \dfrac{1}{1 + \dfrac{1}{1 + \dfrac{1}{2}}}}$$

76. In Exercise 75, what is the pattern in the numerators and denominators of the four answers? What would be the next answer?

Solving Equations That Contain Rational Expressions

Objectives

1 Solve an equation that contains rational expressions.
2 Identify any extraneous solutions.
3 Solve a formula for an indicated variable.

Vocabulary

extraneous solution

Getting Ready

Simplify.

1. $3\left(x + \dfrac{1}{3}\right)$ **2.** $8\left(x - \dfrac{1}{8}\right)$ **3.** $x\left(\dfrac{3}{x} + 2\right)$

4. $3y\left(\dfrac{1}{3} - \dfrac{2}{y}\right)$ **5.** $6x\left(\dfrac{5}{2x} + \dfrac{2}{3x}\right)$ **6.** $9x\left(\dfrac{7}{9} + \dfrac{2}{3x}\right)$

7. $(y - 1)\left(\dfrac{1}{y - 1} + 1\right)$ **8.** $(x + 2)\left(3 - \dfrac{1}{x + 2}\right)$

We will now use our knowledge of rational expressions to solve equations that contain rational expressions with variables in their denominators. To do so, we will use new equation-solving methods that sometimes lead to false solutions. For this reason, it is important to check all answers.

1 **Solve an equation that contains rational expressions.**

To solve equations containing rational expressions, it is usually best to eliminate the denominators. To do so, we multiply both sides of the equation by the LCD of the rational expressions that appear in the equation. For example, to solve $\dfrac{x}{3} + 1 = \dfrac{x}{6}$, we multiply both sides of the equation by 6:

$$\frac{x}{3} + 1 = \frac{x}{6}$$

$$6\left(\frac{x}{3} + 1\right) = 6\left(\frac{x}{6}\right)$$

We then use the distributive property to remove parentheses, simplify, and solve the resulting equation for x.

$$6 \cdot \frac{x}{3} + 6 \cdot 1 = 6 \cdot \frac{x}{6}$$

$$2x + 6 = x$$

$$x + 6 = 0 \qquad \text{Subtract } x \text{ from both sides.}$$

$$x = -6 \qquad \text{Subtract 6 from both sides.}$$

Check: $\dfrac{x}{3} + 1 = \dfrac{x}{6}$

$$\frac{-6}{3} + 1 \stackrel{?}{=} \frac{-6}{6} \qquad \text{Substitute } -6 \text{ for } x.$$

$$-2 + 1 \stackrel{?}{=} -1 \qquad \text{Simplify.}$$

$$-1 = -1$$

Because -6 satisfies the original equation, it is the solution.

EXAMPLE 1 Solve: $\dfrac{4}{x} + 1 = \dfrac{6}{x} \quad (x \neq 0)$.

Solution To clear the equation of rational expressions, we multiply both sides of the equation by the LCD of $\frac{4}{x}$, 1, and $\frac{6}{x}$, which is x.

$$\frac{4}{x} + 1 = \frac{6}{x}$$

$$x\left(\frac{4}{x} + 1\right) = x\left(\frac{6}{x}\right) \qquad \text{Multiply both sides by } x.$$

$$x \cdot \frac{4}{x} + x \cdot 1 = x \cdot \frac{6}{x} \qquad \text{Remove parentheses.}$$

$$4 + x = 6 \qquad \text{Simplify.}$$

$$x = 2 \qquad \text{Subtract 4 from both sides.}$$

Check: $\dfrac{4}{x} + 1 = \dfrac{6}{x}$

$$\frac{4}{2} + 1 \stackrel{?}{=} \frac{6}{2} \qquad \text{Substitute 2 for } x.$$

$$2 + 1 \stackrel{?}{=} 3 \qquad \text{Simplify.}$$

$$3 = 3$$

Because 2 satisfies the original equation, it is the solution.

⇨ **SELF CHECK 1** Solve: $\dfrac{6}{x} - 1 = \dfrac{3}{x} \quad (x \neq 0)$.

2 **Identify any extraneous solutions.**

If we multiply both sides of an equation by an expression that involves a variable, as we did in Example 1, we must check the apparent solutions. The next example shows why.

EXAMPLE 2   Solve: $\dfrac{x+3}{x-1} = \dfrac{4}{x-1}$ $(x \neq 1)$.

Solution   To clear the equation of rational expressions, we multiply both sides by $x - 1$, the LCD of the fractions contained in the equation.

$$\frac{x+3}{x-1} = \frac{4}{x-1}$$

$$(x-1)\frac{x+3}{x-1} = (x-1)\frac{4}{x-1} \qquad \text{Multiply both sides by } x - 1.$$

$$x + 3 = 4 \qquad\qquad \text{Simplify.}$$

$$x = 1 \qquad\qquad \text{Subtract 3 from both sides.}$$

Because both sides were multiplied by an expression containing a variable, we must check the apparent solution.

$$\frac{x+3}{x-1} = \frac{4}{x-1}$$

$$\frac{1+3}{1-1} \overset{?}{=} \frac{4}{1-1} \qquad \text{Substitute 1 for } x.$$

$$\frac{4}{0} = \frac{4}{0} \qquad \text{Division by 0 is undefined.}$$

COMMENT   Whenever a restricted (excluded) value is a possible solution, it will be extraneous.

Such false solutions are often called **extraneous solutions**. Because 1 does not satisfy the original equation, there is no solution. The solution set of the equation is $\varnothing$.

⮕ **SELF CHECK 2**   Solve: $\dfrac{x+5}{x-2} = \dfrac{7}{x-2}$ $(x \neq 2)$.

The next two examples suggest the steps to follow when solving equations that contain rational expressions.

Solving Equations Containing Rational Expressions

1. Find any restrictions on the variable. Remember that the denominator of a fraction cannot be 0.
2. Multiply both sides of the equation by the LCD of the rational expressions appearing in the equation to clear the equation of fractions.
3. Solve the resulting equation.
4. Check the solutions to determine any extraneous roots. If an apparent solution of an equation is a restricted value, that value must be excluded.

EXAMPLE 3   Solve: $\dfrac{3x+1}{x+1} - 2 = \dfrac{3(x-3)}{x+1}$.

Solution   Since the denominator $x + 1$ cannot be 0, x cannot be -1. To clear the equation of rational expressions, we multiply both sides by $x + 1$, the LCD of the rational expressions contained in the equation. We then can solve the resulting equation.

$$\frac{3x + 1}{x + 1} - 2 = \frac{3(x - 3)}{x + 1}$$

$$(x + 1)\left[\frac{3x + 1}{x + 1} - 2\right] = (x + 1)\left[\frac{3(x - 3)}{x + 1}\right] \quad \text{Multiply both sides by } x + 1.$$

$$3x + 1 - 2(x + 1) = 3(x - 3) \qquad \begin{array}{l}\text{Use the distributive property to} \\ \text{remove brackets.}\end{array}$$

$$3x + 1 - 2x - 2 = 3x - 9 \qquad \text{Remove parentheses.}$$

$$x - 1 = 3x - 9 \qquad \text{Combine like terms.}$$

$$-2x = -8 \qquad \text{On both sides, subtract } 3x \text{ and add 1.}$$

$$x = 4 \qquad \text{Divide both sides by } -2.$$

Check:
$$\frac{3x + 1}{x + 1} - 2 = \frac{3(x - 3)}{x + 1}$$

$$\frac{3(4) + 1}{4 + 1} - 2 \stackrel{?}{=} \frac{3(4 - 3)}{4 + 1} \qquad \text{Substitute 4 for } x.$$

$$\frac{13}{5} - \frac{10}{5} \stackrel{?}{=} \frac{3(1)}{5}$$

$$\frac{3}{5} = \frac{3}{5}$$

Because 4 satisfies the original equation, it is the solution.

⇨ **SELF CHECK 3**   Solve: $\frac{12}{x + 1} - 5 = \frac{2}{x + 1}$.

To solve an equation with rational expressions, we often will have to factor a denominator to determine the least common denominator.

EXAMPLE 4   Solve: $\dfrac{x + 2}{x + 3} + \dfrac{1}{x^2 + 2x - 3} = 1$.

Solution   To find any restricted values of x and the LCD, we must factor the second denominator.

$$\frac{x + 2}{x + 3} + \frac{1}{x^2 + 2x - 3} = 1$$

$$\frac{x + 2}{x + 3} + \frac{1}{(x + 3)(x - 1)} = 1 \quad \text{Factor } x^2 + 2x - 3.$$

Since $x + 3$ and $x - 1$ cannot be 0, x cannot be -3 or 1.

To clear the equation of rational expressions, we multiply both sides by $(x + 3)(x - 1)$, the LCD of the fractions contained in the equation.

$$(x + 3)(x - 1)\left[\frac{x + 2}{x + 3} + \frac{1}{(x + 3)(x - 1)}\right] = (x + 3)(x - 1)1 \quad \text{Multiply both sides by } (x + 3)(x - 1).$$

$$(x + 3)(x - 1)\frac{x + 2}{x + 3} + (x + 3)(x - 1)\frac{1}{(x + 3)(x - 1)} = (x + 3)(x - 1)1 \quad \text{Remove brackets.}$$

$$(x - 1)(x + 2) + 1 = (x + 3)(x - 1) \quad \text{Simplify.}$$

$$x^2 + x - 2 + 1 = x^2 + 2x - 3 \qquad \text{Remove parentheses.}$$
$$x - 2 + 1 = 2x - 3 \qquad \text{Subtract } x^2 \text{ from both sides.}$$
$$x - 1 = 2x - 3 \qquad \text{Combine like terms.}$$
$$-x - 1 = -3 \qquad \text{Subtract } 2x \text{ from both sides.}$$
$$-x = -2 \qquad \text{Add 1 to both sides.}$$
$$x = 2 \qquad \text{Divide both sides by } -1.$$

Verify that 2 is the solution of the given equation.

SELF CHECK 4   Solve: $\dfrac{x-4}{x-3} + \dfrac{x-2}{x-3} = x - 3$.

EXAMPLE 5   Solve: $\dfrac{4}{5} + y = \dfrac{4y - 50}{5y - 25}$.

Solution   Since $5y - 25$ cannot be 0, y cannot be 5. Thus, 5 is a restricted value.

$$\frac{4}{5} + y = \frac{4y - 50}{5y - 25}$$

$$\frac{4}{5} + y = \frac{4y - 50}{5(y - 5)} \qquad \text{Factor } 5y - 25.$$

$$5(y - 5)\left[\frac{4}{5} + y\right] = 5(y - 5)\left[\frac{4y - 50}{5(y - 5)}\right] \qquad \text{Multiply both sides by } 5(y - 5).$$

$$4(y - 5) + 5y(y - 5) = 4y - 50 \qquad \text{Remove brackets.}$$

$$4y - 20 + 5y^2 - 25y = 4y - 50 \qquad \text{Remove parentheses.}$$

$$5y^2 - 25y - 20 = -50 \qquad \begin{array}{l}\text{Subtract } 4y \text{ from both sides and} \\ \text{rearrange terms.}\end{array}$$

$$5y^2 - 25y + 30 = 0 \qquad \text{Add 50 to both sides.}$$

$$y^2 - 5y + 6 = 0 \qquad \text{Divide both sides by 5.}$$

$$(y - 3)(y - 2) = 0 \qquad \text{Factor } y^2 - 5y + 6.$$

$$y - 3 = 0 \quad \text{or} \quad y - 2 = 0 \qquad \text{Set each factor equal to 0.}$$

$$y = 3 \quad \big| \quad y = 2$$

Verify that 3 and 2 both satisfy the original equation.

SELF CHECK 5   Solve: $\dfrac{x-6}{3x-9} - \dfrac{1}{3} = \dfrac{x}{2}$.

3   **Solve a formula for an indicated variable.**

Many formulas are equations that contain fractions.

EXAMPLE 6   The formula $\dfrac{1}{r} = \dfrac{1}{r_1} + \dfrac{1}{r_2}$ is used in electronics to calculate parallel resistances. Solve the formula for r.

Solution   We eliminate the denominators by multiplying both sides by the LCD, which is rr_1r_2.

$$\frac{1}{r} = \frac{1}{r_1} + \frac{1}{r_2}$$

$$rr_1r_2\left(\frac{1}{r}\right) = rr_1r_2\left(\frac{1}{r_1} + \frac{1}{r_2}\right) \qquad \text{Multiply both sides by } rr_1r_2.$$

$$\frac{rr_1r_2}{r} = \frac{rr_1r_2}{r_1} + \frac{rr_1r_2}{r_2} \qquad \text{Remove parentheses.}$$

$$r_1r_2 = rr_2 + rr_1 \qquad \text{Simplify.}$$

$$r_1r_2 = r(r_2 + r_1) \qquad \text{Factor out } r.$$

$$\frac{r_1r_2}{r_2 + r_1} = r \qquad \text{Divide both sides by } r_2 - r_1.$$

or

$$r = \frac{r_1r_2}{r_2 + r_1}$$

⇨ **SELF CHECK 6** Solve the formula for r_1.

⇨ **SELF CHECK ANSWERS** **1.** 3 **2.** $\varnothing$, 2 is extraneous **3.** 1 **4.** 5; 3 is extraneous **5.** 1, 2 **6.** $r_1 = \frac{rr_2}{r_2 - r}$

NOW TRY THIS

1. Solve: $\dfrac{4}{x} + x = 5$.

2. Solve: $\dfrac{x - 2}{(x + 3)^2} - \dfrac{5}{x + 3} + 1 = 0$.

3. Explain the procedure for identifying extraneous solutions.

6.5 EXERCISES

WARM-UPS *Indicate your first step when solving each equation. Assume no denominators are zero.*

1. $\dfrac{x - 3}{5} = \dfrac{x}{2}$

2. $\dfrac{1}{x - 1} = \dfrac{8}{x}$

3. $\dfrac{y}{9} + 5 = \dfrac{y + 1}{3}$

4. $\dfrac{5x - 8}{3} + 3x = \dfrac{x}{5}$

REVIEW *Factor each expression.*

5. $x^2 + 4x$

6. $x^2 - 16y^2$

7. $2x^2 + x - 3$

8. $6a^2 - 5a - 6$

9. $x^4 - 16$

10. $4x^2 + 10x - 6$

VOCABULARY AND CONCEPTS *Fill in the blanks.*

11. False solutions that result from multiplying both sides of an equation by a variable are called _____ solutions.

12. If the product of two numbers is 1, the numbers are called
_____.

13. To clear an equation of rational expressions, we multiply
both sides by the _____ of the expressions in the equation.

14. If you multiply both sides of an equation by an expression
that involves a variable, you must _____ the solution.

15. To clear the equation $\frac{1}{x} + \frac{2}{y} = 5$ of denominators, we multiply both sides by ___.

16. To clear the equation $\frac{x}{x-2} - \frac{x}{x-1} = 5$ of denominators,
we multiply both sides by _____.

GUIDED PRACTICE

Solve each equation and check the solution. **See Example 1.**
(Objective 1)

17. $\frac{x}{2} + 4 = \frac{3x}{2}$ **18.** $\frac{y}{3} + 6 = \frac{4y}{3}$

19. $\frac{2y}{5} - 8 = \frac{4y}{5}$ **20.** $\frac{3x}{4} - 6 = \frac{x}{4}$

21. $\frac{x}{3} + 1 = \frac{x}{2}$ **22.** $\frac{x}{2} - 3 = \frac{x}{5}$

23. $\frac{x}{5} - \frac{x}{3} = -8$ **24.** $\frac{2}{3} + \frac{x}{4} = 7$

25. $\frac{3a}{2} + \frac{a}{3} = -22$ **26.** $\frac{x}{2} + x = \frac{9}{2}$

27. $\frac{x-3}{3} + 2x = -1$ **28.** $\frac{x+2}{2} - 3x = x + 8$

29. $\frac{z-3}{2} = z + 2$ **30.** $\frac{b+2}{3} = b - 2$

31. $\frac{5(x+1)}{8} = x + 1$ **32.** $\frac{3(x-1)}{2} + 2 = x$

*Solve each equation and check the solution. Identify any
extraneous root.* **See Example 2.** (Objective 2)

33. $\frac{a^2}{a+2} - \frac{4}{a+2} = a$ **34.** $\frac{z^2}{z+1} + 2 = \frac{1}{z+1}$

35. $\frac{x}{x-5} - \frac{5}{x-5} = 3$ **36.** $\frac{3}{y-2} + 1 = \frac{3}{y-2}$

*Solve each equation and check the solution. Identify any
extraneous root.* **See Example 3.** (Objective 2)

37. $\frac{3}{x} + 2 = 3$ **38.** $\frac{2}{x} + 9 = 11$

39. $\frac{5}{a} - \frac{4}{a} = 8 + \frac{1}{a}$ **40.** $\frac{11}{b} + \frac{13}{b} = 12$

41. $\frac{2}{y+1} + 5 = \frac{12}{y+1}$ **42.** $\frac{1}{t-3} = \frac{-2}{t-3} + 1$

43. $\frac{1}{x-1} + \frac{3}{x-1} = 1$ **44.** $\frac{3}{p+6} - 2 = \frac{7}{p+6}$

*Solve each equation and check the solution. Identify any
extraneous root.* **See Example 4.** (Objective 2)

45. $\frac{u}{u-1} + \frac{1}{u} = \frac{u^2+1}{u^2-u}$ **46.** $\frac{v}{v+2} + \frac{1}{v-1} = 1$

47. $\frac{3}{x-2} + \frac{1}{x} = \frac{2(3x+2)}{x^2-2x}$

48. $\frac{5}{x} + \frac{3}{x+2} = \frac{-6}{x(x+2)}$

49. $\frac{-5}{s^2+s-2} + \frac{3}{s+2} = \frac{1}{s-1}$

50. $\frac{7}{q^2-q-2} + \frac{1}{q+1} = \frac{3}{q-2}$

51. $\frac{3y}{3y-6} + \frac{8}{y^2-4} = \frac{2y}{2y+4}$

52. $\frac{x-3}{4x-4} + \frac{1}{9} = \frac{x-5}{6x-6}$

53. $\frac{n}{n^2-9} + \frac{n+8}{n+3} = \frac{n-8}{n-3}$

54. $\frac{x-3}{x-2} - \frac{1}{x} = \frac{x-3}{x}$

55. $\frac{b+2}{b+3} + 1 = \frac{-7}{b-5}$

56. $\frac{x-4}{x-3} + \frac{x-2}{x-3} = x - 3$

*Solve each equation and check the solution. Identify any
extraneous root.* **See Example 5.** (Objective 2)

57. $y + \frac{2}{3} = \frac{2y-12}{3y-9}$

58. $y + \frac{3}{4} = \frac{3y-50}{4y-24}$

59. $\frac{3}{5x-20} + \frac{4}{5} = \frac{3}{5x-20} - \frac{x}{5}$

60. $\frac{x}{x-1} - \frac{12}{x^2-x} = \frac{-1}{x-1}$

Solve each formula for the specified variable. **See Example 6.**
(Objective 3)

61. $\frac{1}{a} + \frac{1}{b} = 1$ for a.

62. $\frac{1}{a} - \frac{1}{b} = 1$ for b.

63. $\frac{a}{b} + \frac{c}{d} = 1$ for b.

64. $\frac{a}{b} - \frac{c}{d} = 1$ for a.

ADDITIONAL EXERCISES   *Solve each equation.*

65. $\dfrac{c-4}{4} = \dfrac{c+4}{8}$

66. $\dfrac{t+3}{2} = \dfrac{t-3}{3}$

67. $\dfrac{x+1}{3} + \dfrac{x-1}{5} = \dfrac{2}{15}$

68. $\dfrac{y-5}{7} + \dfrac{y-7}{5} = \dfrac{-2}{5}$

69. $\dfrac{3x-1}{6} - \dfrac{x+3}{2} = \dfrac{3x+4}{3}$

70. $\dfrac{2x+3}{3} + \dfrac{3x-4}{6} = \dfrac{x-2}{2}$

71. $\dfrac{3r}{2} - \dfrac{3}{r} = \dfrac{3r}{2} + 3$

72. $\dfrac{2p}{3} - \dfrac{1}{p} = \dfrac{2p-1}{3}$

73. $\dfrac{1}{3} + \dfrac{2}{x-3} = 1$

74. $\dfrac{3}{5} + \dfrac{7}{x+2} = 2$

75. $\dfrac{5}{4y+12} - \dfrac{3}{4} = \dfrac{5}{4y+12} - \dfrac{y}{4}$

76. $1 - \dfrac{3}{b} = \dfrac{-8b}{b^2+3b}$

77. $\dfrac{z-4}{z-3} = \dfrac{z+2}{z+1}$

78. $\dfrac{a+2}{a+8} = \dfrac{a-3}{a-2}$

APPLICATIONS

79. Optics   The focal length f of a lens is given by the formula

$$\frac{1}{f} = \frac{1}{d_1} + \frac{1}{d_2}$$

where d_1 is the distance from the object to the lens and d_2 is the distance from the lens to the image. Solve the formula for f.

80. Solve the formula in Exercise 79 for d_1.

WRITING ABOUT MATH

81. Explain how you would decide what to do first when you solve an equation that involves fractions.

82. Explain why it is important to check your solutions to an equation that contains fractions with variables in the denominator.

SOMETHING TO THINK ABOUT

83. What numbers are equal to their own reciprocals?

84. Solve: $x^{-2} + x^{-1} = 0$.

SECTION 6.6   Solving Applications of Equations That Contain Rational Expressions

Objectives

1 Solve an application problem using a rational equation.

Getting Ready

1. If it takes 5 hours to fill a pool, what part could be filled in 1 hour?
2. x is invested at 5% annual interest. Write an expression for the interest earned in one year.
3. Write an expression for the amount of an investment that earns y interest in one year at 5%.
4. Express how long it takes to travel y miles at 52 mph.

In this section, we will consider problems whose solutions depend on solving equations containing rational expressions.

1 Solve an application problem using a rational equation.

EXAMPLE 1   **NUMBER PROBLEM**   If the same number is added to both the numerator and denominator of the fraction $\frac{3}{5}$, the result is $\frac{4}{5}$. Find the number.

Analyze the problem   We are asked to find a number. We will let n represent the unknown number.

Form an equation   If we add the number n to both the numerator and denominator of the fraction $\frac{3}{5}$, we will get $\frac{4}{5}$. This gives the equation

$$\frac{3 + n}{5 + n} = \frac{4}{5}$$

Solve the equation   To solve the equation, we proceed as follows:

$$\frac{3 + n}{5 + n} = \frac{4}{5}$$

$$5(5 + n)\frac{3 + n}{5 + n} = 5(5 + n)\frac{4}{5} \qquad \text{Multiply both sides by } 5(5 + n).$$

$$5(3 + n) = (5 + n)4 \qquad \text{Simplify.}$$

$$15 + 5n = 20 + 4n \qquad \text{Use the distributive property to remove parentheses.}$$

$$5n = 5 + 4n \qquad \text{Subtract 15 from both sides.}$$

$$n = 5 \qquad \text{Subtract } 4n \text{ from both sides.}$$

State the conclusion   The number is 5.

Check the result   Add 5 to both the numerator and denominator of $\frac{3}{5}$ and get

$$\frac{3 + 5}{5 + 5} = \frac{8}{10} = \frac{4}{5}$$

The result checks.

As we did in Example 1, it is important to state the conclusion after solving an application problem.

EXAMPLE 2   **FILLING AN OIL TANK**   An inlet pipe can fill an oil tank in 7 days, and a second inlet pipe can fill the same tank in 9 days. If both pipes are used, how long will it take to fill the tank?

Analyze the problem   We are asked to find how long it will take to fill the tank, so we let x represent the number of days it will take to fill the tank.

Form an equation   The key is to note what each pipe can do in 1 day. If you add what the first pipe can do in 1 day to what the second pipe can do in 1 day, the sum is what they can do together in 1 day. Since the first pipe can fill the tank in 7 days, it can do $\frac{1}{7}$ of the job in 1 day. Since the second pipe can fill the tank in 9 days, it can do $\frac{1}{9}$ of the job in 1 day. If it takes x days for both pipes to fill the tank, together they can do $\frac{1}{x}$ of the job in 1 day. This gives the equation

What the first inlet pipe can do in 1 day	plus	what the second inlet pipe can do in 1 day	equals	what they can do together in 1 day.
$\frac{1}{7}$	$+$	$\frac{1}{9}$	$=$	$\frac{1}{x}$

Solve the equation   To solve the equation, we proceed as follows:

$$\frac{1}{7} + \frac{1}{9} = \frac{1}{x}$$

$$63x\left(\frac{1}{7} + \frac{1}{9}\right) = 63\left(\frac{1}{x}\right) \quad \text{Multiply both sides by } 63x.$$

$$9x + 7x = 63 \qquad \text{Use the distributive property to remove parentheses and simplify.}$$

$$16x = 63 \qquad \text{Combine like terms.}$$

$$x = \frac{63}{16} \qquad \text{Divide both sides by 16.}$$

State the conclusion   It will take $\frac{63}{16}$ or $3\frac{15}{16}$ days for both inlet pipes to fill the tank.

Check the result   In $\frac{63}{16}$ days, the first pipe fills $\frac{1}{7}\left(\frac{63}{16}\right)$ of the tank, and the second pipe fills $\frac{1}{9}\left(\frac{63}{16}\right)$ of the tank. The sum of these efforts, $\frac{9}{16} + \frac{7}{16}$, is equal to one full tank.

EXAMPLE 3   **TRACK AND FIELD**   A coach can run 10 miles in the same amount of time that her best student athlete can run 12 miles. If the student can run 1 mph faster than the coach, how fast can the student run?

Analyze the problem   We are asked to find how fast the student can run. Since we know that the student runs 1 mph faster than the coach, we will let r represent the rate of the coach and $r + 1$ represent the rate of the student. In this case, we want to find the rate of the student, which is $r + 1$.

Form an equation   This is a uniform motion problem, based on the formula $d = rt$, where d is the distance traveled, r is the rate, and t is the time. If we solve this formula for t, we obtain

$$t = \frac{d}{r}$$

If the coach runs 10 miles at some unknown rate of r mph, it will take $\frac{10}{r}$ hours. If the student runs 12 miles at some unknown rate of $(r + 1)$ mph, it will take $\frac{12}{r + 1}$ hours. We can organize the information of the problem as in Table 6-1.

	d	$=$	r	$\cdot$	t
Student	12		$r + 1$		$\dfrac{12}{r + 1}$
Coach	10		r		$\dfrac{10}{r}$

Table 6-1

Because the times are given to be equal, we know that $\frac{12}{r + 1} = \frac{10}{r}$. This gives the equation

The time it takes the student to run 12 miles	equals	the time it takes the coach to run 10 miles.
$\dfrac{12}{r + 1}$	$=$	$\dfrac{10}{r}$

Solve the equation   We can solve the equation as follows:

$$\frac{12}{r + 1} = \frac{10}{r}$$

COMMENT   This problem could have been set up with r representing the student's rate and $r - 1$ the coach's rate.

$$r(r + 1)\frac{12}{r + 1} = r(r + 1)\frac{10}{r} \qquad \text{Multiply both sides by } r(r + 1).$$

$$12r = 10(r + 1) \qquad \text{Simplify.}$$

$$12r = 10r + 10 \qquad \text{Use the distributive property to remove parentheses.}$$

$$2r = 10 \qquad \text{Subtract } 10r \text{ from both sides.}$$

$$r = 5 \qquad \text{Divide both sides by 2.}$$

State the conclusion   The coach can run 5 mph. The student, running 1 mph faster, can run 6 mph.

Check the result   Verify that this result checks.

EXAMPLE 4   **COMPARING INVESTMENTS**   At one bank, a sum of money invested for one year will earn $96 interest. If invested in bonds, that same money would earn $120, because the interest rate paid by the bonds is 1% greater than that paid by the bank. Find the bank's rate of interest.

Analyze the problem   We are asked to find the bank's rate of interest, so we can let r represent the bank's rate. If the interest on the bonds is 1% greater, then the bonds' interest rate will be $r + 0.01$.

Form an equation   This is an interest problem that is based on the formula $i = pr$, where i is the interest, p is the principal (the amount invested), and r is the annual rate of interest.

    If we solve this formula for p, we obtain

$$p = \frac{i}{r}$$

If an investment at a bank earns $96 interest at some unknown rate r, the principal invested is $\frac{96}{r}$. If an investment in bonds earns $120 interest at some unknown rate $(r + 0.01)$, the principal invested is $\frac{120}{r + 0.01}$. We can organize the information of the problem as in Table 6-2.

	Interest	=	Principal	·	Rate
Bank	96		$\dfrac{96}{r}$		r
Bonds	120		$\dfrac{120}{r + 0.01}$		$r + 0.01$

Table 6-2

Because the same principal would be invested in either account, we can set up the following equation:

$$\frac{96}{r} = \frac{120}{r + 0.01}$$

Solve the equation   We can solve the equation as follows:

$$\frac{96}{r} = \frac{120}{r + 0.01}$$

$$r(r + 0.01) \cdot \frac{96}{r} = \frac{120}{r + 0.01} \cdot r(r + 0.01) \qquad \text{Multiply both sides by } r(r + 0.01).$$

$$96(r + 0.01) = 120r$$

$$96r + 0.96 = 120r \qquad\qquad \text{Remove parentheses.}$$

$$0.96 = 24r \qquad\qquad\qquad \text{Subtract } 96r \text{ from both sides.}$$

$$0.04 = r \qquad\qquad\qquad\quad \text{Divide both sides by 24.}$$

State the conclusion   The bank's interest rate is 0.04 or 4%. The bonds pay 5% interest, a rate 1% greater than that paid by the bank.

Check the results   Verify that these rates check.

NOW TRY THIS

1. Chris can clean a house in 3 hours and Cheryl can clean the house in 2 hours. Their son, Tyler, can scatter toys all over the house in 4 hours. If Tyler starts scattering toys at the same time Chris and Cheryl start cleaning, when (if ever) will the house be clean?

6.6 EXERCISES

WARM-UPS

1. Write the formula that relates the principal p that is invested, the earned interest i, and the rate r for 1 year.
2. Write the formula that relates the distance d traveled at a speed r, for a time t.
3. Write the formula that relates the cost C of purchasing q items that cost $\$d$ each.
4. Write the formula that relates the value v of a mixture of n pounds costing $\$p$ per pound.

REVIEW   *Solve each equation.*

5. $x^2 - 5x - 6 = 0$
6. $x^2 - 25 = 0$
7. $(t + 2)(t^2 + 7t + 12) = 0$
8. $(x^2 - 1)(x^2 - 4) = 0$
9. $y^3 - y^2 = 0$
10. $5a^3 - 125a = 0$
11. $2(y - 4) = -y^2$
12. $6t^3 + 35t^2 = 6t$

VOCABULARY AND CONCEPTS

13. List the five steps used in problem solving.
14. Write 6% as a decimal.

APPLICATIONS

Solve and verify your answer. See Example 1. (Objective 1)

15. **Number problem**   If the denominator of $\frac{3}{4}$ is increased by a number and the numerator is doubled, the result is 1. Find the number.
16. **Number problem**   If a number is added to the numerator of $\frac{7}{8}$ and the same number is subtracted from the denominator, the result is 2. Find the number.
17. **Number problem**   If a number is added to the numerator of $\frac{3}{4}$ and twice as much is added to the denominator, the result is $\frac{4}{7}$. Find the number.
18. **Number problem**   If a number is added to the numerator of $\frac{5}{7}$ and twice as much is subtracted from the denominator, the result is 8. Find the number.

Solve and verify your answer. See Example 2. (Objective 1)

19. **Grading papers**   It takes a teacher 45 minutes to grade a set of quizzes and takes her aide twice as long to do the same amount of grading. How long will it take them to grade a set of quizzes if they work together?
20. **Printing schedules**   It takes a printer 8 hours to print the class schedules for all of the students in a college. A faster printer can do the job in 6 hours. How long will it take to do the job if both printers are used?

21. Filling a pool   An inlet pipe can fill an empty swimming pool in 5 hours, and another inlet pipe can fill the pool in 4 hours. How long will it take both pipes to fill the pool?

22. Roofing a house   A homeowner estimates that it will take 7 days to roof his house. A professional roofer estimates that he could roof the house in 4 days. How long will it take if the homeowner helps the roofer?

Solve and verify your answer. **See Example 3. (Objective 1)**

23. Flying speeds   On average, a Canada goose can fly 10 mph faster than a Great Blue heron. Find their flying speeds if a goose can fly 120 miles in the same time it takes a heron to fly 80 miles.

24. Touring   A tourist can bicycle 28 miles in the same time as he can walk 8 miles. If he can ride 10 mph faster than he can walk, how much time should he allow to walk a 30-mile trail?   (*Hint:* How fast can he walk?)

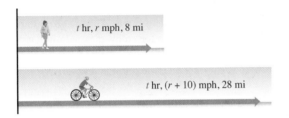

25. Comparing travel   A plane can fly 300 miles in the same time as it takes a car to go 120 miles. If the car travels 90 mph slower than the plane, find the speed of the plane.

26. Wind speed   A plane can fly 300 miles downwind in the same amount of time as it can travel 210 miles upwind. Find the velocity of the wind if the plane can fly 255 mph in still air.

Solve and verify your answer. **See Example 4. (Objective 1)**

27. Comparing investments   Two certificates of deposit pay interest at rates that differ by 1%. Money invested for one year in the first CD earns $175 interest. The same principal invested in the other CD earns $200. Find the two rates of interest.

28. Comparing interest rates   Two bond funds pay interest at rates that differ by 2%. Money invested for one year in the first fund earns $315 interest. The same amount invested in the other fund earns $385. Find the lower rate of interest.

29. Comparing interest rates   Two mutual funds pay interest at rates that differ by 3%. Money invested for one year in the first fund earns $225 interest. The same amount invested in the other fund earns $450. Find the higher rate of interest.

30. Comparing interest rates   Two banks pay interest at rates that differ by 1%. Money invested for one year in the first account earns $105 interest. The same amount invested in the other account earns $125. Find the two rates of interest.

Solve and verify your answer.

31. Number problem   The sum of a number and its reciprocal is $\frac{13}{6}$. Find the numbers.

32. Number problem   The sum of the reciprocals of two consecutive even integers is $\frac{7}{24}$. Find the integers.

33. Filling a pool   One inlet pipe can fill an empty pool in 4 hours, and a drain can empty the pool in 8 hours. How long will it take the pipe to fill the pool if the drain is left open?

34. Sewage treatment   A sludge pool is filled by two inlet pipes. One pipe can fill the pool in 15 days and the other pipe can fill it in 21 days. However, if no sewage is added, waste removal will empty the pool in 36 days. How long will it take the two inlet pipes to fill an empty pool?

35. Boating   A boat that can travel 18 mph in still water can travel 22 miles downstream in the same amount of time that it can travel 14 miles upstream. Find the speed of the current in the river.

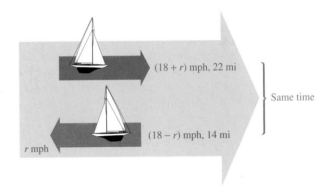

36. Conveyor belts   The diagram shows how apples are processed for market. Although the second conveyor belt is shorter, an apple spends the same time on each belt because the second belt moves 1 ft/sec slower than the first. Find the speed of each belt.

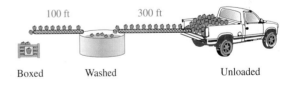

37. Sales   A bookstore can purchase several calculators for a total cost of $120. If each calculator cost $1 less, the bookstore could purchase 10 additional calculators at the same total cost. How many calculators can be purchased at the regular price?

38. Furnace repairs   A repairman purchased several furnace-blower motors for a total cost of $210. If his cost per motor had been $5 less, he could have purchased 1 additional motor. How many motors did he buy at the regular rate?

39. River tours   A river boat tour begins by going 60 miles upstream against a 5 mph current. Then the boat turns around and returns with the current. What still-water speed should the captain use to complete the tour in 5 hours?

40. Travel time   A company president flew 680 miles in a corporate jet but returned in a smaller plane that could fly only half as fast. If the total travel time was 6 hours, find the speeds of the planes.

41. Sharing costs   Some office workers bought a $35 gift for their boss. If there had been two more employees to contribute, everyone's cost would have been $2 less. How many workers contributed to the gift?

42. Sales   A dealer bought some radios for a total of $1,200. She gave away 6 radios as gifts, sold each of the rest for $10 more than she paid for each radio, and broke even. How many radios did she buy?

43. The London to Tashkent, Uzbekistan, Charity Road Rallye takes roughly 2 weeks to complete. One leg of the race, from Nurburgring, Germany, to Wroclaw, Poland, covers 512 miles and the leg from Krakow, Poland, to Kiev, Ukraine, covers 528 miles. If the speed from Germany to Poland is 20 mph faster than that from Poland to Ukraine and the difference in times is 4 hours, find the rates of travel for the 2 legs. (*Hint:* Add the 4 hours to the expression for the faster rate.)

Available at http://www.londontashkent.com

44. The Pony Express carried mail from St. Joseph, MO, to Sacramento, CA, between 1860 and 1861. Pony Express riders stopped only long enough to change horses and these were saddled and waiting. The distance covered was 1,800 miles. A car travels 52 mph faster than the horse. If it took the Pony Express riders 7.5 times as long to make the trip as by car, find how long it took the Pony Express to make the trip.
Available at
http://www.americanwest.com/trails/pages/ponyexp1.htm

WRITING ABOUT MATH

45. The key to solving shared work problems is to ask, "How much of the job could be done in 1 unit of time?" Explain.

46. It is difficult to check the solution of a shared work problem. Explain how you could decide if the answer is at least reasonable.

SOMETHING TO THINK ABOUT

47. Create a problem, involving either investment income or shared work, that can be solved by an equation that contains rational expressions.

48. Solve the problem you created in Exercise 47.

SECTION 6.7   Ratios

Objectives

1. Express a ratio in simplest form.
2. Translate an English sentence to a ratio.
3. Write a ratio as a unit cost.
4. Write a ratio as a rate.

Vocabulary

ratio   unit cost   rate
equal ratios

Simplify each fraction.

1. $\dfrac{2}{4}$ **2.** $\dfrac{8}{12}$ **3.** $-\dfrac{20}{25}$ **4.** $\dfrac{-45}{81}$

In this section, we will discuss ratios, unit costs, and rates. These ideas are important in many areas of everyday life.

1 **Express a ratio in simplest form.**

Ratios appear often in real-life situations. For example,

- To prepare fuel for a Lawnboy lawnmower, gasoline must be mixed with oil in the ratio of 50 to 1.
- To make 14-karat jewelry, gold is mixed with other metals in the ratio of 14 to 10.
- At Rock Valley College, the ratio of students to faculty is 16 to 1.

Ratios give us a way to compare numerical quantities.

Ratios

A **ratio** is a comparison of two numbers by their indicated quotient. In symbols,

If a and b are two numbers, the ratio of a to b is $\dfrac{a}{b}$.

COMMENT The denominator b cannot be 0 in the fraction $\dfrac{a}{b}$, but b can be 0 in the ratio a to b. For example, the ratio of women to men on a women's softball team could be 25 to 0. However, these applications are rare.

Some examples of ratios are

$$\frac{7}{9}, \quad \frac{21}{27}, \quad \text{and} \quad \frac{2,290}{1,317}$$

- The fraction $\dfrac{7}{9}$ can be read as "the ratio of 7 to 9."
- The fraction $\dfrac{21}{27}$ can be read as "the ratio of 21 to 27."
- The fraction $\dfrac{2,290}{1,317}$ can be read as "the ratio of 2,290 to 1,317."

Because $\dfrac{7}{9}$ and $\dfrac{21}{27}$ represent equal numbers, they are **equal ratios.**

EXAMPLE 1 Express each phrase as a ratio in simplest form.
a. the ratio of 15 to 12   **b.** the ratio of 0.3 to 1.2

Solution **a.** The ratio of 15 to 12 can be written as the fraction $\dfrac{15}{12}$. After simplifying, the ratio is $\dfrac{5}{4}$.

b. The ratio of 0.3 to 1.2 can be written as the fraction $\frac{0.3}{1.2}$. We can simplify this fraction as follows:

$$\frac{0.3}{1.2} = \frac{0.3 \cdot 10}{1.2 \cdot 10}$$ To clear the decimals, multiply both numerator and denominator by 10.

$$= \frac{3}{12}$$ Multiply: $0.3 \cdot 10 = 3$ and $1.2 \cdot 10 = 12$.

$$= \frac{1}{4}$$ Simplify the fraction: $\frac{3}{12} = \frac{\overset{1}{\cancel{3}} \cdot 1}{\cancel{3} \cdot 4} = \frac{1}{4}$.

⇨ **SELF CHECK 1** Express each ratio in simplest form.
a. the ratio of 8 to 12   **b.** the ratio of 3.2 to 16

EXAMPLE 2 Express each phrase as a ratio in simplest form.
a. the ratio of 3 meters to 8 meters   **b.** the ratio of 4 ounces to 1 pound

Solution **a.** The ratio of 3 meters to 8 meters can be written as the fraction $\frac{3 \text{ meters}}{8 \text{ meters}}$, or just $\frac{3}{8}$.

b. Ratios should be expressed in the same units. Since there are 16 ounces in 1 pound, the proper ratio is $\frac{4 \text{ ounces}}{16 \text{ ounces}}$, which simplifies to $\frac{1}{4}$.

⇨ **SELF CHECK 2** Express each ratio in simplest form.
a. the ratio of 8 ounces to 2 pounds
b. the ratio of 1 foot to 2 yards   (*Hint:* 3 feet = 1 yard.)

2 Translate an English sentence to a ratio.

EXAMPLE 3 **STUDENT/FACULTY RATIOS** At a college, there are 2,772 students and 154 faculty members. Write a fraction in simplified form that expresses the ratio of students per faculty member.

Solution The ratio of students to faculty is 2,772 to 154. We can write this ratio as the fraction $\frac{2,772}{154}$ and simplify it.

$$\frac{2,772}{154} = \frac{18 \cdot \overset{1}{\cancel{154}}}{1 \cdot \underset{1}{\cancel{154}}}$$

$$= \frac{18}{1} \qquad \frac{154}{154} = 1$$

The ratio of students to faculty is 18 to 1.

⇨ **SELF CHECK 3** In a college graduating class, 224 students out of 632 went on to graduate school. Write a fraction in simplified form that expresses the ratio of the number of students going on to graduate school to the number in the graduating class.

3 Write a ratio as a unit cost.

The *unit cost* of an item is the ratio of its cost to its quantity. For example, the unit cost (the cost per pound) of 5 pounds of coffee priced at $20.75 is given by

$$\frac{\$20.75}{5 \text{ pounds}} = \$4.15 \text{ per pound}$$ $\quad \$20.75 \div 5 = \$4.15$

The unit cost is $4.15 per pound.

EXAMPLE 4   **SHOPPING**   Olives come packaged in a 12-ounce jar, which sells for $3.09, or in a 6-ounce jar, which sells for $1.53. Which is the better buy?

Solution   To find the better buy, we must find each unit cost. The unit cost of the 12-ounce jar is

$$\frac{\$3.09}{12 \text{ ounces}} = \frac{309 ¢}{12 \text{ ounces}}$$ Change $3.09 to 309 cents.

$$= 25.75 ¢ \text{ per ounce}$$

The unit cost of the 6-ounce jar is

$$\frac{\$1.53}{6 \text{ ounces}} = \frac{153 ¢}{6 \text{ ounces}}$$ Change $1.53 to 153 cents.

$$= 25.5 ¢ \text{ per ounce}$$

Since the unit cost is less when olives are packaged in 6-ounce jars, that is the better buy.

⇨ **SELF CHECK 4**   A fast-food restaurant sells a 12-ounce soft drink for 79¢ and a 16-ounce soft drink for 99¢. Which is the better buy?

4 Write a ratio as a rate.

When ratios are used to compare quantities with different units, they often are called **rates.** For example, if we drive 413 miles in 7 hours, the average rate of speed is the quotient of the miles driven to the length of time of the trip.

$$\text{Average rate of speed} = \frac{413 \text{ miles}}{7 \text{ hours}} = \frac{59 \text{ miles}}{1 \text{ hour}}$$ $\frac{413}{7} = \frac{7 \cdot 59}{7 \cdot 1} = \frac{59}{1}$

The rate $\frac{59 \text{ miles}}{1 \text{ hour}}$ can be expressed in any of the following forms:

$$59 \frac{\text{miles}}{\text{hour}}, \quad 59 \text{ miles per hour}, \quad 59 \text{ miles/hour}, \quad \text{or} \quad 59 \text{ mph}$$

EXAMPLE 5   **HOURLY PAY**   Find the hourly rate of pay for a student who earns $370 for working 40 hours.

Solution   We can write the rate of pay as

$$\text{Rate of pay} = \frac{\$370}{40 \text{ hours}}$$

and simplify by dividing 370 by 40.

$$\text{Rate of pay} = 9.25 \frac{\text{dollars}}{\text{hour}}$$

The rate is $9.25 per hour.

SELF CHECK 5 Lawanda earns $716 per 40-hour week managing a dress shop. Find her hourly rate of pay.

EXAMPLE 6 **ENERGY CONSUMPTION** One household used 813.75 kilowatt hours of electricity during a 31-day period. Find the rate of energy consumption in kilowatt hours per day.

Solution We can write the rate of energy consumption as

$$\text{Rate of energy consumption} = \frac{813.75 \text{ kilowatt hours}}{31 \text{ days}}$$

and simplify by dividing 813.75 by 31.

$$\text{Rate of energy consumption} = 26.25 \frac{\text{kilowatt hours}}{\text{day}}$$

The rate of consumption is 26.25 kilowatt hours per day.

SELF CHECK 6 To heat a house for 30 days, a furnace burned 72 therms of natural gas. Find the rate of gas consumption in therms per day.

ACCENT ON TECHNOLOGY

Computing Gas Mileage

A man drove a total of 775 miles. Along the way, he stopped for gas three times, pumping 10.5, 11.3, and 8.75 gallons of gas. He started with the tank half-full and ended with the tank half-full. To find how many miles he got per gallon, we need to divide the total distance by the total number of gallons of gas consumed.

$$\frac{775}{10.5 + 11.3 + 8.75} \quad \begin{array}{l} \leftarrow \text{ Total distance} \\ \leftarrow \text{ Total number of gallons consumed} \end{array}$$

We can make this calculation by entering these numbers and pressing these keys.

775 ÷ (10.5 + 11.3 + 8.75) =   Using a scientific calculator
775 ÷ (10.5 + 11.3 + 8.75) **ENTER**   Using a graphing calculator

Either way, the display will read 25.36824877. To the nearest one-hundredth, he got 25.37 mpg.

SELF CHECK ANSWERS 1. a. $\frac{2}{3}$ b. $\frac{1}{5}$ 2. a. $\frac{1}{4}$ b. $\frac{1}{6}$ 3. $\frac{28}{79}$ 4. the 16-oz drink 5. $17.90 per hour
6. 2.4 therms per day

NOW TRY THIS

1. Express $(x + 2)$ to $(2x + 4)$ as a ratio in simplest form.
2. Express $(x^2 - 25)$ to $(x^2 - 4x - 5)$ as a ratio in simplest form.

6.7 EXERCISES

WARM-UPS *Express as a ratio in simplest form.*

1. 5 to 8

2. 50 to 1

3. 3 to 9

4. 7 to 10

REVIEW

Solve each equation.

5. $2x + 4 = 38$

6. $\dfrac{x}{2} - 4 = 38$

7. $3(x + 2) = 24$

8. $\dfrac{x - 6}{3} = 20$

Factor each expression.

9. $2x + 6$

10. $x^2 - 49$

11. $2x^2 - x - 6$

12. $x^3 + 27$

VOCABULARY AND CONCEPTS   *Fill in the blanks.*

13. A ratio is a _____ of two numbers.

14. The _____ of an item is the quotient of its cost to its quantity.

15. The ratios $\frac{2}{3}$ and $\frac{4}{6}$ are _____ ratios.

16. The quotient $\frac{500 \text{ miles}}{15 \text{ hours}}$ is called a _____.

17. Give three examples of ratios that you have encountered this past week.

18. Suppose that a basketball player made 8 free throws out of 12 tries. The ratio of $\frac{8}{12}$ can be simplified as $\frac{2}{3}$. Interpret this result.

GUIDED PRACTICE

Express each phrase as a ratio in simplest form. See Example 1. (Objective 1)

19. 5 to 7

20. 3 to 5

21. 17 to 34

22. 19 to 38

23. 22 to 33

24. 14 to 21

25. 7 to 24.5

26. 0.65 to 0.15

Express each phrase as a ratio in simplest form. See Example 2. (Objective 1)

27. 4 ounces to 12 ounces

28. 3 inches to 15 inches

29. 12 minutes to 1 hour

30. 8 ounces to 1 pound

31. 3 days to 1 week

32. 4 inches to 2 yards

33. 18 months to 2 years

34. 8 feet to 4 yards

Express each result in simplest form. See Example 3. (Objective 2)

35. **Faculty-to-student ratio**   At a college, there are 125 faculty members and 2,000 students. Find the faculty-to-student ratio.

36. **Ratio of men to women**   In a state senate, there are 94 men and 24 women. Find the ratio of men to women.

Refer to the monthly family budget shown in the table. Give each ratio in simplest form.

Item	Amount
Rent	$750
Food	$652
Gas and electric	$188
Phone	$125
Entertainment	$110

37. Find the total amount of the budget.

38. Find the ratio of the amount budgeted for rent to the total budget.

39. Find the ratio of the amount budgeted for entertainment to the total budget.

40. Find the ratio of the amount budgeted for phone to the amount budgeted for entertainment.

Find the unit cost. See Example 4. (Objective 3)

41. **Unit cost of gasoline**   A driver pumped 17 gallons of gasoline into his tank at a cost of $53.55. Write a quotient of dollars to gallons, and give the unit cost of gasoline.

42. **Unit cost of grass seed**   A 50-pound bag of grass seed costs $222.50. Write a quotient of dollars to pounds, and give the unit cost of grass seed.

43. **Comparative shopping**   A 6-ounce can of orange juice sells for 89¢, and an 8-ounce can sells for $1.19. Which is the better buy?

44. **Comparative shopping**   A 30-pound bag of fertilizer costs $12.25, and an 80-pound bag costs $30.25. Which is the better buy?

Express each result in simplest form. See Examples 5–7. (Objective 3)

45. **Rate of pay**   Ricardo worked for 27 hours to help insulate a hockey arena. For his work, he received $337.50. Write a quotient of dollars to hours, and find his hourly rate of pay.

46. **Real estate taxes**   The real estate taxes on a summer home assessed at $75,000 were $1,500. Find the tax rate as a percent.

47. Rate of speed A car travels 325 miles in 5 hours. Find its rate of speed in mph.

48. Rate of speed An airplane travels from Chicago to San Francisco, a distance of 1,883 miles, in 3.5 hours. Find the average rate of speed of the plane.

ADDITIONAL PRACTICE

Express each result in simplest form.

49. Unit cost of cranberry juice A 12-ounce can of cranberry juice sells for 84¢. Give the unit cost in cents per ounce.

50. Unit cost of beans A 24-ounce package of green beans sells for $1.29. Give the unit cost in cents per ounce.

51. Comparing speeds A car travels 345 miles in 6 hours, and a truck travels 376 miles in 6.2 hours. Which vehicle travels faster?

52. Comparing reading speeds One seventh-grader read a 54-page book in 40 minutes, and another read an 80-page book in 62 minutes. If the books were equally difficult, which student read faster?

53. Comparing gas mileage One car went 1,235 miles on 51.3 gallons of gasoline, and another went 1,456 miles on 55.78 gallons. Which car had the better mpg rating?

54. Comparing electric rates In one community, a bill for 575 kilowatt hours (kwh) of electricity was $38.81. In a second community, a bill for 831 kwh was $58.10. In which community is electricity cheaper?

55. Emptying a tank An 11,880-gallon tank can be emptied in 27 minutes. Write a quotient of gallons to minutes, and give the rate of flow in gallons per minute.

56. Filling a gas tank It took 2.5 minutes to put 17 gallons of gas in a car. Write a quotient of gallons to minutes, and give the rate of flow in gallons per minute.

Refer to the tax deductions listed in the table. Give each ratio in simplest form.

Item	Amount
Medical	$ 995
Real estate tax	$1,245
Contributions	$1,680
Mortgage interest	$4,580
Union dues	$ 225

57. Find the total amount of deductions.

58. Find the ratio of real estate tax deductions to the total deductions.

59. Find the ratio of the contributions to the total deductions.

60. Find the ratio of the mortgage interest deduction to the union dues deduction.

WRITING ABOUT MATH

61. Some people think that the word *ratio* comes from the words *rational number*. Explain why this may be true.

62. In the fraction $\frac{a}{b}$, b cannot be 0. Explain why. In the ratio a to b, b can be 0. Explain why.

SOMETHING TO THINK ABOUT

63. Which ratio is the larger? How can you tell?

$$\frac{17}{19} \quad \text{or} \quad \frac{19}{21}$$

64. Which ratio is the smaller? How can you tell?

$$-\frac{13}{29} \quad \text{or} \quad -\frac{17}{31}$$

SECTION 6.8 Proportions and Similar Triangles

Objectives

1. Determine whether an equation is a proportion.
2. Solve a proportion.
3. Solve an application problem using a proportion.
4. Solve an application problem using the properties of similar triangles.

Vocabulary

proportion   means   similar triangles
extremes   proportional

Getting Ready

Solve each equation.

1. $\dfrac{5}{2} = \dfrac{x}{4}$ **2.** $\dfrac{7}{9} = \dfrac{y}{3}$ **3.** $\dfrac{y}{10} = \dfrac{2}{7}$ **4.** $\dfrac{1}{x} = \dfrac{8}{40}$

5. $\dfrac{w}{14} = \dfrac{7}{21}$ **6.** $\dfrac{c}{12} = \dfrac{5}{12}$ **7.** $\dfrac{3}{q} = \dfrac{1}{7}$ **8.** $\dfrac{16}{3} = \dfrac{8}{z}$

A statement that two ratios are equal is called a *proportion.* In this section, we will discuss proportions and use them to solve problems.

❶ Determine whether an equation is a proportion.

Consider Table 6-3, in which we are given the costs of various numbers of gallons of gasoline.

Number of gallons	Cost (in $)
2	7.60
5	19.00
8	30.40
12	45.60
20	76.00

Table 6-3

If we find the ratios of the costs to the numbers of gallons purchased, we will see that they are equal. In this example, each ratio represents the cost of 1 gallon of gasoline, which is $3.80 per gallon.

$$\frac{7.60}{2} = 3.80, \qquad \frac{19.00}{5} = 3.80, \qquad \frac{30.40}{8} = 3.80, \qquad \frac{45.60}{12} = 3.80, \qquad \frac{76.00}{20} = 3.80$$

When two ratios such as $\frac{7.60}{2}$ and $\frac{19.00}{5}$ are equal, they form a *proportion.*

Proportions

A **proportion** is a statement that two ratios are equal.

Some examples of proportions are

$$\frac{1}{2} = \frac{3}{6}, \qquad \frac{7}{3} = \frac{21}{9}, \qquad \frac{8x}{1} = \frac{40x}{5}, \qquad \text{and} \qquad \frac{a}{b} = \frac{c}{d}$$

- The proportion $\dfrac{1}{2} = \dfrac{3}{6}$ can be read as "1 is to 2 as 3 is to 6."

- The proportion $\dfrac{7}{3} = \dfrac{21}{9}$ can be read as "7 is to 3 as 21 is to 9."

- The proportion $\dfrac{8x}{1} = \dfrac{40x}{5}$ can be read as "$8x$ is to 1 as $40x$ is to 5."

- The proportion $\dfrac{a}{b} = \dfrac{c}{d}$ can be read as "a is to b as c is to d."

The terms of the proportion $\dfrac{a}{b} = \dfrac{c}{d}$ are numbered as follows:

$$\begin{array}{l} \text{First term} \rightarrow\ a \\ \text{Second term} \rightarrow\ b \end{array} \begin{array}{l} c \leftarrow \text{Third term} \\ d \leftarrow \text{Fourth term} \end{array}$$

In the proportion $\dfrac{1}{2} = \dfrac{3}{6}$, the numbers 1 and 6 are called the **extremes,** and the numbers 2 and 3 are called the **means.**

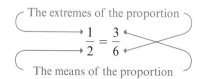

In this proportion, the product of the extremes is equal to the product of the means.

$$1 \cdot 6 = 6 \qquad \text{and} \qquad 2 \cdot 3 = 6$$

This illustrates a fundamental property of proportions.

Fundamental Property of Proportions   In any proportion, the product of the extremes is equal to the product of the means.

In the proportion $\dfrac{a}{b} = \dfrac{c}{d}$, a and d are the extremes, and b and c are the means. We can show that the product of the extremes (ad) is equal to the product of the means (bc) by multiplying both sides of the proportion by bd to clear the fractions, and observing that $ad = bc$.

$$\frac{a}{b} = \frac{c}{d}$$

$$\frac{bd}{1} \cdot \frac{a}{b} = \frac{bd}{1} \cdot \frac{c}{d} \qquad \text{To eliminate the fractions, multiply both sides by } \tfrac{bd}{1}.$$

$$\frac{abd}{b} = \frac{bcd}{d} \qquad \text{Multiply the numerators and multiply the denominators.}$$

$$ad = bc \qquad \text{Divide out the common factors: } \tfrac{b}{b} = 1 \text{ and } \tfrac{d}{d} = 1.$$

Since $ad = bc$, the product of the extremes equals the product of the means.

To determine whether an equation is a proportion, we can check to see whether the product of the extremes is equal to the product of the means.

EXAMPLE 1   Determine whether each equation is a proportion.

a. $\dfrac{3}{7} = \dfrac{9}{21}$ **b.** $\dfrac{8}{3} = \dfrac{13}{5}$

Solution   In each part, we check to see whether the product of the extremes is equal to the product of the means.

a. The product of the extremes is $3 \cdot 21 = 63$. The product of the means is $7 \cdot 9 = 63$. Since the products are equal, the equation is a proportion: $\frac{3}{7} = \frac{9}{21}$.

b. The product of the extremes is $8 \cdot 5 = 40$. The product of the means is $3 \cdot 13 = 39$. Since the products are not equal, the equation is not a proportion: $\frac{8}{3} \neq \frac{13}{5}$.

⇨ **SELF CHECK 1**   Determine whether the equation is a proportion: $\frac{6}{13} = \frac{24}{53}$.

When two pairs of numbers such as 2, 3 and 8, 12 form a proportion, we say that they are **proportional.** To show that 2, 3, 8, and 12 are proportional, we check to see whether the equation

$$\frac{2}{3} = \frac{8}{12}$$

is a proportion. To do so, we find the product of the extremes and the product of the means:

$2 \cdot 12 = 24$ The product of the extremes $3 \cdot 8 = 24$ The product of the means

Since the products are equal, the equation is a proportion, and the numbers are proportional.

EXAMPLE 2   Determine whether 3, 7, 36, and 91 are proportional.

Solution   We check to see whether $\frac{3}{7} = \frac{36}{91}$ is a proportion by finding two products:

$3 \cdot 91 = 273$ This is the product of the extremes.
$7 \cdot 36 = 252$ This is the product of the means.

Since the products are not equal, the numbers are not proportional.

⇨ **SELF CHECK 2**   Determine whether 6, 11, 54, and 99 are proportional.

2   **Solve a proportion.**

Suppose that we know three of the terms in the proportion

$$\frac{x}{5} = \frac{24}{20}$$

To find the unknown term, we multiply the extremes and multiply the means, set them equal, and solve for x:

$$\frac{x}{5} = \frac{24}{20}$$

$20x = 5 \cdot 24$ In a proportion, the product of the extremes is equal to the product of the means.

$$20x = 120 \qquad \text{Multiply: } 5 \cdot 24 = 120.$$

$$\frac{20x}{20} = \frac{120}{20} \qquad \text{To undo the multiplication by 20, divide both sides by 20.}$$

$$x = 6 \qquad \text{Simplify: } \tfrac{20}{20} = 1 \text{ and } \tfrac{120}{20} = 6.$$

The first term is 6.

EXAMPLE 3   Find the fourth term of the proportion: $\dfrac{12}{18} = \dfrac{3}{x}$.

Solution   To solve the proportion, we clear the fractions by multiplying the extremes and multiplying the means. Then, we solve for x.

$$\frac{12}{18} = \frac{3}{x}$$

$$12 \cdot x = 18 \cdot 3 \qquad \text{In a proportion, the product of the extremes equals the product of the means.}$$

$$12x = 54 \qquad \text{Multiply: } 18 \cdot 3 = 54.$$

$$\frac{12x}{12} = \frac{54}{12} \qquad \text{To undo the multiplication by 12, divide both sides by 12.}$$

$$x = \frac{9}{2} \qquad \text{Simplify: } \tfrac{12}{12} = 1 \text{ and } \tfrac{54}{12} = \tfrac{9}{2}.$$

The fourth term is $\dfrac{9}{2}$.

⇨ **SELF CHECK 3**   Solve: $\dfrac{15}{x} = \dfrac{25}{40}$.

EXAMPLE 4   Find the third term of the proportion $\dfrac{3.5}{7.2} = \dfrac{x}{15.84}$.

Solution   To find the third term of the proportion, we clear the fractions by multiplying the extremes and multiplying the means. Then, we solve for x.

$$\frac{3.5}{7.2} = \frac{x}{15.84}$$

$$3.5(15.84) = 7.2x \qquad \text{In a proportion, the product of the extremes equals the product of the means.}$$

$$55.44 = 7.2x \qquad \text{Multiply: } 3.5 \cdot 15.84 = 55.44.$$

$$\frac{55.44}{7.2} = \frac{7.2x}{7.2} \qquad \text{To undo the multiplication by 7.2, divide both sides by 7.2.}$$

$$7.7 = x \qquad \text{Simplify: } \tfrac{55.44}{7.2} = 7.7 \text{ and } \tfrac{7.2}{7.2} = 1.$$

The third term is 7.7.

⇨ **SELF CHECK 4**   Find the second term of the proportion $\dfrac{6.7}{x} = \dfrac{33.5}{38}$.

ACCENT ON TECHNOLOGY	To solve the equation in Example 4 with a calculator, we can proceed as follows.

**Solving Equations
with a Calculator**

$$\frac{3.5}{7.2} = \frac{x}{15.84}$$

$$\frac{3.5(15.84)}{7.2} = x \qquad \text{Multiply both sides by 15.84.}$$

We can find x by entering these numbers and pressing these keys.

3.5 $\boxed{\times}$ 15.84 $\boxed{\div}$ 7.2 $\boxed{=}$ Using a scientific calculator

3.5 $\boxed{\times}$ 15.84 $\boxed{\div}$ 7.2 $\boxed{\textbf{ENTER}}$ Using a graphing calculator

Either way, the display will read 7.7. Thus, $x = 7.7$.

EXAMPLE 5   Solve: $\dfrac{2x + 1}{4} = \dfrac{10}{8}$.

Solution   To solve the proportion, we clear the fractions by multiplying the extremes and multiplying the means. Then, we solve for x.

$$\frac{2x + 1}{4} = \frac{10}{8}$$

$8(2x + 1) = 40$ In a proportion, the product of the extremes equals the product of the means.

$16x + 8 = 40$ Use the distributive property to remove parentheses.

$16x + 8 - \mathbf{8} = 40 - \mathbf{8}$ To undo the addition of 8, subtract 8 from both sides.

$16x = 32$ Simplify: $8 - 8 = 0$ and $40 - 8 = 32$.

$\dfrac{16x}{\mathbf{16}} = \dfrac{32}{\mathbf{16}}$ To undo the multiplication by 16, divide both sides by 16.

$x = 2$ Simplify: $\frac{16}{16} = 1$ and $\frac{32}{16} = 2$.

Thus, $x = 2$.

SELF CHECK 5   Solve: $\frac{3x - 1}{2} = \frac{12.5}{5}$.

3   **Solve an application problem using a proportion.**

When solving application problems, we often need to set up and solve a proportion.

EXAMPLE 6   If 6 apples cost $1.38, how much will 16 apples cost?

Solution   Let c represent the cost of 16 apples. The ratios of the numbers of apples to their costs are equal.

6 apples is to $1.38 as 16 apples is to c.

$$\begin{array}{r} \text{6 apples} \rightarrow \\ \text{Cost of 6 apples} \rightarrow \end{array} \frac{6}{1.38} = \frac{16}{c} \begin{array}{l} \leftarrow \text{16 apples} \\ \leftarrow \text{Cost of 16 apples} \end{array}$$

$$6 \cdot c = 1.38(16)$$ In a proportion, the product of the extremes is equal to the product of the means.

$$6c = 22.08$$ Do the multiplication: $1.38 \cdot 16 = 22.08$.

$$\frac{6c}{6} = \frac{22.08}{6}$$ To undo the multiplication by 6, divide both sides by 6.

$$c = 3.68$$ Simplify: $\frac{6}{6} = 1$ and $\frac{22.08}{6} = 3.68$.

Sixteen apples will cost $3.68.

 **SELF CHECK 6**   If 9 tickets to a concert cost $112.50, how much will 15 tickets cost?

EXAMPLE 7   **MIXING SOLUTIONS**   A solution contains 2 quarts of antifreeze and 5 quarts of water. How many quarts of antifreeze must be mixed with 18 quarts of water to have the same concentration?

Solution   Let q represent the number of quarts of antifreeze to be mixed with the water. The ratios of the quarts of antifreeze to the quarts of water are equal.

2 quarts antifreeze is to 5 quarts water as q quarts antifreeze is to 18 quarts water.

2 quarts antifreeze → $\quad \dfrac{2}{5} = \dfrac{q}{18}$ ← q quarts of antifreeze
5 quarts water → $\qquad\qquad\qquad$ ← 18 quarts water

$$2 \cdot 18 = 5q$$ In a proportion, the product of the extremes is equal to the product of the means.

$$36 = 5q$$ Do the multiplication: $2 \cdot 18 = 36$.

$$\frac{36}{5} = \frac{5q}{5}$$ To undo the multiplication by 5, divide both sides by 5.

$$\frac{36}{5} = q$$ Simplify: $\frac{5}{5} = 1$.

The mixture should contain $\frac{36}{5}$ or 7.2 quarts of antifreeze.

 **SELF CHECK 7**   A solution should contain 2 ounces of alcohol for every 7 ounces of water. How much alcohol should be added to 20 ounces of water to get the proper concentration?

EXAMPLE 8   **BAKING**   A recipe for rhubarb cake calls for $1\frac{1}{4}$ cups of sugar for every $2\frac{1}{2}$ cups of flour. How many cups of flour are needed if the baker intends to use 3 cups of sugar?

Solution   Let f represent the number of cups of flour to be mixed with the sugar. The ratios of the cups of sugar to the cups of flour are equal.

$1\frac{1}{4}$ cups sugar is to $2\frac{1}{2}$ cups flour as 3 cups sugar is to f cups flour.

$1\frac{1}{4}$ cups sugar → $\quad \dfrac{1\frac{1}{4}}{2\frac{1}{2}} = \dfrac{3}{f}$ ← 3 cups sugar
$2\frac{1}{2}$ cups flour → $\qquad\qquad\qquad$ ← f cups flour

$$\frac{1.25}{2.5} = \frac{3}{f}$$ Change the fractions to decimals.

$$1.25f = 2.5 \cdot 3 \qquad \text{In a proportion, the product of the extremes is equal to the product of the means.}$$

$$1.25f = 7.5 \qquad \text{Do the multiplication: } 2.5 \cdot 3 = 7.5.$$

$$\frac{1.25f}{\mathbf{1.25}} = \frac{7.5}{\mathbf{1.25}} \qquad \text{To undo the multiplication by 1.25, divide both sides by 1.25.}$$

$$f = 6 \qquad \text{Divide: } \frac{1.25}{1.25} = 1 \text{ and } \frac{7.5}{1.25} = 6.$$

The baker should use 6 cups of flour.

⇨ **SELF CHECK 8**   How many cups of sugar will be needed to make several cakes that will require a total of 25 cups of flour?

EXAMPLE 9   **QUALITY CONTROL**   In a manufacturing process, 15 parts out of 90 were found to be defective. How many defective parts will be expected in a run of 120 parts?

Solution   Let d represent the expected number of defective parts. In each run, the ratio of the defective parts to the total number of parts should be the same.

15 defective parts is to 90 as d defective parts is to 120.

$$\begin{array}{r}\text{15 defective parts} \rightarrow \\ \text{90 parts} \rightarrow\end{array} \quad \frac{15}{90} = \frac{d}{120} \begin{array}{l} \leftarrow d \text{ defective parts} \\ \leftarrow 120 \text{ parts}\end{array}$$

$$15 \cdot 120 = 90d \qquad \text{In a proportion, the product of the extremes is equal to the product of the means.}$$

$$1{,}800 = 90d \qquad \text{Do the multiplication: } 15 \cdot 120 = 1{,}800.$$

$$\frac{1{,}800}{\mathbf{90}} = \frac{90d}{\mathbf{90}} \qquad \text{To undo the multiplication by 90, divide both sides by 90.}$$

$$20 = d \qquad \text{Divide: } \frac{1{,}800}{90} = 20 \text{ and } \frac{90}{90} = 1.$$

The expected number of defective parts is 20.

⇨ **SELF CHECK 9**   How many defective parts will be expected in a run of 3,000 parts?

---

4   **Solve an application problem using the properties of similar triangles.**

If two angles of one triangle have the same measure as two angles of a second triangle, the triangles will have the same shape. Triangles with the same shape are called **similar triangles**. In Figure 6-1, $\triangle ABC \sim \triangle DEF$ (read the symbol $\sim$ as "is similar to").

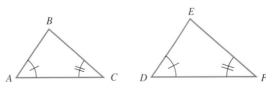

Figure 6-1

Property of Similar Triangles	If two triangles are similar, the lengths of all pairs of corresponding sides are in proportion.

In the similar triangles shown in Figure 6-1, the following proportions are true.

$$\frac{AB}{DE} = \frac{BC}{EF}, \qquad \frac{BC}{EF} = \frac{CA}{FD}, \qquad \text{and} \qquad \frac{CA}{FD} = \frac{AB}{DE}$$

EXAMPLE 10   **HEIGHT OF A TREE**   A tree casts a shadow 18 feet long at the same time as a woman 5 feet tall casts a shadow that is 1.5 feet long. Find the height of the tree.

Solution   We let h represent the height of the tree. Figure 6-2 shows the triangles determined by the tree and its shadow and the woman and her shadow.

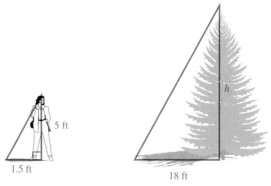

5 ft

1.5 ft

h

18 ft

Figure 6-2

Since the triangles have the same shape, they are similar, and the lengths of their corresponding sides are in proportion. We can find h by solving the following proportion.

$$\frac{h}{5} = \frac{18}{1.5} \qquad \frac{\text{Height of the tree}}{\text{Height of the woman}} = \frac{\text{Shadow of the tree}}{\text{Shadow of the woman}}$$

$1.5h = 5(18)$ In a proportion, the product of the extremes is equal to the product of the means.

$h = 60$ To undo the multiplication by 1.5, divide both sides by 1.5 and simplify.

The tree is 60 feet tall.

⇨ **SELF CHECK 10**   Find the height of the tree if the woman is 5 feet 6 inches tall and her shadow is still 1.5 feet long.

⇨ **SELF CHECK ANSWERS**   **1.** no   **2.** yes   **3.** 24   **4.** 7.6   **5.** 2   **6.** $187.50   **7.** $\frac{40}{7}$ oz   **8.** 12.5 cups   **9.** 500   **10.** 66 ft

NOW TRY THIS

1. To monitor the population of wild animals, the Fish and Wildlife department uses a method called "tag and release." A number of animals are captured, tagged, and returned to the wild. A year later, another group of the animals is captured and the ratio of the tagged animals to the total captured is believed to be approximately the same as the ratio of the original number tagged to the total population.

   If 25 wolves were tagged and released and a year later 21 wolves were captured, 3 of which were tagged, predict the total population of the wolves.

6.8 EXERCISES

WARM-UPS *Which expressions are proportions?*

1. $\dfrac{3}{5} = \dfrac{6}{10}$

2. $\dfrac{1}{2} = \dfrac{1}{3}$

3. $\dfrac{1}{2} + \dfrac{1}{4}$

4. $\dfrac{1}{x} = \dfrac{2}{2x}$

REVIEW

5. Change $\dfrac{9}{10}$ to a percent.

6. Change $\dfrac{7}{8}$ to a percent.

7. Change $33\frac{1}{3}\%$ to a fraction.

8. Change 75% to a fraction.

9. Find 30% of 1,600.

10. Find $\frac{1}{2}\%$ of 520.

11. **Shopping** If Maria bought a dress for 25% off the original price of $98, how much did the dress cost?

12. **Shopping** Bill purchased a shirt on sale for $17.50. Find the original cost of the shirt if it was marked down 30%.

VOCABULARY AND CONCEPTS *Fill in the blanks.*

13. A _____ is a statement that two _____ are equal.

14. The first and fourth terms of a proportion are called the _____ of the proportion.

15. The second and third terms of a proportion are called the _____ of the proportion.

16. When two pairs of numbers form a proportion, we say that the numbers are _____.

17. If two triangles have the same shape, they are said to be _____.

18. If two triangles are similar, the lengths of their corresponding sides are in _____.

19. The equation $\dfrac{a}{b} = \dfrac{c}{d}$ is a proportion if the product ___ is equal to the product ___.

20. If $3 \cdot 10 = 17x$, then _____ is a proportion. (Note that answers may differ.)

21. Read $\triangle ABC$ as _____ ABC.

22. The symbol $\sim$ is read as _____.

GUIDED PRACTICE

Determine whether each statement is a proportion. **See Example 1.**
(Objective 1)

23. $\dfrac{9}{7} = \dfrac{81}{70}$

24. $\dfrac{5}{2} = \dfrac{20}{8}$

25. $\dfrac{-7}{3} = \dfrac{14}{-6}$

26. $\dfrac{13}{-19} = \dfrac{-65}{95}$

27. $\dfrac{9}{19} = \dfrac{38}{80}$

28. $\dfrac{40}{29} = \dfrac{29}{22}$

29. $\dfrac{10.4}{3.6} = \dfrac{41.6}{14.4}$

30. $\dfrac{13.23}{3.45} = \dfrac{39.96}{11.35}$

Determine whether the given values are proportional. **See Example 2.** (Objective 1)

31. 6, 10, 15, 25

32. 4, 2, 17, 8.5

33. 3, 7, 4, 8

34. 4.5, 6, 8.5, 10

Solve for the variable in each proportion. **See Examples 3–4.**
(Objective 2)

35. $\dfrac{2}{3} = \dfrac{x}{6}$

36. $\dfrac{3}{6} = \dfrac{x}{8}$

37. $\dfrac{5}{10} = \dfrac{3}{c}$

38. $\dfrac{7}{14} = \dfrac{2}{b}$

Solve for the variable in each proportion. **See Example 5.**
(Objective 2)

39. $\dfrac{x+1}{5} = \dfrac{3}{15}$

40. $\dfrac{x-1}{7} = \dfrac{2}{21}$

41. $\dfrac{x + 3}{12} = \dfrac{-7}{6}$

42. $\dfrac{x + 7}{-4} = \dfrac{3}{12}$

ADDITIONAL PRACTICE

43. $\dfrac{-6}{x} = \dfrac{8}{4}$

44. $\dfrac{4}{x} = \dfrac{2}{8}$

45. $\dfrac{x}{3} = \dfrac{9}{3}$

46. $\dfrac{x}{2} = \dfrac{-18}{6}$

47. $\dfrac{4 - x}{13} = \dfrac{11}{26}$

48. $\dfrac{5 - x}{17} = \dfrac{13}{34}$

49. $\dfrac{2x + 1}{18} = \dfrac{14}{3}$

50. $\dfrac{2x - 1}{18} = \dfrac{9}{54}$

51. $\dfrac{3p - 2}{12} = \dfrac{p + 1}{3}$

52. $\dfrac{12}{m} = \dfrac{18}{m + 2}$

APPLICATIONS

Set up and solve a proportion. See Examples 6–9. (Objective 3)

53. Grocery shopping If 3 pints of yogurt cost $1, how much will 51 pints cost?

54. Shopping for clothes If shirts are on sale at two for $25, how much will 5 shirts cost?

55. Gardening Garden seed is on sale at 3 packets for 50¢. How much will 39 packets cost?

56. Cooking A recipe for spaghetti sauce requires four 16-ounce bottles of catsup to make two gallons of sauce. How many bottles of catsup are needed to make 10 gallons of sauce?

57. Mixing perfume A perfume is to be mixed in the ratio of 3 drops of pure essence to 7 drops of alcohol. How many drops of pure essence should be mixed with 56 drops of alcohol?

58. Making cologne A cologne can be made by mixing 2 drops of pure essence with 5 drops of distilled water. How many drops of water should be used with 15 drops of pure essence?

59. Making cookies A recipe for chocolate chip cookies calls for $1\frac{1}{4}$ cups of flour and 1 cup of sugar. The recipe will make $3\frac{1}{2}$ dozen cookies. How many cups of flour will be needed to make 12 dozen cookies?

60. Making brownies A recipe for brownies calls for 4 eggs and $1\frac{1}{2}$ cups of flour. If the recipe makes 15 brownies, how many cups of flour will be needed to make 130 brownies?

61. Quality control In a manufacturing process, 95% of the parts made are to be within specifications. How many defective parts would be expected in a run of 940 pieces?

62. Quality control Out of a sample of 500 men's shirts, 17 were rejected because of crooked collars. How many crooked collars would you expect to find in a run of 15,000 shirts?

63. Gas consumption If a car can travel 42 miles on 1 gallon of gas, how much gas will it need to travel 315 miles?

64. Gas consumption If a truck gets 12 mpg, how far can it go on 17 gallons of gas?

65. Computing paychecks Chen earns $412 for a 40-hour week. If he missed 10 hours of work last week, how much did he get paid?

66. Computing paychecks Danielle has a part-time job earning $169.50 for a 30-hour week. If she works a full 40-hour week, how much will she earn?

67. Model railroading An HO-scale model railroad engine is 9 inches long. If HO scale is 87 feet to 1 foot, how long is a real engine?

68. Model railroading An N-scale model railroad caboose is 3.5 inches long. If N scale is 169 feet to 1 foot, how long is a real caboose to the nearest half inch?

69. Model houses A model house is built to a scale of 1 inch to 8 inches. If a model house is 36 inches wide, how wide is the real house?

70. Drafting In a scale drawing, a 280-foot antenna tower is drawn 7 inches high. The building next to it is drawn 2 inches high. How tall is the actual building?

71. Mixing fuel The instructions on a can of oil intended to be added to lawnmower gasoline read:

Recommended	Gasoline	Oil
50 to 1	6 gal	16 oz

Are these instructions correct? (*Hint:* There are 128 ounces in 1 gallon.)

72. Mixing fuel See Exercise 71. How much oil should be mixed with 28 gallons of gas?

Set up and solve a proportion. See Example 10. (Objective 4)

73. Height of a tree A tree casts a shadow of 26 feet at the same time as a 6-foot man casts a shadow of 4 feet. The two triangles in the illustration are similar. Find the height of the tree.

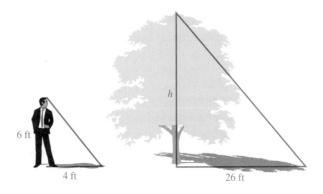

74. Height of a flagpole   A man places a mirror on the ground and sees the reflection of the top of a flagpole, as in the illustration. The two triangles in the illustration are similar. Find the height h of the flagpole.

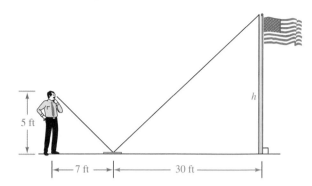

75. Width of a river   Use the dimensions in the illustration to find w, the width of the river. The two triangles in the illustration are similar.

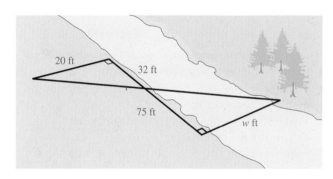

76. Flight path   An airplane ascends 100 feet as it flies a horizontal distance of 1,000 feet. The two triangles in the illustration are similar. How much altitude will it gain as it flies a horizontal distance of 1 mile?   (*Hint:* 5,280 feet = 1 mile.)

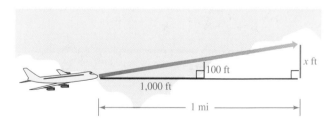

77. Flight path   An airplane descends 1,350 feet as it flies a horizontal distance of 1 mile. How much altitude is lost as it flies a horizontal distance of 5 miles?

78. Ski runs   A ski course falls 100 feet in every 300 feet of horizontal run. If the total horizontal run is $\frac{1}{2}$ mile, find the height of the hill.

79. Mountain travel   A road ascends 750 feet in every 2,500 feet of travel. By how much will the road rise in a trip of 10 miles?

80. Photo enlargements   The 3-by-5 photo in the illustration is to be blown up to the larger size. Find x.

WRITING ABOUT MATH

81. Explain the difference between a ratio and a proportion.

82. Explain how to tell whether the equation $\frac{3.2}{3.7} = \frac{5.44}{6.29}$ is a proportion.

SOMETHING TO THINK ABOUT

83. Verify that $\frac{3}{5} = \frac{12}{20} = \frac{3 + 12}{5 + 20}$. Is the following rule always true?

$$\frac{a}{b} = \frac{c}{d} = \frac{a + c}{b + d}$$

84. Verify that since $\frac{3}{5} = \frac{9}{15}$, then $\frac{3 + 5}{5} = \frac{9 + 15}{15}$. Is the following rule always true?

$$\text{If } \frac{a}{b} = \frac{c}{d}, \text{ then } \frac{a + b}{b} = \frac{c + d}{d}$$

PROJECTS

1. If the sides of two similar triangles are in the ratio of 1 to 1, the triangles are said to be **congruent.** Congruent triangles have the same shape and the same size (area).

a. Draw several triangles with sides of length 1, 1.5, and 2 inches. Are the triangles all congruent? What general rule could you make?

b. Draw several triangles with the dimensions shown in the illustration on the right. Are the triangles all congruent? What general rule could you make?

c. Draw several triangles with the dimensions shown in the illustration on the right. Are the triangles all congruent? What general rule could you make?

40° 50°
1 inch

1.5 inch
30°
1 inch

2. If y is equal to a polynomial divided by a polynomial, we call the resulting function a **rational function.** The simplest of these functions is defined by the equation $f(x) = \frac{1}{x}$. Since the denominator of this fraction cannot be 0, the domain of the function is the set of real numbers, except 0. Since a fraction with a numerator of 1 cannot be 0, the range is also the set of real numbers, except 0.

Construct the graph of this function by making a table of values containing at least eight ordered pairs, plotting the ordered pairs, and joining the points with two curves. Then graph each of the following rational functions and find each one's domain and range.

a. $f(x) = \frac{2}{x}$ **b.** $f(x) = -\frac{1}{x}$

c. $f(x) = -\frac{1}{x + 1}$ **d.** $f(x) = \frac{2}{x - 1}$

3. Suppose that the cost of telephone service is $6 per month plus 5¢ per call. If n represents the number of calls made one month, the cost C of phone service that month will be given by $C = 0.05n + 6$. If we divide the total cost C by the number of calls n, we will obtain the average cost per call, which we will denote as $\bar{c}$.

(1) $\bar{c} = \dfrac{C}{n} = \dfrac{0.05n + 6}{n}$ $\bar{c}$ is the average cost per call, C is the total monthly cost, and n is the number of phone calls made that month.

Use the rational function in Equation 1 to find the average monthly cost per call when

a. 5 calls were made   **b.** 25 calls were made.

Assume that a phone company charges $15 a month and 5¢ per phone call and answer the following questions.

a. Write a function that will give the cost C per month for making n phone calls.

b. Write a function that will give the average cost $\bar{c}$ per call during the month.

c. Find the cost if 45 phone calls were made during the month.

d. Find the average cost per call if 45 calls were made that month.

Chapter 6   REVIEW

SECTION 6.1   Simplifying Rational Expressions

DEFINITIONS AND CONCEPTS	EXAMPLES
Fractions that are the quotient of two integers are *rational numbers*.	**Rational numbers:** $\dfrac{2}{13}$ $\dfrac{15}{28}$
Fractions that are the quotient of two polynomials are *rational expressions*.	**Rational expressions:** $\dfrac{x}{x - 5}$ $\dfrac{5x - 2}{x^2 + x - 3}$

If b and c are not 0, then

$$\frac{a \cdot c}{b \cdot c} = \frac{a}{b}$$

$$\frac{22xy^3}{33x^2y} = \frac{2 \cdot \cancel{11} \cdot x \cdot y \cdot y \cdot y}{3 \cdot \cancel{11} \cdot x \cdot x \cdot y}$$ Factor the numerator and denominator.

$$= \frac{2y^2}{3x}$$ Divide out the common factors of 11, x, and y.

$$\frac{a}{1} = a$$

$$\frac{2x^3 - 2x^2}{x - 1} = \frac{2x^2(x - 1)}{x - 1}$$ Factor the numerator.

$$= \frac{2x^2}{1}$$ Divide out the common factor of $x - 1$.

$$= 2x^2$$ Denominators of 1 need not be written.

$\dfrac{a}{0}$ is undefined.

x cannot be 2 in the rational expression $\frac{x + 1}{x - 2}$ because the denominator will be 0; $\frac{2 + 1}{2 - 2} = \frac{3}{0}$. The expression is undefined.

$$\frac{a - b}{b - a} = -1$$

Because $x - 3$ and $3 - x$ are opposites (additive inverses), their quotient is -1.

$$\frac{x - 3}{3 - x} = -1$$

REVIEW EXERCISES

For what values of x is the rational expression undefined?

1. $\dfrac{x + 4}{(x + 3)(x - 3)}$

2. $\dfrac{x - 3}{x^2 + x - 6}$

Write each fraction in lowest terms.

3. $\dfrac{10}{25}$

4. $-\dfrac{12}{18}$

5. $-\dfrac{51}{153}$

6. $\dfrac{105}{45}$

7. $\dfrac{3x^2}{6x^3}$

8. $\dfrac{5xy^2}{2x^2y^2}$

9. $\dfrac{x^2}{x^2 + x}$

10. $\dfrac{x + 2}{x^2 + 2x}$

11. $\dfrac{6xy}{3xy}$

12. $\dfrac{8x^2y}{2x(4xy)}$

13. $\dfrac{3p - 2}{2 - 3p}$

14. $\dfrac{x^2 - x - 56}{x^2 - 5x - 24}$

15. $\dfrac{2x^2 - 16x}{2x^2 - 18x + 16}$

16. $\dfrac{a^2 + 2a + ab + 2b}{a^2 + 2ab + b^2}$

SECTION 6.2 Multiplying and Dividing Rational Expressions

DEFINITIONS AND CONCEPTS	EXAMPLES

$$\frac{a}{b} \cdot \frac{c}{d} = \frac{a \cdot c}{b \cdot d} \quad b, d \neq 0$$

$$\frac{x + 1}{x + 4} \cdot \frac{x^2 - 16}{x^2 - x - 2} = \frac{(x + 1)(x^2 - 16)}{(x + 4)(x^2 - x - 2)}$$ Multiply the numerators and multiply the denominators.

$$= \frac{(x + 1)(x + 4)(x - 4)}{(x + 4)(x + 1)(x - 2)}$$ Factor and divide out the common factors.

$$= \frac{x - 4}{x - 2}$$

$$\frac{a}{b} \div \frac{c}{d} = \frac{a}{b} \cdot \frac{d}{c} \quad (b, c, d \neq 0)$$

$$\frac{6x^2}{2x + 8} \div \frac{3x}{x^2 - 2x - 24}$$

$$= \frac{6x^2}{2x + 8} \cdot \frac{x^2 - 2x - 24}{3x}$$ Invert the denominator and multiply.

$$= \frac{6x^2(x^2 - 2x - 24)}{(2x + 8)(3x)}$$ Multiply the fractions.

$$= \frac{6x^2(x + 4)(x - 6)}{2(x + 4)3x}$$ Factor and divide out the common factors.

$$= \frac{x(x - 6)}{1}$$

$$= x(x - 6)$$ Denominators of 1 need not be written.

REVIEW EXERCISES

Perform each multiplication and simplify.

17. $\dfrac{3xy}{2x} \cdot \dfrac{4x}{2y^2}$ **18.** $\dfrac{3x}{x^2 - x} \cdot \dfrac{2x - 2}{x^2}$

19. $\dfrac{x^2 + 3x + 2}{x^2 + 2x} \cdot \dfrac{x}{x + 1}$ **20.** $\dfrac{x^2 + x}{3x - 15} \cdot \dfrac{6x - 30}{x^2 + 2x + 1}$

Perform each division and simplify.

21. $\dfrac{3x^2}{5x^2y} \div \dfrac{6x}{15xy^2}$ **22.** $\dfrac{x^2 + 5x}{x^2 + 4x - 5} \div \dfrac{x^2}{x - 1}$

23. $\dfrac{x^2 - x - 6}{2x - 1} \div \dfrac{x^2 - 2x - 3}{2x^2 + x - 1}$

24. $\dfrac{x^2 - 3x}{x^2 - x - 6} \div \dfrac{x^2 - x}{x^2 + x - 2}$

25. $\dfrac{x^2 + 4x + 4}{x^2 + x - 6}\left(\dfrac{x - 2}{x - 1} \div \dfrac{x + 2}{x^2 + 2x - 3}\right)$

SECTION 6.3   Adding and Subtracting Rational Expressions

DEFINITIONS AND CONCEPTS	EXAMPLES
$\dfrac{a}{d} + \dfrac{b}{d} = \dfrac{a + b}{d}$ $(d \neq 0)$	$\dfrac{4x + 3}{2x} + \dfrac{x + 1}{2x} = \dfrac{4x + 3 + x + 1}{2x}$ Add the numerators and keep the common denominator.
	$\qquad\qquad = \dfrac{5x + 4}{2x}$ Combine like terms.
$\dfrac{a}{d} - \dfrac{b}{d} = \dfrac{a - b}{d}$ $(d \neq 0)$	$\dfrac{4x + 3}{2x} - \dfrac{x + 1}{2x} = \dfrac{4x + 3 - (x + 1)}{2x}$ Subtract the numerators and keep the common denominator.
	$\qquad\qquad = \dfrac{4x + 3 - x - 1}{2x}$ Remove the parentheses.
	$\qquad\qquad = \dfrac{3x + 2}{2x}$ Combine like terms.

The least common denominator (LCD) for a set of fractions is the smallest number that each denominator will divide exactly.

Finding the Least Common Denominator (LCD)

1. List the different denominators that appear in the rational expressions.
2. Completely factor each denominator.
3. Form a product using each different factor obtained in Step 2. Use each different factor the *greatest* number of times it appears in any one factorization. The product formed by multiplying these factors is the LCD.

The LCD of 6 and 9 is 18.

The LCD of 10 and 15 is 30.

Find the LCD of $\dfrac{2x}{3y}, \dfrac{4x}{15y}$, and $\dfrac{5x}{18y}$.

$$3y = 3 \cdot y$$
$$15y = 3 \cdot 5 \cdot y$$
$$18y = 2 \cdot 3 \cdot 3 \cdot y$$

Form a product with factors of 2, 3 and y. We use 2 one time, because it appears only once as a factor of 18. We use 3 two times because it appears twice as a factor of 18. We use 5 one time, because it appears only once as a factor of 15. We use y once because it only occurs once in each factor of $3y$, $15y$, and $18y$.

$$\text{LCD} = 2 \cdot 3 \cdot 3 \cdot 5 \cdot y = 90y$$

To add or subtract rational expressions with unlike denominators, first find the LCD of the expressions. Then express each one in equivalent form with this LCD. Finally, add or subtract the expressions. Simplify, if possible.

To perform the subtraction $\frac{x+1}{x^2-9} - \frac{2}{x+3}$, we factor $x^2 - 9$ and discover the LCD is $(x+3)(x-3)$. Then we proceed as follows:

$$\frac{x+1}{x^2-9} - \frac{2}{x+3}$$

$$= \frac{x+1}{(x+3)(x-3)} - \frac{2(x-3)}{(x+3)(x-3)}$$
Build the second fraction and factor the denominator of the first fraction.

$$= \frac{x+1-2(x-3)}{(x+3)(x-3)}$$
Subtract the numerators and keep the common denominator.

$$= \frac{x+1-2x+6}{(x+3)(x-3)}$$
Remove parentheses.

$$= \frac{-x+7}{(x+3)(x-3)}$$
Combine like terms.

REVIEW EXERCISES
Perform each operation. Simplify all answers.

26. $\dfrac{x}{x+y} + \dfrac{y}{x+y}$

27. $\dfrac{3x}{x-7} - \dfrac{x-2}{x-7}$

28. $\dfrac{x}{x-1} + \dfrac{1}{x}$

29. $\dfrac{1}{7} - \dfrac{1}{x}$

30. $\dfrac{3}{x+1} - \dfrac{2}{x}$

31. $\dfrac{x+2}{2x} - \dfrac{2-x}{x^2}$

32. $\dfrac{x}{x+2} + \dfrac{3}{x} - \dfrac{4}{x^2+2x}$

33. $\dfrac{2}{x-1} - \dfrac{3}{x+1} + \dfrac{x-5}{x^2-1}$

SECTION 6.4   Simplifying Complex Fractions

DEFINITIONS AND CONCEPTS	EXAMPLES

To simplify a complex fraction, use either of these methods:

1. Write the numerator and denominator of the complex fraction as single fractions, do the division of the fractions, and simplify.

Method 1

$$\frac{\dfrac{2x}{x+1} + \dfrac{3}{x}}{\dfrac{1}{x} + \dfrac{2}{x+1}}$$

$$= \frac{\dfrac{2x \cdot x}{x(x+1)} + \dfrac{3(x+1)}{x(x+1)}}{\dfrac{1(x+1)}{x(x+1)} + \dfrac{2x}{x(x+1)}}$$
Build each fraction so each fraction has a denominator of $x(x+1)$.

$$= \frac{\dfrac{2x^2}{x(x+1)} + \dfrac{3x+3}{x(x+1)}}{\dfrac{x+1}{x(x+1)} + \dfrac{2x}{x(x+1)}}$$
Simplify wherever possible.

$$= \frac{2x^2+3x+3}{x(x+1)} \div \frac{x+1+2x}{x(x+1)}$$
Add the fractions and write the resulting complex fraction as an equivalent division problem.

$$= \frac{2x^2+3x+3}{x(x+1)} \div \frac{3x+1}{x(x+1)}$$
Simplify the numerators.

$$= \frac{2x^2+3x+3}{x(x+1)} \cdot \frac{x(x+1)}{3x+1}$$
Invert the divisor and multiply.

$$= \frac{2x^2+3x+3}{3x+1}$$
Multiply the fractions and simplify.

2. Multiply both the numerator and the denominator of the complex fraction by the LCD of the fractions that appear in the numerator and the denominator, then simplify.

Method 2

$$\frac{\dfrac{2x}{x+1} + \dfrac{3}{x}}{\dfrac{1}{x} + \dfrac{2}{x+1}}$$

$$= \frac{x(x+1)\left(\dfrac{2x}{x+1} + \dfrac{3}{x}\right)}{x(x+1)\left(\dfrac{1}{x} + \dfrac{2}{x+1}\right)}$$

Multiply the numerator and the denominator by the LCD of $x(x+1)$.

$$= \frac{x(x+1)\left(\dfrac{2x}{x+1}\right) + x(x+1)\left(\dfrac{3}{x}\right)}{x(x+1)\left(\dfrac{1}{x}\right) + x(x+1)\left(\dfrac{2}{x+1}\right)}$$

Remove parentheses.

$$= \frac{x \cdot 2x + 3(x+1)}{x+1+2x}$$

Do the multiplication.

$$= \frac{2x^2 + 3x + 3}{3x+1}$$

Simplify.

REVIEW EXERCISES
Simplify each complex fraction.

34. $\dfrac{\dfrac{3}{2}}{\dfrac{2}{3}}$

35. $\dfrac{\dfrac{3}{2} + 1}{\dfrac{2}{3} + 1}$

36. $\dfrac{\dfrac{1}{x} + 1}{\dfrac{1}{x} - 1}$

37. $\dfrac{1 + \dfrac{3}{x}}{2 - \dfrac{1}{x^2}}$

38. $\dfrac{\dfrac{2}{x-1} + \dfrac{x-1}{x+1}}{\dfrac{1}{x^2 - 1}}$

39. $\dfrac{\dfrac{a}{b} + c}{\dfrac{b}{a} + c}$

SECTION 6.5   Solving Equations That Contain Rational Expressions

DEFINITIONS AND CONCEPTS	**EXAMPLES**

To solve an equation that contains rational expressions, change it to another equation without rational expressions. Do so by multiplying both sides by the LCD of the rational expressions. Check all solutions for extraneous roots.

Solve: $\dfrac{1}{x+1} + \dfrac{2}{x} = \dfrac{x}{x^2 + x}$.

$$x(x+1)\left(\frac{1}{x+1} + \frac{2}{x}\right) = x(x+1)\left[\frac{x}{x(x+1)}\right]$$
Multiply both sides by $x(x+1)$.

$$x(x+1)\left(\frac{1}{x+1}\right) + x(x+1)\left(\frac{2}{x}\right) = x(x+1)\left[\frac{x}{x(x+1)}\right]$$
Use the distributive property.

$$x + 2(x+1) = x$$
Multiply each term by $x(x+1)$.

$$x + 2x + 2 = x$$
Remove parentheses.

$$3x + 2 = x$$
Combine like terms.

$$2x = -2$$
Subtract x and 2 from both sides.

$$x = -1$$
Divide both sides by 2.

Check: $\dfrac{1}{-1+1}+\dfrac{2}{-1}=\dfrac{(-1)}{(-1)^2+(-1)}$

$\dfrac{1}{0}-2=\dfrac{-1}{0}$

Since division by 0 is undefined, $x=-1$ is extraneous. Since there is no solution, the solution set is $\varnothing$.

REVIEW EXERCISES
Solve each equation and check all answers.

40. $\dfrac{3}{x}=\dfrac{2}{x-1}$

41. $\dfrac{5}{x+4}=\dfrac{3}{x+2}$

42. $\dfrac{2}{3x}+\dfrac{1}{x}=\dfrac{5}{9}$

43. $\dfrac{2x}{x+4}=\dfrac{3}{x-1}$

44. $\dfrac{2}{x-1}+\dfrac{3}{x+4}=\dfrac{-5}{x^2+3x-4}$

45. $\dfrac{4}{x+2}-\dfrac{3}{x+3}=\dfrac{6}{x^2+5x+6}$

46. Solve for r_1: $\dfrac{1}{r}=\dfrac{1}{r_1}+\dfrac{1}{r_2}$.

47. The efficiency E of a Carnot engine is given by the formula

$$E=1-\dfrac{T_2}{T_1}$$

Solve the formula for T_1.

48. Nuclear medicine Radioactive tracers are used for diagnostic work in nuclear medicine. The **effective half-life H** of a radioactive material in a biological organism is given by the formula

$$H=\dfrac{RB}{R+B}$$

where R is the radioactive half-life and B is the biological half-life of the tracer. Solve the formula for R.

SECTION 6.6   Applications of Equations That Contain Rational Expressions

DEFINITIONS AND CONCEPTS	EXAMPLES
Use the methods for solving rational equations discussed in Section 6.5 to solve application problems.	An inlet pipe can fill a pond in 4 days, and a second inlet pipe can fill the same pond in 3 days. If both pipes are used, how long will it take to fill the pond?

Let x represent the number of days it takes to fill the pond.

What the first inlet pipe can do in 1 day	plus	what the second inlet pipe can do in 1 day	equals	what they can do together in 1 day.
$\dfrac{1}{4}$	$+$	$\dfrac{1}{3}$	$=$	$\dfrac{1}{x}$

To solve the equation, we proceed as follows:

$\dfrac{1}{4}+\dfrac{1}{3}=\dfrac{1}{x}$

$12x\left(\dfrac{1}{4}+\dfrac{1}{3}\right)=12x\left(\dfrac{1}{x}\right)$ Multiply both sides by $12x$.

$3x+4x=12$ Use the distributive property to remove parentheses and simplify.

$7x=12$ Combine like terms.

$x=\dfrac{12}{7}$ Divide both sides by 7.

It will take $\dfrac{12}{7}$ or $1\dfrac{5}{7}$ days for both inlet pipes to fill the pond.
REVIEW EXERCISES

49. Pumping a basement If one pump can empty a flooded basement in 18 hours and a second pump can empty the basement in 20 hours, how long will it take to empty the basement when both pumps are used?

50. Painting houses If a homeowner can paint a house in 14 days and a professional painter can paint it in 10 days, how long will it take if they work together?

51. Jogging A jogger can bicycle 30 miles in the same time as he can jog 10 miles. If he can ride 10 mph faster than he can jog, how fast can he jog?

52. Wind speed A plane can fly 400 miles downwind in the same amount of time as it can travel 320 miles upwind. If the plane can fly at 360 mph in still air, find the velocity of the wind.

SECTION 6.7   Ratios

DEFINITIONS AND CONCEPTS	EXAMPLES
A **ratio** is the comparison of two numbers by their indicated quotient.	**Ratios:** $\dfrac{1}{2}$ $\dfrac{4}{5}$ $\dfrac{x}{y}$
The **unit cost** of an item is the ratio of its cost to its quantity.	If 3 pounds of peanuts costs \$6.75, the unit cost (the cost per pound) is $\dfrac{6.75}{3} =$ \$2.25 per pound.
Rates are ratios that are used to compare quantities with different units.	If a student drives 120 miles in 3 hours, her average rate is $\dfrac{120\text{ miles}}{3\text{ hours}}$, or 40 mph.

REVIEW EXERCISES

Write each ratio as a fraction in lowest terms.

53. 3 to 6   **54.** $12x$ to $15x$

55. 2 feet to 1 yard   **56.** 5 pints to 3 quarts

57. If three pounds of coffee cost \$8.79, find the unit cost (the cost per pound).

58. If a factory used 2,275 kwh of electricity in February, what was the rate of energy consumption in kwh per week?

SECTION 6.8   Proportions and Similar Triangles

DEFINITIONS AND CONCEPTS	EXAMPLES
A **proportion** is a statement that two ratios are equal.	**Proportions:** $\dfrac{6}{7} = \dfrac{12}{14}$ $\dfrac{9}{11} = \dfrac{27}{33}$
In any proportion, the product of the extremes is equal to the product of the means.	Solve: $\dfrac{x-2}{6} = \dfrac{x}{7}$
	$7(x-2) = 6 \cdot x$ In a proportion, the product of the extremes is equal to the product of the means.
	$7x - 14 = 6x$ Do the multiplication.
	$x = 14$ Subtract $6x$ and add 14 to both sides.
The measures of corresponding sides of similar triangles are in proportion.	A tree casts a shadow 14 feet long at the same time as a woman 5.6 feet tall casts a shadow that is 2.8 feet long. Find the height of the tree.
	Let h represent the height of the tree. Since the triangles formed are similar, the lengths of their corresponding sides are in proportion.
	$\dfrac{h}{5.6} = \dfrac{14}{2.8}$ $\dfrac{\text{Height of tree}}{\text{Height of the woman}} = \dfrac{\text{Shadow of tree}}{\text{Shadow of the woman}}$
	$2.8 \cdot h = 5.6 \cdot 14$ In a proportion, the product of the extremes is equal to the product of the means.
	$2.8h = 78.4$ Do the multiplication.
	$h = 28$ Divide both sides by 2.8.
	The tree is 28 feet tall.

REVIEW EXERCISES

Determine whether the following equations are proportions.

59. $\dfrac{4}{7} = \dfrac{20}{34}$ **60.** $\dfrac{5}{7} = \dfrac{30}{42}$

Solve each proportion.

61. $\dfrac{3}{x} = \dfrac{6}{9}$ **62.** $\dfrac{x}{3} = \dfrac{x}{5}$

63. $\dfrac{x-2}{5} = \dfrac{x}{7}$ **64.** $\dfrac{4x-1}{18} = \dfrac{x}{6}$

65. Height of a pole A telephone pole casts a shadow 12 feet long at the same time that a man 6 feet tall casts a shadow of 3.6 feet. How tall is the pole?

Chapter 6 TEST

Assume no division by 0.

1. Simplify: $\dfrac{48x^2y}{54xy^2}$.

2. Simplify: $\dfrac{2x^2 - x - 3}{4x^2 - 9}$.

3. Simplify: $\dfrac{3(x+2) - 3}{2x - 4 - (x-5)}$.

4. Multiply and simplify: $\dfrac{12x^2y}{15xyz} \cdot \dfrac{25y^2z}{16xt}$.

5. Multiply and simplify: $\dfrac{x^2 + 3x + 2}{3x + 9} \cdot \dfrac{x+3}{x^2 - 4}$.

6. Divide and simplify: $\dfrac{8x^2y}{25xt} \div \dfrac{16x^2y^3}{30xyt^3}$.

7. Divide and simplify: $\dfrac{x^2 - x}{3x^2 + 6x} \div \dfrac{3x - 3}{3x^3 + 6x^2}$.

8. Simplify: $\dfrac{x^2 + xy}{x - y} \cdot \dfrac{x^2 - y^2}{x^2 - 2x} \div \dfrac{x^2 + 2xy + y^2}{x^2 - 4}$.

9. Add: $\dfrac{5x - 4}{x - 1} + \dfrac{5x + 3}{x - 1}$.

10. Subtract: $\dfrac{3y + 7}{2y + 3} - \dfrac{3(y-2)}{2y + 3}$.

11. Add: $\dfrac{x + 1}{x} + \dfrac{x - 1}{x + 1}$.

12. Subtract: $\dfrac{5x}{x - 2} - 3$.

13. Simplify: $\dfrac{\dfrac{8x^2}{xy^3}}{\dfrac{4y^3}{x^2y^3}}$.

14. Simplify: $\dfrac{1 + \dfrac{y}{x}}{\dfrac{y}{x} - 1}$.

15. Solve for x: $\dfrac{x}{10} - \dfrac{1}{2} = \dfrac{x}{5}$.

16. Solve for x: $3x - \dfrac{2(x+3)}{3} = 16 - \dfrac{x+2}{2}$.

17. Solve for x: $\dfrac{7}{x + 4} - \dfrac{1}{2} = \dfrac{3}{x + 4}$.

18. Solve for B: $H = \dfrac{RB}{R + B}$.

19. Cleaning highways One highway worker could pick up all the trash on a strip of highway in 7 hours, and his helper could pick up the trash in 9 hours. How long will it take them if they work together?

20. Boating A boat can motor 28 miles downstream in the same amount of time as it can motor 18 miles upstream. Find the speed of the current if the boat can motor at 23 mph in still water.

21. Flight path A plane drops 575 feet as it flies a horizontal distance of $\frac{1}{2}$ mile. How much altitude will it lose as it flies a horizontal distance of 7 miles?

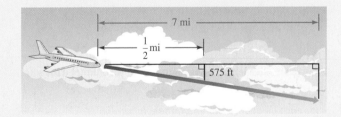

22. Express as a ratio in lowest terms: 6 feet to 3 yards.

23. Is the equation $\dfrac{3xy}{5xy} = \dfrac{3xt}{5xt}$ a proportion?

24. Solve for y: $\dfrac{y}{y - 1} = \dfrac{y - 2}{y}$.

25. A tree casts a shadow that is 30 feet long when a 6-foot-tall man casts a shadow that is 4 feet long. How tall is the tree?

Cumulative Review Exercises

Simplify each expression.

1. $x^2 x^5$

2. $(x^2)^5$

3. $\dfrac{x^5}{x^2}$

4. $(3x^5)^0$

5. $(3x^2 - 2x) + (6x^3 - 3x^2 - 1)$

6. $(4x^3 - 2x) - (2x^3 - 2x^2 - 3x + 1)$

7. $3(5x^2 - 4x + 3) + 2(-x^2 + 2x - 4)$

8. $4(3x^2 - 4x - 1) - 2(-2x^2 + 4x - 3)$

Perform each operation. Assume no division by 0.

9. $(3x^3 y^2)(-4x^2 y^3)$

10. $-5x^2(7x^3 - 2x^2 - 2)$

11. $(3x + 1)(2x + 4)$

12. $(5x - 4y)(3x + 2y)$

13. $x + 3 \overline{)\, x^2 + 7x + 12}$

14. $2x - 3 \overline{)\, 2x^3 - x^2 - x - 3}$

Factor each expression.

15. $3x^2 y - 6xy^2$

16. $3(a + b) + x(a + b)$

17. $2a + 2b + ab + b^2$

18. $25p^4 - 16q^2$

19. $x^2 - 11x - 12$

20. $x^2 - xy - 6y^2$

21. $6a^2 - 7a - 20$

22. $8m^2 - 10mn - 3n^2$

23. $p^3 - 27q^3$

24. $8r^3 + 64s^3$

Solve each equation.

25. $\dfrac{4}{5}x + 6 = 18$

26. $5 - \dfrac{x + 2}{3} = 7 - x$

27. $6x^2 - x - 2 = 0$

28. $5x^2 = 10x$

29. $x^2 + 3x + 2 = 0$

30. $2y^2 + 5y - 12 = 0$

Solve each inequality and graph the solution set.

31. $5x - 3 > 7$

32. $7x - 9 < 5$

33. $-2 < -x + 3 < 5$

34. $0 \le \dfrac{4 - x}{3} \le 2$

Graph each equation.

35. $4x - 3y = 12$

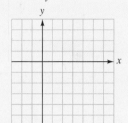

36. $3x + 4y = 4y + 12$

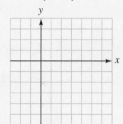

If f(x) = 2x² − 3, find each value.

37. $f(0)$

38. $f(3)$

39. $f(-2)$

40. $f(2x)$

Simplify each fraction.

41. $\dfrac{x^2 + 2x + 1}{x^2 - 1}$

42. $\dfrac{x^2 + 2x - 15}{x^2 + 3x - 10}$

Perform the operation(s) and simplify when possible. Assume no division by 0.

43. $\dfrac{x^2 + x - 6}{5x - 5} \cdot \dfrac{5x - 10}{x + 3}$

44. $\dfrac{p^2 - p - 6}{3p - 9} \div \dfrac{p^2 + 6p + 9}{p^2 - 9}$

45. $\dfrac{3x}{x + 2} + \dfrac{5x}{x + 2} - \dfrac{7x - 2}{x + 2}$

46. $\dfrac{x - 1}{x + 1} + \dfrac{x + 1}{x - 1}$

47. $\dfrac{a + 1}{2a + 4} - \dfrac{a^2}{2a^2 - 8}$

48. $\dfrac{\dfrac{1}{x} + \dfrac{1}{y}}{\dfrac{1}{x} - \dfrac{1}{y}}$

More Equations, Inequalities, and Factoring

© Shutterstock.com/Monkey Business Images

Careers and Mathematics

AIRCRAFT PILOTS AND FLIGHT ENGINEERS

Pilots are highly trained professionals who fly either airplanes or helicopters. Civilian aircraft pilots and flight engineers held about 106,000 jobs in 2004. Of these, about 84,000 worked as airline pilots, copilots, and flight engineers. The remainder were commercial pilots who worked as flight instructors at local airports or for large businesses that fly company cargo and executives in their own airplanes.

Every pilot who is paid to transport passengers or cargo must have a commercial pilot's license with an instrument rating issued by the FAA.

Job Outlook:
Job opportunities for pilots are projected to increase about as fast as average for all occupations through 2014.

Annual Earnings:
$53,870–$129,250

For More Information:
http://www.bls.gov/oco/ocos107.htm

For a Sample Application:
See Project 2 at the end of this chapter.

In this chapter ▶

In this chapter, we will review many concepts covered in the first six chapters and extend them to the intermediate algebra level. If you have trouble with any topic in this chapter, review the sections in the text in which we first discussed that topic.

Review of Solving Linear Equations and Inequalities in One Variable

1. Solve a linear equation in one variable.
2. Solve a linear equation in one variable that results in an identity or a contradiction.
3. Solve a formula for a specified variable.
4. Solve an application problem using a linear equation in one variable.
5. Solve a linear inequality in one variable.
6. Solve a compound inequality.

Vocabulary

contradiction	closed interval	conditional inequalities
empty set	half-open interval	trichometry property
interval	unbounded interval	transitive property
open interval	absolute inequalities	linear inequality
interval notation		

Getting Ready

Find the value of x that will make each statement true.

1. $x + 3 = 5$ **2.** $x - 5 = 3$

3. $\dfrac{3x}{5} = 6$ **4.** $2x + 3 = x - 4$

In this section, we will review how to solve equations and inequalities.

 Solve a linear equation in one variable.

Recall that an *equation* is a statement indicating that two mathematical expressions are equal. The set of numbers that satisfy an equation is called its *solution set,* and the elements in the solution set are called *solutions* or *roots* of the equation. Finding the solution set of an equation is called *solving the equation.*

To solve an equation, we will use the following two properties of equality to replace the equation with simpler equivalent equations that have the same solution set. We continue this process until we have isolated the variable on one side of the = sign.

1. If any quantity is added to (or subtracted from) both sides of an equation, a new equation is formed that is equivalent to the original equation.

2. If both sides of an equation are multiplied (or divided) by the same nonzero constant, a new equation is formed that is equivalent to the original equation.

EXAMPLE 1   Solve: $3(2x - 1) = 2x + 9$.

Solution   We can use the distributive property to remove parentheses and then isolate x on the left side of the equation.

$$3(2x - 1) = 2x + 9$$
$$6x - 3 = 2x + 9 \qquad \text{To remove parentheses, use the distributive property.}$$
$$6x - 3 + 3 = 2x + 9 + 3 \qquad \text{To undo the subtraction by 3, add 3 to both sides.}$$
$$6x = 2x + 12 \qquad \text{Combine like terms.}$$
$$6x - 2x = 2x + 12 - 2x \qquad \text{To eliminate } 2x \text{ from the right side, subtract } 2x \text{ from both sides.}$$
$$4x = 12 \qquad \text{Combine like terms.}$$
$$x = 3 \qquad \text{To undo the multiplication by 4, divide both sides by 4.}$$

Check: We substitute 3 for x in the original equation to see whether it satisfies the equation.

$$3(2x - 1) = 2x + 9$$
$$3(2 \cdot 3 - 1) \overset{?}{=} 2 \cdot 3 + 9$$
$$3(5) \overset{?}{=} 6 + 9 \qquad \text{On the left side, do the work in parentheses first.}$$
$$15 = 15$$

Since 3 satisfies the original equation, it is a solution. The solution set of the equation is $\{3\}$.

SELF CHECK 1   Solve: $2(3x - 2) = 3x - 13$.

To solve more complicated linear equations, we will follow these steps.

Solving Equations

1. If an equation contains fractions, multiply both sides of the equation by their least common denominator (LCD) to eliminate the denominators.
2. Use the distributive property to remove all grouping symbols and combine like terms.
3. Use the addition and subtraction properties to get all variables on one side of the equation and all numbers on the other side. Combine like terms, if necessary.
4. Use the multiplication and division properties to make the coefficient of the variable equal to 1.
5. Check the result by replacing the variable with the possible solution and verifying that the number satisfies the equation.

EXAMPLE 2   Solve: $\dfrac{5}{3}(x - 3) = \dfrac{3}{2}(x - 2) + 2$.

Solution   **Step 1:**   Since 6 is the smallest number that can be divided by both 2 and 3, we multiply both sides of the equation by 6, the LCD, to eliminate the fractions:

$$\frac{5}{3}(x - 3) = \frac{3}{2}(x - 2) + 2$$

$$6\left[\frac{5}{3}(x-3)\right] = 6\left[\frac{3}{2}(x-2)+2\right] \quad \text{Multiply both sides of the equation by 6.}$$

$$10(x-3) = 9(x-2)+12 \quad 6\cdot\frac{5}{3}=10, 6\cdot\frac{3}{2}=9, \text{ and } 6\cdot 2 = 12.$$

Step 2: We use the distributive property to remove parentheses and then combine like terms.

$$10x - 30 = 9x - 18 + 12 \quad \text{To remove parentheses, use the distributive property.}$$

$$10x - 30 = 9x - 6 \quad \text{Combine like terms.}$$

Step 3: We use the addition and subtraction properties by adding 30 to both sides and subtracting $9x$ from both sides.

$$10x - 30 - 9x + 30 = 9x - 6 - 9x + 30$$

$$x = 24 \quad \text{Combine like terms.}$$

Since 1 is the coefficient of x in the above equation, Step 4 is unnecessary.

Step 5: We check by substituting 24 for x in the original equation and simplifying:

$$\frac{5}{3}(x-3) = \frac{3}{2}(x-2)+2$$

$$\frac{5}{3}(24-3) \stackrel{?}{=} \frac{3}{2}(24-2)+2$$

$$\frac{5}{3}(21) \stackrel{?}{=} \frac{3}{2}(22)+2$$

$$5(7) \stackrel{?}{=} 33 + 2$$

$$35 = 35$$

Since 24 satisfies the equation, it is a solution. The solution set of the equation is {24}.

⇨ **SELF CHECK 2** Solve: $\frac{2}{3}(x-2) = \frac{5}{2}(x-1)+3$.

2 Solve a linear equation in one variable that results in an identity or a contradiction.

The equations discussed so far have been *conditional equations*. For these equations, some numbers x are solutions and others are not. An *identity* is an equation that is satisfied by every number x for which both sides of the equation are defined.

EXAMPLE 3 Solve: $2(x-1)+4 = 4(1+x)-(2x+2)$.

Solution
$$2(x-1)+4 = 4(1+x)-(2x+2)$$
$$2x - 2 + 4 = 4 + 4x - 2x - 2 \quad \text{Use the distributive property to remove parentheses.}$$

$$2x + 2 = 2x + 2 \qquad \text{Combine like terms.}$$
$$2 = 2 \qquad \text{Subtract } 2x \text{ from both sides.}$$

Since $2 = 2$, the equation is true for every number x. Since every number x satisfies this equation, it is an identity. The solution set of the equation is the set of real numbers $\mathbb{R}$.

⇨ **SELF CHECK 3**   Solve: $3(x + 1) - (20 + x) = 5(x - 1) - 3(x + 4)$.

A **contradiction** is an equation that has no solution.

EXAMPLE 4   Solve: $\dfrac{x - 1}{3} + 4x = \dfrac{3}{2} + \dfrac{13x - 2}{3}$.

Solution

$$\frac{x - 1}{3} + 4x = \frac{3}{2} + \frac{13x - 2}{3}$$

$$6\left(\frac{x - 1}{3} + 4x\right) = 6\left(\frac{3}{2} + \frac{13x - 2}{3}\right) \qquad \begin{array}{l}\text{To eliminate the fractions, multiply both} \\ \text{sides by 6.}\end{array}$$

$$2(x - 1) + 6(4x) = 9 + 2(13x - 2) \qquad \begin{array}{l}\text{Use the distributive property to remove} \\ \text{parentheses.}\end{array}$$

$$2x - 2 + 24x = 9 + 26x - 4 \qquad \text{Remove parentheses.}$$

$$26x - 2 = 26x + 5 \qquad \text{Combine like terms.}$$

$$-2 = 5 \qquad \text{Subtract } 26x \text{ from both sides.}$$

Since $-2 = 5$ is false, no number x satisfies the equation. The solution set of the equation is $\varnothing$, called the **empty set.**

⇨ **SELF CHECK 4**   Solve: $\dfrac{x - 2}{3} - 3 = \dfrac{1}{5} + \dfrac{x + 1}{3}$.

3   **Solve a formula for a specified variable.**

To solve a formula for a variable means to isolate that variable on one side of the $=$ sign and place all other quantities on the other side.

EXAMPLE 5   **WAGES AND COMMISSIONS**   A sales clerk earns \$200 per week plus a 5% commission on the value of the merchandise she sells. What dollar volume must she sell each week to earn \$250, \$300, and \$350 in three successive weeks?

Solution   The weekly earnings e are computed using the formula

(1) $e = 200 + 0.05v$

where v represents the value of the merchandise sold. To find v for the three values of e, we first solve Equation 1 for v.

$$e = 200 + 0.05v$$

$$e - 200 = 0.05v \qquad \text{Subtract 200 from both sides.}$$

$$\frac{e - 200}{0.05} = v \qquad \text{Divide both sides by 0.05.}$$

We can now substitute $250, $300, and $350 for e and compute v.

$v = \dfrac{e - 200}{0.05}$	$v = \dfrac{e - 200}{0.05}$	$v = \dfrac{e - 200}{0.05}$
$v = \dfrac{250 - 200}{0.05}$	$v = \dfrac{300 - 200}{0.05}$	$v = \dfrac{350 - 200}{0.05}$
$v = 1{,}000$	$v = 2{,}000$	$v = 3{,}000$

She must sell $1,000 worth of merchandise the first week, $2,000 worth in the second week, and $3,000 worth in the third week.

⇨ **SELF CHECK 5**   What dollar volume must the clerk sell to earn $500?

---

4 **Solve an application problem using a linear equation in one variable.**

EXAMPLE 6   **BUILDING A DOG RUN**   A man has 28 meters of fencing to make a rectangular dog run. He wants the dog run to be 6 meters longer than it is wide. Find its dimensions.

Analyze the problem   To find the dimensions, we need to find both the length and the width. If w is chosen to represent the width of the dog run, then $w + 6$ represents its length. (See Figure 7-1.)

Form an equation   The perimeter P of a rectangle is the distance around it. Because the dog run is a rectangle, opposite sides have the same length. The perimeter can be expressed as $2w + 2(w + 6)$ or as 28.

Figure 7-1

Two widths	plus	two lengths	equals	the perimeter.
$2 \cdot w$	$+$	$2 \cdot (w + 6)$	$=$	28

Solve the equation   We can solve this equation as follows:

$$2w + 2(w + 6) = 28$$

$$2w + 2w + 12 = 28 \qquad \text{Use the distributive property to remove parentheses.}$$

$$4w + 12 = 28 \qquad \text{Combine like terms.}$$

$$4w = 16 \qquad \text{Subtract 12 from both sides.}$$

$$w = 4 \qquad \text{Divide both sides by 4. This is the width.}$$

$$w + 6 = 10 \qquad \text{Add 6 to the width to find the length.}$$

State the conclusion   The dimensions of the dog run are 4 meters by 10 meters.

Check the result   If the dog run has a width of 4 meters and a length of 10 meters, its length is 6 meters longer than its width, and the perimeter is $2(4) + 2(10) = 28$.

5   ## Solve a linear inequality in one variable.

Recall that *inequalities* are statements indicating that two quantities might be unequal.

- $a < b$ means "*a* is less than *b*."
- $a > b$ means "*a* is greater than *b*."
- $a \le b$ means "*a* is less than or equal to *b*."
- $a \ge b$ means "*a* is greater than or equal to *b*."

In Chapter 1, we saw that many inequalities can be graphed as regions on the number line, called **intervals**. For example, the graph of the inequality $-4 < x < 2$ is shown in Figure 7-2(a). Since neither endpoint is included, we say that the graph is an **open interval**. In **interval notation**, this interval is denoted as $(-4, 2)$, where the parentheses indicate that the endpoints are not included.

The graph of the inequality $-2 \le x \le 5$ is shown in Figure 7-2(b). Since both endpoints are included, we say that the graph is a **closed interval**. This interval is denoted as $[-2, 5]$, where the brackets indicate that the endpoints are included.

Since one endpoint is included and one is not in the interval shown in Figure 7-2(c), we call the interval a **half-open interval**. This interval is denoted as $[-10, 10)$. Since the interval shown in Figure 7-2(d) extends forever in one direction, it is called an **unbounded interval**. This interval is denoted as $[-6, \infty)$, where the symbol ∞ is read as "infinity."

(a)   (b)   (c)   (d)

Figure 7-2

If *a* and *b* are real numbers, Table 7-1 shows the different types of intervals that can occur.

Kind of interval	Inequality	Graph	Interval
Open interval	$a < x < b$		(a, b)
Half-open interval	$a \le x < b$		$[a, b)$
	$a < x \le b$		$(a, b]$
Closed interval	$a \le x \le b$		$[a, b]$
Unbounded interval	$x > a$		(a, ∞)
	$x \ge a$		$[a, \infty)$
	$x < a$		$(-\infty, a)$
	$x \le a$		$(-\infty, a]$
	$-\infty < x < \infty$		$(-\infty, \infty)$

Table 7-1

Inequalities such as $x + 1 > x$, which are true for all numbers x, are called **absolute inequalities.** Inequalities such as $3x + 2 < 8$, which are true for some numbers x, but not all numbers x, are called **conditional inequalities.**

If a and b are two real numbers, then $a < b$, $a = b$, or $a > b$. This property, called the **trichotomy property,** indicates that one and only one of three statements is true about any two real numbers. Either

- the first number is less than the second,
- the first number is equal to the second,
- or the first number is greater than the second.

If a, b, and c are real numbers with $a < b$ and $b < c$, then $a < c$. This property, called the **transitive property,** indicates that if we have three numbers and the first number is less than the second and the second number is less than the third, then the first number is less than the third.

To solve an inequality, we use the following properties of inequalities.

Properties of Inequalities	**1.** Any real number can be added to (or subtracted from) both sides of an inequality to produce another inequality with the same direction as the original inequality.
	2. If both sides of an inequality are multiplied (or divided) by a positive number, another inequality results with the same direction as the original inequality.
	3. If both sides of an inequality are multiplied (or divided) by a negative number, another inequality results, but with the opposite direction from the original inequality.

Property 1 indicates that any number can be added to both sides of a true inequality to get another true inequality with the same direction. For example, if 4 is added to both sides of the inequality $3 < 12$, we get

$$3 + 4 < 12 + 4$$
$$7 < 16$$

and the $<$ symbol remains an $<$ symbol. Adding 4 to both sides does not change the direction (sometimes called the *order*) of the inequality.

Subtracting 4 from both sides of $3 < 12$ does not change the direction of the inequality either.

$$3 - 4 < 12 - 4$$
$$-1 < 8$$

Property 2 indicates that both sides of a true inequality can be multiplied by any positive number to get another true inequality with the same direction. For example, if both sides of the true inequality $-4 < 6$ are multiplied by 2, we get

$$2(-4) < 2(6)$$
$$-8 < 12$$

and the $<$ symbol remains an $<$ symbol. Multiplying both sides by 2 does not change the direction of the inequality.

Dividing both sides by 2 doesn't change the direction of the inequality either.

$$\frac{-4}{2} < \frac{6}{2}$$
$$-2 < 3$$

Property 3 indicates that if both sides of a true inequality are multiplied by any negative number, another true inequality results, but with the opposite direction. For example, if both sides of the true inequality $-4 < 6$ are multiplied by -2, we get

$$-4 < 6$$
$$-2(-4) > -2(6)$$
$$8 > -12$$

and the $<$ symbol becomes an $>$ symbol. Multiplying both sides by -2 reverses the direction of the inequality.

Dividing both sides by -2 also reverses the direction of the inequality.

$$-4 < 6$$
$$\frac{-4}{-2} > \frac{6}{-2}$$
$$2 > -3$$

A *linear inequality* in one variable is any inequality that can be expressed in the form

COMMENT   We must remember to reverse the inequality symbol every time we multiply or divide both sides by a negative number.

$$ax + c < 0 \qquad ax + c > 0 \qquad ax + c \leq 0 \qquad \text{or} \qquad ax + c \geq 0 \quad (a \neq 0)$$

We can solve linear inequalities by using the same steps that we use for solving linear equations, with one exception. If we multiply or divide both sides by a *negative* number, we must reverse the direction of the inequality.

EXAMPLE 7   Solve: **a.** $3(2x - 9) < 9$ **b.** $-4(3x + 2) \leq 16$.

Solution   **a.** We solve the inequality as if it were an equation:

$$3(2x - 9) < 9$$

$\qquad 6x - 27 < 9$ Use the distributive property to remove parentheses.

$\qquad\qquad 6x < 36$ Add 27 to both sides.

$\qquad\qquad\quad x < 6$ Divide both sides by 6.

The solution set is the interval $(-\infty, 6)$. The graph of the solution set is shown in Figure 7-3(a).

b. We solve the inequality as if it were an equation:

$$-4(3x + 2) \leq 16$$

$\qquad -12x - 8 \leq 16$ Use the distributive property to remove parentheses.

$\qquad\qquad -12x \leq 24$ Add 8 to both sides.

$\qquad\qquad\quad x \geq -2$ Divide both sides by -12 and reverse the $\leq$ symbol.

The solution set is the interval $[-2, \infty)$. The graph of the solution set is shown in Figure 7-3(b).

(a)   (b)

Figure 7-3

⇨ **SELF CHECK 7**   Solve: $-3(2x + 1) > 9$.

EXAMPLE 8 Solve: $\dfrac{2}{3}(x + 2) > \dfrac{4}{5}(x - 3)$.

Solution

$$\dfrac{2}{3}(x + 2) > \dfrac{4}{5}(x - 3)$$

$$15 \cdot \dfrac{2}{3}(x + 2) > 15 \cdot \dfrac{4}{5}(x - 3) \qquad \text{To eliminate the fractions, multiply both sides by 15.}$$

$$10(x + 2) > 12(x - 3) \qquad 15 \cdot \tfrac{2}{3} = 10 \text{ and } 15 \cdot \tfrac{4}{5} = 12.$$

$$10x + 20 > 12x - 36 \qquad \text{Use the distributive property to remove parentheses.}$$

$$-2x + 20 > -36 \qquad \text{Subtract } 12x \text{ from both sides.}$$

$$-2x > -56 \qquad \text{Subtract 20 from both sides.}$$

$$x < 28 \qquad \text{Divide both sides by } -2 \text{ and reverse the } > \text{ symbol.}$$

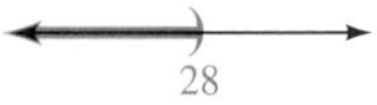

Figure 7-4 (number line marked at 28)

The solution set is the interval $(-\infty, 28)$, whose graph is shown in Figure 7-4.

⇨ **SELF CHECK 8** Solve: $\dfrac{1}{2}(x - 1) \le \dfrac{2}{3}(x + 1)$.

6 **Solve a compound inequality.**

To say that x is between -3 and 8, we write a double inequality:

$$-3 < x < 8 \qquad \text{Read as ``}-3 \text{ is less than } x \text{ and } x \text{ is less than 8.''}$$

This double inequality contains two different linear inequalities:

$$-3 < x \qquad \text{and} \qquad x < 8$$

These two inequalities mean that $-3 < x$ and $x < 8$. The word *and* indicates that these two inequalities are true at the same time.

Double Inequalities

The double inequality $c < x < d$ is equivalent to $c < x$ and $x < d$.

COMMENT Note that the inequality $c < x < d$ is not equivalent to $c < x$ or $x < d$.

EXAMPLE 9 Solve: $-3 \le 2x + 5 < 7$.

Solution This inequality means that $2x + 5$ is between -3 and 7 or possibly equal to -3. We can solve it by isolating x between the inequality symbols:

$$-3 \le 2x + 5 < 7$$

$$-8 \le 2x < 2 \qquad \text{Subtract 5 from all three parts.}$$

$$-4 \le x < 1 \qquad \text{Divide all three parts by 2.}$$

Figure 7-5 (number line marked at -4 and 1)

The solution set is the interval $[-4, 1)$. Its graph is shown in Figure 7-5.

⇨ **SELF CHECK 9** Solve: $-3 < 2x - 5 \le 9$.

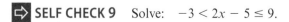

EXAMPLE 10   Solve: $x + 3 < 2x - 1 < 4x - 3$.

Solution   Since it is impossible to isolate x between the inequality symbols, we solve each of its linear inequalities separately.

$$x + 3 < 2x - 1 \quad \text{and} \quad 2x - 1 < 4x - 3$$
$$4 < x \qquad\qquad 2 < 2x$$
$$\qquad\qquad\qquad 1 < x$$

Figure 7-6

Only those numbers x where $x > 4$ and $x > 1$ are in the solution set. Since all numbers greater than 4 are also greater than 1, the solutions are the numbers x where $x > 4$. The solution set is the interval $(4, \infty)$. The graph is shown in Figure 7-6.

SELF CHECK 10   Solve: $x - 5 \le 3x - 1 \le 5x + 5$.

EXAMPLE 11   Solve the compound inequality: $x \le -3$ or $x \ge 8$.

Solution   The graph of $x \le -3$ or $x \ge 8$ is the union of two intervals:

$$(-\infty, -3] \cup [8, \infty)$$

Figure 7-7

Its graph is shown in Figure 7-7.
    The word *or* in the statement $x \le -3$ or $x \ge 8$ indicates that only one of the inequalities needs to be true to make the statement true.

SELF CHECK 11   Solve: $x < -2$ or $x > 4$.

COMMENT   In the statement $x \le -3$ or $x \ge 8$, it is incorrect to string the inequalities together as $8 \le x \le -3$, because that would imply that $8 \le -3$, which is false.

SELF CHECK ANSWERS   **1.** -3 **2.** -1 **3.** $\mathbb{R}$ **4.** $\varnothing$ **5.** \$6,000   **7.** $(-\infty, -2)$ $(-\infty, -2)$

-2

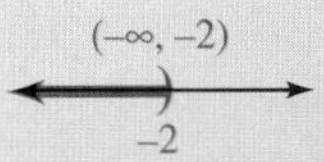

8. $[-7, \infty)$ $[-7, \infty)$ **9.** $(1, 7]$ $(1, 7]$ **10.** $[-2, \infty)$ $[-2, \infty)$

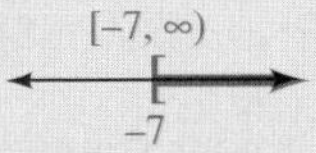

-7 $1 \quad 7$ -2

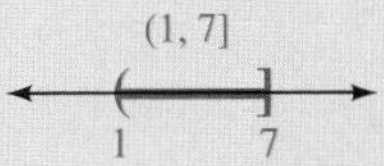

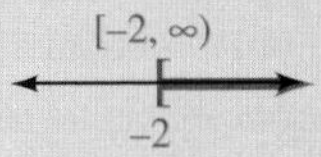

11. $(-\infty, -2) \cup (4, \infty)$ $(-\infty, -2) \cup (4, \infty)$

$-2 \quad 4$

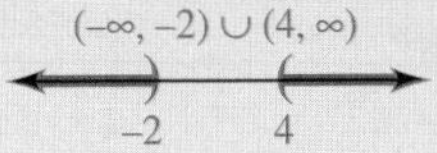

NOW TRY THIS

Solve each inequality, and express the result as a graph and in interval notation, if appropriate.
1. $6x - 2(x + 1) < 10$ or $-5x < -10$

2. $4x \ge 2(x - 6)$ and $-5x \ge 30$

7.1 EXERCISES

WARM-UPS *Solve each equation or inequality.*

1. $2x + 4 = 6$
2. $3x - 4 = 8$
3. $2x < 4$
4. $3x + 1 \geq 10$
5. $-3x > 12$
6. $-\dfrac{x}{2} \leq 4$

REVIEW *Simplify each expression. Assume no variable is 0.*

7. $\left(\dfrac{t^3 t^5 t^{-6}}{t^2 t^{-4}}\right)^{-3}$
8. $\left(\dfrac{a^{-2} b^3 a^5 b^{-2}}{a^6 b^{-5}}\right)^{-4}$

9. **Baking** A man invested \$1,200 in baking equipment to make pies. Each pie requires \$3.40 in ingredients. If he can sell all the pies he can make for \$5.95 each, how many pies will he have to make to earn a profit?

10. **Investing** A woman invested \$15,000, part at 7% annual interest and the rest at 8%. If she earned \$1,100 in income over a one-year period, how much did she invest at 7%?

VOCABULARY AND CONCEPTS *Fill in the blanks.*

11. An _____ is a statement indicating that two mathematical expressions are equal.
12. If any quantity is _____ to both sides of an equation, a new equation is formed that is equivalent to the original equation.
13. If both sides of an equation are _____ (or _____) by the same nonzero number, a new equation is formed that is equivalent to the original equation.
14. An _____ is an equation that is true for all values of its variable.
15. A _____ is an equation that is true for no values of its variable.
16. The symbol $<$ is read as "_____."
17. The symbol $\geq$ is read as "_____ or equal to."
18. An open interval has no _____.
19. A _____ interval has one endpoint.
20. If $a < b$ and $b < c$, then _____.
21. If both sides of an inequality are multiplied by a _____ number, a new inequality is formed that has the same direction as the first.
22. If both sides of an inequality are multiplied by a _____ number, a new inequality is formed that has the opposite direction from the first.

GUIDED PRACTICE

Solve each equation. See Example 1. (Objective 1)

23. $2x + 1 = 13$
24. $2x - 4 = 16$
25. $3(x + 1) = 15$
26. $-2(x + 5) = 30$
27. $2r - 5 = 1 - r$
28. $5s - 13 = s - 1$
29. $3(2y - 4) - 6 = 3y$
30. $2x + (2x - 3) = 5$
31. $5(5 - a) = 37 - 2a$
32. $4a + 17 = 7(a + 2)$
33. $4(y + 1) = -2(4 - y)$
34. $5(r + 4) = -2(r - 3)$

Solve each equation. See Example 2. (Objective 1)

35. $\dfrac{x}{2} - \dfrac{x}{3} = 4$
36. $\dfrac{x}{2} + \dfrac{x}{3} = 10$
37. $\dfrac{x}{6} + 1 = \dfrac{x}{3}$
38. $\dfrac{3}{2}(y + 4) = \dfrac{20 - y}{2}$
39. $\dfrac{a + 1}{3} + \dfrac{a - 1}{5} = \dfrac{2}{15}$
40. $\dfrac{a + 1}{4} + \dfrac{2a - 3}{4} = \dfrac{a}{2} - 2$
41. $\dfrac{2z + 3}{3} + \dfrac{3z - 4}{6} = \dfrac{z - 2}{2}$
42. $\dfrac{y - 8}{5} + 2 = \dfrac{2}{5} - \dfrac{y}{3}$

Solve each equation and indicate whether it is an identity or a contradiction. See Examples 3–4. (Objective 2)

43. $4(2 - 3t) + 6t = -6t + 8$
44. $2x - 6 = -2x + 4(x - 2)$
45. $3(x - 4) + 6 = -2(x + 4) + 5x$
46. $2(x - 3) = \dfrac{3}{2}(x - 4) + \dfrac{x}{2}$

Solve each formula for the indicated variable. See Example 5. (Objective 3)

47. $V = \dfrac{1}{3} Bh$ for B
48. $A = \dfrac{1}{2} bh$ for b
49. $P = 2l + 2w$ for w
50. $P = 2l + 2w$ for l
51. $z = \dfrac{x - \mu}{\sigma}$ for x
52. $z = \dfrac{x - \mu}{\sigma}$ for μ
53. $y = mx + b$ for x
54. $y = mx + b$ for m

Solve each inequality. Give the result in interval notation and graph the solution set. See Examples 7–8. (Objective 5)

55. $5x - 3 > 7$

56. $7x - 9 < 5$

57. $-3x - 1 \leq 5$

58. $-2x + 6 \geq 16$

59. $-3(a + 2) > 2(a + 1)$

60. $-4(y - 1) < y + 8$

61. $\dfrac{1}{2}y + 2 \geq \dfrac{1}{3}y - 4$

62. $\dfrac{1}{4}x - \dfrac{1}{3} \leq x + 2$

Solve each inequality. Give the result in interval notation and graph the solution set. See Examples 9–10. (Objective 5)

63. $-2 < -b + 3 < 5$

64. $4 < -t - 2 < 9$

65. $15 > 2x - 7 > 9$

66. $25 > 3x - 2 > 7$

67. $-6 < -3(x - 4) \leq 24$

68. $-4 \leq -2(x + 8) < 8$

69. $0 \geq \dfrac{1}{2}x - 4 > 6$

70. $-2 \leq \dfrac{5 - 3x}{2} \leq 2$

Solve each inequality. Give the result in interval notation and graph the solution set. See Example 11. (Objective 6)

71. $3x + 2 < 8$ or $2x - 3 > 11$

72. $3x + 4 < -2$ or $3x + 4 > 10$

73. $-4(x + 2) \geq 12$ or $3x + 8 < 11$

74. $x < 3$ or $x > -3$

ADDITIONAL PRACTICE   *Solve each equation or inequality. If an inequality, give the answer as a graph and in interval notation, where appropriate.*

75. $2(a - 5) - (3a + 1) = 0$

76. $8(3a - 5) - 4(2a + 3) = 12$

77. $y(y + 2) = (y + 1)^2 - 1$

78. $x(x - 3) = (x - 1)^2 - (5 + x)$

79. $8 - 9y \geq -y$

80. $4 - 3x \leq x$

81. $5(x - 2) \geq 0$ and $-3x < 9$

82. $x < -3$ and $x > 3$

83. $-6 \leq \dfrac{1}{3}a + 1 < 0$

84. $0 \leq \dfrac{4 - x}{3} \leq 2$

85. $P = L + \dfrac{s}{f}i$ for s **86.** $P = L + \dfrac{s}{f}i$ for f

APPLICATIONS

Solve each application. See Example 6. (Objective 4)

87. Finding dimensions   The rectangular garden below is twice as long as it is wide. Find its dimensions.

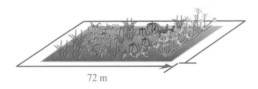

88. Fencing pastures   A farmer has 624 feet of fencing to enclose the rectangular pasture shown below. Because a river runs along one side, fencing will be needed on only three sides. Find the dimensions of the pasture if its length is parallel to the river and is double its width.

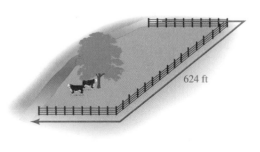

89. Fencing pens   A man has 150 feet of fencing to build the pen shown below. If one end is a square, find the outside dimensions of the entire pen.

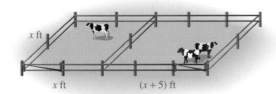

x ft

x ft $(x + 5)$ ft

90. Enclosing swimming pools   A woman wants to enclose the swimming pool shown in the illustration and have a walkway of uniform width all the way around. How wide will the walkway be if the woman uses 180 feet of fencing?

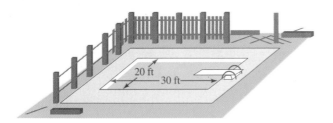

20 ft
30 ft

Solve each application.

91. Cutting boards   The carpenter below saws a board into two pieces. He wants one piece to be 1 foot longer than twice the length of the shorter piece. Find the length of each piece.

x

22 ft

92. Cutting beams   A 30-foot steel beam is to be cut into two pieces. The longer piece is to be 2 feet more than 3 times as long as the shorter piece. Find the length of each piece.

93. Finding profit   The wholesale cost of a radio is $27. A store owner knows that for the radio to sell, it must be priced under $42. If p is the profit, express the possible profit as an inequality.

94. Investing   If a woman invests $10,000 at 8% annual interest, how much more must she invest at 9% so that her annual income will exceed $1,250?

95. Buying compact discs   A student can afford to spend up to $330 on a stereo system and some compact discs. If the stereo costs $175 and the discs are $8.50 each, find the greatest number of discs the student can buy.

96. Grades   A student has scores of 70, 77, and 85 on three exams. What score is needed on a fourth exam to make the student's average 80 or better?

WRITING ABOUT MATH

97. Explain the difference between a conditional equation, an identity, and a contradiction.

98. The techniques for solving linear equations and linear inequalities are similar, yet different. Explain.

SOMETHING TO THINK ABOUT

99. Find the error.

$$4(x + 3) = 16$$
$$4x + 3 = 16$$
$$4x = 13$$
$$x = \frac{13}{4}$$

100. Which of these relations is transitive?

    a. $=$ **b.** $\leq$ **c.** $\not\geq$ **d.** $\neq$

Solving Equations in One Variable Containing Absolute Values

Objectives

1 Find the absolute value of a number.
2 Solve an equation containing a single absolute-value term.
3 Solve an equation where two absolute-value terms are equal.

Getting Ready

Simplify each expression.

1. $-(-6)$ **2.** $-(-5)$ **3.** $-(x - 2)$ **4.** $-(2 - \pi)$

In this section, we will review the definition of absolute value and show how to solve equations that contain absolute values.

1 Find the absolute value of a number.

Recall the definition of the absolute value of x.

Absolute Value

If $x \geq 0$, then $|x| = x$.

If $x < 0$, then $|x| = -x$.

This definition associates a nonnegative real number with any real number.

- If $x \geq 0$, then x is its own absolute value.
- If $x < 0$, then $-x$ (which is positive) is the absolute value.

Either way, $|x|$ is positive or 0:

$|x| \geq 0$ for all real numbers x

EXAMPLE 1 Find each absolute value.
a. $|9|$ **b.** $|-5|$ **c.** $|0|$ and   **d.** $|2 - \pi|$

Solution   **a.** Since $9 \geq 0$, 9 is its own absolute value: $|9| = 9$.

b. Since $-5 < 0$, the negative of -5 is the absolute value:

$|-5| = -(-5) = 5$

COMMENT   The placement of a $-$ sign in an expression containing an absolute value symbol is important. For example, $|-19| = 19$, but $-|19| = -19$.

c. Since $0 \geq 0$, 0 is its own absolute value: $|0| = 0$.

d. Since $\pi \approx 3.14$, it follows that $2 - \pi < 0$. Thus,

$$|2 - \pi| = -(2 - \pi) = \pi - 2$$

 **SELF CHECK 1**   Find each absolute value.
   a. $|-12|$ **b.** $|4 - \pi|$

EXAMPLE 2   Find each value.
   a. $-|-10|$ **b.** $-|13|$ and   **c.** $-(-|-3|)$

Solution   **a.** $-|-10| = -(10) = -10$
   b. $-|13| = -13$
   c. $-(-|-3|) = -(-3) = 3$

 **SELF CHECK 2**   Find the value: $-|-15|$.

2   **Solve an equation containing a single absolute-value term.**

In the equation $|x| = 5$, x can be either 5 or -5, because

$$|5| = 5 \quad \text{and} \quad |-5| = 5$$

Thus, if $|x| = 5$, then $x = 5$ or $x = -5$. In general, the following is true.

Absolute Value Equations

If $k > 0$, then

$$|x| = k \qquad \text{is equivalent to} \qquad x = k \text{ or } x = -k$$

The absolute value of x can be interpreted as the distance on the number line from a point to the origin. The solutions of $|x| = k$ are represented by the two points that lie exactly k units from the origin. (See Figure 7-8.)

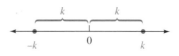

Figure 7-8

The equation $|x - 3| = 7$ indicates that a point on the number line with a coordinate of $x - 3$ is 7 units from the origin. Thus, $x - 3$ can be either 7 or -7.

$$x - 3 = 7 \quad \text{or} \quad x - 3 = -7$$
$$x = 10 \qquad \qquad x = -4$$

Figure 7-9

The solutions of $|x - 3| = 7$ are 10 and -4. (See Figure 7-9). If either of these numbers is substituted for x in the equation, it is satisfied:

$$|x - 3| = 7 \qquad\qquad |x - 3| = 7$$
$$|10 - 3| \overset{2}{=} 7 \qquad |-4 - 3| \overset{2}{=} 7$$
$$|7| \overset{2}{=} 7 \qquad\qquad |-7| \overset{2}{=} 7$$
$$7 = 7 \qquad\qquad\quad 7 = 7$$

EXAMPLE 3   Solve: $|3x - 2| = 5$.

Solution   We can write $|3x - 2| = 5$ as

$$3x - 2 = 5 \qquad \text{or} \qquad 3x - 2 = -5$$

and solve each equation for x:

$$3x - 2 = 5 \quad \text{or} \quad 3x - 2 = -5$$
$$3x = 7 \qquad\qquad 3x = -3$$
$$x = \frac{7}{3} \qquad\qquad x = -1$$

Verify that both solutions check.

⇨ **SELF CHECK 3**   Solve: $|2x + 3| = 5$.

To solve more complicated equations with a term involving an absolute value, we must isolate the absolute value before attempting to solve for the variable.

EXAMPLE 4   Solve: $\left| \dfrac{2}{3}x + 3 \right| + 4 = 10$.

Solution   We first isolate the absolute value on the left side.

$$\left| \frac{2}{3}x + 3 \right| + 4 = 10$$

(1) $\qquad \left| \dfrac{2}{3}x + 3 \right| = 6 \qquad$ Subtract 4 from both sides.

We can now write Equation 1 as

$$\frac{2}{3}x + 3 = 6 \qquad \text{or} \qquad \frac{2}{3}x + 3 = -6$$

and solve each equation for x:

$$\frac{2}{3}x + 3 = 6 \quad \text{or} \quad \frac{2}{3}x + 3 = -6$$

$$\frac{2}{3}x = 3 \qquad\qquad \frac{2}{3}x = -9 \qquad \text{Subtract 3 from both sides of each equation.}$$

$$2x = 9 \qquad\qquad 2x = -27 \qquad \text{Multiply both sides of each equation by 3.}$$

$$x = \frac{9}{2} \qquad\qquad x = -\frac{27}{2} \qquad \text{Divide both sides of each equation by 2.}$$

Verify that both solutions check.

⇨ **SELF CHECK 4** Solve: $\left|\dfrac{3}{2}x - 3\right| + 1 = 7$.

EXAMPLE 5 Solve: $\left|7x + \dfrac{1}{2}\right| = -4$.

Solution Since the absolute value of a number cannot be negative, no value of x can make $\left|7x + \dfrac{1}{2}\right| = -4$. Since this equation has no solutions, its solution set is $\varnothing$.

⇨ **SELF CHECK 5** Solve: $-|3x + 2| = 4$.

EXAMPLE 6 Solve: $\left|\dfrac{1}{2}x - 5\right| - 4 = -4$.

Solution We first isolate the absolute value on the left side.

$$\left|\dfrac{1}{2}x - 5\right| - 4 = -4$$

$$\left|\dfrac{1}{2}x - 5\right| = 0 \qquad \text{Add 4 to both sides.}$$

Since 0 is the only number whose absolute value is 0, the binomial $\dfrac{1}{2}x - 5$ must be 0, and we have

$$\dfrac{1}{2}x - 5 = 0$$

$$\dfrac{1}{2}x = 5 \qquad \text{Add 5 to both sides.}$$

$$x = 10 \qquad \text{Multiply both sides by 2.}$$

Verify that 10 satisfies the original equation.

⇨ **SELF CHECK 6** Solve: $\left|\dfrac{2}{3}x - 4\right| + 2 = 2$.

ACCENT ON TECHNOLOGY

Solving Absolute Value Equations

We can solve absolute value equations with a graphing calculator. For example, to solve $|2x - 3| = 9$, we graph the equations $y_1 = |2x - 3|$ and $y_2 = 9$ on the same coordinate system, as shown in Figure 7-10. To enter the equation $y_1 = |2x - 3|$ on a TI-84 Plus calculator, press these keys.

$$\boxed{Y=}\ \boxed{\text{MATH}}\ \boxed{\blacktriangleright}\ \boxed{1}\ \boxed{2}\ \boxed{x}\ \boxed{-}\ \boxed{3}\ \boxed{)}$$

The equation $|2x - 3| = 9$ will be true for all x-coordinates of points that lie on both graphs. By using the TRACE or INTERSECT feature, we can see that the graphs intersect when $x = -3$ and $x = 6$. These are the solutions of the equation.

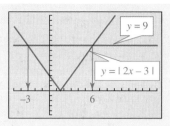

Figure 7-10

3 **Solve an equation where two absolute-value terms are equal.**

The equation $|a| = |b|$ is true when $a = b$ or when $a = -b$. For example,

$$|3| = |3| \qquad\qquad |3| = |-3|$$
$$3 = 3 \qquad\qquad\quad 3 = 3$$

Thus, we have the following result.

Equations with Two Absolute Values	If a and b represent algebraic expressions, the equation $|a| = |b|$ is equivalent to the pair of equations $$a = b \qquad \text{or} \qquad a = -b$$

EXAMPLE 7   Solve: $|5x + 3| = |3x + 25|$.

Solution   This equation is true when $5x + 3 = 3x + 25$, or when $5x + 3 = -(3x + 25)$. We solve each equation for x.

$$5x + 3 = 3x + 25 \quad \text{or} \quad 5x + 3 = -(3x + 25)$$
$$2x = 22 \qquad\qquad\qquad 5x + 3 = -3x - 25$$
$$x = 11 \qquad\qquad\qquad\qquad 8x = -28$$
$$x = -\frac{28}{8}$$
$$x = -\frac{7}{2}$$

Verify that both solutions check.

SELF CHECK 7   Solve: $|4x - 3| = |2x + 5|$.

SELF CHECK ANSWERS   **1. a.** 12   **b.** $4 - \pi$ **2.** -15 **3.** $1, -4$ **4.** $6, -2$ **5.** $\emptyset$ **6.** 6   **7.** $4, -\frac{1}{3}$

NOW TRY THIS

Express each of the following as an absolute value equation:

1. $x = 2$ or $x = -2$

2. $2x - 3 = 7$ or $2x - 3 = -7$

3. $x + 4 = 6$ or $x + 2 = -8$

7.2 EXERCISES

WARM-UPS

Find each absolute value.

1. $|-5|$ **2.** $-|5|$

3. $-|-6|$ **4.** $-|4|$

Solve each equation.

5. $|x| = 8$ **6.** $|x| = -5$

7. $|x - 5| = 0$ **8.** $|x + 1| = 1$

REVIEW   *Solve each equation.*

9. $3(2a - 1) = 2a$ **10.** $\dfrac{t}{6} - \dfrac{t}{3} = -1$

11. $\dfrac{5x}{2} - 1 = \dfrac{x}{3} + 12$ **12.** $4b - \dfrac{b + 9}{2} = \dfrac{b + 2}{5} - \dfrac{8}{5}$

VOCABULARY AND CONCEPTS   *Fill in the blanks.*

13. If $x \geq 0$, then $|x| = $ __.

14. If $x < 0$, then $|x| = $ ____.

15. $|x| \geq $ __ for all real numbers x.

16. If $k > 0$, then $|x| = k$ is equivalent to _____.

17. If $|a| = |b|$, then $a = b$ or _____.

18. If $k > 0$, the equation $|x| = k$ has ____ solutions.

GUIDED PRACTICE

Find each value. See Examples 1–2. (Objective 1)

19. $|8|$ **20.** $|-18|$

21. $|-12|$ **22.** $|15|$

23. $-|2|$ **24.** $-|-20|$

25. $-|-30|$ **26.** $-|25|$

27. $-(-|50|)$ **28.** $-(-|-20|)$

29. $|\pi - 4|$ **30.** $|2\pi - 4|$

Select the smaller of the two numbers. (Objective 1)

31. $|2|, |5|$ **32.** $|-6|, |2|$

33. $|5|, |-8|$ **34.** $|6|, |3|$

35. $|-2|, |10|$ **36.** $|-6|, -|6|$

37. $|-3|, -|-4|$ **38.** $|-3|, |-2|$

39. $-|-5|, -|-7|$ **40.** $-|-8|, -|20|$

41. $-x, |x + 1| \quad (x > 0)$ **42.** $y, |y - 1| \quad (y > 1)$

Solve each equation. See Examples 3–4. (Objective 2)

43. $|x| = 8$ **44.** $|x| = 9$

45. $|x - 3| = 6$ **46.** $|x + 4| = 8$

47. $|2x - 3| = 5$ **48.** $|4x - 4| = 20$

49. $|3x + 2| = 16$ **50.** $|5x - 3| = 22$

51. $|x + 3| + 7 = 10$ **52.** $|2 - x| + 3 = 5$

53. $|0.3x - 3| - 2 = 7$ **54.** $|0.1x + 8| - 1 = 1$

Solve each equation. See Examples 5–6. (Objective 2)

55. $\left| \dfrac{7}{2}x + 3 \right| = -5$ **56.** $|2x + 10| = 0$

57. $|3x + 24| = 0$ **58.** $|x - 21| = -8$

Solve each equation. See Example 7. (Objective 3)

59. $|2x + 1| = |3x + 3|$ **60.** $|5x - 7| = |4x + 1|$

61. $|3x - 1| = |x + 5|$ **62.** $|3x + 1| = |x - 5|$

63. $|2 - x| = |3x + 2|$ **64.** $|4x + 3| = |9 - 2x|$

65. $\left| \dfrac{x}{2} + 2 \right| = \left| \dfrac{x}{2} - 2 \right|$ **66.** $|7x + 12| = |x - 6|$

ADDITIONAL PRACTICE

Solve each equation.

67. $\left| \dfrac{x}{2} - 1 \right| = 3$ **68.** $\left| \dfrac{4x - 64}{4} \right| = 32$

69. $|3 - 4x| = 5$ **70.** $|8 - 5x| = 18$

71. $\left| \dfrac{3}{5}x - 4 \right| - 2 = -2$ **72.** $\left| \dfrac{3}{4}x + 2 \right| + 4 = 4$

73. $\left| x + \dfrac{1}{3} \right| = |x - 3|$ **74.** $\left| x - \dfrac{1}{4} \right| = |x + 4|$

75. $|3x + 7| = -|8x - 2|$ **76.** $-|17x + 13| = |3x - 14|$

77. $\left| \dfrac{3x + 48}{3} \right| = 12$ **78.** $\left| \dfrac{x}{2} + 2 \right| = 4$

🖩 *Use a graphing calculator to solve each equation. Give the result to the nearest tenth.*

79. $|0.75x + 0.12| = 12.3$

80. $|-0.47x - 1.75| = 5.1$

WRITING ABOUT MATH

81. Explain how to find the absolute value of a number.

82. Explain why the equation $|x| + 5 = 0$ has no solution.

SOMETHING TO THINK ABOUT

83. For what values of k does $|x| + k = 0$ have exactly two solutions?

84. For what value of k does $|x| + k = 0$ have exactly one solution?

85. Construct several examples to show that $|a \cdot b| = |a| \cdot |b|$.

86. Construct several examples to show that $\left| \dfrac{a}{b} \right| = \dfrac{|a|}{|b|}$.

87. Construct several examples to show that $|a + b| \neq |a| + |b|$.

88. Construct several examples to show that $|a - b| \neq |a| - |b|$.

SECTION 7.3

Solving Inequalities in One Variable Containing an Absolute-Value Term

Objectives

1 Solve an inequality in one variable containing one absolute-value term.

Getting Ready

Solve each inequality.

1. $2x + 3 > 5$ **2.** $-3x - 1 < 5$ **3.** $2x - 5 \leq 9$

In this section, we will show how to solve inequalities that have a term containing an absolute value.

1 **Solve an inequality in one variable containing one absolute-value term.**

The inequality $|x| < 5$ indicates that a point with coordinate x is *less than* 5 units from the origin. (See Figure 7-11.) Thus, x is between -5 and 5, and

$$|x| < 5 \qquad \text{is equivalent to} \qquad -5 < x < 5$$

The solution to the inequality $|x| < k$ $(k > 0)$ includes the coordinates of the points on the number line that are *less than* k units from the origin. (See Figure 7-12.)

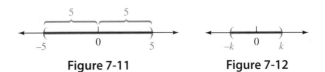

Figure 7-11   Figure 7-12

We have the following facts.

$$|x| < k \qquad \text{is equivalent to} \qquad -k < x < k \quad (k > 0)$$
$$|x| \le k \qquad \text{is equivalent to} \qquad -k \le x \le k \quad (k \ge 0)$$

To solve an inequality containing a term with an absolute value, we first isolate the absolute-value term on one side of the inequality. Then we use one of the previous properties to write the inequality as a double inequality.

EXAMPLE 1 Solve: $|2x - 3| - 2 < 7$.

Solution We first add 2 to both sides of the inequality to obtain

$$|2x - 3| < 9$$

We can then write the inequality as the double inequality

$$-9 < 2x - 3 < 9$$

and solve for x:

$$-9 < 2x - 3 < 9$$
$$-6 < 2x < 12 \qquad \text{Add 3 to all three parts.}$$
$$-3 < x < 6 \qquad \text{Divide all three parts by 2.}$$

Figure 7-13

Any number between -3 and 6, not including either -3 or 6, is in the solution set. This is the interval $(-3, 6)$. The graph is shown in Figure 7-13.

⇨ SELF CHECK 1 Solve: $|3x + 1| < 5$.

EXAMPLE 2 Solve: $|3x + 2| \le 5$.

Solution We write the expression as the double inequality

$$-5 \le 3x + 2 \le 5$$

and solve for x:

$$-5 \le 3x + 2 \le 5$$
$$-7 \le 3x \le 3 \qquad \text{Subtract 2 from all three parts.}$$
$$-\frac{7}{3} \le x \le 1 \qquad \text{Divide all three parts by 3.}$$

Figure 7-14

The solution set is the interval $\left[-\frac{7}{3}, 1\right]$, whose graph is shown in Figure 7-14.

➡ **SELF CHECK 2** Solve: $|2x - 3| \le 5$.

The inequality $|x| > 5$ can be interpreted to mean that a point with coordinate x is *more than* 5 units from the origin. (See Figure 7-15.)

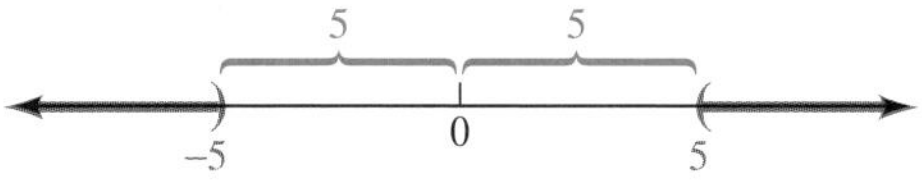

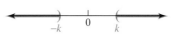

Figure 7-15

Thus, $x < -5$ or $x > 5$.

In general, the inequality $|x| > k$ ($k > 0$) can be interpreted to mean that a point with coordinate x is *more than* k units from the origin. (See Figure 7-16.)

Figure 7-16

Thus,

$$|x| > k \qquad \text{is equivalent to} \qquad x < -k \text{ or } x > k$$

The *or* indicates union, an either/or situation. It is necessary for x to satisfy only one of the two conditions to be in the solution set.

To summarize,

OR

If k is a nonnegative constant, then

$|x| > k$	is equivalent to	$x < -k$ or $x > k$
$|x| \ge k$	is equivalent to	$x \le -k$ or $x \ge k$

EXAMPLE 3   Solve: $|5x - 10| > 20$.

$x < -k \text{ or } x > k$

$5x - 10 < -20 \text{ or } 5x + 10 >$

Solution   We write the inequality as two separate inequalities

$$5x - 10 < -20 \qquad \text{or} \qquad 5x - 10 > 20$$

and solve each one for x:

$$5x - 10 < -20 \quad \text{or} \quad 5x - 10 > 20$$
$$5x < -10 \qquad\qquad 5x > 30 \qquad \text{Add 10 to both sides.}$$
$$x < -2 \qquad\qquad\quad x > 6 \qquad \text{Divide both sides by 5.}$$

Thus, x is either less than -2 or greater than 6.

$$x < -2 \qquad \text{or} \qquad x > 6$$

Figure 7-17

This is the union of two intervals $(-\infty, -2) \cup (6, \infty)$. The graph appears in Figure 7-17.

⇨ **SELF CHECK 3**   Solve: $|3x - 2| > 4$.

EXAMPLE 4   Solve: $\left| \dfrac{3 - x}{5} \right| \geq 6$.

Solution   We write the inequality as two separate inequalities

$$\frac{3 - x}{5} \leq -6 \qquad \text{or} \qquad \frac{3 - x}{5} \geq 6$$

and solve each one for x:

$$\frac{3 - x}{5} \leq -6 \quad \text{or} \quad \frac{3 - x}{5} \geq 6$$

$3 - x \leq -30$	$3 - x \geq 30$	Multiply both sides by 5.
$-x \leq -33$	$-x \geq 27$	Subtract 3 from both sides.
$x \geq 33$	$x \leq -27$	Divide both sides by -1 and reverse the direction of the inequality symbol.

Figure 7-18

The solution set is $(-\infty, -27] \cup [33, \infty)$, whose graph appears in Figure 7-18.

⇨ **SELF CHECK 4**   Solve: $\left| \dfrac{4 - x}{3} \right| \geq 2$.

EVERYDAY CONNECTIONS   The Shortest Distance Between Two Points

Perhaps one of the most famous examples of an inequality involving absolute values is the so-called Triangle Inequality describing one of the Propositions in Euclid's *Elements*. In layman's terms, the Triangle Inequality provides the basis for the rule of thumb, "The shortest distance between two points is a straight line." Using mathematical terminology, we say that given any triangle formed by the points A, B, and C, the length of any one side of the triangle must be shorter than the sum of the other two sides. Using mathematical notation

for the triangle in the illustration, we write
$$|x + y| < |x| + |y|.$$

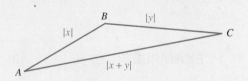

Use the Triangle Inequality to determine whether the given numbers represent the lengths of the sides of a triangle.

1. 8, 14, 20

2. 10, 11, 22

EXAMPLE 5   Solve: $\left| \dfrac{2}{3}x - 2 \right| - 3 > 6$.

Solution   We begin by adding 3 to both sides to isolate the absolute value on the left side. We then proceed as follows:

$$\left| \frac{2}{3}x - 2 \right| - 3 > 6$$

$$\left| \frac{2}{3}x - 2 \right| > 9 \qquad \text{Add 3 to both sides.}$$

$$\frac{2}{3}x - 2 < -9 \quad \text{or} \quad \frac{2}{3}x - 2 > 9$$

$$\frac{2}{3}x < -7 \qquad\qquad \frac{2}{3}x > 11 \qquad \text{Add 2 to both sides.}$$

$$2x < -21 \qquad\qquad 2x > 33 \qquad \text{Multiply both sides by 3.}$$

$$x < -\frac{21}{2} \qquad\qquad x > \frac{33}{2} \qquad \text{Divide both sides by 2.}$$

Figure 7-19

The solution set is $\left(-\infty, -\frac{21}{2}\right) \cup \left(\frac{33}{2}, \infty\right)$, whose graph appears in Figure 7-19.

⇨ **SELF CHECK 5**   Solve: $\left| \dfrac{3}{2}x + 1 \right| - 2 > 1$.

EXAMPLE 6   Solve: $|3x - 5| \geq -2$.

Solution   Since the absolute value of any number is nonnegative, and since any nonnegative number is larger than -2, the inequality is true for all x. The solution set is $(-\infty, \infty)$, whose graph appears in Figure 7-20.

Figure 7-20

⇨ **SELF CHECK 6**   Solve: $|2x + 3| > -5$.

ACCENT ON TECHNOLOGY

Solving Absolute Value Inequalities

We can solve many absolute value inequalities by a graphing method. For example, to solve $|2x - 3| < 9$, we graph the equations $y_1 = |2x - 3|$ and $y_2 = 9$ on the same coordinate system. If we use window settings of $[-5, 15]$ for x and $[-5, 15]$ for y, we get the graph shown in Figure 7-21.

The inequality $|2x - 3| < 9$ will be true for all x-coordinates of points that lie on the graph of $y = |2x - 3|$ and below the graph of $y = 9$. By using the TRACE feature, we can see that these values of x are in the interval $(-3, 6)$.

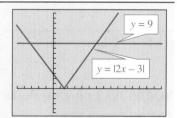

Figure 7-21

The inequality $|2x - 3| > 9$ will be true for all x-coordinates of points that lie on the graph of $y = |2x - 3|$ and above the graph of $y = 9$. By using the TRACE feature, we can see that these values of x are in the union of two intervals $(-\infty, -3) \cup (6, \infty)$.

⇨ **SELF CHECK ANSWERS**

1. $\left(-2, \frac{4}{3}\right)$ (−2, 4/3)

2. $[-1, 4]$ [−1, 4]

3. $\left(-\infty, -\frac{2}{3}\right) \cup (2, \infty)$ (−∞, −2/3) ∪ (2, ∞)

4. $(-\infty, -2] \cup [10, \infty)$ (−∞, −2] ∪ [10, ∞)

5. $\left(-\infty, -\frac{8}{3}\right) \cup \left(\frac{4}{3}, \infty\right)$ (−∞, −8/3) ∪ (4/3, ∞)

6. $(-\infty, \infty)$ (−∞, ∞)

NOW TRY THIS

1. Express each of the following as an absolute value inequality.
 a. $-5 \le x \le 5$
 b. $3x - 5 < -7$ or $3x - 5 > 7$

2. Solve the inequality $|x + 5| \le 2x - 9$. Write the solution in interval notation and graph it.

7.3 EXERCISES

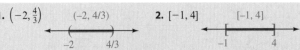

WARM-UPS   *Solve each inequality.*

1. $|x| < 8$ **2.** $|x| > 8$

3. $|x| \ge 4$ **4.** $|x| \le 7$

5. $|x + 1| < 2$ **6.** $|x + 1| > 2$

REVIEW   *Solve each formula for the given variable.*

7. $A = p + prt$ for t **8.** $A = p + prt$ for r

9. $P = 2w + 2l$ for l **10.** $V = \frac{1}{3}Bh$ for B

VOCABULARY AND CONCEPTS

Fill in the blanks.

11. If $k > 0$, then $|x| < k$ is equivalent to _____.
12. If $k > 0$, then _____ is equivalent to $-k \le x \le k$.
13. If k is a nonnegative constant, then $|x| > k$ is equivalent to _____.
14. If k is a nonnegative constant, then _____ is equivalent to $x \le -k$ or $x \ge k$.

GUIDED PRACTICE

Solve each inequality. Write the solution set in interval notation and graph it. See Examples 1–2. (Objective 1)

15. $|2x| < 8$ **16.** $|3x| < 27$

17. $|x + 9| \le 12$ **18.** $|x - 8| \le 12$

19. $|3x - 2| \le 10$ **20.** $|4x - 1| \le 7$

21. $|3 - 2x| < 7$ **22.** $|4 - 3x| \le 13$

Solve each inequality. Write the solution set in interval notation and graph it. See Examples 3–4. (Objective 1)

23. $|5x| > 5$

24. $|7x| > 7$

25. $|x - 12| > 24$

26. $|x + 5| \geq 7$

27. $|3x + 2| > 14$

28. $|2x - 5| \geq 25$

29. $|2 - 3x| \geq 8$

30. $|-1 - 2x| > 5$

Solve each inequality. Write the solution set in interval notation and graph it. See Example 5. (Objective 1)

31. $\left| \dfrac{1}{3}x + 7 \right| + 5 > 6$

32. $\left| \dfrac{1}{2}x - 3 \right| - 4 < 2$

33. $-|2x - 3| < -7$

34. $-|3x + 1| < -8$

35. $-|5x - 1| + 2 < 0$

36. $\left| \dfrac{x - 2}{3} \right| \leq 4$

37. $\left| \dfrac{x - 2}{3} \right| > 4$

38. $|3x + 1| + 2 < 6$

Solve each inequality. Write the solution set in interval notation and graph it. See Example 6. (Objective 1)

39. $-2|3x - 4| < 16$

40. $|7x + 2| > -8$

41. $|5x - 1| + 4 \leq 0$

42. $|3x + 2| \leq -3$

43. $|2x + 1| + 2 \leq 2$

44. $\left| \dfrac{x - 5}{10} \right| \leq 0$

45. $\left| 3\left(\dfrac{x + 4}{4}\right) \right| > 0$

46. $|4x + 3| > 0$

ADDITIONAL PRACTICE

Solve each inequality. Write the solution set in interval notation and graph it.

47. $3|2x + 5| \geq 9$

48. $\left| \dfrac{3}{5}x + \dfrac{7}{3} \right| < 2$

49. $\left| \dfrac{1}{7}x + 1 \right| \leq 0$

50. $\left| \dfrac{3}{5}x - 2 \right| + 3 \leq 3$

51. $\left| \dfrac{1}{5}x - 5 \right| + 4 > 4$

52. $\left| \dfrac{7}{3}x - \dfrac{3}{5} \right| \geq 1$

53. $3\left| \dfrac{1}{3}(x - 2) \right| + 2 \leq 3$

54. $|8x - 3| > 0$

55. $|3x - 2| + 2 \geq 0$
56. $|5x - 12| < -5$
57. $|4x + 3| > -5$

58. $\left| \dfrac{1}{6}x + 6 \right| + 2 < 2$

Use a calculator to solve each inequality. Give each answer in interval notation. Round to the nearest tenth.

59. $|0.5x + 0.7| < 2.6$
60. $|1.25x - 0.75| < 3.15$
61. $|2.15x - 3.05| > 3.8$
62. $|-3.57x + 0.12| > 2.75$

WRITING ABOUT MATH

63. Explain how parentheses and brackets are used when graphing inequalities.
64. If $k > 0$, explain the difference between the solution sets of $|x| < k$ and $|x| > k$.

SOMETHING TO THINK ABOUT

65. Under what conditions is $|x| + |y| > |x + y|$?

66. Under what conditions is $|x| + |y| = |x + y|$?

7.4A Review of Factoring

Objectives

1 Factoring out the greatest common factor
2 Factoring by grouping
3 Formulas
4 Factoring trinomials
5 Using substitution to factor trinomials
6 Using grouping to factor trinomials

Getting Ready *Perform each multiplication.*

1. $3x^2y(2x - y)$ 2. $(x + 2)(x - 3)$

2. $(2x + 3)(x - 3)$ 4. $(3a - b)(2s + 3b)$

In Chapter 5, we discussed how to factor polynomials. In the next two sections, we will review that material. Recall that *when we factor a polynomial, we write a sum of terms as a product of factors.* To perform the most basic type of factoring, we determine whether the terms of the given polynomial have any common factors.

Factoring Out the Greatest Common Factor

Factoring out a common monomial factor is based on the distributive property.

EXAMPLE 1   Factor: $3xy^2z^3 + 6xz^2 - 9xyz^4$.

Solution   We begin by factoring each term:

$$\left.\begin{array}{l} 3xy^2z^3 = 3 \cdot x \cdot y \cdot y \cdot z \cdot z \cdot z \\ 6xz^2 = 3 \cdot 2 \cdot x \cdot z \cdot z \\ 9xyz^4 = 3 \cdot 3 \cdot x \cdot y \cdot z \cdot z \cdot z \cdot z \end{array}\right\} \qquad \text{GCF} = 3 \cdot x \cdot z \cdot z = 3xz^2$$

Since each term has one factor of 3, one factor of x, and two factors of z, and there are no other common factors, $3xz^2$ is the greatest common factor of the three terms. We can use the distributive property to factor out $3xz^2$.

$$\begin{aligned} 3xy^2z^3 + 6xz^2 - 9xyz^4 &= 3xz^2 \cdot y^2z + 3xz^2 \cdot 2 - 3xz^2 \cdot 3yz^2 \\ &= 3xz^2(y^2z + 2 - 3yz^2) \end{aligned}$$

Check: $3xz^2(y^2z + 2 - 3yz^2) = 3xy^2z^3 + 6xz^2 - 9xyz^4$.

Self Check   Factor: $6a^2b^2 - 4ab^3 + 2ab^2$.

EXAMPLE 2   Factor the negative of the greatest common factor from $-6u^2v^3 + 8u^3v^2$.

Solution   Because the greatest common factor of the two terms is $2u^2v^2$, the negative of the greatest common factor is $-2u^2v^2$. To factor out $-2u^2v^2$, we proceed as follows:

$$\begin{aligned} -6u^2v^3 + 8u^3v^2 &= -2u^2v^2 \cdot 3v + 2u^2v^2 \cdot 4u \\ &= -2u^2v^2 \cdot 3v - (-2u^2v^2)4u \\ &= -2u^2v^2(3v - 4u) \end{aligned}$$

Self Check   Factor the opposite of the greatest common factor from $-3p^3q + 6p^2q^2$.

A polynomial that cannot be factored is called a **prime polynomial** or an **irreducible polynomial.**

EXAMPLE 3   Factor $3x^2 + 4y + 7$, if possible.

Solution   We factor each term:

$$3x^2 = 3 \cdot x \cdot x \qquad 4y = 2 \cdot 2 \cdot y \qquad 7 = 7$$

Since there are no common factors other than 1, this polynomial cannot be factored. It is a prime polynomial.

Self Check   Factor: $6a^3 + 7b^2 + 5$.

A common factor can have more than one term.

EXAMPLE 4   Factor: $a(x - y + z) - b(x - y + z) + 3(x - y + z)$.

Solution   Since the trinomial $x - y + z$ is a factor of each term of the given polynomial, we factor it out.

$$a(x - y + z) - b(x - y + z) + 3(x - y + z) = (x - y + z)(a - b + 3)$$

Self Check   Factor: $c^2(y^2 + 1) + d^2(y^2 + 1)$.

Factoring by Grouping

Sometimes polynomials having four or more terms can be factored by removing common factors from groups of terms. This process is called **factoring by grouping.**

EXAMPLE 5   Factor: $2c - 2d + cd - d^2$.

Solution   The first two terms have a common factor of 2, and the last two terms have a common factor, d.

$$2c - 2d + cd - d^2 = 2(c - d) + d(c - d)$$
$$= (c - d)(2 + d)$$

We check by multiplying:

$$(c - d)(2 + d) = 2c + cd - 2d - d^2$$
$$= 2c - 2d + cd - d^2$$

Self Check   Factor: $7m - 7n + mn - n^2$.

To factor a polynomial, it is often necessary to factor more than once. When factoring a polynomial, **always look for a common factor first.**

EXAMPLE 6   Factor: $3x^3y - 4x^2y^2 - 6x^2y + 8xy^2$.

Solution   We begin by factoring out the common factor of xy.

$$3x^3y - 4x^2y^2 - 6x^2y + 8xy^2 = xy(3x^2 - 4xy - 6x + 8y)$$

We can now factor $3x^2 - 4xy - 6x + 8y$ by grouping:

$$
\begin{aligned}
3x^3y &- 4x^2y^2 - 6x^2y + 8xy^2 \\
&= xy(3x^2 - 4xy - 6x + 8y) \\
&= xy[x(3x - 4y) - 2(3x - 4y)] \\
&= xy(3x - 4y)(x - 2)
\end{aligned}
$$

Because no more factoring can be done, the factorization is complete.

Self Check   Factor: $3a^3b + 3a^2b - 2a^2b^2 - 2ab^2$.

Formulas

Factoring is often required to solve a formula for one of its variables.

EXAMPLE 7   The formula $r_1r_2 = rr_2 + rr_1$ is used in electronics. Solve for r_2.

Solution   To isolate r_2 on one side of the equation, we get all terms involving r_2 on the left-hand side and all terms not involving r_2 on the right-hand side. We then proceed as follows:

$$
\begin{aligned}
r_1r_2 &= rr_2 + rr_1 \\
r_1r_2 - rr_2 &= rr_1 \\
r_2(r_1 - r) &= rr_1 \\
r_2 &= \frac{rr_1}{r_1 - r}
\end{aligned}
$$

Self Check   Solve $f_1f_2 = ff_1 + ff_2$ for f_1.

Factoring Trinomials

Recall that many trinomials factor as the product of two binomials.

EXAMPLE 8   Factor: $x^2 - 6x + 8$.

Solution   We attempt to factor $x^2 - 6x + 8$ as the product of two binomials. Since the first term of the trinomial is x^2, we enter x and x as the first terms of the binomial factors.

$$x^2 - 6x + 8 = \left(x\ \boxed{}\ \right)\left(x\ \boxed{}\ \right)$$

The second terms of the binomials must be two integers whose product is 8 and whose sum is -6. All possible integer-pair factors of 8 are listed in the table.

Factors of 8	Sum of factors
1(8)	$1 + 8 = 9$
2(4)	$2 + 4 = 6$
$-1(-8)$	$-1 + (-8) = -9$
$-2(-4)$	$-2 + (-4) = -6$

The fourth row of the table contains the correct pair of integers -2 and -4, whose product is 8 and whose sum is -6. To complete the factorization, we enter -2 and -4 as the second terms of the binomial factors.

$$x^2 - 6x + 8 = (x - 2)(x - 4)$$

Check: We can verify this result by multiplication:

$$(x - 2)(x - 4) = x^2 - 4x - 2x + 8$$
$$= x^2 - 6x + 8$$

Self Check   Factor: $a^2 - 7a + 12$.

EXAMPLE 9   Factor: $30x - 4xy - 2xy^2$.

Solution   We begin by writing the trinomial in descending powers of y:

$$30x - 4xy - 2xy^2 = -2xy^2 - 4xy + 30x$$

Each term in this trinomial has a common factor of $-2x$, which can be factored out.

$$30x - 4xy - 2xy^2 = -2x(y^2 + 2y - 15)$$

To factor $y^2 + 2y - 15$, we list the factors of -15 and find the pair whose sum is 2.

$$15(-1) \qquad 5(-3) \qquad 1(-15) \qquad 3(-5)$$

The only factorization where the sum of the factors is 2 (the coefficient of the middle term of $y^2 + 2y - 15$) is $5(-3)$. Thus,

$$30x - 4xy - 2xy^2 = -2x(y^2 + 2y - 15)$$
$$= -2x(y + 5)(y - 3)$$

Verify this result by multiplication.

Self Check   Factor: $16a - 2ap^2 - 4ap$.

There are more combinations of coefficients to consider when factoring trinomials with lead coefficients other than 1. It is not easy to give specific rules for factoring such trinomials. However, the following hints are helpful. This approach is called the **trial-and-check method.**

EXAMPLE 10   Factor: $3p^2 - 4p - 4$.

Solution   **To factor the trinomial, we note that the first terms of the binomial factors must be $3p$ and p to give the first term of $3p^2$.**

$$3p^2 - 4p - 4 = \left(3p \;\boxed{}\right)\left(p \;\boxed{}\right)$$

The product of the last terms must be -4, and the sum of the products of the outer terms and the inner terms must be $-4p$.

$$3p^2 - 4p - 4 = \left(3p \;\boxed{}\right)\left(p \;\boxed{}\right)$$

$$O + I = -4p$$

Because $1(-4)$, $-1(4)$, and $-2(2)$ all give a product of -4, there are six possible combinations to consider:

$$(3p + 1)(p - 4) \qquad (3p - 4)(p + 1)$$
$$(3p - 1)(p + 4) \qquad (3p + 4)(p - 1)$$
$$(3p - 2)(p + 2) \qquad (3p + 2)(p - 2)$$

Of these possibilities, only the one in blue gives the required middle term of $-4p$.

$$3p^2 - 4p - 4 = (3p + 2)(p - 2)$$

Self Check   Factor: $4q^2 - 9q - 9$.

EXAMPLE 11   Factor: $6y^3 + 13x^2y^3 + 6x^4y^3$.

Solution   **We write the expression in descending powers of x and then factor out the common factor y^3.**

$$6y^3 + 13x^2y^3 + 6x^4y^3 = 6x^4y^3 + 13x^2y^3 + 6y^3$$
$$= y^3(6x^4 + 13x^2 + 6)$$

A test for factorability will show that $6x^4 + 13x^2 + 6$ will factor.

To factor $6x^4 + 13x^2 + 6$, we examine its terms.

• Since the first term is $6x^4$, the first terms of the binomial factors must be either $2x^2$ and $3x^2$ or x^2 and $6x^2$.

$$6x^4 + 13x^2 + 6 = \left(2x^2 \boxed{}\right)\left(3x^2 \boxed{}\right) \quad \text{or} \quad \left(x^2 \boxed{}\right)\left(6x^2 \boxed{}\right)$$

- Since the signs of the middle term and the last term of the trinomial are positive, the signs within each binomial factor will be positive.
- Since the product of the last terms of the binomial factors must be 6, we must find two numbers whose product is 6 that will lead to a middle term of $13x^2$.

After trying some combinations, we find the one that works.

$$6x^4y^3 + 13x^2y^3 + 6y^3 = y^3(6x^4 + 13x^2 + 6)$$
$$= y^3(2x^2 + 3)(3x^2 + 2)$$

Self Check   Factor: $4b + 11a^2b + 6a^4b$.

Using Substitution to Factor Trinomials

For more complicated expressions, a substitution sometimes helps to simplify the factoring process.

EXAMPLE 12   Factor: $(x + y)^2 + 7(x + y) + 12$.

Solution   **We rewrite the trinomial $(x + y)^2 + 7(x + y) + 12$ as $z^2 + 7z + 12$, where $z = x + y$. The trinomial $z^2 + 7z + 12$ factors as $(z + 4)(z + 3)$.**
To find the factorization of $(x + y)^2 + 7(x + y) + 12$, we substitute $x + y$ for z in the expression $(z + 4)(z + 3)$ to obtain

$$z^2 + 7z + 12 = (z + 4)(z + 3)$$
$$(x + y)^2 + 7(x + y) + 12 = (x + y + 4)(x + y + 3)$$

Self Check   Factor: $(a + b)^2 - 3(a + b) - 10$.

Using Grouping to Factor Trinomials

Another way to factor trinomials is to write them as equivalent four-termed polynomials and factor by grouping.

EXAMPLE 13   Factor by grouping: **a.** $x^2 + 8x + 15$ and **b.** $10x^2 + 13x - 3$.

Solution   **a.** Since $x^2 + 8x + 15 = 1x^2 + 8x + 15$, we identify a as 1, b as 8, and c as 15. The key number is $ac = 1(15) = 15$. We must find two integers whose product is 15 and whose sum is $b = 8$. Since the integers must have a positive product and a positive sum, we consider only positive factors of 15.

Key number = 15

Positive factors of 15	Sum of the factors
$1 \cdot 15 = 15$	$1 + 15 = 16$
$3 \cdot 5 = 15$	$3 + 5 = 8$

The second row of the table contains the correct pair of integers 3 and 5, whose product is 15 and whose sum is 8. They serve as the coefficients of $3x$ and $5x$ that we place between x^2 and 15.

$$\begin{aligned} x^2 + 8x + 15 &= x^2 + 3x + 5x + 15 \\ &= x(x + 3) + 5(x + 3) \\ &= (x + 3)(x + 5) \end{aligned}$$

The factorization is $(x + 3)(x + 5)$. Check by multiplying.

b. In $10x^2 + 13x - 3$, $a = 10$, $b = 13$, and $c = -3$. The key number is $ac = 10(-3) = -30$. We must find a factorization of -30 in which the sum of the factors is $b = 13$. Since the factors must have a negative product, their signs must be different. The possible factor pairs are listed in the table.

Key number = −30

Factors of −30	Sum of the factors
$1(-30) = -30$	$1 + (-30) = -29$
$2(-15) = -30$	$2 + (-15) = -13$
$3(-10) = -30$	$3 + (-10) = -7$
$5(-6) = -30$	$5 + (-6) = -1$
$6(-5) = -30$	$6 + (-5) = 1$
$10(-3) = -30$	$10 + (-3) = 7$
$15(-2) = -30$	$15 + (-2) = 13$
$30(-1) = -30$	$30 + (-1) = 29$

The seventh row contains the correct pair of numbers 15 and -2, whose product is -30 and whose sum is 13. They serve as the coefficients of two terms, $15x$ and $-2x$, that we place between $10x^2$ and -3.

$$10x^2 + 13x - 3 = 10x^2 + 15x - 2x - 3$$

Finally, we factor by grouping.

$$\begin{aligned} 10x^2 + 15x - 2x - 3 &= 5x(2x + 3) - 1(2x + 3) \\ &= (2x + 3)(5x - 1) \end{aligned}$$

So $10x^2 + 13x - 3 = (2x + 3)(5x - 1)$. Check by multiplying.

SELF CHECK   Factor by grouping: **a.** $m^2 + 13m + 42$ and **b.** $15a^2 + 17a - 4$.

Self Check Answers

1. $2ab^2(3a - 2b + 1)$ **2.** $-3p^2q(p - 2q)$ **3.** a prime polynomial **4.** $(y^2 + 1)(c^2 + d^2)$
5. $(m - n)(7 + n)$ **6.** $ab(3a - 2b)(a + 1)$ **7.** $f_1 = \dfrac{ff_2}{f_2 - f}$ **8.** $(a - 4)(a - 3)$
9. $-2a(p + 4)(p - 2)$ **10.** $(4q + 3)(q - 3)$ **11.** $b(2a^2 + 1)(3a^2 + 4)$
12. $(a + b + 2)(a + b - 5)$ **13. a.** $(m + 7)(m + 6)$, **b.** $(3a + 4)(5a - 1)$

ORALS Factor each expression, if possible.

1. $3xy^2 - 6x^2y$ **2.** $x^2 + 5x - 6$
3. $2x^2 - x - 1$ **4.** $3a^2 - 5ab - 2b^2$

STUDY SET

VOCABULARY AND CONCEPTS *Fill in the blanks.*

1. When we write $2x + 4$ as $2(x + 2)$, we say that we have _____ $2x + 4$.

2. When we _____ a polynomial, we write a sum of terms as a product of factors.

3. The abbreviation GCF stands for _____ _____ _____.

4. If a polynomial cannot be factored, it is called a _____ polynomial or an irreducible polynomial.

5. To factor means to factor _____. Each factor of a completely factored expression will be _____.

6. To factor $ab + 6a + 2b + 12$ by _____, we begin by factoring out a from the first two terms and 2 from the last two terms.

7. A polynomial with three terms, such as $3x^2 - 2x + 4$, is called a _____.

8. The trinomial $4a^2 - 5a - 6$ is written in _____ powers of a.

9. The _____ coefficient of the trinomial $x^2 - 3x + 2$ is 1, the _____ of the middle term is -3, and the last term is _____.

10. The statement $x^2 - x - 12 = (x - 4)(x + 3)$ shows that $x^2 - x - 12$ factors into the _____ of two binomials.

11. The prime factorizations of three terms are shown here. Find their GCF.

$$2 \cdot 2 \cdot 3 \cdot x \cdot x \cdot y \cdot y \cdot y$$
$$2 \cdot 3 \cdot 3 \cdot x \cdot y \cdot y \cdot y \cdot y$$
$$2 \cdot 3 \cdot 3 \cdot 7 \cdot x \cdot x \cdot x \cdot y \cdot y$$

12. Check to see whether $(3t - 1)(5t - 6)$ is the correct factorization of $15t^2 - 19t + 6$.

13. Complete the table.

Factors of 8	Sum of the factors of 8
$1(8) = 8$	
$2(4) = 8$	
$-1(-8) = 8$	
$-2(-4) = 8$	

14. Find two integers whose
a. product is 10 and whose sum is 7.
b. product is 8 and whose sum is -6.
c. product is -6 and whose sum is 1.
d. product is -9 and whose sum is -8.

15. Complete the key number table.

Key number = 12

Negative factors of 12	Sum of factors of 12
$-1(-12) = 12$	
$-3(-4) = 12$	

16. Use the substitution $x = a + b$ to rewrite the trinomial $6(a + b)^2 - 17(a + b) - 3$.

Complete each factorization.

17. $15c^3d^4 - 25c^2d^4 + 5c^3d^6 = \qquad (3c - 5 + cd^2)$

18. $x^3 - x^2 + 2x - 2 = \quad (x - 1) + \quad (x - 1)$

$\qquad = (\quad)(x^2 + 2)$

19. $6m^2 + 7m - 3 = (\quad - 1)(2m + \quad)$

20. $2y^2 + 10y + 12 = \quad (y^2 + 5y + 6)$

$\qquad = 2(y + \quad)(\quad + 2)$

PRACTICE. Factor each expression. Factor out all common factors first (including −1 if the first term is negative). If an expression is prime, so indicate.

21. $2x^2 - 6x$

22. $3y^3 + 3y^2$

23. $15x^2y - 10x^2y^2$

24. $63x^3y^2 + 81x^2y^4$

25. $27z^3 + 12z^2 + 3z$

26. $25t^6 - 10t^3 + 5t^2$

27. $11m^3n^2 - 12x^2y$

28. $14r^2s^3 + 15t^6$

29. $-5xy + y - 4$

30. $-7m - 12n + 16$

31. $24s^3 - 12s^2t + 6st^2$

32. $18y^2z^2 + 12y^2z^3 - 24y^4z^3$

33. $(x + y)u + (x + y)v$

34. $4(x + y) + t(x + y)$

35. $-18a^2b - 12ab^2$

36. $-21t^5 + 28t^3$

37. $\dfrac{3}{5}ax^4 + \dfrac{1}{5}bx^2 - \dfrac{4}{5}ax^3$

38. $\dfrac{3}{2}t^2y^4 - \dfrac{1}{2}ty^4 - \dfrac{5}{2}ry^3$

39. $5(a - b) - t(a - b)$

40. $(a - b)r - (a - b)s$

41. $3(m + n + p) + x(m + n + p)$

42. $x(x - y - z) + y(x - y - z)$

43. $-63u^3v^6z^9 + 28u^2v^7z^2 - 21u^3v^3z^4$

44. $-56x^4y^3z^2 - 72x^3y^4z^5 + 80xy^2z^3$

45. $4(x^2 + 1)^2 + 2(x^2 + 1)^3$

46. $6(x^3 - 7x + 1)^2 - 3(x^3 - 7x + 1)^3$

Solve for the indicated variable.

47. $r_1r_2 = rr_2 + rr_1$ for r_1

48. $r_1r_2 = rr_2 + rr_1$ for r

49. $S(1 - r) = a - \ell r$ for r

50. $Sn = (n - 2)180°$ for n

51. $b^2x^2 + a^2y^2 = a^2b^2$ for a^2

52. $b^2x^2 + a^2y^2 = a^2b^2$ for b^2

Factor by grouping. Factor out the GCF first.

53. $ax + bx + ay + by$

54. $ar - br + as - bs$

55. $x^2 + yx + x + y$

56. $c + d + cd + d^2$

57. $a^2 - 4b + ab - 4a$

58. $3c - cd + 3d - c^2$

59. $x^2 + 4y - xy - 4x$

60. $7u + v^2 - 7v - uv$

61. $a^2x + bx - a^2 - b$

62. $x^2y - ax - xy + a$

63. $x^2 + xy + xz + xy + y^2 + zy$

64. $ab - b^2 - bc + ac - bc - c^2$

65. $1 - m + mn - n$

66. $a^2x^2 - 10 - 2x^2 + 5a^2$

67. $2ax^2 - 4 + a - 8x^2$

68. $a^3b^2 - 3 + a^3 - 3b^2$

69. $mpx + mqx + npx + nqx$

70. $abd - abe + acd - ace$

71. $x^2y + xy^2 + 2xyz + xy^2 + y^3 + 2y^2z$

72. $a^3 - 2a^2b + a^2c - a^2b + 2ab^2 - abc$

Factor each trinomial. Factor out all common factors first (including −1 if the first term is negative). If a trinomial is prime, so indicate.

73. $x^2 - 5x + 6$

74. $y^2 + 7y + 6$

75. $x^2 - 7x + 10$

76. $c^2 - 7c + 12$

77. $b^2 + 8b + 18$

78. $x^2 + 4x - 28$

79. $-x + x^2 - 30$

80. $a^2 - 45 + 4a$

81. $a^2 - 18a + 81$

82. $b^2 + 12b + 36$

83. $x^2 - 4xy - 21y^2$

84. $a^2 + 4ab - 5b^2$

85. $s^2 - 10st + 16t^2$

86. $h^2 - 8hk + 15k^2$

87. $3x^2 + 12x - 63$

88. $2y^2 + 4y - 48$

89. $32 - a^2 + 4a$

90. $15 - x^2 - 2x$

91. $-3a^2x^2 + 15a^2x - 18a^2$

92. $-2bcy^2 - 16bcy + 40bc$

93. $y^4 - 13y^2 + 30$

94. $y^4 - 13y^2 + 42$

95. $b^4x^2 - 12b^2x^2 + 35x^2$

96. $c^3x^4 + 11c^3x^2 - 42c^3$

97. $6y^2 + 7y + 2$

98. $6x^2 - 11x + 3$

99. $8a^2 + 6a - 9$

100. $15b^2 + 4b - 4$

101. $6x^2 - 5xy - 4y^2$

102. $18y^2 - 3yz - 10z^2$

103. $5x^2 + 4x + 1$

104. $3 + 4a^2 + 20a$

105. $6z^2 + 17z + 12$

106. $3 - 10x + 8x^2$

107. $4y^2 + 4y + 1$

108. $9x^2 + 6x + 1$

109. $-3a^2 + ab + 2b^2$

110. $-2x^2 + 3xy + 5y^2$

111. $20a^2 + 60b^2 + 45ab$

112. $-4x^2 - 9 + 12x$

113. $64h^6 + 24h^5 - 4h^4$

114. $27x^2yz + 90xyz - 72yz$

115. $6a^2(m + n) + 13a(m + n) - 15(m + n)$

116. $15n^2(q - r) - 17n(q - r) - 18(q - r)$

Use substitution to help factor each expression.

117. $(x + a)^2 + 2(x + a) + 1$

118. $(a + b)^2 - 2(a + b) + 1$

119. $(a + b)^2 - 2(a + b) - 24$

120. $(x - y)^2 + 3(x - y) - 10$

121. $14(q - r)^2 - 17(q - r) - 6$

122. $8(h + s)^2 + 34(h + s) + 35$

SOMETHING TO THINK ABOUT Factor out the designated factor.

123. x^2 from $x^{n+2} + x^{n+3}$

124. y^n from $2y^{n+2} - 3y^{n+3}$

Factor. Assume that n is a natural number.

125. $x^{2n} + 2x^n + 1$ **126.** $2a^{6n} - 3a^{3n} - 2$

127. $x^{4n} + 2x^{2n}y^{2n} + y^{4n}$ **128.** $6x^{2n} + 7x^n - 3$

APPLICATIONS

129. CRAYONS The amount of colored wax used to make the crayon shown in the illustration can be found by computing its volume using the formula

$$V = \pi r^2 h_1 + \frac{1}{3}\pi r^2 h_2$$

Factor the expression on the right-hand side of this equation.

130. PACKAGING The amount of cardboard needed to make the following cereal box can be found by finding the area A, which is given by the formula
$$A = 2wh + 4wl + 2lh$$
where w is the width, h the height, and l the length. Solve the equation for the width.

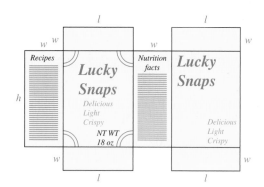

131. ICE The surface area of the ice cube is $6x^2 + 36x + 54$. Find the length of an edge of the cube.

132. CHECKERS The area of the checkerboard is $25x^2 - 40x + 16$. Find the length of each side.

WRITING

133. Explain the error in the following solution.

$$\text{Solve for } r_1: \qquad r_1 r_2 = r r_2 + r r_1$$

$$\frac{r_1 r_2}{r_2} = \frac{r r_2 + r r_1}{r_2}$$

$$r_1 = \frac{r r_2 + r r_1}{r_2}$$

134. Explain the error.
Factor: $2x^2 - 4x - 6$.

$$2x^2 - 4x - 6 = (2x + 2)(x - 3)$$

REVIEW

135. INVESTMENTS Equal amounts are invested in each of three accounts paying 7%, 8%, and 10.5% annually. If one year's combined interest income is \$1,249.50, how much is invested in each account?

136. SEARCH AND RESCUE Two search-and-rescue teams leave base at the same time looking for a lost boy. The first team, on foot, heads north at 2 mph and the other, on horseback, south at 4 mph. How long will it take them to search a distance of 21 miles between them?

The Difference of Two Squares; the Sum and Difference of Two Cubes

Objectives

1 Factoring the difference of two squares
2 Factoring polynomials with four terms
3 Factoring the sum and difference of two cubes

Getting Ready *Perform each multiplication.*

1. $(x + 2)(x - 2)$ 2. $(3x + 3y)(2x - 3y)$

3. $(x - 3)(x^2 + 3x + 9)$ 4. $(x + 2)(x^2 - 2x + 4)$

We will now review some special rules of factoring. These rules are applied to polynomials that can be written as the difference of two squares or the sum or difference of two cubes.

Factoring the Difference of Two Squares

Recall that the difference of the squares of two quantities factors into the product of two binomials.

Difference of Two Squares $x^2 - y^2 = (x + y)(x - y)$

If we think of the difference of two squares as the square of a **First** quantity minus the square of a **Last** quantity, we have the formula

$$F^2 - L^2 = (F + L)(F - L)$$

and we say: *To factor the square of a **First** quantity minus the square of a **Last** quantity, we multiply the **First** plus the **Last** by the **First** minus the **Last**.*

To factor differences of squares, it is helpful to know these **perfect integer squares:** 1, 4, 9, 16, 25, 36, 49, 64, 81, 100, 121, 144.

EXAMPLE 1   Factor: $49x^2 - 16$.

Solution   We begin by rewriting the binomial $49x^2 - 16$ as a difference of two squares: $(7x)^2 - (4)^2$. Then we use the formula for factoring the difference of two squares:

$$F^2 - L^2 = (F + L)(F - L)$$
$$(7x)^2 - 4^2 = (7x + 4)(7x - 4)$$

We can verify this result using the FOIL method to do the multiplication.

$$(7x + 4)(7x - 4) = 49x^2 - 28x + 28x - 16$$
$$= 49x^2 - 16$$

Self Check   Factor: $81p^2 - 25$.

EXAMPLE 2   Factor: $x^4 - 1$.

Solution   Because the binomial is the difference of the squares of x^2 and 1, it factors into the sum of x^2 and 1 and the difference of x^2 and 1.

$$x^4 - 1 = (x^2)^2 - (1)^2$$
$$= (x^2 + 1)(x^2 - 1)$$

The factor $x^2 + 1$ is the sum of two quantities and is prime. However, the factor $x^2 - 1$ is the difference of two squares and can be factored as $(x + 1)(x - 1)$. Thus,

$$x^4 - 1 = (x^2 + 1)(x^2 - 1)$$
$$= (x^2 + 1)(x + 1)(x - 1)$$

Self Check   Factor: $a^4 - 81$.

EXAMPLE 3   Factor: $(x + y)^4 - z^4$.

Solution   This expression is the difference of two squares and can be factored:

$$(x + y)^4 - z^4 = \left[(x + y)^2\right]^2 - (z^2)^2$$
$$= \left[(x + y)^2 + z^2\right]\left[(x + y)^2 - z^2\right]$$

The factor $(x + y)^2 + z^2$ is the sum of two squares and is prime. However, the factor $(x + y)^2 - z^2$ is the difference of two squares and can be factored as $(x + y + z)(x + y - z)$. Thus,

$$(x + y)^4 - z^4 = \left[(x + y)^2 + z^2\right]\left[(x + y)^2 - z^2\right]$$
$$= \left[(x + y)^2 + z^2\right](x + y + z)(x + y - z)$$

Self Check   Factor: $(a - b)^4 - c^4$.

When possible, we always factor out a common factor before factoring the difference of two squares. The factoring process is easier when all common factors are factored out first.

EXAMPLE 4   Factor: $2x^4y - 32y$.

Solution $$2x^4y - 32y = 2y(x^4 - 16)$$
$$= 2y(x^2 + 4)(x^2 - 4)$$
$$= 2y(x^2 + 4)(x + 2)(x - 2)$$

Self Check   Factor: $3a^4 - 3$.

Factoring Polynomials with Four Terms

EXAMPLE 5   Factor: $x^2 - y^2 + x - y$.

Solution   If we group the first two terms and factor the difference of two squares, we have

$$x^2 - y^2 + x - y = (x + y)(x - y) + (x - y)$$
$$= (x - y)(x + y + 1)$$

Self Check   Factor: $a^2 - b^2 + a + b$.

EXAMPLE 6   Factor: $x^2 + 6x + 9 - z^2$.

Solution   We group the first three terms together and factor the trinomial to get

$$x^2 + 6x + 9 - z^2 = (x + 3)(x + 3) - z^2$$
$$= (x + 3)^2 - z^2$$

We can now factor the difference of two squares to get

$$x^2 + 6x + 9 - z^2 = (x + 3 + z)(x + 3 - z)$$

Self Check   Factor: $a^2 + 4a + 4 - b^2$.

Factoring the Sum and Difference of Two Cubes

Recall that the sum and difference of two cubes factor as the product of a binomial and a trinomial.

Sum and Difference of Two Cubes	$x^3 + y^3 = (x + y)(x^2 - xy + y^2)$ $x^3 - y^3 = (x - y)(x^2 + xy + y^2)$

If we think of the sum of two cubes as the sum of the cube of a **F**irst quantity plus the cube of a **L**ast quantity, we have the formula

$$F^3 + L^3 = (F + L)(F^2 - FL + L^2)$$

*To factor the cube of a **F**irst quantity plus the cube of a **L**ast quantity, we multiply the sum of the **F**irst and **L**ast by*

- *the **F**irst squared*
- *minus the **F**irst times the **L**ast*
- *plus the **L**ast squared.*

The formula for the difference of two cubes is

$$F^3 - L^3 = (F - L)(F^2 + FL + L^2)$$

To factor the cube of a First quantity minus the cube of a Last quantity, we multiply the difference of the First and Last by

- *the First squared*
- *plus the First times the Last*
- *plus the Last squared.*

EXAMPLE 7   Factor: $a^3 + 8$.

Solution   Since $a^3 + 8$ can be written as $a^3 + 2^3$, we have the sum of two cubes, which factors as follows:

$$F^3 + L^3 = (F + L)(F^2 - FL + L^2)$$
$$a^3 + 2^3 = (a + 2)(a^2 - a2 + 2^2)$$
$$= (a + 2)(a^2 - 2a + 4)$$

Therefore, $a^3 + 8 = (a + 2)(a^2 - 2a + 4)$. We can check by multiplying.

$$(a + 2)(a^2 - 2a + 4) = a^3 - 2a^2 + 4a + 2a^2 - 4a + 8$$
$$= a^3 + 8$$

Self Check   Factor: $p^3 + 27$.

You should memorize the formulas for factoring the sum and the difference of two cubes. Note that each has the form

(a binomial)(a trinomial)

and that there is a relationship between the signs that appear in these forms.

$$F^3 + L^3 = (F + L)(F^2 - FL + L^2) \quad F^3 - L^3 = (F - L)(F^2 + FL + L^2)$$

To factor sums or differences of cubes, it is helpful to know these **perfect integer cubes:** 1, 8, 27, 64, 125, 216, 343, 512, 729, 1,000.

EXAMPLE 8   Factor: $27a^3 - 64b^3$.

Solution   Since $27a^3 - 64b^3$ can be written as $(3a)^3 - (4b)^3$, we have the difference of two cubes, which factors as follows:

$$F^3 \;-\; L^3 \;=\; (F \;-\; L)\,(F^2 \;+\; F \;\; L \;+\; L^2)$$

$$\downarrow \quad\quad \downarrow \quad\quad \downarrow \quad \downarrow \quad \downarrow \quad\quad \downarrow \quad \downarrow \quad\quad \downarrow$$

$$(3a)^3 - (4b)^3 = (3a - 4b)[(3a)^2 + (3a)(4b) + (4b)^2]$$

$$= (3a - 4b)(9a^2 + 12ab + 16b^2)$$

Thus, $27a^3 - 64b^3 = (3a - 4b)(9a^2 + 12ab + 16b^2)$.

Self Check   Factor: $8c^3 - 125d^3$.

EXAMPLE 9   Factor: $a^3 - (c + d)^3$.

Solution $$a^3 - (c + d)^3 = [a - (c + d)][a^2 + a(c + d) + (c + d)^2]$$

Now we simplify the expressions inside both sets of brackets.

$$a^3 - (c + d)^3 = (a - c - d)(a^2 + ac + ad + c^2 + 2cd + d^2)$$

Self Check   Factor: $(p + q)^3 - r^3$.

EXAMPLE 10   Factor: $x^6 - 64$.

Solution   This expression is both the difference of two squares and the difference of two cubes. It is easier to factor it as the difference of two squares first.

$$x^6 - 64 = (x^3)^2 - 8^2$$
$$= (x^3 + 8)(x^3 - 8)$$

Each of these factors can be factored further. One is the sum of two cubes and the other is the difference of two cubes:

$$x^6 - 64 = (x + 2)(x^2 - 2x + 4)(x - 2)(x^2 + 2x + 4)$$

Self Check   Factor: $x^6 - 1$.

EXAMPLE 11   Factor: $2a^5 + 250a^2$.

Solution   We first factor out the common monomial factor of $2a^2$ to obtain

$$2a^5 + 250a^2 = 2a^2(a^3 + 125)$$

Then we factor $a^3 + 125$ as the sum of two cubes to obtain

$$2a^5 + 250a^2 = 2a^2(a + 5)(a^2 - 5a + 25)$$

Self Check Factor: $3x^5 + 24x^2$.

Self Check Answers

1. $(9p + 5)(9p - 5)$ **2.** $(a^2 + 9)(a + 3)(a - 3)$
3. $[(a - b)^2 + c^2](a - b + c)(a - b - c)$ **4.** $3(a^2 + 1)(a + 1)(a - 1)$
5. $(a + b)(a - b + 1)$ **6.** $(a + 2 + b)(a + 2 - b)$ **7.** $(p + 3)(p^2 - 3p + 9)$
8. $(2c - 5d)(4c^2 + 10cd + 25d^2)$ **9.** $(p + q - r)(p^2 + 2pq + q^2 + pr + qr + r^2)$
10. $(x + 1)(x^2 - x + 1)(x - 1)(x^2 + x + 1)$ **11.** $3x^2(x + 2)(x^2 - 2x + 4)$

ORALS Factor each expression, if possible.

1. $x^2 - 1$

2. $4a^2 - 9b^2$

3. $a^3 + 8$

4. $b^3 - 27$

STUDY SET

VOCABULARY *Fill in the blanks.*

1. When the polynomial $4x^2 - 25$ is written as $(2x)^2 - (5)^2$, we see that it is the difference of two _____.

2. When the polynomial $8x^3 + 125$ is written as $(2x)^3 + (5)^3$, we see that it is the sum of two _____.

CONCEPTS

3. Write the first ten perfect integer squares.

4. Write the first ten perfect integer cubes.

5. a. Use multiplication to verify that the sum of two squares $x^2 + 25$ does not factor as $(x + 5)(x + 5)$.

   b. Use multiplication to verify that the difference of two squares $x^2 - 25$ factors as $(x + 5)(x - 5)$.

6. Explain the error.

   a. Factor: $4g^2 - 16 = (2g + 4)(2g - 4)$

   b. Factor: $1 - t^8 = (1 + t^4)(1 - t^4)$

7. When asked to factor $81t^2 - 16$, one student answered $(9t - 4)(9t + 4)$, and another answered $(9t + 4)(9t - 4)$. Explain why both students are correct.

8. Factor each polynomial.

   a. $5p^2 + 20$

   b. $5p^2 - 20$

   c. $5p^3 + 20$

   d. $5p^3 + 40$

Complete each factorization.

9. $p^2 - q^2 = (p + q)$

10. $36y^2 - 49m^2 = (\quad)^2 - (7m)^2$
$$= (6y \quad 7m)(6y - \quad)$$

11. $p^2q + pq^2 = \quad(p + q)$

12. $p^3 + q^3 = (p + q)$

13. $p^3 - q^3 = (p - q)$

14. $h^3 - 27k^3 = (h)^3 - (\quad)^3$
$$= (h \quad 3k)(h^2 + \quad + 9k^2)$$

15. Give an example of each.

   a. A difference of 2 squares.

   b. A square of a difference.

   c. A sum of two squares.

   d. A sum of two cubes.

   e. A cube of a sum.

16. Fill in the blanks.

   a. $x^2 - y^2 = (x \quad y)(x \quad y)$

   b. $x^3 + y^3 = (x \quad y)(x^2 \quad xy \quad y^2)$

   c. $x^3 - y^3 = (x \quad y)(x^2 \quad xy \quad y^2)$

PRACTICE Factor, if possible.

17. $x^2 - 4$

18. $y^2 - 9$

19. $9y^2 - 64$

20. $16x^4 - 81y^2$

21. $x^2 + 25$

22. $144a^2 - b^4$

23. $400 - c^2$

24. $900 - t^2$

25. $625a^2 - 169b^4$

26. $4y^2 + 9z^4$

27. $81a^4 - 49b^2$

28. $64r^6 - 121s^2$

29. $36x^4y^2 - 49z^4$

30. $4a^2b^4c^6 - 9d^8$

31. $(x + y)^2 - z^2$

32. $a^2 - (b - c)^2$

33. $(a - b)^2 - c^2$

34. $(m + n)^2 - p^4$

35. $x^4 - y^4$

36. $16a^4 - 81b^4$

37. $256x^4y^4 - z^8$

38. $225a^4 - 16b^8c^{12}$

39. $\dfrac{1}{36} - y^4$

40. $\dfrac{4}{81} - m^4$

41. $2x^2 - 288$

42. $8x^2 - 72$

43. $2x^3 - 32x$

44. $3x^3 - 243x$

45. $5x^3 - 125x$

46. $6x^4 - 216x^2$

47. $r^2s^2t^2 - t^2x^4y^2$

48. $16a^4b^3c^4 - 64a^2bc^6$

49. $a^2 - b^2 + a + b$

50. $x^2 - y^2 - x - y$

51. $a^2 - b^2 + 2a - 2b$

52. $m^2 - n^2 + 3m + 3n$

53. $2x + y + 4x^2 - y^2$

54. $m - 2n + m^2 - 4n^2$

55. $x^3 - xy^2 - 4x^2 + 4y^2$

56. $m^2n - 9n + 9m^2 - 81$

57. $x^2 + 4x + 4 - y^2$

58. $x^2 - 6x + 9 - 4y^2$

59. $x^2 + 2x + 1 - 9z^2$

60. $x^2 + 10x + 25 - 16z^2$

61. $c^2 - 4a^2 + 4ab - b^2$

62. $4c^2 - a^2 - 6ab - 9b^2$

63. $r^3 + s^3$

64. $t^3 - v^3$

65. $x^3 - 8y^3$

66. $27a^3 + b^3$

67. $64a^3 - 125b^6$

68. $8x^6 + 125y^3$

69. $125x^3y^6 + 216z^9$

70. $1{,}000a^6 - 343b^3c^6$

71. $x^6 + y^6$

72. $x^9 + y^9$

73. $5x^3 + 625$

74. $2x^3 - 128$

75. $4x^5 - 256x^2$

76. $2x^6 + 54x^3$

77. $128u^2v^3 - 2t^3u^2$

78. $56rs^2t^3 + 7rs^2v^6$

79. $(a + b)x^3 + 27(a + b)$

80. $(c - d)r^3 - (c - d)s^3$

81. $x^9 - y^{12}z^{15}$

82. $r^{12} + s^{18}t^{24}$

83. $(a + b)^3 + 27$

84. $(b - c)^3 - 1{,}000$

85. $y^3(y^2 - 1) - 27(y^2 - 1)$

86. $z^3(y^2 - 4) + 8(y^2 - 4)$

Factor each expression completely. Factor a difference of two squares first.

87. $x^6 - 1$

88. $x^6 - y^6$

89. $x^{12} - y^6$

90. $a^{12} - 64$

Factor each trinomial.

91. $a^4 - 13a^2 + 36$

92. $b^4 - 17b^2 + 16$

SOMETHING TO THINK ABOUT Factor. Assume all variables are natural numbers.

93. $4x^{2n} - 9y^{2n}$

94. $25 - x^{6n}$

95. $a^{3b} - c^{3b}$

96. $8 - x^{3n}$

97. $27x^{3n} + y^{3n}$

98. $a^{3b} + b^{3c}$

99. Factor: $x^{32} - y^{32}$.

100. Find the error in this proof that $2 = 1$.

$$x = y$$
$$x^2 = xy$$
$$x^2 - y^2 = xy - y^2$$
$$(x + y)(x - y) = y(x - y)$$
$$\frac{(x + y)(x - y)}{(x - y)} = \frac{y(x - y)}{x - y}$$
$$x + y = y$$
$$y + y = y$$
$$2y = y$$
$$\frac{2y}{y} = \frac{y}{y}$$
$$2 = 1$$

APPLICATIONS

101. CANDY To find the amount of chocolate used in the outer coating of the malted-milk ball shown in the illustration, we can find the volume V of the chocolate shell using the formula

$$V = \frac{4}{3}\pi r_1^3 - \frac{4}{3}\pi r_2^3$$

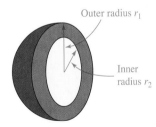

Outer radius r_1

Inner radius r_2

Factor the expression on the right-hand side of the formula.

102. MOVIE STUNTS The function that gives the distance a stuntwoman is above the ground t seconds after she falls over the side of a 144-foot tall building is $h(t) = 144 - 16t^2$. Factor the right-hand side.

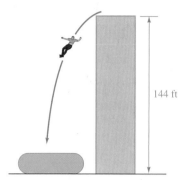

144 ft

WRITING

103. Describe the pattern used to factor the difference of two squares.

104. Describe the patterns used to factor the sum and the difference of two cubes.

REVIEW For each of the following purchases, determine the better buy.

105. Flute lessons: 45 minutes for $25 or 1 hour for $35.

106. Tissue paper: 15 sheets for $1.39 or a dozen sheets for $1.10.

SECTION 7.5

Review of Rational Expressions

Objectives

1. Simplify a rational expression.
2. Multiply and divide two rational expressions.
3. Add and subtract two rational expressions.
4. Simplify a complex fraction.

Getting Ready

Perform each operation.

1. $\dfrac{2}{3} \cdot \dfrac{5}{2}$
    2. $\dfrac{2}{3} \div \dfrac{5}{2}$
    3. $\dfrac{2}{3} + \dfrac{5}{2}$
    4. $\dfrac{2}{3} - \dfrac{5}{2}$

1 Simplify a rational expression.

Recall that a rational expression is an algebraic fraction with a polynomial numerator and a polynomial denominator. To manipulate rational expressions, we use the same rules as we use to simplify, multiply, divide, add, and subtract arithmetic fractions.

EXAMPLE 1 Simplify: $\dfrac{-8y^3z^5}{6y^4z^3}$.

Solution We factor the numerator and denominator and divide out all common factors:

$$\frac{-8y^3z^5}{6y^4z^3} = \frac{-2\cdot 4\cdot y\cdot y\cdot y\cdot z\cdot z\cdot z\cdot z\cdot z}{2\cdot 3\cdot y\cdot y\cdot y\cdot y\cdot z\cdot z\cdot z}$$

$$= -\frac{\overset{1}{\cancel{2}}\cdot 4\cdot \overset{1}{\cancel{y}}\cdot \overset{1}{\cancel{y}}\cdot \overset{1}{\cancel{y}}\cdot \overset{1}{\cancel{z}}\cdot \overset{1}{\cancel{z}}\cdot \overset{1}{\cancel{z}}\cdot z\cdot z}{\underset{1}{\cancel{2}}\cdot 3\cdot \underset{1}{\cancel{y}}\cdot \underset{1}{\cancel{y}}\cdot \underset{1}{\cancel{y}}\cdot y\cdot \underset{1}{\cancel{z}}\cdot \underset{1}{\cancel{z}}\cdot \underset{1}{\cancel{z}}}$$

$$= -\frac{4z^2}{3y}$$

SELF CHECK 1 Simplify: $\dfrac{10k}{25k^2}$.

The rational expressions in Example 1 and Self Check 1 can be simplified using the rules of exponents:

$$\frac{10k}{25k^2} = \frac{5\cdot 2}{5\cdot 5}k^{1-2} \qquad\qquad \frac{-8y^3z^5}{6y^4z^3} = \frac{-2\cdot 4}{2\cdot 3}y^{3-4}z^{5-3}$$

$$= \frac{2}{5}\cdot k^{-1} \qquad\qquad\qquad\quad = \frac{-4}{3}\cdot y^{-1}z^2$$

$$= \frac{2}{5k} \qquad\qquad\qquad\qquad\quad = -\frac{4}{3}\cdot \frac{1}{y}\cdot \frac{z^2}{1}$$

$$\qquad\qquad\qquad\qquad\qquad\qquad\qquad = -\frac{4z^2}{3y}$$

EXAMPLE 2 Simplify: $\dfrac{2x^2 + 11x + 12}{3x^2 + 11x - 4}$.

Solution We factor the numerator and denominator and divide out all common factors:

$$\frac{2x^2 + 11x + 12}{3x^2 + 11x - 4} = \frac{(2x + 3)\overset{1}{\cancel{(x+4)}}}{(3x - 1)\underset{1}{\cancel{(x+4)}}}$$

$$= \frac{2x + 3}{3x - 1} \qquad \frac{x+4}{x+4} = 1$$

COMMENT Do not divide out the x's in $\frac{2x + 3}{3x - 1}$. The x in the numerator is a factor of the first term only. It is not a factor of the entire numerator. Likewise, the x in the denominator is not a factor of the entire denominator.

SELF CHECK 2 Simplify: $\dfrac{2x^2 + 5x + 2}{3x^2 + 5x - 2}$.

EXAMPLE 3   Simplify: $\dfrac{3x^2 - 10xy - 8y^2}{4y^2 - xy}$.

Solution   We factor the numerator and denominator and proceed as follows:

$$\dfrac{3x^2 - 10xy - 8y^2}{4y^2 - xy} = \dfrac{(3x + 2y)\overset{-1}{\cancel{(x - 4y)}}}{y\underset{1}{\cancel{(4y - x)}}} \qquad \text{Because } x - 4y \text{ and } 4y - x \text{ are negatives,}$$
$$\text{their quotient is } -1.$$

$$= \dfrac{-(3x + 2y)}{y}$$

$$= \dfrac{-3x - 2y}{y}$$

⇨ **SELF CHECK 3**   Simplify: $\dfrac{-2a^2 - ab + 3b^2}{a^2 - ab}$.

2   **Multiply and divide two rational expressions.**

To multiply two rational expressions, we multiply the numerators and multiply the denominators.

EXAMPLE 4   Multiply: $\dfrac{x^2 - 6x + 9}{x} \cdot \dfrac{x^2}{x - 3}$.

Solution   We multiply the numerators and multiply the denominators and simplify the resulting fraction.

$$\dfrac{x^2 - 6x + 9}{x} \cdot \dfrac{x^2}{x - 3} = \dfrac{(x^2 - 6x + 9)(x^2)}{x(x - 3)} \qquad \text{Multiply the numerators and multiply the denominators.}$$

$$= \dfrac{(x - 3)(x - 3)xx}{x(x - 3)} \qquad \text{Factor the numerator and the denominator.}$$

$$= \dfrac{\overset{1}{\cancel{(x - 3)}}(x - 3)\overset{1}{x}x}{\underset{1}{x}\underset{1}{\cancel{(x - 3)}}} \qquad \text{Divide out common factors.}$$

$$= x(x - 3)$$

⇨ **SELF CHECK 4**   Multiply: $\dfrac{a^2 - 2a + 1}{a} \cdot \dfrac{a^3}{a - 1}$.

EXAMPLE 5   Multiply: $\dfrac{6x^2 + 5x - 4}{2x^2 + 5x + 3} \cdot \dfrac{8x^2 + 6x - 9}{12x^2 + 7x - 12}$.

Solution   We multiply the rational expressions, factor each polynomial, and simplify.

$$\frac{6x^2 + 5x - 4}{2x^2 + 5x + 3} \cdot \frac{8x^2 + 6x - 9}{12x^2 + 7x - 12}$$

$$= \frac{(6x^2 + 5x - 4)(8x^2 + 6x - 9)}{(2x^2 + 5x + 3)(12x^2 + 7x - 12)}$$ Multiply the numerators and multiply the denominators.

$$= \frac{(3x + 4)(2x - 1)(4x - 3)(2x + 3)}{(2x + 3)(x + 1)(3x + 4)(4x - 3)}$$ Factor the polynomials.

$$= \frac{(3x + 4)(2x - 1)\overset{1}{\cancel{(4x - 3)}}\overset{1}{\cancel{(2x + 3)}}}{\cancel{(2x + 3)}(x + 1)\cancel{(3x + 4)}\cancel{(4x - 3)}}$$ Divide out the common factors.

$$= \frac{2x - 1}{x + 1}$$

SELF CHECK 5 Multiply: $\dfrac{2x^2 + 5x + 3}{3x^2 + 5x + 2} \cdot \dfrac{2x^2 - 5x + 3}{4x^2 - 9}$.

In Examples 4 and 5, we would obtain the same answers if we factored first and divided out the common factors before we multiplied.

To divide two rational expressions, we invert the divisor and multiply.

EXAMPLE 6 Divide: $\dfrac{x^3 + 8}{x + 1} \div \dfrac{x^2 - 2x + 4}{2x^2 - 2}$.

Solution Using the rule for division of fractions, we invert the divisor and multiply.

$$\frac{x^3 + 8}{x + 1} \div \frac{x^2 - 2x + 4}{2x^2 - 2}$$

$$= \frac{x^3 + 8}{x + 1} \cdot \frac{2x^2 - 2}{x^2 - 2x + 4}$$

$$= \frac{(x^3 + 8)(2x^2 - 2)}{(x + 1)(x^2 - 2x + 4)}$$

$$= \frac{(x + 2)\overset{1}{\cancel{(x^2 - 2x + 4)}}2\overset{1}{\cancel{(x + 1)}}(x - 1)}{\cancel{(x + 1)}\cancel{(x^2 - 2x + 4)}}$$ $\begin{aligned} 2x^2 - 2 &= 2(x^2 - 1) \\ &= 2(x + 1)(x - 1) \end{aligned}$

$$= 2(x + 2)(x - 1)$$

SELF CHECK 6 Divide: $\dfrac{x^3 + 27}{x^2 - 4} \div \dfrac{x^2 - 3x + 9}{x + 2}$.

EXAMPLE 7 Simplify: $\dfrac{x^2 + 2x - 3}{6x^2 + 5x + 1} \div \dfrac{2x^2 - 2}{2x^2 - 5x - 3} \cdot \dfrac{6x^2 + 4x - 2}{x^2 - 2x - 3}$.

Solution We change the division to a multiplication by inverting the divisor. Since multiplications and divisions are done from left to right, only the middle rational expression should be inverted. Finally, we multiply the rational expressions, factor each polynomial, and divide out the common factors.

$$\frac{x^2 + 2x - 3}{6x^2 + 5x + 1} \div \frac{2x^2 - 2}{2x^2 - 5x - 3} \cdot \frac{6x^2 + 4x - 2}{x^2 - 2x - 3}$$

$$= \frac{x^2 + 2x - 3}{6x^2 + 5x + 1} \cdot \frac{2x^2 - 5x - 3}{2x^2 - 2} \cdot \frac{6x^2 + 4x - 2}{x^2 - 2x - 3}$$

$$= \frac{(x^2 + 2x - 3)(2x^2 - 5x - 3)(6x^2 + 4x - 2)}{(6x^2 + 5x + 1)(2x^2 - 2)(x^2 - 2x - 3)}$$

$$= \frac{(x + 3)\overset{1}{\cancel{(x - 1)}}\overset{1}{\cancel{(2x + 1)}}\overset{1}{\cancel{(x - 3)}}2(3x - 1)\overset{1}{\cancel{(x + 1)}}}{(3x + 1)\underset{1}{\cancel{(2x + 1)}}2(x + 1)\underset{1}{\cancel{(x - 1)}}\underset{1}{\cancel{(x - 3)}}\underset{1}{\cancel{(x + 1)}}}$$

$$= \frac{(x + 3)(3x - 1)}{(3x + 1)(x + 1)}$$

3 **Add and subtract two rational expressions.**

To add or subtract rational expressions with like denominators, we add or subtract the numerators and keep the same denominator. Whenever possible, we should simplify the result.

EXAMPLE 8 Simplify: $\dfrac{4x}{x + 2} + \dfrac{7x}{x + 2}$.

Solution $\dfrac{4x}{x + 2} + \dfrac{7x}{x + 2} = \dfrac{4x + 7x}{x + 2}$

$$= \dfrac{11x}{x + 2}$$

⇨ **SELF CHECK 8** Simplify: $\dfrac{4a}{a + 3} + \dfrac{2a}{a + 3}$.

To add or subtract rational expressions with unlike denominators, we must convert them to rational expressions with the same denominator.

EXAMPLE 9 Simplify: $\dfrac{4x}{x + 2} - \dfrac{7x}{x - 2}$.

Solution $\dfrac{4x}{x + 2} - \dfrac{7x}{x - 2} = \dfrac{4x(x - 2)}{(x + 2)(x - 2)} - \dfrac{(x + 2)7x}{(x + 2)(x - 2)}$ $\quad \frac{x - 2}{x - 2} = 1; \frac{x + 2}{x + 2} = 1$

COMMENT The − sign between the fractions in Step 1 applies to both terms of $7x^2 + 14x$.

$$= \dfrac{(4x^2 - 8x) - (7x^2 + 14x)}{(x + 2)(x - 2)}$$

Subtract the numerators and keep the common denominator.

$$= \frac{4x^2 - 8x - 7x^2 - 14x}{(x + 2)(x - 2)}$$

To remove parentheses, use the distributive property.

$$= \frac{-3x^2 - 22x}{(x + 2)(x - 2)}$$

Combine like terms.

▷ SELF CHECK 9 Simplify: $\dfrac{3a}{a + 3} - \dfrac{2a}{a - 3}$.

EXAMPLE 10 Add: $\dfrac{x}{x^2 - 2x + 1} + \dfrac{3}{x^2 - 1}$.

Solution We factor each denominator and find the LCD:

$$x^2 - 2x + 1 = (x - 1)(x - 1) = (x - 1)^2$$
$$x^2 - 1 = (x + 1)(x - 1)$$

We take the highest power of each factor to form the LCD of $(x - 1)^2(x + 1)$.

We now write each rational expression with its denominator in factored form and write each rational expression with an LCD of $(x - 1)^2(x + 1)$. Finally, we add them.

$$\frac{x}{x^2 - 2x + 1} + \frac{3}{x^2 - 1} = \frac{x}{(x - 1)(x - 1)} + \frac{3}{(x + 1)(x - 1)}$$

$$= \frac{x(x + 1)}{(x - 1)(x - 1)(x + 1)} + \frac{3(x - 1)}{(x + 1)(x - 1)(x - 1)}$$

$$= \frac{x^2 + x + 3x - 3}{(x - 1)(x - 1)(x + 1)}$$

$$= \frac{x^2 + 4x - 3}{(x - 1)^2(x + 1)}$$

This result does not simplify.

▷ SELF CHECK 10 Add: $\dfrac{3}{a^2 + a} + \dfrac{2}{a^2 - 1}$.

4 **Simplify a complex fraction.**

Recall that a *complex fraction* is a fraction with a rational expression in its numerator and/or its denominator. Examples of complex fractions are

$$\frac{\dfrac{3}{5}}{\dfrac{6}{7}}, \qquad \frac{\dfrac{x + 2}{3}}{x - 4}, \qquad \text{and} \qquad \frac{\dfrac{3x^2 - 2}{2x}}{3x - \dfrac{2}{y}}$$

We will discuss two methods for simplifying complex fractions.

EXAMPLE 11 Simplify: $\dfrac{\dfrac{3a}{b}}{\dfrac{6ac}{b^2}}$.

Solution   **Method 1:**   We write the complex fraction as a division and proceed as follows:

$$\frac{\dfrac{3a}{b}}{\dfrac{6ac}{b^2}} = \frac{3a}{b} \div \frac{6ac}{b^2}$$

$$= \frac{3a}{b} \cdot \frac{b^2}{6ac} \qquad \text{Invert the divisor and multiply.}$$

$$= \frac{b}{2c} \qquad \text{Multiply the fractions and simplify.}$$

Method 2:   We multiply the numerator and denominator by b^2, the LCD of $\frac{3a}{b}$ and $\frac{6ac}{b^2}$, and simplify:

$$\frac{\dfrac{3a}{b}}{\dfrac{6ac}{b^2}} = \frac{\dfrac{3a}{b} \cdot b^2}{\dfrac{6ac}{b^2} \cdot b^2} \qquad \frac{b^2}{b^2} = 1$$

$$= \frac{\dfrac{3ab^2}{b}}{\dfrac{6ab^2c}{b^2}}$$

$$= \frac{3ab}{6ac} \qquad \text{Simplify the fractions in the numerator and denominator.}$$

$$= \frac{b}{2c} \qquad \text{Divide out the common factor of } 3a.$$

⇨ **SELF CHECK 11**   Simplify: $\dfrac{\dfrac{2x}{y^2}}{\dfrac{6xz}{y}}$.

EXAMPLE 12   Simplify: $\dfrac{\dfrac{1}{x} + \dfrac{1}{y}}{\dfrac{1}{x} - \dfrac{1}{y}}$.

Solution   **Method 1:**   We add the rational expressions in the numerator and in the denominator and proceed as follows:

$$\frac{\dfrac{1}{x} + \dfrac{1}{y}}{\dfrac{1}{x} - \dfrac{1}{y}} = \frac{\dfrac{1y}{xy} + \dfrac{x1}{xy}}{\dfrac{1y}{xy} - \dfrac{x1}{xy}}$$

$$= \frac{\dfrac{y + x}{xy}}{\dfrac{y - x}{xy}}$$

Norbert Wiener
(1894–1964)

A child prodigy, Norbert Wiener received his PhD from Harvard University at the age of 19. As a professor of mathematics at MIT, Wiener analyzed the nature of information and communication, and created a new field called cybernetics. Without this study, modern computers would not exist.

$$= \frac{y + x}{xy} \div \frac{y - x}{xy}$$

$$= \frac{y + x}{xy} \cdot \frac{xy}{y - x}$$

$$= \frac{y + x}{y - x} \qquad \text{Multiply and then divide out the factors of } x \text{ and } y.$$

Method 2: We multiply the numerator and denominator by xy (the LCD of the rational expressions appearing in the complex fraction) and simplify.

$$\frac{\dfrac{1}{x} + \dfrac{1}{y}}{\dfrac{1}{x} - \dfrac{1}{y}} = \frac{xy\left(\dfrac{1}{x} + \dfrac{1}{y}\right)}{xy\left(\dfrac{1}{x} - \dfrac{1}{y}\right)} \qquad \frac{xy}{xy} = 1$$

$$= \frac{\dfrac{xy}{x} + \dfrac{xy}{y}}{\dfrac{xy}{x} - \dfrac{xy}{y}}$$

$$= \frac{y + x}{y - x} \qquad \text{Simplify the fractions.}$$

⇨ SELF CHECK 12 Simplify: $\dfrac{\dfrac{1}{x} - \dfrac{1}{y}}{\dfrac{1}{x} + \dfrac{1}{y}}$.

EXAMPLE 13 Simplify: $\dfrac{x^{-1} + y^{-1}}{x^{-2} - y^{-2}}$.

Solution **Method 1:** We proceed as follows:

$$\frac{x^{-1} + y^{-1}}{x^{-2} - y^{-2}} = \frac{\dfrac{1}{x} + \dfrac{1}{y}}{\dfrac{1}{x^2} - \dfrac{1}{y^2}} \qquad \text{Write the fraction without using negative exponents.}$$

$$= \frac{\dfrac{y}{xy} + \dfrac{x}{xy}}{\dfrac{y^2}{x^2y^2} - \dfrac{x^2}{x^2y^2}} \qquad \text{Get a common denominator in the numerator and denominator.}$$

$$= \frac{\dfrac{y + x}{xy}}{\dfrac{y^2 - x^2}{x^2y^2}} \qquad \text{Add the fractions in the numerator and denominator.}$$

$$= \frac{y + x}{xy} \div \frac{y^2 - x^2}{x^2y^2} \qquad \text{Write the complex fraction as a division.}$$

$$= \frac{y + x}{xy} \cdot \frac{xxyy}{(y - x)(y + x)} \qquad \text{Invert, multiply, and factor.}$$

$$= \frac{(y + x)xxyy}{xy(y - x)(y + x)} \qquad \begin{array}{l}\text{Multiply the numerators and the} \\ \text{denominators.}\end{array}$$

$$= \frac{xy}{y - x} \qquad \begin{array}{l}\text{Divide out the common factors of } x, y, \text{ and} \\ y + x \text{ in the numerator and denominator.}\end{array}$$

Method 2: We multiply both numerator and denominator by x^2y^2, the LCD of the rational expressions in the problem, and proceed as follows:

$$\frac{x^{-1} + y^{-1}}{x^{-2} - y^{-2}} = \frac{\dfrac{1}{x} + \dfrac{1}{y}}{\dfrac{1}{x^2} - \dfrac{1}{y^2}} \qquad \text{Write the fraction without negative exponents.}$$

$$= \frac{x^2y^2\left(\dfrac{1}{x} + \dfrac{1}{y}\right)}{x^2y^2\left(\dfrac{1}{x^2} - \dfrac{1}{y^2}\right)} \qquad \dfrac{x^2y^2}{x^2y^2} = 1$$

$$= \frac{xy^2 + x^2y}{y^2 - x^2} \qquad \begin{array}{l}\text{Use the distributive property to remove parentheses,} \\ \text{and simplify.}\end{array}$$

$$= \frac{xy(y + x)}{(y + x)(y - x)} \qquad \text{Factor the numerator and denominator.}$$

$$= \frac{xy}{y - x} \qquad \text{Divide out } y + x.$$

➡ **SELF CHECK 13**   Simplify: $\dfrac{x^{-1} - y^{-1}}{x^{-2}}$.

COMMENT $x^{-1} + y^{-1}$ means $\dfrac{1}{x} + \dfrac{1}{y}$, and $(x + y)^{-1}$ means $\dfrac{1}{x + y}$. Since $\dfrac{1}{x} + \dfrac{1}{y} \neq \dfrac{1}{x + y}$, it follows that

$$x^{-1} + y^{-1} \neq (x + y)^{-1}$$

EXAMPLE 14   Simplify: $\dfrac{\dfrac{2x}{1 - \dfrac{1}{x}} + 3}{3 - \dfrac{2}{x}}$.

Solution   We begin by multiplying the numerator and denominator of

$$\frac{2x}{1 - \dfrac{1}{x}}$$

by x. This will eliminate the complex fraction in the numerator of the given fraction.

$$\frac{\dfrac{2x}{1 - \dfrac{1}{x}} + 3}{3 - \dfrac{2}{x}} = \frac{\dfrac{x2x}{x\left(1 - \dfrac{1}{x}\right)} + 3}{3 - \dfrac{2}{x}} \qquad \frac{x}{x} = 1$$

$$= \frac{\dfrac{2x^2}{x - 1} + 3}{3 - \dfrac{2}{x}}$$

We then multiply the numerator and denominator of the previous complex fraction by $x(x - 1)$, the LCD of $\frac{2x^2}{x - 1}$, 3, and $\frac{2}{x}$, and simplify:

PERSPECTIVE

Each of the complex fractions in the list

$$1 + \frac{1}{2},\; 1 + \frac{1}{1 + \dfrac{1}{2}},\; 1 + \frac{1}{1 + \dfrac{1}{1 + \dfrac{1}{2}}},\; 1 + \frac{1}{1 + \dfrac{1}{1 + \dfrac{1}{1 + \dfrac{1}{2}}}},\; \ldots$$

can be simplified by using the value of the expression preceding it. For example, to simplify the second expression in the list, replace $1 + \frac{1}{2}$ with $\frac{3}{2}$.

$$1 + \frac{1}{1 + \dfrac{1}{2}} = 1 + \frac{1}{\dfrac{3}{2}} = 1 + \frac{2}{3} = \frac{5}{3}$$

To simplify the third expression, replace $1 + \dfrac{1}{1 + \dfrac{1}{2}}$ with $\frac{5}{3}$:

$$1 + \frac{1}{1 + \dfrac{1}{1 + \dfrac{1}{2}}} = 1 + \frac{1}{\dfrac{5}{3}} = 1 + \frac{3}{5} = \frac{8}{5}$$

Can you show that the expressions in the list simplify to the fractions $\frac{3}{2}, \frac{5}{3}, \frac{8}{5}, \frac{13}{8}, \frac{21}{13}, \frac{34}{21}, \ldots$?

Do you see a pattern, and can you predict the next fraction?

Use a calculator to write each of these fractions as a decimal. The values produced get closer and closer to the irrational number 1.61803398875 . . . , which is known as the **golden ratio**. This number often appears in the architecture of the ancient Greeks and Egyptians. The width of the stairs in front of the Greek Parthenon (Illustration 1), divided by the building's height, is the golden ratio. The height of the triangular face of the Great Pyramid of Cheops (Illustration 2), divided by the pyramid's width, is also the golden ratio.

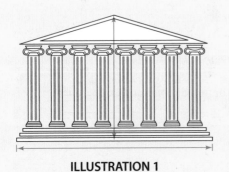

ILLUSTRATION 1

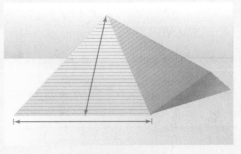

ILLUSTRATION 2

$$\frac{\dfrac{2x}{1 - \dfrac{1}{x}} + 3}{3 + \dfrac{2}{x}} = \frac{x(x - 1)\left(\dfrac{2x^2}{x - 1} + 3\right)}{x(x - 1)\left(3 + \dfrac{2}{x}\right)} \qquad \frac{x(x - 1)}{x(x - 1)} = 1$$

$$= \frac{2x^3 + 3x(x - 1)}{3x(x - 1) - 2(x - 1)}$$

$$= \frac{2x^3 + 3x^2 - 3x}{3x^2 - 5x + 2}$$

This result does not simplify.

▷ **SELF CHECK 14**   Simplify: $\dfrac{\dfrac{3}{1 - \dfrac{2}{x}} + 1}{2 - \dfrac{1}{x}}$.

▷ **SELF CHECK ANSWERS**

1. $\frac{2}{5k}$ **2.** $\frac{2x + 1}{3x - 1}$ **3.** $\frac{-2a - 3b}{a}$ **4.** $a^2(a - 1)$ **5.** $\frac{x - 1}{3x + 2}$ **6.** $\frac{x + 3}{x - 2}$ **8.** $\frac{6a}{a + 3}$ **9.** $\frac{a^2 - 15a}{(a + 3)(a - 3)}$

10. $\frac{5a - 3}{a(a + 1)(a - 1)}$ **11.** $\frac{1}{3yz}$ **12.** $\frac{y - x}{y + x}$ **13.** $\frac{xy - x^2}{y}$ **14.** $\frac{4x^2 - 2x}{2x^2 - 5x + 2}$

NOW TRY THIS

1. $5x(x - 2)^{-1} - 6(x + 3)^{-1}$

2. $8(x - 2)^{-2} - 30(x - 2)^{-1} + 7$

7.5 EXERCISES

Assume no division by 0.

WARM-UPS   *Simplify each fraction.*

1. $\dfrac{4}{6}$

2. $\dfrac{10}{15}$

3. $-\dfrac{25}{30}$

4. $-\dfrac{22}{55}$

5. $\dfrac{x^2}{xy}$

6. $\dfrac{2x - 4}{x - 2}$

7. $\dfrac{x - 2}{2 - x}$

8. $\dfrac{x^2 - 1}{x + 1}$

REVIEW

Graph each interval.

9. $(-\infty, -4) \cup [5, \infty)$

10. $(4, 8]$

Solve each formula for the indicated letter.

11. $P = 2l + 2w$ for w

12. $S = \dfrac{a - lr}{1 - r}$ for a

Solve each equation.

13. $a^4 - 13a^2 + 36 = 0$ **14.** $|2x - 1| = 9$

VOCABULARY AND CONCEPTS   *Fill in the blanks.*

15. $\dfrac{ax}{bx} = \underline{\quad}$ $(b, x \neq 0)$

16. $\dfrac{a}{b} \cdot \dfrac{c}{d} = \underline{\quad}$ $(b, d \neq 0)$

17. $\dfrac{a}{b} \div \dfrac{c}{d} = \underline{\quad}$ $(b, c, d \neq 0)$

18. $\dfrac{a}{b} + \dfrac{c}{b} = \underline{\qquad}$ $(b \neq 0)$

GUIDED PRACTICE

Simplify each rational expression. **See Example 1. (Objective 1)**

19. $\dfrac{12x^3}{3x}$

20. $-\dfrac{15a^2}{25a^3}$

21. $\dfrac{-24x^3y^4}{18x^4y^3}$

22. $\dfrac{15a^5b^4}{21b^3c^2}$

23. $\dfrac{9y^2(y - z)}{21y(y - z)^2}$

24. $\dfrac{-3ab^2(a - b)}{9ab(b - a)}$

25. $\dfrac{(a - b)(b - c)(c - d)}{(c - d)(b - c)(a - b)}$

26. $\dfrac{(p + q)(p - r)(r + s)}{(r - p)(s + r)(p + q)}$

Simplify each rational expression. **See Example 2. (Objective 1)**

27. $\dfrac{12 - 3x^2}{x^2 - x - 2}$

28. $\dfrac{x^2 + 2x - 15}{x^2 - 25}$

29. $\dfrac{x^3 + 8}{x^2 - 2x + 4}$

30. $\dfrac{x^2 + 3x + 9}{x^3 - 27}$

31. $\dfrac{x^2 + 2x + 1}{x^2 + 4x + 3}$

32. $\dfrac{6x^2 + x - 2}{8x^2 + 2x - 3}$

33. $\dfrac{4x^2 + 24x + 32}{16x^2 + 8x - 48}$

34. $\dfrac{a^2 - 4}{a^3 - 8}$

Simplify each rational expression. **See Example 3. (Objective 1)**

35. $\dfrac{x + y}{x^2 - y^2}$

36. $\dfrac{x - y}{x^2 - y^2}$

37. $\dfrac{3m - 6n}{3n - 6m}$

38. $\dfrac{ax + by + ay + bx}{a^2 - b^2}$

39. $\dfrac{3x^2 - 3y^2}{x^2 + 2y + 2x + yx}$

40. $\dfrac{x^2 + 2xy}{x + 2y + x^2 - 4y^2}$

41. $\dfrac{x - y}{x^3 - y^3 - x + y}$

42. $\dfrac{2x^2 + 2x - 12}{x^3 + 3x^2 - 4x - 12}$

Perform the operation and simplify. **See Examples 4–5. (Objective 2)**

43. $\dfrac{x^2y^2}{cd} \cdot \dfrac{c^{-2}d^2}{x}$

44. $\dfrac{a^{-2}b^2}{x^{-1}y} \cdot \dfrac{a^4b^4}{x^2y^3}$

45. $\dfrac{x^2 + 2x + 1}{x} \cdot \dfrac{x^2 - x}{x^2 - 1}$

46. $\dfrac{a + 6}{a^2 - 16} \cdot \dfrac{3a - 12}{3a + 18}$

47. $\dfrac{2x^2 - x - 3}{x^2 - 1} \cdot \dfrac{x^2 + x - 2}{2x^2 + x - 6}$

48. $\dfrac{9x^2 + 3x - 20}{3x^2 - 7x + 4} \cdot \dfrac{3x^2 - 5x + 2}{9x^2 + 18x + 5}$

49. $\dfrac{3t^2 - t - 2}{6t^2 - 5t - 6} \cdot \dfrac{4t^2 - 9}{2t^2 + 5t + 3}$

50. $\dfrac{2p^2 - 5p - 3}{p^2 - 9} \cdot \dfrac{2p^2 + 5p - 3}{2p^2 + 5p + 2}$

Perform the operation and simplify. **See Example 6. (Objective 2)**

51. $\dfrac{-x^2y^{-2}}{x^{-1}y^{-3}} \div \dfrac{x^{-3}y^2}{x^4y^{-1}}$

52. $\dfrac{(a^3)^2}{b^{-1}} \div \dfrac{(a^3)^{-2}}{b^{-1}}$

53. $\dfrac{x^2 - 16}{x^2 - 25} \div \dfrac{x + 4}{x - 5}$

54. $\dfrac{a^2 - 9}{a^2 - 49} \div \dfrac{a + 3}{a + 7}$

55. $\dfrac{a^2 + 2a - 35}{12x} \div \dfrac{ax - 3x}{a^2 + 4a - 21}$

56. $\dfrac{x^2 - 4}{2b - bx} \div \dfrac{x^2 + 4x + 4}{2b + bx}$

57. $(2x^2 - 15x + 25) \div \dfrac{2x^2 - 3x - 5}{x + 1}$

58. $(x^2 - 6x + 9) \div \dfrac{x^2 - 9}{x + 3}$

Perform the operations and simplify. **See Example 7. (Objective 2)**

59. $\dfrac{3x^2y^2}{6x^3y} \cdot \dfrac{-4x^7y^{-2}}{18x^{-2}y} \div \dfrac{36x}{18y^{-2}}$

60. $\dfrac{9ab^3}{7xy} \cdot \dfrac{14xy^2}{27z^3} \div \dfrac{18a^2b^2x}{3z^2}$

61. $(4x + 12) \cdot \dfrac{x^2}{2x - 6} \div \dfrac{2}{x - 3}$

62. $(4x^2 - 9) \div \dfrac{2x^2 + 5x + 3}{x + 2} \div (2x - 3)$

63. $\dfrac{2x^2 - 2x - 4}{x^2 + 2x - 8} \cdot \dfrac{3x^2 + 15x}{x + 1} \div \dfrac{4x^2 - 100}{x^2 - x - 20}$

64. $\dfrac{6a^2 - 7a - 3}{a^2 - 1} \div \dfrac{4a^2 - 12a + 9}{a^2 - 1} \cdot \dfrac{2a^2 - a - 3}{3a^2 - 2a - 1}$

65. $\dfrac{2x^2 + 5x - 3}{x^2 + 2x - 3} \div \left(\dfrac{x^2 + 2x - 35}{x^2 - 6x + 5} \div \dfrac{x^2 - 9x + 14}{2x^2 - 5x + 2} \right)$

66. $\dfrac{x^2 - 4}{x^2 - x - 6} \div \left(\dfrac{x^2 - x - 2}{x^2 - 8x + 15} \cdot \dfrac{x^2 - 3x - 10}{x^2 + 3x + 2} \right)$

Perform the operation(s) and simplify. **See Example 8. (Objective 3)**

67. $\dfrac{x}{x + 4} + \dfrac{5}{x + 4}$

68. $\dfrac{3x}{2x + 2} + \dfrac{x + 4}{2x + 2}$

69. $\dfrac{5x}{x+1} + \dfrac{3}{x+1} - \dfrac{2x}{x+1}$

70. $\dfrac{4}{a+4} - \dfrac{2a}{a+4} + \dfrac{3a}{a+4}$

71. $\dfrac{4y}{y-4} - \dfrac{16}{y-4}$

72. $\dfrac{3}{a+b} - \dfrac{a}{a+b}$

73. $\dfrac{3(x^2+x)}{x^2-5x+6} + \dfrac{-3(x^2-x)}{x^2-5x+6}$

74. $\dfrac{2x+4}{x^2+13x+12} - \dfrac{x+3}{x^2+13x+12}$

Perform the operation and simplify. See Example 9. (Objective 3)

75. $\dfrac{a+b}{3} + \dfrac{a-b}{7}$

76. $\dfrac{x-y}{2} + \dfrac{x+y}{3}$

77. $\dfrac{a}{2} + \dfrac{2a}{5}$

78. $\dfrac{b}{6} + \dfrac{3a}{4}$

79. $\dfrac{3}{4x} + \dfrac{2}{3x}$

80. $\dfrac{2}{5a} + \dfrac{3}{2b}$

81. $\dfrac{3}{x+2} + \dfrac{5}{x-4}$

82. $\dfrac{7}{x+3} + \dfrac{4x}{x+6}$

83. $x + \dfrac{1}{x}$

84. $2 - \dfrac{1}{x+1}$

85. $\dfrac{2}{a+4} - \dfrac{6}{a+3}$

86. $\dfrac{x+2}{x+5} - \dfrac{x-3}{x+7}$

Perform the operation(s) and simplify. See Example 10. (Objective 3)

87. $\dfrac{x}{x^2+5x+6} + \dfrac{x}{x^2-4}$

88. $\dfrac{x}{3x^2-2x-1} + \dfrac{4}{3x^2+10x+3}$

89. $\dfrac{8}{x^2-9} + \dfrac{2}{x-3} - \dfrac{6}{x}$

90. $\dfrac{x}{x^2-4} - \dfrac{x}{x+2} + \dfrac{2}{x}$

91. $1 + x - \dfrac{x}{x-5}$

92. $2 - x + \dfrac{3}{x-9}$

93. $\dfrac{3}{x+1} - \dfrac{2}{x-1} + \dfrac{x+3}{x^2-1}$

94. $\dfrac{2}{x-2} + \dfrac{3}{x+2} - \dfrac{x-1}{x^2-4}$

Simplify each complex fraction. See Example 11. (Objective 4)

95. $\dfrac{\dfrac{4x}{y}}{\dfrac{6xz}{y^2}}$

96. $\dfrac{\dfrac{5t^4}{9x}}{\dfrac{2t}{18x}}$

97. $\dfrac{\dfrac{x-y}{xy}}{\dfrac{y-x}{x}}$

98. $\dfrac{\dfrac{x^2+5x+6}{3xy}}{\dfrac{x^2-9}{6xy}}$

Simplify each complex fraction. See Example 12. (Objective 4)

99. $\dfrac{\dfrac{1}{a} + \dfrac{1}{b}}{\dfrac{1}{a}}$

100. $\dfrac{\dfrac{1}{b}}{\dfrac{1}{a} - \dfrac{1}{b}}$

101. $\dfrac{\dfrac{y}{x} - \dfrac{x}{y}}{\dfrac{1}{x} + \dfrac{1}{y}}$

102. $\dfrac{\dfrac{y}{x} - \dfrac{x}{y}}{\dfrac{1}{y} - \dfrac{1}{x}}$

103. $\dfrac{\dfrac{1}{a} - \dfrac{1}{b}}{\dfrac{a}{b} - \dfrac{b}{a}}$

104. $\dfrac{\dfrac{1}{a} + \dfrac{1}{b}}{\dfrac{a}{b} - \dfrac{b}{a}}$

105. $\dfrac{1 + \dfrac{6}{x} + \dfrac{8}{x^2}}{1 + \dfrac{1}{x} - \dfrac{12}{x^2}}$

106. $\dfrac{1 - x - \dfrac{2}{x}}{\dfrac{6}{x^2} + \dfrac{1}{x} - 1}$

Simplify each complex fraction. See Example 13. (Objective 4)

107. $\dfrac{x^{-1} + y^{-1}}{x^{-1} - y^{-1}}$

108. $\dfrac{(x+y)^{-1}}{x^{-1} + y^{-1}}$

109. $\dfrac{x - y^{-2}}{y - x^{-2}}$

110. $\dfrac{x^{-2} - y^{-2}}{x^{-1} - y^{-1}}$

Simplify each complex fraction. See Example 14. (Objective 4)

111. $\dfrac{1 + \dfrac{a}{b}}{1 - \dfrac{a}{1 - \frac{a}{b}}}$

112. $\dfrac{1 + \dfrac{2}{1 + \frac{a}{b}}}{1 - \dfrac{a}{b}}$

113. $a + \dfrac{a}{1 + \dfrac{a}{a+1}}$

114. $b + \dfrac{b}{1 - \dfrac{b+1}{b}}$

ADDITIONAL PRACTICE *Simplify each expression.*

115. $\dfrac{m^2 - n^2}{2x^2 + 3x - 2} \cdot \dfrac{2x^2 + 5x - 3}{n^2 - m^2}$

116. $\dfrac{x^2 - y^2}{2x^2 + 2xy + x + y} \cdot \dfrac{2x^2 - 5x - 3}{yx - 3y - x^2 + 3x}$

117. $\dfrac{ax + ay + bx + by}{x^3 - 27} \cdot \dfrac{x^2 + 3x + 9}{xc + xd + yc + yd}$

118. $\dfrac{x^2 + 3x + xy + 3y}{x^2 - 9} \cdot \dfrac{x - 3}{x + 3}$

119. $\dfrac{x^3 + y^3}{x^3 - y^3} \div \dfrac{x^2 - xy + y^2}{x^2 + xy + y^2}$

120. $\dfrac{x^2 - 6x + 9}{4 - x^2} \div \dfrac{x^2 - 9}{x^2 - 8x + 12}$

121. $\dfrac{2x^2 - 7x - 4}{20 - x - x^2} \div \dfrac{2x^2 - 9x - 5}{x^2 - 25}$

122. $\dfrac{2x^2 + 3xy + y^2}{y^2 - x^2} \div \dfrac{6x^2 + 5xy + y^2}{2x^2 - xy - y^2}$

123. $\dfrac{x^2 - x - 6}{x^2 - 4} \cdot \dfrac{x^2 - x - 2}{9 - x^2}$

124. $\dfrac{p^3 - q^3}{q^2 - p^2} \cdot \dfrac{q^2 + pq}{p^3 + p^2q + pq^2}$

125. $\dfrac{3n^2 + 5n - 2}{12n^2 - 13n + 3} \div \dfrac{n^2 + 3n + 2}{4n^2 + 5n - 6}$

126. $\dfrac{8y^2 - 14y - 15}{6y^2 - 11y - 10} \div \dfrac{4y^2 - 9y - 9}{3y^2 - 7y - 6}$

127. $\dfrac{x^2 - x - 12}{x^2 + x - 2} \div \dfrac{x^2 - 6x + 8}{x^2 - 3x - 10} \cdot \dfrac{x^2 - 3x + 2}{x^2 - 2x - 15}$

128. $\dfrac{4x^2 - 10x + 6}{x^4 - 3x^3} \div \dfrac{2x - 3}{2x^3} \cdot \dfrac{x - 3}{2x - 2}$

129. $\dfrac{x + 8}{x - 3} - \dfrac{x - 14}{3 - x}$ **130.** $\dfrac{3 - x}{2 - x} + \dfrac{x - 1}{x - 2}$

131. $\dfrac{x - 2}{x^2 - 3x} + \dfrac{2x - 1}{x^2 + 3x} - \dfrac{2}{x^2 - 9}$

132. $\dfrac{2}{x - 1} - \dfrac{2x}{x^2 - 1} - \dfrac{x}{x^2 + 2x + 1}$

133. $\dfrac{\dfrac{1}{a + 1} + 1}{\dfrac{3}{a - 1} + 1}$ **134.** $\dfrac{2 + \dfrac{3}{x + 1}}{\dfrac{1}{x} + x + x^2}$

135. $\dfrac{x + y}{x^{-1} + y^{-1}}$ **136.** $\dfrac{x - y}{x^{-1} - y^{-1}}$

WRITING ABOUT MATH

137. Explain how to simplify a rational expression.

138. Explain how to multiply two rational expressions.

139. Explain how to divide two rational expressions.

140. Explain how to add two rational expressions.

SOMETHING TO THINK ABOUT

141. A student compared his answer, $\dfrac{a - 3b}{2b - a}$, with the answer, $\dfrac{3b - a}{a - 2b}$, in the back of the text. Is the student's answer correct?

142. Another student shows this work:

$$\dfrac{3x^2 + 6}{3y} = \dfrac{\cancel{3}x^2 + \overset{2}{\cancel{6}}}{\cancel{3}y} = \dfrac{x^2 + 2}{y}$$

Is the student's work correct?

143. In which parts can you divide out the 4's?

a. $\dfrac{4x}{4y}$ **b.** $\dfrac{4x}{x + 4}$ **c.** $\dfrac{4 + x}{4 + y}$ **d.** $\dfrac{4x}{4 + 4y}$

144. In which parts can you divide out the 3's?

a. $\dfrac{3x + 3y}{3z}$ **b.** $\dfrac{3(x + y)}{3x + y}$ **c.** $\dfrac{x + 3}{3y}$ **d.** $\dfrac{3x + 3y}{3a - 3b}$

SECTION 7.6 Synthetic Division

Objectives

1 Divide a polynomial by a binomial of the form $x - r$ using synthetic division.

2 Apply the remainder theorem to evaluate a polynomial.

3 Apply the factor theorem to determine whether a specific value is a zero of a polynomial.

Vocabulary

synthetic division   remainder theorem   factor theorem

Getting Ready

Divide each polynomial P(x) by x − 2 and find P(2).

1. $P(x) = x^2 - x - 1$ **2.** $P(x) = x^2 + x + 3$

1 Divide a polynomial by a binomial of the form $x - r$ using synthetic division.

There is a shortcut method, called **synthetic division,** that we can use to divide a polynomial by a binomial of the form $x - r$. To see how it works, we consider the division of $4x^3 - 5x^2 - 11x + 20$ by $x - 2$.

$$
\begin{array}{r}
4x^2 + 3x - 5 \\
x - 2 \overline{) 4x^3 - 5x^2 - 11x + 20} \\
\underline{4x^3 - 8x^2} \\
3x^2 - 11x \\
\underline{3x^2 - 6x} \\
-5x + 20 \\
\underline{-5x + 10} \\
10 \quad \text{(remainder)}
\end{array}
\qquad
\begin{array}{r}
4 \quad 3 \quad -5 \\
1 - 2 \overline{) 4 - 5 - 11 \quad 20} \\
\underline{4 - 8} \\
3 - 11 \\
\underline{3 - 6} \\
-5 \quad 20 \\
\underline{-5 \quad 10} \\
10 \quad \text{(remainder)}
\end{array}
$$

On the left is the long division, and on the right is the same division with the variables and their exponents removed. The various powers of x can be remembered without actually writing them, because the exponents of the terms in the divisor, dividend, and quotient were written in descending order.

We can further shorten the version on the right. The numbers printed in red need not be written, because they are duplicates of the numbers above them. Thus, we can write the division in the following form:

$$
\begin{array}{r}
4 \quad 3 \quad -5 \\
1 - 2 \overline{) 4 - 5 - 11 \quad 20} \\
\underline{-8} \\
3 \\
\underline{-6} \\
-5 \\
\underline{10} \\
10
\end{array}
$$

We can shorten the process further by compressing the work vertically and eliminating the 1 (the coefficient of x in the divisor):

$$
\begin{array}{r}
4 \quad 3 \quad -5 \\
\hline
-2)\,4 - 5 - 11 \quad 20 \\
-8 \quad -6 \quad 10 \\
\hline
3 \quad -5 \quad 10
\end{array}
$$

If we write the 4 in the quotient on the bottom line, the bottom line gives the coefficients of the quotient and the remainder. If we eliminate the top line, the division appears as follows:

$$
\begin{array}{r}
-2|\ \ 4 \quad -5 \quad -11 \quad 20 \\
-8 \quad\ \ -6 \quad 10 \\
\hline
4 \quad\ \ 3 \quad\ \ -5 \quad 10
\end{array}
$$

The bottom line was obtained by subtracting the middle line from the top line. If we replace the -2 in the divisor with $+2$, the division process will reverse the signs of every entry in the middle line, and then the bottom line can be obtained by addition. This gives the final form of the synthetic division.

$$
\begin{array}{r}
+2|\ \ 4 \quad -5 \quad -11 \quad\ \ 20 \\
8 \quad\ \ 6 \quad -10 \\
\hline
4 \quad\ \ 3 \quad\ \ -5 \quad\ \ 10
\end{array}
$$

    The coefficients of the dividend

    The coefficients of the quotient and the remainder

Thus,

$$
\frac{4x^3 - 5x^2 - 11x + 20}{x - 2} = 4x^2 + 3x - 5 + \frac{10}{x - 2}
$$

EXAMPLE 1   Use synthetic division to divide $6x^2 + 5x - 2$ by $x - 5$ $(x \neq 5)$.

Solution   We write the coefficients in the dividend and the 5 in the divisor in the following form:

$$
\begin{array}{r}
5|\ \ 6 \quad 5 \quad -2 \\
\hline

\end{array}
$$

Then we follow these steps:

$$
\begin{array}{r}
5|\ \ 6 \quad 5 \quad -2 \\
\hline
6
\end{array}
$$
Begin by bringing down the 6.

$$
\begin{array}{r}
5|\ \ 6 \quad 5 \quad -2 \\
30 \\
\hline
6
\end{array}
$$
Multiply 5 by 6 to get 30.

$$
\begin{array}{r}
5|\ \ 6 \quad 5 \quad -2 \\
30 \\
\hline
6 \quad 35
\end{array}
$$
Add 5 and 30 to get 35.

$$
\begin{array}{r}
5|\ \ 6 \quad 5 \quad -2 \\
30 \quad 175 \\
\hline
6 \quad 35
\end{array}
$$
Multiply 35 by 5 to get 175.

$$
\begin{array}{r}
5|\ \ 6 \quad 5 \quad -2 \\
30 \quad 175 \\
\hline
6 \quad 35 \quad 173
\end{array}
$$
Add -2 and 175 to get 173.

The numbers 6 and 35 represent the quotient $6x + 35$, and 173 is the remainder. Thus,

$$\frac{6x^2 + 5x - 2}{x - 5} = 6x + 35 + \frac{173}{x - 5}$$

⇨ **SELF CHECK 1**   Use synthetic division to divide $6x^2 - 5x + 2$ by $x - 5$ $(x \neq 5)$.

EXAMPLE 2   Use synthetic division to divide $5x^3 + x^2 - 3$ by $x - 2$ $(x \neq 2)$.

Solution   We begin by writing

$$2\rfloor\ 5\quad 1\quad 0\quad -3$$

Write 0 for the coefficient of x, the missing term.

and complete the division as follows:

$$
\begin{array}{r}
2\rfloor\ 5\quad 1\quad 0\quad -3 \\
\underline{\quad 10\qquad\qquad} \\
5\quad 11
\end{array}
\qquad
\begin{array}{r}
2\rfloor\ 5\quad 1\quad 0\quad -3 \\
\underline{\quad 10\ \ 22\qquad} \\
5\quad 11\quad 22
\end{array}
\qquad
\begin{array}{r}
2\rfloor\ 5\quad 1\quad 0\quad -3 \\
\underline{\quad 10\ \ 22\ \ 44} \\
5\quad 11\quad 22\quad 41
\end{array}
$$

Thus,

$$\frac{5x^3 + x^2 - 3}{x - 2} = 5x^2 + 11x + 22 + \frac{41}{x - 2}$$

⇨ **SELF CHECK 2**   Use synthetic division to divide $5x^3 - x^2 + 3$ by $x - 2$ $(x \neq 2)$.

EXAMPLE 3   Use synthetic division to divide $5x^2 + 6x^3 + 2 - 4x$ by $x + 2$ $(x \neq -2)$.

Solution   First, we write the dividend with the exponents in descending order.

$$6x^3 + 5x^2 - 4x + 2$$

Then we write the divisor in $x - r$ form: $x - (-2)$. Using synthetic division, we begin by writing

$$-2\rfloor\ 6\quad\ \ 5\quad -4\quad\ \ 2$$

and complete the division.

$$
\begin{array}{r}
-2\rfloor\ 6\quad\ \ 5\quad -4\quad\ \ 2 \\
\underline{\quad\ -12\ \ \ 14\ \ -20} \\
6\quad -7\quad 10\quad -18
\end{array}
$$

Thus,

$$\frac{5x^2 + 6x^3 + 2 - 4x}{x + 2} = 6x^2 - 7x + 10 + \frac{-18}{x + 2}$$

⇨ **SELF CHECK 3**   Divide $2x - 4x^2 + 3x^3 - 3$ by $x + 1$.

2 Apply the remainder theorem to evaluate a polynomial

Synthetic division is important in mathematics because of the **remainder theorem.**

Remainder Theorem	If a polynomial $P(x)$ is divided by $x - r$, the remainder is $P(r)$.

We illustrate the remainder theorem in the next example.

EXAMPLE 4 Let $P(x) = 2x^3 - 3x^2 - 2x + 1$. Find
a. $P(3)$ **b.** the remainder when $P(x)$ is divided by $x - 3$.

Solution   **a.** $P(3) = 2(3)^3 - 3(3)^2 - 2(3) + 1$ Substitute 3 for x.

$= 2(27) - 3(9) - 6 + 1$

$= 54 - 27 - 6 + 1$

$= 22$

b. Use synthetic division to find the remainder when $P(x) = 2x^3 - 3x^2 - 2x + 1$ is divided by $x - 3$.

$$
\begin{array}{r|rrrr}
3 & 2 & -3 & -2 & 1 \\
  &   & 6 & 9 & 21 \\
\hline
  & 2 & 3 & 7 & 22
\end{array}
$$

The remainder is 22.

The results of parts **a** and **b** show that when $P(x)$ is divided by $x - 3$, the remainder is $P(3)$.

⇨ **SELF CHECK 4** Use the polynomial of Example 4 and find:
a. $P(2)$ **b.** the remainder when the polynomial is divided by $x - 2$.

COMMENT It is often easier to find $P(r)$ by using synthetic division than by substituting r for x in $P(x)$. This is especially true if r is a decimal.

3 Apply the factor theorem to determine whether a specific value is a zero of a polynomial.

Recall that if two quantities are multiplied, each is called a *factor* of the product. Thus, $x - 2$ is one factor of $6x - 12$, because $6(x - 2) = 6x - 12$. A theorem, called the **factor theorem,** tells us how to find one factor of a polynomial if the remainder of a certain division is 0.

Factor Theorem	If $P(x)$ is a polynomial in x, then $P(r) = 0$ if and only if $x - r$ is a factor of $P(x)$

If $P(x)$ is a polynomial in x and if $P(r) = 0$, r is a *zero* of the polynomial.

EXAMPLE 5 Let $P(x) = 3x^3 - 5x^2 + 3x - 10$. Show that
a. $P(2) = 0$ **b.** $x - 2$ is a factor of $P(x)$.

Solution **a.** We can use the remainder theorem to evaluate $P(2)$ by dividing
$P(x) = 3x^3 - 5x^2 + 3x - 10$ by $x - 2$.

$$
\begin{array}{r|rrrr}
2 & 3 & -5 & 3 & -10 \\
  &   & 6 & 2 & 10 \\
\hline
  & 3 & 1 & 5 & 0
\end{array}
$$

The remainder in this division is 0. By the remainder theorem, the remainder is $P(2)$.
Thus, $P(2) = 0$, and 2 is a zero of the polynomial.

b. Because the remainder is 0, the numbers 3, 1, and 5 in the synthetic division in
part **a** represent the quotient $3x^2 + x + 5$. Thus,

$$
\underbrace{(x - 2)}_{\text{Divisor}} \cdot \underbrace{(3x^2 + x + 5)}_{\text{quotient}} + \underbrace{0}_{\text{remainder}} = \underbrace{3x^3 - 5x^2 + 3x - 10}_{\text{the dividend, } P(x)}
$$

or

$$
(x - 2)(3x^2 + x + 5) = 3x^3 - 5x^2 + 3x - 10
$$

Thus, $x - 2$ is a factor of $P(x)$.

⇨ **SELF CHECK 5** Use the polynomial $P(x) = x^2 - 5x + 6$ to show that $P(2) = 0$ and that $x - 2$ is a factor of $P(x)$.

The result in Example 5 is true, because the remainder, $P(2)$, is 0. If the remainder had not been 0, then $x - 2$ would not have been a factor of $P(x)$.

ACCENT ON TECHNOLOGY

Approximating Zeros of Polynomials

We can use a graphing calculator to approximate the real zeros of a polynomial function $f(x)$. For example, to find the real zeros of $f(x) = 2x^3 - 6x^2 + 7x - 21$, we graph the function as in Figure 7-22.

It is clear from the figure that the function f has a zero at $x = 3$.

$$
\begin{aligned}
f(3) &= 2(3)^3 - 6(3)^2 + 7(3) - 21 \quad \text{Substitute 3 for } x. \\
&= 2(27) - 6(9) + 21 - 21 \\
&= 0
\end{aligned}
$$

From the factor theorem, we know that $x - 3$ is a factor of the polynomial. To find the other factor, we can synthetically divide by 3.

$$
\begin{array}{r|rrrr}
3 & 2 & -6 & 7 & -21 \\
  &   & 6 & 0 & 21 \\
\hline
  & 2 & 0 & 7 & 0
\end{array}
$$

Thus, $f(x) = (x - 3)(2x^2 + 7)$. Since $2x^2 + 7$ cannot be factored over the real numbers, we can conclude that 3 is the only real zero of the polynomial function.

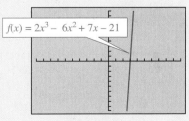

$f(x) = 2x^3 - 6x^2 + 7x - 21$

Figure 7-22

NOW TRY THIS

1. Given that $x + 2$ is a factor of $2x^3 - 3x^2 - 11x + 6$, find the remaining factors.

2. Solve $2x^3 - 3x^2 - 11x + 6 = 0$ without a calculator.

3. Find the x-intercepts for $f(x) = 2x^3 - 3x^2 - 11x + 6$.

7.6 EXERCISES

Assume no division by 0.

WARM-UPS

Find the remainder in each division.

1. $(x^2 + 2x + 1) \div (x - 2)$ **2.** $(x^2 - 4) \div (x + 1)$

Determine whether $x - 2$ is a factor of each polynomial.

3. $x^3 - 2x^2 + x - 2$ **4.** $x^3 + 4x^2 - 1$

REVIEW

Let $f(x) = 3x^2 + 2x - 1$ and find each value.

5. $f(1)$ **6.** $f(-2)$
7. $f(2a)$ **8.** $f(-t)$

Remove parentheses and simplify.

9. $2(x^2 + 4x - 1) + 3(2x^2 - 2x + 2)$
10. $-2(3y^3 - 2y + 7) - 3(y^2 + 2y - 4) + 4(y^3 + 2y - 1)$

VOCABULARY AND CONCEPTS

Fill in the blanks.

11. In order to use synthetic division, the divisor must be in the form _____.

12. If the leading term of the dividend is x^5 and the divisor is $x - r$, the leading term of the quotient will be ___.

13. The remainder theorem states that if a polynomial $P(x)$ is divided by $x - r$, the remainder is _____.

14. The factor theorem states that if $P(x)$ is a polynomial in x, then $P(r) = 0$ if and only if _____ is a factor of $P(x)$.

GUIDED PRACTICE

Use synthetic division to perform each division. **See Example 1.**
(Objective 1)

15. $(x^2 + x - 2) \div (x - 1)$
16. $(x^2 + x - 6) \div (x - 2)$
17. $(x^2 - 7x + 12) \div (x - 4)$
18. $(x^2 - 6x + 5) \div (x - 5)$
19. $(x^2 - 5x + 14) \div (x + 2)$
20. $(x^2 + 13x + 42) \div (x + 6)$
21. $(3x^3 - 10x^2 + 5x - 6) \div (x - 3)$
22. $(2x^3 - 9x^2 + 10x - 3) \div (x - 3)$

Use synthetic division to perform each division. **See Examples 2–3.**
(Objective 1)

23. $(2x^3 - 5x - 6) \div (x - 2)$
24. $(4x^3 + 5x^2 - 1) \div (x + 2)$
25. $(x^2 + 8 + 6x) \div (x + 4)$
26. $(x^2 - 15 - 2x) \div (x + 3)$
27. $(-6x^2 + 4x^3 + 2 - 5x) \div (x - 2)$
28. $(4 - 3x^2 + x) \div (x - 4)$
29. $(5x^2 + 6x^3 + 4) \div (x + 1)$
30. $(4x^2 + 3x^3 + 8) \div (x + 2)$

Let $P(x) = 2x^3 - 4x^2 + 2x - 1$. Evaluate $P(x)$ by substituting the given value of x into the polynomial and simplifying. Then evaluate the polynomial by using the remainder theorem and synthetic division. **See Example 4. (Objective 2)**

31. $P(-2)$ **32.** $P(-1)$
33. $P(3)$ **34.** $P(-4)$
35. $P(0)$ **36.** $P(4)$
37. $P(1)$ **38.** $P(2)$

Let $Q(x) = x^4 - 3x^3 + 2x^2 + x - 3$. Evaluate $Q(x)$ by substituting the given value of x into the polynomial and simplifying. Then evaluate the polynomial by using the remainder theorem and synthetic division. See Example 4. (Objective 2)

39. $Q(2)$ **40.** $Q(-2)$
41. $Q(3)$ **42.** $Q(0)$
43. $Q(-3)$ **44.** $Q(-4)$
45. $Q(-1)$ **46.** $Q(1)$

Use the factor theorem and determine whether the first expression is a factor of $P(x)$. See Example 5. (Objective 3)

47. $x - 3$; $P(x) = x^3 - 3x^2 + 5x - 15$
48. $x + 1$; $P(x) = x^3 + 2x^2 - 2x - 3$
  (*Hint:* Write $x + 1$ as $x - (-1)$.)
49. $x + 2$; $P(x) = 3x^2 - 7x + 4$
  (*Hint:* Write $x + 2$ as $x - (-2)$.)
50. x; $P(x) = 7x^3 - 5x^2 - 8x$ (*Hint:* $x = x - 0$.)

ADDITIONAL PRACTICE

Use the remainder theorem and synthetic division to find $P(r)$.

51. $P(x) = x^3 - 4x^2 + x - 2$; $r = 2$
52. $P(x) = x^3 - 3x^2 + x + 1$; $r = 1$
53. $P(x) = 2x^3 + x + 2$; $r = 3$
54. $P(x) = x^3 + x^2 + 1$; $r = -2$
55. $P(x) = x^4 - 2x^3 + x^2 - 3x + 2$; $r = -2$
56. $P(x) = x^5 + 3x^4 - x^2 + 1$; $r = -1$
57. $P(x) = 3x^5 + 1$; $r = -\dfrac{1}{2}$
58. $P(x) = 5x^7 - 7x^4 + x^2 + 1$; $r = 2$

Use a calculator and synthetic division to perform each division.

59. $(7.2x^2 - 2.1x + 0.5) \div (x - 0.2)$
60. $(8.1x^2 + 3.2x - 5.7) \div (x - 0.4)$
61. $(2.7x^2 + x - 5.2) \div (x + 1.7)$
62. $(1.3x^2 - 0.5x - 2.3) \div (x + 2.5)$
63. $(9x^3 - 25) \div (x + 57)$
64. $(0.5x^3 + x) \div (x - 2.3)$

Use a calculator to work each problem.

65. Find 2^6 by using synthetic division to evaluate the polynomial $P(x) = x^6$ at $x = 2$. Then check the answer by evaluating 2^6 with a calculator.
66. Find $(-3)^5$ by using synthetic division to evaluate the polynomial $P(x) = x^5$ at $x = -3$. Then check the answer by evaluating $(-3)^5$ with a calculator.

WRITING ABOUT MATH

67. If you are given $P(x)$, explain how to use synthetic division to calculate $P(a)$.
68. Explain the factor theorem.

SOMETHING TO THINK ABOUT   *Suppose that* $P(x) = x^{100} - x^{99} + x^{98} - x^{97} + \cdots + x^2 - x + 1.$

69. Find the remainder when $P(x)$ is divided by $x - 1$.
70. Find the remainder when $P(x)$ is divided by $x + 1$.

PROJECTS

Project 1

The expression $1 + x + x^2 + x^3$ is a polynomial of degree 3. The polynomial $1 + x + x^2 + x^3 + x^4$ has the same pattern, but one more term. Its degree is 4. As the pattern continues and more terms are added, the degree of the polynomial increases. If there were no end to the number of terms, the "polynomial" would have infinitely many terms, and no defined degree:

$$1 + x + x^2 + x^3 + x^4 + x^5 + x^6 + \cdots$$

Such "unending polynomials," called **power series,** are studied in calculus. However, this particular series is the result of a division of polynomials:

■ Consider the division $\dfrac{1}{1-x}$. Find the quotient by filling in more steps of this long division:

Step 1:
$$\begin{array}{r} 1 \\ 1 - x \overline{)1 + 0x + 0x^2 +} \\ \underline{1 - x} \\ x \end{array}$$

Step 2:
$$\begin{array}{r} 1 \\ 1 - x \overline{)1 + 0x + 0x^2 +} \\ \underline{1 - x} \\ x + 0x^2 \\ \underline{x - x^2} \\ x^2 \end{array}$$

To determine how the fraction $\dfrac{1}{1-x}$ and the series $1 + x + x^2 + x^3 + x^4 + x^5 + x^6 + \cdots$ could be equal, try this experiment.

- Let $x = \frac{1}{2}$ and evaluate $\frac{1}{1-x}$.

- Again, let $x = \frac{1}{2}$ and evaluate the series. Because you cannot add infinitely many numbers, just add the first 3 or 4 or 5 terms and see if you find a pattern. Use a calculator to complete this table:

Polynomial	Value at $x = \frac{1}{2}$
$1 + x + x^2$	
$1 + x + x^2 + x^3$	
$1 + x + x^2 + x^3 + x^4$	
$1 + x + x^2 + x^3 + x^4 + x^5$	
$1 + x + x^2 + x^3 + x^4 + x^5 + x^6$	

What number do the values in the second column seem to be approaching? That number is called the *sum* of the series.

- Explain why the nonterminating decimal 1.1111111 . . . represents the infinite series

$$1 + \left(\frac{1}{10}\right) + \left(\frac{1}{10}\right)^2 + \left(\frac{1}{10}\right)^3 + \left(\frac{1}{10}\right)^4 + \left(\frac{1}{10}\right)^5 + \left(\frac{1}{10}\right)^6 + \cdots$$

- Using the fraction $\frac{1}{1-x}$, explain why $1.11111 \ldots = \frac{10}{9}$.

- Verify that $\frac{10}{9} = 1.11111 \ldots$ by dividing 10 by 9.

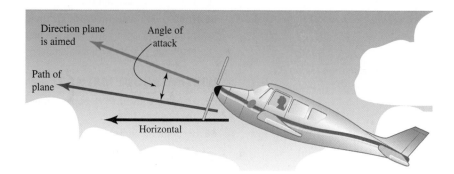

Project 2

We began this chapter by discussing *lift* provided by the wing of an airplane. We learned that two factors that determine lift are controlled by the pilot. One is the speed (or velocity) of the plane, and the other is the *angle of attack,* which is the angle between the direction the plane is aimed and the direction it is actually moving, as shown in the illustration.

For one particular plane weighing 2,050 pounds, the lift, velocity, and angle of attack are related by the equation

$$L = (0.017a + 0.023)V^2$$

where L is the lift in pounds, a is the angle of attack in degrees, and V is the velocity in feet per second. To support the plane, the lift must equal the plane's weight.

a. Find the correct angle of attack when the velocity of the plane is 88.64 mph. (*Hint:* You must change the velocity to units of feet per second.)

b. As the angle of attack approaches 17°, the plane begins to stall. With more cargo on the return trip, the same plane weighs 2,325 pounds. If the pilot allows the velocity to drop to 80 feet per second (about 55 mph), will the plane stall?

Chapter 7 REVIEW

SECTION 7.1 Review of Solving Linear Equations and Inequalities in One Variable

DEFINITIONS AND CONCEPTS	EXAMPLES
If a and b are real numbers and $a = b$, then $$a + c = b + c \qquad a - c = b - c$$ $$ac = bc \quad (c \neq 0) \qquad \frac{a}{c} = \frac{b}{c} \quad (c \neq 0)$$	If $a = b$, then $$a + 3 = b + 3 \qquad a - 5 = b - 5$$ $$4a = 4b \qquad \frac{a}{7} = \frac{b}{7}$$

Solving linear equations:

To solve a linear equation in one variable, follow these steps:

1. If the equation contains fractions, multiply both sides of the equation by a number that will eliminate the denominators.
2. Use the distributive property to remove all sets of parentheses and combine like terms.
3. Use the addition and subtraction properties to get all variables on one side of the equation and all numbers on the other side. Combine like terms, if necessary.
4. Use the multiplication and division properties to make the coefficient of the variable equal to 1.
5. Check the result.

To solve $\frac{x-2}{5} - x = \frac{8}{5} - x + 2$, we first eliminate the fractions by multiplying both sides by 5 and proceeding as follows:

$$5\left(\frac{x-2}{5} - x\right) = 5\left(\frac{8}{5} - x + 2\right)$$

$$x - 2 - 5x = 8 - 5x + 10 \qquad \text{Remove parentheses.}$$

$$-4x - 2 = 18 - 5x \qquad \text{Combine like terms.}$$

$$x = 20 \qquad \text{Add } 5x \text{ and } 2 \text{ to both sides.}$$

Show that 20 satisfies the equation.

An **identity** is an equation that is satisfied by every number x for which both sides of the equation are defined. The solution of an identity is the set of *all real numbers* and is denoted by $\mathbb{R}$.

Show that the equation is an identity.

$$-5(2x + 3) + 8x - 9 = 6x - 8(x + 3)$$

$$-10x - 15 + 8x - 9 = 6x - 8x - 24 \qquad \text{Remove parentheses.}$$

$$-2x - 24 = -2x - 24 \qquad \text{Combine like terms.}$$

Since the left side of the equation is the same as the right side, every number x will satisfy the equation. The equation is an identity and its solution set is all real numbers, $\mathbb{R}$.

A **contradiction** is an equation that has no solution. Its solution set is the **empty set, $\varnothing$**.

Show that the equation is a contradiction.

$$5(2x + 3) - 8x - 9 = 8x - 6(x + 3)$$

$$10x + 15 - 8x - 9 = 8x - 6x - 18 \qquad \text{Remove parentheses.}$$

$$2x + 6 = 2x - 18 \qquad \text{Combine like terms.}$$

$$6 = -18 \qquad \text{Subtract } 2x \text{ from both sides.}$$

Because $6 \neq -18$, there is no number that will satisfy the equation. Therefore, it is a contradiction and the solution set is the empty set, $\varnothing$.

To solve a formula for an indicated variable means to isolate that variable on one side of the equation.	To solve $ax + by = c$ for y, we proceed as follows: $ax + by = c$ $by = c - ax$ Subtract ax from both sides. $\dfrac{by}{b} = \dfrac{c - ax}{b}$ Divide both sides by b. $y = \dfrac{c - ax}{b}$ $\dfrac{b}{b} = 1$

Solving linear inequalities:

Trichotomy property:

$a < b$, $a = b$, or $a > b$

Either $x < 3$, $x = 3$, or $x > 3$.

Transitive properties:

If $a < b$ and $b < c$, then $a < c$.

If $a > b$ and $b > c$, then $a > c$.

If $-2 < 5$ and $5 < 10$, then $-2 < 10$.

If $20 > 7$ and $7 > -5$, then $20 > -5$.

Properties of inequality:

If a and b are real numbers and $a < b$, then

$a + c < b + c$

$a - c < b - c$

$ac < bc$ $(c > 0)$

$ac > bc$ $(c < 0)$

$\dfrac{a}{c} < \dfrac{b}{c}$ $(c > 0)$

$\dfrac{a}{c} > \dfrac{b}{c}$ $(c < 0)$

To solve the linear inequality $3(2x + 6) < 18$, use the same steps as for solving equations.

$$3(2x + 6) < 18$$
$$6x + 18 < 18 \qquad \text{Remove parentheses.}$$
$$6x < 0 \qquad \text{Subtract 18 from both sides.}$$
$$x < 0 \qquad \text{Divide both sides by 6.}$$

The solution set is $\{x \mid x < 0\}$ or, in interval notation, $(-\infty, 0)$. The graph is shown. The parenthesis at 0 indicates that 0 is not included in the solution set.

To solve $-4(3x - 4) \le -8$, proceed as follows:

$$-4(3x - 4) \le -8$$
$$-12x + 16 \le -8 \qquad \text{Remove parentheses.}$$
$$-12x \le -24 \qquad \text{Subtract 16 from both sides.}$$
$$x \ge 2 \qquad \text{Divide both sides by } -12 \text{ and reverse the inequality symbol.}$$

The solution set is $\{x \mid x \ge 2\}$ or, in interval notation, $[2, \infty)$. The graph is shown. The bracket at 2 indicates that 2 is included in the solution set.

Compound inequalities:

$c < x < d$ is equivalent to $c < x$ and $x < d$.

To solve the inequality $-7 \le 2x - 5 < 3$, isolate x between the inequality symbols.

$$-7 \le 2x - 5 < 3$$
$$-2 \le 2x < 8 \qquad \text{Add 5 to all three parts.}$$
$$-1 \le x < 4 \qquad \text{Divide all three parts by 2.}$$

The solution set is $\{x \mid -1 \le x < 4\}$ or, in interval notation, $[-1, 4)$. The graph is shown.

REVIEW EXERCISES
Solve and check each equation.

1. $4(y - 1) = 28$

2. $3(x + 7) = 42$

3. $13(x - 9) - 2 = 7x - 5$

4. $\dfrac{8(x - 5)}{3} = 2(x - 4)$

5. $2x + 4 = 2(x + 3) - 2$

6. $(3x - 2) - x = 2(x - 4)$

Solve for the indicated variable.

7. $V = \dfrac{1}{3}\pi r^2 h$ for h

8. $V = \dfrac{1}{6}ab(x + y)$ for x

9. Carpentry A carpenter wants to cut a 20-foot rafter so that one piece is 3 times as long as the other. Where should he cut the board?

10. Geometry A rectangle is 4 meters longer than it is wide. If the perimeter of the rectangle is 28 meters, find its area.

Solve each inequality. Give each solution set in interval notation and graph it.

11. $\dfrac{1}{3}y - 2 \geq \dfrac{1}{2}y + 2$

12. $\dfrac{7}{4}(x + 3) < \dfrac{3}{8}(x - 3)$

13. $3 < 3x + 4 < 10$

14. $4x > 3x + 2 > x - 3$

SECTION 7.2 Solving Equations in One Variable Containing Absolute Values

DEFINITIONS AND CONCEPTS	EXAMPLES
If $x \geq 0$, $\lvert x \rvert = x$. If $x < 0$, $\lvert x \rvert = -x$. If $k > 0$, $\lvert x \rvert = k$ is equivalent to $x = k$ or $x = -k$. 	$\lvert 4 \rvert = 4$ $\lvert -4 \rvert = -(-4) = 4$ To solve the equation $\lvert 2x - 3 \rvert = 1$, write $\lvert 2x - 3 \rvert = 1$ as $2x - 3 = 1 \quad$ or $\quad 2x - 3 = -1$ and solve each equation for x: $\begin{array}{c\|c} 2x - 3 = 1 & 2x - 3 = -1 \\ 2x = 4 & 2x = 2 \\ x = 2 & x = 1 \end{array}$ Verify that both solutions check.
$\lvert a \rvert = \lvert b \rvert$ is equivalent to $a = b$ or $a = -b$.	To solve the equation $\lvert 4x - 3 \rvert = \lvert 2x + 15 \rvert$, note that the equation is true when $4x - 3 = 2x + 15$ or when $4x - 3 = -(2x + 15)$. Then solve each equation for x. $\begin{array}{c\|c} 4x - 3 = 2x + 15 & 4x - 3 = -(2x + 15) \\ 4x = 2x + 18 & 4x - 3 = -2x - 15 \\ 2x = 18 & 6x = -12 \\ x = 9 & x = -2 \end{array}$ Verify that both solutions check.

REVIEW EXERCISES
Solve and check each equation.

15. $\lvert 3x + 1 \rvert = 10$

16. $\left\lvert \dfrac{3}{2}x - 4 \right\rvert = 9$

17. $\lvert 3x + 2 \rvert = \lvert 2x - 3 \rvert$

18. $\lvert 5x - 4 \rvert = \lvert 4x - 5 \rvert$

SECTION 7.3 Solving Inequalities in One Variable Containing an Absolute Value Term

DEFINITIONS AND CONCEPTS	EXAMPLES
If $k > 0$, $|x| < k$ is equivalent to $-k < x < k$.	To solve the inequality $|2x - 3| < 1$, note that $|2x - 3| < 1$ is equivalent to $-1 < 2x - 3 < 1$, an inequality that we can solve. $\quad -1 < 2x - 3 < 1$ $\quad\quad 2 < 2x < 4$ Add 3 to all three parts. $\quad\quad 1 < x < 2$ Divide all three parts by 2. The solution set contains all numbers between 1 and 2, not including either 1 or 2. This is the interval $(1, 2)$, whose graph is shown below.
$|x| > k$ is equivalent to $x < -k$ or $x > k$.	To solve the inequality $|5x - 5| > 15$, write the inequality as two separate inequalities and solve each one. Since $|5x - 5| > 15$ is equivalent to $\quad 5x - 5 < -15 \quad$ or $\quad 5x - 5 > 15$ we have $5x - 5 < -15 \quad$ or $\quad 5x - 5 > 15$ $\quad 5x < -10 \quad\quad\quad\quad 5x > 20$ Add 5 to both sides. $\quad\quad x < -2 \quad\quad\quad\quad\quad x > 4$ Divide both sides by 5. Thus, x is either less than -2 or greater than 4. $\quad x < -2 \quad$ or $\quad x > 4$ This is the union of two intervals $(-\infty, -2) \cup (4, \infty)$, whose graph appears below.

REVIEW EXERCISES
Solve each inequality. Give each solution in interval notation and graph it.

19. $|2x + 7| < 3$

20. $|3x - 8| \geq 4$

21. $\left| \dfrac{3}{2}x - 14 \right| \geq 0$

22. $\left| \dfrac{2}{3}x + 14 \right| < 0$

SECTION 7.4 Review of Factoring

DEFINITIONS AND CONCEPTS	EXAMPLES
GCF and factoring by grouping: Always factor out common factors as the first step in a factoring problem.	To factor $36x^3 - 6x^2 + 12x$, use the distributive property to factor out the greatest common factor of $6x$. $\quad 6x(6x^2 - x + 2)$ Factor the common term.

If an expression has four or more terms, try to factor the expression by grouping.	$25x^3 - 10x^2 + 20x - 8$ $= (25x^3 - 10x^2) + (20x - 8)$ Group the first two terms and the last two terms. $= 5x^2(5x - 2) + 4(5x - 2)$ Factor each grouping. $= (5x - 2)(5x^2 + 4)$ Factor out $5x - 2$.
Difference of two squares: $x^2 - y^2 = (x + y)(x - y)$	$64x^2 - 25$ $= (8x)^2 - (5)^2$ Write each factor as a perfect square. $= (8x + 5)(8x - 5)$ Factor.
Sum of two cubes: $x^3 + y^3 = (x + y)(x^2 - xy + y^2)$	$64x^3 + 125$ $= (4x)^3 + (5)^3$ Write each factor as a cube. $= (4x + 5)[(4x)^2 - (4x)(5) + (5)^2]$ Factor. $= (4x + 5)(16x^2 - 20x + 25)$ Simplify.
Difference of two cubes: $x^3 - y^3 = (x - y)(x^2 + xy + y^2)$	$27a^3 - 1$ $= (3a)^3 - (1)^3$ Write each factor as a cube. $= (3a - 1)[(3a)^2 + (3a)(1) + (1)^2]$ Factor. $= (3a - 1)(9a^2 + 3a + 1)$ Simplify.
Factoring a trinomial with a leading coefficient of 1: **1.** Write the trinomial in descending powers of one variable. **2.** List the factorizations of the third term of the trinomial. **3.** Pick the factorization in which the sum of the factors is the coefficient of the middle term.	To factor $x^2 - 8x + 12$, first note that the trinomial is written in descending powers of x. Then note that the factors of 12 are 1 and 12 -1 and -12 2 and 6 -2 and -6 3 and 4 -3 and -4 Since -2 and -6 are the only pair whose sum is -8, the factorization is $(x - 2)(x - 6)$.
Test for factorability: A trinomial of the form $ax^2 + bx + c$ $(a \neq 0)$ will factor with integer coefficients if $b^2 - 4ac$ is a perfect square.	To determine whether $5x^2 - 8x + 3$ is factorable with integer coefficients, note that $a = 5$, $b = -8$, and $c = 3$. Then calculate $b^2 - 4ac$. $b^2 - 4ac = (-8)^2 - 4(5)(3) = 64 - 60 = 4$ Since 4 is a perfect square, $5x^2 - 8x + 3$ is factorable with integer coefficients.

Factoring a trinomial with a leading coefficient other than 1:
 	
1. Write the trinomial in descending powers of one variable.
2. Factor out any greatest common factor (including -1 if that is necessary to make the coefficient of the first term positive).
3. Test the trinomial for factorability.
4. When the sign of the first term of a trinomial is $+$ and the sign of the third term is $+$, the signs between the terms of each binomial factor are the same as the sign of the middle term of the trinomial.
     When the sign of the first term is $+$ and the sign of the third term is $-$, the signs between the terms of the binomials are opposites.
	To factor $5x^2 - 8x + 3$, follow the steps shown on the left.
	
	1. The polynomial is already written in descending powers of x.
	
	2. In this polynomial, there are no common factors.
	
	3. We have previously seen that $5x^2 - 8x + 3$ is factorable.
	4. Since the last term is $+$ and the middle term $-$, the signs in both sets of parentheses will be $-$.
	
	     The factors of the first term $5x^2$ are 5 and 1.
	     The factors of the last term 3 are 3 and 1.

5. Try various combinations of first terms and last terms until you find the one that works.

5. The possible combinations are

$$(5x - 3)(x - 1) \quad \text{and} \quad (5x - 1)(x - 3)$$

6. Check the factorization by multiplication.

6. The pair that will give a middle term of $-8x$ is

$$(5x - 3)(x - 1)$$

REVIEW EXERCISES

Factor each polynomial.

23. $4x + 8$

24. $5x^2y^3 - 10xy^2$

25. $-8x^2y^3z^4 - 12x^4y^3z^2$

26. $12a^6b^4c^2 + 15a^2b^4c^6$

27. $xy + 2y + 4x + 8$

28. $ac + bc + 3a + 3b$

29. Factor x^n from $x^{2n} + x^n$.

30. Factor y^{2n} from $y^{2n} - y^{3n}$.

Factor each polynomial.

31. $x^4 + 4y + 4x^2 + x^2y$

32. $a^5 + b^2c + a^2c + a^3b^2$

33. $z^2 - 16$

34. $y^2 - 121$

35. $2x^4 - 98$

36. $3x^6 - 300x^2$

37. $y^2 + 21y + 20$

38. $z^2 - 11z + 30$

39. $-x^2 - 3x + 28$

40. $-y^2 + 5y + 24$

41. $y^3 + y^2 - 2y$

42. $2a^4 + 4a^3 - 6a^2$

43. $15x^2 - 57xy - 12y^2$

44. $30x^2 + 65xy + 10y^2$

45. $x^2 + 4x + 4 - 4p^4$

46. $y^2 + 3y + 2 + 2x + xy$

Factor each polynomial.

47. $x^3 + 343$

48. $a^3 - 125$

49. $8y^3 - 512$

50. $4x^3y + 108yz^3$

SECTION 7.5　Review of Rational Expressions

DEFINITIONS AND CONCEPTS	EXAMPLES

Simplifying a rational expression:
To simplify a rational expression, factor the numerator and denominator and divide out all factors common to the numerator and denominator.

$$\frac{ak}{bk} = \frac{a}{b} \quad (b \neq 0 \text{ and } k \neq 0)$$

To simplify $\dfrac{x^2 - 5x + 6}{x^2 - 9}$ ($x \neq 3, -3$), factor the numerator and the denominator and divide out any resulting common factors:

$$\frac{x^2 - 5x + 6}{x^2 - 9} = \frac{\overset{1}{\cancel{(x - 3)}}(x - 2)}{(x + 3)\underset{1}{\cancel{(x - 3)}}} = \frac{x - 2}{x + 3}$$

Multiplying rational expressions:
To multiply two rational expressions, follow the same procedure as multiplying two fractions.

$$\frac{a}{b} \cdot \frac{c}{d} = \frac{ac}{bd} \quad (b, d \neq 0)$$

Simplify the result, if possible.

$$\frac{a + 6}{(ax + 4a - 4x - 16)} \cdot \frac{3a - 12}{3a + 18}$$

$$= \frac{(a + 6)(3a - 12)}{(ax + 4a - 4x - 16)(3a + 18)} \quad \text{Multiply the numerators and multiply the denominators.}$$

$$= \frac{(a + 6)3(a - 4)}{(a - 4)(x + 4)3(a + 6)} \quad \text{Factor.}$$

$$= \frac{1}{x + 4} \quad \text{Divide all common factors.}$$

Dividing rational expressions:
To divide two rational expressions, follow the same procedure as dividing two fractions.

$$\frac{a}{b} \div \frac{c}{d} = \frac{a}{b} \cdot \frac{d}{c} \quad (b, d, c \neq 0)$$

Simplify the result, if possible.

$$\frac{x^2 - 4}{2b - bx} \div \frac{x^2 + 4x + 4}{2b + bx}$$

$$= \frac{x^2 - 4}{2b - bx} \cdot \frac{2b + bx}{x^2 + 4x + 4} \qquad \text{Multiply by the reciprocal of the second expression.}$$

$$= \frac{(x^2 - 4)(2b + bx)}{(2b - bx)(x^2 + 4x + 4)} \qquad \text{Multiply the numerators and multiply the denominators.}$$

$$= \frac{(x - 2)(x + 2)b(2 + x)}{b(2 - x)(x + 2)(x + 2)} \qquad \text{Factor.}$$

$$= \frac{x - 2}{2 - x} \qquad \text{Divide out all common factors.}$$

$$= -1 \qquad x - 2 \text{ and } 2 - x \text{ are opposites.}$$

Adding and subtracting rational expressions with the same denominator:
To add or subtract two rational expressions with like denominators, add the numerators and keep the denominator. Simplify, if possible.

$$\frac{a}{b} + \frac{c}{b} = \frac{a + c}{b} \quad (b \neq 0)$$

$$\frac{a}{b} - \frac{c}{b} = \frac{a - c}{b} \quad (b \neq 0)$$

$$\frac{2x + 4}{x^2 + 13x + 12} - \frac{x + 3}{x^2 + 13x + 12}$$

$$= \frac{2x + 4 - x - 3}{x^2 + 13x + 12} \qquad \text{Subtract the numerators and keep the common denominator.}$$

$$= \frac{x + 1}{x^2 + 13x + 12} \qquad \text{Combine like terms.}$$

$$= \frac{x + 1}{(x + 12)(x + 1)} \qquad \text{Factor the denominator.}$$

$$= \frac{1}{x + 12} \qquad \text{Divide out } x + 1.$$

Finding the LCD of two rational expressions:
To find the LCD of the denominators of two fractions, factor each denominator and use each factor the greatest number of times that it appears in any one denominator. The product of these factors is the LCD.

To find the LCD of $\frac{2a}{a^2 - 2a - 8}$ and $\frac{3}{a^2 - 5a + 4}$, factor each denominator to get

$$\frac{2a}{(a - 4)(a + 2)} \qquad \frac{3}{(a - 4)(a - 1)}$$

The LCD is $(a - 4)(a + 2)(a - 1)$.

Adding and subtracting rational expressions with different denominators.

To add or subtract two rational expressions with different denominators, find the LCD of the two expressions and write each fraction as an equivalent fraction with the new denominator. Add the numerators and keep the denominator. Simplify if possible.

$$\frac{2a}{a^2 - 2a - 8} + \frac{3}{a^2 - 5a + 4}$$

$$= \frac{2a}{(a - 4)(a + 2)} + \frac{3}{(a - 4)(a - 1)} \qquad \text{Factor each denominator.}$$

Write each fraction with the LCD of $(a - 4)(a + 2)(a - 1)$, found above.

$$= \frac{2a(a - 1)}{(a - 4)(a + 2)(a - 1)} + \frac{3(a + 2)}{(a - 4)(a - 1)(a + 2)}$$

$$= \frac{2a^2 - 2a}{(a - 4)(a + 2)(a - 1)} + \frac{3a + 6}{(a - 4)(a - 1)(a + 2)}$$

$$= \frac{2a^2 + a + 6}{(a - 4)(a + 2)(a - 1)}$$

This expression cannot be simplified.

REVIEW EXERCISES

Simplify each rational expression.

51. $\dfrac{248x^2y}{576xy^2}$

52. $\dfrac{x^2 - 49}{x^2 + 14x + 49}$

Perform the operations and simplify. Assume no division by 0.

53. $\dfrac{x^2 + 4x + 4}{x^2 - x - 6} \cdot \dfrac{x^2 - 9}{x^2 + 5x + 6}$

54. $\dfrac{x^3 - 64}{x^2 + 4x + 16} \div \dfrac{x^2 - 16}{x + 4}$

55. $\dfrac{5y}{x - y} - \dfrac{3}{x - y}$

56. $\dfrac{3x - 1}{x^2 + 2} + \dfrac{3(x - 2)}{x^2 + 2}$

57. $\dfrac{3}{x + 2} + \dfrac{2}{x + 3}$

58. $\dfrac{4x}{x - 4} - \dfrac{3}{x + 3}$

59. $\dfrac{x^2 + 3x + 2}{x^2 - x - 6} \cdot \dfrac{3x^2 - 3x}{x^2 - 3x - 4} \div \dfrac{x^2 + 3x + 2}{x^2 - 2x - 8}$

60. $\dfrac{x^2 - x - 6}{x^2 - 3x - 10} \div \dfrac{x^2 - x}{x^2 - 5x} \cdot \dfrac{x^2 - 4x + 3}{x^2 - 6x + 9}$

61. $\dfrac{2x}{x + 1} + \dfrac{3x}{x + 2} + \dfrac{4x}{x^2 + 3x + 2}$

62. $\dfrac{5x}{x - 3} + \dfrac{5}{x^2 - 5x + 6} + \dfrac{x + 3}{x - 2}$

63. $\dfrac{3(x + 2)}{x^2 - 1} - \dfrac{2}{x + 1} + \dfrac{4(x + 3)}{x^2 - 2x + 1}$

64. $\dfrac{x}{x^2 + 4x + 4} + \dfrac{2x}{x^2 - 4} - \dfrac{x^2 - 4}{x - 2}$

Simplify each complex fraction.

65. $\dfrac{\dfrac{3}{x} - \dfrac{2}{y}}{xy}$

66. $\dfrac{\dfrac{1}{x} + \dfrac{2}{y}}{\dfrac{2}{x} - \dfrac{1}{y}}$

67. $\dfrac{2x + 3 + \dfrac{1}{x}}{x + 2 + \dfrac{1}{x}}$

68. $\dfrac{x^{-1} - y^{-1}}{x^{-1} + y^{-1}}$

SECTION 7.6   Synthetic Division

DEFINITIONS AND CONCEPTS	EXAMPLES
Dividing a polynomial by a binomial of the form $x - r$ **using synthetic division:** Write the coefficients of the polynomial in the dividend and r in the divisor. Use multiplication and addition to complete the division.	Use synthetic division to perform the division $$(5x^2 - 8x - 2) \div (x - 2)$$ $$\begin{array}{r} 2 \rfloor\ 5 \quad -8 \quad -2 \\ \quad 10 \quad 4 \\ \hline 5 \quad \ \ 2 \quad \ \ 2 \end{array}$$ Thus, $(5x^2 - 8x - 2) \div (x - 2) = 5x + 2 + \dfrac{2}{x - 2}$.
Using the remainder theorem to evaluate a polynomial: **Remainder theorem:** If a polynomial $P(x)$ is divided by $x - r$, then the remainder is $P(r)$.	Given $P(x) = 8x^3 - 2x^2 - 9$, find $P(-2)$. $$\begin{array}{r} -2 \rfloor\ 8 \quad -2 \quad 0 \quad -9 \\ \quad -16 \quad 36 \quad -72 \\ \hline 8 \quad -18 \quad 36 \quad -81 \end{array}$$ Insert a 0 for the missing term. Thus, $P(-2) = -81$.
Using the factor theorem to determine if a binomial is a factor of a polynomial: **Factor theorem:** If $P(x)$ is divided by $x - r$, then $P(r) = 0$ if and only if $x - r$ is a factor of $P(x)$.	Determine whether $x + 4$ is a factor of $x^4 + 4x^3 + 9x^2 + 37x + 4$. $$\begin{array}{r} -4 \rfloor\ 1 \quad 4 \quad 9 \quad 37 \quad 4 \\ \quad -4 \quad 0 \quad -36 \quad -4 \\ \hline 1 \quad 0 \quad 9 \quad 1 \quad 0 \end{array}$$ Since the remainder is 0, $x + 4$ is a factor of $x^4 + 4x^3 + 9x^2 + 37x + 4$.

REVIEW EXERCISES
Use synthetic division to find the remainder in each division.
Assume no division by 0.

69. $x - 2\overline{)3x^3 + 2x^2 - 7x + 2}$

70. $x + 2\overline{)2x^3 - 4x^2 - 14x + 3}$

Use the factor theorem to decide whether the first expression is a factor of $P(x)$.

71. $x - 5$; $P(x) = x^3 - 3x^2 - 8x - 10$

72. $x + 5$; $P(x) = x^3 + 4x^2 - 5x + 5$
  (*Hint:* Write $x + 5$ as $x - (-5)$.)

Chapter 7   TEST

Solve each equation.

1. $9(x + 4) + 4 = 4(x - 5)$

2. $\dfrac{y - 1}{5} + 2 = \dfrac{2y - 3}{3}$

3. Solve $P = L + \dfrac{s}{f}i$ for i.

4. Solve $n = \dfrac{360}{180 - a}$ for a.

5. Cutting pipe   A 20-foot pipe is to be cut into three pieces. One piece is to be twice as long as another, and the third piece is to be six times as long as the shortest. Find the length of the longest piece.

6. Geometry   A rectangle with a perimeter of 26 centimeters is 5 centimeters longer than it is wide. Find its area.

Solve each equation or inequality.

7. $-2(2x + 3) \geq 14$

8. $-2 < \dfrac{x - 4}{3} < 4$

9. $|2x + 3| = 11$

10. $|3x + 4| = |x + 12|$

11. $|x + 3| \leq 4$

12. $|2x - 4| > 22$

Factor each polynomial.

13. $3xy^2 + 6x^2y$

14. $12a^3b^2c - 3a^2b^2c^2 + 6abc^3$

15. $ax - xy + ay - y^2$

16. $ax + ay + bx + by - cx - cy$

17. $x^2 - 49$

18. $2x^2 - 32$

19. $4y^4 - 64$

20. $b^3 + 125$

21. $b^3 - 27$

22. $3u^3 - 24$

23. $x^2 + 8x + 15$

24. $6b^2 + b - 2$

25. $6u^2 + 9u - 6$

26. $x^2 + 6x + 9 - y^2$

In Exercises 27–30, assume no division by 0.
Simplify each rational expression.

27. $\dfrac{-12x^2y^3z^2}{18x^3y^4z^2}$

28. $\dfrac{2x^2 + 7x + 3}{4x + 12}$

Perform the operations and simplify, if necessary. Write all answers without negative exponents.

29. $\dfrac{x^2y^{-2}}{x^3z^2} \cdot \dfrac{x^2z^4}{y^2z}$

30. $\dfrac{u^2 + 5u + 6}{u^2 - 4} \cdot \dfrac{u^2 - 5u + 6}{u^2 - 9}$

31. $\dfrac{x^3 + y^3}{4} \div \dfrac{x^2 - xy + y^2}{2x + 2y}$

32. $\dfrac{x + 2}{x + 1} - \dfrac{x + 1}{x + 2}$

Simplify each complex fraction.

33. $\dfrac{\dfrac{2u^2w^3}{v^2}}{\dfrac{4uw^4}{uv}}$

34. $\dfrac{\dfrac{x}{y} + \dfrac{1}{2}}{\dfrac{x}{2} - \dfrac{1}{y}}$

35. Find the remainder in the division.

$$\dfrac{x^3 - 4x^2 + 5x + 3}{x + 1}$$

36. Use synthetic division to find the remainder when $4x^3 + 3x^2 + 2x - 1$ is divided by $x - 2$.

Writing Equations of Lines, Functions, and Variation

In this chapter ▶

In this chapter, we will review how to graph linear equations and then consider the reverse problem of writing equations of lines with known graphs. In Sections 8.4 and 8.5, we will continue the discussion of functions, one of the most important concepts in mathematics. Finally, we will conclude by discussing variation.

© Shutterstock.com/Lisa F. Young

Careers and Mathematics

ATMOSPHERIC SCIENTISTS—WEATHER FORECASTERS

Atmospheric science is the study of the atmosphere—the blanket of air covering the Earth. Atmospheric scientists, often called *meteorologists,* study the atmosphere's physical characteristics, motions, and processes. The best-known application of this knowledge is in forecasting the weather.

Atmospheric scientists held about 8,800 jobs in 2006. A bachelor's degree in meteorology is usually the minimum educational requirement for an entry-level position in the field.

Job Outlook:
Employment of atmospheric scientists is projected to grow about 11% in the decade from 2006–2016. This is about as fast as the average for all occupations. Opportunities will be greater in private industry than in the federal government.

Annual Earnings:
$55,530–$96,490

For More Information:
http://www.bls.gov/oco/ocos051.htm

For a Sample Application:
See Exercise 82 in Section 8.2.

A Review of the Rectangular Coordinate System

1 Plot an ordered pair on a coordinate plane and identify the coordinates of a point on a coordinate plane.

2 Graph a linear equation in two variables by plotting points.

3 Graph a linear equation in two variables by using the intercepts.

4 Graph a horizontal line and a vertical line.

5 Find the midpoint of a line segment between two points.

quadrants	xy-plane	ordered pairs
x-axis	rectangular coordinate	x-coordinate
y-axis	system	y-coordinate
origin	coordinates of a point	midpoint

In the equation $2x + y = 5$, find y when x has the following values.

1 $x = 2$ **2.** $x = -2$ **3.** $x = 0$ **4.** $x = \dfrac{3}{2}$

1 **Plot an ordered pair on a coordinate plane and identify the coordinates of a point on a coordinate plane.**

René Descartes (1596–1650) is credited with the idea of associating ordered pairs of real numbers with points in the geometric plane. His idea is based on two perpendicular number lines, one horizontal and one vertical, that divide the plane into four **quadrants,** numbered as in Figure 8-1.

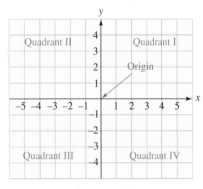

Figure 8-1

533

The horizontal number line is the **x-axis** and the vertical number line is the **y-axis.** The point where the axes intersect, called the **origin,** is the 0 point on each number line.

The positive direction on the x-axis is to the right, the positive direction on the y-axis is upward, and the unit distance on each axis is the same. This **xy-plane** is called a **rectangular coordinate system** or a *Cartesian coordinate system.*

To plot the point associated with the pair of real numbers $(2, 3)$, we start at the origin and count 2 units to the right and then 3 units up, as in Figure 8-2. The point P, which lies in the first quadrant, is the *graph* of the pair $(2, 3)$. The pair $(2, 3)$ gives the **coordinates** of point P.

To plot point Q with coordinates $(-4, 6)$, we start at the origin and count 4 units to the left and then 6 units up. Point Q lies in the second quadrant. Point R with coordinates $(6, -4)$ lies in the fourth quadrant.

COMMENT   The pairs $(-4, 6)$ and $(6, -4)$ represent different points. One is in the second quadrant, and one is in the fourth quadrant. Since order is important when graphing pairs of real numbers, such pairs are called **ordered pairs.**

In the ordered pair (a, b), a is called the **x-coordinate** and b is called the **y-coordinate.**

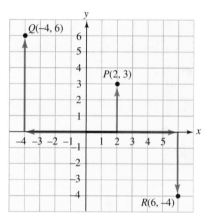

Figure 8-2

2   Graph a linear equation in two variables by plotting points.

The *graph of an equation* in the variables x and y is the set of all points on a rectangular coordinate system with coordinates (x, y) that satisfy the equation.

EXAMPLE 1   Graph the equation: $3x + 2y = 12$.

Solution   To graph an equation, we can pick values for either x or y, substitute them in the equation, and solve for the other variable. For example, if $x = 2$, then

$$3x + 2y = 12$$
$$3(2) + 2y = 12 \qquad \text{Substitute 2 for } x.$$
$$6 + 2y = 12 \qquad \text{Simplify.}$$
$$2y = 6 \qquad \text{Subtract 6 from both sides.}$$
$$y = 3 \qquad \text{Divide both sides by 2.}$$

One ordered pair that satisfies the equation is $(2, 3)$. If $y = 6$, we have

$$3x + 2y = 12$$
$$3x + 2(6) = 12 \quad \text{Substitute 6 for } y.$$
$$3x + 12 = 12 \quad \text{Simplify.}$$
$$3x = 0 \quad \text{Subtract 12 from both sides.}$$
$$x = 0 \quad \text{Divide both sides by 3.}$$

A second ordered pair that satisfies the equation is $(0, 6)$.

The pairs $(2, 3)$ and $(0, 6)$ and others that satisfy the equation are shown in the table in Figure 8-3. We plot each pair on a rectangular coordinate system and join the points to get the line shown in the figure. This line is the graph of the equation.

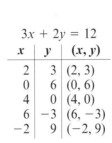

$3x + 2y = 12$

x	y	(x, y)
2	3	(2, 3)
0	6	(0, 6)
4	0	(4, 0)
6	−3	(6, −3)
−2	9	(−2, 9)

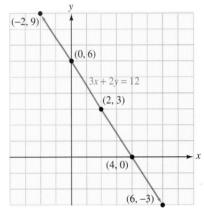

Figure 8-3

⇨ **SELF CHECK 1**   Graph $2x + 3y = 6$.

---

3   **Graph a linear equation in two variables by using the intercepts.**

Intercepts of a Line

The **y-intercept** of a line is the point $(0, b)$ where the line intersects the y-axis. To find b, substitute 0 for x in the equation of the line and solve for y.

The **x-intercept** of a line is the point $(a, 0)$ where the line intersects the x-axis. To find a, substitute 0 for y in the equation of a line and solve for x.

In Example 1, the y-intercept of the line is the point with coordinates of $(0, 6)$, and the x-intercept is the point with coordinates of $(4, 0)$.

EXAMPLE 2   Use the x- and y-intercepts to graph $2x + 5y = 10$.

Solution   To find the y-intercept we substitute 0 for x and solve for y.

$$2x + 5y = 10$$
$$2(0) + 5y = 10 \quad \text{Substitute 0 for } x.$$
$$5y = 10 \quad \text{Simplify.}$$
$$y = 2 \quad \text{Divide both sides by 5.}$$

The y-intercept is the point $(0, 2)$.

To find the x-intercept we substitute 0 for y and solve for x.

$$2x + 5y = 10$$
$$2x + 5(0) = 10 \qquad \text{Substitute 0 for } y.$$
$$2x = 10 \qquad \text{Simplify.}$$
$$x = 5 \qquad \text{Divide both sides by 2.}$$

The x-intercept is the point $(5, 0)$.

Although two points are sufficient to draw the line, it is a good idea to find and plot a third point as a check. To find the coordinates of a third point, we can substitute any convenient number (such as -5) for x and solve for y:

$$2x + 5y = 10$$
$$2(-5) + 5y = 10 \qquad \text{Substitute } -5 \text{ for } x.$$
$$-10 + 5y = 10 \qquad \text{Simplify.}$$
$$5y = 20 \qquad \text{Add 10 to both sides.}$$
$$y = 4 \qquad \text{Divide both sides by 5.}$$

The line will also pass through the point $(-5, 4)$. The graph is shown in Figure 8-4.

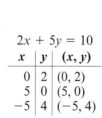

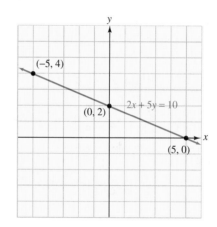

Figure 8-4

⇨ **SELF CHECK 2**   Graph $5x - 2y = 10$.

EXAMPLE 3   Graph $y = 3x + 4$.

Solution   We find the y- and x-intercepts. If $x = 0$, then

$$y = 3x + 4$$
$$y = 3(0) + 4 \qquad \text{Substitute 0 for } x.$$
$$y = 4 \qquad \text{Simplify.}$$

The y-intercept is the point $(0, 4)$.

If $y = 0$, then

$$y = 3x + 4$$

$$0 = 3x + 4 \quad \text{Substitute 0 for } y.$$

$$-4 = 3x \quad \text{Subtract 4 from both sides.}$$

$$-\frac{4}{3} = x \quad \text{Divide both sides by 3.}$$

The x-intercept is the point $\left(-\frac{4}{3}, 0\right)$.

To find the coordinates of a third point, we can substitute 1 for x and solve for y.

$$y = 3x + 4$$

$$y = 3(1) + 4 \quad \text{Substitute 1 for } x.$$

$$y = 7 \quad \text{Simplify.}$$

The point $(1, 7)$ lies on the graph, as shown in Figure 8-5.

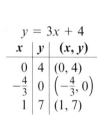

$$y = 3x + 4$$

x	y	(x, y)
0	4	$(0, 4)$
$-\frac{4}{3}$	0	$\left(-\frac{4}{3}, 0\right)$
1	7	$(1, 7)$

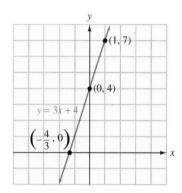

Figure 8-5

⇨ **SELF CHECK 3**   Graph $y = -2x + 3$.

---

4   **Graph a horizontal line and a vertical line.**

EXAMPLE 4   Graph: **a.** $y = 3$ **b.** $x = -2$.

Solution   **a.** Since the equation $y = 3$ does not contain x, the numbers chosen for x have no effect on y. The value of y is always 3.

After plotting the pairs (x, y) shown in Figure 8-6 on the next page and joining them with a straight line, we see that the graph is a horizontal line, parallel to the x-axis, with a y-intercept of $(0, 3)$. The line has no x-intercept.

b. Since the equation $x = -2$ does not contain y, the value of y can be any number. The value of x is always -2.

After plotting the pairs (x, y) shown in Figure 8-6 and joining them with a straight line, we see that the graph is a vertical line, parallel to the y-axis with an x-intercept of $(-2, 0)$. The line has no y-intercept.

$y = 3$		
x	y	(x, y)
-3	3	$(-3, 3)$
0	3	$(0, 3)$
2	3	$(2, 3)$
4	3	$(4, 3)$

$x = -2$		
x	y	(x, y)
-2	-2	$(-2, -2)$
-2	0	$(-2, 0)$
-2	2	$(-2, 2)$
-2	6	$(-2, 6)$

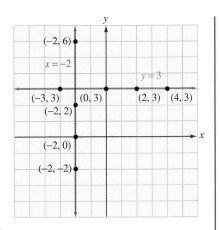

Figure 8-6

➡ **SELF CHECK 4**   Graph: **a.** $x = 4$ **b.** $y = -2$.

The results of Example 4 suggest the following facts.

Equations of Horizontal and Vertical Lines	If a and b are real numbers, then
	The graph of $y = b$ is a horizontal line with y-intercept at $(0, b)$. If $b = 0$, the line is the x-axis.
	The graph of $x = a$ is a vertical line with x-intercept at $(a, 0)$. If $a = 0$, the line is the y-axis.

5 **Find the midpoint of a line segment between two points.**

If point M in Figure 8-7 lies midway between points $P(x_1, y_1)$ and $Q(x_2, y_2)$, point M is called the **midpoint** of segment PQ. To find the coordinates of M, we average the x-coordinates and average the y-coordinates of P and Q.

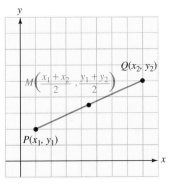

Figure 8-7

The Midpoint Formula	The midpoint of the line segment $P(x_1, y_1)$ and $Q(x_2, y_2)$ is the point M with coordinates of

$$\left(\frac{x_1 + x_2}{2}, \frac{y_1 + y_2}{2}\right)$$

EXAMPLE 5   Find the midpoint of the segment joining $(-2, 3)$ and $(3, -5)$.

Solution   To find the midpoint, we average the x-coordinates and the y-coordinates to get

$$\frac{x_1 + x_2}{2} = \frac{-2 + 3}{2} \qquad \text{and} \qquad \frac{y_1 + y_2}{2} = \frac{3 + (-5)}{2}$$

$$= \frac{1}{2} \qquad\qquad\qquad = -1$$

The midpoint of the segment is the point $\left(\frac{1}{2}, -1\right)$.

 SELF CHECK 5   Find the midpoint of $(5, -3)$ and $(-2, 5)$.

SELF CHECK ANSWERS

1.
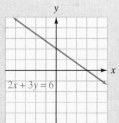
$2x + 3y = 6$

2.
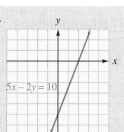
$5x - 2y = 10$

3.
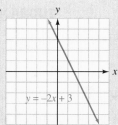
$y = -2x + 3$

4.
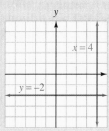
$x = 4$
$y = -2$

5. $\left(\frac{3}{2}, 1\right)$

NOW TRY THIS

1. Find the center of a circle with a diameter having endpoints at $(-5, 2)$ and $(-9, -7)$.

2. Find the midpoint of the segment joining
   a. $(p - 2, p)$ and $(4 - p, 5p - 2)$
   b. $(p + 5, 3p - 1)$ and $(6p, p + 9)$

8.1 EXERCISES

WARM-UPS

Find the x- and y-intercepts of each line.

1. $x + y = 3$

2. $3x + y = 6$

3. $x + 4y = 8$

4. $3x - 4y = 12$

Find the midpoint of a line segment with endpoints at

5. $(2, 4), (6, 8)$

6. $(4, -8), (-4, 6)$

REVIEW

Graph each interval on the number line.

7. $(-\infty, -2) \cup [2, \infty)$

8. $(-2, 4]$

Factor each expression completely.

9. $x^2 - x$

10. $x^2 - 1$

11. $x^3 - 1$

12. $x^4 - 1$

VOCABULARY AND CONCEPTS   *Fill in the blanks.*

13. The point where the x- and y-axes intersect is called the
_____.

14. The x-coordinate of a point is the first number in an
ordered _____.

15. The _____ of a point is the second number in an
ordered pair.

16. The y-intercept of a line is the point where the line intersects the _____.

17. The x-intercept of a line is the point where the line intersects the _____.

18. The graph of any equation of the form $x = a$, where a is a
constant, is a _____ line.

19. The graph of any equation of the form $y = b$, where b is a
constant, is a _____ line.

20. The midpoint of a segment with endpoints at (a, b) and
(c, d) has coordinates of _____.

GUIDED PRACTICE

Plot each point on the rectangular coordinate system. (Objective 1)

21. $A(4, 3)$

22. $B(-2, 1)$

23. $C(3, -2)$

24. $D(-2, -3)$

25. $E(0, 5)$

26. $F(-4, 0)$

27. $G(2, 0)$

28. $H(0, 3)$

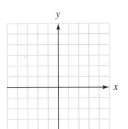

Give the coordinates of each point shown in the illustration.
(Objective 1)

29. A

30. B

31. C

32. D

33. E

34. F

35. G

36. H

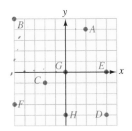

Graph each equation. See Examples 1–3. (Objective 2)

37. $x + y = 4$

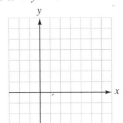

38. $x - y = 2$

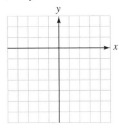

39. $2x - y = 3$

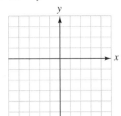

40. $x + 2y = 5$

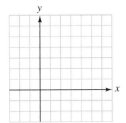

Graph each equation using x- and y-intercepts. **See Examples 2 and 3. (Objective 3)**

41. $3x + 4y = 12$

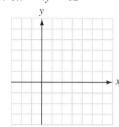

42. $4x - 3y = 12$

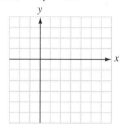

43. $y = -3x + 2$

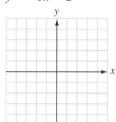

44. $y = 2x - 3$

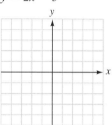

Graph each equation. **See Example 4. (Objective 4)**

45. $x = 3$

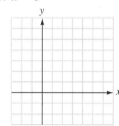

46. $y = -4$

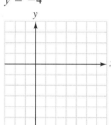

47. $-3y + 2 = 5$

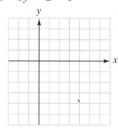

48. $-2x + 3 = 11$

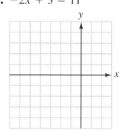

Find the midpoint of the segment joining the given points. **See Example 5. (Objective 5)**

49. $(0, 0), (6, 8)$

50. $(10, 12), (0, 0)$

51. $(6, 8), (12, 16)$

52. $(10, 4), (2, -2)$

53. $(2, 4), (5, 8)$

54. $(5, 9), (8, 13)$

55. $(-2, -8), (3, 4)$

56. $(-5, -2), (7, 3)$

ADDITIONAL PRACTICE

Graph each equation.

57. $3y = 6x - 9$

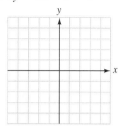

58. $2x = 4y - 10$

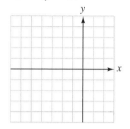

59. $3x + 4y - 8 = 0$

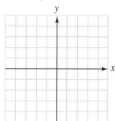

60. $-2y - 3x + 9 = 0$

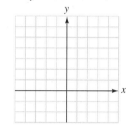

Find the midpoint of the segment joining the given points.

61. $(-3, 5), (-5, -5)$

62. $(2, -3), (4, -8)$

63. $(a, b), (4a, 3b)$

64. $(a + b, b), (-b, -a)$

65. $(a - b, b), (a + b, 3b)$

66. $(3a, a + b), (a + 2b, a - b)$

Find an endpoint if the midpoint and one endpoint of a segment are given.

67. If $M(-2, 3)$ is the midpoint of segment PQ and the coordinates of P are $(-8, 5)$, find the coordinates of Q.

68. If $M(6, -5)$ is the midpoint of segment PQ and the coordinates of Q are $(-5, -8)$, find the coordinates of P.

APPLICATIONS

69. House appreciation   A house purchased for $125,000 is expected to appreciate according to the formula $y = 7,500x + 125,000$, where y is the value of the house after x years. Find the value of the house 5 years later and 10 years later.

70. Car depreciation   A car purchased for $17,000 is expected to depreciate according to the formula $y = -1,360x + 17,000$. When will the car be worthless?

71. Demand equations   The number of television sets that consumers buy depends on price. The higher the price, the fewer people will buy. The equation that relates price to the number of TVs sold at that price is called a **demand equation.**

For a 25-inch TV, this equation is $p = -\frac{1}{10}q + 170$,

where p is the price and q is the number of TVs sold at that price. How many TVs will be sold at a price of $150?

72. Supply equations The number of TVs that manufacturers produce depends on price. The higher the price, the more TVs manufacturers will produce. The equation that relates price to the number of TVs produced at that price is called a **supply equation.**

For a 25-inch TV, the supply equation is $p = \frac{1}{10}q + 130$, where p is the price and q is the number of TVs produced for sale at that price. How many TVs will be produced if the price is $150?

73. Meshing gears The rotational speed V of a large gear (with N teeth) is related to the speed v of the smaller gear (with n teeth) by the equation $V = \frac{nv}{N}$. If the larger gear in the illustration is making 60 revolutions per minute, how fast is the smaller gear spinning?

74. Crime prevention The number n of incidents of family violence requiring police response appears to be related to d, the money spent on crisis intervention, by the equation

$$n = 430 - 0.005d$$

What expenditure would reduce the number of incidents to 350?

WRITING ABOUT MATH

75. Explain how to graph a line using the intercept method.

76. Explain how to determine in which quadrant the point (a, b) lies.

SOMETHING TO THINK ABOUT

77. If the line $y = ax + b$ passes through only quadrants I and II, what can be known about a and b?

78. What are the coordinates of the three points that divide the segment joining $P(a, b)$ and $Q(c, d)$ into four equal parts?

SECTION 8.2 Slope of a Line

Objectives

1. Find the slope of a line given a graph.
2. Find the slope of a line passing through two given points.
3. Find the slope of a line given its equation.
4. Identify the slope of a horizontal line and a vertical line.
5. Determine whether two lines are parallel, perpendicular, or neither.
6. Interpret slope in an application problem.

Vocabulary

slope	run	negative reciprocals
rise	perpendicular lines	parallel lines

Simplify each expression.

1. $\dfrac{6-3}{8-5}$ **2.** $\dfrac{10-4}{2-8}$ **3.** $\dfrac{25-12}{9-(-5)}$ **4.** $\dfrac{-9-(-6)}{-4-10}$

In Section 8.1, we graphed equations of lines. Later, we will show that we can graph a line if we know the coordinates of one point on the line and the slant (steepness) of the line. A measure of this slant is called the *slope* of the line.

1 **Find the slope of a line given a graph.**

A service offered by an online research company costs $2 per month plus $3 for each hour of connect time. The table in Figure 8-8(a) gives the cost y for certain numbers of hours x of connect time. If we construct a graph from these data, we get the line shown in Figure 8-8(b).

Grace Murray Hopper
(1906–1992)

Grace Hopper graduated from Vassar College in 1928 and obtained a Master's degree from Yale in 1930. In 1943, she entered the U.S. Naval Reserve. While in the Navy, she became a programmer of the Mark I, the world's first large computer. She is credited for first using the word "bug" to refer to a computer problem. The first bug was actually a moth that flew into one of the relays of the Mark II. From then on, locating computer problems was called "debugging" the system.

			Hours of connect time			
x	0	1	2	3	4	5
y	2	5	8	11	14	17
			Cost			

(a)

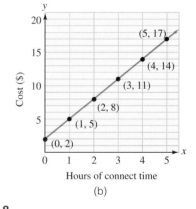

(b)

Figure 8-8

From the graph, we can see that if x changes from 0 to 1, y changes from 2 to 5. As x changes from 1 to 2, y changes from 5 to 8, and so on. The ratio of the change in y divided by the change in x is the constant 3.

$$\frac{\text{Change in } y}{\text{Change in } x} = \frac{5-2}{1-0} = \frac{8-5}{2-1} = \frac{11-8}{3-2} = \frac{14-11}{4-3} = \frac{17-14}{5-4} = \frac{3}{1} = 3$$

The ratio of the change in y divided by the change in x between any two points on any line is always a constant. This constant rate of change is called the **slope of the line.**

Slope of a Nonvertical Line	The slope m of the nonvertical line passing through points (x_1, y_1) and (x_2, y_2) is $$m = \frac{\text{change in } y}{\text{change in } x} = \frac{y_2 - y_1}{x_2 - x_1}$$

2 **Find the slope of a line passing through two given points.**

EXAMPLE 1 Use the two points shown in Figure 8-9 to find the slope of the line passing through the points with coordinates $(-2, 4)$ and $(3, -4)$.

Solution We can let $(x_1, y_1) = (-2, 4)$ and $(x_2, y_2) = (3, -4)$. Then

$$m = \frac{\text{change in } y}{\text{change in } x}$$

$$= \frac{y_2 - y_1}{x_2 - x_1}$$

$$= \frac{-4 - 4}{3 - (-2)} \qquad \text{Substitute } -4 \text{ for } y_2, \\ 4 \text{ for } y_1, 3 \text{ for } x_2, \text{ and} \\ -2 \text{ for } x_1.$$

$$= \frac{-8}{5}$$

$$= -\frac{8}{5}$$

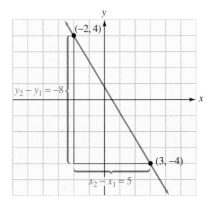

Figure 8-9

The slope of the line is $-\frac{8}{5}$. We would obtain the same result if we let $(x_1, y_1) = (3, -4)$ and $(x_2, y_2) = (-2, 4)$.

⇨ **SELF CHECK 1** Find the slope of the line joining the points $(-3, 6)$ and $(4, -8)$.

COMMENT When calculating slope, always subtract the y-values and the x-values in the same order.

$$m = \frac{y_2 - y_1}{x_2 - x_1} \qquad \text{or} \qquad m = \frac{y_1 - y_2}{x_1 - x_2}$$

However, the following are not true:

$$m = \frac{y_2 - y_1}{x_1 - x_2} \qquad \text{and} \qquad m = \frac{y_1 - y_2}{x_2 - x_1}$$

The change in y (often denoted as Δy) is the **rise** of the line between two points. The change in x (often denoted as Δx) is the **run.** Using this terminology, we can define slope to be the ratio of the rise to the run:

$$m = \frac{\Delta y}{\Delta x} = \frac{\text{rise}}{\text{run}} \qquad (\Delta x \neq 0)$$

3 Find the slope of a line given its equation.

To find the slope of a line from a given equation, we could graph the equation and count squares on the resulting line graph to determine the rise and the run. A better way is to find the x- and y-intercepts of the graph and use the slope formula.

EXAMPLE 2   Find the slope of the line determined by $3x - 4y = 12$.

Solution   We first find the coordinates of two points on the line.

- If $x = 0$, then $y = -3$, and the point $(0, -3)$ is on the line.
- If $y = 0$, then $x = 4$, and the point $(4, 0)$ is on the line.

We then refer to Figure 8-10 and find the slope of the line between $(0, -3)$ and $(4, 0)$ by substituting 0 for y_2, -3 for y_1, 4 for x_2, and 0 for x_1 in the formula for slope.

$$m = \frac{\Delta y}{\Delta x}$$

$$= \frac{y_2 - y_1}{x_2 - x_1}$$

$$= \frac{0 - (-3)}{4 - 0}$$

$$= \frac{3}{4}$$

The slope of the line is $\frac{3}{4}$.

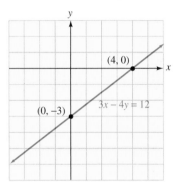

Figure 8-10

⇨ **SELF CHECK 2**   Find the slope of the line determined by $2x + 5y = 12$.

4 Identify the slope of a horizontal line and a vertical line.

If $P(x_1, y_1)$ and $Q(x_2, y_2)$ are points on the horizontal line shown in Figure 8-11(a) on the next page, then $y_1 = y_2$, and the numerator of the fraction

$$\frac{y_2 - y_1}{x_2 - x_1} \qquad \text{On a horizontal line, } x_2 \neq x_1.$$

is 0. Thus, the value of the fraction is 0, and the slope of the horizontal line is 0.

If $P(x_1, y_1)$ and $Q(x_2, y_2)$ are two points on the vertical line shown in Figure 8-11(b) on the next page, then $x_1 = x_2$, and the denominator of the fraction

$$\frac{y_2 - y_1}{x_2 - x_1} \qquad \text{On a vertical line, } y_2 \neq y_1.$$

is 0. Since the denominator cannot be 0, a vertical line has no defined slope.

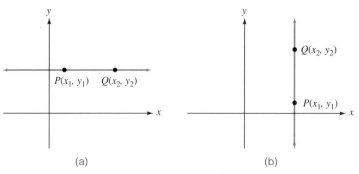

Figure 8-11

Slopes of Horizontal and Vertical Lines	All horizontal lines (lines with equations of the form $y = b$) have a slope of 0.
	All vertical lines (lines with equations of the form $x = a$) have no defined slope.

If a line rises as we follow it from left to right, as in Figure 8-12(a), its slope is positive. If a line drops as we follow it from left to right, as in Figure 8-12(b), its slope is negative. If a line is horizontal, as in Figure 8-12(c), its slope is 0. If a line is vertical, as in Figure 8-12(d), it has no defined slope.

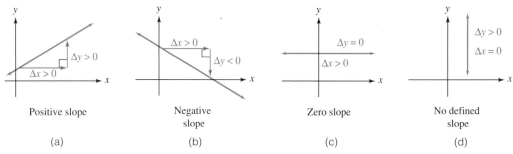

Figure 8-12

5 **Determine whether two lines are parallel, perpendicular, or neither.**

To see a relationship between parallel lines and their slopes, we refer to the parallel lines l_1 and l_2 shown in Figure 8-13, with slopes of m_1 and m_2, respectively. Because right triangles ABC and DEF are similar, it follows that

$$m_1 = \frac{\Delta y \text{ of } l_1}{\Delta x \text{ of } l_1}$$

$$= \frac{\Delta y \text{ of } l_2}{\Delta x \text{ of } l_2}$$

$$= m_2$$

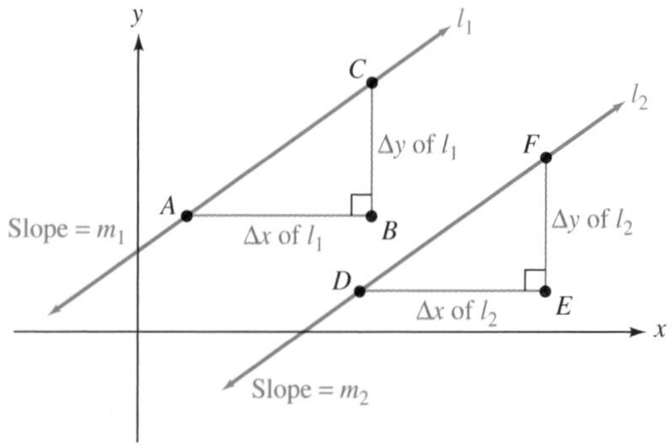

Figure 8-13

Thus, if two nonvertical lines are parallel, they have the same slope. It is also true that when two lines have the same slope, they are parallel.

Slopes of Parallel Lines   Nonvertical parallel lines have the same slope, and lines having the same slope are parallel.

Since vertical lines are parallel, lines with no defined slope are parallel.

EXAMPLE 3   The lines in Figure 8-14 are parallel. Find the slope of l_2.

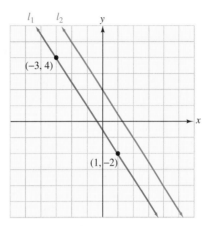

Figure 8-14

Solution   From the figure, we can find the slope of line l_1. Since the lines are parallel, they will have equal slopes. Therefore, the slope of line l_2 will be equal to the slope of line l_1. We can use the points with coordinates $(-3, 4)$ and $(1, -2)$ on line l_1 to find the slope of l_1 as follows:

$$m = \frac{y_2 - y_1}{x_2 - x_1}$$

$$= \frac{-2 - 4}{1 - (-3)} \quad \text{Substitute } -2 \text{ for } y_2, 4 \text{ for } y_1, 1 \text{ for } x_2, \text{ and } -3 \text{ for } x_1.$$

$$= \frac{-6}{4}$$

$$= -\frac{3}{2}$$

The slope of l_1 is $-\frac{3}{2}$ and because the lines are parallel, the slope of l_2 is also $-\frac{3}{2}$.

➡ SELF CHECK 3   Find the slope of any line parallel to a line with a slope of -3.

Two real numbers a and b are called **negative reciprocals** if $ab = -1$. For example,

$$-\frac{4}{3} \quad \text{and} \quad \frac{3}{4}$$

are negative reciprocals, because $-\frac{4}{3}\left(\frac{3}{4}\right) = -1$.

The following theorem relates perpendicular lines and their slopes.

Slopes of Perpendicular Lines	If two nonvertical lines are perpendicular, their slopes are negative reciprocals.
	If the slopes of two lines are negative reciprocals, the lines are perpendicular.

Because a horizontal line is perpendicular to a vertical line, a line with a slope of 0 is perpendicular to a line with no defined slope.

EXAMPLE 4   Are the lines shown in Figure 8-15 perpendicular?

Solution   We find the slopes of the lines and see whether they are negative reciprocals.

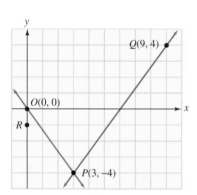

Slope of line $OP = \dfrac{\Delta y}{\Delta x}$

$= \dfrac{y_2 - y_1}{x_2 - x_1}$

$= \dfrac{-4 - 0}{3 - 0}$

$= -\dfrac{4}{3}$

Slope of line $PQ = \dfrac{\Delta y}{\Delta x}$

$= \dfrac{y_2 - y_1}{x_2 - x_1}$

$= \dfrac{4 - (-4)}{9 - 3}$

$= \dfrac{8}{6}$

$= \dfrac{4}{3}$

Figure 8-15   Since their slopes are not negative reciprocals, the lines are not perpendicular.

 **SELF CHECK 4**   In Figure 8-15, is line PR perpendicular to line PQ?

6   **Interpret slope in an application problem.**

Many applied problems involve equations of lines and their slopes.

EXAMPLE 5   **COST OF CARPET**   A store sells a carpet for $25 per square yard, plus a $20 delivery charge. The total cost c of n square yards is given by the following formula.

c	equals	cost per square yard	times	the number of square yards	plus	the delivery charge.
c	$=$	25	$\cdot$	n	$+$	20

Graph the equation $c = 25n + 20$ and interpret the slope of the line.

Solution   We can graph the equation on a coordinate system with a vertical c-axis and a horizontal n-axis. Figure 8-16 shows a table of ordered pairs and the graph.

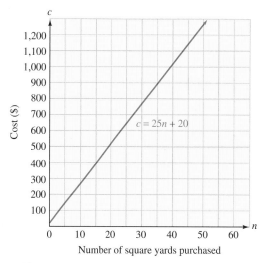

$$c = 25n + 20$$

n	c	(n, c)
10	270	(10, 270)
20	520	(20, 520)
30	770	(30, 770)
40	1,020	(40, 1,020)
50	1,270	(50, 1,270)

Figure 8-16

COMMENT Recall that any two points on a line can be used to find the slope. In this example, we chose (30, 770) and (50, 1,270), but we could have chosen any two points and obtained the same result.

If we choose the points (30, 770) and (50, 1,270) to find the slope, we have

$$m = \frac{\Delta c}{\Delta n}$$

$$= \frac{c_2 - c_1}{n_2 - n_1}$$

$$= \frac{1,270 - 770}{50 - 30} \qquad \text{Substitute 1,270 for } c_2, 770 \text{ for } c_1, 50 \text{ for } n_2, \text{ and } 30 \text{ for } n_1.$$

$$= \frac{500}{20}$$

$$= 25$$

The slope of 25 is the cost of the carpet in dollars per square yard.

⇨ **SELF CHECK 5**   Interpret the y-intercept of the graph in Figure 8-16.

EXAMPLE 6   **RATE OF DESCENT** It takes a skier 25 minutes to complete the course shown in Figure 8-17. Find his average rate of descent in feet per minute.

Solution   To find the average rate of descent, we must find the ratio of the change in altitude to the change in time. To find this ratio, we calculate the slope of the line passing through the points with coordinates (0, 12,000) and (25, 8,500).

$$\text{Average rate of descent} = \frac{12,000 - 8,500}{0 - 25}$$

$$= \frac{3,500}{-25}$$

$$= -140$$

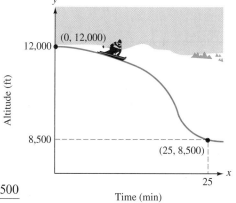

Figure 8-17

The slope is -140. Thus, the rate of change of descent is 140 ft/min.

⇨ **SELF CHECK 6**   Find the average rate of descent if the skier completes the course in 20 minutes.

EVERYDAY CONNECTIONS

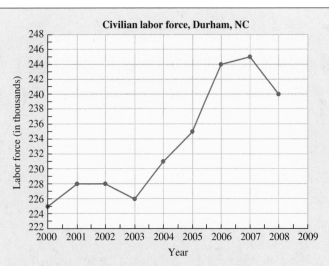

Civilian labor force, Durham, NC

Source: http://www.bls.gov/eag/eag.nc_durham_msa.htm

We can approximate the **rate of growth (or decrease)** of a quantity during a given time interval by calculating the slope of the line segment that connects the endpoints of the graph on the given interval.

Use the data from the graph to compute the rate of growth (or decrease) of the following:

1. labor force from 2002 to 2003.

2. labor force from 2005 to 2006.

3. During which 1-year interval was a positive rate of growth of the labor force the smallest?

⇨ **SELF CHECK ANSWERS**   **1.** -2 **2.** $-\frac{2}{5}$ **3.** -3 **4.** no   **5.** The y-coordinate of the y-intercept is the delivery charge.
6. 175 ft/min

NOW TRY THIS

Find the slope of a line

1. parallel to $3x - 2 = 0$

2. perpendicular to $6x = 4$

3. perpendicular to $5y + 4 = 0$

8.2 EXERCISES

WARM-UPS   *Find the slope of the line passing through*

1. $(0, 0), (1, 3)$ **2.** $(0, 0), (3, 6)$

3. Are lines with slopes of -2 and $-\frac{8}{4}$ parallel?

4. Find the negative reciprocal of -0.2.

5. Are lines with slopes of -2 and $\frac{1}{2}$ perpendicular?

REVIEW   *Simplify each expression. Write all answers without negative exponents. Assume no variable is zero.*

6. $(x^3y^2)^3$

7. $\left(\dfrac{x^5}{x^3}\right)^3$

8. $(x^{-3}y^2)^{-4}$

9. $\left(\dfrac{x^{-6}}{y^3}\right)^{-4}$

10. $\left(\dfrac{3x^2y^3}{8}\right)^0$

11. $\left(\dfrac{x^3x^{-7}y^{-6}}{x^4y^{-3}y^{-2}}\right)^{-2}$

VOCABULARY AND CONCEPTS   *Fill in the blanks.*

12. Slope is defined as the change in ___ divided by the change in ___.

13. A slope is a rate of _____.

14. The formula to compute slope is $m =$ _____.

15. The change in y (denoted as Δy) is the _____ of the line between two points.

16. The change in x (denoted as Δx) is the _____ of the line between two points.

17. The slope of a _____ line is 0.

18. The slope of a _____ line has no defined slope.

19. If a line rises as x increases, its slope is _____.

20. _____ lines have the same slope.

21. The slopes of nonvertical _____ lines are negative _____.

22. A line with no defined slope and a line with a slope of ___ are perpendicular.

GUIDED PRACTICE

Find the slope of the line that passes through the given points, if possible. See Example 1. (Objectives 1–2)

23.
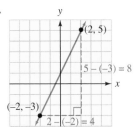

24.
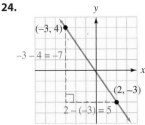

25. $(0, 0), (3, 9)$ **26.** $(9, 6), (0, 0)$

27. $(-1, 8), (6, 1)$ **28.** $(-5, -8), (3, 8)$

29. $(3, -1), (-6, 2)$ **30.** $(0, -8), (-5, 0)$

31. $(7, 5), (-9, 5)$ **32.** $(2, -8), (3, -8)$

33. $(-7, -5), (-7, -2)$ **34.** $(3, -5), (3, 14)$

Find the slope of the line determined by each equation. See Example 2. (Objective 3)

35. $3x + 2y = 12$ **36.** $2x - y = 6$

37. $3x = 4y - 2$ **38.** $x = y$

39. $y = \dfrac{x - 4}{2}$ **40.** $x = \dfrac{3 - y}{4}$

41. $4y = 3(y + 2)$ **42.** $x + y = \dfrac{2 - 3y}{3}$

Determine whether the slope of the line in each graph is positive, negative, 0, or not defined. (Objective 4)

43.
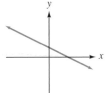

44.
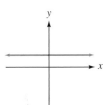

45.
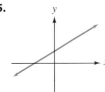

46.
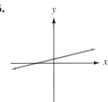

47.
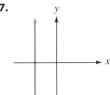

48.
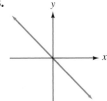

49.

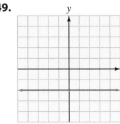

50.

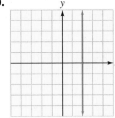

Determine whether the lines with the given slopes are parallel, perpendicular, or neither. See Examples 3–4. (Objective 5)

51. $m_1 = 3, m_2 = -\dfrac{1}{3}$

52. $m_1 = \dfrac{1}{4}, m_2 = 4$

53. $m_1 = 4, m_2 = 0.25$

54. $m_1 = -5, m_2 = \dfrac{1}{-0.2}$

Determine whether the line PQ is parallel or perpendicular or neither parallel nor perpendicular to a line with a slope of −2. See Examples 3–4. (Objective 5)

55. $P(3, 4), Q(4, 2)$

56. $P(6, 4), Q(8, 5)$

57. $P(-2, 1), Q(6, 5)$

58. $P(3, 4), Q(-3, -5)$

ADDITIONAL PRACTICE

59. Are the lines passing through the points $(2.5, 3.7), (3.7, 2.5)$ and $(1.7, -2.3), (2.3, -1.7)$ parallel, perpendicular, or neither parallel nor perpendicular?

60. Are the lines with slopes $m_1 = \dfrac{5.5}{2.7}$ and $m_2 = \left(\dfrac{2.7}{5.5}\right)^{-1}$ parallel, perpendicular, or neither parallel nor perpendicular ?

61. Are the lines with slopes $m_1 = \dfrac{3.2}{-9.1}$ and $m_2 = \dfrac{-9.1}{3.2}$ parallel, perpendicular, or neither parallel nor perpendicular?

62. Is the line passing through the points $P(5, 4)$ and $Q(6, 6)$ parallel, perpendicular, or neither parallel nor perpendicular to a line with a slope of -2?

63. Is the line passing through the points $P(-2, 3)$ and $Q(4, -9)$ parallel, perpendicular, or neither parallel nor perpendicular to a line with a slope of -2?

Find the slopes of lines PQ and PR and tell whether the points P, Q, and R lie on the same line. (Hint: Two lines with the same slope and a point in common must be the same line.)

64. $P(-2, 4), Q(4, 8), R(8, 12)$

65. $P(6, 10), Q(0, 6), R(3, 8)$

66. $P(-4, 10), Q(-6, 0), R(-1, 5)$

67. $P(-10, -13), Q(-8, -10), R(-12, -16)$

68. $P(-2, 4), Q(0, 8), R(2, 12)$

69. $P(8, -4), Q(0, -12), R(8, -20)$

70. Find the equation of the x-axis and its slope, if any.

71. Find the equation of the y-axis and its slope, if any.

72. Show that points with coordinates of $(-3, 4), (4, 1),$ and $(-1, -1)$ are the vertices of a right triangle.

73. Show that a triangle with vertices at $(0, 0), (12, 0),$ and $(13, 12)$ is not a right triangle.

74. A square has vertices at points $(a, 0), (0, a), (-a, 0),$ and $(0, -a)$, where $a \neq 0$. Show that its adjacent sides are perpendicular.

75. If a and b are not both 0, show that the points $(2b, a), (b, b),$ and $(a, 0)$ are the vertices of a right triangle.

76. Show that the points $(0, 0), (0, a), (b, c),$ and $(b, a + c)$ are the vertices of a parallelogram. (*Hint:* Opposite sides of a parallelogram are parallel.)

77. If $b \neq 0$, show that the points $(0, 0), (0, b), (8, b + 2),$ and $(12, 3)$ are the vertices of a trapezoid. (*Hint:* A **trapezoid** is a four-sided figure with exactly two sides parallel.)

APPLICATIONS   See Examples 5–6. (Objective 6)

78. Grade of a road Find the slope of the road. (*Hint:* 1 mi = 5,280 ft.)

79. Slope of a roof Find the slope of the roof.

80. Slope of a ladder A ladder reaches 18 feet up the side of a building with its base 5 feet from the building. Find the slope of the ladder.

81. Physical fitness   Find the slope of the treadmill for each setting listed in the table.

Height setting
2 in.
5 in.
8 in.

82. Global warming   The following line graphs estimate the global temperature rise between the years of 1990 and 2040. Find the average rate of temperature change (the slope) of Model A: Status quo.

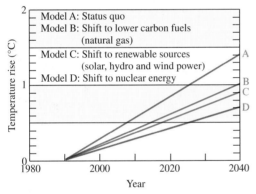

Based on data from The Blue Planet (Wiley, 1995)

83. Global warming   Find the average rate of temperature change of Model D: Shift to nuclear energy.

84. Rate of growth   When a college started an aviation program, the administration agreed to predict enrollments using a straight-line method. If the enrollment during the first year was 8, and the enrollment during the fifth year was 20, find the rate of growth per year (the slope of the line). (See the illustration.)

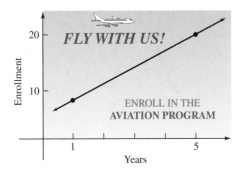

85. Wheelchair ramps   The illustration shows two designs for a ramp to make a platform wheelchair accessible.
   a. Find the slope of the ramp shown in design 1.
   b. Find the slope of each part of the ramp shown in design 2.
   c. Give one advantage and one disadvantage of each design.

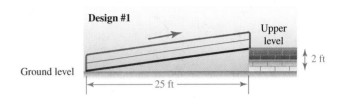

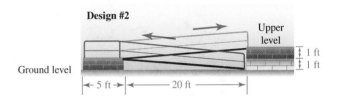

86. Rate of growth   A small business predicts sales according to a straight-line method. If sales were $85,000 in the first year and $125,000 in the third year, find the rate of growth in sales per year (the slope of the line).

87. Rate of decrease   The price of computer technology has been dropping for the past ten years. If a desktop PC cost $5,700 ten years ago, and the same computing power cost $1,499 two years ago, find the rate of decrease per year. (Assume a straight-line model.)

WRITING ABOUT MATH

88. Explain why a vertical line has no defined slope.

89. Explain how to determine from their slopes whether two lines are parallel, perpendicular, or neither.

SOMETHING TO THINK ABOUT

90. Find the slope of the line $Ax + By = C$. Follow the procedure of Example 2.

91. Follow Example 2 to find the slope of the line $y = mx + b$.

92. The points $(3, a)$, $(5, 7)$, and $(7, 10)$ lie on a line. Find a.

93. The line passing through points $(1, 3)$ and $(-2, 7)$ is perpendicular to the line passing through points $(4, b)$ and $(8, -1)$. Find b.

SECTION 8.3 Writing Equations of Lines

Objectives

1. Find the point-slope equation of a line with a given slope that passes through a given point.

2. Write the equation in slope-intercept form of a line that has a given slope and passes through a given point.

3. Graph a linear equation using the slope and y-intercept.

4. Determine whether two linear equations define lines that are parallel, perpendicular, or neither.

5. Write an equation of the line passing through a given point and parallel or perpendicular to a given line.

6. Use the general form of an equation of a line to determine whether two equations are parallel, perpendicular, or neither.

7. Write an equation of a line representing real-world data.

Vocabulary

point-slope form   slope-intercept form   general form

Getting Ready

Solve each equation.

1. $3 = \dfrac{x - 2}{4}$ 2. $-2 = 3(x + 1)$

3. Solve $y - 2 = 3(x - 2)$ for y.

4. Solve $Ax + By + 3 = 0$ for x.

We now apply the concept of slope to write the equation of a line passing through two fixed points. We also will use slope as an aid in graphing lines.

1 Find the point-slope equation of a line with a given slope that passes through a given point.

Suppose that the line shown in Figure 8-18 has a slope of m and passes through the point (x_1, y_1). If (x, y) is a second point on the line, we have

$$m = \frac{y - y_1}{x - x_1}$$

or if we multiply both sides by $x - x_1$, we have

$$(1) \qquad y - y_1 = m(x - x_1)$$

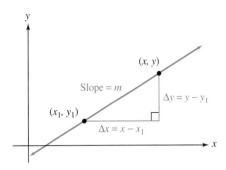

Figure 8-18

Because Equation 1 displays the coordinates of the point (x_1, y_1) on the line and the slope m of the line, it is called the **point-slope form** of the equation of a line.

Point-Slope Form	The **point-slope equation** of the line passing through $P(x_1, y_1)$ and with slope m is
	$$y - y_1 = m(x - x_1)$$

EXAMPLE 1   Write the point-slope equation of the line with a slope of $-\frac{2}{3}$ and passing through $(-4, 5)$.

Solution   We substitute $-\frac{2}{3}$ for m, -4 for x_1, and 5 for y_1 into the point-slope form and simplify.

$$y - y_1 = m(x - x_1)$$

$$y - 5 = -\frac{2}{3}[x - (-4)] \quad \text{Substitute } -\tfrac{2}{3} \text{ for } m, -4 \text{ for } x_1, \text{ and 5 for } y_1.$$

$$y - 5 = -\frac{2}{3}(x + 4) \qquad -(-4) = 4$$

The point-slope equation of the line is $y - 5 = -\frac{2}{3}(x + 4)$.

SELF CHECK 1   Write the point-slope equation of the line with slope of $\frac{5}{4}$ and passing through $(0, 5)$.

EXAMPLE 2   Write the point-slope equation of the line passing through $(-5, 4)$ and $(8, -6)$. Then solve the equation for y.

Solution   First we find the slope of the line.

$$m = \frac{y_2 - y_1}{x_2 - x_1}$$

$$= \frac{-6 - 4}{8 - (-5)} \quad \text{Substitute } -6 \text{ for } y_2, 4 \text{ for } y_1, 8 \text{ for } x_2, \text{ and } -5 \text{ for } x_1.$$

$$= -\frac{10}{13}$$

Because the line passes through both points, we can choose either one and substitute its coordinates into the point-slope form. If we choose $(-5, 4)$, we substitute -5 for x_1, 4 for y_1, and $-\frac{10}{13}$ for m and proceed as follows.

$$y - y_1 = m(x - x_1)$$

$$y - 4 = -\frac{10}{13}[x - (-5)] \quad \text{Substitute } -\frac{10}{13} \text{ for } m, -5 \text{ for } x_1, \text{ and } 4 \text{ for } y_1.$$

$$y - 4 = -\frac{10}{13}(x + 5) \qquad -(-5) = 5$$

To solve the equation for y, we proceed as follows:

$$y - 4 = -\frac{10}{13}x - \frac{50}{13} \quad \text{Remove parentheses.}$$

$$y = -\frac{10}{13}x + \frac{2}{13} \quad \text{Add 4 to both sides and simplify.}$$

The equation of the line is $y = -\frac{10}{13}x + \frac{2}{13}$.

⇨ **SELF CHECK 2**   Write the equation of the line passing through the points $(-2, 5)$ and $(4, -3)$ in point-slope form and then solve for y.

---

2 **Write the equation in slope-intercept form of a line that has a given slope and passes through a given point.**

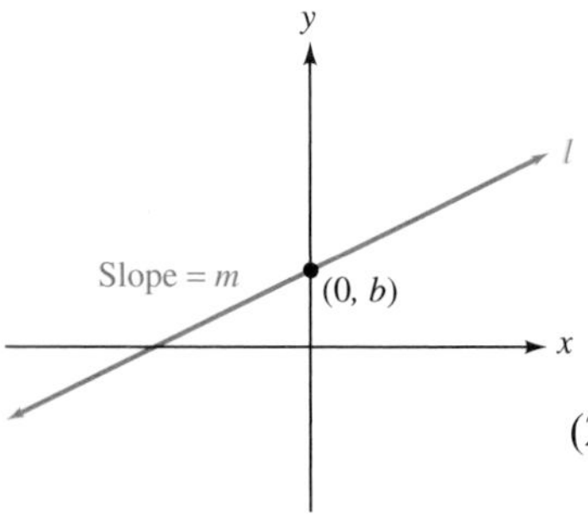

Since the y-intercept of the line shown in Figure 8-19 is the point $(0, b)$, we can write the equation of the line by substituting 0 for x_1 and b for y_1 in the point-slope form and then simplifying.

Figure 8-19

$$y - y_1 = m(x - x_1) \quad \text{This is the point-slope form of the equation of a line.}$$

$$y - b = m(x - 0) \quad \text{Substitute } b \text{ for } y_1 \text{ and } 0 \text{ for } x_1.$$

$$y - b = mx \quad \text{Remove parentheses.}$$

$$(2) \qquad y = mx + b \quad \text{Add } b \text{ to both sides.}$$

Because Equation 2 displays the slope m and the y-coordinate b of the y-intercept, it is called the **slope-intercept form** of the equation of a line.

Slope-Intercept Form

The **slope-intercept equation** of a line with slope m and y-intercept $(0, b)$ is

$$y = mx + b$$

EXAMPLE 3   Use the slope-intercept form to write an equation of the line with slope 4 that passes through the point $(5, 9)$.

Solution   Since we are given that $m = 4$ and that the ordered pair $(5, 9)$ satisfies the equation, we can substitute 5 for x, 9 for y, and 4 for m in the equation $y = mx + b$ and solve for b.

$$y = mx + b$$

$$9 = 4(5) + b \quad \text{Substitute 9 for } y, 4 \text{ for } m, \text{ and 5 for } x.$$

$$9 = 20 + b \qquad \text{Simplify.}$$
$$-11 = b \qquad \text{Subtract 20 from both sides.}$$

Because $m = 4$ and $b = -11$, the equation is $y = 4x - 11$.

SELF CHECK 3   Write the slope-intercept equation of the line with slope -2 that passes through the point $(-2, 8)$.

3   **Graph a linear equation using the slope and y-intercept.**

It is easy to graph a linear equation when it is written in slope-intercept form. For example, to graph $y = \frac{4}{3}x - 2$, we note that $b = -2$ so the y-intercept is $(0, b) = (0, -2)$. (See Figure 8-20.)

Because the slope of the line is $\frac{\Delta y}{\Delta x} = \frac{4}{3}$, we can locate another point on the line by starting at the point $(0, -2)$ and counting 3 units to the right and 4 units up. The line joining the two points is the graph of the equation.

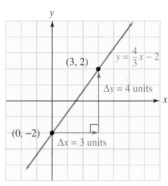

Figure 8-20

EXAMPLE 4   Find the slope and the y-intercept of the line with the equation $2(x - 3) = -3(y + 5)$. Then graph the line.

Solution   We write the equation in the form $y = mx + b$ to find the slope m and the y-intercept $(0, b)$.

$$2(x - 3) = -3(y + 5)$$
$$2x - 6 = -3y - 15 \qquad \text{Use the distributive property to remove parentheses.}$$
$$2x + 3y - 6 = -15 \qquad \text{Add } 3y \text{ to both sides.}$$
$$3y - 6 = -2x - 15 \qquad \text{Subtract } 2x \text{ from both sides.}$$
$$3y = -2x - 9 \qquad \text{Add 6 to both sides.}$$
$$y = -\frac{2}{3}x - 3 \qquad \text{Divide both sides by 3 and simplify.}$$

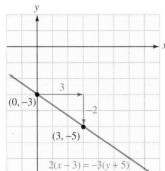

Figure 8-21

The slope is $-\frac{2}{3}$, and the y-intercept is $(0, -3)$. To draw the graph, we plot the y-intercept $(0, -3)$ and then locate a second point on the line by moving 3 units to the right and 2 units down. We draw a line through the two points to obtain the graph shown in Figure 8-21.

SELF CHECK 4   Find the slope and the y-intercept of the line with the equation $2(y - 1) = 3x + 2$ and graph the line.

4 **Determine whether two linear equations define lines that are parallel, perpendicular, or neither.**

EXAMPLE 5 Show that the lines represented by $4x + 8y = 10$ and $2x = 12 - 4y$ are parallel.

Solution In the previous section, we saw that distinct lines are parallel when their slopes are equal. To see whether this is true in this case, we can solve each equation for y.

$$4x + 8y = 10 \qquad\qquad 2x = 12 - 4y$$
$$8y = -4x + 10 \qquad\qquad 4y = -2x + 12$$
$$y = -\frac{1}{2}x + \frac{5}{4} \qquad\qquad y = -\frac{1}{2}x + 3$$

Because the values of b $\left(\frac{5}{4} \text{ and } 3\right)$ are different, the lines are distinct. Since the lines are distinct and have the same slope $\left(-\frac{1}{2}\right)$, they are parallel.

⇨ **SELF CHECK 5** Are lines represented by $3x - 2y = 4$ and $6x = 4(y + 1)$ parallel?

EXAMPLE 6 Show that the lines represented by $4x + 8y = 10$ and $4x - 2y = 21$ are perpendicular.

Solution Since two lines are perpendicular when their slopes are negative reciprocals, we can solve each equation for y to see whether the slopes of their graphs are negative reciprocals.

$$4x + 8y = 10 \qquad\qquad 4x - 2y = 21$$
$$8y = -4x + 10 \qquad\qquad -2y = -4x + 21$$
$$y = -\frac{1}{2}x + \frac{5}{4} \qquad\qquad y = 2x - \frac{21}{2}$$

Since the slopes are $-\frac{1}{2}$ and 2 (which are negative reciprocals), the lines are perpendicular.

⇨ **SELF CHECK 6** Are lines represented by $3x + 2y = 6$ and $2x - 3y = 6$ perpendicular?

5 **Write an equation of the line passing through a given point and parallel or perpendicular to a given line.**

We will now use the slope properties of parallel and perpendicular lines to write equations of lines.

EXAMPLE 7 Write the equation of the line passing through $(-2, 5)$ and parallel to the line $y = 8x - 3$.

Solution Since the equation is solved for y, the slope of the line given by $y = 8x - 3$ is the coefficient of x, which is 8. Since the desired equation is to have a graph that is parallel to the graph of $y = 8x - 3$, its slope also must be 8.

We substitute -2 for x_1, 5 for y_1, and 8 for m in the point-slope form and simplify.

$$y - y_1 = m(x - x_1)$$
$$y - 5 = 8[x - (-2)] \quad \text{Substitute 5 for } y_1, \text{8 for } m, \text{ and } -2 \text{ for } x_1.$$
$$y - 5 = 8(x + 2) \quad -(-2) = 2$$
$$y - 5 = 8x + 16 \quad \text{Use the distributive property to remove parentheses.}$$
$$y = 8x + 21 \quad \text{Add 5 to both sides.}$$

The equation is $y = 8x + 21$.

SELF CHECK 7   Write the equation of the line that is parallel to the line $y = 8x - 3$ and passes through the origin.

EXAMPLE 8   Write the equation of the line passing through $(-2, 5)$ and perpendicular to the line $y = 8x - 3$.

Solution   The slope of the given line is 8. Thus, the slope of the desired line must be $-\frac{1}{8}$, which is the negative reciprocal of 8.

We substitute -2 for x_1, 5 for y_1, and $-\frac{1}{8}$ for m into the point-slope form and simplify:

$$y - y_1 = m(x - x_1)$$
$$y - 5 = -\frac{1}{8}[x - (-2)] \quad \text{Substitute 5 for } y_1, -\frac{1}{8} \text{ for } m, \text{ and } -2 \text{ for } x_1.$$
$$y - 5 = -\frac{1}{8}(x + 2) \quad -(-2) = 2$$
$$y - 5 = -\frac{1}{8}x - \frac{1}{4} \quad \text{Remove parentheses.}$$
$$y = -\frac{1}{8}x - \frac{1}{4} + 5 \quad \text{Add 5 to both sides.}$$
$$y = -\frac{1}{8}x + \frac{19}{4} \quad \text{Combine terms: } -\frac{1}{4} + \frac{20}{4} = \frac{19}{4}.$$

The equation is $y = -\frac{1}{8}x + \frac{19}{4}$.

SELF CHECK 8   Write the equation of the line that is perpendicular to the line $y = 8x - 3$ and passes through $(2, 4)$.

6   **Use the general form of an equation of a line to determine whether two equations are parallel, perpendicular, or neither.**

Recall that any linear equation that is written in the form $Ax + By = C$, where A, B, and C are constants, is said to be written in **general form.**

COMMENT   When writing equations in general form, we usually clear the equation of fractions and make A positive. We also will make A, B, and C as small as possible. For example, the equation $6x + 12y = 24$ can be written as $x + 2y = 4$ by dividing both sides by 6.

Finding the Slope and y-Intercept from the General Form

If A, B, and C are real numbers and $B \neq 0$, the graph of the equation

$$Ax + By = C$$

is a nonvertical line with slope of $-\frac{A}{B}$ and a y-intercept of $\left(0, \frac{C}{B}\right)$.

You will be asked to justify the previous results in the exercises. You also will be asked to show that if $B = 0$, the equation $Ax + By = C$ represents a vertical line with x-intercept of $\left(\frac{C}{A}, 0\right)$.

EXAMPLE 9 Show that the lines represented by $4x + 3y = 7$ and $3x - 4y = 12$ are perpendicular.

Solution To show that the lines are perpendicular, we will show that their slopes are negative reciprocals. The first equation, $4x + 3y = 7$, is written in general form, with $A = 4$, $B = 3$, and $C = 7$. By the previous result, the slope of the line is

$$m_1 = -\frac{A}{B} = -\frac{4}{3} = -\frac{4}{3}$$

The second equation, $3x - 4y = 12$, also is written in general form, with $A = 3$, $B = -4$, and $C = 12$. The slope of this line is

$$m_2 = -\frac{A}{B} = -\frac{3}{-4} = \frac{3}{4}$$

Since the slopes are negative reciprocals, the lines are perpendicular.

⇨ **SELF CHECK 9** Are the lines $4x + 3y = 7$ and $y = -\frac{4}{3}x + 2$ parallel?

We summarize the various forms for the equation of a line in Table 8-1.

Point-slope form of a linear equation	$y - y_1 = m(x - x_1)$ The slope is m, and the line passes through (x_1, y_1).
Slope-intercept form of a linear equation	$y = mx + b$ The slope is m, and the y-intercept is $(0, b)$.
General form of a linear equation	$Ax + By = C$ A and B cannot both be 0.
A horizontal line	$y = b$ The slope is 0, and the y-intercept is $(0, b)$.
A vertical line	$x = a$ There is no defined slope, and the x-intercept is $(a, 0)$.

Table 8-1

7 ## Write an equation of a line representing real-world data.

For tax purposes, many businesses use straight-line depreciation to find the declining value of aging equipment.

EXAMPLE 10   **VALUE OF A LATHE**   The owner of a machine shop buys a lathe for $1,970 and expects it to last for ten years. It can then be sold as scrap for an estimated **salvage value** of $270. If y represents the value of the lathe after x years of use, and y and x are related by the equation of a line,
a. Find the equation of the line.
b. Find the value of the lathe after $2\frac{1}{2}$ years.
c. Find the economic meaning of the y-intercept of the line.
d. Find the economic meaning of the slope of the line.

Solution   **a.** To find the equation of the line, we find its slope and use point-slope form to find its equation.

When the lathe is new, its age x is 0, and its value y is $1,970. When the lathe is 10 years old, $x = 10$ and its value is $y = $270. Since the line passes through the points (0, 1,970) and (10, 270), as shown in Figure 8-22, the slope of the line is

$$m = \frac{y_2 - y_1}{x_2 - x_1}$$
$$= \frac{270 - 1{,}970}{10 - 0}$$
$$= \frac{-1{,}700}{10}$$
$$= -170$$

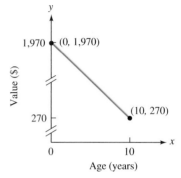

Figure 8-22

COMMENT   When the size of data is large, we can insert a // (break) symbol on the x- or y-axis to indicate that the scale does not begin until the first value is listed.

To find the equation of the line, we substitute -170 for m, 0 for x_1, and 1,970 for y_1 into the point-slope form and solve for y.

$$y - y_1 = m(x - x_1)$$
$$y - 1{,}970 = -170(x - 0)$$
(3) $$y = -170x + 1{,}970$$

The current value y of the lathe is related to its age x by the equation $y = -170x + 1{,}970$.

b. To find the value of the lathe after $2\frac{1}{2}$ years, we substitute 2.5 for x in Equation 3 and solve for y.

$$y = -170x + 1{,}970$$
$$= -170(2.5) + 1{,}970$$
$$= -425 + 1{,}970$$
$$= 1{,}545$$

After $2\frac{1}{2}$ years, the lathe will be worth $1,545.

c. The y-intercept of the graph is (0, b), where b is the value of y when $x = 0$.

$$y = -170x + 1{,}970$$
$$y = -170(0) + 1{,}970$$
$$y = 1{,}970$$

Thus, b is the value of a 0-year-old lathe, which is the lathe's original cost, $1,970.

d. Each year, the value of the lathe decreases by $170, because the slope of the line is -170. The slope of the line is the **annual depreciation rate.**

In statistics, the process of using one variable to predict another is called *regression.* For example, if we know a man's height, we can make a good prediction about his weight, because taller men usually weigh more than shorter men.

Figure 8-23 shows the result of sampling ten men at random and finding their heights and weights. The graph of the ordered pairs (h, w) is called a **scattergram.**

Man	Height in inches	Weight in pounds
1	66	140
2	68	150
3	68	165
4	70	180
5	70	165
6	71	175
7	72	200
8	74	190
9	75	210
10	75	215

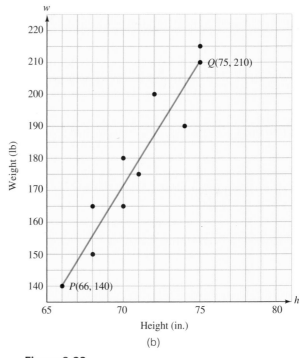

(a)   (b)

Figure 8-23

To write a prediction equation (sometimes called a *regression equation*), we must find the equation of the line that comes closer to all of the points in the scattergram than any other possible line. There are exact methods to find this equation, but we can only approximate it here.

To write an approximation of the regression equation, we place a straightedge on the scattergram shown in Figure 8-23 and draw the line joining two points that seems to best fit all the points. In the figure, line PQ is drawn, where point P has coordinates of $(66, 140)$ and point Q has coordinates of $(75, 210)$.

Our approximation of the regression equation will be the equation of the line passing through points P and Q. To find the equation of this line, we first find its slope.

$$m = \frac{y_2 - y_1}{x_2 - x_1}$$

$$= \frac{210 - 140}{75 - 66}$$

$$= \frac{70}{9}$$

We can then use point-slope form to find its equation.

$$y - y_1 = m(x - x_1)$$

$$y - 140 = \frac{70}{9}(x - 66) \quad \text{Choose } (66, 140) \text{ for } (x_1, y_1).$$

$$y = \frac{70}{9}x - \frac{4{,}620}{9} + 140 \qquad \text{Remove parentheses and add 140 to both sides.}$$

$$(4) \qquad y = \frac{70}{9}x - \frac{1{,}120}{3} \qquad -\frac{4{,}620}{9} + 140 = -\frac{1{,}120}{3}$$

Our approximation of the regression equation is $y = \frac{70}{9}x - \frac{1{,}120}{3}$.

To predict the weight of a man who is 73 inches tall, for example, we substitute 73 for x in Equation 4 and simplify.

$$y = \frac{70}{9}x - \frac{1{,}120}{3}$$

$$y = \frac{70}{9}(73) - \frac{1{,}120}{3}$$

$$y \approx 194.4$$

We would predict that a 73-inch-tall man chosen at random will weigh about 194 pounds.

➡ SELF CHECK ANSWERS

1. $y - 5 = \frac{5}{4}x$ **2.** $y = -\frac{4}{3}x + \frac{7}{3}$ **3.** $y = -2x + 4$

4. $m = \frac{3}{2}, (0, 2)$ **5.** yes **6.** yes **7.** $y = 8x$ **8.** $y = -\frac{1}{8}x + \frac{17}{4}$ **9.** yes

$2(y - 1) = 3x + 2$

NOW TRY THIS

1. Which of the following graphs could be the graph of $y = -px - q$?

a.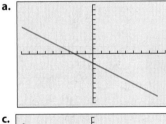

b.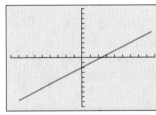

c.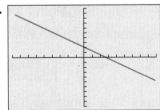

d.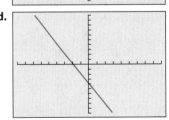

2. Write an equation of a line in slope-intercept form (if possible) with the given information.
   a. parallel to $y = -3$ through $(4, 6)$
   b. perpendicular to $x = 4$ through $(0, 0)$
   c. parallel to $3x = 2y + 8$ through $(-4, -6)$

8.3 EXERCISES

WARM-UPS

Write the point-slope form of the equation of a line with m = 2, passing through the given point.

1. $(2, 3)$ **2.** $(-3, 8)$

Write the equation of a line with m = −3 and the given y-intercept.

3. $(0, 5)$ **4.** $(0, -7)$

Determine whether the lines are parallel, perpendicular, or neither.

5. $y = 3x - 4, y = 3x + 5$ **6.** $y = -3x + 7, x = 3y - 1$

REVIEW EXERCISES   *Solve each equation.*

7. $3(x + 2) + x = 5x$ **8.** $12b + 6(3 - b) = b + 3$

9. $\dfrac{5(2 - x)}{3} - 1 = x + 5$ **10.** $\dfrac{r - 1}{3} = \dfrac{r + 2}{6} + 2$

11. Mixing alloys In 60 ounces of alloy for watch cases, there are 20 ounces of gold. How much copper must be added to the alloy so that a watch case weighing 4 ounces, made from the new alloy, will contain exactly 1 ounce of gold?

12. Mixing coffee To make a mixture of 80 pounds of coffee worth $272, a grocer mixes coffee worth $3.25 a pound with coffee worth $3.85 a pound. How many pounds of the cheaper coffee should the grocer use?

VOCABULARY AND CONCEPTS   *Fill in the blanks.*

13. The point-slope form of the equation of a line is _____.

14. The slope-intercept form of the equation of a line is _____.

15. The general form of the equation of a line is _____.

16. Two nonvertical lines are parallel when they have the _____ slope.

17. If the slopes of two lines are negative reciprocals, the lines are _____.

18. The process that recognizes that equipment loses value with age is called _____.

GUIDED PRACTICE

Use point-slope form to write the equation of the line with the given properties. See Example 1. (Objective 1)

19. $m = 5$, passing through $(0, 7)$

20. $m = -8$, passing through $(0, -2)$
21. $m = -3$, passing through $(2, 0)$
22. $m = 4$, passing through $(-5, 0)$

Use point-slope form to write the equation of the line passing through the two given points and solve for y. See Example 2. (Objective 1)

23. $P(0, 0), Q(4, 4)$
24. $P(-5, -5), Q(0, 0)$
25. $P(3, 4), Q(0, -3)$
26. $P(4, 0), Q(6, -8)$

Use slope-intercept form to write the equation of the line with the given properties. See Example 3. (Objective 2)

27. $m = 3, b = 17$
28. $m = -2, b = 11$
29. $m = -7$, passing through $(7, 5)$
30. $m = 3$, passing through $(-2, -5)$
31. $m = 0$, passing through $(2, -4)$
32. $m = -7$, passing through the origin
33. Passing through $(6, 8)$ and $(2, 10)$
34. Passing through $(-4, 5)$ and $(2, -6)$

Find the slope and the y-intercept of the line determined by the given equation. See Example 4. (Objective 3)

35. $3x - 2y = 8$ **36.** $-2x + 4y = 12$

37. $-2(x + 3y) = 5$ **38.** $5(2x - 3y) = 4$

Write each equation in slope-intercept form to find the slope and the y-intercept. Then use the slope and y-intercept to graph the line. See Example 4. (Objective 3)

39. $y + 1 = x$ **40.** $x + y = 2$

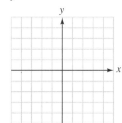   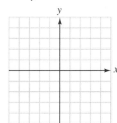

41. $x = \dfrac{3}{2}y - 3$

42. $x = -\dfrac{4}{5}y + 2$

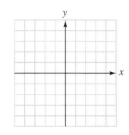
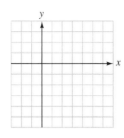

Determine whether the graphs of each pair of equations are parallel, perpendicular, or neither parallel nor perpendicular. See Examples 5–6. (Objective 4)

43. $y = 3x + 4, y = 3x - 7$

44. $y = 4x - 13, y = \dfrac{1}{4}x + 13$

45. $x + y = 2, y = x + 5$

46. $x = y + 2, y = x + 3$

47. $y = 3x + 7, 2y = 6x - 9$

48. $2x + 3y = 9, 3x - 2y = 5$

49. $x = 3y + 4, y = -3x + 7$

50. $3x + 6y = 1, y = \dfrac{1}{2}x$

51. $y = 3, x = 4$

52. $y = -3, y = -7$

53. $x = \dfrac{y - 2}{3}, 3(y - 3) + x = 0$

54. $2y = 8, 3(2 + x) = 2(x + 2)$

Write the equation of the line that passes through the given point and is parallel or perpendicular to the given line. Write the answer in slope-intercept form. See Examples 7–8. (Objective 5)

55. $(0, 0)$, parallel to $y = 4x - 7$

56. $(0, 0)$, parallel to $x = -3y - 12$

57. $(2, 5)$, parallel to $4x - y = 7$

58. $(-6, 3)$, parallel to $y + 3x = -12$

59. $(0, 0)$, perpendicular to $y = 4x - 7$

60. $(0, 0)$, perpendicular to $x = -3y - 12$

61. $(2, 5)$, perpendicular to $4x - y = 7$

62. $(-6, 3)$, perpendicular to $y + 3x = -12$

63. $(4, -2)$, parallel to $x = \dfrac{5}{4}y - 2$

64. $(1, -5)$, parallel to $x = -\dfrac{3}{4}y + 5$

65. $(4, -2)$, perpendicular to $x = \dfrac{5}{4}y - 2$

66. $(1, -5)$, perpendicular to $x = -\dfrac{3}{4}y + 5$

Find whether the graphs determined by each pair of equations are parallel, perpendicular, or neither parallel nor perpendicular. See Example 9. (Objective 6)

67. $4x + 5y = 20, 5x - 4y = 20$

68. $9x - 12y = 17, 3x - 4y = 17$

69. $2x + 3y = 12, 6x + 9y = 32$

70. $5x + 6y = 30, 6x + 5y = 24$

ADDITIONAL PRACTICE

Find the slope and y-intercept and then graph the line.

71. $x = \dfrac{2y - 4}{7}$

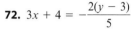

72. $3x + 4 = -\dfrac{2(y - 3)}{5}$

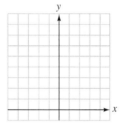
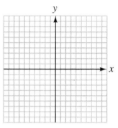

73. $3(y - 4) = -2(x - 3)$

74. $-4(2x + 3) = 3(3y + 8)$

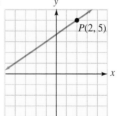
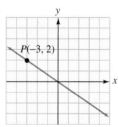

Use point-slope form to write the equation of each line and then write each answer in slope-intercept form.

75.

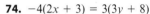

$P(2, 5)$

76.

$P(-3, 2)$

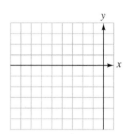

77.

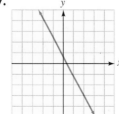

78.

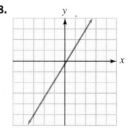

79. Find the equation of the line perpendicular to the line $y = 3$ and passing through the midpoint of the segment joining $(2, 4)$ and $(-6, 10)$.

80. Find the equation of the line parallel to the line $y = -8$ and passing through the midpoint of the segment joining $(-4, 2)$ and $(-2, 8)$.

81. Find the equation of the line parallel to the line $x = 3$ and passing through the midpoint of the segment joining $(2, -4)$ and $(8, 12)$.

82. Find the equation of the line perpendicular to the line $x = 3$ and passing through the midpoint of the segment joining $(-2, 2)$ and $(4, -8)$.

83. Solve $Ax + By = C$ for y and thereby show that the slope of its graph is $-\frac{A}{B}$ and its y-intercept is $\left(0, \frac{C}{B}\right)$.

84. Show that the x-intercept of the graph of $Ax + By = C$ is $\left(\frac{C}{A}, 0\right)$.

APPLICATIONS *For problems involving depreciation or appreciation, assume straight-line depreciation or straight-line appreciation.* See Example 10. (Objective 7)

85. Depreciation equations A truck was purchased for $19,984. Its salvage value at the end of 8 years is expected to be $1,600. Find the depreciation equation.

86. Depreciation equations A business purchased the computer shown. It will be depreciated over a 5-year period, when it will probably be worth $200. Find the depreciation equation.

$2,350

87. Art In 1987, the painting *Rising Sunflowers* by Vincent van Gogh sold for $36,225,000. Suppose that an appraiser expected the painting to double in value in 20 years. Let x represent the time in years after 1987. Find the straight-line appreciation equation.

88. Real estate listings Use the information given in the following description of the property to write a straight-line appreciation equation for the house.

Vacation Home
$122,000
Only 2 years old

• Great investment property!
• Expected to appreciate $4,000/yr

Sq ft: 1,635	Fam rm: yes	Den: no
Bdrm: 3	Ba: 1.5	Gar: enclosed
A/C: yes	Firepl: yes	Kit: built-ins

89. Appreciation equations A famous oil painting was purchased for $250,000 and is expected to double in value in 5 years. Find the appreciation equation.

90. Appreciation equations A house purchased for $142,000 is expected to double in value in 8 years. Find its appreciation equation.

91. Depreciation equations Find the depreciation equation for the TV in the want ad in the illustration.

For Sale: 3-year-old 65-inch TV, $1,750 new. Asking $800. Call 715-5588. Ask for Joe.

92. Depreciating a lawn mower A lawn mower cost $450 when new and is expected to last 10 years. What will it be worth in $6\frac{1}{2}$ years?

93. Salvage value A copy machine that cost $1,750 when new will be depreciated at the rate of $180 per year. If the useful life of the copier is 7 years, find its salvage value.

94. Annual rate of depreciation A machine that cost $47,600 when new will have a salvage value of $500 after its useful life of 15 years. Find its annual rate of depreciation.

95. Real estate A vacation home is expected to appreciate about $4,000 a year. If the home will be worth $122,000 in 2 years, what will it be worth in 10 years?

96. Car repair A garage charges a fixed amount, plus an hourly rate, to service a car. Use the information in the table to find the hourly rate.

A-1 Car Repair Typical charges	
2 hours	$143
5 hours	$320

97. Printer charges A printer charges a fixed setup cost, plus $15 for every 100 copies. If 300 copies cost $75, how much will 1,000 copies cost?

98. Predicting burglaries A police department knows that city growth and the number of burglaries are related by a linear equation. City records show that 575 burglaries were reported in a year when the local population was 77,000, and 675 were reported in a year when the population was 87,000. How many burglaries can be expected when the population reaches 110,000?

WRITING ABOUT MATH

99. Explain how to find the equation of a line passing through two given points.

100. In straight-line depreciation, explain why the slope of the line is called the *rate of depreciation*.

SOMETHING TO THINK ABOUT *Investigate the properties of the slope and the y-intercept by experimenting with the following problems.*

101. Graph $y = mx + 2$ for several positive values of m. What do you notice?

102. Graph $y = mx + 2$ for several negative values of m. What do you notice?

103. Graph $y = 2x + b$ for several increasing positive values of b. What do you notice?

104. Graph $y = 2x + b$ for several decreasing negative values of b. What do you notice?

105. How will the graph of $y = \frac{1}{2}x + 5$ compare to the graph of $y = \frac{1}{2}x - 5$?

106. How will the graph of $y = \frac{1}{2}x - 5$ compare to the graph of $y = \frac{1}{2}x$?

107. If the graph of $y = ax + b$ passes through quadrants I, II, and IV, what can be known about the constants a and b?

108. The graph of $Ax + By = C$ passes only through quadrants I and IV. What is known about the constants A, B, and C?

SECTION 8.4
A Review of Functions

Objectives

1 Find the domain and range of a relation and determine whether the relation is a function.

2 Find the domain and range from a graph and determine whether the graph represents a function.

3 Use function notation to evaluate a function at a given value.

4 Find the domain of a function given its equation.

5 Graph a linear function.

Vocabulary

relation	function	independent variable
domain	vertical line test	linear function
range	dependent variable	

If $y = \frac{3}{2}x - 2$, find the value of y for each value of x.

1. $x = 2$ **2.** $x = 6$ **3.** $x = -12$ **4.** $x = -\frac{1}{2}$

In this section, we will discuss *relations* and review *functions*. We include these concepts in this chapter because they involve ordered pairs.

1 **Find the domain and range of a relation and determine whether the relation is a function.**

Table 8-2 shows the number of women serving in the U.S. House of Representatives for several recent sessions of Congress.

Women in the U.S. House of Representatives					
Session of Congress	106th	107th	108th	109th	110th
Number of Female Representatives	56	59	59	68	71

Table 8-2

We can display the data in the table as a set of ordered pairs, where the first component (or *input*) represents the session of Congress and the second component (or *output*) represents the number of women serving in that session.

(106, 56)   (107, 59)   (108, 59)   (109, 68)   (110, 71)

Sets of ordered pairs like this are called **relations.** The set of all *first components* {106, 107, 108, 109, 110} is called the **domain** of the relation, and the set of all *second components* {56, 59, 68, 71} is called the **range** of the relation. Although 59 occurs twice as an output value, we list it only once in the range.

When each first component in a relation determines exactly one second component, the relation is called a **function.**

Functions

A **function** is any set of ordered pairs (a relation) in which each first component (or input value) determines exactly one second component (or output value).

EXAMPLE 1 Find the domain and range of the relation $\{(3, 2), (5, -7), (-8, 2), (-9, -12)\}$ and determine whether the relation represents a function.

Solution Because the set of first components is the domain, the domain is $\{3, 5, -8, -9\}$. Because the set of second components is the range, the range is $\{2, -7, -12\}$. In this relation

the first component of 3 determines a second component of 2

the first component of 5 determines a second component of -7

the first component of -8 determines a second component of 2

the first component of -9 determines a second component of -12

Since each component in the domain determines exactly one component in the range, this relation is a function.

⇨ **SELF CHECK 1**   Find the domain and range of the relation {(5, 6), (−12, 4), (8, 6), (5, 4)} and determine whether it defines a function.

2 **Find the domain and range from a graph and determine whether the graph represents a function.**

A **vertical line test** can be used to determine whether the graph of an equation represents a function. If every vertical line that intersects a graph does so exactly once, the graph represents a function, because every number x determines a single value of y. If any vertical line that intersects a graph does so more than once, the graph cannot represent a function, because to one number x there would correspond more than one value of y.

The graph in Figure 8-24(a) represents a function, because every vertical line that intersects the graph does so exactly once. The graph in Figure 8-24(b) does not represent a function, because some vertical lines intersect the graph more than once.

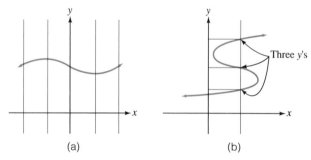

(a)   (b)

Figure 8-24

EXAMPLE 2   Find the domain and range of the relation determined by each graph and then tell whether the graph defines a function.

a.

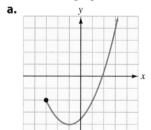

b.

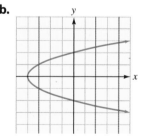

a. To find the domain, we look at the left-most point on the graph and identify −3 as its x-coordinate. Since the graph continues forever to the right, there is no right-most point. Therefore, the domain is [−3, ∞).

　　　　To find the range, we look for the lowest point on the graph and identify −4 as its y-coordinate. Since the graph continues upward forever, there is no highest point. Therefore, the range is [−4, ∞).

　　　　Since every vertical line that intersects the graph will do so exactly once, the vertical line test indicates that the graph is a function.

b. To find the domain, we note that the x-coordinate of the left-most point is -4 and that there is no right-most point. Therefore, the domain is $[-4, \infty)$.

To find the range, we note that there is no lowest point or highest point. Therefore, the range is $(-\infty, \infty)$.

Since many vertical lines that intersect the graph will do so more than once, the vertical line test indicates that the graph is not a function.

⇨ **SELF CHECK 2**   Find the domain and range of the relation determined by the graph and then tell whether the graph defines a function.

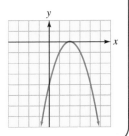

---

3 **Use function notation to evaluate a function at a given value.**

In Chapter 4, we introduced the following special notation, which is used to denote functions.

Function Notation   The notation $y = f(x)$ denotes that the variable y is a function of x.

COMMENT The notation $f(x)$ does not mean "f times x."

The notation $y = f(x)$ is read as "y equals f of x." Note that y and $f(x)$ are two notations for the same quantity. Thus, the equations $y = 4x + 3$ and $f(x) = 4x + 3$ are equivalent.

The notation $y = f(x)$ provides a way of denoting the value of y (the **dependent variable**) that corresponds to some number x (the **independent variable**).

EXAMPLE 3   Let $f(x) = 4x + 3$. Find: **a.** $f(3)$ **b.** $f(-1)$ **c.** $f(0)$
d. the value of x for which $f(x) = 7$.

Solution **a.** We replace x with 3:

$$f(x) = 4x + 3$$
$$f(3) = 4(3) + 3$$
$$= 12 + 3$$
$$= 15$$

b. We replace x with -1:

$$f(x) = 4x + 3$$
$$f(-1) = 4(-1) + 3$$
$$= -4 + 3$$
$$= -1$$

c. We replace x with 0:

$$f(x) = 4x + 3$$
$$f(0) = 4(0) + 3$$
$$= 3$$

d. We replace $f(x)$ with 7.

$$f(x) = 4x + 3$$
$$7 = 4x + 3$$
$$4 = 4x \quad \text{Subtract 3 from both sides.}$$
$$x = 1 \quad \text{Divide each side by 4.}$$

⇨ **SELF CHECK 3**   If $f(x) = -2x - 1$, find: **a.** $f(2)$ **b.** $f(-3)$
c. the value of x for which $f(x) = -7$.

We can think of a function as a machine that takes some input x and turns it into some output $f(x)$, as shown in Figure 8-25. The machine shown in Figure 8-26 turns the input number 2 into the output value -3 and turns the input number 6 into the output value -11. The set of numbers that we can put into the machine is the domain of the function, and the set of numbers that comes out is the range.

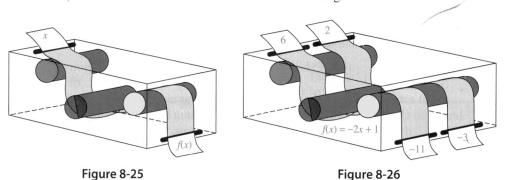

Figure 8-25   **Figure 8-26**

The letter f used in the notation $y = f(x)$ represents the word *function*. However, other letters can be used to represent functions. The notations $y = g(x)$ and $y = h(x)$ also denote functions involving the independent variable x.

EXAMPLE 4   Let $f(x) = 4x - 1$. Find: **a.** $f(3) + f(2)$ **b.** $f(a) - f(b)$.

Solution   **a.** We find $f(3)$ and $f(2)$ separately.

$$f(x) = 4x - 1 \qquad\qquad f(x) = 4x - 1$$
$$f(3) = 4(3) - 1 \qquad\qquad f(2) = 4(2) - 1$$
$$= 12 - 1 \qquad\qquad\quad = 8 - 1$$
$$= 11 \qquad\qquad\qquad\ = 7$$

We then add the results to obtain $f(3) + f(2) = 11 + 7 = 18$.

b. We find $f(a)$ and $f(b)$ separately.

$$f(x) = 4x - 1 \qquad\qquad f(x) = 4x - 1$$
$$f(a) = 4a - 1 \qquad\qquad f(b) = 4b - 1$$

We then subtract the results to obtain

$$f(a) - f(b) = (4a - 1) - (4b - 1)$$
$$= 4a - 1 - 4b + 1$$
$$= 4a - 4b$$

⇨ **SELF CHECK 4**   Let $g(x) = -2x + 3$. Find: **a.** $g(-2) + g(3)$ **b.** $g\left(\frac{1}{2}\right) - g(2)$.

4 **Find the domain of a function given its equation.**

The domain of a function that is defined by an equation is the <u>set of all numbers that are permissible replacements for its variable.</u>

EXAMPLE 5   Find the domain of the functions defined by

a. $f(x) = x^2 + 8x - 3$ **b.** $f(x) = \dfrac{1}{x - 2}$.

Solution   **a.** Since any real number can be substituted for x in the function $f(x) = x^2 + 8x - 3$ to obtain a single value y, the domain is $(-\infty, \infty)$.

b. The number 2 cannot be substituted for x in the function $f(x) = \dfrac{1}{x - 2}$, because that would make the denominator 0. However, any real number, except 2, can be substituted for x to obtain a single value y. Therefore, the domain is the set of all real numbers except 2. This is the interval $(-\infty, 2) \cup (2, \infty)$.

⇨ **SELF CHECK 5**   Find the domain of the function defined by $y = \dfrac{2}{x + 3}$.

---

5   **Graph a linear function.**

The *graph of a function* is the graph of the ordered pairs $(x, f(x))$ that define the function. For the graph of the function shown in Figure 8-27, the domain is shown on the x-axis, and the range is shown on the y-axis. For any x in the domain, there corresponds one value $y = f(x)$ in the range.

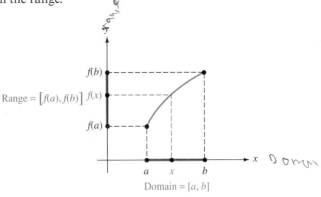

Figure 8-27

EXAMPLE 6   Graph the function $f(x) = -2x + 1$ and find its domain and range.

Solution   We graph the equation as in Figure 8-28. Since every real number x on the x-axis determines a corresponding value of y, the domain is the interval $(-\infty, \infty)$ shown on the x-axis. Since the values of y can be any real number, the range is the interval $(-\infty, \infty)$ shown on the y-axis.

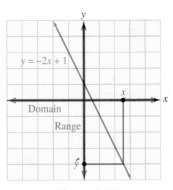

Figure 8-28

In Section 8.1, we graphed equations whose graphs were lines. These equations define basic functions, called **linear functions.**

Linear Functions	A **linear function** is a function defined by an equation that can be written in the form

$$f(x) = mx + b \quad \text{or} \quad y = mx + b$$

where m is the slope of the line graph and $(0, b)$ is the y-intercept.

EXAMPLE 7   Solve the equation $3x + 2y = 10$ for y to show that it defines a linear function. Then graph the function and find its domain and range.

Solution   We solve the equation for y as follows:

$$3x + 2y = 10$$
$$2y = -3x + 10 \quad \text{Subtract } 3x \text{ from both sides.}$$
$$y = -\frac{3}{2}x + 5 \quad \text{Divide both sides by 2.}$$

Because the given equation is written in the form $y = mx + b$, it defines a linear function, $f(x) = -\frac{3}{2}x + 5$. The slope of its line graph is $-\frac{3}{2}$, and the y-intercept is $(0, 5)$. The graph appears in Figure 8-29. From the graph, we can see that both the domain and the range are the interval $(-\infty, \infty)$.

A special case of a linear function is the *constant function,* defined by the equation $f(x) = b$, where b is a constant. Its graph, domain, and range are shown in Figure 8-30.

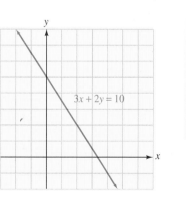

$3x + 2y = 10$

Figure 8-29

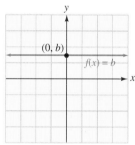

$(0, b)$

$f(x) = b$

Constant function
Domain: $(-\infty, \infty)$
Range: $\{b\}$

Figure 8-30

EXAMPLE 8   **CUTTING HAIR**   A barber earns $26 per day plus $6.50 for each haircut she gives that day. Write a linear function that describes her daily income if she gives x haircuts each day.

Solution   The barber earns $6.50 per haircut, so if she serves x customers a day, her earnings for haircuts will be $6.50x$. To find her total daily income, we must add $26 to $6.50. Thus, her total daily income $I(x)$ is described by the function

$$I(x) = 6.50x + 26$$

⇨ **SELF CHECK 8** Write a linear function that describes her daily income if she gets a raise of $0.50 per haircut.

⇨ **SELF CHECK ANSWERS** **1.** D: $\{5, -12, 8\}$; R: $\{6, 4\}$, not a function **2.** D: $(-\infty, \infty)$, R: $(-\infty, 0]$, yes **3. a.** -5 **b.** 5
c. 3 **4. a.** 4 **b.** 3 **5.** $(-\infty, -3) \cup (-3, \infty)$ **8.** $I(x) = 7x + 26$

NOW TRY THIS

Given $f(x) = 3x - 4$, find

1. $f(x - 2)$

2. $f(x + h)$
3. $f(x + h) - f(x)$

8.4 EXERCISES

WARM-UPS

Determine whether each equation or inequality determines y to be a function of x.

1. $y = 2x + 1$ **2.** $y \geq 2x$
3. $y^2 = x$

If f(x) = 2x + 1, find

4. $f(0)$ **5.** $f(1)$
6. $f(-2)$

REVIEW   *Solve each equation.*

7. $\dfrac{y + 2}{2} = 4(y + 2)$

8. $\dfrac{3z - 1}{6} - \dfrac{3z + 4}{3} = \dfrac{z + 3}{2}$

9. $\dfrac{2a}{3} + \dfrac{1}{2} = \dfrac{6a - 1}{6}$

10. $\dfrac{2x + 3}{5} - \dfrac{3x - 1}{3} = \dfrac{x - 1}{15}$

VOCABULARY AND CONCEPTS

Fill in the blanks.

11. Any set of ordered pairs defines a _____.

12. A _____ is a correspondence between a set of input values and a set of output values, where each _____ value determines exactly one _____ value.

13. In a function, the set of all inputs is called the _____ of the function.

14. In a function, the set of all outputs is called the _____ of the function.

15. The denominator of a fraction can never be __.

16. To decide whether a graph determines a function, use the _____.

17. If a vertical line intersects a graph more than once, the graph _____ represent a function.

18. A linear function is any function that can be written in the form _____.

19. In the function $f(x) = mx + b$, m is the _____ of its graph, and b is the y-coordinate of the _____.

Consider the function y = f(x) = 5x − 4. Fill in the blanks.

20. Any substitution for x is called an _____ value.
21. The value __ is called an output value.
22. The independent variable is __.
23. The dependent variable is __.
24. The notation $f(3)$ is the value of __ when $x = 3$.

GUIDED PRACTICE

Find the domain and range of each relation and determine if it is a function. See Example 1. (Objective 1)

25. $\{(3, -2), (5, 0), (-4, -5), (0, 0)\}$

26. $\{(9, 2), (3, 3), (-6, -9), (2, 9)\}$

27. $\{(-2, 3), (6, 8), (-2, 5), (5, 4)\}$

28. $\{(3, -2), (5, 2), (4, 5), (3, 0)\}$

State the domain and range of the relation determined by each graph in interval notation and determine whether the relation represents a function. See Example 2. (Objective 2)

29.

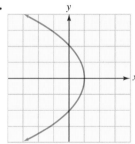

30.

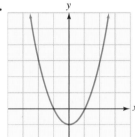

31.

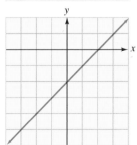

32.

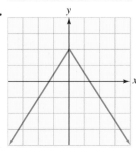

Find $f(3)$, $f(-1)$ and all values of x for which $f(x) = 0$. See Example 3. (Objective 3)

33. $f(x) = 3x$ **34.** $f(x) = -4x$

35. $f(x) = 2x - 3$ **36.** $f(x) = 3x - 5$

Find $f(2)$ and $f(3)$. See Example 3. (Objective 3)

37. $f(x) = x^2$ **38.** $f(x) = x^2 - 2$

39. $f(x) = x^3 - 1$ **40.** $f(x) = x^3$

Find $f(2)$ and $f(-2)$. See Example 3. (Objective 3)

41. $f(x) = |x| + 2$ **42.** $f(x) = |x| - 5$

43. $f(x) = x^2 - 2$ **44.** $f(x) = x^2 + 3$

Find $g(w)$ and $g(w + 1)$. See Example 4. (Objective 3)

45. $g(x) = 2x$ **46.** $g(x) = -3x$

47. $g(x) = 3x - 5$ **48.** $g(x) = 2x - 7$

Find each value given that $f(x) = 2x + 1$. See Example 4. (Objective 3)

49. $f(3) + f(2)$ **50.** $f(1) - f(-1)$

51. $f(b) - f(a)$ **52.** $f(b) + f(a)$

Find the domain of each function. See Example 5. (Objective 4)

53. $\{(-2, 3), (4, 5), (6, 7)\}$ **54.** $\{(0, 2), (1, 2), (3, 4)\}$

55. $f(x) = \dfrac{1}{x - 4}$ **56.** $f(x) = \dfrac{5}{x + 1}$

57. $f(x) = \dfrac{1}{x + 3}$ **58.** $f(x) = \dfrac{3}{x - 4}$

59. $f(x) = \dfrac{x}{x^2 + 2}$ **60.** $f(x) = \dfrac{x}{x - 3}$

Sketch the graph of each linear function and give the domain and range. See Example 6. (Objective 5)

61. $f(x) = 2x - 1$ **62.** $f(x) = -x + 2$

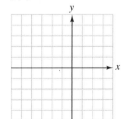
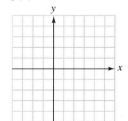

63. $2x - 3y = 6$

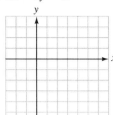

64. $3x + 2y = -6$

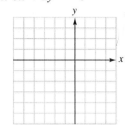

Determine whether each equation defines a linear function.
See Example 7. (Objective 5)

65. $y = 3x^2 + 2$

66. $y = \dfrac{x - 3}{2}$

67. $x = 3y - 4$

68. $x = \dfrac{8}{y}$

ADDITIONAL PRACTICE

For each function, find f(2) and f(3).

69. $f(x) = (x + 1)^2$

70. $f(x) = (x - 3)^2$

71. $f(x) = 2x^2 - x$

72. $f(x) = 5x^2 + 2x$

For each function, find f(3) and f(−1).

73. $f(x) = 7 + 5x$

74. $f(x) = 3 + 3x$

75. $f(x) = 9 - 2x$

76. $f(x) = 12 + 3x$

Find each value given that f(x) = 2x + 1.

77. $f(b) - 1$

78. $f(b) - f(1)$

79. $f(0) + f\left(-\dfrac{1}{2}\right)$

80. $f(a) + f(2a)$

APPLICATIONS   *For problems 81–84, set up a linear equation.* See Example 8. (Objective 5)

81. Selling DVD players An electronics firm manufactures portable DVD players, receiving $120 for each unit it makes. If x represents the number of units produced, the income received is determined by the *revenue function* $R(x) = 120x$. The manufacturer has fixed costs of $12,000 per month and variable costs of $57.50 for each unit manufactured. Thus, the *cost function* is $C(x) = 57.50x + 12,000$. How many DVD players must the company sell for revenue to equal cost?

82. Selling tires A tire company manufactures premium tires, receiving $130 for each tire it makes. If the manufacturer has fixed costs of $15,512.50 per month and variable costs of $93.50 for each tire manufactured, how many tires must the company sell for revenue to equal cost? (*Hint:* See Exercise 81.)

83. Selling hot dogs At a football game, a vendor sells hot dogs. He earns $50 per game plus $0.10 for each hot dog sold.

   a. Write a linear function that describes the vendor's income if he sells h hot dogs.

   b. Find his income if he sells 115 hot dogs.

84. Housing A housing contractor lists the following costs.

Fees and permits	$14,000
Cost per square foot	$102

   a. Write a linear function that describes the cost of building a house with s square feet.

   b. Find the cost to build a house having 1,800 square feet.

85. Ballistics A bullet shot straight up is s feet above the ground after t seconds, where $s = f(t) = -16t^2 + 256t$. Find the height of the bullet 3 seconds after it is shot.

86. Artillery fire A mortar shell is s feet above the ground after t seconds, where $s = f(t) = -16t^2 + 512t + 64$. Find the height of the shell 20 seconds after it is fired.

87. Dolphins See the illustration. The height h in feet reached by a dolphin t seconds after breaking the surface of the water is given by

$$h = -16t^2 + 32t$$

How far above the water will the dolphin be 1.5 seconds after a jump?

88. Forensic medicine The kinetic energy E of a moving object is given by $E = \frac{1}{2}mv^2$, where m is the mass of the object (in kilograms) and v is the object's velocity (in meters per second). Kinetic energy is measured in joules. Examining the damage done to a victim, a police pathologist estimates that the velocity of a club with a 3-kilogram mass was 6 meters per second. Find the kinetic energy of the club.

89. Conversion from degrees Celsius to degrees Fahrenheit The temperature in degrees Fahrenheit that is equivalent to a temperature in degrees Celsius is given by the function $F(C) = \frac{9}{5}C + 32$. Find the Fahrenheit temperature that is equivalent to 25°C.

90. Conversion from degrees Fahrenheit to degrees Celsius The temperature in degrees Celsius that is equivalent to a temperature in degrees Fahrenheit is given by the function $C(F) = \frac{5}{9}F - \frac{160}{9}$. Find the Celsius temperature that is equivalent to 14°F.

92. Explain why the constant function is a special case of a linear function.

SOMETHING TO THINK ABOUT *Let $f(x) = 2x + 1$ and $g(x) = x^2$. Assume that $f(x) \neq 0$ and $g(x) \neq 0$.*

93. Is $f(x) + g(x)$ equal to $g(x) + f(x)$?

94. Is $f(x) - g(x)$ equal to $g(x) - f(x)$?

WRITING ABOUT MATH

91. Explain the concepts of function, domain, and range.

SECTION 8.5

Graphs of Nonlinear Functions

Objectives

1. Graph the squaring, cubing, and absolute value functions.
2. Graph a vertical and horizontal translation of the squaring, cubing, and absolute value functions.
3. Graph a reflection of the squaring, cubing, and absolute value functions about the *x*-axis.
4. Graph a rational function.
5. Find the domain and range of a rational function.

Vocabulary

squaring function	vertical translation	asymptote
cubing function	horizontal translation	horizontal asymptote
absolute value function	reflection	vertical asymptote

Getting Ready

Give the slope and the y-intercept of each linear function.

1. $f(x) = 2x - 3$ **2.** $f(x) = -3x + 4$

Find the value of $f(x)$ when $x = 2$ and $x = -1$.

3. $f(x) = 5x - 4$ **4.** $f(x) = \frac{1}{2}x + 3$

In the previous section, we discussed linear functions, functions whose graphs are straight lines. We now extend the discussion to include nonlinear functions, functions whose graphs are not straight lines.

1 Graph the squaring, cubing, and absolute value functions.

If f is a function whose domain and range are sets of real numbers, its graph is the set of all points $(x, f(x))$ in the xy-plane. In other words, the graph of f is the graph of the equation $y = f(x)$. In this section, we will draw the graphs of many basic functions. The first is $f(x) = x^2$ (or $y = x^2$), often called the **squaring function.**

EXAMPLE 1   Graph the function: $f(x) = x^2$.

Solution   We substitute values for x in the equation and compute the corresponding values of $f(x)$. For example, if $x = -3$, we have

$$f(x) = x^2$$
$$f(-3) = (-3)^2 \quad \text{Substitute } -3 \text{ for } x.$$
$$= 9$$

The ordered pair $(-3, 9)$ satisfies the equation and will lie on the graph. We list this pair and the others that satisfy the equation in the table shown in Figure 8-31. We plot the points and draw a smooth curve through them to get the graph, called a *parabola*.

$$f(x) = x^2$$

x	$f(x)$	$(x, f(x))$
-3	9	$(-3, 9)$
-2	4	$(-2, 4)$
-1	1	$(-1, 1)$
0	0	$(0, 0)$
1	1	$(1, 1)$
2	4	$(2, 4)$
3	9	$(3, 9)$

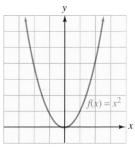

Figure 8-31

From the graph, we see that x can be any real number. This indicates that the domain of the squaring function is the set of real numbers, which is the interval $(-\infty, \infty)$. We can also see that y is always positive or zero. This indicates that the range is the set of nonnegative real numbers, which is the interval $[0, \infty)$.

⇨ **SELF CHECK 1**   Graph $f(x) = x^2 - 2$ and compare the graph to the graph of $f(x) = x^2$.

The second basic function is $f(x) = x^3$ (or $y = x^3$), often called the **cubing function.**

EXAMPLE 2   Graph the function: $f(x) = x^3$.

Solution   We substitute values for x in the equation and compute the corresponding values of $f(x)$. For example, if $x = -2$, we have

$$f(x) = x^3$$
$$f(-2) = (-2)^3 \quad \text{Substitute } -2 \text{ for } x.$$
$$= -8$$

The ordered pair $(-2, -8)$ satisfies the equation and will lie on the graph. We list this pair and others that satisfy the equation in the table shown in Figure 8-32. We plot the points and draw a smooth curve through them to get the graph.

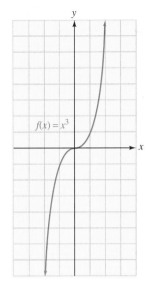

$$f(x) = x^3$$

x	$f(x)$	$(x, f(x))$
-2	-8	$(-2, -8)$
-1	-1	$(-1, -1)$
0	0	$(0, 0)$
1	1	$(1, 1)$
2	8	$(2, 8)$

Figure 8-32

From the graph, we can see that x can be any real number. This indicates that the domain of the cubing function is the set of real numbers, which is the interval $(-\infty, \infty)$. We can also see that y can be any real number. This indicates that the range is the set of real numbers, which is the interval $(-\infty, \infty)$.

⇨ SELF CHECK 2   Graph $f(x) = x^3 + 1$ and compare the graph to the graph of $f(x) = x^3$.

The third basic function is $f(x) = |x|$ (or $y = |x|$), often called the **absolute value function**.

EXAMPLE 3   Graph the function: $f(x) = |x|$.

Solution   We substitute values for x in the equation and compute the corresponding values of y. For example, if $x = -3$, we have

$$f(x) = |x|$$
$$f(-3) = |-3| \quad \text{Substitute } -3 \text{ for } x.$$
$$= 3$$

The ordered pair $(-3, 3)$ satisfies the equation and will lie on the graph. We list this pair and others that satisfy the equation in the table shown in Figure 8-33 on the next page. We plot the points and draw a V-shaped graph through them.

From the graph, we see that x can be any real number. This indicates that the domain of the absolute value function is the set of real numbers, which is the interval $(-\infty, \infty)$. We can also see that y is always positive or zero. This indicates that the range is the set of nonnegative real numbers, which is the interval $[0, \infty)$.

$f(x) = |x|$

x	$f(x)$	$(x, f(x))$
-3	3	$(-3, 3)$
-2	2	$(-2, 2)$
-1	1	$(-1, 1)$
0	0	$(0, 0)$
1	1	$(1, 1)$
2	2	$(2, 2)$
3	3	$(3, 3)$

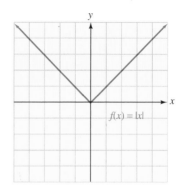

Figure 8-33

⇨ **SELF CHECK 3**   Graph $f(x) = |x - 2|$ and compare the graph to the graph of $f(x) = |x|$.

ACCENT ON TECHNOLOGY

Graphing Functions

We can graph nonlinear functions with a graphing calculator. For example, to graph $f(x) = x^2$ in a standard window of $[-10, 10]$ for x and $[-10, 10]$ for y, we enter the function by using the **y =** key and typing x $^\wedge$ 2 and pressing the **GRAPH** key. We will obtain the graph shown in Figure 8-34(a).

To graph $f(x) = x^3$, we enter the function by typing x $^\wedge$ 3 and press the **GRAPH** key to obtain the graph in Figure 8-34(b). To graph $f(x) = |x|$, we enter the function by selecting "abs" from the MATH menu, typing x, and pressing the **GRAPH** key to obtain the graph in Figure 8-34(c).

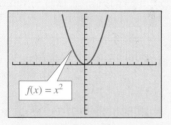

The squaring function

(a)

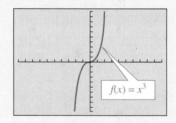

The cubing function

(b)

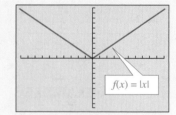

The absolute value function

(c)

Figure 8-34

When using a graphing calculator, we must be sure that the viewing window does not show a misleading graph. For example, if we graph $f(x) = |x|$ in the window $[0, 10]$ for x and $[0, 10]$ for y, we will obtain a misleading graph that looks like a line. (See Figure 8-35.) This is not true. The proper graph is the V-shaped graph shown in Figure 8-34(c).

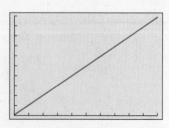

Figure 8-35

2 Graph a vertical and horizontal translation of the squaring, cubing, and absolute value functions.

Examples 1–3 and their Self Checks suggest that the graphs of different functions may be identical except for their positions in the xy-plane. For example, Figure 8-36 shows the graph of $f(x) = x^2 + k$ for three different values of k. If $k = 0$, we get the graph of $f(x) = x^2$. If $k = 3$, we get the graph of $f(x) = x^2 + 3$, which is identical to the graph of $f(x) = x^2$, except that it is shifted 3 units upward. If $k = -4$, we get the graph of $f(x) = x^2 - 4$, which is identical to the graph of $f(x) = x^2$, except that it is shifted 4 units downward. These shifts are called **vertical translations.**

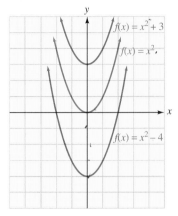

Figure 8-36

In general, we can make these observations.

Vertical Translations	If f is a function and k is a positive number, then

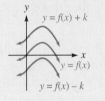

- The graph of $y = f(x) + k$ is identical to the graph of $y = f(x)$, except that it is translated k units upward.
- The graph of $y = f(x) - k$ is identical to the graph of $y = f(x)$, except that it is translated k units downward.

EXAMPLE 4 Graph: $f(x) = |x| + 2$.

Solution The graph of $f(x) = |x| + 2$ will be the same V-shaped graph as $f(x) = |x|$, except that it is shifted 2 units up. The graph appears in Figure 8-37.

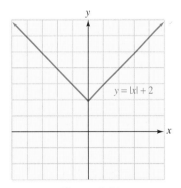

Figure 8-37

➡ **SELF CHECK 4** Graph: $f(x) = |x| - 3$.

Figure 8-38 shows the graph of $f(x) = (x + h)^2$ for three different values of h. If $h = 0$, we get the graph of $f(x) = x^2$. The graph of $f(x) = (x - 3)^2$ is identical to the graph of $f(x) = x^2$, except that it is shifted 3 units to the right. The graph of $f(x) = (x + 2)^2$ is identical to the graph of $f(x) = x^2$, except that it is shifted 2 units to the left. These shifts are called **horizontal translations.**

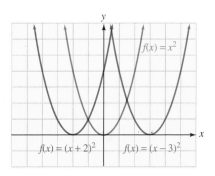

Figure 8-38

In general, we can make these observations.

Horizontal Translations

If f is a function and k is a positive number, then

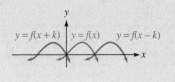

- The graph of $y = f(x - k)$ is identical to the graph of $y = f(x)$, except that it is translated k units to the right.

- The graph of $y = f(x + k)$ is identical to the graph of $y = f(x)$, except that it is translated k units to the left.

EXAMPLE 5   Graph: $f(x) = (x - 2)^2$.

Solution   The graph of $f(x) = (x - 2)^2$ will be the same shape as the graph of $f(x) = x^2$, except that it is shifted 2 units to the right. The graph appears in Figure 8-39.

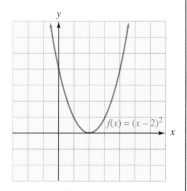

Figure 8-39

⇨ **SELF CHECK 5**   Graph: $f(x) = (x + 3)^3$.

EXAMPLE 6   Graph: $f(x) = (x - 3)^2 + 2$.

Solution   We can graph this function by translating the graph of $f(x) = x^2$ to the right 3 units and then up 2 units, as shown in Figure 8-40.

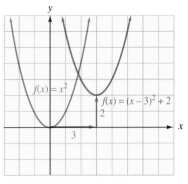

Figure 8-40

⇨ **SELF CHECK 6**   Graph: $f(x) = |x + 2| - 3$.

3 **Graph a reflection of the squaring, cubing, and absolute value functions about the *x*-axis.**

We now consider the graph of $y = f(x) = -|x|$. To graph this function, we can make a table of values, plot each point, and draw the graph, as in Figure 8-41.

$y = f(x) = -|x|$

x	$f(x)$	$(x, f(x))$
-3	-3	$(-3, -3)$
-2	-2	$(-2, -2)$
-1	-1	$(-1, -1)$
0	0	$(0, 0)$
1	-1	$(1, -1)$
2	-2	$(2, -3)$
3	-3	$(3, -3)$

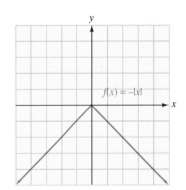

Figure 8-41

As we can see from the graph, its shape is the same as the graph of $y = f(x) = |x|$, except that it has been flipped upside down. We say that the graph of $y = f(x) = |x|$ has been *reflected* about the *x*-axis. In general, we can make the following statement.

Reflections about the *x*-Axis   The graph of $y = -f(x)$ is identical to the graph of $y = f(x)$, except that it is reflected about the *x*-axis.

EXAMPLE 7   Graph the absolute value function: $y = f(x) = -|x - 1| + 3$.

Solution   We graph this function by translating the graph of $y = f(x) = -|x|$ to the right 1 unit and up 3 units, as shown in Figure 8-42 on the next page.

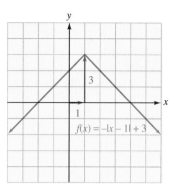

Figure 8-42

⇨ **SELF CHECK 7**   Graph: $y = f(x) = -|x + 2| - 3.$

PERSPECTIVE   Graphs in Space

In an xy-coordinate system, graphs of equations containing the two variables x and y are lines or curves. Other equations have more than two variables, and graphing them often requires some ingenuity and perhaps the aid of a computer. Graphs of equations with the three variables x, y, and z are viewed in a three-dimensional coordinate system with three axes. The coordinates of points in a three-dimensional coordinate system are ordered triples (x, y, z). For example, the points $P(2, 3, 4)$ and $Q(-1, 2, 3)$ are plotted in Illustration 1.

Graphs of equations in three variables are not lines or curves, but flat planes or curved surfaces. Only the simplest of these equations can be conveniently graphed by hand; a computer provides the best images of others. The graph in Illustration 2 is called a **paraboloid;** it is the three-dimensional version of a parabola. Illustration 3 models a portion of the vibrating surface of a drum head.

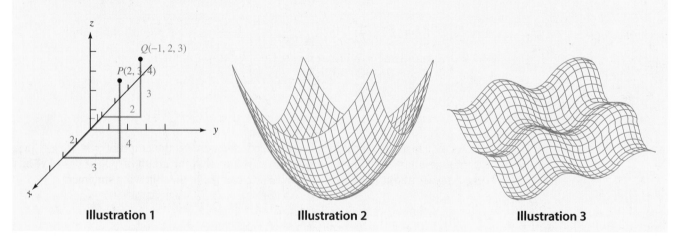

Illustration 1   **Illustration 2**   **Illustration 3**

4   Graph a rational function.

Rational expressions often define functions. For example, if the cost of subscribing to an online information network is $6 per month plus $1.50 per hour of access time, the average (mean) hourly cost of the service is the total monthly cost, divided by the number of hours of access time:

$$\overline{c} = \frac{C}{n} = \frac{1.50n + 6}{n}$$ $\overline{c}$ is the mean hourly cost, C is the total monthly cost, and n is the number of hours the service is used.

The function

(1) $\overline{c} = f(n) = \dfrac{1.50n + 6}{n}$ $(n > 0)$

gives the mean hourly cost of using the information network for n hours per month.

Figure 8-43 shows the graph of the rational function $\overline{c} = f(n) = \frac{1.50n + 6}{n}$ $(n > 0)$. Since $n > 0$, the domain of this function is the interval $(0, \infty)$.

From the graph, we can see that the mean hourly cost decreases as the number of hours of access time increases. Since the cost of each extra hour of access time is \$1.50, the mean hourly cost can approach \$1.50 but never drop below it. Thus, the graph of the function approaches the line $y = 1.5$ as n increases without bound.

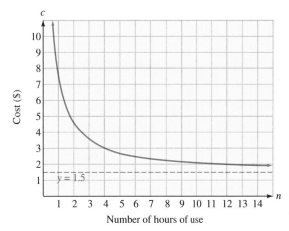

Figure 8-43

When a graph approaches a line as the dependent variable gets large, we call the line an **asymptote**. The line $y = 1.5$ is a **horizontal asymptote** of the graph.

As n gets smaller and approaches 0, the graph approaches the y-axis but never touches it. The y-axis is a **vertical asymptote** of the graph.

EXAMPLE 8   Find the mean hourly cost when the network described above is used for   **a.** 3 hours **b.** 70.4 hours.

Solution   **a.** To find the mean hourly cost for 3 hours of access time, we substitute 3 for n in Equation 1 and simplify:

$$\overline{c} = f(3) = \frac{1.50(3) + 6}{3} = 3.5$$

The mean hourly cost for 3 hours of access time is \$3.50.

b. To find the mean hourly cost for 70.4 hours of access time, we substitute 70.4 for n in Equation 1 and simplify:

$$\overline{c} = f(70.4) = \frac{1.50(70.4) + 6}{70.4} = 1.585227273$$

The mean hourly cost for 70.4 hours of access time is approximately \$1.59.

⇨ **SELF CHECK 8**   Find the mean hourly cost when the network is used for 5 hours.

5   **Find the domain and range of a rational function.**

Since division by 0 is undefined, any values that make the denominator 0 in a rational function must be excluded from the domain of the function.

EXAMPLE 9   Find the domain: $f(x) = \dfrac{3x + 2}{x^2 + x - 6}$.

Solution   From the set of real numbers, we must exclude any values of x that make the denominator 0. To find these values, we set $x^2 + x - 6$ equal to 0 and solve for x.

$$x^2 + x - 6 = 0$$
$$(x + 3)(x - 2) = 0 \qquad \text{Factor.}$$
$$x + 3 = 0 \qquad \text{or} \qquad x - 2 = 0 \qquad \text{Set each factor equal to 0.}$$
$$x = -3 \qquad\qquad x = 2 \qquad \text{Solve each linear equation.}$$

Thus, the domain of the function is the set of all real numbers except -3 and 2. In interval notation, the domain is $(-\infty, -3) \cup (-3, 2) \cup (2, \infty)$.

⇨ **SELF CHECK 9**   Find the domain: $f(x) = \dfrac{x^2 + 1}{x - 2}$.

ACCENT ON TECHNOLOGY

Finding the Domain and Range of a Function

We can find the domain and range of the function in Example 9 by looking at its graph. If we use window settings of $[-10, 10]$ for x and $[-10, 10]$ for y and graph the function

$$f(x) = \frac{3x + 2}{x^2 + x - 6}$$

we will obtain the graph in Figure 8-44(a).

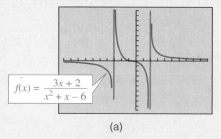
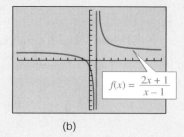

(a)   (b)

Figure 8-44

From the figure, we can see that

- As x approaches -3 from the left, the values of y decrease, and the graph approaches the vertical line $x = -3$.
- As x approaches -3 from the right, the values of y increase, and the graph approaches the vertical line $x = -3$.

From the figure, we also can see that

- As x approaches 2 from the left, the values of y decrease, and the graph approaches the vertical line $x = 2$.
- As x approaches 2 from the right, the values of y increase, and the graph approaches the vertical line $x = 2$.

The lines $x = -3$ and $x = 2$ are vertical asymptotes. Although the vertical lines in the graph appear to be the graphs of $x = -3$ and $x = 2$, they are not. Graphing calculators draw graphs by connecting dots whose x-coordinates are close together. Often, when two such points straddle a vertical asymptote and their y-coordinates are far apart, the calculator draws a line between them anyway, producing what appears to be a vertical asymptote. If you set your calculator to dot mode instead of connected mode, the vertical lines will not appear.

From Figure 8-44(a), we also can see that

- As x increases to the right of 2, the values of y decrease and approach the value $y = 0$.
- As x decreases to the left of -3, the values of y increase and approach the value $y = 0$.

The line $y = 0$ (the x-axis) is a horizontal asymptote. Graphing calculators do not draw lines that appear to be horizontal asymptotes. From the graph, we can see that all real numbers x, except -3 and 2, give a value of y. This confirms that the domain of the function is $(-\infty, -3) \cup (-3, 2) \cup (2, \infty)$. We also can see that y can be any value. Thus, the range is $(-\infty, \infty)$.

To find the domain and range of the function $f(x) = \frac{2x + 1}{x - 1}$, we use a calculator to draw the graph shown in Figure 8-44(b). From this graph, we can see that the line $x = 1$ is a vertical asymptote and that the line $y = 2$ is a horizontal asymptote. Since x can be any real number except 1, the domain is the interval $(-\infty, 1) \cup (1, \infty)$. Since y can be any value except 2, the range is $(-\infty, 2) \cup (2, \infty)$.

⇨ **SELF CHECK ANSWERS**

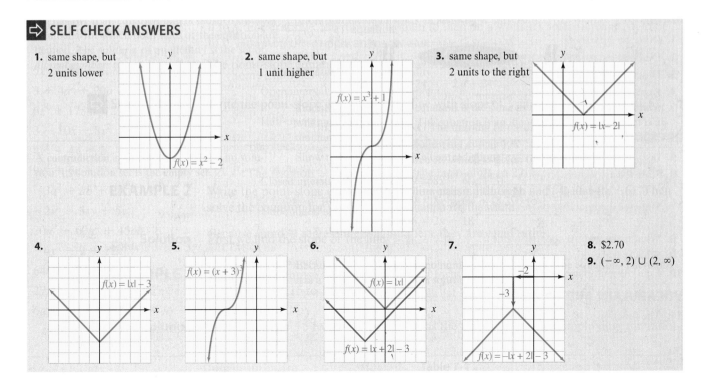

1. same shape, but 2 units lower $f(x) = x^2 - 2$

2. same shape, but 1 unit higher $f(x) = x^3 + 1$

3. same shape, but 2 units to the right $f(x) = |x - 2|$

4. $f(x) = |x| - 3$

5. $f(x) = (x + 3)^3$

6. $f(x) = |x| \qquad f(x) = |x + 2| - 3$

7. $f(x) = -|x + 2| - 3$

8. \$2.70

9. $(-\infty, 2) \cup (2, \infty)$

NOW TRY THIS

1. Given the graph of $f(x)$ below, sketch a graph of each translation or reflection.

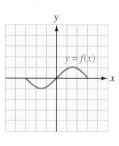

a. $f(x) + 2$

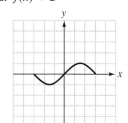

b. $-f(x)$

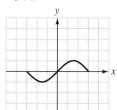

c. $f(x - 1)$

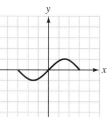

8.5 EXERCISES

WARM-UPS

1. Describe a parabola.
2. Describe the graph of $f(x) = |x| + 3$.
3. Describe the graph of $f(x) = x^3 - 4$.
4. Explain why the choice of a viewing window is important when using a graphing calculator.

REVIEW

5. List the prime numbers between 40 and 50.
6. State the associative property of addition.

7. State the commutative property of multiplication.

8. What is the additive identity element?
9. What is the multiplicative identity element?
10. Find the multiplicative inverse of $\frac{5}{3}$.

VOCABULARY AND CONCEPTS   *Fill in the blanks.*

11. The function $f(x) = x^2$ is called the _____ function.

12. The function $f(x) = x^3$ is called the _____ function.
13. The function $f(x) = |x|$ is called the _____ function.
14. Shifting the graph of an equation up or down is called a _____ translation.
15. Shifting the graph of an equation to the left or to the right is called a _____ translation.
16. The graph of $f(x) = x^3 + 5$ is the same as the graph of $f(x) = x^3$, except that it is shifted __ units ___.
17. The graph of $f(x) = x^3 - 2$ is the same as the graph of $f(x) = x^3$, except that it is shifted __ units _____.
18. The graph of $f(x) = (x - 5)^3$ is the same as the graph of $f(x) = x^3$, except that it is shifted __ units _____.
19. The graph of $f(x) = (x + 4)^3$ is the same as the graph of $f(x) = x^3$, except that it is shifted __ units _____.
20. The graph of $y = -f(x)$ is identical to the graph of $y = f(x)$, except that it is reflected about the _____.
21. If a fraction is the quotient of two polynomials, it is called a _____ expression.
22. If a graph approaches a vertical line but never touches it, the line is called an _____.

GUIDED PRACTICE

Graph each function by plotting points. Check your work with a graphing calculator. See Examples 1–3. (Objective 1)

23. $f(x) = x^2 - 3$

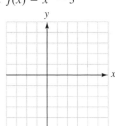

24. $f(x) = x^2 + 2$

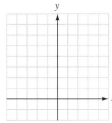

25. $f(x) = (x - 1)^3$

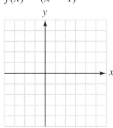

26. $f(x) = (x + 1)^3$

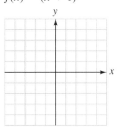

27. $f(x) = |x| - 2$

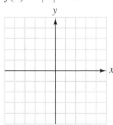

28. $f(x) = |x| + 1$

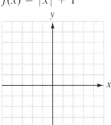

29. $f(x) = |x - 1|$

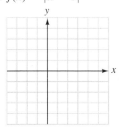

30. $f(x) = |x + 2|$

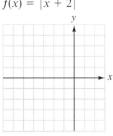

Sketch each graph using a translation of the graph of $f(x) = x^2$, $f(x) = x^3$, or $f(x) = |x|$. See Examples 4–6. (Objective 2)

31. $f(x) = x^2 - 5$

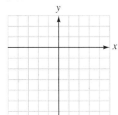

32. $f(x) = x^3 + 4$

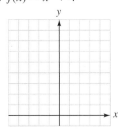

33. $f(x) = (x - 1)^3$

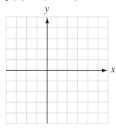

34. $f(x) = (x + 4)^2$

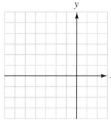

35. $f(x) = |x - 2| - 1$

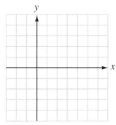

36. $f(x) = (x + 2)^2 - 1$

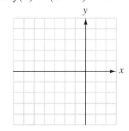

37. $f(x) = (x + 1)^3 - 2$

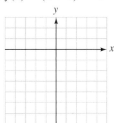

38. $f(x) = |x + 4| + 3$

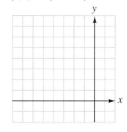

Graph each function. See Example 7. (Objective 3)

39. $f(x) = -x^2$

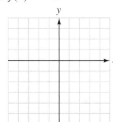

40. $f(x) = -x^3 + 2$

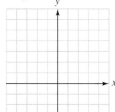

41. $f(x) = -(x - 2)^2 - 3$

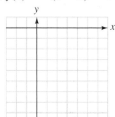

42. $f(x) = -|x - 2| - 3$

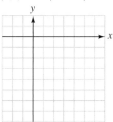

The time t it takes to travel 600 miles is a function of the mean rate of speed r: $t = f(r) = \dfrac{600}{r}$. Find t for each value of r. See Example 8. (Objective 4)

43. 30 mph

44. 40 mph

45. 50 mph

46. 60 mph

Find the domain of each rational function and write it in interval notation. Use a graphing calculator to graph each rational function to verify the domain and find the range. See Example 9. (Objective 5)

47. $f(x) = \dfrac{x}{x - 2}$

48. $f(x) = \dfrac{x + 2}{x}$

49. $f(x) = \dfrac{x + 1}{x^2 - 4}$

50. $f(x) = \dfrac{x - 2}{x^2 - 3x - 4}$

ADDITIONAL PRACTICE

Use a graphing calculator to graph each function, using values of $[-4, 4]$ for x and $[-4, 4]$ for y. The graph is not what it appears to be. Pick a better viewing window and find the true graph.

51. $f(x) = x^2 + 8$

52. $f(x) = x^3 - 8$

53. $f(x) = |x + 5|$

54. $f(x) = |x - 5|$

55. $f(x) = (x - 6)^2$

56. $f(x) = (x + 9)^2$

57. $f(x) = x^3 + 8$

58. $f(x) = x^3 - 12$

Suppose the cost (in dollars) of removing p% of the pollution in a river is given by the function $c = f(p) = \dfrac{50{,}000p}{100 - p}$ $(0 \le p < 100)$. Find the cost of removing each percent of pollution.

59. 10%

60. 30%

61. 50%

62. 80%

APPLICATIONS

A service club wants to publish a directory of its members. Some investigation shows that the cost of typesetting and photography will be $700, and the cost of printing each directory will be $1.25.

63. Find a function that gives the total cost c of printing x directories.

64. Find a function that gives the mean cost per directory $\bar{c}$ of printing x directories.

65. Find the total cost of printing 500 directories.

66. Find the mean cost per directory if 500 directories are printed.

67. Find the mean cost per directory if 1,000 directories are printed.

68. Find the mean cost per directory if 2,000 directories are printed.

An electric company charges $7.50 per month plus 9¢ for each kilowatt hour (kwh) of electricity used.

69. Find a function that gives the total cost c of n kwh of electricity.

70. Find a function that gives the mean cost per kwh $\bar{c}$ when using n kwh.

71. Find the total cost for using 775 kwh.

72. Find the mean cost per kwh when 775 kwh are used.

73. Find the mean cost per kwh when 1,000 kwh are used.

74. Find the mean cost per kwh when 1,200 kwh are used.

Assume that a person buys a horse for $5,000 and plans to pay $350 per month to board the horse.

75. Find a function that will give the total cost of owning the horse for x months.

76. Find a function that will give the mean cost per month $\bar{c}$ after owning the horse for x months.

77. Find the total cost of owning the horse for 10 years.

78. Find the mean cost per month if the horse is owned for 10 years.

WRITING ABOUT MATH

79. Explain how to graph an equation by plotting points.

80. Explain how the graphs of $y = (x - 4)^2 - 3$ and $y = x^2$ are related.

SOMETHING TO THINK ABOUT

81. Can a rational function have two horizontal asymptotes? Explain.

82. Use a graphing calculator to investigate the positioning of the vertical asymptotes of a rational function by graphing $y = \dfrac{x}{x - k}$ for several values of k. What do you observe?

SECTION
8.6

Variation

Objectives

1. Solve a proportion.
2. Solve a direct variation problem.
3. Solve an inverse variation problem.
4. Solve a joint variation problem.
5. Solve a combined variation problem.

Vocabulary

ratio	direct variation	constant of variation
proportion	constant of proportionality	joint variation
extremes	inverse variation	combined variation
means		

Getting Ready

Solve each equation.

1. $\dfrac{x}{2} = \dfrac{3}{4}$ **2.** $\dfrac{5}{7} = \dfrac{x}{2}$ **3.** $8 = 2k$ **4.** $12 = \dfrac{k}{3}$

1 Solve a proportion.

Recall that the quotient of two numbers is often called a **ratio.** For example, the fraction $\frac{2}{3}$ can be read as "the ratio of 2 to 3." An equation indicating that two ratios are equal is called a **proportion.** Two examples of proportions are

$$\frac{1}{4} = \frac{2}{8} \quad \text{and} \quad \frac{4}{7} = \frac{12}{21}$$

In the proportion $\frac{a}{b} = \frac{c}{d}$, the terms a and d are called the **extremes** of the proportion, and the terms b and c are called the **means.**

To develop a fundamental property of proportions, we suppose that

$$\frac{a}{b} = \frac{c}{d}$$

is a proportion and multiply both sides by bd to obtain

$$bd\left(\frac{a}{b}\right) = bd\left(\frac{c}{d}\right)$$

$$\frac{\cancel{b}da}{\cancel{b}} = \frac{b\cancel{d}c}{\cancel{d}} \qquad \frac{b}{b} = 1 \text{ and } \frac{d}{d} = 1.$$

$$ad = bc$$

Thus, if $\frac{a}{b} = \frac{c}{d}$, then $ad = bc$. In a proportion, *the product of the extremes equals the product of the means.*

EXAMPLE 1   Solve the proportion: $\dfrac{x+1}{x} = \dfrac{x}{x+2}$.

Solution

$$\frac{x+1}{x} = \frac{x}{x+2}$$

$$(x+1)(x+2) = x \cdot x \qquad \text{The product of the extremes equals the product of the means.}$$

$$x^2 + 3x + 2 = x^2 \qquad \text{Multiply.}$$

$$3x + 2 = 0 \qquad \text{Subtract } x^2 \text{ from both sides.}$$

$$x = -\frac{2}{3} \qquad \text{Subtract 2 from both sides and divide both sides by 3.}$$

⇨ **SELF CHECK 1**   Solve: $\dfrac{x-2}{x} = \dfrac{x}{x-3}$.

2   **Solve a direct variation problem.**

To introduce **direct variation,** we consider the formula

$$C = \pi D$$

for the circumference of a circle, where C is the circumference, D is the diameter, and $\pi \approx 3.14159$. If we double the diameter of a circle, we determine another circle with a larger circumference C_1 such that

$$C_1 = \pi(2D) = 2\pi D = 2C$$

Thus, doubling the diameter results in doubling the circumference. Likewise, if we triple the diameter, we triple the circumference.

In this formula, we say that the variables C and D *vary directly,* or that they are *directly proportional.* This is because as one variable gets larger, so does the other, in a predictable way. In this example, the constant π is called the *constant of variation* or the *constant of proportionality.*

Direct Variation

The words "y varies directly with x" or "y is directly proportional to x" mean that $y = kx$ for some nonzero constant k. The constant k is called the **constant of variation** or the **constant of proportionality.**

Since the formula for direct variation ($y = kx$) defines a linear function, its graph is always a line with a y-intercept at the origin. The graph of $y = kx$ appears in Figure 8-45 for three positive values of k.

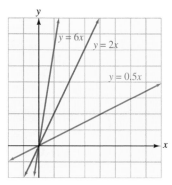

Figure 8-45

One example of direct variation is Hooke's law from physics. Hooke's law states that the distance a spring will stretch varies directly with the force that is applied to it.

If d represents a distance and f represents a force, Hooke's law is expressed mathematically as

$$d = kf$$

where k is the constant of variation. If the spring stretches 10 inches when a weight of 6 pounds is attached, k can be found as follows:

$$d = kf$$

$10 = k(6)$ Substitute 10 for d and 6 for f.

$\dfrac{5}{3} = k$ Divide both sides by 6 and simplify.

To find the force required to stretch the spring a distance of 35 inches, we can solve the equation $d = kf$ for f, with $d = 35$ and $k = \frac{5}{3}$.

$$d = kf$$

$35 = \dfrac{5}{3}f$ Substitute 35 for d and $\frac{5}{3}$ for k.

$105 = 5f$ Multiply both sides by 3.

$21 = f$ Divide both sides by 5.

The force required to stretch the spring a distance of 35 inches is 21 pounds.

EXAMPLE 2   **DIRECT VARIATION**   The distance traveled in a given time is directly proportional to the speed. If a car travels 70 miles at 30 mph, how far will it travel in the same time at 45 mph?

Solution   The words *distance is directly proportional to speed* can be expressed by the equation

(1) $d = ks$

where d is distance, k is the constant of variation, and s is the speed. To find k, we substitute 70 for d and 30 for s, and solve for k.

$$d = ks$$

$$70 = k(30)$$

$$k = \dfrac{7}{3}$$

To find the distance traveled at 45 mph, we substitute $\frac{7}{3}$ for k and 45 for s in Equation 1 and simplify.

$$d = ks$$

$$d = \dfrac{7}{3}(45)$$

$$= 105$$

In the time it took to go 70 miles at 30 mph, the car could travel 105 miles at 45 mph.

➡ **SELF CHECK 2**   How far will the car travel in the same time at 60 mph?

3 Solve an inverse variation problem.

In the formula $w = \frac{12}{l}$, w gets smaller as l gets larger, and w gets larger as l gets smaller. Since these variables vary in opposite directions in a predictable way, we say that the variables **vary inversely,** or that they are *inversely proportional.* The constant 12 is the constant of variation.

Inverse Variation	The words "y varies inversely with x" or "y is inversely proportional to x" mean that $y = \frac{k}{x}$ for some nonzero constant k. The constant k is called the **constant of variation.**

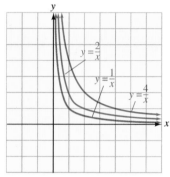

Figure 8-46

The formula for inverse variation $\left(y = \frac{k}{x}\right)$ defines a rational function. The graph of $y = \frac{k}{x}$ appears in Figure 8-46 for three positive values of k.

Because of gravity, an object in space is attracted to Earth. The force of this attraction varies inversely with the square of the distance from the object to the center of the Earth. If f represents the force and d represents the distance, this information can be expressed by the equation

$$f = \frac{k}{d^2}$$

If we know that an object 4,000 miles from the center of the Earth is attracted to Earth with a force of 90 pounds, we can find k.

$$f = \frac{k}{d^2}$$

$$90 = \frac{k}{4{,}000^2} \qquad \text{Substitute 90 for } f \text{ and 4,000 for } d.$$

$$k = 90(4{,}000^2)$$

$$= 1.44 \times 10^9$$

To find the force of attraction when the object is 5,000 miles from the center of the Earth, we proceed as follows:

$$f = \frac{k}{d^2}$$

$$f = \frac{1.44 \times 10^9}{5{,}000^2} \qquad \text{Substitute } 1.44 \times 10^9 \text{ for } k \text{ and 5,000 for } d.$$

$$= 57.6$$

The object will be attracted to the Earth with a force of 57.6 pounds when it is 5,000 miles from Earth's center.

EXAMPLE 3   **LIGHT INTENSITY**   The intensity I of light received from a light source varies inversely with the square of the distance d from the light source. If the intensity of a light source 4 feet from an object is 8 candelas, find the intensity at a distance of 2 feet.

Solution   The words *intensity varies inversely with the square of the distance d* can be expressed by the equation

$$I = \frac{k}{d^2}$$

To find k, we substitute 8 for I and 4 for d and solve for k.

$$I = \frac{k}{d^2}$$

$$8 = \frac{k}{4^2}$$

$$128 = k$$

To find the intensity when the object is 2 feet from the light source, we substitute 2 for d and 128 for k and simplify.

$$I = \frac{k}{d^2}$$

$$I = \frac{128}{2^2}$$

$$= 32$$

The intensity at 2 feet is 32 candelas.

 **SELF CHECK 3**   Find the intensity at a distance of 8 feet.

4 Solve a joint variation problem.

There are times when one variable varies with the product of several variables. For example, the area of a triangle varies directly with the product of its base and height:

$$A = \frac{1}{2}bh$$

Such variation is called **joint variation.**

Joint Variation

If one variable varies directly with the product of two or more variables, the relationship is called **joint variation.** If y varies jointly with x and z, then $y = kxz$. The nonzero constant k is called the **constant of variation.**

EXAMPLE 4   The volume V of a cone varies jointly with its height h and the area of its base B. If $V = 6$ cm^3 when $h = 3$ cm and $B = 6$ cm^2, find V when $h = 2$ and $B = 8$ cm^2.

Solution   The words V varies jointly with h and B can be expressed by the equation

$$V = khB \qquad \text{The relationship can also be read as "}V\text{ is directly proportional to the product of }h\text{ and }B\text{."}$$

We can find k by substituting 6 for V, 3 for h, and 6 for B.

$$V = khB$$

$$6 = k(3)(6)$$

$$6 = k(18)$$

$$\frac{1}{3} = k \qquad \text{Divide both sides by 18; } \frac{6}{18} = \frac{1}{3}.$$

To find V when $h = 2$ and $b = 8$, we substitute these values into the formula $V = \frac{1}{3}hB$.

$$V = \frac{1}{3}hB$$

$$V = \left(\frac{1}{3}\right)(2)(8)$$

$$= \frac{16}{3}$$

When $h = 2$ and $B = 8$, the volume is $5\frac{1}{3}$ cm^3.

5 **Solve a combined variation problem.**

Many applied problems involve a combination of direct and inverse variation. Such variation is called **combined variation.**

EXAMPLE 5   **BUILDING HIGHWAYS**   The time it takes to build a highway varies directly with the length of the road, but inversely with the number of workers. If it takes 100 workers 4 weeks to build 2 miles of highway, how long will it take 80 workers to build 10 miles of highway?

Solution   We can let t represent the time in weeks, l represent the length in miles, and w represent the number of workers. The relationship among these variables can be expressed by the equation

$$t = \frac{kl}{w}$$

We substitute 4 for t, 100 for w, and 2 for l to find k:

$$4 = \frac{k(2)}{100}$$

$400 = 2k$ Multiply both sides by 100.

$200 = k$ Divide both sides by 2.

We now substitute 80 for w, 10 for l, and 200 for k in the equation $t = \frac{kl}{w}$ and simplify:

$$t = \frac{kl}{w}$$ Substitute the values for the variables.

$$t = \frac{200(10)}{80}$$

$$= 25$$

It will take 25 weeks for 80 workers to build 10 miles of highway.

⇨ **SELF CHECK 5**   How long will it take 60 workers to build 6 miles of highway?

⇨ **SELF CHECK ANSWERS**   **1.** $\frac{6}{5}$ **2.** 140 mi   **3.** 2 candelas   **5.** 20 weeks

> **NOW TRY THIS**
>
> *The time t, in hours, required for a satellite to orbit the Earth varies directly as the radius r of the orbit, measured from the center of the Earth, and inversely as the velocity v, in mph. The radius of the Earth is approximately 4,000 miles.*
>
> **1.** The space shuttle makes one orbit around the Earth in 1.5 hours at a rate of 17,000 mph. Its altitude above the Earth's surface is about 200 miles. Find the constant of variation rounded to 8 decimal places.
>
> **2.** The Pentagon's Defense Satellite Communications System (DSCS) orbits at 23,500 miles above the Earth's surface at a speed of approximately 6,955 mph. Using the same constant of variation, how often does it complete an orbit to the nearest hour? What can you conclude about the satellite?

8.6 EXERCISES

WARM-UPS

Solve each proportion.

1. $\dfrac{x}{2} = \dfrac{3}{6}$

2. $\dfrac{3}{x} = \dfrac{4}{12}$

Express each sentence with a formula.

3. a varies directly with b.

4. a varies inversely with b.

5. a varies jointly with b and c.

6. a varies directly with b and inversely with c.

REVIEW   *Simplify each expression.*

7. $(x^2x^3)^2$

8. $\left(\dfrac{a^3a^5}{a^{-2}}\right)^3$

9. $\dfrac{b^0 - 2b^0}{b^0}$

10. $\left(\dfrac{2r^{-2}r^{-3}}{4r^{-5}}\right)^{-3}$

11. Write 35,000 in scientific notation.

12. Write 0.00035 in scientific notation.

13. Write 2.5×10^{-3} in standard notation.

14. Write 2.5×10^4 in standard notation.

VOCABULARY AND CONCEPTS

Fill in the blanks.

15. An equation stating that two ratios are equal is called a _____.

16. In a proportion, the product of the _____ is equal to the product of the _____.

17. The equation $y = kx$ indicates _____ variation.

18. The equation $y = \dfrac{k}{x}$ indicates _____ variation.

19. Inverse variation is represented by a _____ function.

20. Direct variation is represented by a _____ function whose graph passes through the origin.

21. The equation $y = kxz$ indicates _____ variation.

22. The equation $y = \dfrac{kx}{z}$ indicates _____ variation.

Determine whether the graph represents direct variation, inverse variation, or neither.

23.

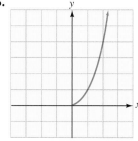

24.

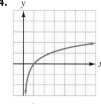

25.

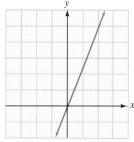

26.

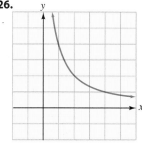

GUIDED PRACTICE

Solve each proportion, if possible. **See Example 1. (Objective 1)**

27. $\dfrac{x}{5} = \dfrac{15}{25}$

28. $\dfrac{4}{y} = \dfrac{6}{27}$

29. $\dfrac{r-2}{3} = \dfrac{r}{5}$

30. $\dfrac{x+1}{x-1} = \dfrac{6}{4}$

31. $\dfrac{3}{n} = \dfrac{2}{n+1}$

32. $\dfrac{4}{x+3} = \dfrac{3}{5}$

33. $\dfrac{5}{5z+3} = \dfrac{2z}{2z^2+6}$

34. $\dfrac{9t+6}{t(t+3)} = \dfrac{7}{t+3}$

Express each sentence as a formula. **See Examples 2–5. (Objectives 2–5)**

35. A varies directly with the square of p.

36. z varies inversely with the cube of t.

37. v varies inversely with the cube of r.

38. r varies directly with the square of s.

39. B varies jointly with m and n.

40. C varies jointly with x, y, and z.

41. P varies directly with the square of a, and inversely with the cube of j.

42. M varies inversely with the cube of n, and jointly with x and the square of z.

Express each formula in words. In each formula, k is the constant of variation. **See Examples 2–5. (Objectives 2–5)**

43. $L = kmn$

44. $P = \dfrac{km}{n}$

45. $E = kab^2$

46. $U = krs^2t$

47. $X = \dfrac{kx^2}{y^2}$

48. $Z = \dfrac{kw}{xy}$

49. $R = \dfrac{kL}{d^2}$

50. $e = \dfrac{kPL}{A}$

ADDITIONAL PRACTICE   *Solve each proportion.*

51. $\dfrac{2}{c} = \dfrac{c-3}{2}$

52. $\dfrac{y}{4} = \dfrac{4}{y}$

53. $\dfrac{2}{3x} = \dfrac{6x}{36}$

54. $\dfrac{2}{x+6} = \dfrac{-2x}{5}$

55. $\dfrac{2(x+3)}{3} = \dfrac{4(x-4)}{5}$

56. $\dfrac{x+4}{5} = \dfrac{3(x-2)}{3}$

57. $\dfrac{1}{x+3} = \dfrac{-2x}{x+5}$

58. $\dfrac{x-1}{x+1} = \dfrac{2}{3x}$

APPLICATIONS   *Solve each variation problem.*
See Examples 2–5. (Objectives 2–5)

59. Area of a circle   The area of a circle varies directly with the square of its radius. The constant of variation is π. Find the area of a circle with a radius of 6 inches.

60. Falling objects   An object in free fall travels a distance s that is directly proportional to the square of the time t. If an object falls 1,024 feet in 8 seconds, how far will it fall in 10 seconds?

61. Finding distance   The distance that a car can go is directly proportional to the number of gallons of gasoline it consumes. If a car can go 288 miles on 12 gallons of gasoline, how far can it go on a full tank of 18 gallons?

62. Farming   A farmer's harvest in bushels varies directly with the number of acres planted. If 8 acres can produce 144 bushels, how many acres are required to produce 1,152 bushels?

63. Farming   The length of time that a given number of bushels of corn will last when feeding cattle varies inversely with the number of animals. If x bushels will feed 25 cows for 10 days, how long will the feed last for 10 cows?

64. Geometry   For a fixed area, the length of a rectangle is inversely proportional to its width. A rectangle has a width of 18 feet and a length of 12 feet. If the length is increased to 16 feet, find the width.

65. Gas pressure   Under constant temperature, the volume occupied by a gas is inversely proportional to the pressure applied. If the gas occupies a volume of 20 cubic inches under a pressure of 6 pounds per square inch, find the volume when the gas is subjected to a pressure of 10 pounds per square inch.

66. Value of a car   The value of a car usually varies inversely with its age. If a car is worth $7,000 when it is 3 years old, how much will it be worth when it is 7 years old?

67. Organ pipes   The frequency of vibration of air in an organ pipe is inversely proportional to the length of the pipe. If a pipe 2 feet long vibrates 256 times per second, how many times per second will a 6-foot pipe vibrate?

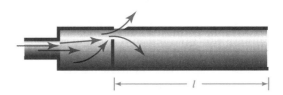

68. Geometry   The area of a rectangle varies jointly with its length and width. If both the length and the width are tripled, by what factor is the area multiplied?

69. Geometry   The volume of a rectangular solid varies jointly with its length, width, and height. If the length is doubled, the width is tripled, and the height is doubled, by what factor is the volume multiplied?

70. Costs of a trucking company The costs incurred by a trucking company vary jointly with the number of trucks in service and the number of hours they are used. When 4 trucks are used for 6 hours each, the costs are $1,800. Find the costs of using 10 trucks, each for 12 hours.

71. Storing oil The number of gallons of oil that can be stored in a cylindrical tank varies jointly with the height of the tank and the square of the radius of its base. The constant of proportionality is 23.5. Find the number of gallons that can be stored in the cylindrical tank in the illustration.

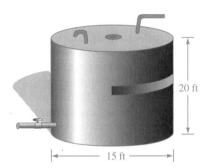

20 ft

15 ft

72. Finding the constant of variation A quantity l varies jointly with x and y and inversely with z. If the value of l is 30 when $x = 15$, $y = 5$, and $z = 10$, find k.

73. Electronics The voltage (in volts) measured across a resistor is directly proportional to the current (in amperes) flowing through the resistor. The constant of variation is the **resistance** (in ohms). If 6 volts is measured across a resistor carrying a current of 2 amperes, find the resistance.

74. Electronics The power (in watts) lost in a resistor (in the form of heat) is directly proportional to the square of the current (in amperes) passing through it. The constant of proportionality is the resistance (in ohms). What power is lost in a 5-ohm resistor carrying a 3-ampere current?

75. Building construction The deflection of a beam is inversely proportional to its width and the cube of its depth. If the deflection of a 4-inch-by-4-inch beam is 1.1 inches, find the deflection of a 2-inch-by-8-inch beam positioned as in the illustration.

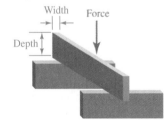

Width | Force

Depth

76. Building construction Find the deflection of the beam in Exercise 75 when the beam is positioned as shown.

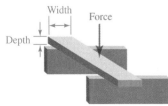

Width | Force

Depth

77. Gas pressure The pressure of a certain amount of gas is directly proportional to the temperature (measured in Kelvin) and inversely proportional to the volume. A sample of gas at a pressure of 1 atmosphere occupies a volume of 1 cubic meter at a temperature of 273 Kelvin. When heated, the gas expands to twice its volume, but the pressure remains constant. To what temperature is it heated?

78. Tension A ball, twirled at the end of a string, is kept in its circular path by the tension of the string. The tension T is directly proportional to the square of the speed s and inversely proportional to the radius r of the circle. If the tension is 32 pounds when the speed is 8 ft/sec and the radius is 6 feet, find the tension when the speed is 4 ft/sec and the radius is 3 feet.

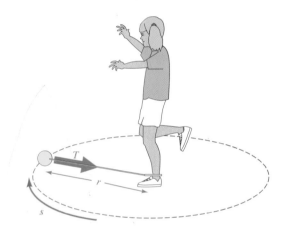

WRITING ABOUT MATH

79. Explain the terms *means* and *extremes*.

80. Distinguish between a *ratio* and a *proportion*.

81. Explain the term *joint variation*.

82. Explain why the equation $\frac{y}{x} = k$ indicates that y varies directly with x.

SOMETHING TO THINK ABOUT

83. As temperature increases on the Fahrenheit scale, it also increases on the Celsius scale. Is this direct variation? Explain.

84. As the cost of a purchase (less than $5) increases, the amount of change received from a five-dollar bill decreases. Is this inverse variation? Explain.

85. Is a proportion useful for solving this problem?

A water bill for 1,000 gallons was $15, and a bill for 2,000 gallons was $25. Find the bill for 3,000 gallons.

Explain.

86. How would you solve the problem in Exercise 85?

PROJECTS

Project 1

The graph of a line is determined by two pieces of information. If we know the line's slope and its y-intercept, we would use the *slope-intercept* form to find the equation of the line. If we know the slope of the line and the coordinates of some point on that line, we would use the *point-slope* form. We have studied several standard forms of the equation of a line. Here is one more standard form that is useful when we know a line's x- and y-intercepts.

The Intercept Form of the Equation of a Line

The equation of a line with x-intercept $(a, 0)$ and y-intercept $(0, b)$ is

$$\frac{x}{a} + \frac{y}{b} = 1$$

- Derive the intercept form of the equation of a line. (*Hint:* You know two points on the line.)

- Find the x- and y-intercepts of the line $\frac{x}{5} + \frac{y}{9} = 1$.

- Find the equation of the line with x-intercept $(3, 0)$ and y-intercept $(0, 7)$.

- Find the x- and y-intercepts of the line $4x + 5y = 20$ by writing the equation in intercept form.

- Graph the line $\frac{x}{k} + \frac{y}{k} = 1$ for five different values of k (your choice). What do these lines have in common?

- Graph the line $\frac{x}{3} + \frac{y}{k} = 1$ for five different values of k. What do these lines have in common?

- Can the equation of every line be written in intercept form? If not, discuss which lines can and which ones can't.

Project 2

You are representing your branch of the large Buy-from-Us Corporation at the company's regional meeting, and you are looking forward to presenting your revenue and cost reports to the other branch representatives. But now disaster strikes! The graphs you had planned to present, containing cost and revenue information for this year and last year, are unlabeled! You cannot immediately recognize which graphs represent costs, which represent revenues, and which represent which year. Without these graphs, your presentation will not be effective.

The only other information you have with you is in the notes you made for your talk. From these you are able to glean the following financial data about your branch.

1. All cost and revenue figures on the graphs are rounded to the nearest $50,000.

2. Costs for the fourth quarter of last year were $400,000.

3. Revenue was not above $400,000 for any quarter last year.

4. Last year, your branch lost money during the first quarter.

5. This year, your branch made money during three of the four quarters.

6. Profit during the second quarter of this year was $150,000.

And, of course, you know that profit = revenue − cost.

With this information, you must match each of the graphs (Illustrations 1–4) with one of the following titles:

Costs, This Year   Costs, Last Year

Revenues, This Year   Revenues, Last Year

You should be sure to have sound reasons for your choices—reasons ensuring that no other arrangement of the titles will fit the data. The *last* thing you want to do is present incorrect information to the company bigwigs!

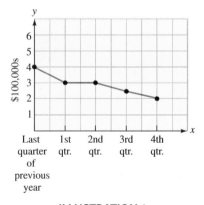

ILLUSTRATION 1

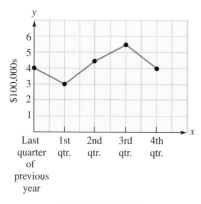

ILLUSTRATION 2

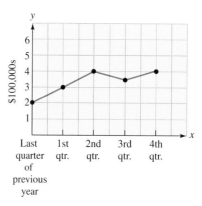

ILLUSTRATION 3

ILLUSTRATION 4

Chapter 8   REVIEW

SECTION 8.1   A Review of the Rectangular Coordinate System

DEFINITIONS AND CONCEPTS	EXAMPLES
Any ordered pair of real numbers represents a point on the rectangular coordinate system.	On the coordinate axis, plot $(0, -2)$, $(2, -4)$, and $(-3, 5)$.
The point where the axes cross is called the *origin*. The four regions of a coordinate plane are called *quadrants*.	The origin is represented by the ordered pair $(0, 0)$. The point with coordinates $(5, 3)$ is in quadrant I. The point with coordinates $(-5, 3)$ is in quadrant II. The point with coordinates $(-5, -3)$ is in quadrant III. The point with coordinates $(5, -3)$ is in quadrant IV.
An ordered pair of real numbers is a **solution** of an equation in two variables if it satisfies the equation.	The ordered pair $(-1, 5)$ is a solution of the equation $x - 2y = -11$ because it satisfies the equation. $$x - 2y = -11$$ $$(-1) - 2(5) \stackrel{?}{=} -11 \quad \text{Substitute } -1 \text{ for } x \text{ and } 5 \text{ for } y.$$ $$-1 - 10 \stackrel{?}{=} -11$$ $$-11 = -11 \quad \text{True.}$$ Since the results are equal, $(-1, 5)$ is a solution.

General form of an equation of a line:

$$Ax + By = C \quad (A \text{ and } B \text{ are not both } 0.)$$

To graph a linear equation,

1. Find three ordered pairs (x, y) that satisfy the equation.
2. Plot each pair on the rectangular coordinate system.
3. Draw a line passing through the three points.

The equation $x + y = -2$ is written in general form.

To graph it, find three ordered pairs that satisfy the equation.

x	y	(x, y)
1	-3	$(1, -3)$
2	-4	$(2, -4)$
3	-5	$(3, -5)$

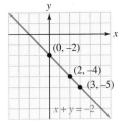

Then plot the points and draw a line passing through them.

The y-intercept of a line is the point where the line intersects the y-axis.

The x-intercept of a line is the point where the line intersects the x-axis.

The y-intercept of the graph above is the point with coordinates $(0, -2)$.

The x-intercept of the graph above is the point with coordinates $(-2, 0)$.

Graph of a horizontal line:

$$y = b \qquad y\text{-intercept at } (0, b)$$

Graph of a vertical line:

$$x = a \qquad x\text{-intercept at } (a, 0)$$

The graph of $y = -3$ is a horizontal line passing through $(0, -3)$.

The graph of $x = 2$ is a vertical line passing through $(2, 0)$.

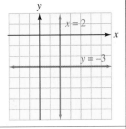

Midpoint formula:

If $P(x_1, y_1)$ and $Q(x_2, y_2)$, the midpoint of segment PQ is

$$M\left(\frac{x_1 + x_2}{2}, \frac{y_1 + y_2}{2}\right)$$

To find the midpoint of the line segment joining $P(3, -2)$ and $Q(2, -5)$, find the mean of the x-coordinates and the mean of the y-coordinates:

$$\frac{x_1 + x_2}{2} = \frac{3 + 2}{2} = \frac{5}{2}$$

$$\frac{y_1 + y_2}{2} = \frac{-2 + (-5)}{2} = -\frac{7}{2}$$

The midpoint of segment PQ is the point $M\left(\frac{5}{2}, -\frac{7}{2}\right)$.

REVIEW EXERCISES

Graph each equation.

1. $x + y = 4$

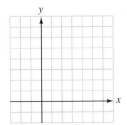

2. $2x - y = 8$

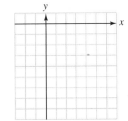

3. $y = 3x + 4$

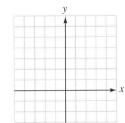

4. $x = 4 - 2y$

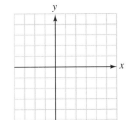

5. $y = 4$

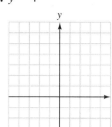

6. $x = -2$

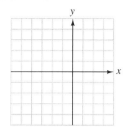

7. $2(x + 3) = x + 2$

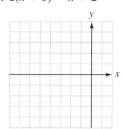

8. $3y = 2(y - 1)$

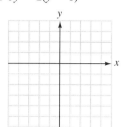

9. Find the midpoint of the line segment joining $(-3, 5)$ and $(6, 11)$.

SECTION 8.2   Slope of a Line

DEFINITIONS AND CONCEPTS	EXAMPLES
Slope of a nonvertical line: If $x_2 \neq x_1$, $$m = \frac{\Delta y}{\Delta x} = \frac{y_2 - y_1}{x_2 - x_1}$$	The slope of a line passing through $(-1, 4)$ and $(5, -3)$ is given by $$m = \frac{y_2 - y_1}{x_2 - x_1} = \frac{-3 - 4}{5 - (-1)} = \frac{-7}{6}$$
Horizontal lines have a slope of 0.	$y = 5$ is a horizontal line with slope 0.
Vertical lines have no defined slope.	$x = 5$ is a vertical line with no defined slope.
Parallel lines have the same slope.	Two lines with slopes $\frac{3}{2}$ and $\frac{3}{2}$ are parallel if they have different y-intercepts.
The slopes of two nonvertical perpendicular lines are negative reciprocals.	Two lines with slopes 5 and $-\frac{1}{5}$ are perpendicular.

REVIEW EXERCISES
Find the slope of the line passing through points P and Q, if possible.

10. $P(2, 5)$ and $Q(5, 8)$

11. $P(-3, -2)$ and $Q(6, 12)$

12. $P(-3, 4)$ and $Q(-5, -6)$

13. $P(5, -4)$ and $Q(-6, -9)$

14. $P(-2, 4)$ and $Q(8, 4)$

15. $P(-5, -4)$ and $Q(-5, 8)$

Find the slope of the graph of each equation, if one exists.

16. $2x - 3y = 18$

17. $2x + y = 8$

18. $-2(x - 3) = 10$

19. $3y + 1 = 7$

Determine whether the lines with the given slopes are parallel, perpendicular, or neither.

20. $m_1 = 4, m_2 = -\frac{1}{4}$

21. $m_1 = 0.5, m_2 = \frac{1}{2}$

22. $m_1 = 0.5, m_2 = -\frac{1}{2}$

23. $m_1 = 5, m_2 = -0.2$

24. Sales growth If the sales of a new business were $65,000 in its first year and $130,000 in its fourth year, find the rate of growth in sales per year.

SECTION 8.3   Writing Equations of Lines

DEFINITIONS AND CONCEPTS	EXAMPLES
Equations of a line: *Point-slope form:* $$y - y_1 = m(x - x_1)$$	Write the point-slope form of a line passing through $(-3, 5)$ with slope $\frac{1}{2}$. $y - y_1 = m(x - x_1)$ This is point-slope form. $y - 5 = \frac{1}{2}[x - (-3)]$ Substitute. $y - 5 = \frac{1}{2}(x + 3)$

Slope-intercept form:	Write the slope-intercept form of a line with slope $\frac{1}{2}$ and y-intercept $(0, -4)$.
$y = mx + b$	$y = mx + b$ This is slope-intercept form. $y = \frac{1}{2}x - 4$ Substitute. $y = \frac{1}{2}x - 4$

REVIEW EXERCISES

Write the equation of the line with the given properties. Write the equation in general form.

25. Slope of 3; passing through $P(-8, 5)$

26. Passing through $(-2, 4)$ and $(6, -9)$

27. Passing through $(-3, -5)$; parallel to the graph of $3x - 2y = 7$

28. Passing through $(-3, -5)$; perpendicular to the graph of $3x - 2y = 7$

29. Use the slope of a line to help graph the function $y = \frac{2}{3}x + 1$.

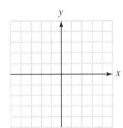

30. Are the lines represented by $2x + 3y = 8$ and $3x - 2y = 10$ parallel or perpendicular?

31. Depreciation A business purchased a copy machine for \$8,700 and will depreciate it on a straight-line basis over the next 5 years. At the end of its useful life, it will be sold as scrap for \$100. Find its depreciation equation.

SECTION 8.4   A Review of Functions

DEFINITIONS AND CONCEPTS	EXAMPLES
A **relation** is any set of ordered pairs. A **function** is any set of ordered pairs (a relation) in which each first component (input value) determines exactly one second component (output value).	Find the domain and range of the relation $\{(2, -1), (6, 3), (2, 5)\}$ and determine whether it defines a function.
The **domain** of a function is the set of input values.	**Domain:** $\{2, 6\}$ because 2 and 6 are the first components in the ordered pairs.
The **range** is the set of output values.	**Range:** $\{-1, 3, 5\}$ because $-1, 3$, and 5 are the second components in the ordered pairs. The relation does not define a function because the first component 2 determines two different second components.
The **vertical line test** can be used to determine whether a graph represents a function.	Find the domain and range of the function represented by the graph and determine whether it is a function.

	Since the graph extends forever to the left, and stops at $x = 3$ on the right, the domain is $(-\infty, 3]$.
	Since the graph extends forever downward and ends at $y = 4$, the domain is $(-\infty, 4]$.
	Since every vertical line that intersects the graph will do so exactly once, the vertical line test indicates that the graph is a function.
$f(k)$ represents the value of $f(x)$ when $x = k$.	If $f(x) = -7x + 4$, find $f(2)$. $$\begin{aligned} f(x) &= -7x + 4 \\ f(2) &= -7(2) + 4 \quad \text{Substitute 2 for } x. \\ &= -14 + 4 \\ &= -10 \end{aligned}$$ In ordered pair form, we can write $(2, -10)$.
The domain of a function of x that is defined by an equation is the set of all numbers that are permissible replacements for x.	Find the domain of $f(x) = \dfrac{-5}{x + 7}$. The number -7 cannot be substituted for x in the function, because that would make the denominator 0. However, any real number, except -7, can be substituted for x to obtain a single value y. Therefore, the domain is the set of all real numbers except -7. This is the union of two intervals $(-\infty, -7) \cup (-7, \infty)$.
A **linear function** is a function defined by an equation that can be written in the form $$f(x) = mx + b \quad \text{or} \quad y = mx + b$$ where m is the slope of the line graph and $(0, b)$ is the y-intercept.	The graph of $f(x) = 4x - 1$ is a line with slope 4 and y-intercept $(0, -1)$. The domain is the set of real numbers $\mathbb{R}$, and the range is the set of real numbers $\mathbb{R}$.

REVIEW EXERCISES

Determine whether each equation determines y to be a function of x.

32. $y = 6x - 4$ **33.** $y = 4 - x$

34. $y^2 = x$ **35.** $|y| = x^2$

Assume that $f(x) = 3x + 2$ and $g(x) = x^2 - 4$ and find each value.

36. $f(-3)$ **37.** $g(8)$

38. $g(-2)$ **39.** $f(5)$

Find the domain of each function and graph the function to find its range.

40. $f(x) = 4x - 1$

41. $f(x) = 3x - 10$

42. $f(x) = x^2 + 1$

43. $f(x) = \dfrac{4}{2 - x}$

44. $f(x) = \dfrac{7}{x - 3}$

45. $y = 7$

Use the vertical line test to determine whether each graph represents a function.

46.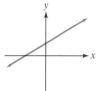

47.

48.

49.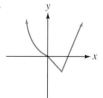

SECTION 8.5   Graphs of Nonlinear Functions

DEFINITIONS AND CONCEPTS	EXAMPLES
Graphs of nonlinear equations are not lines. **Vertical translations:** If f is a function and k is a positive number, then • The graph of $f(x) + k$ is identical to the graph of $f(x)$, except that it is translated k units upward. • The graph of $f(x) - k$ is identical to the graph of $f(x)$, except that it is translated k units downward. **Horizontal translations:** If f is a function and k is a positive number, then • The graph of $f(x - k)$ is identical to the graph of $f(x)$, except that it is translated k units to the right. • The graph of $f(x + k)$ is identical to the graph of $f(x)$, except that it is translated k units to the left. **Reflections:** The graph of $y = -f(x)$ is the graph of $f(x)$ reflected about the x-axis.	The graph of $f(x) = |x| + 4$ will be the same shape as the graph of $f(x) = |x|$, but shifted up 4 units. The graph of $f(x) = |x| - 3$ will be the same shape as the graph of $f(x) = |x|$, but shifted down 3 units. The graph of $f(x) = (x - 3)^2$ will be the same shape as the graph of $f(x) = x^2$, but shifted 3 units to the right. The graph of $f(x) = (x + 4)^2$ will be the same shape as the graph of $f(x) = x^2$, but shifted 4 units to the left. The graph of $f(x) = -x^3$ is the graph of $f(x) = x^3$ reflected about the x-axis.
Finding the domain of a rational function: The domain of a rational function is all values for which the function is defined.	Since the denominator of the fraction in $f(x) = \frac{x + 1}{x - 2}$ cannot be 0, the domain of $f(x)$ is all real numbers except 2. In interval notation, this is $(-\infty, 2) \cup (2, \infty)$.
Vertical asymptotes occur where a rational function is not defined.	In the graph of $f(x) = \frac{x + 1}{x - 2}$, there will be a vertical asymptote at $x = 2$ because the function is not defined when x is 2. 
We obtain the range from the graph. A horizontal asymptote occurs when a value is excluded from the range.	From the graph, we see that the range is $(-\infty, 1) \cup (1, \infty)$. There will be a horizontal asymptote at $y = 1$.

REVIEW EXERCISES
Graph each function.

50. $f(x) = x^2 - 3$

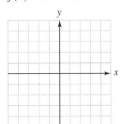

51. $f(x) = |x| - 4$

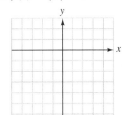

52. $f(x) = (x - 2)^3$

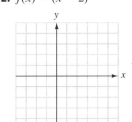

53. $f(x) = (x + 4)^2 - 3$

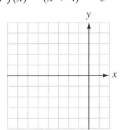

54. $f(x) = -x^3 - 2$ **55.** $f(x) = -|x - 1| + 2$ **60.** $f(x) = -x^3 - 2$ **61.** $f(x) = -|x - 1| + 2$

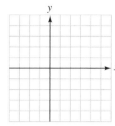

Use a graphing calculator to graph each rational function and find its domain and range.

62. $f(x) = \dfrac{2}{x - 2}$ **63.** $f(x) = \dfrac{x}{x + 3}$

Use a graphing calculator to graph each function. Compare the results in Problems 50–55.

56. $f(x) = x^2 - 3$ **57.** $f(x) = |x| - 4$

58. $f(x) = (x - 2)^3$ **59.** $f(x) = (x + 4)^2 - 3$

SECTION 8.6   Variation

DEFINITIONS AND CONCEPTS	EXAMPLES
Solving a proportion: In a proportion, the product of the extremes is equal to the product of the means.	To solve $\dfrac{x - 1}{x + 1} = \dfrac{2}{3x}$, proceed as follows: $3x(x - 1) = 2(x + 1)$ The product of the extremes is equal to the product of the means. $3x^2 - 3x = 2x + 2$ Remove parentheses. $3x^2 - 5x - 2 = 0$ Subtract $2x$ and 2 from both sides. $(3x + 1)(x - 2) = 0$ Factor. $3x + 1 = 0$ or $x - 2 = 0$ Use the zero factor property. $x = -\dfrac{1}{3}$ $\bigg|$ $x = 2$ Solve each linear equation. The solutions are $-\dfrac{1}{3}$, 2.
Solving variation problems **Direct variation:** $y = kx$ (k is a constant)	Express each sentence as a formula: The distance, d, a car travels is directly proportional to the time, t, it has been traveling. $d = kt$
Inverse variation: $y = \dfrac{k}{x}$ (k is a constant)	The temperature, T, of the coffee in the mug varies inversely to the time, t, it has been sitting on the counter. $T = \dfrac{k}{t}$
Joint variation: $y = kxz$ (k is a constant)	The interest, I, on the money is jointly proportional to the principle, p, and the interest rate, r. $I = kpr$

Combined variation:

$$y = \frac{kx}{y} \quad (k \text{ is a constant})$$

The pressure, P, of the gas varies directly as the temperature, t, and inversely as the volume, V.

$$P = \frac{kt}{V}$$

REVIEW EXERCISES
Solve each proportion.

64. $\dfrac{x+1}{8} = \dfrac{4x-2}{23}$

65. $\dfrac{1}{x+6} = \dfrac{x+10}{12}$

66. Assume that y varies directly with x. If $x = 12$ when $y = 2$, find the value of y when $x = 12$.

67. Assume that y varies inversely with x. If $x = 24$ when $y = 3$, find the value of y when $x = 12$.

68. Assume that y varies jointly with x and z. Find the constant of variation if $x = 24$ when $y = 3$ and $z = 4$.

69. Assume that y varies directly with t and inversely with x. Find the constant of variation if $x = 2$ when $t = 8$ and $y = 64$.

Chapter 8 TEST

1. Graph the equation $2x - 5y = 10$.

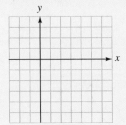

2. Find the coordinates of the midpoint of the line segment shown in the illustration.

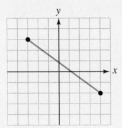

3. Find the x- and y-intercepts of the graph of $y = \dfrac{x-3}{5}$.

4. Is the graph of $x - 7 = 0$ a horizontal or a vertical line?

Find the slope of each line, if possible.

5. The line through $(-2, 4)$ and $(6, 8)$

6. The graph of $2x - 3y = 8$

7. The graph of $x = 12$

8. The graph of $y = 12$

9. Write the equation of the line with slope of $\frac{2}{3}$ that passes through $(4, -5)$. Give the answer in slope-intercept form.

10. Write the equation of the line that passes through $(-2, 6)$ and $(-4, -10)$. Give the answer in general form.

11. Find the slope and the y-intercept of the graph of $-2(x - 3) = 3(2y + 5)$.

12. Determine whether the graphs of $4x - y = 12$ and $y = \frac{1}{4}x + 3$ are parallel, perpendicular, or neither.

13. Determine whether the graphs of $y = -\frac{2}{3}x + 4$ and $2y = 3x - 3$ are parallel, perpendicular, or neither.

14. Write the equation of the line that passes through the origin and is parallel to the graph of $y = \frac{3}{2}x - 7$.

15. Write the equation of the line that passes through $(-3, 6)$ and is perpendicular to the graph of $y = -\frac{2}{3}x - 7$.

16. Does $|y| = x$ define y to be a function of x?

17. Find the domain and range of the function $f(x) = |x|$ by graphing.

18. Find the domain and range of the function $f(x) = x^3$ by graphing.

Let $f(x) = 3x + 1$ and $g(x) = x^2 - 2$. Find each value.

19. $f(3)$

20. $g(0)$

21. $f(a)$

22. $g(-x)$

Determine whether each graph represents a function.

23.

24.

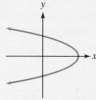

25. Graph: $f(x) = x^2 - 1$.

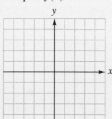

26. Graph: $f(x) = -|x + 2|$.

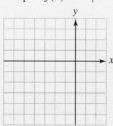

27. Solve the proportion: $\frac{3}{x - 2} = \frac{x + 3}{2x}$.

28. Assume that y varies directly with x. If $x = 30$ when $y = 4$, find y when $x = 9$.

29. Assume that V varies inversely with t. If $= 55$ when $t = 20$, find t when $V = 75$.

30. Does the graph define a function?

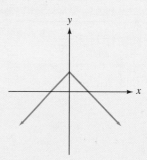

Cumulative Review Exercises

Determine which numbers in the set $\left\{-2, 0, 1, 2, \frac{13}{12}, 6, 7, \sqrt{5}, \pi\right\}$ are in each category.

1. Natural numbers

2. Whole numbers

3. Rational numbers

4. Irrational numbers

5. Negative numbers

6. Real numbers

7. Prime numbers

8. Composite numbers

9. Even numbers

10. Odd numbers

Graph each interval on the number line.

11. $-2 < x \le 5$

12. $[-5, 0) \cup [3, 6]$

Simplify each expression.

13. $-|5| + |-3|$

14. $\dfrac{|-5| + |-3|}{-|4|}$

Perform the operations.

15. $2 + 4 \cdot 5$

16. $\dfrac{8 - 4}{2 - 4}$

17. $20 \div (-10 \div 2)$

18. $\dfrac{6 + 3(6 + 4)}{2(3 - 9)}$

Let $x = 2$ and $y = -3$ and evaluate each expression.

19. $-x - 2y$

20. $\dfrac{x^2 - y^2}{2x + y}$

Determine which property of real numbers justifies each statement.

21. $(a + b) + c = a + (b + c)$

22. $3(x + y) = 3x + 3y$

23. $(a + b) + c = c + (a + b)$

24. $(ab)c = a(bc)$

Simplify each expression. Assume that all variables are positive numbers and write all answers without negative exponents.

25. $(x^2 y^3)^4$

26. $\dfrac{c^4 c^8}{(c^5)^2}$

27. $\left(-\dfrac{a^3 b^{-2}}{ab}\right)^{-1}$

28. $\left(\dfrac{-3a^3 b^{-2}}{6a^{-2} b^3}\right)^0$

29. Change 0.00000497 to scientific notation.

30. Change 9.32×10^8 to standard notation.

Radicals and Rational Exponents

Careers and Mathematics

PHOTOGRAPHERS

Photographers produce and preserve images that paint a picture, tell a story, or record an event. They use either a traditional camera that records images on silver halide film that is developed into prints or a digital camera that electronically records images.
Photographers held about 129,000 jobs in 2004. More than half were self-employed. Employers usually seek applicants with a "good eye," imagination, and creativity. Entry-level positions in photojournalism generally require a college degree in journalism or photography.

Job Outlook:
Employment of photographers is expected to increase about as fast as the average for all occupations through 2014. However, photographers can expect keen competition for job openings because the work is attractive to many people.

Annual Earnings:
$18,380–$37,370

For More Information:
http://www.bls.gov/oco/ocos264.htm

For a Sample Application:
See Problem 107 in Section 9.5.

In this chapter ▶

In this chapter, we will reverse the squaring process and learn how to find square roots of numbers. We also will learn how to find other roots of numbers, solve radical equations, and discuss complex numbers.

Radical Expressions

1. Simplify a perfect-square root.
2. Simplify a perfect-square root expression.
3. Simplify a perfect-cube root.
4. Simplify a perfect nth root.
5. Find the domain of a square-root function and a cube-root function.
6. Use a square root to find the standard deviation of a set of data.

Vocabulary

square root	integer squares	index
radical sign	cube root	square-root function
radicand	odd root	cube-root function
principal square root	even root	standard deviation

Getting Ready

Find each power.

1. 0^2 **2.** 4^2 **3.** $(-4)^2$ **4.** -4^2

5. $\left(\dfrac{2}{5}\right)^3$ **6.** $\left(-\dfrac{3}{4}\right)^4$ **7.** $(7xy)^2$ **8.** $(7xy)^3$

In this section, we will discuss square roots and other roots of algebraic expressions. We also will consider their related functions.

1 Simplify a perfect-square root.

When solving problems, we often must find what number must be squared to obtain a second number a. If such a number can be found, it is called a **square root** of a. For example,

- 0 is a square root of 0, because $0^2 = 0$.
- 4 is a square root of 16, because $4^2 = 16$.
- -4 is a square root of 16, because $(-4)^2 = 16$.
- $7xy$ is a square root of $49x^2y^2$, because $(7xy)^2 = 49x^2y^2$.
- $-7xy$ is a square root of $49x^2y^2$, because $(-7xy)^2 = 49x^2y^2$.

All positive numbers have two real-number square roots: one that is positive and one that is negative.

EXAMPLE 1   Find the two square roots of 121.

Solution   The two square roots of 121 are 11 and −11, because

$$11^2 = 121 \quad \text{and} \quad (-11)^2 = 121$$

⇨ **SELF CHECK 1**   Find the square roots of 144.

To express square roots, we use the symbol $\sqrt{}$, called a **radical sign.** For example,

$$\sqrt{121} = 11 \qquad \text{Read as "The positive square root of 121 is 11."}$$
$$-\sqrt{121} = -11 \qquad \text{Read as "The negative square root of 121 is −11."}$$

The number under the radical sign is called a **radicand.**

Square Root of a	If $a > 0$, $\sqrt{a}$ is the positive number whose square is a. In symbols, $$\left(\sqrt{a}\right)^2 = a$$ The positive number $\sqrt{a}$ is called the **principal square root of a.** If $a = 0$, $\sqrt{a} = \sqrt{0} = 0$. The principal square root of 0 is 0. If $a < 0$, $\sqrt{a}$ is not a real number.

COMMENT   These examples suggest that if any number a can be factored into two equal factors, either of those factors is a square root of a.

COMMENT   The principal square root of a positive number is always positive. Although 5 and −5 are both square roots of 25, only 5 is the principal square root. The radical expression $\sqrt{25}$ represents 5. The radical expression $-\sqrt{25}$ represents −5.

Because of the previous definition, the square root of any number squared is that number. For example,

$$\left(\sqrt{10}\right)^2 = \sqrt{10} \cdot \sqrt{10} = 10 \quad \left(\sqrt{a}\right)^2 = \sqrt{a} \cdot \sqrt{a} = a$$

EXAMPLE 2   Simplify each radical.

a. $\sqrt{1} = 1$ **b.** $\sqrt{81} = 9$

c. $-\sqrt{81} = -9$ **d.** $-\sqrt{225} = -15$

e. $\sqrt{\dfrac{1}{4}} = \dfrac{1}{2}$ **f.** $-\sqrt{\dfrac{16}{121}} = -\dfrac{4}{11}$

g. $\sqrt{0.04} = 0.2$ **h.** $-\sqrt{0.0009} = -0.03$

⇨ **SELF CHECK 2**   Simplify: **a.** $-\sqrt{49}$ **b.** $\sqrt{\dfrac{25}{49}}$.

Numbers such as 1, 4, 9, 16, 49, and 1,600 are called **integer squares,** because each one is the square of an integer. The square root of every integer square is an integer.

$$\sqrt{1} = 1 \qquad \sqrt{4} = 2 \qquad \sqrt{9} = 3 \qquad \sqrt{16} = 4 \qquad \sqrt{49} = 7 \qquad \sqrt{1,600} = 40$$

PERSPECTIVE Calculating Square Roots

The Bakhshali manuscript is an early mathematical manuscript that was discovered in India in the late 19th century. Mathematical historians estimate that the manuscript was written sometime around 400 A.D. One section of the manuscript presents a procedure for calculating square roots using basic arithmetic. Specifically, we can use the formula

$$\sqrt{Q} = A + \frac{b}{2A} - \left(\frac{b^2}{4A(2A^2 + b)} \right)$$

where $A^2 = $ a perfect square close to the number Q, and $b = Q - A^2$.

Source: http://www.gap-system.org/~history/HistTopics/Bakhshali_manuscript.html

For example, if we want to compute an approximation of $\sqrt{21}$, we can choose $A^2 = 16$. Thus, $A = 4$ and $b = 21 - 16 = 5$. So we get

$$\sqrt{21} = 4 + \frac{5}{(2)(4)} - \left(\frac{5^2}{(4)(4)((2)(4)^2 + 5)} \right)$$

$$= 4 + \frac{5}{8} - \left(\frac{25}{(16)(37)} \right)$$

$$= 4 + \frac{5}{8} - \frac{25}{592} \approx 4.58277027$$

Using the square root key on a calculator, we see that, to nine decimal places, $\sqrt{21} = 4.582575695$. Therefore, the formula gives an answer that is correct to three decimal places.

1. Use the formula to approximate $\sqrt{105}$. How accurate is your answer?

2. Use the formula to approximate $\sqrt{627}$. How accurate is your answer?

The square roots of many positive integers are not rational numbers. For example, $\sqrt{11}$ is an *irrational number*. To find an approximate value of $\sqrt{11}$ with a calculator, we enter these numbers and press these keys.

11 **2ND** $\sqrt{\ }$ Using a scientific calculator

2ND $\sqrt{\ }$ 11 **ENTER**   Using a graphing calculator

Either way, we will see that

$$\sqrt{11} \approx 3.31662479$$

Square roots of negative numbers are not real numbers. For example, $\sqrt{-9}$ is not a real number, because no real number squared equals -9. Square roots of negative numbers come from a set called *imaginary numbers,* which we will discuss later in this chapter.

2 Simplify a perfect-square root expression.

If $x \neq 0$, the positive number x^2 has x and $-x$ for its two square roots. To denote the positive square root of $\sqrt{x^2}$, we must know whether x is positive or negative.

If $x > 0$, we can write

$$\sqrt{x^2} = x \qquad \sqrt{x^2} \text{ represents the positive square root of } x^2, \text{ which is } x.$$

If x is negative, then $-x > 0$, and we can write

$$\sqrt{x^2} = -x \qquad \sqrt{x^2} \text{ represents the positive square root of } x^2, \text{ which is } -x.$$

If we don't know whether x is positive or negative, we must use absolute value symbols to guarantee that $\sqrt{x^2}$ is positive.

Definition of $\sqrt{x^2}$	If x can be any real number, then
	$$\sqrt{x^2} = |x|$$

EXAMPLE 3 Simplify each expression. Assume that x can be any real number.

a. $\sqrt{16x^2} = \sqrt{(4x)^2}$ Write $16x^2$ as $(4x)^2$.

$= |4x|$ Because $(|4x|)^2 = 16x^2$. Since x could be negative, absolute value symbols are needed.

$= 4|x|$ Since 4 is a positive constant in the product $4x$, we can write it outside the absolute value symbols.

b. $\sqrt{x^2 + 2x + 1}$

$= \sqrt{(x + 1)^2}$ Factor $x^2 + 2x + 1$.

$= |x + 1|$ Because $(x + 1)^2 = x^2 + 2x + 1$. Since $x + 1$ can be negative (for example, when $x = -5$), absolute value symbols are needed.

c. $\sqrt{x^4} = x^2$ Because $(x^2)^2 = x^4$. Since $x^2 \geq 0$, no absolute value symbols are needed.

⇨ **SELF CHECK 3** Simplify: **a.** $\sqrt{25a^2}$ **b.** $\sqrt{x^2 + 4x + 4}$ **c.** $\sqrt{16a^4}$.

---

3 **Simplify a perfect-cube root.**

The **cube root of x** is any number whose cube is x. For example,

4 is a cube root of 64, because $4^3 = 64$.

$3x^2y$ is a cube root of $27x^6y^3$, because $(3x^2y)^3 = 27x^6y^3$.

$-2y$ is a cube root of $-8y^3$, because $(-2y)^3 = -8y^3$.

Cube Root of a	The cube root of a is denoted as $\sqrt[3]{a}$ and is the number whose cube is a. In symbols,
	$$\left(\sqrt[3]{a}\right)^3 = a$$
	If a is any real number, then
	$$\sqrt[3]{a^3} = a$$

We note that 64 has two real-number square roots, 8 and -8. However, 64 has only one real-number cube root, 4, because 4 is the only real number whose cube is 64. Since every real number has exactly one real cube root, it is unnecessary to use absolute value symbols when simplifying cube roots.

EXAMPLE 4 Simplify each radical.

a. $\sqrt[3]{125} = 5$ Because $5^3 = 5 \cdot 5 \cdot 5 = 125$

b. $\sqrt[3]{\dfrac{1}{8}} = \dfrac{1}{2}$ Because $\left(\dfrac{1}{2}\right)^3 = \dfrac{1}{2} \cdot \dfrac{1}{2} \cdot \dfrac{1}{2} = \dfrac{1}{8}$

c. $\sqrt[3]{-27x^3} = -3x$ Because $(-3x)^3 = (-3x)(-3x)(-3x) = -27x^3$

d. $\sqrt[3]{-\dfrac{8a^3}{27b^3}} = -\dfrac{2a}{3b}$ Because $\left(-\dfrac{2a}{3b}\right)^3 = \left(-\dfrac{2a}{3b}\right)\left(-\dfrac{2a}{3b}\right)\left(-\dfrac{2a}{3b}\right) = -\dfrac{8a^3}{27b^3}$

e. $\sqrt[3]{0.216x^3y^6} = 0.6xy^2$ Because $(0.6xy^2)^3 = (0.6xy^2)(0.6xy^2)(0.6xy^2) = 0.216x^3y^6$

⇨ **SELF CHECK 4**   Simplify: **a.** $\sqrt[3]{1,000}$ **b.** $\sqrt[3]{\dfrac{1}{27}}$ **c.** $\sqrt[3]{125a^3}$.

COMMENT   The previous examples suggest that if a can be factored into three equal factors, any one of those factors is a cube root of a.

4   **Simplify a perfect nth root.**

Just as there are square roots and cube roots, there are fourth roots, fifth roots, sixth roots, and so on.

When n is an odd natural number greater than 1, $\sqrt[n]{x}$ represents an **odd root.** Since every real number has only one real nth root when n is odd, we don't need to use absolute value symbols when finding odd roots. For example,

$$\sqrt[5]{243} = 3 \qquad \text{because } 3^5 = 243$$
$$\sqrt[7]{-128x^7} = -2x \qquad \text{because } (-2x)^7 = -128x^7$$

When n is an even natural number greater than 1, $\sqrt[n]{x}$ represents an **even root.** In this case, there will be one positive and one negative real nth root. For example, the two real sixth roots of 729 are 3 and -3, because $3^6 = 729$ and $(-3)^6 = 729$. When finding even roots, we use absolute value symbols to guarantee that the principal nth root is positive.

$$\sqrt[4]{(-3)^4} = |-3| = 3 \qquad \text{Because } 3^4 = (-3)^4. \text{ We also could simplify this as follows:}$$
$$\sqrt[4]{(-3)^4} = \sqrt[4]{81} = 3.$$

$$\sqrt[6]{729x^6} = |3x| = 3|x| \qquad \text{Because } (3|x|)^6 = 729x^6. \text{ The absolute value symbols}$$
$$\text{guarantee that the sixth root is positive.}$$

In the radical $\sqrt[n]{x}$, n is called the **index** (or **order**) of the radical. When the index is 2, the radical is a square root, and we usually do not write the index.

$$\sqrt[2]{x} = \sqrt{x}$$

COMMENT   When n is an even number greater than 1 and $x < 0$, $\sqrt[n]{x}$ is not a real number. For example, $\sqrt[4]{-81}$ is not a real number, because no real number raised to the 4th power is -81. However, when n is odd, $\sqrt[n]{x}$ is a real number.

EXAMPLE 5   Simplify each radical.

a. $\sqrt[4]{625} = 5$, because $5^4 = 625$ Read $\sqrt[4]{625}$ as "the fourth root of 625."

b. $\sqrt[5]{-32} = -2$, because $(-2)^5 = -32$ Read $\sqrt[5]{-32}$ as "the fifth root of -32."

c. $\sqrt[6]{\dfrac{1}{64}} = \dfrac{1}{2}$, because $\left(\dfrac{1}{2}\right)^6 = \dfrac{1}{64}$ Read $\sqrt[6]{\dfrac{1}{64}}$ as "the sixth root of $\dfrac{1}{64}$."

d. $\sqrt[7]{10^7} = 10$, because $10^7 = 10^7$ Read $\sqrt[7]{10^7}$ as "the seventh root of 10^7."

⇨ **SELF CHECK 5**   Simplify: **a.** $\sqrt[4]{\dfrac{1}{81}}$ **b.** $\sqrt[5]{10^5}$.

When finding the *n*th root of an *n*th power, we can use the following rules.

Definition of $\sqrt[n]{a^n}$	If n is an odd natural number greater than 1, then $\sqrt[n]{a^n} = a$.
	If n is an even natural number, then $\sqrt[n]{a^n} = |a|$.

EXAMPLE 6 Simplify each radical. Assume that x can be any real number.

Solution

a. $\sqrt[5]{x^5} = x$ — Since n is odd, absolute value symbols aren't needed.

b. $\sqrt[4]{16x^4} = |2x| = 2|x|$ — Since n is even and x can be negative, absolute value symbols are needed to guarantee that the result is positive.

c. $\sqrt[6]{(x + 4)^6} = |x + 4|$ — Absolute value symbols are needed to guarantee that the result is positive.

d. $\sqrt[3]{(x + 1)^3} = x + 1$ — Since n is odd, absolute value symbols aren't needed.

e. $\sqrt{(x^2 + 6x + 9)^2} = \sqrt{[(x + 3)^2]^2}$ Factor $x^2 + 6x + 9$.

$\qquad = \sqrt{(x + 3)^4}$

$\qquad = (x + 3)^2$ — Since $(x + 3)^2$ is always positive, absolute value symbols aren't needed.

⇨ **SELF CHECK 6** Simplify: **a.** $\sqrt[4]{16a^4}$ **b.** $\sqrt[5]{(a + 5)^5}$.

We summarize the possibilities for $\sqrt[n]{x}$ as follows:

Definition for $\sqrt[n]{x}$	If n is a natural number greater than 1 and x is a real number, then
	If $x > 0$, then $\sqrt[n]{x}$ is the positive number such that $\left(\sqrt[n]{x}\right)^n = x$.
	If $x = 0$, then $\sqrt[n]{x} = 0$.
	If $x < 0$ $\begin{cases} \text{and } n \text{ is odd, then } \sqrt[n]{x} \text{ is the real number such that } \left(\sqrt[n]{x}\right)^n = x. \\ \text{and } n \text{ is even, then } \sqrt[n]{x} \text{ is not a real number.} \end{cases}$

5 **Find the domain of a square-root function and a cube-root function.**

Since there is one principal square root for every nonnegative real number x, the equation $f(x) = \sqrt{x}$ determines a function, called the **square-root function.**

EXAMPLE 7 Consider the function $f(x) = \sqrt{x}$.
a. Find its domain.   **b.** Graph the function.   **c.** Find its range.

Solution **a.** To find the domain, we note that $x \geq 0$ in the function because the radicand must be nonnegative. Thus, the domain is the set of nonnegative real numbers. In interval notation, the domain is the interval $[0, \infty)$.

b. We can make a table of values and plot points to get the graph shown in Figure 9-1(a). If we use a graphing calculator, we can choose window settings of $[-1, 9]$ for x and $[-2, 5]$ for y to get the graph shown in Figure 9-1(b). Since the equation defines a function, its graph passes the vertical line test.

$f(x) = \sqrt{x}$

x	$f(x)$	$(x, f(x))$
0	0	$(0, 0)$
1	1	$(1, 1)$
4	2	$(4, 2)$
9	3	$(9, 3)$

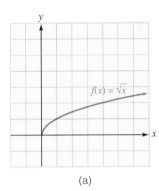

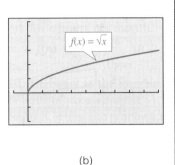

(a)   (b)

Figure 9-1

c. From either graph, we can see that the range of the function is the set of nonnegative real numbers, which is the interval $[0, \infty)$. The graph also confirms that the domain is the interval $[0, \infty)$.

⇨ **SELF CHECK 7**   Graph $f(x) = \sqrt{x} + 2$ and compare it to the graph of $f(x) = \sqrt{x}$. Find the domain and the range.

The graphs of many functions are translations or reflections of the square-root function. For example, if $k > 0$,

- The graph of $f(x) = \sqrt{x} + k$ is the graph of $f(x) = \sqrt{x}$ translated k units up.
- The graph of $f(x) = \sqrt{x} - k$ is the graph of $f(x) = \sqrt{x}$ translated k units down.
- The graph of $f(x) = \sqrt{x + k}$ is the graph of $f(x) = \sqrt{x}$ translated k units to the left.
- The graph of $f(x) = \sqrt{x - k}$ is the graph of $f(x) = \sqrt{x}$ translated k units to the right.
- The graph of $f(x) = -\sqrt{x}$ is the graph of $f(x) = \sqrt{x}$ reflected about the x-axis.

EXAMPLE 8   Consider the function $f(x) = -\sqrt{x + 4} - 2$.
     a. Find its domain.   **b.** Graph the function.   **c.** Find its range.

Solution   **a.** To find the domain, we note that the radicand must be nonnegative and solve the following inequality:

$$x + 4 \geq 0$$
$$x \geq -4$$

In interval notation, the domain is the interval $[-4, \infty)$.

b. This graph will be the reflection of $f(x) = \sqrt{x}$ about the x-axis, translated 4 units to the left and 2 units down. (See Figure 9-2(a).) We can confirm this graph by using a graphing calculator. If we choose window settings of $[-5, 6]$ for x and $[-6, 2]$ for y, we will get the graph shown in Figure 9-2(b).

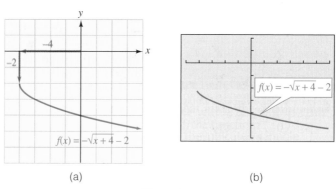

(a)   (b)

Figure 9-2

c. From either graph, we can see that the range is the interval $(-\infty, -2]$. The graph also confirms that the domain is the interval $[-4, \infty)$.

⇨ **SELF CHECK 8**   Graph $f(x) = \sqrt{x - 2} - 4$ and find the domain and range.

EXAMPLE 9   **PERIOD OF A PENDULUM**   The *period of a pendulum* is the time required for the pendulum to swing back and forth to complete one cycle. (See Figure 9-3.) The period t (in seconds) is a function of the pendulum's length l, which is defined by the formula

$$t = f(l) = 2\pi\sqrt{\frac{l}{32}}$$

Find the period of a pendulum that is 5 feet long.

Solution   We substitute 5 for l in the formula and simplify.

$$t = 2\pi\sqrt{\frac{l}{32}}$$

$$t = 2\pi\sqrt{\frac{5}{32}} \qquad \text{Substitute.}$$

$$\approx 2.483647066 \qquad \text{Use a calculator.}$$

To the nearest tenth, the period is 2.5 seconds.

Figure 9-3

⇨ **SELF CHECK 9**   To the nearest hundredth, find the period of a pendulum that is 3 feet long.

ACCENT ON TECHNOLOGY

Finding the Period of a Pendulum

To solve Example 9 with a graphing calculator with window settings of $[-2, 10]$ for x and $[-2, 10]$ for y, we graph the function $f(x) = 2\pi\sqrt{\frac{x}{32}}$, as in Figure 9-4(a) on the next page. We then trace and move the cursor toward an x-value of 5 until we see the coordinates shown in Figure 9-4(b). The period is given by the y-value shown on the screen. By zooming in, we can get better results.

(continued)

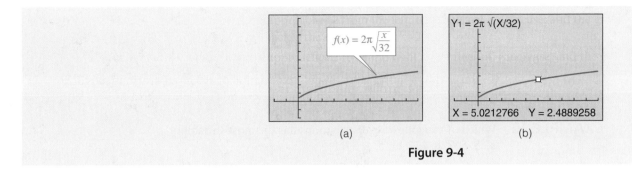

Figure 9-4

The equation $f(x) = \sqrt[3]{x}$ defines the **cube-root function.** From the graph shown in Figure 9-5(a), we can see that the domain and range of the function $f(x) = \sqrt[3]{x}$ are the set of real numbers. Note that the graph of $f(x) = \sqrt[3]{x}$ passes the vertical line test. Figures 9-5(b) and 9-5(c) show several translations of the cube-root function.

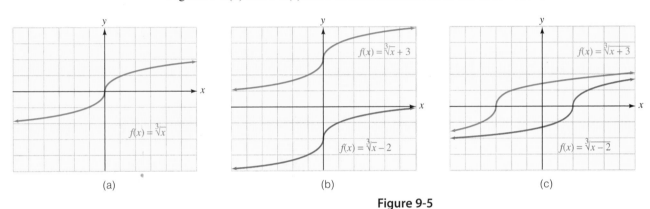

Figure 9-5

6 **Use a square root to find the standard deviation of a set of data.**

In statistics, the **standard deviation** of a data set is a measure of how tightly the data points are grouped around the mean (average) of the data set.

To see how to compute the standard deviation of a distribution, we consider the distribution 4, 5, 5, 8, 13 and construct the following table.

Original terms	Mean of the distribution	Differences (original term minus mean)	Squares of the differences from the mean
4	7	−3	9
5	7	−2	4
5	7	−2	4
8	7	1	1
13	7	6	36

The population *standard deviation* of the distribution is the positive square root of the mean of the numbers shown in column 4 of the table.

$$\text{Standard deviation} = \sqrt{\frac{\text{sum of the squares of the differences from the mean}}{\text{number of differences}}}$$

$$= \sqrt{\frac{9 + 4 + 4 + 1 + 36}{5}}$$

$$= \sqrt{\frac{54}{5}}$$

$$\approx 3.286335345 \quad \text{Use a calculator.}$$

To the nearest hundredth, the standard deviation of the given distribution is 3.29.
The symbol for the population standard deviation is σ, the lowercase Greek letter *sigma*.

EXAMPLE 10   Which of the following distributions has the most variability?
a. 3, 5, 7, 8, 12   **b.** 1, 4, 6, 11

Solution   We compute the standard deviation of each distribution.

a.

Original terms	Mean of the distribution	Differences (original term minus mean)	Squares of the differences from the mean
3	7	-4	16
5	7	-2	4
7	7	0	0
8	7	1	1
12	7	5	25

$$\sigma = \sqrt{\frac{16 + 4 + 0 + 1 + 25}{5}} = \sqrt{\frac{46}{5}} \approx 3.03$$

b.

Original terms	Mean of the distribution	Differences (original term minus mean)	Squares of the differences from the mean
1	5.5	-4.5	20.25
4	5.5	-1.5	2.25
6	5.5	0.5	0.25
11	5.5	5.5	30.25

$$\sigma = \sqrt{\frac{20.25 + 2.25 + 0.25 + 30.25}{4}} = \sqrt{\frac{53}{4}} \approx 3.64$$

Since the standard deviation for the second distribution is greater than the standard deviation for the first distribution, the second distribution has the greater variability.

⇨ **SELF CHECK ANSWERS**   **1.** 12, -12 **2. a.** -7 **b.** $\frac{5}{7}$ **3. a.** $5|a|$ **b.** $|x + 2|$ **c.** $4a^2$
4. a. 10   **b.** $\frac{1}{3}$ **c.** $5a$ **5. a.** $\frac{1}{3}$ **b.** 10   **6. a.** $2|a|$ **b.** $a + 5$
7. It is 2 units higher.   **8.**   **9.** 1.92 sec

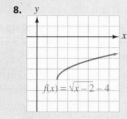

D: $[0, \infty)$
R: $[2, \infty)$

D: $[2, \infty)$
R: $[-4, \infty)$

NOW TRY THIS

1. Simplify: $\sqrt{100x^{100}}$.

2. Without using a calculator, between which two integers will the value of each expression be found?
   a. $\sqrt{8}$
   b. $\sqrt{54}$
   c. $\sqrt[3]{54}$

3. Given that $2^{-1} = \frac{1}{2}$, $2^0 = 1$, $2^1 = 2$, $2^2 = 4$, and $2^3 = 8$, between which two integers would you expect the value of each expression to be found?
   a. $2^{1/2}$
   b. $2^{3/2}$
   c. $2^{5/2}$

9.1 EXERCISES

WARM-UPS *Simplify each radical, if possible.*

1. $\sqrt{9}$
2. $-\sqrt{16}$
3. $\sqrt[3]{-8}$
4. $\sqrt[5]{32}$
5. $\sqrt{64x^2}$
6. $\sqrt[3]{-27x^3}$
7. $\sqrt{-3}$
8. $\sqrt[4]{(x+1)^8}$

REVIEW

Simplify each rational expression. Assume no division by zero.

9. $\dfrac{x^2 + 7x + 12}{x^2 - 16}$

10. $\dfrac{a^3 - b^3}{b^2 - a^2}$

Perform the operations. Assume no division by zero.

11. $\dfrac{x^2 - x - 6}{x^2 - 2x - 3} \cdot \dfrac{x^2 - 1}{x^2 + x - 2}$

12. $\dfrac{x^2 - 3x - 4}{x^2 - 5x + 6} \div \dfrac{x^2 - 2x - 3}{x^2 - x - 2}$

13. $\dfrac{3}{m+1} + \dfrac{3m}{m-1}$

14. $\dfrac{2x+3}{3x-1} - \dfrac{x-4}{2x+1}$

VOCABULARY AND CONCEPTS

Fill in the blanks.

15. $5x^2$ is the square root of $25x^4$, because _____ $= 25x^4$ and 6 is a square root of 36 because _____.

16. The numbers 1, 4, 9, 16, 25, . . . are called _____.

17. The principal square root of x ($x > 0$) is the _____ square root of x.

18. The graph of $f(x) = \sqrt{x} + 3$ is the graph of $f(x) = \sqrt{x}$ translated __ units ___.

19. The graph of $f(x) = \sqrt{x + 5}$ is the graph of $f(x) = \sqrt{x}$ translated __ units to the ____.

20. When n is an odd number greater than 1, $\sqrt[n]{x}$ represents an _____ root.

21. Given the radical $\sqrt[a]{b}$, the symbol $\sqrt{}$ is the _____ sign, a is the _____, and b is the _____.

22. The square-root function has the domain _____, while the cube-root function has the domain _____.

23. $\sqrt{x^2} = $ ___
24. $\left(\sqrt[3]{x}\right)^3 = $ ___
25. $\sqrt[3]{x^3} = $ __
26. $\sqrt{0} = $ __

27. When n is a positive _____ number, $\sqrt[n]{x}$ represents an even root.

28. The _____ deviation of a set of numbers is the positive square root of the mean of the squares of the differences of the numbers from the mean.

Identify the radicand in each expression.

29. $\sqrt{3x^2}$
30. $5\sqrt{x}$
31. $ab^2\sqrt{a^2 + b^3}$
32. $\dfrac{1}{2}x\sqrt{\dfrac{x}{y}}$

GUIDED PRACTICE

Find each square root, if possible. **See Examples 1–2. (Objective 1)**

33. $\sqrt{121}$
34. $\sqrt{144}$
35. $-\sqrt{64}$
36. $-\sqrt{1}$
37. $\sqrt{\dfrac{1}{9}}$
38. $-\sqrt{\dfrac{4}{25}}$

39. $-\sqrt{\dfrac{25}{49}}$

40. $\sqrt{\dfrac{49}{81}}$

41. $\sqrt{-25}$

42. $\sqrt{0.25}$

43. $\sqrt{0.16}$

44. $\sqrt{-49}$

Find each square root. Assume that all variables are unrestricted, and use absolute value symbols when necessary. See Example 3. (Objective 2)

45. $\sqrt{4x^2}$

46. $\sqrt{16y^4}$

47. $\sqrt{9a^4}$

48. $\sqrt{16b^2}$

49. $\sqrt{(t+5)^2}$

50. $\sqrt{(a+6)^2}$

51. $\sqrt{a^2+6a+9}$

52. $\sqrt{x^2+10x+25}$

Simplify each cube root. See Example 4. (Objective 3)

53. $\sqrt[3]{1}$

54. $\sqrt[3]{-8}$

55. $\sqrt[3]{-125}$

56. $\sqrt[3]{512}$

57. $\sqrt[3]{-\dfrac{8}{27}}$

58. $\sqrt[3]{\dfrac{125}{216}}$

59. $\sqrt[3]{0.064}$

60. $\sqrt[3]{0.001}$

61. $\sqrt[3]{8a^3}$

62. $\sqrt[3]{-27x^6}$

63. $\sqrt[3]{-1,000p^3q^3}$

64. $\sqrt[3]{343a^6b^3}$

Simplify each radical, if possible. See Example 5. (Objective 4)

65. $\sqrt[4]{81}$

66. $\sqrt[6]{64}$

67. $-\sqrt[5]{243}$

68. $-\sqrt[4]{625}$

69. $\sqrt[5]{-32}$

70. $\sqrt[6]{729}$

71. $\sqrt[4]{\dfrac{16}{625}}$

72. $\sqrt[5]{-\dfrac{243}{32}}$

73. $-\sqrt[5]{-\dfrac{1}{32}}$

74. $\sqrt[6]{-729}$

75. $\sqrt[4]{-256}$

76. $-\sqrt[4]{\dfrac{81}{256}}$

Simplify each radical. Assume that all variables are unrestricted, and use absolute value symbols where necessary. See Example 6. (Objective 4)

77. $\sqrt[4]{16x^4}$

78. $\sqrt[5]{32a^5}$

79. $\sqrt[3]{8a^3}$

80. $\sqrt[6]{64x^6}$

81. $\sqrt[4]{\dfrac{1}{16}x^4}$

82. $\sqrt[4]{\dfrac{1}{81}x^8}$

83. $\sqrt[4]{x^{12}}$

84. $\sqrt[8]{x^{24}}$

85. $\sqrt[5]{-x^5}$

86. $\sqrt[3]{-x^6}$

87. $\sqrt[3]{-27a^6}$

88. $\sqrt[5]{-32x^5}$

Find each value given that f(x) = $\sqrt{x-4}$. (Objective 5)

89. $f(4)$

90. $f(8)$

91. $f(20)$

92. $f(29)$

Find each value given that g(x) = $\sqrt{x-8}$. (Objective 5)

93. $g(9)$

94. $g(17)$

95. $g(8.25)$

96. $g(8.64)$

Graph each function and find its domain and range. See Examples 7–8. (Objective 5)

97. $f(x)=\sqrt{x+4}$

98. $f(x)=-\sqrt{x-2}$

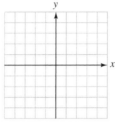

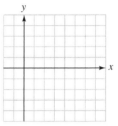

99. $f(x)=\sqrt[3]{x}-1$

100. $f(x)=-\sqrt{x}-3$

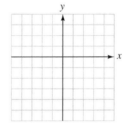

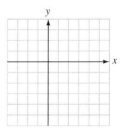

ADDITIONAL PRACTICE

Simplify each radical. Assume that all variables are unrestricted, and use absolute value symbols where necessary.

101. $\sqrt{(-4)^2}$

102. $\sqrt{(-9)^2}$

103. $\sqrt{-36}$

104. $-\sqrt{-4}$

105. $\sqrt{(-5b)^2}$

106. $\sqrt{(-8c)^2}$

107. $\sqrt{t^2+24t+144}$

108. $\sqrt{m^2+30m+225}$

109. $\sqrt[3]{-\dfrac{1}{8}m^6n^3}$

110. $\sqrt[3]{\dfrac{27}{1,000}a^6b^6}$

111. $\sqrt[3]{0.008z^9}$

112. $\sqrt[3]{0.064s^9t^6}$

113. $\sqrt[25]{(x+2)^{25}}$

114. $\sqrt[44]{(x+4)^{44}}$

115. $\sqrt[8]{0.00000001x^{16}y^8}$

116. $\sqrt[5]{0.00032x^{10}y^5}$

Use a calculator to find each square root. Give the answer to four decimal places.

117. $\sqrt{12}$

118. $\sqrt{340}$

119. $\sqrt{679.25}$

120. $\sqrt{0.0063}$

Find each value given that f(x) = $\sqrt{x^2+1}$. Give each answer to four decimal places.

121. $f(4)$

122. $f(6)$

123. $f(2.35)$

124. $f(21.57)$

APPLICATIONS *Use a calculator to solve each problem.* See Examples 9–10. (Objectives 2 and 6)

125. Find the standard deviation of the following distribution to the nearest hundredth: 2, 5, 5, 6, 7.

126. Find the standard deviation of the following distribution to the nearest hundredth: 3, 6, 7, 9, 11, 12.

127. Statistics In statistics, the formula

$$s_{\bar{x}} = \frac{s}{\sqrt{N}}$$

gives an estimate of the standard error of the mean. Find $s_{\bar{x}}$ to four decimal places when $s = 65$ and $N = 30$.

128. Statistics In statistics, the formula

$$\sigma_{\bar{x}} = \frac{\sigma}{\sqrt{N}}$$

gives the standard deviation of means of samples of size N. Find $\sigma_{\bar{x}}$ to four decimal places when $\sigma = 12.7$ and $N = 32$.

129. Radius of a circle The radius r of a circle is given by the formula $r = \sqrt{\frac{A}{\pi}}$, where A is its area. Find the radius of a circle whose area is 9π square units.

130. Diagonal of a baseball diamond The diagonal d of a square is given by the formula $d = \sqrt{2s^2}$, where s is the length of each side. Find the diagonal of the baseball diamond.

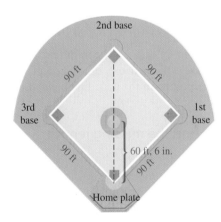

131. Falling objects The time t (in seconds) that it will take for an object to fall a distance of s feet is given by the formula

$$t = \frac{\sqrt{s}}{4}$$

If a stone is dropped down a 256-foot well, how long will it take it to hit bottom?

132. Law enforcement Police sometimes use the formula $s = k\sqrt{l}$ to estimate the speed s (in mph) of a car involved in an accident. In this formula, l is the length of the skid in feet, and k is a constant depending on the condition of the pavement. For wet pavement, $k \approx 3.24$. How fast was a car going if its skid was 400 feet on wet pavement?

133. Electronics When the resistance in a circuit is 18 ohms, the current I (measured in amperes) and the power P (measured in watts) are related by the formula

$$I = \sqrt{\frac{P}{18}}$$

Find the current used by an electrical appliance that is rated at 980 watts.

134. Medicine The approximate pulse rate p (in beats per minute) of an adult who is t inches tall is given by the formula

$$p = \frac{590}{\sqrt{t}}$$

Find the approximate pulse rate of an adult who is 71 inches tall.

WRITING ABOUT MATH

135. If x is any real number, then $\sqrt{x^2} = x$ is not correct. Explain.

136. If x is any real number, then $\sqrt[3]{x^3} = |x|$ is not correct. Explain.

SOMETHING TO THINK ABOUT

137. Is $\sqrt{x^2 - 4x + 4} = x - 2$? What are the exceptions?

138. When is $\sqrt{x^2} \neq x$?

SECTION 9.2 Applications of the Pythagorean Theorem and the Distance Formula

Objectives

1. Apply the Pythagorean theorem to find the missing length of one side of a right triangle.
2. Find the distance between two points on the coordinate plane.

Vocabulary

hypotenuse   Pythagorean theorem

Getting Ready

Evaluate each expression.

1. $3^2 + 4^2$ **2.** $5^2 + 12^2$
3. $(5 - 2)^2 + (2 + 1)^2$ **4.** $(111 - 21)^2 + (60 - 4)^2$

In this section, we will discuss the Pythagorean theorem, a theorem that shows the relationship of the sides of a right triangle. We will then use this theorem to develop a formula that gives the distance between two points on the coordinate plane.

1 Apply the Pythagorean theorem to find the missing length of one side of a right triangle.

If we know the lengths of two legs of a right triangle, we can find the length of the **hypotenuse** (the side opposite the 90° angle) by using the **Pythagorean theorem.** In fact, if we know the lengths of any two sides of a right triangle, we can find the length of the third side.

Pythagorean Theorem

If a and b are the lengths of two legs of a right triangle and c is the length of the hypotenuse, then

$$a^2 + b^2 = c^2$$

In words, the Pythagorean theorem says,

In any right triangle, the square of the length of the hypotenuse is equal to the sum of the squares of the lengths of the two legs.

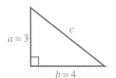

Figure 9-6

Suppose the right triangle shown in Figure 9-6 has legs of length 3 and 4 units. To find the length of the hypotenuse, we can use the Pythagorean theorem.

$$a^2 + b^2 = c^2$$
$$3^2 + 4^2 = c^2 \quad \text{Substitute.}$$
$$9 + 16 = c^2 \quad \text{Simplify.}$$
$$25 = c^2 \quad \text{Add.}$$

To find c, we ask "what number, when squared is equal to 25?" There are two such numbers: the positive square root of 25 and the negative square root of 25. Since c represents the length of the hypotenuse and cannot be negative, it follows that c is the positive square root of 25.

$$\sqrt{25} = c \quad \text{Recall that the radical symbol } \sqrt{} \text{ represents the positive, or principal,}$$
$$\text{square root of a number.}$$
$$5 = c$$

The length of the hypotenuse is 5 units.

EXAMPLE 1   **FIGHTING FIRES**   To fight a forest fire, the forestry department plans to clear a rectangular fire break around the fire, as shown in Figure 9-7. Crews are equipped with mobile communications with a 3,000-yard range. Can crews at points A and B remain in radio contact?

Solution   Points A, B, and C form a right triangle. The lengths of its sides are represented as a, b, and c where a is opposite point A, b is opposite point B, and c is opposite point C. To find the distance c, we can use the Pythagorean theorem, substituting 2,400 for a and 1,000 for b and solving for c.

$$a^2 + b^2 = c^2$$
$$2{,}400^2 + 1{,}000^2 = c^2 \quad \text{Substitute.}$$
$$5{,}760{,}000 + 1{,}000{,}000 = c^2 \quad \text{Square each value.}$$
$$6{,}760{,}000 = c^2 \quad \text{Add.}$$
$$\sqrt{6{,}760{,}000} = c \quad \text{Since } c \text{ represents a length, it must be the positive}$$
$$\text{square root of 6,760,000.}$$
$$2{,}600 = c \quad \text{Use a calculator to find the square root.}$$

**Pythagoras of Samos
(569?–475? B.C.)**

Pythagoras is thought to be the world's first pure mathematician. Although he is famous for the theorem that bears his name, he is often called "the father of music," because a society he led discovered some of the fundamentals of musical harmony. This secret society had numerology as its religion. The society is also credited with the discovery of irrational numbers.

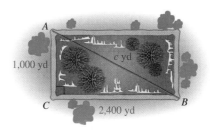

Figure 9-7

The two crews are 2,600 yards apart. Because this distance is less than the range of the radios, they can communicate.

⇨ **SELF CHECK 1**   Can the crews communicate if $b = 1,500$ yards?

PERSPECTIVE

Pythagoras was a teacher. Although it was unusual at that time, his classes were coeducational. He and his followers formed a secret society with two rules: Membership was for life, and members could not reveal the secrets they knew.

Much of their teaching was good mathematics, but some ideas were strange. To them, numbers were sacred. Because beans were used as counters to represent numbers, Pythagoreans refused to eat beans. They also believed that the *only* numbers were the whole numbers. To them, fractions were not numbers; $\frac{2}{3}$ was just a way of comparing the whole numbers 2 and 3. They believed that whole numbers were the building blocks of the universe. The basic Pythagorean doctrine was, "All things are numbers," and they meant *whole* numbers.

The Pythagorean theorem was an important discovery of the Pythagorean school, yet it caused some controversy. The right triangle in the illustration has two legs of length 1. By the Pythagorean theorem, the length of the hypotenuse is $\sqrt{2}$. One of their own group, Hippasus of Metapontum, discovered that $\sqrt{2}$ is an irrational number: There are *no* whole numbers a and b that make the fraction $\frac{a}{b}$ exactly equal to $\sqrt{2}$. This discovery was not appreciated by the other Pythagoreans. How could everything in the universe be described with whole numbers, when the side of this simple triangle couldn't? The Pythagoreans had a choice. Either expand their beliefs, or cling to the old. According to legend, the group was at sea at the time of the discovery. Rather than upset the system, they threw Hippasus overboard.

---

2 ### Find the distance between two points on the coordinate plane.

We can use the Pythagorean theorem to develop a formula to find the distance between any two points that are graphed on a rectangular coordinate system.

To find the distance d between points P and Q shown in Figure 9-8, we construct the right triangle PRQ. Because line segment RQ is vertical, point R will have the same x-coordinate as point Q. Because line segment PR is horizontal, point R will have same y-coordinate as point P. The distance between P and R is $|x_2 - x_1|$, and the distance between R and Q is $|y_2 - y_1|$. We apply the Pythagorean theorem to the right triangle PRQ to get

$$(PQ)^2 = (PR)^2 + (RQ)^2 \qquad \text{Read } PQ \text{ as "the length of segment } PQ.\text{"}$$

$$d^2 = |x_2 - x_1|^2 + |y_2 - y_1|^2 \qquad \text{Substitute the value of each expression.}$$

$$d^2 = (x_2 - x_1)^2 + (y_2 - y_1)^2 \qquad \text{Because } |x_2 - x_1|^2 = (x_2 - x_1)^2 \text{ and } |y_2 - y_1|^2 = (y_2 - y_1)^2$$

$$(1) \qquad d = \sqrt{(x_2 - x_1)^2 + (y_2 - y_1)^2} \qquad \text{Since } d \text{ represents a length, it must be the positive square root of } (x_2 - x_1)^2 + (y_2 - y_1)^2.$$

Equation 1 is called the **distance formula.**

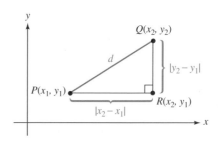

Figure 9-8

Distance Formula	The distance d between two points (x_1, y_1) and (x_2, y_2) is given by the formula $$d = \sqrt{(x_2 - x_1)^2 + (y_2 - y_1)^2}$$

EXAMPLE 2   Find the distance between the points $(-2, 3)$ and $(4, -5)$.

Solution   To find the distance, we can use the distance formula by substituting 4 for x_2, -2 for x_1, -5 for y_2, and 3 for y_1.

COMMENT   Recall that $\sqrt{a^2 + b^2} \neq \sqrt{a} + \sqrt{b}$.

$$
\begin{aligned}
d &= \sqrt{(x_2 - x_1)^2 + (y_2 - y_1)^2} \\
&= \sqrt{[4 - (-2)]^2 + (-5 - 3)^2} \qquad \text{Substitute.} \\
&= \sqrt{(4 + 2)^2 + (-5 - 3)^2} \qquad \text{Simplify.} \\
&= \sqrt{6^2 + (-8)^2} \qquad \text{Simplify.} \\
&= \sqrt{36 + 64} \qquad \text{Square each value.} \\
&= \sqrt{100} \qquad \text{Add.} \\
&= 10 \qquad \text{Take the square root.}
\end{aligned}
$$

The distance between the two points is 10 units.

➡ **SELF CHECK 2**   Find the distance between $P(-2, -2)$ and $Q(3, 10)$.

EXAMPLE 3   **BUILDING A FREEWAY**   In a city, streets run north and south, and avenues run east and west. Streets are 850 feet apart and avenues are 850 feet apart. The city plans to construct a straight freeway from the intersection of 25th Street and 8th Avenue to the intersection of 115th Street and 64th Avenue. How long will the freeway be?

Solution   We can represent the roads by the coordinate system in Figure 9-9, where the units on each axis represent 850 feet. We represent the end of the freeway at 25th Street and 8th Avenue by the point $(x_1, y_1) = (25, 8)$. The other end is $(x_2, y_2) = (115, 64)$.

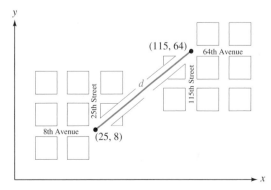

Figure 9-9

We can use the distance formula to find the number of units between the two designated points.

$$d = \sqrt{(x_2 - x_1)^2 + (y_2 - y_1)^2}$$

$$d = \sqrt{(115 - 25)^2 + (64 - 8)^2} \qquad \text{Substitute.}$$

$$= \sqrt{90^2 + 56^2} \qquad \text{Remove parentheses.}$$

$$= \sqrt{8,100 + 3,136} \qquad \text{Square each value.}$$

$$= \sqrt{11,236} \qquad \text{Add.}$$

$$= 106 \qquad \text{Use a calculator to find the square root.}$$

There are 106 units between the two designated points, and because each unit is 850 feet, the length of the freeway is 106(850) = 90,100 feet. Since 5,280 feet = 1 mile, we can divide 90,100 by 5,280 to convert 90,100 feet to 17.064394 miles. Thus, the freeway will be about 17 miles long.

SELF CHECK 3   Find the diagonal distance in feet from the intersection of 25th Street and 8th Avenue to the intersection of 28th Street and 12th Avenue.

EXAMPLE 4   **BOWLING**   The velocity, v, of an object after it has fallen d feet is given by the equation $v^2 = 64d$. If an inexperienced bowler lofts the ball 4 feet, with what velocity does it strike the alley?

Solution   We find the velocity by substituting 4 for d in the equation $v^2 = 64d$ and solving for v.

$$v^2 = 64d$$

$$v^2 = 64(4) \qquad \text{Substitute.}$$

$$v^2 = 256 \qquad \text{Multiply.}$$

$$v = \sqrt{256} \qquad \text{Since } v \text{ represents a velocity, it must be the positive square root of 256.}$$

$$= 16 \qquad \text{Simplify.}$$

The ball strikes the alley with a velocity of 16 feet per second.

SELF CHECK 4   Find the velocity if the bowler lofts the ball 3 feet. Round to the nearest tenth.

SELF CHECK ANSWERS   **1.** yes   **2.** 13 units   **3.** 4,250 ft   **4.** 13.9 ft/sec

---

NOW TRY THIS

1. Determine whether the points $(4, -2)$, $(-2, -4)$, and $(-4, 2)$ are the vertices of an *isosceles triangle* (two equal sides), an *equilateral triangle* (three equal sides), or neither. Is the triangle a right triangle?

2. Find the distance between points with coordinates of $(2x + 1, x + 1)$ and $(2x - 3, x - 2)$.

9.2 EXERCISES

WARM-UPS   *Evaluate each expression.*

1. $\sqrt{25}$

2. $\sqrt{169}$

3. $\sqrt{3^2 + 4^2}$

4. $\sqrt{5^2 + 12^2}$

5. $\sqrt{5^2 - 3^2}$

6. $\sqrt{5^2 - 4^2}$

REVIEW   *Find each product.*

7. $(4x + 2)(3x - 5)$

8. $(3y - 5)(2y + 3)$

9. $(5t + 4s)(3t - 2s)$

10. $(4r - 3)(2r^2 + 3r - 4)$

VOCABULARY AND CONCEPTS   *Fill in the blanks.*

11. In a right triangle, the side opposite the 90° angle is called the _____.

12. In a right triangle, the two shorter sides are called ____.

13. If a and b are the lengths of two legs of a right triangle and c is the length of the hypotenuse, then _____.

14. In any right triangle, the square of the length of the hypotenuse is equal to the ____ of the squares of the lengths of the two ____. This fact is known as the _____.

15. If $x^2 = 25$ and x is positive, we can conclude that x is the _____ square root of 25. Thus, $x = 5$.

16. The formula for finding the distance between two points on a rectangular coordinate system is

$d = $ _____.

GUIDED PRACTICE

The lengths of two sides of the right triangle ABC shown in the illustration are given. Find the length of the missing side.
See Example 1. (Objective 1)

17. $a = 6$ ft and $b = 8$ ft

18. $a = 10$ cm and $c = 26$ cm

19. $b = 18$ m and $c = 82$ m

20. $b = 7$ ft and $c = 25$ ft

21. $a = 14$ in. and $c = 50$ in.

22. $a = 8$ cm and $b = 15$ cm

23. $a = \sqrt{6}$ mi and $b = \sqrt{3}$ mi

24. $a = \sqrt{15}$ ft and $b = \sqrt{21}$ ft

Find the distance between the given points. If an answer is not exact, use a calculator and give an approximation to the nearest tenth. See Example 2. (Objective 2)

25. $(0, 0), (3, -4)$

26. $(0, 0), (-6, 8)$

27. $(2, 4), (5, 8)$

28. $(5, 9), (8, 13)$

29. $(-2, -8), (3, 4)$

30. $(-5, -2), (7, 3)$

31. $(6, 8), (12, 16)$

32. $(10, 4), (2, -2)$

33. $(-3, 5), (-5, -5)$

34. $(2, -3), (4, -8)$

35. $(-9, 3), (4, 7)$

36. $(-1, -3), (-5, 8)$

ADDITIONAL PRACTICE

In Exercises 37–40, use a calculator to approximate each value to the nearest foot. The baseball diamond is a square, 90 feet on a side.

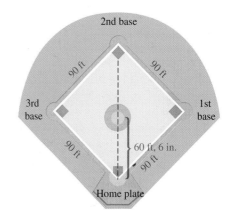

37. Baseball   How far must a catcher throw the ball to throw out a runner stealing second base?

38. Baseball   In baseball, the pitcher's mound is 60 feet, 6 inches from home plate. How far from the mound is second base?

39. Baseball   If the third baseman fields a ground ball 10 feet directly behind third base, how far must he throw the ball to throw a runner out at first base?

40. Baseball   The shortstop fields a grounder at a point one-third of the way from second base to third base. How far will he have to throw the ball to make an out at first base?

For Exercises 41–42, approximate each answer to the nearest tenth.

41. Geometry   Find the length of the diagonal of one of the faces of the cube.

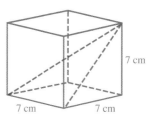

42. Geometry Find the length of the diagonal of the cube shown in the illustration in Exercise 41.

43. Geometry Show that the point (5, 1) is equidistant from points (7, 0) and (3, 0).

44. Geometry Show that a triangle with vertices at (2, 3), (−3, 4), and (1, −2) is a right triangle. (*Hint:* If the Pythagorean theorem holds, the triangle is a right triangle.)

45. Geometry Show that a triangle with vertices at (−2, 4), (2, 8), and (6, 4) is isosceles.

46. Geometry Show that a triangle with vertices at (−2, 13), (−8, 9), and (−2, 5) is isosceles.

APPLICATIONS

See Examples 1, 3, and 4. (Objectives 1–2)

47. Sailing Refer to the sailboat in the illustration. How long must a rope be to fasten the top of the mast to the bow?

48. Carpentry The gable end of the roof shown is divided in half by a vertical brace. Find the distance from an eave to the peak.

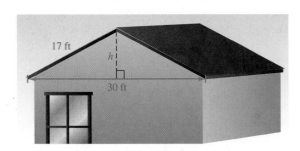

49. Reach of a ladder The base of the 37-foot ladder in the illustration is 9 feet from the wall. Will the top reach a window ledge that is 35 feet above the ground?

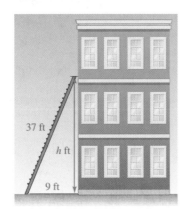

50. Telephone service The telephone cable in the illustration currently runs from A to B to C to D. How much cable is required to run from A to D directly?

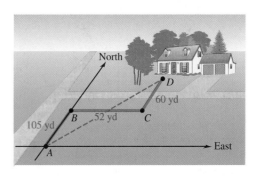

51. Electric service The power company routes its lines as shown in the illustration. How much wire could be saved by going directly from A to E?

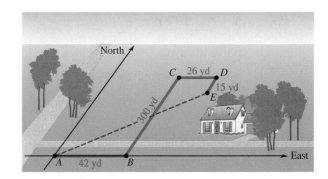

52. Geometry The side, s, of a square with area A square feet is given by the formula $s = \sqrt{A}$. Find the perimeter of a square with an area of 49 square feet.

53. Surface area of a cube The total surface area, A, of a cube is related to its volume, V, by the formula $A = 6\sqrt[3]{V^2}$. Find the surface area of a cube with a volume of 8 cubic centimeters.

54. Area of many cubes A grain of table salt is a cube with a volume of approximately 6×10^{-6} cubic in., and there are about 1.5 million grains of salt in one cup. Find the total surface area of the salt in one cup. (See Exercise 53.)

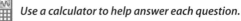

Use a calculator to help answer each question.

55. Packing a tennis racket The diagonal d of a rectangular box with dimensions $a \times b \times c$ is given by

$$d = \sqrt{a^2 + b^2 + c^2}$$

Will the racket shown on the next page fit in the shipping carton?

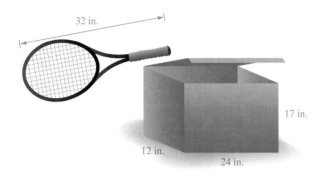

56. Packing a tennis racket Will the racket in Exercise 55 fit in a carton with dimensions that are 15 in. · 15 in. · 17 in.?

57. Shipping packages A delivery service won't accept a package for shipping if any dimension exceeds 21 inches. An archaeologist wants to ship a 36-inch femur bone. Will it fit in a 3-inch-tall box that has a 21-inch-square base?

58. Shipping packages Can the archaeologist in Exercise 57 ship the femur bone in a cubical box 21 inches on an edge?

59. Supporting a weight A weight placed on the tight wire pulls the center down 1 foot. By how much is the wire stretched? Round the answer to the nearest hundredth of a foot.

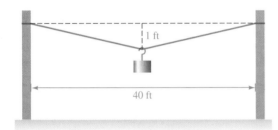

60. Supporting a weight If the weight in Exercise 59 pulls the center down 2 feet, by how much would the wire stretch? Round the answer to the nearest tenth of a foot.

WRITING ABOUT MATH

61. State the Pythagorean theorem.

62. Explain the distance formula.

SOMETHING TO THINK ABOUT

63. Body mass The formula

$$I = \frac{703w}{h^2}$$

(where w is weight in pounds and h is height in inches) can be used to estimate body mass index, I. The scale shown in the table can be used to judge a person's risk of heart attack. A girl weighing 104 pounds is 54.1 inches tall. Find her estimated body mass index.

20–26	normal
27–29	higher risk
30 and above	very high risk

64. What is the risk of a heart attack for a man who is 6 feet tall and weighs 220 pounds?

SECTION 9.3 **Rational Exponents**

Objectives

1 Simplify an expression that contains a positive rational exponent with a numerator of 1.

2 Simplify an expression that contains a positive rational exponent with a numerator other than 1.

3 Simplify an expression that contains a negative rational exponent.

4 Simplify an expression that contains rational exponents by applying the properties of exponents.

5 Simplify a radical expression by first writing it as an expression with a rational exponent.

Simplify each expression. Assume no variable is zero.

1. x^3x^4 **2.** $(a^3)^4$ **3.** $\dfrac{a^8}{a^4}$ **4.** a^0

5. x^{-4} **6.** $\dfrac{1}{x^{-3}}$ **7.** $\left(\dfrac{b^2}{c^3}\right)^3$ **8.** $(a^2a^3)^2$

1 **Simplify an expression that contains a positive rational exponent with a numerator of 1.**

We have seen that positive integer exponents indicate the number of times that a base is to be used as a factor in a product. For example, x^5 means that x is to be used as a factor five times.

$$x^5 = \overbrace{x \cdot x \cdot x \cdot x \cdot x}^{5 \text{ factors of } x}$$

Furthermore, we recall the following properties of exponents.

Rules of Exponents

If there are no divisions by 0, then for all integers m and n,

1. $x^m x^n = x^{m+n}$ **2.** $(x^m)^n = x^{mn}$ **3.** $(xy)^n = x^n y^n$

4. $\left(\dfrac{x}{y}\right)^n = \dfrac{x^n}{y^n}$ **5.** $x^0 = 1$ $(x \neq 0)$ **6.** $x^{-n} = \dfrac{1}{x^n}$

7. $\dfrac{x^m}{x^n} = x^{m-n}$ **8.** $\left(\dfrac{x}{y}\right)^{-n} = \left(\dfrac{y}{x}\right)^n$ **9.** $\dfrac{1}{x^{-n}} = x^n$

To show how to raise bases to rational powers, we consider the expression $10^{1/2}$. Since rational exponents must obey the same rules as integer exponents, the square of $10^{1/2}$ is equal to 10.

$$(10^{1/2})^2 = 10^{(1/2)2} \quad \text{Keep the base and multiply the exponents.}$$
$$= 10^1 \qquad \tfrac{1}{2} \cdot 2 = 1$$
$$= 10 \qquad 10^1 = 10$$

However, we have seen that

$$\left(\sqrt{10}\right)^2 = 10$$

Since $(10^{1/2})^2$ and $\left(\sqrt{10}\right)^2$ both equal 10, we define $10^{1/2}$ to be $\sqrt{10}$. Likewise, we define

$$10^{1/3} \text{ to be } \sqrt[3]{10} \quad \text{and} \quad 10^{1/4} \text{ to be } \sqrt[4]{10}$$

Rational Exponents

If n is a natural number greater than 1, and $\sqrt[n]{x}$ is a real number, then

$$x^{1/n} = \sqrt[n]{x}$$

EXAMPLE 1 Simplify each expression. Assume all variables represent nonnegative values.

a. $9^{1/2} = \sqrt{9} = 3$ **b.** $-\left(\dfrac{16}{9}\right)^{1/2} = -\sqrt{\dfrac{16}{9}} = -\dfrac{4}{3}$

c. $(-64)^{1/3} = \sqrt[3]{-64} = -4$ **d.** $16^{1/4} = \sqrt[4]{16} = 2$

e. $\left(\dfrac{1}{32}\right)^{1/5} = \sqrt[5]{\dfrac{1}{32}} = \dfrac{1}{2}$ **f.** $0^{1/8} = \sqrt[8]{0} = 0$

g. $-(32x^5)^{1/5} = -\sqrt[5]{32x^5} = -2x$ **h.** $(xyz)^{1/4} = \sqrt[4]{xyz}$

SELF CHECK 1 Assume that $x > 0$. Simplify:

a. $16^{1/2}$ **b.** $\left(\dfrac{27}{8}\right)^{1/3}$ **c.** $-(16x^4)^{1/4}$.

EXAMPLE 2 Write each radical using a rational exponent: **a.** $\sqrt[4]{5xyz}$ **b.** $\sqrt[5]{\dfrac{xy^2}{15}}$.

Solution   **a.** $\sqrt[4]{5xyz} = (5xyz)^{1/4}$ **b.** $\sqrt[5]{\dfrac{xy^2}{15}} = \left(\dfrac{xy^2}{15}\right)^{1/5}$

SELF CHECK 2 Write the radical using a rational exponent: $\sqrt[6]{4ab}$.

As with radicals, when n is even in the expression $x^{1/n}$ ($n > 1$), there are two real nth roots and we must use absolute value symbols to guarantee that the simplified result is positive.

When n is odd, there is only one real nth root, and we don't need to use absolute value symbols.

When n is even and x is negative, the expression $x^{1/n}$ is not a real number.

EXAMPLE 3 Assume that all variables can be any real number, and simplify each expression using absolute value symbols when necessary.

a. $(-27x^3)^{1/3} = -3x$ Because $(-3x)^3 = -27x^3$. Since n is odd, no absolute value symbols are needed.

b. $(49x^2)^{1/2} = |7x| = 7|x|$ Because $(|7x|)^2 = 49x^2$. Since $7x$ can be negative, absolute value symbols are needed.

c. $(256a^8)^{1/8} = 2|a|$ Because $(2|a|)^8 = 256a^8$. Since a can be any real number, $2a$ can be negative. Thus, absolute value symbols are needed.

d. $[(y + 1)^2]^{1/2} = |y + 1|$ Because $|y + 1|^2 = (y + 1)^2$. Since y can be any real number, $y + 1$ can be negative, and the absolute value symbols are needed.

e. $(25b^4)^{1/2} = 5b^2$ Because $(5b^2)^2 = 25b^4$. Since $b^2 \geq 0$, no absolute value symbols are needed.

f. $(-256x^4)^{1/4}$ is not a real number.   Because no real number raised to the 4th power is $-256x^4$

⇨ **SELF CHECK 3** Simplify each expression using absolute value symbols when necessary.
a. $(625a^4)^{1/4}$ **b.** $(b^4)^{1/2}$

We summarize the cases as follows.

Summary of the Definitions of $x^{1/n}$

If n is a natural number greater than 1 and x is a real number, then

If $x > 0$, then $x^{1/n}$ is the positive number such that $(x^{1/n})^n = x$.

If $x = 0$, then $x^{1/n} = 0$.

If $x < 0$ $\begin{cases} \text{and } n \text{ is odd, then } x^{1/n} \text{ is the real number such that } (x^{1/n})^n = x. \\ \text{and } n \text{ is even, then } x^{1/n} \text{ is not a real number.} \end{cases}$

2 **Simplify an expression that contains a positive rational exponent with a numerator other than 1.**

We can extend the definition of $x^{1/n}$ to include rational exponents with numerators other than 1. For example, since $4^{3/2}$ can be written as $(4^{1/2})^3$, we have

$$4^{3/2} = (4^{1/2})^3 = \left(\sqrt{4}\right)^3 = 2^3 = 8$$

Thus, we can simplify $4^{3/2}$ by cubing the square root of 4. We can also simplify $4^{3/2}$ by taking the square root of 4 cubed.

$$4^{3/2} = (4^3)^{1/2} = 64^{1/2} = \sqrt{64} = 8$$

In general, we have the following rule.

Changing from Rational Exponents to Radicals

If m and n are positive integers, $x \geq 0$, and $\frac{m}{n}$ is in simplified form, then

$$x^{m/n} = \left(\sqrt[n]{x}\right)^m = \sqrt[n]{x^m}$$

Because of the previous definition, we can interpret $x^{m/n}$ in two ways:

1. $x^{m/n}$ means the mth power of the nth root of x.
2. $x^{m/n}$ means the nth root of the mth power of x.

EXAMPLE 4 Simplify each expression.

a. $27^{2/3} = \left(\sqrt[3]{27}\right)^2$ or $27^{2/3} = \sqrt[3]{27^2}$
$\phantom{27^{2/3}} = 3^2$ $\phantom{27^{2/3} = } = \sqrt[3]{729}$
$\phantom{27^{2/3}} = 9$ $\phantom{27^{2/3} = } = 9$

b. $\left(\dfrac{1}{16}\right)^{3/4} = \left(\sqrt[4]{\dfrac{1}{16}}\right)^3$ or $\left(\dfrac{1}{16}\right)^{3/4} = \sqrt[4]{\left(\dfrac{1}{16}\right)^3}$

$\phantom{\left(\dfrac{1}{16}\right)^{3/4}} = \left(\dfrac{1}{2}\right)^3$ $\phantom{\left(\dfrac{1}{16}\right)^{3/4} = } = \sqrt[4]{\dfrac{1}{4,096}}$

$\phantom{\left(\dfrac{1}{16}\right)^{3/4}} = \dfrac{1}{8}$ $\phantom{\left(\dfrac{1}{16}\right)^{3/4} = } = \dfrac{1}{8}$

COMMENT To avoid large numbers, it is usually better to find the root of the base first, as shown in Example 4.

c. $(-8x^3)^{4/3} = \left(\sqrt[3]{-8x^3}\right)^4$ or $(-8x^3)^{4/3} = \sqrt[3]{(-8x^3)^4}$
$= (-2x)^4$ $= \sqrt[3]{4{,}096x^{12}}$
$= 16x^4$ $= 16x^4$

⇨ **SELF CHECK 4**   Simplify: **a.** $16^{3/2}$ **b.** $(-27x^6)^{2/3}$.

ACCENT ON TECHNOLOGY

Rational Exponents

We can evaluate expressions containing rational exponents using the exponential key y^x or x^y on a scientific calculator. For example, to evaluate $10^{2/3}$, we enter

10 y^x (2 ÷ 3) =   4.641588834

Note that parentheses were used when entering the power. Without them, the calculator would interpret the entry as $10^2 \div 3$.

To evaluate the exponential expression using a graphing calculator, we use the $\wedge$ key, which raises a base to a power. Again, we use parentheses when entering the power.

10 $\wedge$ (2 ÷ 3) **ENTER**   10 $\wedge$ (2/3)
                                                          4.641588834

To the nearest hundredth, $10^{2/3} \approx 4.64$.

---

3 **Simplify an expression that contains a negative rational exponent.**

To be consistent with the definition of negative integer exponents, we define $x^{-m/n}$ as follows.

Definition of $x^{-m/n}$

If m and n are positive integers, $\frac{m}{n}$ is in simplified form, and $x^{1/n}$ is a real number ($x \neq 0$), then

$$x^{-m/n} = \frac{1}{x^{m/n}} \quad \text{and} \quad \frac{1}{x^{-m/n}} = x^{m/n}$$

EXAMPLE 5   Write each expression without negative exponents, if possible.

a. $64^{-1/2} = \dfrac{1}{64^{1/2}}$ **b.** $16^{-3/2} = \dfrac{1}{16^{3/2}}$
$= \dfrac{1}{8}$ $= \dfrac{1}{(16^{1/2})^3}$
                                                     $= \dfrac{1}{64}$ $(16^{1/2})^3 = 4^3 = 64$

c. $(-32x^5)^{-2/5} = \dfrac{1}{(-32x^5)^{2/5}}$ $(x \neq 0)$ **d.** $(-16)^{-3/4}$ is not a real number, because $(-16)^{-1/4}$ is not a real number.
$= \dfrac{1}{[(-32x^5)^{1/5}]^2}$

$$= \frac{1}{(-2x)^2}$$

$$= \frac{1}{4x^2}$$

⇨ **SELF CHECK 5** Write each expression without negative exponents.
a. $25^{-3/2}$ **b.** $(-27a^3)^{-2/3}$

COMMENT By definition, 0^0 is undefined. A base of 0 raised to a negative power is also undefined, because 0^{-2} would equal $\frac{1}{0^2}$, which is undefined since we cannot divide by 0.

4 **Simplify an expression that contains rational exponents by applying the properties of exponents.**

We can use the properties of exponents to simplify many expressions with rational exponents.

EXAMPLE 6 Write all answers without negative exponents. Assume that all variables represent positive numbers. Thus, no absolute value symbols are necessary.

a. $5^{2/7}5^{3/7} = 5^{2/7+3/7}$ Use the rule $x^m x^n = x^{m+n}$.

     $= 5^{5/7}$ Add: $\frac{2}{7} + \frac{3}{7} = \frac{5}{7}$.

b. $(5^{2/7})^3 = 5^{(2/7)(3)}$ Use the rule $(x^m)^n = x^{mn}$.

     $= 5^{6/7}$ Multiply: $\frac{2}{7}(3) = \frac{2}{7}\left(\frac{3}{1}\right) = \frac{6}{7}$.

c. $(a^{2/3}b^{1/2})^6 = (a^{2/3})^6(b^{1/2})^6$ Use the rule $(xy)^n = x^n y^n$.

     $= a^{12/3}b^{6/2}$ Use the rule $(x^m)^n = x^{mn}$ twice.

     $= a^4 b^3$ Simplify the exponents.

d. $\dfrac{a^{8/3}a^{1/3}}{a^2} = a^{8/3+1/3-2}$ Use the rules $x^m x^n = x^{m+n}$ and $\frac{x^m}{x^n} = x^{m-n}$.

     $= a^{8/3+1/3-6/3}$ $2 = \frac{6}{3}$

     $= a^{3/3}$ $\frac{8}{3} + \frac{1}{3} - \frac{6}{3} = \frac{3}{3}$

     $= a$ $\frac{3}{3} = 1$

⇨ **SELF CHECK 6** Simplify: **a.** $(x^{1/3}y^{3/2})^6$ **b.** $\dfrac{x^{5/3}x^{2/3}}{x^{1/3}}$.

EXAMPLE 7 Assume that all variables represent positive numbers and perform the operations.

COMMENT Note that $a + a^{7/5} \neq a^{1+7/5}$. The expression $a + a^{7/5}$ cannot be simplified, because a and $a^{7/5}$ are not like terms.

a. $a^{4/5}(a^{1/5} + a^{3/5}) = a^{4/5}a^{1/5} + a^{4/5}a^{3/5}$ Use the distributive property.

     $= a^{4/5+1/5} + a^{4/5+3/5}$ Use the rule $x^m x^n = x^{m+n}$.

     $= a^{5/5} + a^{7/5}$ Simplify the exponents.

     $= a + a^{7/5}$

Carl Friedrich Gauss
(1777–1855)

Many people consider Gauss to be the greatest mathematician of all time. He made contributions in the areas of number theory, solutions of equations, geometry of curved surfaces, and statistics. For his efforts, he earned the title "Prince of the Mathematicians."

b. $x^{1/2}(x^{-1/2} + x^{1/2}) = x^{1/2}x^{-1/2} + x^{1/2}x^{1/2}$ Use the distributive property.

$= x^{1/2-1/2} + x^{1/2+1/2}$ Use the rule $x^m x^n = x^{m+n}$.

$= x^0 + x^1$ Simplify.

$= 1 + x$ $x^0 = 1$

c. $(x^{2/3} + 1)(x^{2/3} - 1) = x^{4/3} - x^{2/3} + x^{2/3} - 1$ Use the FOIL method.

$= x^{4/3} - 1$ Combine like terms.

d. $(x^{1/2} + y^{1/2})^2 = (x^{1/2} + y^{1/2})(x^{1/2} + y^{1/2})$ Use the FOIL method.

$= x + 2x^{1/2}y^{1/2} + y$

⇨ **SELF CHECK 7**   Assume that all variables represent positive numbers and perform the operations.
a. $p^{1/5}(p^{4/5} + p^{2/5})$ **b.** $(p^{2/3} + q^{1/3})(p^{2/3} - q^{1/3})$

5   **Simplify a radical expression by first writing it as an expression with a rational exponent.**

We can simplify many radical expressions by using the following steps.

Using Fractional Exponents to Simplify Radicals

1. Change the radical expression into an exponential expression with rational exponents.
2. Simplify the rational exponents.
3. Change the exponential expression back into a radical.

EXAMPLE 8   Simplify. Assume variables represent positive values.
a. $\sqrt[4]{3^2}$ **b.** $\sqrt[8]{x^6}$ **c.** $\sqrt[9]{27x^6y^3}$

Solution   **a.** $\sqrt[4]{3^2} = 3^{2/4}$ Use the rule $\sqrt[n]{x^m} = x^{m/n}$.

$= 3^{1/2}$ $\frac{2}{4} = \frac{1}{2}$

$= \sqrt{3}$ Change back to radical notation.

b. $\sqrt[8]{x^6} = x^{6/8}$ Use the rule $\sqrt[n]{x^m} = x^{m/n}$.

$= x^{3/4}$ $\frac{6}{8} = \frac{3}{4}$

$= (x^3)^{1/4}$ $\frac{3}{4} = 3\left(\frac{1}{4}\right)$

$= \sqrt[4]{x^3}$ Change back to radical notation.

c. $\sqrt[9]{27x^6y^3} = (3^3x^6y^3)^{1/9}$ Write 27 as 3^3 and change the radical to an exponential expression.

$= 3^{3/9}x^{6/9}y^{3/9}$ Raise each factor to the $\frac{1}{9}$ power by multiplying the fractional exponents.

$= 3^{1/3}x^{2/3}y^{1/3}$ Simplify each fractional exponent.

$= (3x^2y)^{1/3}$ Use the rule $(xy)^n = x^n y^n$.

$= \sqrt[3]{3x^2y}$ Change back to radical notation.

⇨ SELF CHECK 8   Simplify. Assume variables represent positive values.

     a. $\sqrt[6]{3^3}$ **b.** $\sqrt[4]{49x^2y^2}$

⇨ SELF CHECK ANSWERS   **1. a.** 4   **b.** $\frac{3}{2}$ **c.** $-2x$ **2.** $(4ab)^{1/6}$ **3. a.** $5|a|$ **b.** b^2 **4. a.** 64   **b.** $9x^4$ **5. a.** $\frac{1}{125}$ **b.** $\frac{1}{9a^2}$
6. a. x^2y^9 **b.** x^2 **7. a.** $p + p^{3/5}$ **b.** $p^{4/3} - q^{2/3}$ **8. a.** $\sqrt{3}$ **b.** $\sqrt{7xy}$

NOW TRY THIS

1. Evaluate each exponential expression, if possible.

     a. $-64^{-2/3}$ **b.** $-64^{-3/2}$ **c.** $(-64)^{-2/3}$

     d. $(-64)^{-3/2}$

2. Simplify each expression and then write the answer using radical notation. Assume all variables represent positive numbers.

     a. $x^{a/4} \cdot x^{a/2}$ **b.** $\dfrac{x^{n/m}}{x^{(n-1)/m}}$

3. Simplify $\dfrac{\sqrt{5}}{\sqrt[3]{5}}$ and write the answer using radical notation.

9.3 EXERCISES

Assume no division by zero.

WARM-UPS   *Simplify each expression.*

1. $4^{1/2}$ **2.** $9^{1/2}$

3. $27^{1/3}$ **4.** $1^{1/4}$

5. $4^{3/2}$ **6.** $8^{2/3}$

7. $\left(\dfrac{1}{4}\right)^{1/2}$ **8.** $\left(\dfrac{1}{4}\right)^{-1/2}$

9. $(8x^3)^{1/3}$ **10.** $(16x^8)^{1/4}$

REVIEW   *Solve each inequality.*

11. $5x - 4 < 11$ **12.** $2(3t - 5) \geq 8$

13. $\dfrac{4}{5}(r - 3) > \dfrac{2}{3}(r + 2)$ **14.** $-4 < 2x - 4 \leq 8$

15. Mixing solutions   How much water must be added to 5 pints of a 20% alcohol solution to dilute it to a 15% solution?

16. Selling apples   A grocer bought some boxes of apples for $70. However, 4 boxes were spoiled. The grocer sold the remaining boxes at a profit of $2 each. How many boxes did the grocer sell if she managed to break even?

VOCABULARY AND CONCEPTS   *Fill in the blanks.*

17. $a^4 = $ _____   **18.** $a^m a^n = $ _____

19. $(a^m)^n = $ _____   **20.** $(ab)^n = $ _____

21. $\left(\dfrac{a}{b}\right)^n = $ ____

22. $a^0 = $ __, provided $a \neq $ __.

23. $a^{-n} = $ ____ , provided $a \neq $ __.

24. $\dfrac{a^m}{a^n} = $ _____, provided $a \neq 0$.

25. $\left(\dfrac{a}{b}\right)^{-n} = $ _____

26. $x^{1/n} = $ ____

27. $(x^n)^{1/n} = $ ___, provided n is even.

28. $x^{m/n} = \sqrt[n]{x^m} = $ _____

GUIDED PRACTICE

Change each expression into radical notation. (Objective 1)

29. $7^{1/3}$
30. $26^{1/2}$

31. $8^{1/5}$
32. $13^{1/7}$

33. $(3x)^{1/4}$
34. $(4ab)^{1/6}$

35. $\left(\dfrac{1}{2}x^3y\right)^{1/4}$
36. $\left(\dfrac{3}{4}a^2b^2\right)^{1/5}$

37. $(4a^2b^3)^{1/5}$
38. $(5pq^2)^{1/3}$

39. $(x^2 + y^2)^{1/2}$
40. $(x^3 + y^3)^{1/3}$

Simplify each expression, if possible. See Example 1. (Objective 1)

41. $4^{1/2}$
42. $64^{1/2}$

43. $27^{1/3}$
44. $125^{1/3}$

45. $\left(\dfrac{1}{4}\right)^{1/2}$
46. $\left(\dfrac{1}{16}\right)^{1/2}$

47. $\left(\dfrac{1}{8}\right)^{1/3}$
48. $\left(\dfrac{1}{16}\right)^{1/4}$

49. $-16^{1/4}$
50. $-125^{1/3}$

51. $(-64)^{1/2}$
52. $(-216)^{1/2}$

Change each radical to an exponential expression. See Example 2. (Objective 1)

53. $\sqrt{11}$
54. $\sqrt[3]{12}$

55. $\sqrt[4]{3a}$
56. $\sqrt[7]{12xy}$

57. $3\sqrt[5]{a}$
58. $4\sqrt[3]{p}$

59. $\sqrt[6]{\dfrac{1}{7}abc}$
60. $\sqrt{\dfrac{3}{8}p^2q}$

61. $\sqrt[5]{\dfrac{1}{2}mn}$
62. $\sqrt[8]{\dfrac{2}{7}p^2q}$

63. $\sqrt[3]{a^2 - b^2}$
64. $\sqrt{x^2 + y^2}$

Simplify each expression. Assume that all variables can be any real number, and use absolute value symbols if necessary. See Example 3. (Objective 1)

65. $(25y^2)^{1/2}$
66. $(16x^4)^{1/4}$

67. $(243x^5)^{1/5}$
68. $(-27x^3)^{1/3}$

69. $[(x + 1)^4]^{1/4}$
70. $[(x + 5)^3]^{1/3}$

71. $(-64x^8)^{1/4}$
72. $(-16x^4)^{1/2}$

Simplify each expression, if possible. Assume that all variables are unrestricted, and use absolute value symbols when necessary. See Example 4. (Objective 2)

73. $36^{3/2}$
74. $27^{2/3}$

75. $81^{3/4}$
76. $100^{3/2}$

77. $144^{3/2}$
78. $1{,}000^{2/3}$

79. $\left(\dfrac{1}{8}\right)^{2/3}$
80. $\left(\dfrac{4}{9}\right)^{3/2}$

Write each expression without using negative exponents. Assume that all variables represent positive numbers. See Example 5. (Objective 3)

81. $4^{-1/2}$
82. $8^{-1/3}$

83. $(4)^{-3/2}$
84. $25^{-5/2}$

85. $(16x^2)^{-3/2}$
86. $(81c^4)^{-3/2}$

87. $(-27y^3)^{-2/3}$
88. $(-8z^9)^{-2/3}$

89. $\left(\dfrac{1}{4}\right)^{-3/2}$
90. $\left(\dfrac{4}{25}\right)^{-3/2}$

91. $\left(\dfrac{27}{8}\right)^{-4/3}$
92. $\left(\dfrac{25}{49}\right)^{-3/2}$

Perform the operations. Write answers without negative exponents. Assume that all variables represent positive numbers. See Example 6. (Objective 4)

93. $5^{4/9}5^{4/9}$
94. $4^{2/5}4^{2/5}$

95. $(4^{1/5})^3$
96. $(3^{1/3})^5$

97. $6^{-2/3}6^{-4/3}$
98. $5^{1/3}5^{-5/3}$

99. $\dfrac{9^{4/5}}{9^{3/5}}$
100. $\dfrac{7^{2/3}}{7^{1/2}}$

101. $\dfrac{7^{1/2}}{7^0}$
102. $\dfrac{3^{4/3}3^{1/3}}{3^{2/3}}$

103. $\dfrac{2^{5/6}2^{1/3}}{2^{1/2}}$
104. $\dfrac{5^{1/3}5^{1/2}}{5^{1/3}}$

105. $a^{2/5}a^{1/3}$
106. $b^{3/5}b^{1/5}$

107. $(a^{2/3})^{1/3}$
108. $(t^{4/5})^{10}$

Perform the operations. Write answers without negative exponents. Assume that all variables represent positive numbers. See Example 7. (Objective 4)

109. $y^{1/3}(y^{2/3} + y^{5/3})$
110. $y^{2/5}(y^{-2/5} + y^{3/5})$

111. $x^{3/5}(x^{7/5} - x^{2/5} + 1)$
112. $(x^{1/2} + 2)(x^{1/2} - 2)$

113. $(x^{1/2} + y^{1/2})(x^{1/2} - y^{1/2})$
114. $(x^{2/3} - x)(x^{2/3} + x)$

115. $(x^{2/3} + y^{2/3})^2$
116. $(a^{3/2} - b^{3/2})^2$

Use rational exponents to simplify each radical. Assume that all variables represent positive numbers. **See Example 8. (Objective 5)**

117. $\sqrt[6]{p^3}$

118. $\sqrt[8]{q^2}$

119. $\sqrt[4]{25b^2}$

120. $\sqrt[9]{-8x^6}$

ADDITIONAL PRACTICE

Simplify each expression, if possible. Assume all variables represent positive numbers. Write answers without negative exponents.

121. $16^{1/4}$

122. $625^{1/4}$

123. $32^{1/5}$

124. $0^{1/5}$

125. $0^{1/3}$

126. $(-243)^{1/5}$

127. $(-27)^{1/3}$

128. $(-125)^{1/3}$

129. $(25x^4)^{3/2}$

130. $(27a^3b^3)^{2/3}$

131. $\left(\dfrac{8x^3}{27}\right)^{2/3}$

132. $\left(\dfrac{27}{64y^6}\right)^{2/3}$

133. $(-32p^5)^{-2/5}$

134. $(16q^6)^{-5/2}$

135. $\left(-\dfrac{8x^3}{27}\right)^{-1/3}$

136. $\left(\dfrac{16}{81y^4}\right)^{-3/4}$

137. $(a^{1/2}b^{1/3})^{3/2}$

138. $(a^{3/5}b^{3/2})^{2/3}$

139. $(mn^{-2/3})^{-3/5}$

140. $(r^{-2}s^3)^{1/3}$

141. $\dfrac{(4x^3y)^{1/2}}{(9xy)^{1/2}}$

142. $\dfrac{(27x^3y)^{1/3}}{(8xy^2)^{2/3}}$

143. $(27x^{-3})^{-1/3}$

144. $(16a^{-2})^{-1/2}$

145. $x^{4/3}(x^{2/3} + 3x^{5/3} - 4)$

146. $(x^{1/3} + x^2)(x^{1/3} - x^2)$

147. $(x^{-1/2} - x^{1/2})^2$

148. $(a^{1/2} - b^{2/3})^2$

Use a calculator to evaluate each expression. Round to the nearest hundredth.

149. $15^{1/3}$

150. $50.5^{1/4}$

151. $1.045^{1/5}$

152. $(-1,000)^{2/5}$

Use a calculator to evaluate each expression. Round to the nearest hundredth.

153. $17^{-1/2}$

154. $2.45^{-2/3}$

155. $(-0.25)^{-1/5}$

156. $(-17.1)^{-3/7}$

WRITING ABOUT MATH

157. Explain how you would decide whether $a^{1/n}$ is a real number.

158. The expression $(a^{1/2} + b^{1/2})^2$ is not equal to $a + b$. Explain.

SOMETHING TO THINK ABOUT

159. The fraction $\frac{2}{4}$ is equal to $\frac{1}{2}$. Is $16^{2/4}$ equal to $16^{1/2}$? Explain.

160. How would you evaluate an expression with a mixed-number exponent? For example, what is $8^{1\frac{1}{3}}$? What is $25^{2\frac{1}{2}}$? Explain.

SECTION 9.4

Simplifying and Combining Radical Expressions

Objectives

1. Simplify a radical expression by applying the properties of radicals.
2. Add and subtract two or more radical expressions.
3. Find the length of a side of a 30°–60°–90° triangle and a 45°–45°–90° triangle.

Vocabulary

like (similar) radicals   altitude

Simplify each radical. Assume that all variables represent positive numbers.

1. $\sqrt{225}$ **2.** $\sqrt{576}$ **3.** $\sqrt[3]{125}$ **4.** $\sqrt[3]{343}$

5. $\sqrt{16x^4}$ **6.** $\sqrt{\dfrac{64}{121}x^6}$ **7.** $\sqrt[3]{27a^3b^9}$ **8.** $\sqrt[3]{-8a^{12}}$

In this section, we will introduce several properties of radicals and use them to simplify radical expressions. Then we will add and subtract radical expressions.

1 **Simplify a radical expression by applying the properties of radicals.**

Many properties of exponents have counterparts in radical notation. For example, because $a^{1/n}b^{1/n} = (ab)^{1/n}$, we have

(1) $\sqrt[n]{a}\sqrt[n]{b} = \sqrt[n]{ab}$

For example,

$$\sqrt{5}\sqrt{5} = \sqrt{5 \cdot 5} = \sqrt{5^2} = 5$$

$$\sqrt[3]{7x}\sqrt[3]{49x^2} = \sqrt[3]{7x \cdot 7^2x^2} = \sqrt[3]{7^3 \cdot x^3} = 7x$$

$$\sqrt[4]{2x^3}\sqrt[4]{8x} = \sqrt[4]{2x^3 \cdot 2^3x} = \sqrt[4]{2^4 \cdot x^4} = 2x \quad (x > 0)$$

If we rewrite Equation 1, we have the following rule.

Multiplication Property of Radicals

If $\sqrt[n]{a}$ and $\sqrt[n]{b}$ are real numbers, then

$$\sqrt[n]{ab} = \sqrt[n]{a}\sqrt[n]{b}$$

As long as all radicals represent real numbers, *the nth root of the product of two numbers is equal to the product of their nth roots.*

COMMENT The multiplication property of radicals applies to the nth root of the product of two numbers. There is no such property for sums or differences. For example,

$$\sqrt{9 + 4} \ne \sqrt{9} + \sqrt{4} \qquad\qquad \sqrt{9 - 4} \ne \sqrt{9} - \sqrt{4}$$

$$\sqrt{13} \ne 3 + 2 \qquad\qquad\qquad \sqrt{5} \ne 3 - 2$$

$$\sqrt{13} \ne 5 \qquad\qquad\qquad\qquad \sqrt{5} \ne 1$$

Thus, $\sqrt{a + b} \ne \sqrt{a} + \sqrt{b}$ and $\sqrt{a - b} \ne \sqrt{a} - \sqrt{b}$.

A second property of radicals involves quotients. Because

$$\frac{a^{1/n}}{b^{1/n}} = \left(\frac{a}{b}\right)^{1/n}$$

it follows that

(2) $\dfrac{\sqrt[n]{a}}{\sqrt[n]{b}} = \sqrt[n]{\dfrac{a}{b}} \quad (b \ne 0)$

For example,

$$\frac{\sqrt{8x^3}}{\sqrt{2x}} = \sqrt{\frac{8x^3}{2x}} = \sqrt{4x^2} = 2x \quad (x > 0)$$

$$\frac{\sqrt[3]{54x^5}}{\sqrt[3]{2x^2}} = \sqrt[3]{\frac{54x^5}{2x^2}} = \sqrt[3]{27x^3} = 3x \quad (x \neq 0)$$

If we rewrite Equation 2, we have the following rule.

Division Property of Radicals	If $\sqrt[n]{a}$ and $\sqrt[n]{b}$ are real numbers, then $$\sqrt[n]{\frac{a}{b}} = \frac{\sqrt[n]{a}}{\sqrt[n]{b}} \quad (b \neq 0)$$

As long as all radicals represent real numbers, *the nth root of the quotient of two numbers is equal to the quotient of their nth roots.*

A radical expression is said to be in simplified form when each of the following statements is true.

Simplified Form of a Radical Expression	A radical expression is in simplified form when **1.** Each prime and variable factor in the radicand appears to a power that is less than the index of the radical. **2.** The radicand contains no fractions or negative numbers. **3.** No radicals appear in the denominator of a fraction.

EXAMPLE 1 Simplify: **a.** $\sqrt{12}$ **b.** $\sqrt{98}$ **c.** $\sqrt[3]{54}$.

Solution **a.** Recall that squares of integers, such as 1, 4, 9, 16, 25, and 36, are *perfect squares*. To simplify $\sqrt{12}$, we factor 12 so that one factor is the largest perfect square that divides 12. Since 4 is the largest perfect-square factor of 12, we write 12 as $4 \cdot 3$, use the multiplication property of radicals, and simplify.

$$\begin{aligned} \sqrt{12} &= \sqrt{4 \cdot 3} & \text{Write 12 as } 4 \cdot 3. \\ &= \sqrt{4}\sqrt{3} & \sqrt{4 \cdot 3} = \sqrt{4}\sqrt{3} \\ &= 2\sqrt{3} & \sqrt{4} = 2 \end{aligned}$$

b. Since the largest perfect-square factor of 98 is 49, we have

$$\begin{aligned} \sqrt{98} &= \sqrt{49 \cdot 2} & \text{Write 98 as } 49 \cdot 2. \\ &= \sqrt{49}\sqrt{2} & \sqrt{49 \cdot 2} = \sqrt{49}\sqrt{2} \\ &= 7\sqrt{2} & \sqrt{49} = 7 \end{aligned}$$

c. Numbers that are cubes of integers, such as 1, 8, 27, 64, 125, and 216, are called *perfect cubes*. Since the largest perfect-cube factor of 54 is 27, we have

$$\sqrt[3]{54} = \sqrt[3]{27 \cdot 2} \qquad \text{Write 54 as } 27 \cdot 2.$$
$$= \sqrt[3]{27}\sqrt[3]{2} \qquad \sqrt[3]{27 \cdot 2} = \sqrt[3]{27}\sqrt[3]{2}$$
$$= 3\sqrt[3]{2} \qquad \sqrt[3]{27} = 3$$

⇨ **SELF CHECK 1**   Simplify: **a.** $\sqrt{20}$ **b.** $\sqrt[3]{24}$.

EXAMPLE 2   Simplify: **a.** $\sqrt{\dfrac{15}{49x^2}}$ $(x > 0)$ **b.** $\sqrt[3]{\dfrac{10x^2}{27y^6}}$ $(y \neq 0)$.

Solution   **a.** We can write the square root of the quotient as the quotient of the square roots and simplify the denominator. Since $x > 0$, we have

$$\sqrt{\frac{15}{49x^2}} = \frac{\sqrt{15}}{\sqrt{49x^2}}$$
$$= \frac{\sqrt{15}}{7x}$$

b. We can write the cube root of the quotient as the quotient of two cube roots. Since $y \neq 0$, we have

$$\sqrt[3]{\frac{10x^2}{27y^6}} = \frac{\sqrt[3]{10x^2}}{\sqrt[3]{27y^6}}$$
$$= \frac{\sqrt[3]{10x^2}}{3y^2}$$

⇨ **SELF CHECK 2**   Simplify: **a.** $\sqrt{\dfrac{11}{36a^2}}$ $(a > 0)$ **b.** $\sqrt[3]{\dfrac{8a^2}{125y^3}}$ $(y \neq 0)$.

EXAMPLE 3   Simplify each expression. Assume that all variables represent positive numbers.

   a. $\sqrt{128a^5}$ **b.** $\sqrt[3]{24x^5}$ **c.** $\dfrac{\sqrt{45xy^2}}{\sqrt{5x}}$ **d.** $\dfrac{\sqrt[3]{-432x^5}}{\sqrt[3]{8x}}$

Solution   **a.** We can write $128a^5$ as $64a^4 \cdot 2a$ and use the multiplication property of radicals.

$$\sqrt{128a^5} = \sqrt{64a^4 \cdot 2a} \qquad 64a^4 \text{ is the largest perfect square that divides } 128a^5.$$
$$= \sqrt{64a^4}\sqrt{2a} \qquad \text{Use the multiplication property of radicals.}$$
$$= 8a^2\sqrt{2a} \qquad \sqrt{64a^4} = 8a^2$$

b. We can write $24x^5$ as $8x^3 \cdot 3x^2$ and use the multiplication property of radicals.

$$\sqrt[3]{24x^5} = \sqrt[3]{8x^3 \cdot 3x^2} \qquad 8x^3 \text{ is the largest perfect cube that divides } 24x^5.$$
$$= \sqrt[3]{8x^3}\sqrt[3]{3x^2} \qquad \text{Use the multiplication property of radicals.}$$
$$= 2x\sqrt[3]{3x^2} \qquad \sqrt[3]{8x^3} = 2x$$

c. We can write the quotient of the square roots as the square root of a quotient.

$$\frac{\sqrt{45xy^2}}{\sqrt{5x}} = \sqrt{\frac{45xy^2}{5x}} \qquad \text{Use the quotient property of radicals.}$$

$$= \sqrt{9y^2} \qquad \text{Simplify the fraction.}$$

$$= 3y$$

d. We can write the quotient of the cube roots as the cube root of a quotient.

$$\frac{\sqrt[3]{-432x^5}}{\sqrt[3]{8x}} = \sqrt[3]{\frac{-432x^5}{8x}} \qquad \text{Use the quotient property of radicals.}$$

$$= \sqrt[3]{-54x^4} \qquad \text{Simplify the fraction.}$$

$$= \sqrt[3]{-27x^3 \cdot 2x} \qquad -27x^3 \text{ is the largest perfect cube that divides } -54x^4.$$

$$= \sqrt[3]{-27x^3}\sqrt[3]{2x} \qquad \text{Use the multiplication property of radicals.}$$

$$= -3x\sqrt[3]{2x}$$

⇨ **SELF CHECK 3**   Simplify each expression. Assume that all variables represent positive numbers.

a. $\sqrt{98b^3}$ **b.** $\sqrt[3]{54y^5}$ **c.** $\dfrac{\sqrt{50ab^2}}{\sqrt{2a}}$

To simplify more complicated radicals, we can use the prime factorization of the radicand to find its perfect-square factors. For example, to simplify $\sqrt{3{,}168x^5y^7}$, we first find the prime factorization of $3{,}168x^5y^7$.

$$3{,}168x^5y^7 = 2^5 \cdot 3^2 \cdot 11 \cdot x^5 \cdot y^7$$

Then we have

$$\sqrt{3{,}168x^5y^7} = \sqrt{2^4 \cdot 3^2 \cdot x^4 \cdot y^6 \cdot 2 \cdot 11 \cdot x \cdot y}$$

$$= \sqrt{2^4 \cdot 3^2 \cdot x^4 \cdot y^6}\sqrt{2 \cdot 11 \cdot x \cdot y} \qquad \text{Write each perfect square under the left radical and each nonperfect square under the right radical.}$$

$$= 2^2 \cdot 3x^2y^3\sqrt{22xy}$$

$$= 12x^2y^3\sqrt{22xy}$$

2   ## Add and subtract two or more radical expressions.

Radical expressions with the same index and the same radicand are called **like** or **similar radicals.** For example, $3\sqrt{2}$ and $5\sqrt{2}$ are like radicals. However,

$3\sqrt{5}$ and $5\sqrt{2}$ are not like radicals, because the radicands are different.

$3\sqrt{5}$ and $2\sqrt[3]{5}$ are not like radicals, because the indexes are different.

We often can combine like terms. For example, to simplify the expression $3\sqrt{2} + 2\sqrt{2}$, we use the distributive property to factor out $\sqrt{2}$ and simplify.

$$3\sqrt{2} + 2\sqrt{2} = (3 + 2)\sqrt{2}$$

$$= 5\sqrt{2}$$

Radicals with the same index but different radicands can often be written as like radicals. For example, to simplify the expression $\sqrt{27} - \sqrt{12}$, we simplify both radicals and combine the resulting like radicals.

$$
\begin{aligned}
\sqrt{27} - \sqrt{12} &= \sqrt{9 \cdot 3} - \sqrt{4 \cdot 3} \\
&= \sqrt{9}\sqrt{3} - \sqrt{4}\sqrt{3} && \sqrt{ab} = \sqrt{a}\sqrt{b} \\
&= 3\sqrt{3} - 2\sqrt{3} && \sqrt{9} = 3 \text{ and } \sqrt{4} = 2. \\
&= (3 - 2)\sqrt{3} && \text{Factor out } \sqrt{3}. \\
&= \sqrt{3}
\end{aligned}
$$

As the previous examples suggest, we can use the following rule to add or subtract radicals.

Adding and Subtracting Radicals

To add or subtract radicals, simplify each radical and combine all like radicals. To combine like radicals, add the coefficients and keep the common radical.

EXAMPLE 4   Simplify: $2\sqrt{12} - 3\sqrt{48} + 3\sqrt{3}$.

Solution   We simplify each radical separately and combine like radicals.

$$
\begin{aligned}
2\sqrt{12} - 3\sqrt{48} + 3\sqrt{3} &= 2\sqrt{4 \cdot 3} - 3\sqrt{16 \cdot 3} + 3\sqrt{3} \\
&= 2\sqrt{4}\sqrt{3} - 3\sqrt{16}\sqrt{3} + 3\sqrt{3} \\
&= 2(2)\sqrt{3} - 3(4)\sqrt{3} + 3\sqrt{3} \\
&= 4\sqrt{3} - 12\sqrt{3} + 3\sqrt{3} \\
&= (4 - 12 + 3)\sqrt{3} \\
&= -5\sqrt{3}
\end{aligned}
$$

SELF CHECK 4   Simplify: $3\sqrt{75} - 2\sqrt{12} + 2\sqrt{48}$.

EXAMPLE 5   Simplify: $\sqrt[3]{16} - \sqrt[3]{54} + \sqrt[3]{24}$.

Solution   We simplify each radical separately and combine like radicals.

COMMENT We cannot combine $-\sqrt[3]{2}$ and $2\sqrt[3]{3}$, because the radicals have different radicands.

$$
\begin{aligned}
\sqrt[3]{16} - \sqrt[3]{54} + \sqrt[3]{24} &= \sqrt[3]{8 \cdot 2} - \sqrt[3]{27 \cdot 2} + \sqrt[3]{8 \cdot 3} \\
&= \sqrt[3]{8}\sqrt[3]{2} - \sqrt[3]{27}\sqrt[3]{2} + \sqrt[3]{8}\sqrt[3]{3} \\
&= 2\sqrt[3]{2} - 3\sqrt[3]{2} + 2\sqrt[3]{3} \\
&= -\sqrt[3]{2} + 2\sqrt[3]{3}
\end{aligned}
$$

SELF CHECK 5   Simplify: $\sqrt[3]{24} - \sqrt[3]{16} + \sqrt[3]{54}$.

EXAMPLE 6   Simplify: $\sqrt[3]{16x^4} + \sqrt[3]{54x^4} - \sqrt[3]{-128x^4}$.

Solution   We simplify each radical separately, factor out $\sqrt[3]{2x}$, and combine like radicals.

$$\sqrt[3]{16x^4} + \sqrt[3]{54x^4} - \sqrt[3]{-128x^4}$$
$$= \sqrt[3]{8x^3 \cdot 2x} + \sqrt[3]{27x^3 \cdot 2x} - \sqrt[3]{-64x^3 \cdot 2x}$$
$$= \sqrt[3]{8x^3}\sqrt[3]{2x} + \sqrt[3]{27x^3}\sqrt[3]{2x} - \sqrt[3]{-64x^3}\sqrt[3]{2x}$$
$$= 2x\sqrt[3]{2x} + 3x\sqrt[3]{2x} + 4x\sqrt[3]{2x}$$
$$= (2x + 3x + 4x)\sqrt[3]{2x}$$
$$= 9x\sqrt[3]{2x}$$

⇨ **SELF CHECK 6**   Simplify: $\sqrt{32x^3} + \sqrt{50x^3} - \sqrt{18x^3}$ $(x > 0)$.

---

3   **Find the length of a side of a 30°–60°–90° triangle and a 45°–45°–90° triangle.**

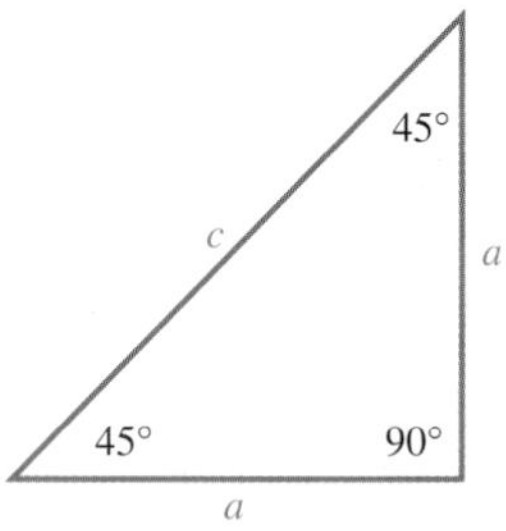

An isosceles right triangle is a right triangle with two legs of equal length. If we know the length of one leg of an isosceles right triangle, we can use the Pythagorean theorem to find the length of the hypotenuse. Since the triangle shown in Figure 9-10 is a right triangle, we have

$$c^2 = a^2 + a^2 \qquad \text{Use the Pythagorean theorem.}$$
$$c^2 = 2a^2 \qquad \text{Combine like terms.}$$
$$c = \sqrt{2a^2} \qquad \text{Since } c \text{ represents a length, take the positive square root.}$$
$$c = a\sqrt{2} \qquad \sqrt{2a^2} = \sqrt{2}\sqrt{a^2} = \sqrt{2}a = a\sqrt{2}. \text{ No absolute value symbols are needed, because } a \text{ is positive.}$$

Thus, *in an isosceles right triangle, the length of the hypotenuse is the length of one leg times* $\sqrt{2}$.

Figure 9-10

EXAMPLE 7   **GEOMETRY**   If one leg of the isosceles right triangle shown in Figure 9-10 is 10 feet long, find the length of the hypotenuse.

Solution   Since the length of the hypotenuse is the length of a leg times $\sqrt{2}$, we have

$$c = 10\sqrt{2}$$

The length of the hypotenuse is $10\sqrt{2}$ feet. To two decimal places, the length is 14.14 feet.

⇨ **SELF CHECK 7**   Find the length of the hypotenuse of an isosceles right triangle if one leg is 12 meters long.

If the length of the hypotenuse of an isosceles right triangle is known, we can use the Pythagorean theorem to find the length of each leg.

EXAMPLE 8   **GEOMETRY**   Find the length of each leg of the isosceles right triangle shown in Figure 9-11 on the next page.

Solution   We use the Pythagorean theorem.

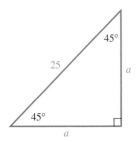

Figure 9-11

$$c^2 = a^2 + a^2$$

$$25^2 = 2a^2 \qquad \text{Substitute 25 for } c \text{ and combine like terms.}$$

$$\frac{625}{2} = a^2 \qquad \text{Square 25 and divide both sides by 2.}$$

$$\sqrt{\frac{625}{2}} = a \qquad \text{Since } a \text{ represents a length, take the positive square root.}$$

$$a \approx 17.67766953 \qquad \text{Use a calculator.}$$

To two decimal places, the length is 17.68 units.

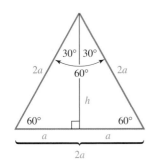

Figure 9-12

From geometry, we know that an *equilateral triangle* is a triangle with three sides of equal length and three 60° angles. If an **altitude** is drawn upon the base of an equilateral triangle, as shown in Figure 9-12, it bisects the base and divides the triangle into two 30°–60°–90° triangles. We can see that the shortest leg of each 30°–60°–90° triangle is a units long. Thus,

The shorter leg of a 30°–60°–90° *triangle is half as long as its hypotenuse.*

We can find the length of the altitude, h, by using the Pythagorean theorem.

$$a^2 + h^2 = (2a)^2$$

$$a^2 + h^2 = 4a^2 \qquad (2a)^2 = (2a)(2a) = 4a^2$$

$$h^2 = 3a^2 \qquad \text{Subtract } a^2 \text{ from both sides.}$$

$$h = \sqrt{3a^2} \qquad \text{Since } h \text{ represents a length, take the positive square root.}$$

$$h = a\sqrt{3} \qquad \sqrt{3a^2} = \sqrt{3}\sqrt{a^2} = a\sqrt{3}. \text{ No absolute value symbols are needed, because } a \text{ is positive.}$$

Thus,

The length of the longer leg is the length of the shorter side times $\sqrt{3}$.

EXAMPLE 9   **GEOMETRY**   Find the length of the hypotenuse and the longer leg of the right triangle shown in Figure 9-13.

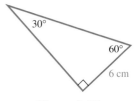

Figure 9-13

Solution   Since the shorter leg of a 30°–60°–90° triangle is half as long as its hypotenuse, the hypotenuse is 12 centimeters long.

Since the length of the longer leg is the length of the shorter leg times $\sqrt{3}$, the longer leg is $6\sqrt{3}$ (about 10.39) centimeters long.

⇨ **SELF CHECK 9**   Find the length of the hypotenuse and the longer leg of a 30°–60°–90° right triangle if the shorter leg is 8 centimeters long.

EXAMPLE 10   **GEOMETRY**   Find the length of each leg of the triangle shown in Figure 9-14.

Solution   Since the shorter leg of a 30°–60°–90° triangle is half as long as its hypotenuse, the shorter leg is $\frac{9}{2}$ centimeters long.

Since the length of the longer leg is the length of the shorter leg times $\sqrt{3}$, the longer leg is $\frac{9}{2}\sqrt{3}$ (or about 7.79) centimeters long.

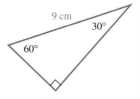

Figure 9-14

⇨ **SELF CHECK 10**   Find the length of the longer leg of the right triangle shown in Figure 9-14 if its hypotenuse is 10 cm long.

⇨ **SELF CHECK ANSWERS**   **1. a.** $2\sqrt{5}$ **b.** $2\sqrt[3]{3}$ **2. a.** $\frac{\sqrt{11}}{6a}$ **b.** $\frac{2\sqrt[3]{a^2}}{5y}$ **3. a.** $7b\sqrt{2b}$ **b.** $3y\sqrt[3]{2y^2}$ **c.** $5b$ **4.** $19\sqrt{3}$
5. $2\sqrt[3]{3} + \sqrt[3]{2}$ **6.** $6x\sqrt{2x}$ **7.** $12\sqrt{2}$ m   **9.** 16 cm, $8\sqrt{3}$ cm   **10.** $5\sqrt{3}$ cm

NOW TRY THIS

Simplify.

1. $\sqrt[3]{8x - 8} + \sqrt[3]{x - 1}$

2. $\sqrt{\dfrac{75x^7 y}{3xy}}$

3. $\dfrac{5\sqrt[3]{32}}{2}$

9.4 EXERCISES

WARM-UPS

Simplify.

1. $\sqrt{7}\sqrt{7}$

2. $\sqrt[3]{4^2}\sqrt[3]{4}$

3. $\dfrac{\sqrt[3]{54}}{\sqrt[3]{2}}$

Simplify each expression. Assume that $b \neq 0$.

4. $\sqrt{18}$

5. $\sqrt[3]{16}$

6. $\sqrt[3]{\dfrac{3x^2}{64b^6}}$

Combine like terms.

7. $3\sqrt{3} + 4\sqrt{3}$

8. $5\sqrt{7} - 2\sqrt{7}$

9. $2\sqrt[3]{9} + 3\sqrt[3]{9}$

10. $10\sqrt[5]{4} - 2\sqrt[5]{4}$

REVIEW   *Perform each operation.*

11. $3x^2 y^2(-5x^3 y^{-3})$

12. $-2a^2 b^{-2}(4a^{-2}b^4 - 2a^2 b + 3a^3 b^2)$

13. $(3t + 2)^2$

14. $(5r - 3s)(5r + 2s)$

15. $2p - 5\overline{)6p^2 - 7p - 25}$

16. $3m + n\overline{)6m^3 - m^2 n + 2mn^2 + n^3}$

VOCABULARY AND CONCEPTS   *Fill in the blanks.*

17. $\sqrt[n]{ab} = $ _____

18. $\sqrt[n]{\dfrac{a}{b}} = $ ____

19. If two radicals have the same index and the same radicand, they are called _____ radicals.

20. The perpendicular distance from a vertex of a triangle to the opposite side is called an _____.

GUIDED PRACTICE

Simplify each expression. Assume that all variables represent positive numbers. (Objective 1)

21. $\sqrt{6}\sqrt{6}$

22. $\sqrt{11}\sqrt{11}$

23. $\sqrt{t}\sqrt{t}$

24. $-\sqrt{z}\sqrt{z}$

25. $\sqrt[3]{5x^2}\sqrt[3]{25x}$

26. $\sqrt[4]{25a}\sqrt[4]{25a^3}$

27. $\dfrac{\sqrt{500}}{\sqrt{5}}$

28. $\dfrac{\sqrt{128}}{\sqrt{2}}$

29. $\dfrac{\sqrt{98x^3}}{\sqrt{2x}}$

30. $\dfrac{\sqrt{75y^5}}{\sqrt{3y}}$

31. $\dfrac{\sqrt{180ab^4}}{\sqrt{5ab^2}}$

32. $\dfrac{\sqrt{112ab^3}}{\sqrt{7ab}}$

33. $\dfrac{\sqrt[3]{48}}{\sqrt[3]{6}}$

34. $\dfrac{\sqrt[3]{64}}{\sqrt[3]{8}}$

35. $\dfrac{\sqrt[3]{189a^4}}{\sqrt[3]{7a}}$

36. $\dfrac{\sqrt[3]{243x^7}}{\sqrt[3]{9x}}$

Simplify each radical. See Example 1. (Objective 1)

37. $\sqrt{20}$

38. $\sqrt{8}$

39. $-\sqrt{200}$

40. $-\sqrt{250}$

41. $\sqrt[3]{80}$

42. $\sqrt[3]{270}$

43. $\sqrt[3]{-81}$

44. $\sqrt[3]{-72}$

45. $\sqrt[4]{32}$

46. $\sqrt[4]{48}$

47. $\sqrt[5]{96}$

48. $\sqrt[7]{256}$

Simplify each radical. Assume no divisions by 0. See Example 2. (Objective 1)

49. $\sqrt{\dfrac{7}{9x^2}}$

50. $\sqrt{\dfrac{3}{4y^2}}$

51. $\sqrt[3]{\dfrac{7a^3}{64}}$

52. $\sqrt[3]{\dfrac{4b^3}{125}}$

53. $\sqrt[4]{\dfrac{3p^4}{10,000q^4}}$

54. $\sqrt[5]{\dfrac{4r^5}{243s^{10}}}$

55. $\sqrt[5]{\dfrac{3m^{15}}{32n^{10}}}$

56. $\sqrt[6]{\dfrac{5a^6}{64b^{12}}}$

Simplify each radical. Assume that all variables represent positive numbers. See Example 3. (Objective 1)

57. $\sqrt{50x^2}$

58. $\sqrt{75a^2}$

59. $\sqrt{32b}$

60. $\sqrt{80c}$

61. $-\sqrt{112a^3}$

62. $\sqrt{147a^5}$

63. $\sqrt{175a^2b^3}$

64. $\sqrt{128a^3b^5}$

65. $-\sqrt{300xy}$

66. $\sqrt{200x^2y}$

67. $\sqrt[3]{-54x^6}$

68. $-\sqrt[3]{-81a^3}$

69. $\sqrt[3]{16x^{12}y^3}$

70. $\sqrt[3]{40a^3b^6}$

71. $\sqrt{\dfrac{z^2}{16x^2}}$

72. $\sqrt{\dfrac{b^4}{64a^8}}$

Simplify and combine like radicals. See Example 4. (Objective 2)

73. $\sqrt{3} + \sqrt{27}$

74. $\sqrt{8} + \sqrt{32}$

75. $\sqrt{2} - \sqrt{8}$

76. $\sqrt{20} - \sqrt{125}$

77. $\sqrt{98} - \sqrt{50}$

78. $\sqrt{72} - \sqrt{200}$

79. $3\sqrt{24} + \sqrt{54}$

80. $\sqrt{18} + 2\sqrt{50}$

81. $\sqrt{18} + \sqrt{300} - \sqrt{243}$

82. $\sqrt{80} - \sqrt{128} + \sqrt{288}$

Simplify and combine like radicals. See Example 5. (Objective 2)

83. $\sqrt[3]{24} + \sqrt[3]{3}$

84. $\sqrt[3]{16} + \sqrt[3]{128}$

85. $\sqrt[3]{32} - \sqrt[3]{108}$

86. $\sqrt[3]{80} - \sqrt[3]{10,000}$

87. $2\sqrt[3]{125} - 5\sqrt[3]{64}$

88. $\sqrt[3]{81} - \sqrt[3]{24}$

89. $2\sqrt[3]{16} - \sqrt[3]{54} - 3\sqrt[3]{128}$

90. $\sqrt[3]{250} - 4\sqrt[3]{5} + \sqrt[3]{16}$

Simplify and combine like radicals. All variables represent positive numbers. See Example 6. (Objective 2)

91. $\sqrt[3]{3x^5} - \sqrt[3]{24x^5}$

92. $\sqrt[3]{16x^4} - \sqrt[3]{54x^4}$

93. $\sqrt{25yz^2} + \sqrt{9yz^2}$

94. $\sqrt{36xy^2} + \sqrt{49xy^2}$

95. $\sqrt{y^5} - \sqrt{9y^5} - \sqrt{25y^5}$

96. $\sqrt{8y^7} + \sqrt{32y^7} - \sqrt{2y^7}$

97. $3\sqrt[3]{2x} - \sqrt[3]{54x}$

98. $2\sqrt[3]{64a} + 2\sqrt[3]{8a}$

For Exercises 99–106, find the lengths of the remaining sides of the triangle. See Examples 7–8. (Objective 3)

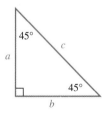

99. $a = 3$

100. $a = 8$

101. $b = \dfrac{2}{3}$

102. $b = \dfrac{3}{10}$

103. $a = 5\sqrt{2}$

104. $a = 12\sqrt{2}$

105. $c = 7\sqrt{2}$

106. $c = 16\sqrt{2}$

For Exercises 107–114, find the lengths of the remaining sides of the triangle. **See Examples 9–10. (Objective 3)**

107. $a = 5$

108. $a = 8$

109. $b = 9\sqrt{3}$

110. $b = 18\sqrt{3}$

111. $c = 24$

112. $c = 8$

113. $c = 15$

114. $c = 25$

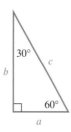

ADDITIONAL PRACTICE

Simplify. Assume that all variables represent positive numbers.

115. $4\sqrt{2x} + 6\sqrt{2x}$

116. $\sqrt{25y^2z} - \sqrt{16y^2z}$

117. $\sqrt[4]{32x^{12}y^4}$

118. $\sqrt[5]{64x^{10}y^5}$

119. $\sqrt[4]{\dfrac{5x}{16z^4}}$

120. $\sqrt{\dfrac{11a^2}{125b^6}}$

121. $\sqrt{98} - \sqrt{50} - \sqrt{72}$

122. $\sqrt{20} + \sqrt{125} - \sqrt{80}$

123. $3\sqrt[3]{27} + 12\sqrt[3]{216}$

124. $14\sqrt[4]{32} - 15\sqrt[4]{162}$

125. $23\sqrt[4]{768} + \sqrt[4]{48}$

126. $3\sqrt[4]{512} + 2\sqrt[4]{32}$

127. $4\sqrt[4]{243} - \sqrt[4]{48}$

128. $\sqrt[4]{48} - \sqrt[4]{243} - \sqrt[4]{768}$

129. $6\sqrt[3]{5y} + 3\sqrt[3]{5y}$

130. $8\sqrt[5]{7a^2} - 7\sqrt[5]{7a^2}$

131. $10\sqrt[6]{12xyz} - \sqrt[6]{12xyz}$

132. $3\sqrt[4]{x^4y} - 2\sqrt[4]{x^4y}$

133. $\sqrt[5]{x^6y^2} + \sqrt[5]{32x^6y^2} + \sqrt[5]{x^6y^2}$

134. $\sqrt[3]{xy^4} + \sqrt[3]{8xy^4} - \sqrt[3]{27xy^4}$

135. $\sqrt{x^2 + 2x + 1} + \sqrt{x^2 + 2x + 1}$

136. $\sqrt{4x^2 + 12x + 9} + \sqrt{9x^2 + 6x + 1}$

Find the missing lengths in each triangle. Give each answer to two decimal places.

137.

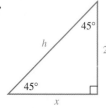

138.

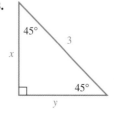

139.

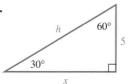

140.

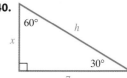

141.

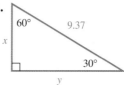

142.

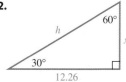

143.

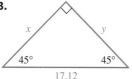

144.

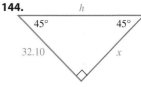

APPLICATIONS

Find the exact answer and then give an approximation to the nearest hundredth.

145. Hardware The sides of a regular hexagonal nut are 10 millimeters long. Find the height h of the nut.

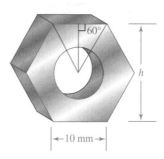

146. Ironing boards Find the height h of the ironing board shown in the illustration.

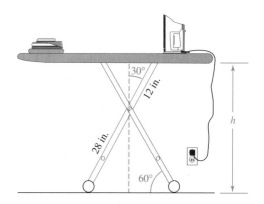

WRITING ABOUT MATH

147. Explain how to recognize like radicals.

148. Explain how to combine like radicals.

SOMETHING TO THINK ABOUT

149. Can you find any numbers a and b such that

$$\sqrt{a + b} = \sqrt{a} + \sqrt{b}$$

150. Find the sum.

$$\sqrt{3} + \sqrt{3^2} + \sqrt{3^3} + \sqrt{3^4} + \sqrt{3^5}$$

SECTION 9.5 Multiplying and Dividing Radical Expressions

Objectives

1 Multiply two radical expressions.

2 Rationalize the denominator of a fraction that contains a radical expression.

3 Rationalize the numerator of a fraction that contains a radical expression.

4 Solve an application problem containing a radical expression.

Vocabulary

rationalize denominators   conjugates   rationalize numerators

Getting Ready

Perform each operation and simplify, if possible.

1. $a^3 a^4$ **2.** $\dfrac{b^5}{b^2}$ **3.** $a(a - 2)$ **4.** $3b^2(2b + 3)$

5. $(a + 2)(a - 5)$ **6.** $(2a + 3b)(2a - 3b)$

We now learn how to multiply and divide radical expressions. Then we will use these skills to solve application problems.

1 Multiply two radical expressions.

Radical expressions with the same index can be multiplied and divided.

EXAMPLE 1 Multiply: **a.** $\left(3\sqrt{6}\right)\left(2\sqrt{3}\right)$ **b.** $\left(\sqrt[3]{3a}\right)\left(\sqrt[3]{9a^4}\right)$.

Solution We use the commutative and associative properties of multiplication to multiply the coefficients and the radicals separately. Then we simplify any radicals in the product, if possible.

a. $3\sqrt{6} \cdot 2\sqrt{3} = 3(2)\sqrt{6}\sqrt{3}$ Multiply the coefficients and multiply the radicals.

$\qquad\qquad = 6\sqrt{18}$ $3(2) = 6$ and $\sqrt{6}\sqrt{3} = \sqrt{18}$.

$\qquad\qquad = 6\sqrt{9}\sqrt{2}$ $\sqrt{18} = \sqrt{9 \cdot 2} = \sqrt{9}\sqrt{2}$.

$\qquad\qquad = 6(3)\sqrt{2}$ $\sqrt{9} = 3$

$\qquad\qquad = 18\sqrt{2}$

b. $\left(\sqrt[3]{3a}\right)\left(\sqrt[3]{9a^4}\right) = \sqrt[3]{27a^5}$ Multiply the radicals.

$\qquad\qquad\qquad = \sqrt[3]{27a^3 \cdot a^2}$ Factor $27a^5$.

$\qquad\qquad\qquad = \sqrt[3]{27a^3}\sqrt[3]{a^2}$ $\sqrt[3]{ab} = \sqrt[3]{a}\sqrt[3]{b}$

$\qquad\qquad\qquad = 3a\sqrt[3]{a^2}$ $\sqrt[3]{27a^3} = 3a$

⇨ **SELF CHECK 1**   Multiply $-2\sqrt{7}$ by $5\sqrt{2}$.

To multiply a radical expression with two or more terms by a radical expression, we use the distributive property to remove parentheses and then simplify each resulting term, if possible.

EXAMPLE 2   Multiply: $3\sqrt{3}\left(4\sqrt{8} - 5\sqrt{10}\right)$.

Solution $3\sqrt{3}\left(4\sqrt{8} - 5\sqrt{10}\right)$

$\qquad = 3\sqrt{3} \cdot 4\sqrt{8} - 3\sqrt{3} \cdot 5\sqrt{10}$ Use the distributive property.

$\qquad = 12\sqrt{24} - 15\sqrt{30}$ Multiply the coefficients and multiply the radicals.

$\qquad = 12\sqrt{4}\sqrt{6} - 15\sqrt{30}$

$\qquad = 12(2)\sqrt{6} - 15\sqrt{30}$

$\qquad = 24\sqrt{6} - 15\sqrt{30}$

⇨ **SELF CHECK 2**   Multiply: $4\sqrt{2}\left(3\sqrt{5} - 2\sqrt{8}\right)$.

To multiply two radical expressions, each with two or more terms, we use the distributive property as we did when we multiplied two polynomials. Then we simplify each resulting term, if possible.

EXAMPLE 3   Multiply: $\left(\sqrt{7} + \sqrt{2}\right)\left(\sqrt{7} - 3\sqrt{2}\right)$.

Solution $\left(\sqrt{7} + \sqrt{2}\right)\left(\sqrt{7} - 3\sqrt{2}\right)$

$\qquad = \left(\sqrt{7}\right)^2 - 3\sqrt{7}\sqrt{2} + \sqrt{2}\sqrt{7} - 3\sqrt{2}\sqrt{2}$

$\qquad = 7 - 3\sqrt{14} + \sqrt{14} - 3(2)$

$$= 7 - 2\sqrt{14} - 6$$
$$= 1 - 2\sqrt{14}$$

⇨ **SELF CHECK 3**   Multiply: $\left(\sqrt{5} + 2\sqrt{3}\right)\left(\sqrt{5} - \sqrt{3}\right)$.

EXAMPLE 4   Multiply: $\left(\sqrt{3x} - \sqrt{5}\right)\left(\sqrt{2x} + \sqrt{10}\right)$.

Solution $\left(\sqrt{3x} - \sqrt{5}\right)\left(\sqrt{2x} + \sqrt{10}\right)$

COMMENT   Note that x is not under the radical in the first term, but it is under the radical in the second and third terms.

$$= \sqrt{3x}\sqrt{2x} + \sqrt{3x}\sqrt{10} - \sqrt{5}\sqrt{2x} - \sqrt{5}\sqrt{10}$$
$$= \sqrt{6x^2} + \sqrt{30x} - \sqrt{10x} - \sqrt{50}$$
$$= \sqrt{6}\sqrt{x^2} + \sqrt{30x} - \sqrt{10x} - \sqrt{25}\sqrt{2}$$
$$\rightarrow \quad = \sqrt{6}x + \sqrt{30x} - \sqrt{10x} - 5\sqrt{2}$$

⇨ **SELF CHECK 4**   Multiply: $\left(\sqrt{x} + 1\right)\left(\sqrt{x} - 3\right)$.

COMMENT   It is important to draw radical signs so they completely cover the radicand, but no more than the radicand. To avoid confusion, we can use the commutative property of multiplication and write an expression such as $\sqrt{6}x$ in the form $x\sqrt{6}$.

2   **Rationalize the denominator of a fraction that contains a radical expression.**

To divide radical expressions, we **rationalize the denominator** of a fraction to replace the denominator with a rational number. For example, to divide $\sqrt{70}$ by $\sqrt{3}$ we write the division as the fraction

$$\frac{\sqrt{70}}{\sqrt{3}}$$

To eliminate the radical in the denominator, we multiply the numerator and the denominator by a number that will give a perfect square under the radical in the denominator. Because $3 \cdot 3 = 9$ and 9 is a perfect square, $\sqrt{3}$ is such a number.

$$\frac{\sqrt{70}}{\sqrt{3}} = \frac{\sqrt{70} \cdot \sqrt{3}}{\sqrt{3} \cdot \sqrt{3}} \qquad \text{Multiply numerator and denominator by } \sqrt{3}.$$
$$= \frac{\sqrt{210}}{3} \qquad \text{Multiply the radicals.}$$

Since there is no radical in the denominator and $\sqrt{210}$ cannot be simplified, the expression $\frac{\sqrt{210}}{3}$ is in simplest form, and the division is complete.

EXAMPLE 5 Rationalize the denominator.

a. $\sqrt{\dfrac{20}{7}}$ **b.** $\dfrac{4}{\sqrt[3]{2}}$

Solution **a.** We first write the square root of the quotient as the quotient of two square roots.

$$\sqrt{\frac{20}{7}} = \frac{\sqrt{20}}{\sqrt{7}}$$

Because the denominator is a square root, we must then multiply the numerator and the denominator by a number that will give a rational number in the denominator. Such a number is $\sqrt{7}$.

$$\frac{\sqrt{20}}{\sqrt{7}} = \frac{\sqrt{20} \cdot \sqrt{7}}{\sqrt{7} \cdot \sqrt{7}} \qquad \text{Multiply numerator and denominator by } \sqrt{7}.$$

$$= \frac{\sqrt{140}}{7} \qquad \text{Multiply the radicals.}$$

$$= \frac{2\sqrt{35}}{7} \qquad \text{Simplify } \sqrt{140}: \sqrt{140} = \sqrt{4 \cdot 35} = \sqrt{4}\sqrt{35} = 2\sqrt{35}.$$

b. Since the denominator is a cube root, we multiply the numerator and the denominator by a number that will give a perfect cube under the radical sign. Since $2 \cdot 4 = 8$ is a perfect cube, $\sqrt[3]{4}$ is such a number.

$$\frac{4}{\sqrt[3]{2}} = \frac{4 \cdot \sqrt[3]{4}}{\sqrt[3]{2} \cdot \sqrt[3]{4}} \qquad \text{Multiply numerator and denominator by } \sqrt[3]{4}.$$

$$= \frac{4\sqrt[3]{4}}{\sqrt[3]{8}} \qquad \text{Multiply the radicals in the denominator.}$$

$$= \frac{4\sqrt[3]{4}}{2} \qquad \sqrt[3]{8} = 2$$

$$= 2\sqrt[3]{4} \qquad \text{Simplify.}$$

⇨ **SELF CHECK 5** Rationalize the denominator: $\dfrac{5}{\sqrt[4]{3}}$.

EXAMPLE 6 Rationalize the denominator: $\dfrac{\sqrt[3]{5}}{\sqrt[3]{18}}$.

Solution We multiply the numerator and the denominator by a number that will result in a perfect cube under the radical sign in the denominator.

Since 216 is the smallest perfect cube that is divisible by 18 ($216 \div 18 = 12$) multiplying the numerator and the denominator by $\sqrt[3]{12}$ will give the smallest possible perfect cube under the radical in the denominator.

$$\frac{\sqrt[3]{5}}{\sqrt[3]{18}} = \frac{\sqrt[3]{5} \cdot \sqrt[3]{12}}{\sqrt[3]{18} \cdot \sqrt[3]{12}} \qquad \text{Multiply numerator and denominator by } \sqrt[3]{12}.$$

$$= \frac{\sqrt[3]{60}}{\sqrt[3]{216}} \qquad \text{Multiply the radicals.}$$

$$= \frac{\sqrt[3]{60}}{6} \qquad \sqrt[3]{216} = 6$$

SELF CHECK 6 Rationalize the denominator: $\dfrac{\sqrt[3]{2}}{\sqrt[3]{9}}$.

EXAMPLE 7 Rationalize the denominator of $\dfrac{\sqrt{5xy^2}}{\sqrt{xy^3}}$ (x and y are positive numbers).

Solution

Method 1

$$\frac{\sqrt{5xy^2}}{\sqrt{xy^3}} = \sqrt{\frac{5xy^2}{xy^3}}$$

$$= \sqrt{\frac{5}{y}}$$

$$= \frac{\sqrt{5}}{\sqrt{y}}$$

$$= \frac{\sqrt{5}\sqrt{y}}{\sqrt{y}\sqrt{y}}$$

$$= \frac{\sqrt{5y}}{y}$$

Method 2

$$\frac{\sqrt{5xy^2}}{\sqrt{xy^3}} = \sqrt{\frac{5xy^2}{xy^3}}$$

$$= \sqrt{\frac{5}{y}}$$

$$= \sqrt{\frac{5 \cdot y}{y \cdot y}}$$

$$= \frac{\sqrt{5y}}{\sqrt{y^2}}$$

$$= \frac{\sqrt{5y}}{y}$$

SELF CHECK 7 Rationalize the denominator: $\dfrac{\sqrt{4ab^3}}{\sqrt{2a^2b^2}}$ ($a > 0, b > 0$).

To rationalize the denominator of a fraction with square roots in a binomial denominator, we can multiply the numerator and denominator by the **conjugate** of the denominator. Conjugate binomials are binomials with the same terms but with opposite signs between their terms.

Conjugate Binomials The conjugate of $a + b$ is $a - b$, and the conjugate of $a - b$ is $a + b$.

If we multiply an expression such as $5 + \sqrt{2}$ by its conjugate $5 - \sqrt{2}$, we will obtain an expression without any radical terms.

$$\left(5 + \sqrt{2}\right)\left(5 - \sqrt{2}\right) = 25 - 5\sqrt{2} + 5\sqrt{2} - 2$$
$$= 23$$

EXAMPLE 8 Rationalize the denominator: $\dfrac{1}{\sqrt{2} + 1}$.

Solution We multiply the numerator and denominator of the fraction by $\sqrt{2} - 1$, which is the conjugate of the denominator.

$$\frac{1}{\sqrt{2} + 1} = \frac{1(\sqrt{2} - 1)}{(\sqrt{2} + 1)(\sqrt{2} - 1)} \qquad \frac{\sqrt{2} - 1}{\sqrt{2} - 1} = 1$$

$$= \frac{\sqrt{2} - 1}{(\sqrt{2})^2 - 1} \qquad (\sqrt{2} + 1)(\sqrt{2} - 1) = (\sqrt{2})^2 - 1$$

$$= \frac{\sqrt{2} - 1}{2 - 1} \qquad (\sqrt{2})^2 = 2$$

$$= \sqrt{2} - 1 \qquad \frac{\sqrt{2} - 1}{2 - 1} = \frac{\sqrt{2} - 1}{1} = \sqrt{2} - 1$$

⇨ **SELF CHECK 8**   Rationalize the denominator: $\dfrac{2}{\sqrt{3} + 1}$.

EXAMPLE 9   Rationalize the denominator: $\dfrac{\sqrt{x} + \sqrt{2}}{\sqrt{x} - \sqrt{2}}$ $(x > 0, x \neq 2)$.

Solution   We multiply the numerator and denominator by $\sqrt{x} + \sqrt{2}$, which is the conjugate of the denominator, and simplify.

$$\frac{\sqrt{x} + \sqrt{2}}{\sqrt{x} - \sqrt{2}} = \frac{(\sqrt{x} + \sqrt{2})(\sqrt{x} + \sqrt{2})}{(\sqrt{x} - \sqrt{2})(\sqrt{x} + \sqrt{2})}$$

$$= \frac{x + \sqrt{2x} + \sqrt{2x} + 2}{x - 2} \qquad \text{Use the FOIL method.}$$

$$= \frac{x + 2\sqrt{2x} + 2}{x - 2}$$

⇨ **SELF CHECK 9**   Rationalize the denominator: $\dfrac{\sqrt{x} - \sqrt{2}}{\sqrt{x} + \sqrt{2}}$ $(x > 0)$.

3   Rationalize the numerator of a fraction that contains a radical expression.

In calculus, we sometimes have to **rationalize a numerator** by multiplying the numerator and denominator of the fraction by the conjugate of the numerator.

EXAMPLE 10   Rationalize the numerator: $\dfrac{\sqrt{x} - 3}{\sqrt{x}}$ $(x > 0)$.

Solution   We multiply the numerator and denominator by $\sqrt{x} + 3$, which is the conjugate of the numerator.

$$\frac{\sqrt{x} - 3}{\sqrt{x}} = \frac{(\sqrt{x} - 3)(\sqrt{x} + 3)}{\sqrt{x}(\sqrt{x} + 3)}$$

$$= \frac{x + 3\sqrt{x} - 3\sqrt{x} - 9}{x + 3\sqrt{x}}$$

$$= \frac{x - 9}{x + 3\sqrt{x}}$$

The final expression is not in simplified form. However, this nonsimplified form is sometimes desirable in calculus.

⇨ **SELF CHECK 10**   Rationalize the numerator: $\dfrac{\sqrt{x}+3}{\sqrt{x}}$ $(x > 0)$.

4   **Solve an application problem containing a radical expression.**

EXAMPLE 11

Figure 9-15

PHOTOGRAPHY   Many camera lenses (see Figure 9-15) have an adjustable opening called the *aperture*, which controls the amount of light passing through the lens. The *f-number* of a lens is its *focal length* divided by the diameter of its circular aperture.

$$f\text{-number} = \dfrac{f}{d} \qquad f \text{ is the focal length, and } d \text{ is the diameter of the aperture.}$$

A lens with a focal length of 12 centimeters and an aperture with a diameter of 6 centimeters has an *f-number* of $\frac{12}{6}$ and is an $f/2$ lens. If the area of the aperture is reduced to admit half as much light, the *f-number* of the lens will change. Find the new *f-number*.

Solution   We first find the area of the aperture when its diameter is 6 centimeters.

$$A = \pi r^2 \qquad \text{The formula for the area of a circle.}$$
$$A = \pi(3)^2 \qquad \text{Since a radius is half the diameter, substitute 3 for } r.$$
$$A = 9\pi$$

When the size of the aperture is reduced to admit half as much light, the area of the aperture will be $\frac{9\pi}{2}$ square centimeters. To find the diameter of a circle with this area, we proceed as follows:

$$A = \pi r^2 \qquad \text{This is the formula for the area of a circle.}$$
$$\frac{9\pi}{2} = \pi\left(\frac{d}{2}\right)^2 \qquad \text{Substitute } \tfrac{9\pi}{2} \text{ for } A \text{ and } \tfrac{d}{2} \text{ for } r.$$
$$\frac{9\pi}{2} = \frac{\pi d^2}{4} \qquad \left(\tfrac{d}{2}\right)^2 = \tfrac{d^2}{4}$$
$$18 = d^2 \qquad \text{Multiply both sides by 4, and divide both sides by } \pi.$$
$$d = 3\sqrt{2} \qquad \sqrt{18} = \sqrt{9}\sqrt{2} = 3\sqrt{2}$$

Since the focal length of the lens is still 12 centimeters and the diameter is now $3\sqrt{2}$ centimeters, the new *f-number* of the lens is

$$f\text{-number} = \frac{f}{d} = \frac{12}{3\sqrt{2}} \qquad \text{Substitute 12 for } f \text{ and } 3\sqrt{2} \text{ for } d.$$
$$= \frac{4}{\sqrt{2}} \qquad \text{Simplify.}$$
$$= \frac{4\sqrt{2}}{2} \qquad \text{Rationalize the denominator.}$$
$$= 2\sqrt{2} \qquad \text{Simplify.}$$
$$\approx 2.828427125 \qquad \text{Use a calculator.}$$

The lens is now an $f/2.8$ lens.

EVERYDAY CONNECTIONS   Traveling Through Water

©Shutterstock.com/Steven Lee

The Froude number, named after William Froude, measures the resistance of an object moving through water. For a ship, the Froude number is calculated by the formula:

$$Fr = \frac{V}{\sqrt{gL}}$$

where V is the ship's velocity, L is the ship's length, and g is the acceleration due to gravity.

Source:
http://www.solarnavigator.net/froude_number_speed_length_ratio.htm

1. Use the formula to compute the Froude number for a ship that is 100 feet long, traveling with a velocity of 74 feet per second. Note that the acceleration due to gravity is 32 ft/s².

2. Use the formula to compute the Froude number for a ship that is 25 meters long, traveling with a velocity of 22 meters per second. Note that the acceleration due to gravity is 9.8 m/s².

➡️ **SELF CHECK ANSWERS**

1. $-10\sqrt{14}$ **2.** $12\sqrt{10} - 32$ **3.** $-1 + \sqrt{15}$ **4.** $x - 2\sqrt{x} - 3$ **5.** $\frac{5\sqrt[4]{27}}{3}$ **6.** $\frac{\sqrt[3]{6}}{3}$ **7.** $\frac{\sqrt{2ab}}{a}$

8. $\sqrt{3} - 1$ **9.** $\frac{x - 2\sqrt{2x} + 2}{x - 2}$ **10.** $\frac{x - 9}{x - 3\sqrt{x}}$

NOW TRY THIS

Find the domain of each of the following. Give your answer in interval notation.

1. $f(x) = \dfrac{3x - 2}{\sqrt{x} + 1}$

2. $g(x) = \dfrac{3x - 2}{\sqrt{x + 1}}$

3. $h(x) = \dfrac{\sqrt{x} - 2}{\sqrt{x} + 1}$

9.5 EXERCISES

WARM-UPS   *Simplify.*

$\sqrt{3}\sqrt{3}$ **2.** $\sqrt[3]{2}\sqrt[3]{2}\sqrt[3]{2}$ **3.** $\sqrt{3}\sqrt{9}$ **4.** $\sqrt{a^3b}\sqrt{ab}$ $(a > 0, b > 0)$

5. $3\sqrt{2}\left(\sqrt{2} + 1\right)$

6. $\left(\sqrt{2} + 1\right)\left(\sqrt{2} - 1\right)$

7. $\dfrac{1}{\sqrt{2}}$

8. $\dfrac{1}{\sqrt{3} - 1}$

REVIEW   *Solve each equation.*

9. $\dfrac{2}{3 - a} = 1$

10. $5(s - 4) = -5(s - 4)$

11. $\dfrac{8}{b - 2} + \dfrac{3}{2 - b} = -\dfrac{1}{b}$

12. $\dfrac{2}{x - 2} + \dfrac{1}{x + 1} = \dfrac{1}{(x + 1)(x - 2)}$

VOCABULARY AND CONCEPTS   *Fill in the blanks.*

13. To multiply $2\sqrt{7}$ by $3\sqrt{5}$, we multiply __ by 3 and then multiply ____ by ____.

14. To multiply $2\sqrt{5}\left(3\sqrt{8} + \sqrt{3}\right)$, we use the _____ property to remove parentheses and simplify each resulting term.

15. The conjugate of $\sqrt{x} + 1$ is _____.

16. To multiply $\left(\sqrt{3} + \sqrt{2}\right)\left(\sqrt{3} - 2\sqrt{2}\right)$, we can use the _____ method.

17. To rationalize the denominator of $\dfrac{1}{\sqrt{3} - 1}$, multiply both the numerator and denominator by the _____ of the denominator.

18. To rationalize the numerator of $\dfrac{\sqrt{5} + 2}{\sqrt{5} - 2}$, multiply both the numerator and denominator by _____.

GUIDED PRACTICE

Simplify. All variables represent positive values. **See Example 1. (Objective 1)**

19. $\sqrt{2}\sqrt{8}$

20. $\sqrt{3}\sqrt{27}$

21. $\sqrt{5}\sqrt{10}$

22. $\sqrt{7}\sqrt{35}$

23. $2\sqrt{3}\sqrt{6}$

24. $3\sqrt{11}\sqrt{33}$

25. $\sqrt[3]{5}\sqrt[3]{25}$

26. $\sqrt[3]{7}\sqrt[3]{49}$

27. $\sqrt[3]{2}\sqrt[3]{12}$

28. $\sqrt[3]{3}\sqrt[3]{18}$

29. $\sqrt{ab^3}\sqrt{ab}$

30. $\sqrt{8x}\sqrt{2x^3y}$

31. $\sqrt[3]{5r^2s}\sqrt[3]{2r}$

32. $\sqrt[3]{3xy^2}\sqrt[3]{9x^3}$

33. $\sqrt{x(x + 3)}\sqrt{x^3(x + 3)}$

34. $\sqrt{y^2(x + y)}\sqrt{(x + y)^3}$

Simplify. **See Example 2. (Objective 1)**

35. $3\sqrt{5}\left(4 - \sqrt{5}\right)$

36. $2\sqrt{7}\left(3\sqrt{7} - 1\right)$

37. $3\sqrt{2}\left(4\sqrt{3} + 2\sqrt{7}\right)$

38. $-\sqrt{3}\left(\sqrt{7} - \sqrt{5}\right)$

Simplify. All variables represent positive values. **See Examples 3–4. (Objective 1)**

39. $\left(\sqrt{2} + 1\right)\left(\sqrt{2} - 3\right)$

40. $\left(2\sqrt{3} + 1\right)\left(\sqrt{3} - 1\right)$

41. $\left(4\sqrt{x} + 3\right)\left(2\sqrt{x} - 5\right)$

42. $\left(7\sqrt{y} + 2\right)\left(3\sqrt{y} - 5\right)$

43. $\left(\sqrt{5z} + \sqrt{3}\right)\left(\sqrt{5z} + \sqrt{3}\right)$

44. $\left(\sqrt{3p} - \sqrt{2}\right)\left(\sqrt{3p} + \sqrt{2}\right)$

45. $\left(2\sqrt{3a} - \sqrt{b}\right)\left(\sqrt{3a} + 3\sqrt{b}\right)$

46. $\left(5\sqrt{p} - \sqrt{3q}\right)\left(\sqrt{p} + 2\sqrt{3q}\right)$

47. $\left(3\sqrt{2r} - 2\right)^2$

48. $\left(2\sqrt{3t} + 5\right)^2$

49. $-2\left(\sqrt{3x} + \sqrt{3}\right)^2$

50. $3\left(\sqrt{5x} - \sqrt{3}\right)^2$

Rationalize each denominator. **See Examples 5–6. (Objective 2)**

51. $\sqrt{\dfrac{1}{7}}$

52. $\sqrt{\dfrac{5}{3}}$

53. $\sqrt{\dfrac{2}{3}}$

54. $\sqrt{\dfrac{3}{2}}$

55. $\dfrac{\sqrt{5}}{\sqrt{8}}$

56. $\dfrac{\sqrt{3}}{\sqrt{50}}$

57. $\dfrac{\sqrt{8}}{\sqrt{2}}$

58. $\dfrac{\sqrt{27}}{\sqrt{3}}$

59. $\dfrac{1}{\sqrt[3]{2}}$

60. $\dfrac{2}{\sqrt[3]{6}}$

61. $\dfrac{\sqrt[3]{2}}{\sqrt[3]{9}}$

62. $\dfrac{\sqrt[3]{9}}{\sqrt[3]{54}}$

Rationalize each denominator. All variables represent positive values. **See Example 7. (Objective 2)**

63. $\dfrac{\sqrt{8x^2y}}{\sqrt{xy}}$

64. $\dfrac{\sqrt{9xy}}{\sqrt{3x^2y}}$

65. $\dfrac{\sqrt{10xy^2}}{\sqrt{2xy^3}}$

66. $\dfrac{\sqrt{5ab^2c}}{\sqrt{10abc}}$

Rationalize each denominator. **See Example 8. (Objective 2)**

67. $\dfrac{1}{\sqrt{2} - 1}$

68. $\dfrac{3}{\sqrt{3} - 1}$

69. $\dfrac{\sqrt{2}}{\sqrt{5} + 3}$

70. $\dfrac{\sqrt{3}}{\sqrt{3} - 2}$

71. $\dfrac{\sqrt{3} + 1}{\sqrt{3} - 1}$

72. $\dfrac{\sqrt{2} - 1}{\sqrt{2} + 1}$

73. $\dfrac{\sqrt{7} - \sqrt{2}}{\sqrt{2} + \sqrt{7}}$

74. $\dfrac{\sqrt{3} + \sqrt{2}}{\sqrt{3} - \sqrt{2}}$

Rationalize each denominator. All variables represent positive values. See Example 9. (Objective 2)

75. $\dfrac{2}{\sqrt{x}+1}$

76. $\dfrac{3}{\sqrt{x}-2}$

77. $\dfrac{x}{\sqrt{x}-4}$

78. $\dfrac{2x}{\sqrt{x}+1}$

79. $\dfrac{\sqrt{x}-\sqrt{y}}{\sqrt{x}+\sqrt{y}}$

80. $\dfrac{\sqrt{x}+\sqrt{y}}{\sqrt{x}-\sqrt{y}}$

Rationalize each numerator. All variables represent positive values. See Example 10. (Objective 3)

81. $\dfrac{\sqrt{3}+1}{2}$

82. $\dfrac{\sqrt{5}-1}{2}$

83. $\dfrac{\sqrt{x}+3}{x}$

84. $\dfrac{2+\sqrt{x}}{5x}$

ADDITIONAL PRACTICE

Simplify each radical expression. All variables represent positive values.

85. $\left(3\sqrt[3]{9}\right)\left(2\sqrt[3]{3}\right)$

86. $\left(2\sqrt[3]{16}\right)\left(-\sqrt[3]{4}\right)$

87. $\sqrt{5ab}\sqrt{5a}$

88. $\sqrt{15rs^2}\sqrt{10r}$

89. $\sqrt[3]{a^5b}\sqrt[3]{16ab^5}$

90. $\sqrt[3]{3x^4y}\sqrt[3]{18x}$

91. $\sqrt[3]{6x^2(y+z)^2}\sqrt[3]{18x(y+z)}$

92. $\sqrt[3]{9x^2y(z+1)^2}\sqrt[3]{6xy^2(z+1)}$

93. $-2\sqrt{5x}\left(4\sqrt{2x}-3\sqrt{3}\right)$

94. $3\sqrt{7t}\left(2\sqrt{7t}+3\sqrt{3t^2}\right)$

Rationalize each denominator. All variables represent positive values.

95. $\dfrac{3}{\sqrt[3]{9}}$

96. $\dfrac{2}{\sqrt[3]{a}}$

97. $\dfrac{1}{\sqrt[4]{4}}$

98. $\dfrac{4}{\sqrt[4]{32}}$

99. $\dfrac{1}{\sqrt[5]{16}}$

100. $\dfrac{1}{\sqrt[5]{2}}$

101. $\dfrac{\sqrt[3]{4a^2}}{\sqrt[3]{2ab}}$

102. $\dfrac{\sqrt[3]{9x}}{\sqrt[3]{3xy}}$

103. $\dfrac{2z-1}{\sqrt{2z}-1}$

104. $\dfrac{3t-1}{\sqrt{3t}+1}$

Rationalize each numerator. All variables represent positive values.

105. $\dfrac{\sqrt{x}+\sqrt{y}}{\sqrt{x}}$

106. $\dfrac{\sqrt{x}-\sqrt{y}}{\sqrt{x}+\sqrt{y}}$

APPLICATIONS   *Solve each application problem.*

See Example 11. (Objective 4)

107. Photography   We have seen that a lens with a focal length of 12 centimeters and an aperture $3\sqrt{2}$ centimeters in diameter is an $f/2.8$ lens. Find the f-number if the area of the aperture is again cut in half.

108. Photography   A lens with a focal length of 12 centimeters and an aperture 3 centimeters in diameter is an $f/4$ lens. Find the f-number if the area of the aperture is cut in half.

109. Targets   The radius r of the target is given by the formula

$$r=\sqrt{\dfrac{A}{\pi}}$$

where A is the area. Write the formula in a form in which the denominator is not part of the radicand.

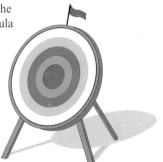

110. Pulse rates   The approximate pulse rate (in beats per minute) of an adult who is t inches tall is given by the function

$$p(t)=\dfrac{590}{\sqrt{t}}$$

Write the formula in a form in which the denominator is a rational expression.

111. If the hypotenuse of an isosceles right triangle is 8 cm, find the length of each leg.

112. The hypotenuse of a 45°–45°–90° triangle is 14 m. Find the length of each leg.

113. The longer leg of a 30°–60°–90° triangle is 6 ft. Find the length of remaining sides.

114. The altitude of an equilateral triangle is 24 mm. Find the lengths of the sides of the triangle.

WRITING ABOUT MATH

115. Explain how to simplify a fraction with the monomial denominator $\sqrt[3]{3}$.

116. Explain how to simplify a fraction with the monomial denominator $\sqrt[3]{9}$.

SOMETHING TO THINK ABOUT   *Assume that x is a rational number.*

117. Change the numerator of $\dfrac{\sqrt{x}-3}{4}$ to a rational number.

118. Rationalize the numerator: $\dfrac{2\sqrt{3x}+4}{\sqrt{3x}-1}$.

SECTION 9.6

Radical Equations

Objectives

1. Solve a radical equation containing one radical.
2. Solve a radical equation containing two radicals.
3. Solve a radical equation containing three radicals.
4. Solve a formula containing a radical for a specified variable.

Vocabulary

power rule

Getting Ready

Find each power.

1. $\left(\sqrt{a}\right)^2$
2. $\left(\sqrt{5x}\right)^2$
3. $\left(\sqrt{x+4}\right)^2$
4. $\left(\sqrt[4]{y-3}\right)^4$

In this section, we will solve equations that contain radicals. To do so, we will use the **power rule.**

1 **Solve a radical equation containing one radical.**

The Power Rule

If x, y, and n are real numbers and $x = y$, then

$$x^n = y^n$$

If we raise both sides of an equation to the same power, the resulting equation might not be equivalent to the original equation. For example, if we square both sides of the equation

(1) $x = 3$ With a solution set of $\{3\}$

we obtain the equation

(2) $x^2 = 9$ With a solution set of $\{3, -3\}$

Equations 1 and 2 are not equivalent, because they have different solution sets, and the solution -3 of Equation 2 does not satisfy Equation 1. Since raising both sides of equation to the same power can produce an equation with roots that don't satisfy the original equation, we must check each suspected solution in the original equation.

EXAMPLE 1   Solve: $\sqrt{x + 3} = 4$.

Solution   To eliminate the radical, we apply the power rule by squaring both sides of the equation, and proceed as follows:

$$\sqrt{x + 3} = 4$$
$$\left(\sqrt{x + 3}\right)^2 = (4)^2 \quad \text{Square both sides.}$$
$$x + 3 = 16$$
$$x = 13 \quad \text{Subtract 3 from both sides.}$$

To check the apparent solution of 13, we can substitute 13 for x and see whether it satisfies the original equation.

$$\sqrt{x + 3} = 4$$
$$\sqrt{13 + 3} \stackrel{?}{=} 4 \quad \text{Substitute 13 for } x.$$
$$\sqrt{16} \stackrel{?}{=} 4$$
$$4 = 4$$

Since 13 satisfies the original equation, it is a solution.

⇨ **SELF CHECK 1**   Solve: $\sqrt{a - 2} = 3$.

To solve an equation with radicals, we follow these steps.

Solving an Equation Containing Radicals

1. Isolate one radical expression on one side of the equation.
2. Raise both sides of the equation to the power that is the same as the index of the radical.
3. Solve the resulting equation. If it still contains a radical, go back to Step 1.
4. Check the possible solutions to eliminate the ones that do not satisfy the original equation.

EXAMPLE 2   **HEIGHT OF A BRIDGE**   The distance d (in feet) that an object will fall in t seconds is given by the formula

$$t = \sqrt{\frac{d}{16}}$$

To find the height of a bridge, a man drops a stone into the water. (See Figure 9-16.) If it takes the stone 3 seconds to hit the water, how far above the river is the bridge?

Solution   We substitute 3 for t in the formula and solve for d.

Figure 9-16

$$t = \sqrt{\dfrac{d}{16}}$$

$$3 = \sqrt{\dfrac{d}{16}}$$

$$9 = \dfrac{d}{16} \qquad \text{Square both sides.}$$

$$144 = d \qquad \text{Multiply both sides by 16.}$$

The bridge is 144 feet above the river.

⇨ **SELF CHECK 2**   How high is the bridge if it takes 4 seconds for the stone to hit the water?

EXAMPLE 3   Solve: $\sqrt{3x + 1} + 1 = x$.

Solution   We first subtract 1 from both sides to isolate the radical. Then, to eliminate the radical, we square both sides of the equation and proceed as follows:

$$\sqrt{3x + 1} + 1 = x$$

$$\sqrt{3x + 1} = x - 1 \qquad \text{Subtract 1 from both sides.}$$

$$\left(\sqrt{3x + 1}\right)^2 = (x - 1)^2 \qquad \text{Square both sides to eliminate the square root.}$$

$$3x + 1 = x^2 - 2x + 1 \qquad \begin{array}{l}(x - 1)^2 = (x - 1)(x - 1) = \\ x^2 - x - x + 1 = x^2 - 2x + 1\end{array}$$

$$0 = x^2 - 5x \qquad \text{Subtract } 3x \text{ and 1 from both sides.}$$

$$0 = x(x - 5) \qquad \text{Factor } x^2 - 5x.$$

$$x = 0 \quad \text{or} \quad x - 5 = 0 \qquad \text{Set each factor equal to 0.}$$

$$x = 0 \qquad\qquad x = 5$$

We must check each apparent solution to see whether it satisfies the original equation.

Check:

$$\sqrt{3x + 1} + 1 = x \qquad\qquad \sqrt{3x + 1} + 1 = x$$

$$\sqrt{3(0) + 1} + 1 \overset{2}{=} 0 \qquad\qquad \sqrt{3(5) + 1} + 1 \overset{2}{=} 5$$

$$\sqrt{1} + 1 \overset{2}{=} 0 \qquad\qquad \sqrt{16} + 1 \overset{2}{=} 5$$

$$2 \neq 0 \qquad\qquad\qquad 5 = 5$$

Since 0 does not check, it is extraneous and must be discarded. The only solution of the original equation is 5.

⇨ **SELF CHECK 3**   Solve: $\sqrt{4x + 1} + 1 = x$.

ACCENT ON TECHNOLOGY

Solving Equations Containing Radicals

To find approximate solutions for $\sqrt{3x + 1} + 1 = x$ with a graphing calculator, we graph the functions $f(x) = \sqrt{3x + 1} + 1$ and $g(x) = x$, and then adjust the window settings to $[-5, 10]$ for x and $[-2, 8]$ for y as in Figure 9-17(a). We then trace to find the approximate x-coordinate of their intersection point, as in Figure 9-17(b). After repeated zooms, we will see that $x = 5$.

We can also find the exact x-coordinate of the intersection point by using the INTERSECT command found in the CALC menu.

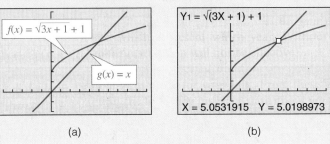

(a)   (b)

Figure 9-17

EXAMPLE 4 Solve: $\sqrt[3]{x^3 + 7} = x + 1$.

Solution To eliminate the radical, we cube both sides of the equation and proceed as follows:

$$\sqrt[3]{x^3 + 7} = x + 1$$
$$\left(\sqrt[3]{x^3 + 7}\right)^3 = (x + 1)^3 \qquad \text{Cube both sides to eliminate the cube root.}$$
$$x^3 + 7 = x^3 + 3x^2 + 3x + 1$$
$$0 = 3x^2 + 3x - 6 \qquad \text{Subtract } x^3 \text{ and 7 from both sides.}$$
$$0 = x^2 + x - 2 \qquad \text{Divide both sides by 3.}$$
$$0 = (x + 2)(x - 1) \qquad \text{Factor the trinomial.}$$
$$x + 2 = 0 \quad \text{or} \quad x - 1 = 0 \qquad \text{Set each factor equal to 0.}$$
$$x = -2 \quad \mid \quad x = 1 \qquad \text{Solve each linear equation.}$$

We check each apparent solution to see whether it satisfies the original equation.

Check:
$$\sqrt[3]{x^3 + 7} = x + 1 \qquad\qquad \sqrt[3]{x^3 + 7} = x + 1$$
$$\sqrt[3]{(-2)^3 + 7} \stackrel{?}{=} -2 + 1 \qquad\qquad \sqrt[3]{1 + 7} \stackrel{?}{=} 1 + 1$$
$$\sqrt[3]{-8 + 7} \stackrel{?}{=} -1 \qquad\qquad\qquad \sqrt[3]{8} \stackrel{?}{=} 2$$
$$\sqrt[3]{-1} \stackrel{?}{=} -1 \qquad\qquad\qquad\quad 2 = 2$$
$$-1 = -1$$

Both solutions satisfy the original equation.

➡ **SELF CHECK 4** Solve: $\sqrt[3]{x^3 + 8} = x + 2$.

2 **Solve a radical equation containing two radicals.**

When more than one radical appears in an equation, it is often necessary to apply the power rule more than once.

EXAMPLE 5 Solve: $\sqrt{x} + \sqrt{x + 2} = 2$.

Solution To remove the radicals, we square both sides of the equation. Since this is easier to do if one radical is on each side of the equation, we subtract $\sqrt{x}$ from both sides to isolate one radical on one side of the equation.

$$\sqrt{x} + \sqrt{x + 2} = 2$$

$$\sqrt{x + 2} = 2 - \sqrt{x} \qquad \text{Subtract } \sqrt{x} \text{ from both sides.}$$

$$\left(\sqrt{x + 2}\right)^2 = \left(2 - \sqrt{x}\right)^2 \qquad \text{Square both sides to eliminate the square root.}$$

$$x + 2 = 4 - 4\sqrt{x} + x \qquad \begin{array}{l}(2 - \sqrt{x})(2 - \sqrt{x}) = \\ 4 - 2\sqrt{x} - 2\sqrt{x} + x = 4 - 4\sqrt{x} + x\end{array}$$

$$4 - 2\sqrt{7} - 2\sqrt{x} +$$

$$2 = 4 - 4\sqrt{x} \qquad \text{Subtract } x \text{ from both sides.}$$

$$-2 = -4\sqrt{x} \qquad \text{Subtract 4 from both sides.}$$

$$\frac{1}{2} = \sqrt{x} \qquad \text{Divide both sides by } -4.$$

$$\frac{1}{4} = x \qquad \text{Square both sides.}$$

Check:
$$\sqrt{x} + \sqrt{x + 2} = 2$$

$$\sqrt{\frac{1}{4}} + \sqrt{\frac{1}{4} + 2} \overset{?}{=} 2$$

$$\frac{1}{2} + \sqrt{\frac{9}{4}} \overset{?}{=} 2$$

$$\frac{1}{2} + \frac{3}{2} \overset{?}{=} 2$$

$$2 = 2$$

The solution checks.

⇨ **SELF CHECK 5**   Solve: $\sqrt{a} + \sqrt{a + 3} = 3$.

ACCENT ON TECHNOLOGY

Solving Equations Containing Radicals

To find approximate solutions for $\sqrt{x} + \sqrt{x + 2} = 5$ with a graphing calculator, we graph the functions $f(x) = \sqrt{x} + \sqrt{x + 2}$ and $g(x) = 5$, and adjust the window settings to [2, 10] for x and [−2, 8] for y as in Figure 9-18(a). We then trace to find an approximation of the x-coordinate of their intersection point, as in Figure 9-18(b). From the figure, we can see that $x \approx 5.15$. We can zoom to get better results.

We also can find the exact x-coordinate of the intersection point by using the INTERSECT command found in the CALC menu.

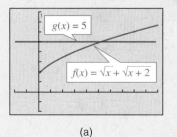

(a)

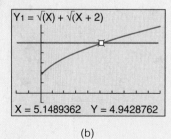

(b)

Figure 9-18

3 Solve a radical equation containing three radicals.

EXAMPLE 6 Solve: $\sqrt{x+2} + \sqrt{2x} = \sqrt{18-x}$.

Solution In this case, it is impossible to isolate one radical on each side of the equation, so we begin by squaring both sides. Then we proceed as follows.

$$\sqrt{x+2} + \sqrt{2x} = \sqrt{18-x}$$

$$\left(\sqrt{x+2} + \sqrt{2x}\right)^2 = \left(\sqrt{18-x}\right)^2 \qquad \text{Square both sides to eliminate one square root.}$$

$$x + 2 + 2\sqrt{x+2}\sqrt{2x} + 2x = 18 - x$$

$$2\sqrt{x+2}\sqrt{2x} = 16 - 4x \qquad \text{Subtract } 3x \text{ and 2 from both sides.}$$

$$\sqrt{x+2}\sqrt{2x} = 8 - 2x \qquad \text{Divide both sides by 2.}$$

$$\left(\sqrt{x+2}\sqrt{2x}\right)^2 = (8-2x)^2 \qquad \text{Square both sides to eliminate the other square roots.}$$

$$(x+2)2x = 64 - 32x + 4x^2$$

$$2x^2 + 4x = 64 - 32x + 4x^2$$

$$0 = 2x^2 - 36x + 64 \qquad \text{Write the equation in quadratic form.}$$

$$0 = x^2 - 18x + 32 \qquad \text{Divide both sides by 2.}$$

$$0 = (x - 16)(x - 2) \qquad \text{Factor the trinomial.}$$

$$x - 16 = 0 \quad \text{or} \quad x - 2 = 0 \qquad \text{Set each factor equal to 0.}$$

$$x = 16 \qquad\qquad x = 2$$

Verify that 2 satisfies the equation, but 16 does not. Thus, the only solution is 2.

SELF CHECK 6 Solve: $\sqrt{3x+4} + \sqrt{x+9} = \sqrt{x+25}$.

4 Solve a formula containing a radical for a specified variable.

To *solve a formula for a variable* means to isolate that variable on one side of the equation, with all other quantities on the other side.

EXAMPLE 7 **DEPRECIATION RATES** Some office equipment that is now worth V dollars originally cost C dollars 3 years ago. The rate r at which it has depreciated is given by

$$r = 1 - \sqrt[3]{\frac{V}{C}}$$

Solve the formula for C.

Solution We begin by isolating the cube root on the right side of the equation.

$$r = 1 - \sqrt[3]{\frac{V}{C}}$$

$$r - 1 = -\sqrt[3]{\frac{V}{C}} \qquad \text{Subtract 1 from both sides.}$$

$$(r - 1)^3 = \left(-\sqrt[3]{\frac{V}{C}}\right)^3 \qquad \text{To eliminate the radical, cube both sides.}$$

$$(r - 1)^3 = -\frac{V}{C} \qquad \text{Simplify the right side.}$$

$$C(r - 1)^3 = -V \qquad \text{Multiply both sides by } C.$$

$$C = -\frac{V}{(r - 1)^3} \qquad \text{Divide both sides by } (r - 1)^3.$$

⇨ **SELF CHECK 7**   A formula used in statistics to determine the size of a sample to obtain a desired degree of accuracy is

$$E = z_0 \sqrt{\frac{pq}{n}}$$

Solve the formula for n.

⇨ **SELF CHECK ANSWERS**   **1.** 11   **2.** 256 ft   **3.** 6; 0 is extraneous   **4.** 0, −2   **5.** 1   **6.** 0   **7.** $n = \frac{z_0^2 pq}{E^2}$

NOW TRY THIS

Solve.

1. $x^{1/3} = 2$

2. $x^{2/3} = 4$

3. $(x + 1)^{-1/2} = 3$

9.6 EXERCISES

WARM-UPS   *Solve each equation.*

1. $\sqrt{x + 2} = 3$

2. $\sqrt{x - 2} = 1$

3. $\sqrt[3]{x + 1} = 1$

4. $\sqrt[3]{x - 1} = 2$

5. $\sqrt[4]{x - 1} = 2$

6. $\sqrt[5]{x + 1} = 2$

REVIEW   *If $f(x) = 3x^2 - 4x + 2$, find each quantity.*

7. $f(0)$

8. $f(-3)$

9. $f(2)$

10. $f\left(\frac{1}{2}\right)$

VOCABULARY AND CONCEPTS   *Fill in the blanks.*

11. If x, y, and n are real numbers and $x = y$, then _____, called the _____.

12. When solving equations containing radicals, try to _____ one radical expression on one side of the equation.

13. To solve the equation $\sqrt{x + 4} = 5$, we first _____ both sides.

14. To solve the equation $\sqrt[3]{x + 4} = 2$, we first _____ both sides.

15. Squaring both sides of an equation can introduce _____ solutions.

16. Always remember to _____ the solutions of an equation containing radicals to eliminate any _____ solutions.

GUIDED PRACTICE

Solve each equation. See Example 1. (Objective 1)

17. $\sqrt{5x - 6} = 2$

18. $\sqrt{7x - 10} = 12$

19. $\sqrt{6x + 1} + 2 = 7$

20. $\sqrt{6x + 13} - 2 = 5$

21. $\sqrt[3]{7n - 1} = 3$

22. $\sqrt[3]{12m + 4} = 4$

23. $x = \dfrac{\sqrt{12x - 5}}{2}$

24. $x = \dfrac{\sqrt{16x - 12}}{2}$

Solve each equation. Identify any extraneous solution.
See Examples 3–4. (Objective 1)

25. $r - 9 = \sqrt{2r - 3}$

26. $-s - 3 = 2\sqrt{5 - s}$

27. $\sqrt{-5x + 24} = 6 - x$

28. $\sqrt{-x + 2} = x - 2$

29. $\sqrt{y + 2} = 4 - y$

30. $\sqrt{22y + 86} = y + 9$

31. $\sqrt[3]{x^3 - 7} = x - 1$

32. $\sqrt[3]{x^3 + 56} - 2 = x$

Solve each equation. Identify any extraneous solution.
See Example 5. (Objective 2)

33. $2\sqrt{4x + 1} = \sqrt{x + 4}$

34. $\sqrt{3(x + 4)} = \sqrt{5x - 12}$

35. $\sqrt{x + 2} = \sqrt{4 - x}$

36. $\sqrt{6 - x} = \sqrt{2x + 3}$

37. $2\sqrt{x} = \sqrt{5x - 16}$

38. $3\sqrt{x} = \sqrt{3x + 12}$

39. $\sqrt{2y + 1} = 1 - 2\sqrt{y}$

40. $\sqrt{u} + 3 = \sqrt{u - 3}$

41. $1 + \sqrt{z} = \sqrt{z + 3}$

42. $\sqrt{x} + 2 = \sqrt{x + 4}$

43. $\sqrt{4s + 1} - \sqrt{6s} = -1$

44. $\sqrt{y + 7} + 3 = \sqrt{y + 4}$

45. $\sqrt{2x + 5} + \sqrt{x + 2} = 5$

46. $\sqrt{2x + 5} + \sqrt{2x + 1} + 4 = 0$

Solve each equation. Identify any extraneous solution.
See Example 6. (Objective 3)

47. $\sqrt{v} + \sqrt{3} = \sqrt{v + 3}$

48. $\sqrt{x + 1} + \sqrt{3x} = \sqrt{5x + 1}$

49. $\sqrt{3x} - \sqrt{x + 1} = \sqrt{x - 2}$

50. $\sqrt{x + 2} + \sqrt{2x - 3} = \sqrt{11 - x}$

Solve each formula for the indicated variable. See Example 7.
(Objective 4)

51. $v = \sqrt{2gh}$ for h

52. $d = 1.4\sqrt{h}$ for h

53. $T = 2\pi\sqrt{\dfrac{l}{32}}$ for l

54. $d = \sqrt[3]{\dfrac{12V}{\pi}}$ for V

55. $r = \sqrt[3]{\dfrac{A}{P}} - 1$ for A

56. $r = \sqrt[3]{\dfrac{A}{P}} - 1$ for P

57. $L_A = L_B\sqrt{1 - \dfrac{v^2}{c^2}}$ for v^2

58. $R_1 = \sqrt{\dfrac{A}{\pi} - R_2{}^2}$ for A

ADDITIONAL PRACTICE   *Solve each equation.*

59. $5r + 4 = \sqrt{5r + 20} + 4r$

60. $\sqrt{x}\sqrt{x + 16} = 15$

61. $\sqrt{x}\sqrt{x + 6} = 4$

62. $\dfrac{6}{\sqrt{x + 5}} = \sqrt{x}$

63. $\sqrt[4]{x^4 + 4x^2 - 4} = -x$

64. $\sqrt[4]{8x - 8} + 2 = 0$

65. $2 + \sqrt{u} = \sqrt{2u + 7}$

66. $\sqrt[4]{12t + 4} + 2 = 0$

67. $u = \sqrt[4]{u^4 - 6u^2 + 24}$

68. $\sqrt{6t + 1} - 3\sqrt{t} = -1$

69. $\sqrt{x - 5} - \sqrt{x + 3} = 4$

70. $\sqrt[4]{10p + 1} = \sqrt[4]{11p - 7}$

71. $\sqrt{x + 8} - \sqrt{x - 4} = -2$

72. $\sqrt[4]{10y + 2} = 2\sqrt[4]{2}$

73. $\sqrt{z - 1} + \sqrt{z + 2} = 3$

74. $\sqrt{16v + 1} + \sqrt{8v + 1} = 12$

75. $\sqrt{\sqrt{a} + \sqrt{a + 8}} = 2$

76. $\sqrt{\sqrt{2y} - \sqrt{y - 1}} = 1$

77. $\dfrac{\sqrt{2x}}{\sqrt{x + 2}} = \sqrt{x - 1}$

78. $\sqrt{8 - x} - \sqrt{3x - 8} = \sqrt{x - 4}$

APPLICATIONS

Solve each application problem. See Example 2. (Objective 1)

79. **Highway design** A curve banked at 8° will accommodate traffic traveling s mph if the radius of the curve is r feet, according to the formula $s = 1.45\sqrt{r}$. If engineers expect 65-mph traffic, what radius should they specify? See the illustration on the next page.

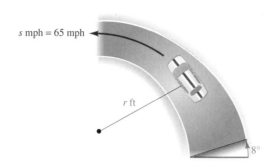

80. Horizon distance The higher a lookout tower is built, the farther an observer can see. That distance d (called the *horizon distance,* measured in miles) is related to the height h of the observer (measured in feet) by the formula $d = 1.4\sqrt{h}$. How tall must a lookout tower be to see the edge of the forest, 25 miles away?

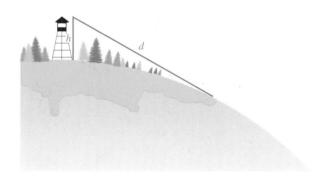

81. Generating power The power generated by a windmill is related to the velocity of the wind by the formula

$$v = \sqrt[3]{\frac{P}{0.02}}$$

where P is the power (in watts) and v is the velocity of the wind (in mph). Find the speed of the wind when the windmill is generating 500 watts of power.

82. Carpentry During construction, carpenters often brace walls as shown in the illustration, where the length of the brace is given by the formula

$$l = \sqrt{f^2 + h^2}$$

If a carpenter nails a 10-ft brace to the wall 6 feet above the floor, how far from the base of the wall should he nail the brace to the floor?

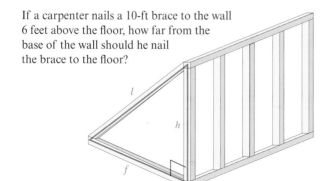

Use a graphing calculator.

83. Depreciation The formula

$$r = 1 - \sqrt[n]{\frac{T}{C}}$$

gives the annual depreciation rate r of a car that had an original cost of C dollars, a useful life of n years, and a trade-in value of T dollars. Find the annual depreciation rate of a car that cost \$22,000 and was sold 5 years later for \$9,000. Give the result to the nearest percent.

84. Savings accounts The interest rate r earned by a savings account after n compoundings is given by the formula

$$\sqrt[n]{\frac{V}{P}} - 1 = r$$

where V is the current value and P is the original principal. What interest rate r was paid on an account in which a deposit of \$1,000 grew to \$1,338.23 after 5 compoundings?

85. Marketing The number of wrenches that will be produced at a given price can be predicted by the formula $s = \sqrt{5x}$, where s is the supply (in thousands) and x is the price (in dollars). If the demand, d, for wrenches can be predicted by the formula $d = \sqrt{100 - 3x^2}$, find the equilibrium price.

86. Marketing The number of footballs that will be produced at a given price can be predicted by the formula $s = \sqrt{23x}$, where s is the supply (in thousands) and x is the price (in dollars). If the demand, d, for footballs can be predicted by the formula $d = \sqrt{312 - 2x^2}$, find the equilibrium price.

87. Medicine The resistance R to blood flow through an artery can be found using the formula

$$r = \sqrt[4]{\frac{8kl}{\pi R}}$$

where r is the radius of the artery, k is the viscosity of blood, and l is the length of the artery. Solve the formula for R.

88. Generating power The power P generated by a windmill is given by the formula

$$s = \sqrt[3]{\frac{P}{0.02}}$$

where s is the speed of the wind. Solve the formula for P.

WRITING ABOUT MATH

89. If both sides of an equation are raised to the same power, the resulting equation might not be equivalent to the original equation. Explain.

90. Explain why you must check each apparent solution of a radical equation.

SOMETHING TO THINK ABOUT

91. Solve: $\sqrt[3]{2x} = \sqrt{x}$.   **92.** Solve: $\sqrt[4]{x} = \sqrt{\dfrac{x}{4}}$.

SECTION 9.7

Complex Numbers

Objectives

1. Simplify an imaginary number.
2. Simplify an expression containing complex numbers.
3. Rationalize the denominator of a fraction that contains a complex number.
4. Find a specified power of i.
5. Find the absolute value of a complex number.

Vocabulary

imaginary number   complex number

Getting Ready

Perform the following operations.

1. $(3x + 5) + (4x - 5)$
2. $(3x + 5) - (4x - 5)$
3. $(3x + 5)(4x - 5)$
4. $(3x + 5)(3x - 5)$

We have seen that square roots of negative numbers are not real numbers. However, there is a broader set of numbers, called the *complex numbers*, in which negative numbers do have square roots. In this section, we will discuss this broader set of numbers.

1 Simplify an imaginary number.

Consider the number $\sqrt{-3}$. Since no real number squared is -3, $\sqrt{-3}$ is not a real number. For years, people believed that numbers such as

$$\sqrt{-1}, \qquad \sqrt{-3}, \qquad \sqrt{-4}, \qquad \text{and} \qquad \sqrt{-9}$$

were nonsense. In the 17th century, René Descartes (1596–1650) called them **imaginary numbers.** Today, imaginary numbers have many important uses, such as describing the behavior of alternating current in electronics.

The imaginary number $\sqrt{-1}$ often is denoted by the letter i:

$$i = \sqrt{-1}$$

Because i represents the square root of -1, it follows that

$$i^2 = -1$$

PERSPECTIVE

The Pythagoreans (ca. 500 B.C.) understood the universe as a harmony of whole numbers. They did not classify fractions as numbers, and were upset that $\sqrt{2}$ was not the ratio of whole numbers. For 2,000 years, little progress was made in the understanding of the various kinds of numbers.

The father of algebra, François Vieta (1540–1603), understood the whole numbers, fractions, and certain irrational numbers. But he was unable to accept negative numbers, and certainly not imaginary numbers.

René Descartes (1596–1650) thought these numbers to be nothing more than figments of his imagination, so he called them *imaginary numbers.* Leonhard Euler (1707–1783) used the letter i for $\sqrt{-1}$; Augustin Cauchy (1789–1857) used the term *conjugate;* and Carl Gauss (1777–1855) first used the word *complex.*

Today, we accept complex numbers without question, but it took many centuries and the work of many mathematicians to make them respectable.

If we assume that multiplication of imaginary numbers is commutative and associative, then

$$(2i)^2 = 2^2 i^2$$
$$= 4(-1) \quad i^2 = -1$$
$$= -4$$

Since $(2i)^2 = -4$, $2i$ is a square root of -4, and we can write

$$\sqrt{-4} = 2i$$

This result also can be obtained by using the multiplication property of radicals:

$$\sqrt{-4} = \sqrt{4(-1)} = \sqrt{4}\sqrt{-1} = 2i$$

We can use the multiplication property of radicals to simplify any imaginary number. For example,

$$\sqrt{-25} = \sqrt{25(-1)} = \sqrt{25}\sqrt{-1} = 5i$$
$$\sqrt{\frac{-100}{49}} = \sqrt{\frac{100}{49}(-1)} = \frac{\sqrt{100}}{\sqrt{49}}\sqrt{-1} = \frac{10}{7}i$$

These examples illustrate the following rule.

Properties of Radicals	If at least one of a and b is a nonnegative real number, then $$\sqrt{ab} = \sqrt{a}\sqrt{b} \quad \text{and} \quad \sqrt{\frac{a}{b}} = \frac{\sqrt{a}}{\sqrt{b}} \quad (b \neq 0)$$

COMMENT   If a and b are negative, then $\sqrt{ab} \neq \sqrt{a}\sqrt{b}$. For example, if $a = -16$ and $b = -4$, we have

$$\sqrt{(-16)}\sqrt{(-4)} = (4i)(2i) = 8i^2 = 8(-1) = -8$$

Note that $\sqrt{(-16)}\sqrt{(-4)}$ does not simplify as $\sqrt{(-16)(-4)} = \sqrt{64} = 8$.

2   Simplify an expression containing complex numbers.

The imaginary numbers are a subset of a set of numbers called the *complex numbers.*

Complex Numbers	A **complex number** is any number that can be written in the standard form $a + bi$, where a and b are real numbers and $i = \sqrt{-1}$.
	In the complex number $a + bi$, a is called the *real part,* and b is called the *imaginary part.*

If $b = 0$, the complex number $a + bi$ is a real number. If $b \neq 0$ and $a = 0$, the complex number $0 + bi$ (or just bi) is an imaginary number.

Any imaginary number can be expressed in bi form. For example,

COMMENT The expression $\sqrt{3}i$ is often written as $i\sqrt{3}$ to make it clear that i is not part of the radicand. Don't confuse $\sqrt{3}i$ with $\sqrt{3i}$.

$$\sqrt{-1} = i$$
$$\sqrt{-9} = \sqrt{9(-1)} = \sqrt{9}\sqrt{-1} = 3i$$
$$\sqrt{-3} = \sqrt{3(-1)} = \sqrt{3}\sqrt{-1} = \sqrt{3}i$$

The relationship between the real numbers, the imaginary numbers, and the complex numbers is shown in Figure 9-19.

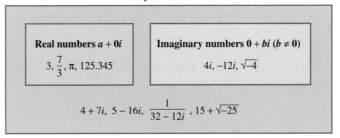

Complex numbers

Real numbers $a + 0i$	Imaginary numbers $0 + bi$ $(b \neq 0)$
$3, \frac{7}{3}, \pi, 125.345$	$4i, -12i, \sqrt{-4}$

$4 + 7i,\ 5 - 16i,\ \dfrac{1}{32 - 12i},\ 15 + \sqrt{-25}$

Figure 9-19

Equality of Complex Numbers	The complex numbers $a + bi$ and $c + di$ are equal if and only if
	$a = c$ $\quad$ and $\quad$ $b = d$

Because of the previous definition, complex numbers are equal when their real parts are equal and their imaginary parts are equal.

EXAMPLE 1 **a.** $2 + 3i = \sqrt{4} + \frac{6}{2}i$ $\quad$ because $\quad$ $2 = \sqrt{4}$ and $3 = \frac{6}{2}$.

b. $4 - 5i = \frac{12}{3} - \sqrt{25}i$ $\quad$ because $\quad$ $4 = \frac{12}{3}$ and $-5 = -\sqrt{25}$.

c. $x + yi = 4 + 7i$ $\quad$ if and only if $\quad$ $x = 4$ and $y = 7$.

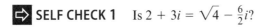 **SELF CHECK 1** $\quad$ Is $2 + 3i = \sqrt{4} - \frac{6}{2}i$?

Addition and Subtraction of Complex Numbers	Complex numbers are added and subtracted as if they were binomials: $(a + bi) + (c + di) = (a + c) + (b + d)i$ $(a + bi) - (c + di) = (a + bi) + (-c - di) = (a - c) + (b - d)i$

The previous definition suggests that when adding or subtracting two complex numbers, we add or subtract the real parts and then add or subtract the imaginary parts.

EXAMPLE 2   Perform the operations.

    a. $(8 + 4i) + (12 + 8i) = 8 + 4i + 12 + 8i$
                                    $= 20 + 12i$

    b. $(7 - 4i) + (9 + 2i) = 7 - 4i + 9 + 2i$
                                    $= 16 - 2i$

    c. $(-6 + i) - (3 - 4i) = -6 + i - 3 + 4i$
                                  $= -9 + 5i$

    d. $(2 - 4i) - (-4 + 3i) = 2 - 4i + 4 - 3i$
                                    $= 6 - 7i$

SELF CHECK 2   Perform the operations.
    a. $(3 - 5i) + (-2 + 7i)$ **b.** $(3 - 5i) - (-2 + 7i)$

To multiply a complex number by an imaginary number, we use the distributive property to remove parentheses and simplify. For example,

$$-5i(4 - 8i) = -5i(4) - (-5i)8i \quad \text{Use the distributive property.}$$
$$= -20i + 40i^2 \quad \text{Simplify.}$$
$$= -20i + 40(-1) \quad \text{Remember that } i^2 = -1.$$
$$= -40 - 20i$$

To multiply two complex numbers, we use the following definition.

Multiplying Complex Numbers	Complex numbers are multiplied as if they were binomials, with $i^2 = -1$: $(a + bi)(c + di) = ac + adi + bci + bdi^2$ $= ac + adi + bci + bd(-1)$ $= (ac - bd) + (ad + bc)i$

EXAMPLE 3   Multiply the complex numbers.

    a. $(2 + 3i)(3 - 2i) = 6 - 4i + 9i - 6i^2 \quad \text{Use the FOIL method.}$
                        $= 6 + 5i + 6 \quad\quad\quad i^2 = -1, \text{combine } -4i \text{ and } 9i.$
                        $= 12 + 5i$

b. $(3 + i)(1 + 2i) = 3 + 6i + i + 2i^2$ Use the FOIL method.

$\qquad\qquad\qquad\quad = 3 + 7i - 2$ $i^2 = -1$, combine $6i$ and i.

$\qquad\qquad\qquad\quad = 1 + 7i$

c. $(-4 + 2i)(2 + i) = -8 - 4i + 4i + 2i^2$ Use the FOIL method.

$\qquad\qquad\qquad\quad = -8 - 2$ $i^2 = -1$, combine $-4i$ and $4i$.

$\qquad\qquad\qquad\quad = -10$

⇨ **SELF CHECK 3** Multiply: $(-2 + 3i)(3 - 2i)$.

The next two examples show how to write complex numbers in $a + bi$ form. It is common to use $a - bi$ as a substitute for $a + (-b)i$.

EXAMPLE 4 Write each number in $a + bi$ form.

a. $7 = 7 + 0i$ $\qquad\qquad\qquad\qquad$ **b.** $3i = 0 + 3i$

c. $4 - \sqrt{-16} = 4 - \sqrt{-1(16)}$ $\qquad$ **d.** $5 + \sqrt{-11} = 5 + \sqrt{-1(11)}$

$\qquad\qquad\qquad = 4 - \sqrt{16}\sqrt{-1}$ $\qquad\qquad\qquad\quad = 5 + \sqrt{11}\sqrt{-1}$

$\qquad\qquad\qquad = 4 - 4i$ $\qquad\qquad\qquad\qquad\quad = 5 + \sqrt{11}i$

⇨ **SELF CHECK 4** Write $3 - \sqrt{-25}$ in $a + bi$ form.

Complex Conjugates

The complex numbers $a + bi$ and $a - bi$ are called **complex conjugates.**

For example,

$3 + 4i$ and $3 - 4i$ are complex conjugates.

$5 - 7i$ and $5 + 7i$ are complex conjugates.

EXAMPLE 5 Find the product of $3 + i$ and its complex conjugate.

Solution The complex conjugate of $3 + i$ is $3 - i$. We can find the product as follows:

$(3 + i)(3 - i) = 9 - 3i + 3i - i^2$ Use the FOIL method.

$\qquad\qquad\quad = 9 - i^2$ Combine like terms.

$\qquad\qquad\quad = 9 - (-1)$ $i^2 = -1$

$\qquad\qquad\quad = 10$

⇨ **SELF CHECK 5** Multiply: $(2 + 3i)(2 - 3i)$.

The product of the complex number $a + bi$ and its complex conjugate $a - bi$ is the real number $a^2 + b^2$, as the following work shows:

$$(a + bi)(a - bi) = a^2 - abi + abi - b^2i^2 \qquad \text{Use the FOIL method.}$$
$$= a^2 - b^2(-1) \qquad\qquad i^2 = -1$$
$$= a^2 + b^2$$

3 ### Rationalize the denominator of a fraction that contains a complex number.

If $b \neq 0$, the complex number $a + bi$ contains the square root $i = \sqrt{-1}$. Since a square root cannot remain in the denominator of a fraction, we often have to rationalize a denominator when dividing complex numbers.

EXAMPLE 6   Divide and write the result in $a + bi$ form: $\dfrac{1}{3 + i}$.

Solution   We can rationalize the denominator by multiplying the numerator and the denominator by the complex conjugate of the denominator.

$$\frac{1}{3 + i} = \frac{1}{3 + i} \cdot \frac{3 - i}{3 - i} \qquad \tfrac{3 - i}{3 - i} = 1$$

$$= \frac{3 - i}{9 - 3i + 3i - i^2} \qquad \text{Multiply the numerators and multiply the denominators.}$$

$$= \frac{3 - i}{9 - (-1)} \qquad\qquad i^2 = -1$$

$$= \frac{3 - i}{10}$$

$$= \frac{3}{10} - \frac{1}{10}i \qquad\qquad \text{Write the result in } a + bi \text{ form.}$$

⇨ **SELF CHECK 6**   Rationalize the denominator: $\dfrac{1}{5 - i}$.

EXAMPLE 7   Write $\dfrac{3 - i}{2 + i}$ in $a + bi$ form.

Solution   We multiply the numerator and the denominator of the fraction by the complex conjugate of the denominator.

$$\frac{3 - i}{2 + i} = \frac{3 - i}{2 + i} \cdot \frac{2 - i}{2 - i} \qquad \tfrac{2 - i}{2 - i} = 1$$

$$= \frac{6 - 3i - 2i + i^2}{4 - 2i + 2i - i^2} \qquad \text{Multiply the numerators and multiply the denominators.}$$

$$= \frac{5 - 5i}{4 - (-1)} \qquad\qquad 6 + i^2 = 6 - 1 = 5$$

$$= \frac{5(1 - i)}{5}$$ Factor out 5 in the numerator.

$$= 1 - i$$ Simplify.

⇨ SELF CHECK 7   Rationalize the denominator: $\dfrac{2 + i}{5 - i}$.

EXAMPLE 8   Write $\dfrac{4 + \sqrt{-16}}{2 + \sqrt{-4}}$ in $a + bi$ form.

Solution $\dfrac{4 + \sqrt{-16}}{2 + \sqrt{-4}} = \dfrac{4 + 4i}{2 + 2i}$ Write each number in $a + bi$ form.

$$= \frac{\overset{1}{\cancel{2(2 + 2i)}}}{\underset{1}{\cancel{2 + 2i}}}$$ Factor out 2 in the numerator and simplify.

$$= 2 + 0i$$

⇨ SELF CHECK 8   Divide: $\dfrac{3 + \sqrt{-25}}{2 + \sqrt{-9}}$.

COMMENT   To avoid mistakes, always put complex numbers in $a + bi$ form before doing any operations with complex numbers.

4   **Find a specified power of i.**

The powers of i produce an interesting pattern:

$$i = \sqrt{-1} = i \qquad\qquad i^5 = i^4i = 1i = i$$
$$i^2 = \left(\sqrt{-1}\right)^2 = -1 \qquad i^6 = i^4i^2 = 1(-1) = -1$$
$$i^3 = i^2i = -1i = -i \qquad i^7 = i^4i^3 = 1(-i) = -i$$
$$i^4 = i^2i^2 = (-1)(-1) = 1 \qquad i^8 = i^4i^4 = (1)(1) = 1$$

The pattern continues: $i, -1, -i, 1, \ldots$.

EXAMPLE 9   Simplify: i^{29}.

Solution   We note that 29 divided by 4 gives a quotient of 7 and a remainder of 1. Thus, $29 = 4 \cdot 7 + 1$, and

$$i^{29} = i^{4 \cdot 7 + 1} \qquad 29 = 4 \cdot 7 + 1$$
$$= (i^4)^7 \cdot i \qquad i^{4 \cdot 7 + 1} = i^{4 \cdot 7} \cdot i^1 = (i^4)^7 \cdot i$$
$$= 1^7 \cdot i \qquad i^4 = 1$$
$$= i$$

⇨ SELF CHECK 9   Simplify: i^{31}.

The results of Example 9 illustrate the following fact.

Powers of i	If n is a natural number that has a remainder of r when divided by 4, then
	$$i^n = i^r$$
	When n is divisible by 4, the remainder r is 0 and $i^0 = 1$.

EXAMPLE 10   Simplify: i^{55}.

Solution   We divide 55 by 4 and get a remainder of 3. Therefore,
$$i^{55} = i^3 = -i$$

⇨ **SELF CHECK 10**   Simplify: i^{62}.

EXAMPLE 11   Simplify each expression. If a denominator has a factor of i, multiply the expression by $\frac{i}{i}$.

a. $2i^2 + 4i^3 = 2(-1) + 4(-i)$
$$= -2 - 4i$$

b. $\dfrac{3}{2i} = \dfrac{3}{2i} \cdot \dfrac{i}{i}$ $\frac{i}{i} = 1$
$$= \dfrac{3i}{2i^2}$$
$$= \dfrac{3i}{2(-1)}$$
$$= \dfrac{3i}{-2}$$
$$= 0 - \dfrac{3}{2}i$$

c. $-\dfrac{5}{i} = -\dfrac{5}{i} \cdot \dfrac{i}{i}$ $\frac{i}{i} = 1$
$$= -\dfrac{5(i)}{i^2}$$
$$= -\dfrac{5i}{-1}$$
$$= 5i$$
$$= 0 + 5i$$

d. $\dfrac{6}{i^3} = \dfrac{6i}{i^3 i}$ $\frac{i}{i} = 1$
$$= \dfrac{6i}{i^4}$$
$$= \dfrac{6i}{1}$$
$$= 6i$$
$$= 0 + 6i$$

⇨ **SELF CHECK 11**   Simplify.   **a.** $3i^3 - 2i^2$ **b.** $\frac{2}{3i}$

5   Find the absolute value of a complex number.

Absolute Value of a Complex Number	The **absolute value** of the complex number $a + bi$ is $\sqrt{a^2 + b^2}$. In symbols,
	$$|a + bi| = \sqrt{a^2 + b^2}$$

EXAMPLE 12 Find each absolute value.

a. $|3 + 4i| = \sqrt{3^2 + 4^2}$

$= \sqrt{9 + 16}$

$= \sqrt{25}$

$= 5$

b. $|3 - 4i| = \sqrt{3^2 + (-4)^2}$

$= \sqrt{9 + 16}$

$= \sqrt{25}$

$= 5$

c. $|-5 - 12i| = \sqrt{(-5)^2 + (-12)^2}$

$= \sqrt{25 + 144}$

$= \sqrt{169}$

$= 13$

d. $|a + 0i| = \sqrt{a^2 + 0^2}$

$= \sqrt{a^2}$

$= |a|$

SELF CHECK 12 Evaluate: $|5 + 12i|$.

SELF CHECK ANSWERS 1. no 2. a. $1 + 2i$ b. $5 - 12i$ 3. $13i$ 4. $3 - 5i$ 5. 13 6. $\frac{5}{26} + \frac{1}{26}i$ 7. $\frac{9}{26} + \frac{7}{26}i$
8. $\frac{21}{13} + \frac{1}{13}i$ 9. $-i$ 10. -1 11. a. $2 - 3i$ b. $0 - \frac{2}{3}i$ 12. 13

NOW TRY THIS

1. Simplify: $-\sqrt{-8}\sqrt{-2}$.

2. Evaluate $3x^2 - 2x - 4$ for $x = 2 - 3i$.

9.7 EXERCISES

WARM-UPS

Write each imaginary number in bi form.

1. $\sqrt{-49}$

2. $\sqrt{-64}$

3. $\sqrt{-100}$

4. $\sqrt{-81}$

Simplify each power of i.

5. i^3

6. i^2

7. i^4

8. i^5

Find each absolute value.

9. $|-3 + 4i|$

10. $|5 - 12i|$

REVIEW *Perform each operation.*

11. $\dfrac{x^2 - x - 6}{9 - x^2} \cdot \dfrac{x^2 + x - 6}{x^2 - 4}$

12. $\dfrac{3x + 4}{x - 2} + \dfrac{x - 4}{x + 2}$

13. **Wind speed** A plane that can fly 200 mph in still air makes a 330-mile flight with a tail wind and returns, flying into the same wind. Find the speed of the wind if the total flying time is $3\frac{1}{3}$ hours.

14. **Finding rates** A student drove a distance of 135 miles at an average speed of 50 mph. How much faster would he have to drive on the return trip to save 30 minutes of driving time?

VOCABULARY AND CONCEPTS   *Fill in the blanks.*

15. $\sqrt{-1} =$ ___

16. $i^6 =$ ____

17. $i^7 =$ ____

18. $i^8 =$ ___

19. $\sqrt{-1}$, $\sqrt{-3}$, $\sqrt{-4}$ are examples of _____ numbers.

20. $\sqrt{ab} =$ _____, provided a and b are not both negative.

21. $\sqrt{\dfrac{a}{b}} =$ ____ $(b \neq 0)$, provided a and b are not both negative.

22. $3 + 5i$, $2 - 7i$, and $5 - \frac{1}{2}i$ are examples of _____ numbers.

23. The real part of $5 + 7i$ is __. The imaginary part is __.

24. $a + bi = c + di$ if and only if $a =$ __ and $b =$ __.

25. $a + bi$ and $a - bi$ are called complex _____.

26. $|a + bi| =$ _____

GUIDED PRACTICE

Write each imaginary number in simplified form. (Objective 1)

27. $\sqrt{-9}$

28. $\sqrt{-16}$

29. $\sqrt{-36}$

30. $\sqrt{-81}$

31. $\sqrt{-7}$

32. $\sqrt{-11}$

33. $\sqrt{-8}$

34. $\sqrt{-24}$

Determine whether the complex numbers are equal.
See Example 1. (Objective 1)

35. $3 + 7i$, $\sqrt{9} + (5 + 2)i$

36. $\sqrt{4} + \sqrt{25}i$, $2 - (-5)i$

37. $\sqrt{4} + \sqrt{-4}$, $2 - 2i$

38. $\sqrt{-9} - i$, $4i$

Simplify each expression. Write all answers in standard form.
See Example 2. (Objective 2)

39. $(3 + 4i) + (5 - 6i)$

40. $(5 + 3i) - (6 - 9i)$

41. $(7 - 3i) - (4 + 2i)$

42. $(8 + 3i) + (-7 - 2i)$

43. $(8 + 5i) + (7 + 2i)$

44. $(-7 + 9i) - (-2 - 8i)$

45. $(1 + i) - 2i + (5 - 7i)$

46. $(-9 + i) - 5i + (2 + 7i)$

Simplify each expression. Write all answers in standard form.
(Objective 2)

47. $3i(2 - i)$

48. $-4i(3 + 4i)$

49. $-5i(5 - 5i)$

50. $2i(7 + 2i)$

Simplify each expression. Write all answers in standard form.
See Example 3. (Objective 2)

51. $(2 + i)(3 - i)$

52. $(4 - i)(2 + i)$

53. $(2 - 4i)(3 + 2i)$

54. $(3 - 2i)(4 - 3i)$

55. $(2 + \sqrt{2}i)(3 - \sqrt{2}i)$

56. $(5 + \sqrt{3}i)(2 - \sqrt{3}i)$

57. $(2 + i)^2$

58. $(3 - 2i)^2$

59. $(2 + 3i)^2$

60. $(1 - 3i)^2$

61. $i(5 + i)(3 - 2i)$

62. $i(-3 - 2i)(1 - 2i)$

Simplify each expression. Write in standard form.
See Examples 4–5. (Objective 2)

63. $(8 - \sqrt{-1})(-2 - \sqrt{-16})$

64. $(-1 + \sqrt{-4})(2 + \sqrt{-9})$

65. $(6 - 5i)(6 + 5i)$

66. $(7 + 2i)(7 - 2i)$

Divide and write each expression in standard form. See Example 6.
(Objective 3)

67. $\dfrac{5}{2 - i}$

68. $\dfrac{26}{3 - 2i}$

69. $\dfrac{13i}{5 + i}$

70. $\dfrac{2i}{5 + 3i}$

71. $\dfrac{-12}{7 - \sqrt{-1}}$

72. $\dfrac{4}{3 + \sqrt{-1}}$

73. $\dfrac{5i}{6 + 2i}$

74. $\dfrac{-4i}{2 - 6i}$

Divide and write each expression in standard form.
See Examples 7–8. (Objective 3)

75. $\dfrac{3 - 2i}{3 + 2i}$

76. $\dfrac{2 + 3i}{2 - 3i}$

77. $\dfrac{3 + 2i}{3 + i}$

78. $\dfrac{2 - 5i}{2 + 5i}$

79. $\dfrac{\sqrt{5} - \sqrt{3}i}{\sqrt{5} + \sqrt{3}i}$

80. $\dfrac{\sqrt{3} + \sqrt{2}i}{\sqrt{3} - \sqrt{2}i}$

81. $\left(\dfrac{i}{3 + 2i}\right)^2$

82. $\left(\dfrac{5 + i}{2 + i}\right)^2$

Simplify each expression. See Examples 9–10. (Objective 4)

83. i^{21}

84. i^{19}

85. i^{27}

86. i^{22}

87. i^{100}

88. i^{42}

89. i^{97}

90. i^{200}

Simplify each expression. See Example 11. (Objectives 3–4)

91. $3i^3 + i^2$

92. $4i^2 - 3i^3$

93. $\dfrac{1}{i}$

94. $\dfrac{1}{i^3}$

95. $\dfrac{4}{5i^3}$

96. $\dfrac{3}{2i}$

97. $\dfrac{3i}{8\sqrt{-9}}$

98. $\dfrac{5i^3}{2\sqrt{-4}}$

99. $\dfrac{-3}{5i^5}$

100. $\dfrac{-4}{6i^7}$

Find each value. **See Example 12. (Objective 5)**

101. $|6 + 8i|$

102. $|12 + 5i|$

103. $|12 - 5i|$

104. $|3 - 4i|$

105. $|5 + 7i|$

106. $|6 - 5i|$

107. $\left| \dfrac{3}{5} - \dfrac{4}{5}i \right|$

108. $\left| \dfrac{5}{13} + \dfrac{12}{13}i \right|$

ADDITIONAL PRACTICE

Are the two numbers equal?

109. $8 + 5i, 2^3 + \sqrt{25}i^3$

110. $4 - 7i, -4i^2 + 7i^3$

Simplify each expression. Write the answer in standard form.

111. $(5 + 3i) - (3 - 5i) + \sqrt{-1}$

112. $(8 + 7i) - \left(-7 - \sqrt{-64}\right) + (3 - i)$

113. $\left(-8 - \sqrt{3}i\right) - \left(7 - 3\sqrt{3}i\right)$

114. $\left(2 + 2\sqrt{2}i\right) + \left(-3 - \sqrt{2}i\right)$

115. $(2 + i)(2 - i)(1 + i)$

116. $(3 + 2i)(3 - 2i)(i + 1)$

117. $(3 + i)[(3 - 2i) + (2 + i)]$

118. $(2 - 3i)[(5 - 2i) - (2i + 1)]$

119. $\dfrac{i(3 - i)}{3 + i}$

120. $\dfrac{5 + 3i}{i(3 - 5i)}$

121. $\dfrac{(2 - 5i) - (5 - 2i)}{5 - i}$

122. $\dfrac{5i}{(5 + 2i) + (2 + i)}$

123. Show that $1 - 5i$ is a solution of $x^2 - 2x + 26 = 0$.

124. Show that $3 - 2i$ is a solution of $x^2 - 6x + 13 = 0$.

125. Show that i is a solution of $x^4 - 3x^2 - 4 = 0$.

126. Show that $2 + i$ is *not* a solution of $x^2 + x + 1 = 0$.

APPLICATIONS

*In electronics, the formula $V = IR$ is called **Ohm's Law**. It gives the relationship in a circuit between the voltage V (in volts), the current I (in amperes), and the resistance R (in ohms).*

127. **Electronics** Find V when $I = 2 - 3i$ amperes and $R = 2 + i$ ohms.

128. **Electronics** Find R when $I = 3 - 2i$ amperes and $V = 18 + i$ volts.

In electronics, the formula $Z = \dfrac{V}{I}$ is used to find the impedance Z of a circuit, where V is the voltage and I is the current.

129. **Electronics** Find the impedance of a circuit when the voltage is $1.7 + 0.5i$ and the current is $0.5i$.

130. **Electronics** Find the impedance of a circuit when the voltage is $1.6 - 0.4i$ and the current is $-0.2i$.

WRITING ABOUT MATH

131. Determine how to decide whether two complex numbers are equal.

132. Define the complex conjugate of a complex number.

SOMETHING TO THINK ABOUT

133. Rationalize the numerator: $\dfrac{3 - i}{2}$.

134. Rationalize the numerator: $\dfrac{2 + 3i}{2 - 3i}$.

PROJECTS

Project 1

The size of a television screen is measured along the diagonal of its screen, as shown in the illustrations. The screen of a traditional TV has an aspect ratio of 4:3. This means that the ratio of the width of the screen to its height is $\frac{4}{3}$. The screen of a wide-screen set has an aspect ratio of 16:9. This means that the ratio of the width of the screen to its height is $\frac{16}{9}$.

50 in.

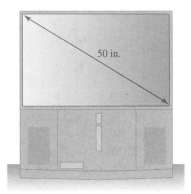

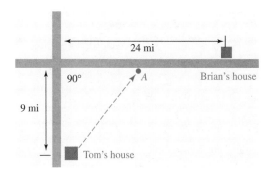

across country for the first part of his trip, averaging 15 mph. When Tom reaches the highway at point *A*, he turns right and follows the highway, averaging 21 mph.

a. Find the width and height of the traditional-screen set shown in the illustration on the previous page. $\left(Hint:\ \dfrac{4}{3} = \dfrac{4x}{3x}.\right)$

b. Find the viewing area of the traditional-screen set in square inches.

c. Find the width and height of the wide-screen set shown in the illustration above.

d. Find the viewing area of the wide-screen set in square inches.

e. Which set has the larger viewing area? Give the answer as a percent.

Project 2

Tom and Brian arrange to have a bicycle race. Each leaves his own house at the same time and rides to the other's house, whereupon the winner of the race calls his own house and leaves a message for the loser. A map of the race is shown in the illustration. Brian stays on the highway, averaging 21 mph. Tom knows that he and Brian are evenly matched when biking on the highway, so he cuts

Tom and Brian never meet during the race and, amazingly, the race is a tie. Each of them calls the other at exactly the same moment!

a. How long (to the nearest second) did it take each person to complete the race?

b. How far from the intersection of the two highways is point *A*? (*Hint:* Set the travel times for Brian and Tom equal to each other. You may find two answers, but only one of them matches all of the information.)

c. Show that if Tom had started straight across country for Brian's house (in order to minimize the distance he had to travel), he would have lost the race. By how much time (to the nearest second) would he have lost? Then show that if Tom had biked across country to a point 9 miles from the intersection of the two highways, he would have won the race. By how much time (to the nearest second) would he have won?

Chapter 9 REVIEW

SECTION 9.1 Radical Expressions

DEFINITIONS AND CONCEPTS	EXAMPLES
Simplifying radicals: If *n* is a natural number greater than 1 and *x* is a real number, then	
If $x > 0$, then $\sqrt[n]{x}$ is the positive number such that $\left(\sqrt[n]{x}\right)^{n} = x$.	$\sqrt{25} = 5$ because $5^{2} = 25$.
If $x = 0$, then $\sqrt[n]{x} = 0$.	$\sqrt[4]{0} = 0$ because $0^{4} = 0$.

If $x < 0$, and n is odd, $\sqrt[n]{x}$ is the real number such that $\left(\sqrt[n]{x}\right)^n = x$. If $x < 0$, and n is even, $\sqrt[n]{x}$ is not a real number.	$\sqrt[3]{-64} = -4$ because $(-4)^3 = -64$. $\sqrt[4]{-8} =$ is not a real number.
If n is an even natural number, $$\sqrt[n]{a^n} = |a|$$ If n is an odd natural number, greater than 1, $$\sqrt[n]{a^n} = a$$	$\sqrt{64x^2} = 8|x|$ Absolute value bars are necessary because x could be a negative number. $\sqrt[3]{-8} = -2$ because $(-2)^3 = -8$.
Finding the domain of a radical function: If $f(x) = \sqrt[n]{x}$, then the domain of $f(x)$ will be [0, ∞) if n is even (−∞, ∞) if n is odd	To find the domain of $f(x) = \sqrt{x + 4}$, set the radicand to be greater than or equal to 0, and solve for x. $x + 4 \geq 0$ The radicand must be ≥ 0. $x \geq -4$ Subtract 4 from each side. The domain is $[-4, \infty)$. To find the domain of $g(x) = \sqrt[3]{x - 9}$, we note that in a cube root the radicand can be any real number. Therefore, x can be any real number, and the domain is $(-\infty, \infty)$.
Standard deviation of a data set: Standard deviation $$= \sqrt{\dfrac{\text{sum of the squares of the differences from the mean}}{\text{number of differences}}}$$	Find the standard deviation of the data set 1, 3, 4, 8. *(see table below)* The sum of the squares of the differences is 26 and there are 4 values in the data set. The standard deviation is $\sqrt{\dfrac{26}{4}} \approx 2.549509757$. To the nearest hundredth, the standard deviation is 2.55.

Original terms	Mean	Difference	Square of the differences
1	4	−3	9
3	4	−1	1
4	4	0	0
8	4	4	16

REVIEW EXERCISES

Simplify each radical. Assume that x can be any number.

1. $\sqrt{49}$
2. $-\sqrt{121}$
3. $-\sqrt{36}$
4. $\sqrt{225}$
5. $\sqrt[3]{-27}$
6. $-\sqrt[3]{216}$
7. $\sqrt[4]{625}$
8. $\sqrt[5]{-32}$
9. $\sqrt{25x^2}$
10. $\sqrt{x^2 + 4x + 4}$
11. $\sqrt[3]{27a^6b^3}$
12. $\sqrt[4]{256x^8y^4}$

Graph each function.

13. $f(x) = \sqrt{x + 2}$

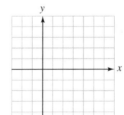

14. $f(x) = -\sqrt{x - 1}$

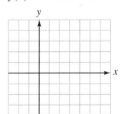

15. $f(x) = -\sqrt{x} + 2$ **16.** $f(x) = -\sqrt[3]{x} + 3$

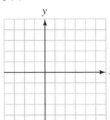

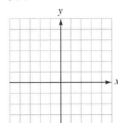

Consider the distribution 4, 8, 12, 16, 20.
17. Find the mean of the distribution.
18. Find the standard deviation.

SECTION 9.2   Applications of the Pythagorean Theorem and the Distance Formula

DEFINITIONS AND CONCEPTS	EXAMPLES
The Pythagorean theorem: If a and b are the lengths of the legs of a right triangle and c is the length of the hypotenuse, then $a^2 + b^2 = c^2$	To find the length of the hypotenuse of a right triangle with legs of length 9 ft and 12 ft, proceed as follows: $a^2 + b^2 = c^2$ The Pythagorean theorem. $(9)^2 + (12)^2 = c^2$ Substitute the values. $81 + 144 = c^2$ Square each value. $225 = c^2$ Add. $\sqrt{225} = c$ Since c is a length, take the positive square root. $15 = c$ $\sqrt{225} = 15$ The hypotenuse is 15 ft.
The distance formula: The distance between two points, (x_1, y_1) and (x_2, y_2), on a coordinate plane is $d = \sqrt{(x_2 - x_1)^2 + (y_2 - y_1)^2}$	To find the distance between $(6, -1)$ and $(3, 3)$, use the distance formula: $d = \sqrt{(x_2 - x_1)^2 + (y_2 - y_1)^2}$ The distance formula. $= \sqrt{(3 - 6)^2 + [3 - (-1)]^2}$ Substitute values. $= \sqrt{(-3)^2 + 4^2}$ Remove parentheses $= \sqrt{9 + 16}$ Square each value. $= \sqrt{25}$ Add. $= 5$ Simplify. The distance between the points is 5 units.

REVIEW EXERCISES
In Exercises 19–20, the horizon distance d (measured in miles) is related to the height h (measured in feet) of the observer by the formula $d = 1.4\sqrt{h}$.

19. View from a submarine A submarine's periscope extends 4.7 feet above the surface. How far away is the horizon?

20. View from a submarine How far out of the water must a submarine periscope extend to provide a 4-mile horizon?

21. Sailing A technique called *tacking* allows a sailboat to make progress into the wind. A sailboat follows the course in the illustration. Find d, the distance the boat advances into the wind.

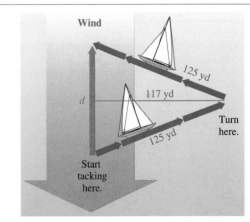

22. Communications Some campers 3,900 yards from a highway are talking to truckers on a citizen's band radio with an 8,900-yard range. Over what length of highway can these conversations take place?

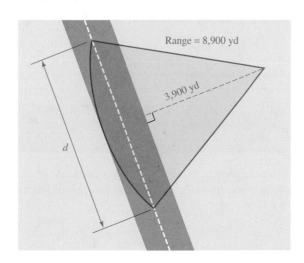

Range = 8,900 yd

3,900 yd

d

23. Find the distance between points $(0, 0)$ and $(5, -12)$.

24. Find the distance between points $(-4, 6)$ and $(-2, 8)$. Give the result to the nearest hundredth.

SECTION 9.3 Rational Exponents

DEFINITIONS AND CONCEPTS	EXAMPLES
Rational exponents with numerator of 1: If n $(n > 1)$ is a natural number and $\sqrt[n]{x}$ is a real number, then $x^{1/n} = \sqrt[n]{x}$. If n is even, $(x^n)^{1/n} = \lvert x \rvert$. If n is a natural number greater than 1 and x is a real number, then	$16^{1/2} = \sqrt{16} = 4$ $(25x^2)^{1/2} = \sqrt{25x^2} = 5\lvert x \rvert$
If $x > 0$, then $x^{1/n}$ is the positive number such that $(x^{1/n})^n = x$.	$64^{1/2} = \sqrt{64} = 8$

If $x = 0$, then $x^{1/n} = 0$.
 	
     If $x < 0$ and n is odd, then $x^{1/n}$ is the real number such that $(x^{1/n})^n = x$.
 	
     If $x < 0$ and n is even, then $x^{1/n}$ is not a real number.
	$0^{1/4} = \sqrt[4]{0} = 0$
	 $(-27)^{1/3} = \sqrt[3]{-27} = -3$
	
	 $(-64)^{1/2} = \sqrt{-64}$ is not a real number.

Rational exponents with numerator other than 1: If m and n are positive integers and $x > 0$, $x^{m/n} = \sqrt[n]{x^m} = \left(\sqrt[n]{x}\right)^m$	$64^{2/3} = \sqrt[3]{(64)^2} = \sqrt[3]{4{,}096} = 16$ $64^{2/3} = \left(\sqrt[3]{64}\right)^2 = 4^2 = 16$

Negative rational exponents:
 	
     $x^{-m/n} = \dfrac{1}{x^{m/n}}$
 	
     $\dfrac{1}{x^{-m/n}} = x^{m/n}$ $(x \neq 0)$
	$25^{-1/2} = \dfrac{1}{25^{1/2}} = \dfrac{1}{\sqrt{25}} = \dfrac{1}{5}$
	
	 $\dfrac{1}{16^{-3/2}} = 16^{3/2} = \left(\sqrt{16}\right)^3 = 4^3 = 64$

Simplifying expressions with rational exponents: Apply the properties of exponents.	$\dfrac{x^{3/4} \cdot x^{2/3}}{x^{7/6}} = x^{3/4+2/3-7/6}$ Use the rules $x^m \cdot x^n = x^{m+n}$ and $\dfrac{x^m}{x^n} = x^{m-n}$.
	$= x^{1/4}$ $\qquad$ $\dfrac{3}{4} + \dfrac{2}{3} - \dfrac{7}{6} = \dfrac{1}{4}$
	$= \sqrt[4]{x}$ $\qquad$ Change to radical notation.

Simplifying radical expressions: 1. Change the radical expression into an exponential expression with rational exponents. 2. Simplify the rational exponents. 3. Change the exponential expression back into a radical.	$\sqrt[4]{81x^2} = (81x^2)^{1/4}$ $\quad$ Use the rule $\sqrt[n]{x} = x^{1/n}$.
	$= (3^4 x^2)^{1/4}$ $\quad$ $81 = 3^4$
	$= 3x^{1/2}$ $\qquad$ Use the rule $(xy)^m = x^m \cdot y^m$.
	$= 3\sqrt{x}$ $\qquad$ Change to radical notation.

REVIEW EXERCISES

Simplify each expression, if possible. Assume that all variables represent positive numbers.

25. $25^{1/2}$ $\qquad\qquad$ **26.** $-36^{1/2}$

27. $9^{3/2}$ $\qquad\qquad$ **28.** $16^{3/2}$

29. $(-8)^{1/3}$ $\qquad\qquad$ **30.** $-8^{2/3}$

31. $8^{-2/3}$ $\qquad\qquad$ **32.** $8^{-1/3}$

33. $-49^{5/2}$ $\qquad\qquad$ **34.** $\dfrac{1}{25^{5/2}}$

35. $\left(\dfrac{1}{4}\right)^{-3/2}$ $\qquad\quad$ **36.** $\left(\dfrac{4}{9}\right)^{-3/2}$

37. $(27x^3y)^{1/3}$ $\qquad$ **38.** $(81x^4y^2)^{1/4}$

39. $(25x^3y^4)^{3/2}$ $\qquad$ **40.** $(8u^2v^3)^{-2/3}$

Perform the multiplications. Assume that all variables represent positive numbers and write all answers without negative exponents.

41. $5^{1/4}5^{1/2}$ $\qquad\qquad$ **42.** $a^{3/7}a^{2/7}$

43. $u^{1/2}(u^{1/2} - u^{-1/2})$ $\qquad$ **44.** $v^{2/3}(v^{1/3} + v^{4/3})$

45. $(x^{1/2} + y^{1/2})^2$

46. $(a^{2/3} + b^{2/3})(a^{2/3} - b^{2/3})$

Simplify each expression. Assume that all variables are positive.

47. $\sqrt[6]{5^2}$ $\qquad\qquad$ **48.** $\sqrt[8]{x^4}$

49. $\sqrt[9]{27a^3b^6}$ $\qquad\qquad$ **50.** $\sqrt[4]{25a^2b^2}$

SECTION 9.4   Simplifying and Combining Radical Expressions

DEFINITIONS AND CONCEPTS	EXAMPLES
Properties of radicals: $\sqrt[n]{ab} = \sqrt[n]{a}\sqrt[n]{b}$	$\begin{aligned} \sqrt{24} &= \sqrt{4 \cdot 6} \\ &= \sqrt{4}\sqrt{6} \\ &= 2\sqrt{6} \end{aligned}$ $\qquad$ $\begin{aligned} \sqrt[3]{24} &= \sqrt[3]{8 \cdot 3} \\ &= \sqrt[3]{8}\sqrt[3]{3} \\ &= 2\sqrt[3]{3} \end{aligned}$
$\sqrt[n]{\dfrac{a}{b}} = \dfrac{\sqrt[n]{a}}{\sqrt[n]{b}}$ $\quad (b \neq 0)$	$\begin{aligned} \sqrt{\dfrac{21}{64x^6}} &= \dfrac{\sqrt{21}}{\sqrt{64x^6}} \\ &= \dfrac{\sqrt{21}}{8x^3} \end{aligned}$ $\qquad$ $\begin{aligned} \sqrt[3]{\dfrac{21}{64x^6}} &= \dfrac{\sqrt[3]{21}}{\sqrt[3]{64x^6}} \\ &= \dfrac{\sqrt[3]{21}}{4x^2} \end{aligned}$
Adding and subtracting radical expressions: Like radicals can be combined by addition and subtraction. Radicals that are not similar often can be simplified to radicals that are similar and then combined.	$9\sqrt{2} + 4\sqrt{2} = (9 + 4)\sqrt{2} = 13\sqrt{2}$ $\begin{aligned} \sqrt{2} + \sqrt{18} &= \sqrt{2} + \sqrt{9}\sqrt{2} \\ &= \sqrt{2} + 3\sqrt{2} \\ &= 4\sqrt{2} \end{aligned}$

Special right triangles:

In a 45°–45°–90° triangle, the length of the hypotenuse is the length of one leg times $\sqrt{2}$.

The shorter leg of a 30°–60°–90° triangle is half as long as the hypotenuse. The longer leg is the length of the shorter leg times $\sqrt{3}$.

If each leg of an isosceles triangle is 17 cm, the hypotenuse measures $17\sqrt{2}$ cm.

If the shorter leg of a 30°–60°–90° triangle is 12 units, the hypotenuse is 24 cm and the longer leg is $12\sqrt{3}$ units.

REVIEW EXERCISES

Simplify each expression. Assume that all variables represent positive numbers.

51. $\sqrt{240}$ **52.** $\sqrt[3]{54}$

53. $\sqrt[4]{32}$ **54.** $\sqrt[5]{96}$

55. $\sqrt{8x^3}$ **56.** $\sqrt{18x^4y^3}$

57. $\sqrt[3]{16x^5y^4}$ **58.** $\sqrt[3]{54x^7y^3}$

59. $\dfrac{\sqrt{32x^3}}{\sqrt{2x}}$ **60.** $\dfrac{\sqrt[3]{16x^5}}{\sqrt[3]{2x^2}}$

61. $\sqrt[3]{\dfrac{2a^2b}{27x^3}}$ **62.** $\sqrt{\dfrac{17xy}{64a^4}}$

Simplify and combine like radicals. Assume that all variables represent positive numbers.

63. $\sqrt{2} + \sqrt{8}$ **64.** $\sqrt{20} - \sqrt{5}$

65. $2\sqrt[3]{3} - \sqrt[3]{24}$ **66.** $\sqrt[4]{32} + 2\sqrt[4]{162}$

67. $2x\sqrt{8} + 2\sqrt{200x^2} + \sqrt{50x^2}$

68. $3\sqrt{27a^3} - 2a\sqrt{3a} + 5\sqrt{75a^3}$

69. $\sqrt[3]{54} - 3\sqrt[3]{16} + 4\sqrt[3]{128}$

70. $2\sqrt[4]{32x^5} + 4\sqrt[4]{162x^5} - 5x\sqrt[4]{512x}$

71. Geometry   Find the length of the hypotenuse of an isosceles right triangle whose legs measure 7 meters.

72. Geometry   The hypotenuse of a 30°–60°–90° triangle measures $12\sqrt{3}$ centimeters. Find the length of each leg.

Find x to two decimal places.

73.

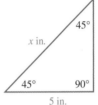

74.

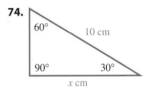

SECTION 9.5   Multiplying and Dividing Radical Expressions

DEFINITIONS AND CONCEPTS	EXAMPLES
Multiplying radical expressions: If two radicals have the same index, they can be multiplied:	$\sqrt{3x}\sqrt{6x} = \sqrt{18x^2}$ $(x > 0)$ $\qquad = \sqrt{9x^2}\sqrt{2}$ $\qquad = 3x\sqrt{2}$ $(5 - 2\sqrt{3})(7 + 6\sqrt{3})$ $\qquad = 35 + 30\sqrt{3} - 14\sqrt{3} - 12\sqrt{9}$ Distribute. $\qquad = 35 + 16\sqrt{3} - 12(3)$ Combine like terms. $\qquad = 35 + 16\sqrt{3} - 36$ Multiply. $\qquad = -1 + 16\sqrt{3}$ Simplify.
Rationalizing the denominator: To eliminate a single radical in the denominator, we multiply the numerator and the denominator by a number that will give a perfect square (or cube, or 4th power, etc.) under the radical in the denominator.	$\sqrt{\dfrac{5}{8}} = \dfrac{\sqrt{5}}{\sqrt{8}}$ $\sqrt{\dfrac{a}{b}} = \dfrac{\sqrt{a}}{\sqrt{b}}$ $\qquad = \dfrac{\sqrt{5}}{\sqrt{8}} \cdot \dfrac{\sqrt{2}}{\sqrt{2}}$ Multiply by 1: $\dfrac{\sqrt{2}}{\sqrt{2}} = 1$. $\qquad = \dfrac{\sqrt{10}}{\sqrt{16}}$ Multiply radicals. $\qquad = \dfrac{\sqrt{10}}{4}$ Simplify.

To rationalize a fraction whose denominator has two terms with one or both containing square roots, we multiply its numerator and denominator by the *conjugate* of its denominator.

$$\frac{5}{4 - \sqrt{2}} \cdot \frac{4 + \sqrt{2}}{4 + \sqrt{2}}$$ Multiply the numerator and the denominator by the conjugate of the denominator.

$$= \frac{20 + 5\sqrt{2}}{16 - 2}$$ Multiply the numerators and denominators.

$$= \frac{20 + 5\sqrt{2}}{14}$$ Simplify.

REVIEW EXERCISES

Simplify each expression. Assume that all variables represent positive numbers.

75. $\left(2\sqrt{5}\right)\left(3\sqrt{2}\right)$

76. $2\sqrt{6}\sqrt{216}$

77. $\sqrt{9x}\sqrt{x}$

78. $\sqrt[3]{3}\sqrt[3]{9}$

79. $-\sqrt[3]{2x^2}\sqrt[3]{4x}$

80. $-\sqrt[4]{256x^5y^{11}}\sqrt[4]{625x^9y^3}$

81. $\sqrt{2}\left(\sqrt{8} - 3\right)$

82. $\sqrt{2}\left(\sqrt{2} + 3\right)$

83. $\sqrt{5}\left(\sqrt{2} - 1\right)$

84. $\sqrt{3}\left(\sqrt{3} + \sqrt{2}\right)$

85. $\left(\sqrt{2} + 1\right)\left(\sqrt{2} - 1\right)$

86. $\left(\sqrt{3} + \sqrt{2}\right)\left(\sqrt{3} + \sqrt{2}\right)$

87. $\left(\sqrt{x} + \sqrt{y}\right)\left(\sqrt{x} - \sqrt{y}\right)$

88. $\left(2\sqrt{u} + 3\right)\left(3\sqrt{u} - 4\right)$

Rationalize each denominator.

89. $\dfrac{1}{\sqrt{3}}$

90. $\dfrac{\sqrt{3}}{\sqrt{5}}$

91. $\dfrac{x}{\sqrt{xy}}$

92. $\dfrac{\sqrt[3]{uv}}{\sqrt[3]{u^5v^7}}$

93. $\dfrac{2}{\sqrt{2} - 1}$

94. $\dfrac{\sqrt{2}}{\sqrt{3} - 1}$

95. $\dfrac{2x - 32}{\sqrt{x} + 4}$

96. $\dfrac{\sqrt{a} + 1}{\sqrt{a} - 1}$

Rationalize each numerator. All variables represent positive numbers.

97. $\dfrac{\sqrt{3}}{5}$

98. $\dfrac{\sqrt[3]{9}}{3}$

99. $\dfrac{3 - \sqrt{x}}{2}$

100. $\dfrac{\sqrt{a} - \sqrt{b}}{\sqrt{a}}$

SECTION 9.6   Radical Equations

DEFINITIONS AND CONCEPTS	EXAMPLES
The power rule: If x, y, and n are real numbers, If $x = y$, then $x^n = y^n$. Raising both sides of an equation to the same power can lead to extraneous solutions. Be sure to check all suspected solutions.	To solve $\sqrt{x + 4} = x - 2$, proceed as follows:

$$\left(\sqrt{x + 4}\right)^2 = \left(x - 2\right)^2$$ Square both sides to eliminate the square root.

$$x + 4 = x^2 - 4x + 4$$ Square the binomial.

$$0 = x^2 - 5x$$ Subtract x and 4 from both sides.

$$0 = x(x - 5)$$ Factor $x^2 - 5x$.

$$x = 0 \quad \text{or} \quad x - 5 = 0$$ Set each factor equal to 0.

$$x = 0 \quad | \quad x = 5$$

Check:

$$\sqrt{x + 4} = x - 2 \qquad \sqrt{x + 4} = x - 2$$

$$\sqrt{0 + 4} \stackrel{?}{=} 0 - 2 \qquad \sqrt{5 + 4} \stackrel{?}{=} 5 - 2$$

$$\sqrt{4} \stackrel{?}{=} -2 \qquad \sqrt{9} \stackrel{?}{=} 3$$

$$2 \neq -2 \qquad 3 = 3$$

Since 0 does not check, it is extraneous and must be discarded. The only solution of the original equation is 5.

REVIEW EXERCISES

Solve each equation.

101. $\sqrt{y + 3} = \sqrt{2y - 19}$ **102.** $u = \sqrt{25u - 144}$ **105.** $\sqrt{2x + 5} - \sqrt{2x} = 1$ **106.** $\sqrt[3]{x^3 + 8} = x + 2$

103. $r = \sqrt{12r - 27}$ **104.** $\sqrt{z + 1} + \sqrt{z} = 2$

SECTION 9.7 Complex Numbers

DEFINITIONS AND CONCEPTS	EXAMPLES
Simplifying imaginary numbers: $\sqrt{-1}$ is defined as the **imaginary number i.**	$\begin{aligned} \sqrt{-12} &= \sqrt{-4}\sqrt{3} &&\text{Write } -12 \text{ as } -4(3).\\ &= \sqrt{-1}\sqrt{4}\sqrt{3} &&\text{Write } -4 \text{ as the product of } -1 \text{ and } 4.\\ &= i(2)\sqrt{3} &&\sqrt{-1} = i\\ &= 2\sqrt{3}i \end{aligned}$
Operations with complex numbers: If a, b, c, and d are real numbers and $i^2 = -1$, $a + bi = c + di$ if and only if $a = c$ and $b = d$ $(a + bi) + (c + di) = (a + c) + (b + d)i$ $(a + bi) - (c + di) = (a - c) + (b - d)i$ $(a + bi)(c + di) = (ac - bd) + (ad + bc)i$	$3 + 5i = \sqrt{9} + \frac{10}{2}i$ because $\sqrt{9} = 3$ and $\frac{10}{2} = 5$. $(6 + 5i) + (2 + 9i) = (6 + 2) + (5 + 9)i = 8 + 14i$ $(6 + 5i) - (2 + 9i) = (6 - 2) + (5 - 9)i = 4 - 4i$ $\begin{aligned} (6 - 5i)(2 + 9i) &= 12 + 54i - 10i - 45i^2\\ &= 12 + 44i - 45(-1)\\ &= 12 + 44i + 45\\ &= 57 + 44i \end{aligned}$
Dividing complex numbers: To divide complex numbers, write the division as a fraction, and rationalize the denominator.	$\begin{aligned} \frac{6}{3 + i} \cdot \frac{3 - i}{3 - i} &= \frac{18 - 6i}{9 - i^2} &&\text{Multiply the numerator and the denominator by the conjugate of the denominator. Multiply the fractions.}\\ &= \frac{18 - 6i}{9 + 1} &&i^2 = -1\\ &= \frac{18 - 6i}{10} &&\text{Add.}\\ &= \frac{18}{10} - \frac{6}{10}i &&\text{Write in } a + bi \text{ form.}\\ &= \frac{9}{5} - \frac{3}{5}i &&\text{Simplify each fraction.} \end{aligned}$
Absolute value of a complex number: $|a + bi| = \sqrt{a^2 + b^2}$	$\begin{aligned} |4 + 8i| &= \sqrt{4^2 + 8^2} &&|a + bi| = \sqrt{a^2 + b^2}\\ &= \sqrt{16 + 64} &&\text{Square each value.}\\ &= \sqrt{80} &&\text{Add.}\\ &= \sqrt{16 \cdot 5} &&\text{Factor: } 80 = 16(5).\\ &= 4\sqrt{5} &&\text{Simplify: } \sqrt{16 \cdot 5} = \sqrt{16}\sqrt{5} = 4\sqrt{5}. \end{aligned}$

REVIEW EXERCISES
Perform the operations and give all answers in *a + bi* form.

107. $(5 + 4i) + (7 - 12i)$

108. $(-6 - 40i) - (-8 + 28i)$

109. $\left(-32 + \sqrt{-144}\right) - \left(64 + \sqrt{-81}\right)$

110. $\left(-8 + \sqrt{-8}\right) + \left(6 - \sqrt{-32}\right)$

111. $(2 - 7i)(-3 + 4i)$

112. $(-5 + 6i)(2 + i)$

113. $\left(5 - \sqrt{-27}\right)\left(-6 + \sqrt{-12}\right)$

114. $\left(2 + \sqrt{-128}\right)\left(3 - \sqrt{-98}\right)$

115. $\dfrac{3}{4i}$

116. $\dfrac{-2}{5i^3}$

117. $\dfrac{6}{2 + i}$

118. $\dfrac{7}{3 - i}$

119. $\dfrac{4 + i}{4 - i}$

120. $\dfrac{3 - i}{3 + i}$

121. $\dfrac{3}{5 + \sqrt{-4}}$

122. $\dfrac{2}{3 - \sqrt{-9}}$

Simplify.

123. $|9 + 12i|$

124. $|24 - 10i|$

125. i^{12}

126. i^{583}

Chapter 9   TEST

Find each root.

1. $\sqrt{49}$

2. $\sqrt[3]{64}$

3. $\sqrt{4x^2}$

4. $\sqrt[3]{8x^3}$

Graph each function and find its domain and range.

5. $f(x) = \sqrt{x - 2}$

6. $f(x) = \sqrt[3]{x} + 3$

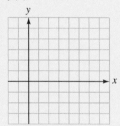

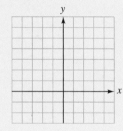

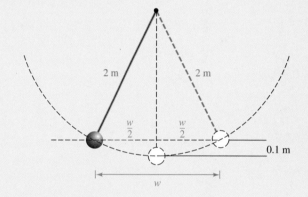

 Use a calculator.

7. Shipping crates The diagonal brace on the shipping crate shown in the illustration is 53 inches. Find the height, *h*, of the crate.

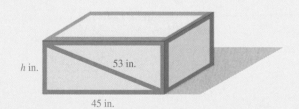

8. Pendulums The 2-meter pendulum rises 0.1 meter at the extremes of its swing. Find the width *w* of the swing.

Find the distance between the points.

9. $(6, 8), (0, 0)$

10. $(-2, 5), (22, 12)$

Simplify each expression. Assume that all variables represent positive numbers, and write answers without using negative exponents.

11. $16^{1/4}$

12. $27^{2/3}$

13. $36^{-3/2}$

14. $\left(-\dfrac{8}{27}\right)^{-2/3}$

15. $\dfrac{2^{5/3}2^{1/6}}{2^{1/2}}$

16. $\dfrac{(8x^3y)^{1/2}(8xy^5)^{1/2}}{(x^3y^6)^{1/3}}$

Simplify each expression. Assume that all variables represent positive numbers.

17. $\sqrt{48}$

18. $\sqrt{250x^3y^5}$

19. $\dfrac{\sqrt[3]{24x^{15}y^4}}{\sqrt[3]{y}}$

20. $\sqrt{\dfrac{3a^5}{48a^7}}$

Simplify each expression. Assume that the variables are unrestricted.

21. $\sqrt{12x^2}$

22. $\sqrt{8x^6}$

23. $\sqrt[3]{81x^3}$

24. $\sqrt{18x^4y^9}$

Simplify and combine like radicals. Assume that all variables represent positive numbers.

25. $\sqrt{12} - \sqrt{27}$

26. $2\sqrt[3]{40} - \sqrt[3]{5{,}000} + 4\sqrt[3]{625}$

27. $2\sqrt{48y^5} - 3y\sqrt{12y^3}$

28. $\sqrt[4]{768z^5} + z\sqrt[4]{48z}$

Perform each operation and simplify, if possible. All variables represent positive numbers.

29. $-2\sqrt{xy}\left(3\sqrt{x} + \sqrt{xy^3}\right)$

30. $\left(3\sqrt{2} + \sqrt{3}\right)\left(2\sqrt{2} - 3\sqrt{3}\right)$

Rationalize each denominator.

31. $\dfrac{1}{\sqrt{5}}$

32. $\dfrac{3t - 1}{\sqrt{3t} - 1}$

Rationalize each numerator.

33. $\dfrac{\sqrt{3}}{\sqrt{7}}$

34. $\dfrac{\sqrt{a} + \sqrt{b}}{\sqrt{a} - \sqrt{b}}$

Solve and check each equation.

35. $\sqrt[3]{6n + 4} - 4 = 0$

36. $1 - \sqrt{u} = \sqrt{u - 3}$

Perform the operations. Give all answers in standard form.

37. $(2 + 4i) + (-3 + 7i)$

38. $\left(3 - \sqrt{-9}\right) - \left(-1 + \sqrt{-16}\right)$

39. $2i(3 - 4i)$

40. $(3 + 2i)(-4 - i)$

41. $\dfrac{1}{i\sqrt{2}}$

42. $\dfrac{2 + i}{3 - i}$

Quadratic Functions, Inequalities, and Algebra of Functions

Careers and Mathematics

POLICE OFFICERS AND DETECTIVES

People depend on police officers and detectives to protect their lives and property. Law enforcement officers, some of whom are state or federal special agents, perform these duties in a variety of ways. Uniformed police officers maintain regular patrols and respond to calls for service. They may direct traffic, investigate a burglary, or give first aid to an accident victim. Police work can be very dangerous and stressful.
Police officers and detectives held about 861,000 jobs in 2006.

Job Outlook:
Employment of police officers and detectives is expected to grow as fast as the average for all occupations through 2016.

Annual Earnings:
$35,600–$59,880

For More Information:
http://www.bls.gov/oco/ocos160.htm

For a Sample Application:
See Problem 83 in Section 10.1.

In this chapter ▶

We have discussed how to solve linear equations and certain quadratic equations in which the quadratic expression is factorable. In this chapter, we will discuss more general methods for solving quadratic equations and quadratic inequalities, and we will consider the graphs of quadratic functions. Finally, we will discuss operations on fuctions.

Solving Quadratic Equations Using the Square-Root Property and by Completing the Square

1. Solve a quadratic equation by factoring.
2. Solve a quadratic equation by applying the square-root property.
3. Solve a quadratic equation by completing the square.
4. Solve an application problem requiring the use of the square-root property.

Vocabulary

square-root property   completing the square

Getting Ready

Factor each expression.

1. $x^2 - 25$ **2.** $b^2 - 81$

3. $6x^2 + x - 2$ **4.** $4x^2 - 4x - 3$

We begin this section by reviewing how to solve quadratic equations by factoring. We will then discuss how to solve these equations by applying the **square-root property** and completing the square and use these skills to solve application problems.

Solve a quadratic equation by factoring.

Recall that a *quadratic equation* is an equation of the form $ax^2 + bx + c = 0$ $(a \neq 0)$, where a, b, and c are real numbers. We will solve the first two examples by factoring.

EXAMPLE 1   Solve: $x^2 = 9$.

Solution   To solve this quadratic equation by factoring, we proceed as follows:

$$x^2 = 9$$
$$x^2 - 9 = 0 \qquad \text{Subtract 9 from both sides.}$$
$$(x + 3)(x - 3) = 0 \qquad \text{Factor the binomial.}$$
$$x + 3 = 0 \quad \text{or} \quad x - 3 = 0 \qquad \text{Set each factor equal to 0.}$$
$$x = -3 \qquad \qquad x = 3 \qquad \text{Solve each linear equation.}$$

Check:

For $x = -3$	For $x = 3$
$x^2 = 9$	$x^2 = 9$
$(-3)^2 \stackrel{?}{=} 9$	$(3)^2 \stackrel{?}{=} 9$
$9 = 9$	$9 = 9$

Since both results check, the solutions are 3 and -3.

⇨ **SELF CHECK 1**   Solve: $p^2 = 64$.

EXAMPLE 2   Solve: $6x^2 - 7x - 3 = 0$.

Solution   To solve this quadratic equation by factoring, we proceed as follows:

$$6x^2 - 7x - 3 = 0$$
$$(2x - 3)(3x + 1) = 0 \qquad \text{Factor.}$$
$$2x - 3 = 0 \quad \text{or} \quad 3x + 1 = 0 \qquad \text{Set each factor equal to 0.}$$
$$x = \frac{3}{2} \qquad\qquad x = -\frac{1}{3} \qquad \text{Solve each linear equation.}$$

Check:

For $x = \frac{3}{2}$	For $x = -\frac{1}{3}$
$6x^2 - 7x - 3 = 0$	$6x^2 - 7x - 3 = 0$
$6\left(\frac{3}{2}\right)^2 - 7\left(\frac{3}{2}\right) - 3 \stackrel{?}{=} 0$	$6\left(-\frac{1}{3}\right)^2 - 7\left(-\frac{1}{3}\right) - 3 \stackrel{?}{=} 0$
$6\left(\frac{9}{4}\right) - 7\left(\frac{3}{2}\right) - 3 \stackrel{?}{=} 0$	$6\left(\frac{1}{9}\right) - 7\left(-\frac{1}{3}\right) - 3 \stackrel{?}{=} 0$
$\frac{27}{2} - \frac{21}{2} - \frac{6}{2} \stackrel{?}{=} 0$	$\frac{2}{3} + \frac{7}{3} - \frac{9}{3} \stackrel{?}{=} 0$
$0 = 0$	$0 = 0$

Since both results check, the solutions are $\frac{3}{2}$ and $-\frac{1}{3}$.

⇨ **SELF CHECK 2**   Solve: $6m^2 - 5m + 1 = 0$.

Unfortunately, many quadratic expressions do not factor easily. For example, it would be difficult to solve $2x^2 + 4x + 1 = 0$ by factoring, because $2x^2 + 4x + 1$ cannot be factored by using only integers.

2   **Solve a quadratic equation by applying the square-root property.**

To develop general methods for solving all quadratic equations, we first solve $x^2 = c$ by a method similar to the one used in Example 1.

$$x^2 = c$$
$$x^2 - c = 0 \qquad \text{Subtract } c \text{ from both sides.}$$
$$x^2 - \left(\sqrt{c}\right)^2 = 0 \qquad c = \left(\sqrt{c}\right)^2$$
$$\left(x + \sqrt{c}\right)\left(x - \sqrt{c}\right) = 0 \qquad \text{Factor the difference of two squares.}$$

$$x + \sqrt{c} = 0 \quad \text{or} \quad x - \sqrt{c} = 0 \qquad \text{Set each factor equal to 0.}$$
$$x = -\sqrt{c} \quad \Big| \quad x = \sqrt{c} \qquad \text{Solve each linear equation.}$$

The two solutions of $x^2 = c$ are $x = \sqrt{c}$ and $x = -\sqrt{c}$.

The Square-Root Property	The equation $x^2 = c$ has two solutions. They are
	$$x = \sqrt{c} \quad \text{or} \quad x = -\sqrt{c}$$

We often use the symbol $\pm\sqrt{c}$ to represent the two solutions $\sqrt{c}$ and $-\sqrt{c}$. The symbol $\pm\sqrt{c}$ is read as "the positive or negative square root of c."

EXAMPLE 3 Use the square-root property to solve $x^2 - 12 = 0$.

Solution We can write the equation as $x^2 = 12$ and use the square-root property.

$$x^2 - 12 = 0$$
$$x^2 = 12 \qquad \text{Add 12 to both sides.}$$
$$x = \sqrt{12} \quad \text{or} \quad x = -\sqrt{12} \qquad \text{Use the square-root property.}$$
$$x = 2\sqrt{3} \quad \Big| \quad x = -2\sqrt{3} \qquad \sqrt{12} = \sqrt{4}\sqrt{3} = 2\sqrt{3}$$

The solutions can be written as $\pm 2\sqrt{3}$. Verify that each one satisfies the equation.

⇨ **SELF CHECK 3** Use the square-root property to solve $x^2 - 18 = 0$.

EXAMPLE 4 Use the square-root property to solve $(x - 3)^2 = 16$.

Solution We can use the square-root property.

$$(x - 3)^2 = 16$$
$$x - 3 = \sqrt{16} \quad \text{or} \quad x - 3 = -\sqrt{16} \qquad \text{Use the square-root property.}$$
$$x - 3 = 4 \quad \Big| \quad x - 3 = -4 \qquad \sqrt{16} = 4 \text{ and } -\sqrt{16} = -4.$$
$$x = 3 + 4 \quad \Big| \quad x = 3 - 4 \qquad \text{Add 3 to both sides.}$$
$$x = 7 \quad \Big| \quad x = -1 \qquad \text{Simplify.}$$

Verify that each solution satisfies the equation.

⇨ **SELF CHECK 4** Use the square-root property to solve $(x + 2)^2 = 9$.

In the following example, the solutions are imaginary numbers.

EXAMPLE 5 Use the square-root property to solve $9x^2 + 25 = 0$.

Solution We can write the equation as $x^2 = -\frac{25}{9}$ and use the square-root property.

$$9x^2 + 25 = 0$$

$$x^2 = -\frac{25}{9} \qquad \text{Subtract 25 from both sides and divide both sides by 9.}$$

$$x = \sqrt{-\frac{25}{9}} \quad \text{or} \quad x = -\sqrt{-\frac{25}{9}} \qquad \text{Use the square-root property.}$$

$$x = \sqrt{\frac{25}{9}}\sqrt{-1} \qquad x = -\sqrt{\frac{25}{9}}\sqrt{-1} \qquad \sqrt{-\frac{25}{9}} = \sqrt{\frac{25}{9}(-1)} = \sqrt{\frac{25}{9}}\sqrt{-1}$$

$$x = \frac{5}{3}i \qquad x = -\frac{5}{3}i \qquad \sqrt{\frac{25}{9}} = \frac{5}{3}; \sqrt{-1} = i$$

Check:

$$9x^2 + 25 = 0 \qquad\qquad 9x^2 + 25 = 0$$

$$9\left(\frac{5}{3}i\right)^2 + 25 \stackrel{?}{=} 0 \qquad 9\left(-\frac{5}{3}i\right)^2 + 25 \stackrel{?}{=} 0$$

$$9\left(\frac{25}{9}\right)i^2 + 25 \stackrel{?}{=} 0 \qquad 9\left(\frac{25}{9}\right)i^2 + 25 \stackrel{?}{=} 0$$

$$25(-1) + 25 \stackrel{?}{=} 0 \qquad 25(-1) + 25 \stackrel{?}{=} 0$$

$$0 = 0 \qquad\qquad 0 = 0$$

Since both results check, the solutions are $\pm\frac{5}{3}i$.

⇨ **SELF CHECK 5** Use the square-root property to solve $4x^2 + 36 = 0$.

3 **Solve a quadratic equation by completing the square.**

All quadratic equations can be solved by a method called **completing the square.** This method is based on the special products

$$x^2 + 2ax + a^2 = (x + a)^2 \qquad \text{and} \qquad x^2 - 2ax + a^2 = (x - a)^2$$

Recall that the trinomials $x^2 + 2ax + a^2$ and $x^2 - 2ax + a^2$ are both *perfect-square trinomials,* because both factor as the square of a binomial. In each case, the coefficient of the first term is 1 and if we take one-half of the coefficient of x in the middle term and square it, we obtain the third term.

$$\left[\frac{1}{2}(2a)\right]^2 = a^2 \qquad\qquad \left[\frac{1}{2}(2a)\right]^2 = (a)^2 = a^2$$

$$\left[\frac{1}{2}(-2a)\right]^2 = (-a)^2 = a^2 \qquad \left[\frac{1}{2}(-2a)\right]^2 = (-a)^2 = a^2$$

EXAMPLE 6 Find the number that when added to each binomial results in a perfect-square trinomial: **a.** $x^2 + 10x$ **b.** $x^2 - 6x$ **c.** $x^2 - 11x$.

Solution **a.** To make $x^2 + 10x$ a perfect-square trinomial, we first find one-half of 10 to get 5 and square 5 to get 25.

$$\left[\frac{1}{2}(10)\right]^2 = (5)^2 = 25$$

Then we add 25 to $x^2 + 10x$ and obtain $x^2 + 10x + 25$. This is a perfect-square trinomial because $x^2 + 10x + 25 = (x + 5)^2$.

b. To make $x^2 - 6x$ a perfect-square trinomial, we first find one-half of -6 to get -3 and square -3 to get 9.

$$\left[\frac{1}{2}(-6)\right]^2 = (-3)^2 = 9$$

Then we add 9 to $x^2 - 6x$ and obtain $x^2 - 6x + 9$. This is a perfect-square trinomial because $x^2 - 6x + 9 = (x - 3)^2$.

c. To make $x^2 - 11x$ a perfect-square trinomial, we first find one-half of -11 to get $-\frac{11}{2}$ and square $-\frac{11}{2}$ to get $\frac{121}{4}$.

$$\left[\frac{1}{2}(-11)\right]^2 = \left(-\frac{11}{2}\right)^2 = \frac{121}{4}$$

Then we add $\frac{121}{4}$ to $x^2 - 11x$ and obtain $x^2 - 11x + \frac{121}{4}$. This is a perfect-square trinomial because $x^2 - 11x + \frac{121}{4} = \left(x - \frac{11}{2}\right)^2$.

⇨ SELF CHECK 6   Find the number that when added to $a^2 - 5a$ results in a perfect-square trinomial.

To see geometrically why completing the square works on $x^2 + 10x$, we refer to Figure 10-1(a), which shows a polygon with an area of $x^2 + 10x$. To turn the polygon into a square, we can divide the area of $10x$ into two areas of $5x$ and then reassemble the polygon as shown in Figure 10-1(b). To fill in the missing corner, we must add a square with an area of $5^2 = 25$. Thus, we complete the square.

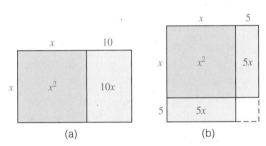

Figure 10-1

To solve an equation of the form $ax^2 + bx + c = 0$ $(a \neq 0)$ by completing the square, we use the following steps.

Completing the Square

1. Make sure that the coefficient of x^2 is 1. If it isn't, make it 1 by dividing both sides of the equation by the coefficient of x^2.

2. If necessary, add a number to both sides of the equation to place the constant term on the right side of the equal sign.

3. Complete the square:

    a. Find one-half of the coefficient of x and square it.

    b. Add the square to both sides of the equation.

4. Factor the trinomial square on one side of the equation and combine like terms on the other side.

5. Solve the resulting equation by using the square-root property.

EXAMPLE 7 Solve $x^2 + 8x + 7 = 0$ by completing the square.

Solution **Step 1** In this example, the coefficient of x^2 is already 1.

Step 2 We add -7 to both sides to place the constant on the right side of the equal sign:

$$x^2 + 8x + 7 = 0$$
$$x^2 + 8x = -7$$

Step 3 The coefficient of x is 8, one-half of 8 is 4, and $4^2 = 16$. To complete the square, we add 16 to both sides.

$$x^2 + 8x + 16 = -7 + 16$$

Step 4 Since the left side of the above equation is a perfect-square trinomial, we can factor it to get $(x + 4)^2$ and simplify on the right side to obtain

$$(x + 4)^2 = 9$$

Step 5 We can then solve the resulting equation by using the square-root property.

$$(x + 4)^2 = 9$$
$$x + 4 = \sqrt{9} \quad \text{or} \quad x + 4 = -\sqrt{9}$$
$$x + 4 = 3 \qquad\qquad x + 4 = -3$$
$$x = -1 \qquad\qquad x = -7$$

After checking both results, we see that the solutions are -1 and -7. Note that this equation could be solved by factoring.

⇨ **SELF CHECK 7** Solve $a^2 + 5a + 4 = 0$ by completing the square.

EXAMPLE 8 Solve $6x^2 + 5x - 6 = 0$ by completing the square.

Solution **Step 1** To make the coefficient of x^2 equal to 1, we divide both sides by 6.

$$6x^2 + 5x - 6 = 0$$
$$\frac{6x^2}{6} + \frac{5}{6}x - \frac{6}{6} = \frac{0}{6} \quad \text{Divide both sides by 6.}$$
$$x^2 + \frac{5}{6}x - 1 = 0 \quad \text{Simplify.}$$

Step 2 We add 1 to both sides to place the constant on the right side.

$$x^2 + \frac{5}{6}x = 1$$

Step 3 The coefficient of x is $\frac{5}{6}$, one-half of $\frac{5}{6}$ is $\frac{5}{12}$, and $\left(\frac{5}{12}\right)^2 = \frac{25}{144}$. To complete the square, we add $\frac{25}{144}$ to both sides.

$$x^2 + \frac{5}{6}x + \frac{25}{144} = 1 + \frac{25}{144}$$

Step 4 Since the left side of the above equation is a perfect-square trinomial, we can factor it to get $\left(x + \frac{5}{12}\right)^2$ and simplify the right side to obtain

$$\left(x + \frac{5}{12}\right)^2 = \frac{169}{144} \qquad 1 + \frac{25}{144} = \frac{144}{144} + \frac{25}{144} = \frac{169}{144}$$

Step 5 We can solve this equation by using the square-root property.

$$x + \frac{5}{12} = \sqrt{\frac{169}{144}} \qquad \text{or} \quad x + \frac{5}{12} = -\sqrt{\frac{169}{144}} \qquad \text{Apply the square-root property.}$$

$$x + \frac{5}{12} = \frac{13}{12} \qquad\qquad x + \frac{5}{12} = -\frac{13}{12} \qquad \sqrt{\frac{169}{144}} = \frac{13}{12}$$

$$x = -\frac{5}{12} + \frac{13}{12} \qquad\qquad x = -\frac{5}{12} - \frac{13}{12} \qquad \text{Subtract } \frac{5}{12} \text{ from both sides.}$$

$$x = \frac{8}{12} \qquad\qquad\qquad x = -\frac{18}{12} \qquad \text{Add.}$$

$$x = \frac{2}{3} \qquad\qquad\qquad x = -\frac{3}{2} \qquad \text{Simplify each fraction.}$$

After checking both results, we see that the solutions are $\frac{2}{3}$ and $-\frac{3}{2}$. Note that this equation could be solved by factoring.

➡ **SELF CHECK 8** Solve $6p^2 - 5p - 6 = 0$ by completing the square.

EXAMPLE 9 Solve $2x^2 + 4x + 1 = 0$ by completing the square.

Solution

$$2x^2 + 4x + 1 = 0$$

$$x^2 + 2x + \frac{1}{2} = \frac{0}{2} \qquad \text{Divide both sides by 2 to make the coefficient of } x^2 \text{ equal to 1.}$$

$$x^2 + 2x = -\frac{1}{2} \qquad \text{Subtract } \frac{1}{2} \text{ from both sides.}$$

$$x^2 + 2x + 1 = -\frac{1}{2} + 1 \qquad \text{Square half the coefficient of } x \text{ and add it to both sides.}$$

$$(x + 1)^2 = \frac{1}{2} \qquad \text{Factor on one side and combine like terms on the other.}$$

$$x + 1 = \sqrt{\frac{1}{2}} \qquad \text{or} \quad x + 1 = -\sqrt{\frac{1}{2}} \qquad \text{Use the square-root property.}$$

COMMENT Note that $-1 \pm \frac{\sqrt{2}}{2}$ can be written as

$$-1 \pm \frac{\sqrt{2}}{2} = \frac{-2}{2} \pm \frac{\sqrt{2}}{2}$$

$$= \frac{-2 \pm \sqrt{2}}{2}$$

$$x + 1 = \frac{\sqrt{2}}{2} \qquad\qquad x + 1 = -\frac{\sqrt{2}}{2} \qquad \sqrt{\frac{1}{2}} = \frac{1}{\sqrt{2}} = \frac{1 \cdot \sqrt{2}}{\sqrt{2}\sqrt{2}} = \frac{\sqrt{2}}{2}$$

$$x = -1 + \frac{\sqrt{2}}{2} \qquad\qquad x = -1 - \frac{\sqrt{2}}{2}$$

These solutions can be written as $-1 \pm \frac{\sqrt{2}}{2}$.

➡ **SELF CHECK 9** Solve $3x^2 + 6x + 1 = 0$ by completing the square.

ACCENT ON TECHNOLOGY

Checking Solutions of Quadratic Equations

We can use a graphing calculator to check the solutions of the equation $2x^2 + 4x + 1 = 0$ found in Example 9. Using a TI-84 Plus calculator, we first find the decimal value of $-1 + \dfrac{\sqrt{2}}{2}$ by pressing these keys:

(−1 + **2ND** √ 2) ÷ 2) **ENTER**

We will obtain the screen shown in Figure 10-2(a). We can now store this decimal value in the calculator by pressing these keys:

STO **X, T, θ, n** **ENTER**   *X, T, θ, n* is one key.

Finally, we enter $2x^2 + 4x + 1$ by pressing

2 **X, T, θ, n** ∧ 2 + 4 **X, T, θ, n** + 1

After pressing **ENTER** one more time, we will obtain the screen shown in Figure 10-2(b). The 0 on the screen confirms that $-1 + \dfrac{\sqrt{2}}{2}$ satisfies the equation $2x^2 + 4x + 1 = 0$ and is a solution.

We can check the other solution in a similar way.

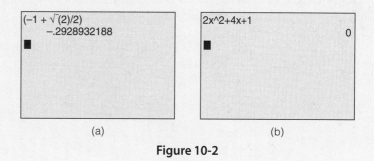

(a)   (b)

Figure 10-2

In the next example, the solutions are complex numbers.

EXAMPLE 10   Solve $3x^2 + 2x + 2 = 0$ by completing the square.

Solution

$$3x^2 + 2x + 2 = 0$$

$$x^2 + \frac{2}{3}x + \frac{2}{3} = \frac{0}{3}$$ Divide both sides by 3 to make the coefficient of x^2 equal to 1.

$$x^2 + \frac{2}{3}x = -\frac{2}{3}$$ Subtract $\frac{2}{3}$ from both sides.

$$x^2 + \frac{2}{3}x + \frac{1}{9} = -\frac{2}{3} + \frac{1}{9}$$ Square half the coefficient of x and add it to both sides.

$$\left(x + \frac{1}{3}\right)^2 = -\frac{5}{9}$$ Factor on one side and combine terms on the other: $\frac{1}{9} - \frac{2}{3} = \frac{1}{9} - \frac{6}{9} = -\frac{5}{9}$.

$$x + \frac{1}{3} = \sqrt{-\frac{5}{9}} \quad \text{or} \quad x + \frac{1}{3} = -\sqrt{-\frac{5}{9}}$$ Use the square-root property.

$$x + \frac{1}{3} = \sqrt{\frac{5}{9}}\sqrt{-1} \quad\quad x + \frac{1}{3} = -\sqrt{\frac{5}{9}}\sqrt{-1}$$ $\sqrt{-\frac{5}{9}} = \sqrt{\frac{5}{9}(-1)} = \sqrt{\frac{5}{9}}\sqrt{-1}$

$$x + \frac{1}{3} = \frac{\sqrt{5}}{3}i \qquad \left| \qquad x + \frac{1}{3} = -\frac{\sqrt{5}}{3}i \qquad \sqrt{\frac{5}{9}} = \frac{\sqrt{5}}{\sqrt{9}} = \frac{\sqrt{5}}{3} \right.$$

$$x = -\frac{1}{3} + \frac{\sqrt{5}}{3}i \qquad \left| \qquad x = -\frac{1}{3} - \frac{\sqrt{5}}{3}i \qquad \text{Subtract } \frac{1}{3} \text{ from both sides.} \right.$$

These solutions can be written as $x = -\frac{1}{3} \pm \frac{\sqrt{5}}{3}i$.

⇨ **SELF CHECK 10**   Solve $x^2 + 4x + 6 = 0$ by completing the square.

---

4   **Solve an application problem requiring the use of the square-root property.**

Many application problems involving equations containing squared terms can be solved using the square-root property.

EXAMPLE 11   **DVDs**   A DVD used for recording movies has a surface area of 17.72 square inches on one side. Find the radius of a disc.

Solution   The formula for the area of a circular disc is $A = \pi r^2$. We can find the radius of a disc by substituting 17.72 for A and solving for r.

$$A = \pi r^2$$
$$\mathbf{17.72} = \pi r^2 \qquad \text{Substitute 17.72 for } A.$$
$$\frac{17.72}{\pi} = r^2 \qquad \text{Divide both sides by } \pi.$$
$$r = \sqrt{\frac{17.72}{\pi}} \quad \text{or} \quad r = -\sqrt{\frac{17.72}{\pi}} \qquad \text{Use the square-root property.}$$

Since the radius of a disc cannot be negative, we will discard the negative result. Thus, the radius of a disc is $\sqrt{\frac{17.72}{\pi}}$ inches or, to the nearest hundredth, 2.37 inches.

When you deposit money in a bank account, it earns interest. If you leave the money in the account, the earned interest is deposited back into the account and also earns interest. When this is the case, the account is earning *compound interest*. There is a formula we can use to compute the amount in an account at any time t.

Formula for Compound Interest   If P dollars is deposited in an account and interest is paid once a year at an annual rate r, the amount A in the account after t years is given by the formula

$$A = P(1 + r)^t$$

EXAMPLE 12   **SAVING MONEY**   A woman invests $10,000 in an account. Find the annual interest rate if the account will be worth $11,025 in 2 years.

Solution   We substitute 11,025 for A, 10,000 for P, and 2 for t in the compound interest formula and solve for r.

$$A = P(1 + r)^t$$

$$11{,}025 = 10{,}000(1 + r)^2 \qquad \text{Substitute.}$$

$$\frac{11{,}025}{10{,}000} = (1 + r)^2 \qquad \text{Divide both sides by 10,000.}$$

$$1.1025 = (1 + r)^2 \qquad \frac{11{,}025}{10{,}000} = 1.1025$$

$$1 + r = 1.05 \quad \text{or} \quad 1 + r = -1.05 \qquad \text{Use the square-root property: } \sqrt{1.1025} = 1.05.$$

$$r = 0.05 \quad | \quad\quad r = -2.05 \qquad \text{Subtract 1 from both sides.}$$

Since an interest rate cannot be negative, we must discard the result of -2.05. Thus, the annual interest rate is 0.05, or 5%.

We can check this result by substituting 0.05 for r, 10,000 for P, and 2 for t in the formula and confirming that the deposit of $10,000 will grow to $11,025 in 2 years.

$$A = P(1 + r)^t = 10{,}000(1 + 0.05)^2 = 10{,}000(1.1025) = 11{,}025$$

⇨ **SELF CHECK ANSWERS**   **1.** $8, -8$ **2.** $\frac{1}{3}, \frac{1}{2}$ **3.** $\pm 3\sqrt{2}$ **4.** $1, -5$ **5.** $\pm 3i$ **6.** $\frac{25}{4}$ **7.** $-1, -4$ **8.** $-\frac{2}{3}, \frac{3}{2}$
9. $-1 \pm \frac{\sqrt{6}}{3}$ **10.** $-2 \pm i\sqrt{2}$

NOW TRY THIS

1. Solve using the square-root property.
   a. $(3x + 5)^2 = 18$

   b. $(x + 6)^2 = 0$

2. Solve $x^2 - 2\sqrt{2}x + 1 = 0$ by completing the square.

10.1 EXERCISES

WARM-UPS

Solve each equation.

1. $x^2 = 49$

2. $x^2 = 10$

Find the number that when added to the binomial will make it a perfect-square trinomial.

3. $x^2 + 4x$

4. $x^2 - 6x$

5. $x^2 - 3x$

6. $x^2 + 5x$

REVIEW   *Solve each equation or inequality.*

7. $\dfrac{t + 9}{2} + \dfrac{t + 2}{5} = \dfrac{8}{5} + 4t$

8. $\dfrac{1 - 5x}{2x} + 4 = \dfrac{x + 3}{x}$

9. $3(t - 3) + 3t \le 2(t + 1) + t + 1$

10. $-2(y + 4) - 3y + 8 \ge 3(2y - 3) - y$

VOCABULARY AND CONCEPTS   *Fill in the blanks.*

11. The square-root property states that the solutions of $x^2 = c$ are _____ and _____.

12. To complete the square on x in $x^2 + 6x = 17$, find one-half of __, square it to get __, and add __ to both sides of the equation.

13. The symbol $\pm$ is read as _____.

14. The formula for annual compound interest is

_____.

GUIDED PRACTICE

Use factoring to solve each equation. See Examples 1–2.
(Objective 1)

15. $2y^2 - 50 = 0$

16. $4y^2 - 64 = 0$

17. $6x^2 + 12x = 0$

18. $5x^2 + 11x = 0$

19. $r^2 + 6r + 8 = 0$

20. $x^2 + 9x + 20 = 0$

21. $6s^2 + 11s - 10 = 0$

22. $3x^2 + 10x - 8 = 0$

Use the square-root property to solve each equation.
See Example 3. (Objective 2)

23. $x^2 = 36$

24. $x^2 = 144$

25. $z^2 = 5$

26. $u^2 = 24$

Use the square-root property to solve each equation.
See Example 4. (Objective 2)

27. $(y + 1)^2 = 1$

28. $(y - 1)^2 = 4$

29. $(x - 2)^2 - 5 = 0$

30. $(x - 5)^2 - 11 = 0$

Use the square-root property to solve each equation.
See Example 5. (Objective 2)

31. $p^2 + 16 = 0$

32. $q^2 + 25 = 0$

33. $4m^2 + 81 = 0$

34. $9n^2 + 121 = 0$

Use completing the square to solve each equation.
See Examples 6–7. (Objective 3)

35. $x^2 + 2x - 8 = 0$

36. $x^2 + 6x + 5 = 0$

37. $x^2 - 6x + 8 = 0$

38. $x^2 + 8x + 15 = 0$

39. $x^2 + 5x + 4 = 0$

40. $x^2 - 11x + 30 = 0$

41. $x^2 - 9x - 10 = 0$

42. $x^2 - 3x + 2 = 0$

Use completing the square to solve each equation. See Example 8.
(Objective 3)

43. $6x^2 + 11x + 3 = 0$

44. $6x^2 + x - 2 = 0$

45. $6x^2 - 7x - 5 = 0$

46. $4x^2 - x - 3 = 0$

47. $9 - 6r = 8r^2$

48. $11m - 10 = 3m^2$

49. $x + 1 = 2x^2$

50. $-2 = 2x^2 - 5x$

Use completing the square to solve each equation.
See Examples 9–10. (Objective 3)

51. $\dfrac{7x + 1}{5} = -x^2$

52. $\dfrac{3x^2}{8} = \dfrac{1}{8} - x$

53. $p^2 + 2p + 2 = 0$

54. $x^2 - 6x + 10 = 0$

55. $y^2 + 8y + 18 = 0$

56. $t^2 + t + 3 = 0$

57. $3m^2 - 2m + 3 = 0$

58. $4p^2 + 2p + 3 = 0$

ADDITIONAL PRACTICE

Solve using any method.

59. $7x - 6 = x^2$

60. $5t - 6 = t^2$

61. $3x^2 - 16 = 0$

62. $5x^2 - 49 = 0$

63. $(s - 7)^2 - 9 = 0$

64. $(t + 4)^2 = 16$

65. $(x + 5)^2 - 3 = 0$

66. $(x + 3)^2 - 7 = 0$

67. $2z^2 - 5z + 2 = 0$

68. $2x^2 - x - 1 = 0$

69. $3x^2 - 6x + 1 = 0$

70. $3x^2 + 9x + 5 = 0$

71. $2x^2 - x + 8 = 0$

72. $4x^2 + 2x + 5 = 0$

Solve for the indicated variable. Assume that all variables represent positive numbers. Express all radicals in simplified form.
See Example 11.

73. $2d^2 = 3h$ for d

74. $2x^2 = d^2$ for d

75. $E = mc^2$ for c

76. $S = \dfrac{1}{2}gt^2$ for t

Find all values of x that will make f(x) = 0.

77. $f(x) = 2x^2 + x - 5$

78. $f(x) = 3x^2 - 2x - 4$

79. $f(x) = x^2 + x - 3$

80. $f(x) = x^2 + 2x - 4$

APPLICATIONS   *Solve each application problem.*
See Examples 11–12. (Objective 4)

81. Falling objects   The distance s (in feet) that an object will fall in t seconds is given by the formula $s = 16t^2$. How long will it take an object to fall 256 feet?

82. Pendulums   The time (in seconds) it takes a pendulum to swing back and forth to complete one cycle is related to its length l (in feet) by the formula:

$$l = \dfrac{32t^2}{4\pi^2}$$

How long will it take a 5-foot pendulum to swing through one cycle? Give the result to the nearest hundredth.

83. Law enforcement   To estimate the speed s (in mph) of a car involved in an accident, police often use the formula $s^2 = 10.5l$, where l is the length of any skid mark. Approximately how fast was a car going that was involved in an accident and left skid marks of 495 feet?

84. Medicine   The approximate pulse rate (in beats per minute) of an adult who is t inches tall is given by the formula

$$p^2 = \frac{348,100}{t}$$

Find the pulse rate of an adult who is 64 inches tall.

85. Saving money   A student invests $8,500 in a savings account drawing interest that is compounded annually. Find the annual rate if the money grows to $9,193.60 in 2 years.

86. Saving money   A woman invests $12,500 in a savings account drawing interest that is compounded annually. Find the annual rate if the money grows to $14,045 in 2 years.

87. Flags   In 1912, an order by President Taft fixed the width and length of the U.S. flag in the ratio 1 to 1.9. If 100 square feet of cloth are to be used to make a U.S. flag, estimate its dimensions to the nearest $\frac{1}{4}$ foot.

88. Accidents   The height h (in feet) of an object that is dropped from a height of s feet is given by the formula $h = s - 16t^2$, where t is the time the object has been falling. A 5-foot-tall woman on a sidewalk looks directly overhead and sees a window washer drop a bottle from 4 stories up. How long does she have to get out of the way? Round to the nearest tenth. (A story is 10 feet.)

WRITING ABOUT MATH

89. Explain how to complete the square.

90. Explain why a cannot be 0 in the quadratic equation $ax^2 + bx + c = 0$.

SOMETHING TO THINK ABOUT

91. What number must be added to $x^2 + \sqrt{3}x$ to make it a perfect-square trinomial?

92. Solve $x^2 + \sqrt{3}x - \frac{1}{4} = 0$ by completing the square.

SECTION 10.2
Solving Quadratic Equations by the Quadratic Formula

Objectives

1. Solve a quadratic equation using the quadratic formula.
2. Solve a formula for a specified variable using the quadratic formula.
3. Solve an application problem involving a quadratic equation.

Vocabulary

quadratic formula

Add a number to each binomial to complete the square. Then write the resulting trinomial as the square of a binomial.

1. $x^2 + 12x$ **2.** $x^2 - 7x$

Evaluate $\sqrt{b^2 - 4ac}$ for the following values.

3. $a = 6, b = 1, c = -2$ **4.** $a = 4, b = -4, c = -3$

Solving quadratic equations by completing the square is often tedious. Fortunately, there is an easier way. In this section, we will develop a formula, called the **quadratic formula,** that we can use to solve quadratic equations with a minimum of effort. To develop this formula, we will use the skills we learned in the last section and complete the square.

1   **Solve a quadratic equation using the quadratic formula.**

To develop a formula to solve quadratic equations, we will solve the general quadratic equation $ax^2 + bx + c = 0$ $(a \neq 0)$ by completing the square.

$$ax^2 + bx + c = 0$$

$$\frac{ax^2}{a} + \frac{bx}{a} + \frac{c}{a} = \frac{0}{a} \qquad \text{To make the coefficient of } x^2 \text{ equal to 1, we divide both sides by } a.$$

$$x^2 + \frac{bx}{a} = -\frac{c}{a} \qquad \frac{0}{a} = 0; \text{ subtract } \frac{c}{a} \text{ from both sides.}$$

$$x^2 + \frac{bx}{a} + \left(\frac{b}{2a}\right)^2 = \left(\frac{b}{2a}\right)^2 - \frac{c}{a} \qquad \text{Complete the square on } x \text{ by adding } \left(\frac{b}{2a}\right)^2 \text{ to both sides.}$$

$$x^2 + \frac{b}{a}x + \frac{b^2}{4a^2} = \frac{b^2}{4a^2} - \frac{4ac}{4aa} \qquad \text{Remove parentheses and get a common denominator on the right side.}$$

$$\text{(1)} \qquad \left(x + \frac{b}{2a}\right)^2 = \frac{b^2 - 4ac}{4a^2} \qquad \text{Factor the left side and add the fractions on the right side.}$$

We can solve Equation 1 using the square-root property.

$$x + \frac{b}{2a} = \sqrt{\frac{b^2 - 4ac}{4a^2}} \qquad \text{or} \qquad x + \frac{b}{2a} = -\sqrt{\frac{b^2 - 4ac}{4a^2}}$$

$$x + \frac{b}{2a} = \frac{\sqrt{b^2 - 4ac}}{2a} \qquad\qquad\qquad x + \frac{b}{2a} = -\frac{\sqrt{b^2 - 4ac}}{2a}$$

$$x = -\frac{b}{2a} + \frac{\sqrt{b^2 - 4ac}}{2a} \qquad\qquad x = -\frac{b}{2a} - \frac{\sqrt{b^2 - 4ac}}{2a}$$

$$= \frac{-b + \sqrt{b^2 - 4ac}}{2a} \qquad\qquad\qquad = \frac{-b - \sqrt{b^2 - 4ac}}{2a}$$

These two solutions give the *quadratic formula.*

The Quadratic Formula   The solutions of $ax^2 + bx + c = 0$ $(a \neq 0)$ are given by the formula

$$x = \frac{-b \pm \sqrt{b^2 - 4ac}}{2a}$$

COMMENT   Be sure to draw the fraction bar under both parts of the numerator, and be sure to draw the radical sign exactly over $b^2 - 4ac$. Don't write the quadratic formula as

$$x = -b \pm \frac{\sqrt{b^2 - 4ac}}{2a} \qquad \text{or as} \qquad x = -b \pm \sqrt{\frac{b^2 - 4ac}{2a}}$$

EXAMPLE 1   Use the quadratic formula to solve $2x^2 - 3x - 5 = 0$.

Solution   In this equation $a = 2$, $b = -3$, and $c = -5$.

$$x = \frac{-b \pm \sqrt{b^2 - 4ac}}{2a}$$

$$= \frac{-(-3) \pm \sqrt{(-3)^2 - 4(2)(-5)}}{2(2)} \qquad \text{Substitute 2 for } a, -3 \text{ for } b, \text{ and } -5 \text{ for } c.$$

$$= \frac{3 \pm \sqrt{9 + 40}}{4} \qquad \text{Simplify.}$$

$$= \frac{3 \pm \sqrt{49}}{4} \qquad \text{Add.}$$

$$= \frac{3 \pm 7}{4} \qquad \text{Simplify the radical.}$$

$$x = \frac{3 + 7}{4} \quad \text{or} \quad x = \frac{3 - 7}{4}$$

$$x = \frac{10}{4} \qquad\qquad x = \frac{-4}{4}$$

$$x = \frac{5}{2} \qquad\qquad x = -1$$

After checking the results, we see that the solutions are $\frac{5}{2}$ and -1. Note that this equation can be solved by factoring.

⇨ **SELF CHECK 1**   Use the quadratic formula to solve $3x^2 - 5x - 2 = 0$.

EXAMPLE 2   Use the quadratic formula to solve $2x^2 + 1 = -4x$.

Solution   We begin by writing the equation in $ax^2 + bx + c = 0$ form (called *standard form*) before identifying a, b, and c.

$$2x^2 + 4x + 1 = 0$$

In this equation, $a = 2$, $b = 4$, and $c = 1$.

$$x = \frac{-b \pm \sqrt{b^2 - 4ac}}{2a}$$

$$= \frac{-4 \pm \sqrt{4^2 - 4(2)(1)}}{2(2)} \qquad \text{Substitute 2 for } a, 4 \text{ for } b, \text{ and } 1 \text{ for } c.$$

$$= \frac{-4 \pm \sqrt{16 - 8}}{4} \qquad \text{Simplify.}$$

$$= \frac{-4 \pm \sqrt{8}}{4} \qquad \text{Subtract.}$$

$$= \frac{-4 \pm 2\sqrt{2}}{4} \qquad \sqrt{8} = \sqrt{4 \cdot 2} = \sqrt{4}\sqrt{2} = 2\sqrt{2}$$

$$= \frac{-2 \pm \sqrt{2}}{2} \qquad \frac{-4 \pm 2\sqrt{2}}{4} = \frac{2(-2 \pm \sqrt{2})}{4} = \frac{-2 \pm \sqrt{2}}{2}$$

Note that these solutions can be written as $-1 \pm \frac{\sqrt{2}}{2}$.

⇨ **SELF CHECK 2** Use the quadratic formula to solve $3x^2 - 2x - 3 = 0$.

In the next example, the solutions are complex numbers.

EXAMPLE 3 Use the quadratic formula to solve $x^2 + x = -1$.

Solution We begin by writing the equation in standard form before identifying a, b, and c.

$$x^2 + x + 1 = 0$$

In this equation, $a = 1$, $b = 1$, and $c = 1$:

$$x = \frac{-b \pm \sqrt{b^2 - 4ac}}{2a}$$

$$= \frac{-1 \pm \sqrt{1^2 - 4(1)(1)}}{2(1)} \qquad \text{Substitute 1 for } a, 1 \text{ for } b, \text{ and 1 for } c.$$

$$= \frac{-1 \pm \sqrt{1 - 4}}{2} \qquad \text{Simplify the expression under the radical.}$$

PERSPECTIVE The Fibonacci Sequence and the Golden Ratio

Perhaps one of the most intriguing examples of how a mathematical idea can represent natural phenomena is the *Fibonacci Sequence,* a list of whole numbers that is generated by a very simple rule. This sequence was first developed by the Italian mathematician Leonardo da Pisa, more commonly known as Fibonacci. The Fibonacci Sequence is the following list of numbers

1, 1, 2, 3, 5, 8, 13, 21, . . .

where each successive number in the list is obtained by adding the two preceding numbers. Although Fibonacci originally developed this sequence to solve a mathematical puzzle, subsequent study of the numbers in this sequence has uncovered

many examples in the natural world in which this sequence emerges. For example, the arrangement of the seeds on the face of a sunflower, the hibernation periods of certain insects, and the branching patterns of many plants all give rise to Fibonacci numbers.

Among the many special properties of these numbers is the fact that, as we generate more and more numbers in the list, the ratio of successive numbers approaches a constant value. This value is designated by the symbol ϕ and often is referred to as the "Golden Ratio." One way to calculate the value of ϕ is to solve the quadratic equation $\phi^2 - \phi - 1 = 0$.

1. Using the quadratic formula, find the exact value of ϕ.

2. Using a calculator, find a decimal approximation of ϕ, correct to three decimal places.

$$= \frac{-1 \pm \sqrt{-3}}{2} \qquad \text{Subtract.}$$

$$= \frac{-1 \pm \sqrt{3}i}{2} \qquad \text{Simplify the radical expression.}$$

Note that these solutions can be written as $-\frac{1}{2} \pm \frac{\sqrt{3}}{2}i$.

⇨ **SELF CHECK 3**   Use the quadratic formula to solve $a^2 + 2a + 3 = 0$.

2 **Solve a formula for a specified variable using the quadratic formula.**

EXAMPLE 4   An object thrown straight up with an initial velocity of v_0 feet per second will reach a height of s feet in t seconds according to the formula $s = -16t^2 + v_0t$. Solve the formula for t.

Solution   We begin by writing the equation in standard form:

$$s = -16t^2 + v_0t$$
$$16t^2 - v_0t + s = 0$$

In this equation, $a = 6$, $b = -v_0$, and $c = s$. Then we can use the quadratic formula to solve for t.

$$t = \frac{-b \pm \sqrt{b^2 - 4ac}}{2a}$$

$$t = \frac{-(-v_0) \pm \sqrt{(-v_0)^2 - 4(16)(s)}}{2(16)} \qquad \text{Substitute into the quadratic formula.}$$

$$t = \frac{v_0 \pm \sqrt{v_0^2 - 64s}}{32} \qquad \text{Simplify.}$$

Thus, $t = \frac{v_0 \pm \sqrt{v_0^2 - 64s}}{32}$.

3 **Solve an application problem involving a quadratic equation.**

EXAMPLE 5   **DIMENSIONS OF A RECTANGLE**   Find the dimensions of the rectangle shown in Figure 10-3, given that its area is 253 cm².

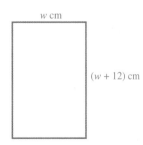

w cm

$(w + 12)$ cm

Figure 10-3

Solution If we let w represent the width of the rectangle, then $w + 12$ represents its length. Since the area of the rectangle is 253 square centimeters, we can form the equation

$$w(w + 12) = 253 \quad \text{Area of a rectangle = width} \cdot \text{length.}$$

and solve it as follows:

$$w(w + 12) = 253$$
$$w^2 + 12w = 253 \quad \text{Use the distributive property to remove parentheses.}$$
$$w^2 + 12w - 253 = 0 \quad \text{Subtract 253 from both sides.}$$

Solution by factoring	*Solution by formula*

Solution by factoring

$$(w - 11)(w + 23) = 0$$
$$w - 11 = 0 \quad \text{or} \quad w + 23 = 0$$
$$w = 11 \quad | \quad w = -23$$

Solution by formula

$$w = \frac{-12 \pm \sqrt{12^2 - 4(1)(-253)}}{2(1)}$$
$$= \frac{-12 \pm \sqrt{144 + 1{,}012}}{2}$$
$$= \frac{-12 \pm \sqrt{1{,}156}}{2}$$
$$= \frac{-12 \pm 34}{2}$$
$$w = 11 \quad \text{or} \quad w = -23$$

Since the rectangle cannot have a negative width, we discard the solution of -23. Thus, the only solution is $w = 11$. Since the rectangle is 11 centimeters wide and $(11 + 12)$ centimeters long, its dimensions are 11 centimeters by 23 centimeters.

Check: 23 is 12 more than 11, and the area of a rectangle with dimensions of 23 centimeters by 11 centimeters is 253 square centimeters.

⇨ **SELF CHECK ANSWERS** **1.** $2, -\frac{1}{3}$ **2.** $\frac{1}{3} \pm \frac{\sqrt{10}}{3}$ **3.** $-1 \pm i\sqrt{2}$

NOW TRY THIS

1. The length of a rectangular garden is 1 ft less than 3 times the width. If the area is 44 sq ft, find the length of the garden.

2. The product of 2 consecutive integers is 90. Find the numbers. (Consecutive means one after another.)

3. Solve $x^3 - 8 = 0$. (*Hint:* Recall how to factor the difference of cubes.)

4. Graph $y = x^3 - 8$ and identify the x-intercept(s).

10.2 EXERCISES

WARM-UPS *Identify a, b, and c in each quadratic equation.*

1. $3x^2 - 4x + 7 = 0$

2. $-2x^2 + x = 5$

REVIEW

Solve for the indicated variable.

3. $Ax + By = C$ for y

4. $R = \dfrac{kL}{d^2}$ for L

Simplify each radical.

5. $\sqrt{24}$

6. $\sqrt{288}$

7. $\dfrac{3}{\sqrt{3}}$

8. $\dfrac{1}{2 - \sqrt{3}}$

VOCABULARY AND CONCEPTS *Fill in the blanks.*

9. In the quadratic equation $3x^2 - 2x + 6 = 0$, $a =$ ___, $b =$ ___, and $c =$ ___.

10. The solutions of $ax^2 + bx + c = 0$ $(a \neq 0)$ are given by the quadratic formula, which is $x =$ _____.

GUIDED PRACTICE

Solve each equation using the quadratic formula. **See Example 1.** (Objective 1)

11. $x^2 + 3x + 2 = 0$

12. $x^2 - 3x + 2 = 0$

13. $x^2 - 2x - 15 = 0$

14. $x^2 - 2x - 35 = 0$

15. $x^2 + 12x = -36$

16. $y^2 - 18y = -81$

17. $2x^2 - x - 3 = 0$

18. $3x^2 - 10x + 8 = 0$

Solve each equation using the quadratic formula. **See Example 2.** (Objective 1)

19. $15x^2 - 14x = 8$

20. $4x^2 = -5x + 6$

21. $8u = -4u^2 - 3$

22. $4t + 3 = 4t^2$

23. $16y^2 + 8y - 3 = 0$

24. $16x^2 + 16x + 3 = 0$

25. $5x^2 + 5x + 1 = 0$

26. $4w^2 + 6w + 1 = 0$

Solve each equation using the quadratic formula. **See Example 3.** (Objective 1)

27. $x^2 + 2x + 2 = 0$

28. $x^2 + 3x + 3 = 0$

29. $2x^2 + x + 1 = 0$

30. $3x^2 + 2x + 1 = 0$

31. $3x^2 - 4x = -2$

32. $2x^2 + 3x = -3$

33. $3x^2 - 2x = -3$

34. $5x^2 = 2x - 1$

Solve each formula for the indicated variable. **See Example 4.** (Objective 2)

35. $C = \dfrac{N^2 - N}{2}$, for n

(The formula for a selection sort in data processing)

36. $A = 2\pi r^2 + 2\pi hr$, for r

(The formula for the surface area of a right circular-cylinder)

37. $x^2 - kx = -ay$ for x

38. $xy^2 + 3xy + 7 = 0$ for y

ADDITIONAL PRACTICE

Solve each equation using any method.

39. $6x^2 - x - 1 = 0$

40. $2x^2 + 5x - 3 = 0$

41. $\dfrac{x^2}{2} + \dfrac{5}{2}x = -1$

42. $-3x = \dfrac{x^2}{2} + 2$

43. $2x^2 - 1 = 3x$

44. $-9x = 2 - 3x^2$

Find all x-values that will make f(x) = 0.

45. $f(x) = 4x^2 + 4x - 19$

46. $f(x) = 9x^2 + 12x - 8$

47. $f(x) = 3x^2 + 2x + 2$

48. $f(x) = 4x^2 + x + 1$

Use the quadratic formula and a calculator to solve each equation. Give all answers to the nearest hundredth.

49. $0.7x^2 - 3.5x - 25 = 0$

50. $-4.5x^2 + 0.2x + 3.75 = 0$

Note that a and b are the solutions to the equation
$(x - a)(x - b) = 0.$

51. Find a quadratic equation that has a solution set of {3, 5}.

52. Find a quadratic equation that has a solution set of {−4, 6}.

53. Find a third-degree equation that has a solution set of {2, 3, −4}.

54. Find a fourth-degree equation that has a solution set of {3, −3, 4, −4}.

APPLICATIONS

Solve each problem. **See Example 5. (Objective 3)**

55. Dimensions of a rectangle
The rectangle has an area of 96 square feet. Find its dimensions.

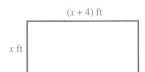
$(x + 4)$ ft
x ft

56. Dimensions of a window The area of the window is 77 square feet. Find its dimensions.

$(2x - 3)$ ft
x ft

57. Side of a square The area of a square is numerically equal to its perimeter. Find the length of each side of the square.

58. Perimeter of a rectangle A rectangle is 2 inches longer than it is wide. Numerically, its area exceeds its perimeter by 11. Find the perimeter.

Solve each problem.

59. Base of a triangle The height of a triangle is 5 centimeters longer than three times its base. Find the base of the triangle if its area is 6 square centimeters.

60. Height of a triangle The height of a triangle is 4 meters longer than twice its base. Find the height if the area of the triangle is 15 square meters.

61. Integer problem The product of two consecutive even integers is 288. Find the integers. (*Hint:* If one even integer is x, the next consecutive even integer is $x + 2$.)

62. Integer problem The product of two consecutive odd integers is 143. Find the integers. (*Hint:* If one odd integer is x, the next consecutive odd integer is $x + 2$.)

63. Integer problem The sum of the squares of two consecutive integers is 85. Find the integers. (*Hint:* If one integer is x, the next consecutive positive integer is $x + 1$.)

64. Integer problem The sum of the squares of three consecutive integers is 77. Find the integers. (*Hint:* If one integer is x, the next consecutive positive integer is $x + 1$, and the third is $x + 2$.)

65. Finding rates A woman drives her snowmobile 150 miles at the rate of r mph. She could have gone the same distance in 2 hours less time if she had increased her speed by 20 mph. Find r.

66. Finding rates Jeff bicycles 160 miles at the rate of r mph. The same trip would have taken 2 hours longer if he had decreased his speed by 4 mph. Find r.

67. Pricing concert tickets Tickets to a concert cost $4, and the projected attendance is 300 people. It is further projected that for every 10¢ increase in ticket price, the average attendance will decrease by 5. At what ticket price will the nightly receipts be $1,248?

68. Setting bus fares A bus company has 3,000 passengers daily, paying a $1.25 fare. For each 25¢ increase in fare, the company estimates that it will lose 80 passengers. What is the smallest increase in fare that will produce a $4,970 daily revenue?

69. Computing profit The *Gazette's* profit is $20 per year for each of its 3,000 subscribers. Management estimates that the profit per subscriber will increase by 1¢ for each additional subscriber over the current 3,000. How many subscribers will bring a total profit of $120,000?

70. Finding interest rates A woman invests $1,000 in a mutual fund for which interest is compounded annually at a rate r. After one year, she deposits an additional $2,000. After two years, the balance A in the account is

$$A = \$1{,}000(1 + r)^2 + \$2{,}000(1 + r)$$

If this amount is $3,368.10, find r.

71. Framing a picture The frame around the picture in the illustration has a constant width. To the nearest hundredth, how wide is the frame if its area equals the area of the picture?

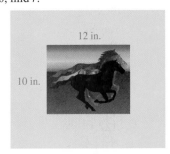
12 in.
10 in.

72. Metal fabrication A box with no top is to be made by cutting a 2-inch square from each corner of the square sheet of metal shown in the illustration. After bending up the sides, the volume of the box is to be 200 cubic inches. How large should the piece of metal be?

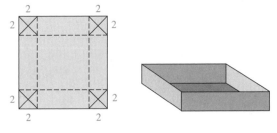

⌨ *Use a calculator.*

73. Labor force   The labor force participation rate P (in percent) for workers ages 16 and older from 1966 to 2008 is approximated by the quadratic equation

$$P = -0.0072x^2 + 0.4904x + 58.2714$$

where $x = 0$ corresponds to the year 1966, $x = 1$ corresponds to 1967, and so on. (Thus, $0 \le x \le 42$.) In what year in this range were 65% of the workers ages 16 and older part of the workforce?

74. Space program   The yearly budget B (in billions of dollars) for the National Aeronautics and Space Administration (NASA) is approximated by the quadratic equation

$$B = 0.0518x^2 - 0.2122x + 14.1112$$

where x is the number of years since 1997 and $0 \le x \le 12$. In what year does the model indicate that NASA's budget was about $17 billion?

75. Chemistry   A weak acid (0.1 M concentration) breaks down into free cations (the hydrogen ion, H^+) and anions (A^-). When this acid dissociates, the following equilibrium equation is established:

$$\frac{[H^+][A^-]}{[HA]} = 4 \times 10^{-4}$$

where $[H^+]$, the hydrogen ion concentration, is equal to $[A^-]$, the anion concentration. $[HA]$ is the concentration of the undissociated acid itself. Find $[H^+]$ at equilibrium. (*Hint:* If $[H^+] = x$, then $[HA] = 0.1 - x$.)

76. Chemistry   A saturated solution of hydrogen sulfide (0.1 M concentration) dissociates into cation $[H^+]$ and anion $[HS^-]$, where $[H^+] = [HS^-]$. When this solution dissociates, the following equilibrium equation is established:

$$\frac{[H^+][HS^-]}{[HHS]} = 1.0 \times 10^{-7}$$

Find $[H^+]$.   (*Hint:* If $[H^+] = x$, then $[HHS] = 0.1 - x$.)

WRITING ABOUT MATH

77. Explain why $x = -b \pm \dfrac{\sqrt{b^2 - 4ac}}{2a}$ is not a correct statement of the quadratic formula.

78. Explain why $x = \dfrac{b \pm \sqrt{b^2 - 4ac}}{2a}$ is not a correct statement of the quadratic formula.

SOMETHING TO THINK ABOUT   *All of the equations we have solved so far have had rational-number coefficients. However, the quadratic formula can be used to solve quadratic equations with irrational or even imaginary coefficients. Try solving each of the following equations.*

79. $x^2 + 2\sqrt{2}x - 6 = 0$ **80.** $\sqrt{2}x^2 + x - \sqrt{2} = 0$

81. $x^2 - 3ix - 2 = 0$ **82.** $ix^2 + 3x - 2i = 0$

SECTION 10.3

The Discriminant and Equations That Can Be Written in Quadratic Form

Objectives

1 Use the discriminant to determine the type of solutions to a given quadratic equation.

2 Solve an equation that can be written in quadratic form.

3 Verify the solutions of a quadratic equation by showing that the sum of the solutions is $-\frac{b}{a}$ and the product is $\frac{c}{a}$.

Vocabulary

discriminant

Evaluate $b^2 - 4ac$ for the following values.

1. $a = 2, b = 3$, and $c = -1$ **2.** $a = -2, b = 4$, and $c = -3$

We can use part of the quadratic formula to predict the type of solutions, if any, that a quadratic equation will have. We don't even have to solve the equation.

1 Use the discriminant to determine the type of solutions to a given quadratic equation.

Suppose that the coefficients a, b, and c in the equation $ax^2 + bx + c = 0$ $(a \neq 0)$ are real numbers. Then the solutions of the equation are given by the quadratic formula

$$x = \frac{-b \pm \sqrt{b^2 - 4ac}}{2a} \quad (a \neq 0)$$

If $b^2 - 4ac \geq 0$, the solutions are real numbers. If $b^2 - 4ac < 0$, the solutions are nonreal complex numbers. Thus, the value of $b^2 - 4ac$, called the **discriminant,** determines the type of solutions for a particular quadratic equation.

The Discriminant

If $ax^2 + bx + c = 0$ $(a \neq 0)$ and if a, b, and c are real numbers, then

$b^2 - 4ac > 0$, there are two unequal real solutions.

$b^2 - 4ac = 0$, there are two equal real solutions (called a *double root*).

$b^2 - 4ac < 0$, the solutions are complex conjugates.

If a, b, and c are rational numbers and the discriminant

is a perfect square greater than 0, there are two unequal rational solutions.

is positive but not a perfect square, the solutions are irrational and unequal.

EXAMPLE 1   Determine the type of solutions for the equations.
a. $x^2 + x + 1 = 0$ **b.** $3x^2 + 5x + 2 = 0$

Solution   **a.** We calculate the discriminant for $x^2 + x + 1 = 0$.

$$b^2 - 4ac = 1^2 - 4(1)(1) \quad a = 1, b = 1, \text{ and } c = 1.$$
$$= -3$$

Since $b^2 - 4ac < 0$, the solutions will be complex conjugates.

b. We calculate the discriminant for $3x^2 + 5x + 2 = 0$.

$$b^2 - 4ac = 5^2 - 4(3)(2) \quad a = 3, b = 5, \text{ and } c = 2.$$
$$= 25 - 24$$
$$= 1$$

Since $b^2 - 4ac > 0$ and $b^2 - 4ac$ is a perfect square, there will be two unequal rational solutions.

⇨ **SELF CHECK 1**   Determine the type of solutions.
a. $x^2 + x - 1 = 0$
b. $4x^2 - 10x + 25 = 0$

EXAMPLE 2   What value of k will make the solutions of the equation $kx^2 - 12x + 9 = 0$ equal?

Solution   We calculate the discriminant:

$$b^2 - 4ac = (-12)^2 - 4(k)(9) \qquad a = k, b = -12, \text{ and } c = 9.$$
$$= 144 - 36k$$
$$= -36k + 144$$

Since the solutions are to be equal, we let $-36k + 144 = 0$ and solve for k.

$$-36k + 144 = 0$$
$$-36k = -144 \qquad \text{Subtract 144 from both sides.}$$
$$k = 4 \qquad \text{Divide both sides by } -36.$$

If $k = 4$, the solutions will be equal. Verify this by solving $4x^2 - 12x + 9 = 0$ and showing that the solutions are equal.

⇨ **SELF CHECK 2**   Find the value of k will make the solutions of $kx^2 - 20x + 25 = 0$ equal.

2   **Solve an equation that can be written in quadratic form.**

Many equations that are not quadratic can be written in quadratic form $(ax^2 + bx + c = 0)$ and then solved using the techniques discussed in previous sections. For example, an inspection of the equation $x^4 - 5x^2 + 4 = 0$ shows that

The leading term x^4 is the square of x^2, the variable part of the middle term:

$$x^4 = (x^2)^2$$

$$x^4 - 5x^2 + 4 = 0$$

The last term is a constant.

To solve the equation $x^4 - 5x^2 + 4 = 0$, we can write the equation in a different form and proceed as follows:

$$x^4 - 5x^2 + 4 = 0$$
$$(x^2)^2 - 5(x^2) + 4 = 0$$

If we replace each x^2 with u, we will obtain a quadratic equation with the variable u that we can solve by factoring.

$$u^2 - 5u + 4 = 0 \qquad \text{Let } x^2 = u.$$
$$(u - 4)(u - 1) = 0 \qquad \text{Factor } u^2 - 5u + 4.$$
$$u - 4 = 0 \quad \text{or} \quad u - 1 = 0 \qquad \text{Set each factor equal to 0.}$$
$$u = 4 \qquad \qquad u = 1$$

Since $u = x^2$, it follows that $x^2 = 4$ or $x^2 = 1$. Thus,

$$x^2 = 4 \qquad \text{or} \qquad x^2 = 1$$
$$x = 2 \quad \text{or} \quad x = -2 \qquad \qquad x = 1 \quad \text{or} \quad x = -1$$

This equation has four solutions: 1, -1, 2, and -2. Verify that each one satisfies the original equation. Note that this equation can be solved by factoring.

EXAMPLE 3   Solve: $x - 7\sqrt{x} + 12 = 0$.

Solution   We examine the leading term and middle term.

The leading term x is the
square of $\sqrt{x}$, the variable $x - 7\sqrt{x} + 12 = 0$
part of the middle term:

$$x = \left(\sqrt{x}\right)^2$$

If we write x as $\left(\sqrt{x}\right)^2$, the equation takes the form

$$\left(\sqrt{x}\right)^2 - 7\sqrt{x} + 12 = 0$$

and it is said to be *quadratic in* $\sqrt{x}$. We can solve this equation by letting $\sqrt{x} = u$ and factoring.

$$u^2 - 7u + 12 = 0 \qquad \text{Replace each } \sqrt{x} \text{ with } u.$$
$$(u - 3)(u - 4) = 0 \qquad \text{Factor } u^2 - 7u + 12.$$
$$u - 3 = 0 \quad \text{or} \quad u - 4 = 0 \quad \text{Set each factor equal to 0.}$$
$$u = 3 \qquad \qquad u = 4$$

To find x, we undo the substitutions by replacing each u with $\sqrt{x}$. Then we solve the radical equations by squaring both sides.

$$\sqrt{x} = 3 \quad \text{or} \quad \sqrt{x} = 4$$
$$x = 9 \qquad \qquad x = 16$$

The solutions are 9 and 16. Verify that both satisfy the original equation.

⇨ **SELF CHECK 3**   Solve: $x + \sqrt{x} - 6 = 0$.

EXAMPLE 4   Solve: $2m^{2/3} - 2 = 3m^{1/3}$.

Solution   First we subtract $3m^{1/3}$ from both sides to write the equation in the form

$$2m^{2/3} - 3m^{1/3} - 2 = 0$$

Then we write the equation in the form

$$2(m^{1/3})^2 - 3m^{1/3} - 2 = 0 \quad (m^{1/3})^2 = m^{2/3}$$

If we substitute u for $m^{1/3}$, this equation can be written in a form that can be solved by factoring.

$$2u^2 - 3u - 2 = 0 \qquad \text{Replace each } m^{1/3} \text{ with } u.$$
$$(2u + 1)(u - 2) = 0 \qquad \text{Factor } 2u^2 - 3u - 2.$$

$$2u + 1 = 0 \quad \text{or} \quad u - 2 = 0 \qquad \text{Set each factor equal to 0.}$$

$$u = -\frac{1}{2} \qquad\qquad u = 2$$

To find m, we undo the substitutions by replacing each u with $m^{1/3}$ and solve each resulting equation by cubing both sides.

$$m^{1/3} = -\frac{1}{2} \quad \text{or} \quad m^{1/3} = 2$$

$$(m^{1/3})^3 = \left(-\frac{1}{2}\right)^3 \qquad (m^{1/3})^3 = (2)^3 \qquad \text{Cube both sides.}$$

$$m = -\frac{1}{8} \qquad\qquad m = 8 \qquad \text{Simplify.}$$

The solutions are $-\frac{1}{8}$ and 8. Verify that both satisfy the original equation.

⇨ **SELF CHECK 4**   Solve: $a^{2/3} = -3a^{1/3} + 10$.

EXAMPLE 5   Solve: $\dfrac{24}{x} + \dfrac{12}{x + 1} = 11$.

Solution   Since the denominator cannot be 0, x cannot be 0 or -1. If either 0 or -1 appears as a suspected solution, it is extraneous and must be discarded.

$$\frac{24}{x} + \frac{12}{x + 1} = 11$$

$$x(x + 1)\left(\frac{24}{x} + \frac{12}{x + 1}\right) = x(x + 1)11 \qquad \text{Multiply both sides by } x(x + 1).$$

$$24(x + 1) + 12x = (x^2 + x)11 \qquad \text{Simplify.}$$

$$24x + 24 + 12x = 11x^2 + 11x \qquad \text{Use the distributive property to remove parentheses.}$$

$$36x + 24 = 11x^2 + 11x \qquad \text{Combine like terms.}$$

$$0 = 11x^2 - 25x - 24 \qquad \text{Subtract } 36x \text{ and 24 from both sides.}$$

$$0 = (11x + 8)(x - 3) \qquad \text{Factor } 11x^2 - 25x - 24.$$

$$11x + 8 = 0 \quad \text{or} \quad x - 3 = 0 \qquad \text{Set each factor equal to 0.}$$

$$x = -\frac{8}{11} \qquad\qquad x = 3$$

Verify that $-\frac{8}{11}$ and 3 satisfy the original equation.

⇨ **SELF CHECK 5**   Solve: $\frac{12}{x} + \frac{6}{x + 3} = 5$.

EXAMPLE 6   Solve: $15a^{-2} - 8a^{-1} + 1 = 0$.

Solution   First we write the equation in the form

$$15(a^{-1})^2 - 8a^{-1} + 1 = 0 \qquad (a^{-1})^2 = a^{-2}$$

If we substitute u for a^{-1}, this equation can be written in a form that can be solved by factoring.

$$15u^2 - 8u + 1 = 0 \qquad \text{Replace each } a^{-1} \text{ with } u.$$
$$(5u - 1)(3u - 1) = 0 \qquad \text{Factor } 15u^2 - 8u + 1.$$
$$5u - 1 = 0 \quad \text{or} \quad 3u - 1 = 0 \qquad \text{Set each factor equal to 0.}$$
$$u = \frac{1}{5} \qquad\qquad u = \frac{1}{3}$$

To find a, we undo the substitutions by replacing each u with a^{-1} and solve each resulting equation.

$$a^{-1} = \frac{1}{5} \qquad\qquad a^{-1} = \frac{1}{3}$$
$$\frac{1}{a} = \frac{1}{5} \qquad\qquad \frac{1}{a} = \frac{1}{3} \qquad a^{-1} = \frac{1}{a}$$
$$5 = a \qquad\qquad 3 = a \qquad \text{Solve the proportions.}$$

The solutions are 5 and 3. Verify that both satisfy the original equation.

SELF CHECK 6   Solve: $28c^{-2} - 3c^{-1} - 1 = 0$.

EXAMPLE 7   Solve the formula $s = 16t^2 - 32$ for t.

Solution   We proceed as follows:

$$s = 16t^2 - 32$$
$$s + 32 = 16t^2 \qquad \text{Add 32 to both sides.}$$
$$\frac{s + 32}{16} = t^2 \qquad \text{Divide both sides by 16.}$$
$$t^2 = \frac{s + 32}{16} \qquad \text{Write } t^2 \text{ on the left side.}$$
$$t = \pm\sqrt{\frac{s + 32}{16}} \qquad \text{Apply the square-root property.}$$
$$t = \pm\frac{\sqrt{s + 32}}{\sqrt{16}} \qquad \sqrt{\frac{a}{b}} = \frac{\sqrt{a}}{\sqrt{b}}$$
$$t = \pm\frac{\sqrt{s + 32}}{4}$$

SELF CHECK 7   Solve $a^2 + b^2 = c^2$ for a.

3   Verify the solutions of a quadratic equation by showing that the sum of the solutions is $-\frac{b}{a}$ and the product is $\frac{c}{a}$.

Solutions of a Quadratic Equation

If r_1 and r_2 are the solutions of the quadratic equation $ax^2 + bx + c = 0$, with $a \neq 0$, then

$$r_1 + r_2 = -\frac{b}{a} \qquad \text{and} \qquad r_1 r_2 = \frac{c}{a}$$

Proof   We note that the solutions to the equation are given by the quadratic formula

$$r_1 = \frac{-b + \sqrt{b^2 - 4ac}}{2a} \quad \text{and} \quad r_2 = \frac{-b - \sqrt{b^2 - 4ac}}{2a}$$

Thus,

$$r_1 + r_2 = \frac{-b + \sqrt{b^2 - 4ac}}{2a} + \frac{-b - \sqrt{b^2 - 4ac}}{2a}$$

$$= \frac{-b + \sqrt{b^2 - 4ac} - b - \sqrt{b^2 - 4ac}}{2a} \qquad \text{Keep the denominator and add the numerators.}$$

$$= -\frac{2b}{2a}$$

$$= -\frac{b}{a}$$

and

$$r_1 r_2 = \frac{-b + \sqrt{b^2 - 4ac}}{2a} \cdot \frac{-b - \sqrt{b^2 - 4ac}}{2a}$$

$$= \frac{b^2 - (b^2 - 4ac)}{4a^2} \qquad \text{Multiply the numerators and multiply the denominators.}$$

$$= \frac{b^2 - b^2 + 4ac}{4a^2}$$

$$= \frac{4ac}{4a^2} \qquad\qquad\qquad b^2 - b^2 = 0$$

$$= \frac{c}{a}$$

It can also be shown that if

$$r_1 + r_2 = -\frac{b}{a} \quad \text{and} \quad r_1 r_2 = \frac{c}{a}$$

then r_1 and r_2 are solutions of $ax^2 + bx + c = 0$. We can use this fact to check the solutions of quadratic equations.

EXAMPLE 8   Show that $\frac{3}{2}$ and $-\frac{1}{3}$ are solutions of $6x^2 - 7x - 3 = 0$.

Solution   Since $a = 6$, $b = -7$, and $c = -3$, we have

$$-\frac{b}{a} = -\frac{-7}{6} = \frac{7}{6} \quad \text{and} \quad \frac{c}{a} = \frac{-3}{6} = -\frac{1}{2}$$

Since $\frac{3}{2} + \left(-\frac{1}{3}\right) = \frac{7}{6}$ and $\left(\frac{3}{2}\right)\left(-\frac{1}{3}\right) = -\frac{1}{2}$, these numbers are solutions. Solve the equation to verify that the roots are $\frac{3}{2}$ and $-\frac{1}{3}$.

⇨ **SELF CHECK 8**   Are $-\frac{3}{2}$ and $\frac{1}{3}$ solutions of $6x^2 + 7x - 3 = 0$?

NOW TRY THIS

1. Solve: $x - 3\sqrt{x} - 4 = 0$.

2. Without substituting, show that $3 + 5i$ and $3 - 5i$ are solutions of $x^2 - 6x + 34 = 0$.

3. Find the discriminant of $\sqrt{2}x^2 - \sqrt{65}x - 2\sqrt{2} = 0$.

10.3 EXERCISES

WARM-UPS

Find $b^2 - 4ac$ when

1. $a = 1, b = 1, c = 1$ **2.** $a = 2, b = 1, c = 1$

Determine the type of solutions for

3. $x^2 - 4x + 1 = 0$ **4.** $8x^2 - x + 2 = 0$

Are the following numbers solutions of $x^2 - 7x + 6 = 0$?

5. 1, 5 **6.** 1, 6

REVIEW *Solve each equation. Assume no division by 0.*

7. $\dfrac{1}{4} + \dfrac{1}{t} = \dfrac{1}{2t}$ **8.** $\dfrac{p-3}{3p} + \dfrac{1}{2p} = \dfrac{1}{4}$

9. Find the slope of the line passing through $(-2, -4)$ and $(3, 5)$.

10. Write an equation of the line passing through $(-2, -4)$ and $(3, 5)$ in general form.

VOCABULARY AND CONCEPTS *Consider the equation $ax^2 + bx + c = 0$ ($a \neq 0$), and fill in the blanks.*

11. The discriminant is _____.

12. If $b^2 - 4ac < 0$, the solutions of the equation are complex _____.

13. If $b^2 - 4ac$ is a nonzero perfect square, the solutions are _____ numbers and _____.

14. If r_1 and r_2 are the solutions of the equation, then $r_1 + r_2 =$ ____ and $r_1r_2 =$ __.

GUIDED PRACTICE

Use the discriminant to determine what type of solutions exist for each quadratic equation. Do not solve the equation.
See Example 1. (Objective 1)

15. $4x^2 - 4x + 1 = 0$ **16.** $6x^2 - 5x - 6 = 0$

17. $5x^2 + x + 2 = 0$ **18.** $3x^2 + 10x - 2 = 0$

19. $2x^2 = 4x - 1$ **20.** $9x^2 = 12x - 4$

21. $x(2x - 3) = 20$ **22.** $x(x - 3) = -10$

Find the values of k that will make the solutions of each given quadratic equation equal. **See Example 2. (Objective 1)**

23. $x^2 + kx + 9 = 0$
24. $kx^2 - 12x + 4 = 0$
25. $9x^2 + 4 = -kx$
26. $9x^2 - kx + 25 = 0$

Solve each equation. (Objective 2)

27. $x^4 - 17x^2 + 16 = 0$ **28.** $x^4 - 10x^2 + 9 = 0$

29. $x^4 - 3x^2 = -2$ **30.** $x^4 - 29x^2 = -100$

31. $x^4 = 6x^2 - 5$ **32.** $x^4 = 8x^2 - 7$

33. $2x^4 - 10x^2 = -8$ **34.** $3x^4 + 12 = 15x^2$

Solve each equation. See Example 3. (Objective 2)

35. $x - 6\sqrt{x} + 8 = 0$

36. $x - 5\sqrt{x} + 4 = 0$

37. $2x - \sqrt{x} = 3$

38. $3x - 4 = -4\sqrt{x}$

39. $2x + x^{1/2} - 3 = 0$

40. $2x - x^{1/2} - 1 = 0$

41. $3x + 5x^{1/2} + 2 = 0$

42. $3x - 4x^{1/2} + 1 = 0$

Solve each equation. See Example 4. (Objective 2)

43. $x^{2/3} + 5x^{1/3} + 6 = 0$

44. $x^{2/3} - 7x^{1/3} + 12 = 0$

45. $x^{2/3} - 2x^{1/3} - 3 = 0$

46. $x^{2/3} + 4x^{1/3} - 5 = 0$

Solve each equation. See Example 5. (Objective 2)

47. $x + 5 + \dfrac{4}{x} = 0$

48. $x - 4 + \dfrac{3}{x} = 0$

49. $x + 1 = \dfrac{20}{x}$

50. $x + \dfrac{15}{x} = 8$

51. $\dfrac{1}{x - 1} + \dfrac{3}{x + 1} = 2$

52. $\dfrac{6}{x - 2} - \dfrac{12}{x - 1} = -1$

53. $\dfrac{1}{x + 2} + \dfrac{24}{x + 3} = 13$

54. $\dfrac{3}{x} + \dfrac{4}{x + 1} = 2$

Solve each equation. See Example 6. (Objective 2)

55. $x^{-4} - 2x^{-2} + 1 = 0$

56. $4x^{-4} + 1 = 5x^{-2}$

57. $8a^{-2} - 10a^{-1} - 3 = 0$

58. $2y^{-2} - 5y^{-1} = 3$

Solve each equation for the indicated variable. See Example 7. (Objective 2)

59. $x^2 + y^2 = r^2$ for x

60. $x^2 + y^2 = r^2$ for y

61. $xy^2 + 3xy + 7 = 0$ for y

62. $kx = ay - x^2$ for x

Solve each equation and verify that the sum of the solutions is $-\dfrac{b}{a}$ and that the product of the solutions is $\dfrac{c}{a}$. See Example 8. (Objective 3)

63. $12x^2 - 5x - 2 = 0$

64. $8x^2 - 2x - 3 = 0$

65. $2x^2 + 5x + 1 = 0$

66. $3x^2 + 9x + 1 = 0$

67. $3x^2 - 2x + 4 = 0$

68. $2x^2 - x + 4 = 0$

69. $x^2 + 2x + 5 = 0$

70. $x^2 - 4x + 13 = 0$

ADDITIONAL PRACTICE

71. Use the discriminant to determine whether the solutions of $1,492x^2 + 1,776x - 1,984 = 0$ are real numbers.

72. Use the discriminant to determine whether the solutions of $1,776x^2 - 1,492x + 1,984 = 0$ are real numbers.

Solve using any method.

73. $4x - 5\sqrt{x} - 9 = 0$

74. $9x - 5\sqrt{x} = 4$

75. $3x^{2/3} - x^{1/3} - 2 = 0$

76. $4x^{2/3} + 4x^{1/3} + 1 = 0$

77. $2x^4 + 24 = 26x^2$

78. $4x^4 = -9 + 13x^2$

79. $t^4 + 3t^2 = 28$

80. $t^4 + 4t^2 - 5 = 0$

81. $4(2x - 1)^2 - 3(2x - 1) - 1 = 0$

82. $4(x^2 - 1)^2 + 13(x^2 - 1) + 9 = 0$

83. $x^{-2/3} - 2x^{-1/3} - 3 = 0$

84. $4x^{-1} - 5x^{-1/2} - 9 = 0$

85. $x + \dfrac{2}{x - 2} = 0$

86. $x + \dfrac{x + 5}{x - 3} = 0$

87. $8(m + 1)^{-2} - 30(m + 1)^{-1} + 7 = 0$

88. $2(p - 2)^{-2} + 3(p - 2)^{-1} - 5 = 0$

89. $I = \dfrac{k}{d^2}$ for d

90. $V = \dfrac{1}{3}\pi r^2 h$ for r

91. $\sigma = \sqrt{\dfrac{\Sigma x^2}{N} - \mu^2}$ for μ^2

92. $\sigma = \sqrt{\dfrac{\Sigma x^2}{N} - \mu^2}$ for N

Find the values of k that will make the solutions of each given quadratic equation equal.

93. $(k - 1)x^2 + (k - 1)x + 1 = 0$

94. $(k + 3)x^2 + 2kx + 4 = 0$

95. $(k + 4)x^2 + 2kx + 9 = 0$

96. $(k + 15)x^2 + (k - 30)x + 4 = 0$

97. Determine k such that the solutions of $3x^2 + 4x = k$ are complex numbers.

98. Determine k such that the solutions of $kx^2 - 4x = 7$ are complex numbers.

WRITING ABOUT MATH

99. Describe how to predict what type of solutions the equation $3x^2 - 4x + 5 = 0$ will have.

100. How is the discriminant related to the quadratic formula?

SOMETHING TO THINK ABOUT

101. Can a quadratic equation with integer coefficients have one real and one complex solution? Why?

102. Can a quadratic equation with complex coefficients have one real and one complex solution? Why?

SECTION 10.4 Graphs of Quadratic Functions

Objectives

1 Graph a quadratic function of the form $f(x) = ax^2$.

2 Use a vertical translation of $f(x) = ax^2$ to graph $f(x) = ax^2 + c$.

3 Use a horizontal translation of $f(x) = ax^2$ to graph $f(x) = a(x - h)^2$.

4 Use both a vertical and horizontal translation of $f(x) = ax^2$ to graph $f(x) = a(x - h)^2 + k$.

5 Graph a quadratic function in standard form by writing it in the form $f(x) = a(x - h)^2 + k$.

6 Find the vertex of a parabola using $\left(-\frac{b}{2a}, f\left(-\frac{b}{2a}\right)\right)$.

7 Graph a quadratic function in standard form by finding the vertex, axis of symmetry, and the x- and y-intercepts.

8 Solve an application problem using a quadratic function.

Vocabulary

quadratic function   vertex   variance
parabola   axis of symmetry

Getting Ready

If $f(x) = 3x^2 + x - 2$, find each value.

1. $f(0)$ **2.** $f(1)$ **3.** $f(-1)$ **4.** $f(-2)$

If $x = -\frac{b}{2a}$, find x when a and b have the following values.

5. $a = 3$ and $b = -6$ **6.** $a = 5$ and $b = -40$

In this section, we consider graphs of second-degree polynomial functions, called *quadratic functions.*

The graph shown in Figure 10-4 on the next page shows the height (in relation to time) of a toy rocket launched straight up into the air.

COMMENT   Note that the graph describes the height of the rocket, not the path of the rocket. The rocket goes straight up and comes straight down.

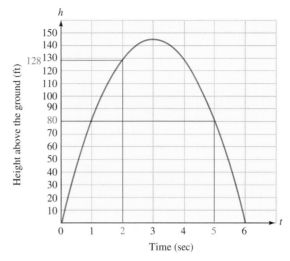

Figure 10-4

From the graph, we can see that the height of the rocket 2 seconds after it was launched is about 128 feet and that the height of the rocket 5 seconds after it was launched is 80 feet.

The parabola shown in Figure 10-4 is the graph of a *quadratic function.*

Quadratic Functions	A **quadratic function** is a second-degree polynomial function of the form $$f(x) = ax^2 + bx + c \quad (a \neq 0)$$ where a, b, and c are real numbers.

We begin the discussion of graphing quadratic functions by considering the graph of $f(x) = ax^2 + bx + c$, where $b = 0$ and $c = 0$.

1   **Graph a quadratic function of the form $f(x) = ax^2$.**

EXAMPLE 1   Graph: **a.** $f(x) = x^2$ **b.** $g(x) = 3x^2$ **c.** $h(x) = \frac{1}{3}x^2$.

Solution   We can make a table of ordered pairs that satisfy each equation, plot each point, and join them with a smooth curve, as in Figure 10-5. We note that the graph of $h(x) = \frac{1}{3}x^2$ is wider than the graph of $f(x) = x^2$, and that the graph of $g(x) = 3x^2$ is narrower than the graph of $f(x) = x^2$. In the function $f(x) = ax^2$, the smaller the value of $|a|$, the wider the graph.

$f(x) = x^2$

x	$f(x)$	$(x, f(x))$
-2	4	$(-2, 4)$
-1	1	$(-1, 1)$
0	0	$(0, 0)$
1	1	$(1, 1)$
2	4	$(2, 4)$

$g(x) = 3x^2$

x	$g(x)$	$(x, g(x))$
-2	12	$(-2, 12)$
-1	3	$(-1, 3)$
0	0	$(0, 0)$
1	3	$(1, 3)$
2	12	$(2, 12)$

$h(x) = \frac{1}{3}x^2$

x	$h(x)$	$(x, h(x))$
-2	$\frac{4}{3}$	$\left(-2, \frac{4}{3}\right)$
-1	$\frac{1}{3}$	$\left(-1, \frac{1}{3}\right)$
0	0	$(0, 0)$
1	$\frac{1}{3}$	$\left(1, \frac{1}{3}\right)$
2	$\frac{4}{3}$	$\left(2, \frac{4}{3}\right)$

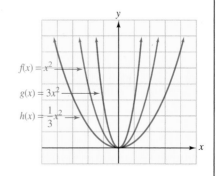

Figure 10-5

⇨ **SELF CHECK 1**   On the same set of coordinate axes, graph each function.
a. $f(x) = 2x^2$ **b.** $f(x) = \frac{1}{2}x^2$

If we consider the graph of $f(x) = -3x^2$, we will see that it opens downward and has the same shape as the graph of $g(x) = 3x^2$.

EXAMPLE 2   Graph: $f(x) = -3x^2$.

Solution   We make a table of ordered pairs that satisfy the equation, plot each point, and join them with a smooth curve, as in Figure 10-6.

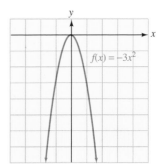

$f(x) = -3x^2$

x	$f(x)$	$(x, f(x))$
-2	-12	$(-2, -12)$
-1	-3	$(-1, -3)$
0	0	$(0, 0)$
1	-3	$(1, -3)$
2	-12	$(2, -12)$

Figure 10-6

⇨ **SELF CHECK 2**   Graph: $f(x) = -\frac{1}{3}x^2$.

The graphs of quadratic functions are called **parabolas.** They open upward when $a > 0$ and downward when $a < 0$. The lowest point (*minimum*) of a parabola that opens upward, or the highest point (*maximum*) of a parabola that opens downward, is called the **vertex** of the parabola. The vertex of the parabola shown in Figure 10-6 is the point $(0, 0)$.

The vertical line, called an **axis of symmetry,** that passes through the vertex divides the parabola into two congruent halves. The axis of symmetry of the parabola shown in Figure 10-6 is the y-axis, written as the equation $x = 0$.

2   Use a vertical translation of $f(x) = ax^2$ to graph $f(x) = ax^2 + c$.

EXAMPLE 3   Graph: **a.** $f(x) = 2x^2$ **b.** $g(x) = 2x^2 + 3$ **c.** $h(x) = 2x^2 - 3$.

Solution   We make a table of ordered pairs that satisfy each equation, plot each point, and join them with a smooth curve, as in Figure 10-7 on the next page. We note that the graph of $g(x) = 2x^2 + 3$ is identical to the graph of $f(x) = 2x^2$, except that it has been translated 3 units upward. The graph of $h(x) = 2x^2 - 3$ is identical to the graph of $f(x) = 2x^2$, except that it has been translated 3 units downward.

$f(x) = 2x^2$		
x	$f(x)$	$(x, f(x))$
-2	8	$(-2, 8)$
-1	2	$(-1, 2)$
0	0	$(0, 0)$
1	2	$(1, 2)$
2	8	$(2, 8)$

$g(x) = 2x^2 + 3$		
x	$g(x)$	$(x, g(x))$
-2	11	$(-2, 11)$
-1	5	$(-1, 5)$
0	3	$(0, 3)$
1	5	$(1, 5)$
2	11	$(2, 11)$

$h(x) = 2x^2 - 3$		
x	$h(x)$	$(x, h(x))$
-2	5	$(-2, 5)$
-1	-1	$(-1, -1)$
0	-3	$(0, -3)$
1	-1	$(1, -1)$
2	5	$(2, 5)$

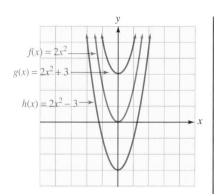

Figure 10-7

⇨ **SELF CHECK 3**   On the same set of coordinate axes, graph each function and tell how it differs from the graph of $f(x) = x^2$.
a. $f(x) = x^2 + 1$
b. $f(x) = x^2 - 5$

The results of Example 3 confirm the following facts.

Vertical Translations of Graphs

If $y = f(x)$ is a function and k is a positive number, then

- The graph of $y = f(x) + k$ is identical to the graph of $y = f(x)$, except that it is translated k units upward.
- The graph of $y = f(x) - k$ is identical to the graph of $y = f(x)$, except that it is translated k units downward.

3 Use a horizontal translation of $f(x) = ax^2$ to graph $f(x) = a(x - h)^2$.

EXAMPLE 4   Graph: **a.** $f(x) = 2x^2$ **b.** $g(x) = 2(x - 3)^2$ **c.** $h(x) = 2(x + 3)^2$.

Solution   We make a table of ordered pairs that satisfy each equation, plot each point, and join them with a smooth curve, as in Figure 10-8. We note that the graph of $g(x) = 2(x - 3)^2$ is identical to the graph of $f(x) = 2x^2$, except that it has been translated 3 units to the right. The graph of $h(x) = 2(x + 3)^2$ is identical to the graph of $f(x) = 2x^2$, except that it has been translated 3 units to the left.

$f(x) = 2x^2$		
x	$f(x)$	$(x, f(x))$
-2	8	$(-2, 8)$
-1	2	$(-1, 2)$
0	0	$(0, 0)$
1	2	$(1, 2)$
2	8	$(2, 8)$

$g(x) = 2(x - 3)^2$		
x	$g(x)$	$(x, g(x))$
1	8	$(1, 8)$
2	2	$(2, 2)$
3	0	$(3, 0)$
4	2	$(4, 2)$
5	8	$(5, 8)$

$h(x) = 2(x + 3)^2$		
x	$h(x)$	$(x, h(x))$
-5	8	$(-5, 8)$
-4	2	$(-4, 2)$
-3	0	$(-3, 0)$
-2	2	$(-2, 2)$
-1	8	$(-1, 8)$

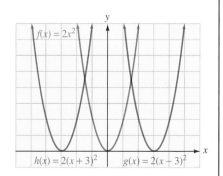

Figure 10-8

⇨ **SELF CHECK 4**   On the same set of coordinate axes, graph each function and tell how it differs from the graph of $f(x) = x^2$.
a. $f(x) = (x - 2)^2$
b. $f(x) = (x + 5)^2$

The results of Example 4 confirm the following facts.

Horizontal Translations of Graphs

If $y = f(x)$ is a function and h is a positive number, then

• The graph of $y = f(x - h)$ is identical to the graph of $y = f(x)$, except that it is translated h units to the right.

• The graph of $y = f(x + h)$ is identical to the graph of $y = f(x)$, except that it is translated h units to the left.

4 Use both a vertical and horizontal translation of $f(x) = ax^2$ to graph $f(x) = a(x - h)^2 + k$.

EXAMPLE 5   Graph: $f(x) = 2(x - 3)^2 - 4$.

Solution   The graph of $f(x) = 2(x - 3)^2 - 4$ is identical to the graph of $g(x) = 2(x - 3)^2$, except that it has been translated 4 units downward. The graph of $g(x) = 2(x - 3)^2$ is identical to the graph of $h(x) = 2x^2$, except that it has been translated 3 units to the right. Thus, to graph $f(x) = 2(x - 3)^2 - 4$, we can graph $h(x) = 2x^2$ and shift it 3 units to the right and then 4 units downward, as shown in Figure 10-9.

The vertex of the graph is the point $(3, -4)$, and the axis of symmetry is the line $x = 3$.

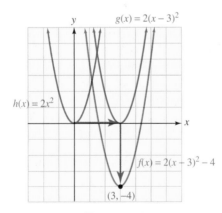

Figure 10-9

⇨ **SELF CHECK 5**   Graph: $f(x) = 2(x + 3)^2 + 1$.

The results of Example 5 confirm the following facts.

Vertex and Axis of Symmetry of a Parabola

The graph of the function

$$f(x) = a(x - h)^2 + k \quad (a \neq 0)$$

is a parabola with vertex at (h, k). (See Figure 10-10.)

The parabola opens upward when $a > 0$ and downward when $a < 0$. The axis of symmetry is the line $x = h$.

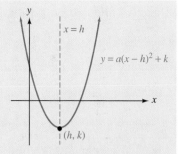

Figure 10-10

5 **Graph a quadratic function in standard form by writing it in the form $f(x) = a(x - h)^2 + k$.**

To graph functions of the form $f(x) = ax^2 + bx + c$, we can complete the square to write the function in the form $f(x) = a(x - h)^2 + k$.

EXAMPLE 6   Graph: $f(x) = 2x^2 - 4x - 1$.

Solution   We complete the square on x to write the function in the form $f(x) = a(x - h)^2 + k$.

$$f(x) = 2x^2 - 4x - 1$$

$$f(x) = 2(x^2 - 2x) - 1 \qquad \text{Factor 2 from } 2x^2 - 4x.$$

$$f(x) = 2(x^2 - 2x + \mathbf{1}) - 1 - \mathbf{2} \qquad \begin{array}{l}\text{Complete the square on } x. \text{ Since this adds 2 to the} \\ \text{right side, we also subtract 2 from the right side.}\end{array}$$

$$(1) \qquad f(x) = 2(x - 1)^2 - 3 \qquad \text{Factor } x^2 - 2x + 1 \text{ and combine like terms.}$$

From Equation 1, we can see that the vertex will be at the point $(1, -3)$. We can plot the vertex and a few points on either side of the vertex and draw the graph, which appears in Figure 10-11.

COMMENT   Note that this is the graph of $f(x) = 2x^2$ translated one unit to the right and three units down.

$$f(x) = 2x^2 - 4x - 1$$

x	$f(x)$	$(x, f(x))$
-1	5	$(-1, 5)$
0	-1	$(0, -1)$
1	-3	$(1, -3)$
2	-1	$(2, -1)$
3	5	$(3, 5)$

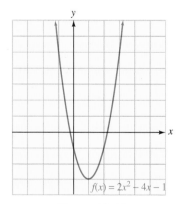

Figure 10-11

⇨ SELF CHECK 6   Graph: $f(x) = 2x^2 - 4x + 1$.

6 Find the vertex of a parabola using $\left(-\frac{b}{2a}, f\left(-\frac{b}{2a}\right)\right)$.

We can derive a formula for the vertex of the graph of $f(x) = ax^2 + bx + c$ by completing the square in the same manner as we did in Example 6. After using similar steps, the result is

$$f(x) = a\left[x - \left(-\frac{b}{2a}\right)\right]^2 + \underbrace{\frac{4ac - b^2}{4a}}$$
$$\quad\quad\quad\quad\quad \underset{h}{\uparrow} \quad\quad\quad\quad \underset{k}{\uparrow}$$

The x-coordinate of the vertex is $-\frac{b}{2a}$. The y-coordinate of the vertex is $\frac{4ac - b^2}{4a}$. We can also find the y-coordinate of the vertex by substituting the x-coordinate, $-\frac{b}{2a}$, for x in the quadratic function and simplifying.

Formula for the Vertex of a Parabola

The vertex of the graph of the quadratic function $f(x) = ax^2 + bx + c$ is

$$\left(-\frac{b}{2a}, f\left(-\frac{b}{2a}\right)\right)$$

and the axis of symmetry of the parabola is the line $x = -\frac{b}{2a}$.

EXAMPLE 7   Find the vertex of the graph of $f(x) = 2x^2 - 4x - 1$.

Solution   The function is written in $f(x) = ax^2 + bx + c$ form, where $a = 2$, $b = -4$, and $c = -1$. We can find the x-coordinate of the vertex by evaluating $-\frac{b}{2a}$.

$$-\frac{b}{2a} = -\frac{-4}{2(2)} = -\frac{-4}{4} = 1$$

COMMENT This is the same as finding $f(1)$.

We can find the y-coordinate by evaluating $f\left(-\frac{b}{2a}\right)$.

$$f\left(-\frac{b}{2a}\right) = f(1) = 2(1)^2 - 4(1) - 1 = -3$$

The vertex is the point $(1, -3)$. This agrees with the result we obtained in Example 6 by completing the square.

 SELF CHECK 7   Find the vertex of the graph of $f(x) = 3x^2 - 12x + 8$.

---

7 Graph a quadratic function in standard form by finding the vertex, axis of symmetry, and the x- and y-intercepts.

Much can be determined about the graph of $f(x) = ax^2 + bx + c$ from the coefficients a, b, and c. This information is summarized as follows:

Graphing a Quadratic Function
$f(x) = ax^2 + bx + c$

Determine whether the parabola opens upward or downward:

If $a > 0$, the parabola opens upward.

If $a < 0$, the parabola opens downward.

The x-coordinate of the vertex of the parabola is $x = -\frac{b}{2a}$.

To find the y-coordinate of the vertex, substitute $-\frac{b}{2a}$ for x and find $f\left(-\frac{b}{2a}\right)$.

The axis of symmetry is the vertical line passing through the vertex. The axis of symmetry is $x = -\frac{b}{2a}$.

The y-intercept is determined by the value of $f(x)$ when $x = 0$. The y-intercept is $(0, c)$.

The x-intercepts (if any) are determined by the values of x that make $f(x) = 0$. To find them, solve the quadratic equation $ax^2 + bx + c = 0$.

EXAMPLE 8   Graph: $f(x) = -2x^2 - 8x - 8$.

Solution   **Step 1**   *Determine whether the parabola opens upward or downward.* The function is in the form $f(x) = ax^2 + bx + c$, with $a = -2$, $b = -8$, and $c = -8$. Since $a < 0$, the parabola opens downward.

Step 2   *Find the vertex and draw the axis of symmetry.* To find the coordinates of the vertex, we evaluate $-\frac{b}{2a}$ by substituting -2 for a and -8 for b.

$$x = -\frac{b}{2a} \quad x = -\frac{-8}{2(-2)} = -2$$

We then find $f(-2)$.

$$f\left(-\frac{b}{2a}\right) = f(-2) = -2(-2)^2 - 8(-2) - 8 = -8 + 16 - 8 = 0$$

The vertex of the parabola is the point $(-2, 0)$. The axis of symmetry is the line $x = -2$.

Step 3   *Find the x- and y-intercepts.* Since $c = -8$, the y-intercept of the parabola is $(0, -8)$. The point $(-4, -8)$, two units to the left of the axis of symmetry, must also be on the graph. We plot both points in black on the graph.

To find the x-intercepts, we set $f(x)$ equal to 0 and solve the resulting quadratic equation.

$$
\begin{aligned}
f(x) &= -2x^2 - 8x - 8 \\
0 &= -2x^2 - 8x - 8 && \text{Set } f(x) = 0. \\
0 &= x^2 + 4x + 4 && \text{Divide both sides by } -2. \\
0 &= (x + 2)(x + 2) && \text{Find the trinomial.} \\
x + 2 = 0 \quad &\text{or} \quad x + 2 = 0 && \text{Set each factor equal to } 0. \\
x = -2 \quad &\phantom{\text{or}} \quad x = -2 &&
\end{aligned}
$$

Since the solutions are the same, the graph has only one x-intercept: $(-2, 0)$. This point is the vertex of the parabola and has already been plotted.

Step 4 *Plot another point.* Finally, we find another point on the parabola. If $x = -3$, then $f(-3) = -2$. We plot $(-3, -2)$ and use symmetry to determine that $(-1, -2)$ is also on the graph. Both points are in black.

Step 5 *Draw a smooth curve through the points,* as shown.

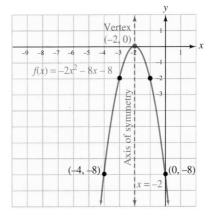

$$f(x) = -2x^2 - 8x - 8$$

x	$f(x)$	$(x, f(x))$
-3	-2	$(-3, -2)$

Figure 10-12

ACCENT ON TECHNOLOGY

Graphing Quadratic Functions

To use a graphing calculator to graph $f(x) = 0.7x^2 + 2x - 3.5$, we can use window settings of $[-10, 10]$ for x and $[-10, 10]$ for y, enter the function, and press **GRAPH** to obtain Figure 10-13(a).

To find approximate coordinates of the vertex of the graph, we trace to move the cursor near the lowest point of the graph as shown in Figure 10-13(b). By zooming in twice and tracing as in Figure 10-13(c), we can see that the vertex is a point whose coordinates are approximately $(-1.422872, -4.928549)$.

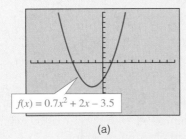
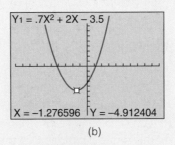
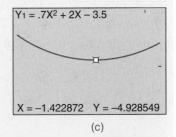

| (a) | (b) | (c) |

Figure 10-13

We can find the vertex more efficiently by using the MINIMUM command found in the CALC menu. We first graph the function $f(x) = 0.7x^2 + 2x - 3.5$ as in Figure 10-13(a). We then select 3 in the CALC menu, enter -3 for a left guess, and press **ENTER**. We then enter 0 for a right guess and press **ENTER**. After pressing **ENTER** again, we will obtain the minimum value $(-1.42857, -4.928571)$.

The solutions of the quadratic equation $0.7x^2 + 2x - 3.5 = 0$ are the numbers x that will make $f(x) = 0$ in the function $f(x) = 0.7x^2 + 2x - 3.5$. To approximate these numbers, we graph the function as shown in Figure 10-14(a) and find the x-intercepts

(continued)

by tracing to move the cursor near each x-intercept, as in Figures 10-14(b) and 10-14(c). From the graphs, we can read the approximate value of the x-coordinate of each x-intercept. For better results, we can zoom in.

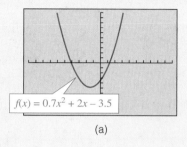
(a)

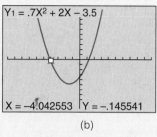
(b)

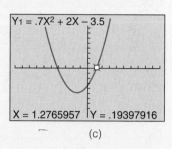
(c)

Figure 10-14

We can also solve the equation by using the ZERO command found in the CALC menu. We first graph the function $f(x) = 0.7x^2 + 2x - 3.5$ as in Figure 10-15(a). We then select 2 in the CALC menu to get Figure 10-15(b). We enter -5 for a left guess and press **ENTER**. We then enter -2 for a right guess and press **ENTER**. After pressing **ENTER** again, we will obtain Figure 10-15(c). We can find the second solution in a similar way.

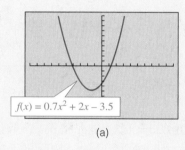
(a)

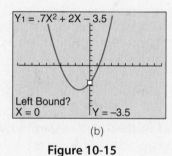
(b)

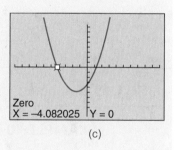
(c)

Figure 10-15

8   Solve an application problem using a quadratic function.

EXAMPLE 9   **BALLISTICS**   The ball shown in Figure 10-16(a) is thrown straight up with a velocity of 128 feet per second. The function $s = h(t) = -16t^2 + 128t$ gives the relation between t (the time measured in seconds) and s (the number of feet the ball is above the ground). How long will it take the ball to reach its maximum height, and what is that height?

Solution   The graph of $s = h(t) = -16t^2 + 128t$ is a parabola. Since the coefficient of t^2 is negative, it opens downward. The time it takes the ball to reach its maximum height is given by the t-coordinate of its vertex, and the maximum height of the ball is given by the s-coordinate of the vertex. To find the vertex, we find its t-coordinate and s-coordinate. To find the t-coordinate, we compute

$$-\frac{b}{2a} = -\frac{128}{2(-16)} \qquad b = 128 \text{ and } a = -16.$$

$$= -\frac{128}{-32}$$

$$= 4$$

To find the s-coordinate, we substitute 4 for t in $h(t) = -16t^2 + 128t$.

$$h(4) = -16(4)^2 + 128(4)$$
$$= -256 + 512$$
$$= 256$$

Since $t = 4$ and $s = 256$ are the coordinates of the vertex, the ball will reach a maximum height in 4 seconds and that maximum height will be 256 feet.

To solve this problem with a graphing calculator with window settings of [0, 10] for x and [0, 300] for y, we graph the function $h(t) = -16t^2 + 128t$ to get the graph in Figure 10-16(b). By using the MAXIMUM command found under the CALC menu in the same way as the MINIMUM command, we can determine that the ball reaches a height of 256 feet in 4 seconds.

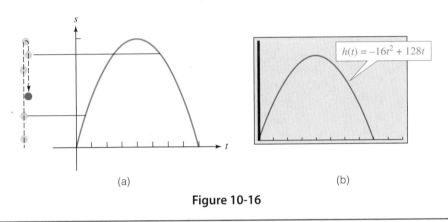

(a)   (b)

Figure 10-16

EXAMPLE 10   **MAXIMIZING AREA**   A man wants to build the rectangular pen shown in Figure 10-17(a) on the next page to house his dog. If he uses one side of his barn, find the maximum area that he can enclose with 80 feet of fencing.

Solution   If we use w to represent the width of the pen, the length is represented by $80 - 2w$. Since the area A of the pen is the product of its length and width, we have

$$A = (80 - 2w)w$$
$$= 80w - 2w^2$$
$$= -2w^2 + 80w$$

Since the graph of $A = -2w^2 + 80w$ is a parabola opening downward, the maximum area will be given by the A-coordinate of the vertex of the graph. To find the vertex, we first find its w-coordinate by letting $b = 80$ and $a = -2$ and computing $-\frac{b}{2a}$.

$$-\frac{b}{2a} = -\frac{80}{2(-2)} = 20$$

We can then find the A-coordinate of the vertex by substituting 20 into the function $A = -2w^2 + 80w$.

$$A = -2w^2 + 80w$$
$$= -2(20)^2 + 80(20)$$
$$= -2(400) + 1,600$$

$$= -800 + 1,600$$
$$= 800$$

Thus, the coordinates of the vertex of the graph of the quadratic function are (20, 800), and the maximum area is 800 square feet. This occurs when the width is 20 feet.

To solve this problem using a graphing calculator with window settings of [0, 50] for x and [0, 1,000] for y, we graph the function $A = -2w^2 + 80w$ to get the graph in Figure 10-17(b). By using the MAXIMUM command, we can determine that the maximum area is 800 square feet when the width is 20 feet.

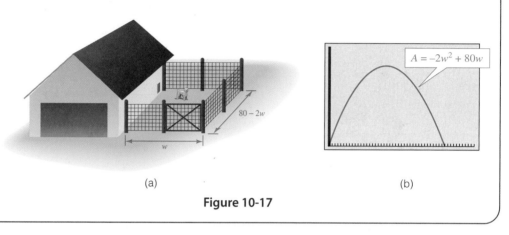

(a)   (b)

Figure 10-17

In statistics, the square of the standard deviation is called the **variance.**

EXAMPLE 11   **VARIANCE**   If p is the chance that a person selected at random has the HIV virus, then $1 - p$ is the chance that the person does not have the HIV virus. If 100 people are randomly sampled, we know from statistics that the variance of this type of sample distribution will be $100p(1 - p)$. Find the value of p that will maximize the variance.

Solution   The variance is given by the function

$$v(p) = 100p(1 - p) \qquad \text{or} \qquad v(p) = -100p^2 + 100p$$

In this setting, all values of p are between 0 and 1, including 0 and 1. We use window settings of [0, 1] for x when graphing the function $v(p) = -100p^2 + 100p$ on a graphing calculator. If we also use window settings of [0, 30] for y, we will obtain the graph shown in Figure 10-18(a). After using the MAXIMUM command to obtain Figure 10-18(b), we can see that a value of 0.5 will give the maximum variance.

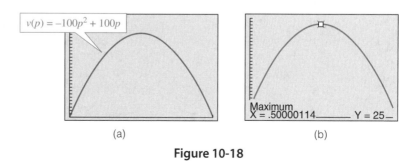

(a)   (b)

Figure 10-18

⇨ SELF CHECK ANSWERS

1.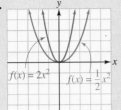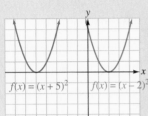

$f(x) = 2x^2$ $f(x) = \frac{1}{2}x^2$

2.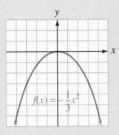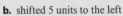

$f(x) = -\frac{1}{3}x^2$

3.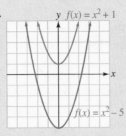

$y \; f(x) = x^2 + 1$

$f(x) = x^2 - 5$

a. shifted 1 unit up
b. shifted 5 units down

4.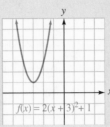

$f(x) = (x + 5)^2$ $f(x) = (x - 2)^2$

a. shifted 2 units to the right
b. shifted 5 units to the left

5.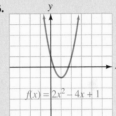

$f(x) = 2(x + 3)^2 + 1$

6.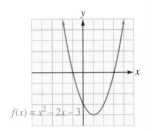

$f(x) = 2x^2 - 4x + 1$

7. $(2, -4)$

NOW TRY THIS

Answer the following questions about the graph of $f(x)$.

1. What is the vertex?

2. What is the axis of symmetry?

3. What is the domain?

4. What is the range?

5. For what values of x will $f(x) = 0$?

6. For what values of x will y be positive? ($f(x) > 0$)

7. For what values of x will y be negative? ($f(x) < 0$)

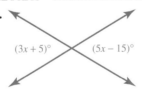

$f(x) = x^2 - 2x - 3$

10.4 EXERCISES

WARM-UPS

Determine whether the graph of each equation opens up or down.

1. $y = -3x^2 + x - 5$ **2.** $y = 4x^2 + 2x - 3$

3. $y = 2(x - 3)^2 - 1$ **4.** $y = -3(x + 2)^2 + 2$

Find the vertex of the parabola determined by each equation.

5. $y = 2(x - 3)^2 - 1$ **6.** $y = -3(x + 2)^2 + 2$

REVIEW   *Find the value of x.*

7.

$(3x + 5)°$ $(5x - 15)°$

8. Lines r and s are parallel.

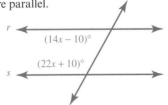

r $(14x - 10)°$

$(22x + 10)°$ s

9. **Travel** Madison and St. Louis are 385 miles apart. One train leaves Madison and heads toward St. Louis at the rate of 30 mph. Three hours later, a second train leaves Madison, bound for St. Louis. If the second train travels at the rate of 55 mph, in how many hours will the faster train overtake the slower train?

10. **Investing** A woman invests $25,000, some at 7% annual interest and the rest at 8%. If the annual income from both investments is $1,900, how much is invested at the higher rate?

VOCABULARY AND CONCEPTS   *Fill in the blanks.*

11. A quadratic function is a second-degree polynomial function that can be written in the form _____, where _____.

12. The graphs of quadratic functions are called _____.

13. The highest (_____) or lowest (_____) point on a parabola is called the _____.

14. A vertical line that divides a parabola into two halves is called an ____ of symmetry.

15. The graph of $y = f(x) + k$ $(k > 0)$ is identical to the graph of $y = f(x)$, except that it is translated k units _____.

16. The graph of $y = f(x) - k$ $(k > 0)$ is a vertical translation of the graph of $y = f(x)$, k units _____.

17. The graph of $y = f(x - h)$ $(h > 0)$ is a horizontal translation of the graph of $y = f(x)$, h units _____.

18. The graph of $y = f(x + h)$ $(h > 0)$ is identical to the graph of $y = f(x)$, except that it is translated h units _____.

19. The graph of $y = f(x) = ax^2 + bx + c$ $(a \neq 0)$ opens _____ when $a > 0$.

20. In statistics, the square of the standard deviation is called the _____.

GUIDED PRACTICE

Graph each function. See Examples 1–3. (Objectives 1–2)

21. $f(x) = x^2$

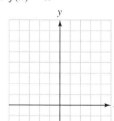

22. $f(x) = -x^2$

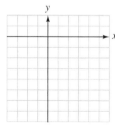

23. $f(x) = x^2 + 2$

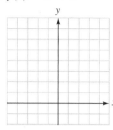

24. $f(x) = x^2 - 3$

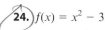
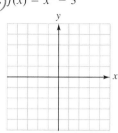

Graph each function. See Examples 4–5. (Objectives 3–4)

25. $f(x) = -(x - 2)^2$

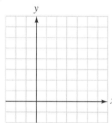

26. $f(x) = (x + 2)^2$

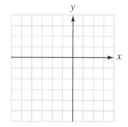

27. $f(x) = (x - 3)^2 + 2$

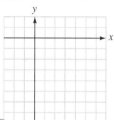

28. $f(x) = (x + 1)^2 - 2$

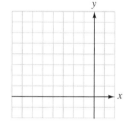

Find the coordinates of the vertex and the axis of symmetry of the graph of each equation. If necessary, complete the square on x to write the equation in the form $y = a(x - h)^2 + k$. Do not graph the equation. See Example 6. (Objective 5)

29. $y = (x - 1)^2 + 2$

30. $y = 2(x - 2)^2 - 1$

31. $y = 2(x + 3)^2 - 4$

32. $y = -3(x + 1)^2 + 3$

33. $y = -3x^2$

34. $y = 3x^2 - 3$

35. $y = 2x^2 - 4x$

36. $y = 3x^2 + 6x$

Find the coordinates of the vertex and the axis of symmetry of the graph of each equation. Use $\left(-\frac{b}{2a}, f\left(-\frac{b}{2a}\right)\right)$ to find the vertex and graph the equation. See Examples 7–8. (Objectives 6–7)

37. $f(x) = -2x^2 + 4x + 1$

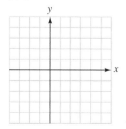

38. $f(x) = -2x^2 + 4x + 3$

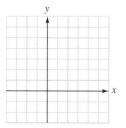

39. $f(x) = 3x^2 - 12x + 10$

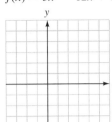

40. $f(x) = 3x^2 - 12x + 9$

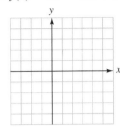

ADDITIONAL PRACTICE

Find the vertex and axis of symmetry using any method. Do not graph.

41. $y = -4x^2 + 16x + 5$

42. $y = 5x^2 + 20x + 25$

43. $y - 7 = 6x^2 - 5x$

44. $y - 2 = 3x^2 + 4x$

Graph each function.

45. $f(x) = x^2 + x - 6$

46. $f(x) = x^2 - x - 6$

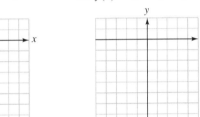

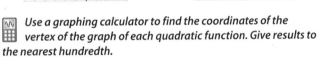 *Use a graphing calculator to find the coordinates of the vertex of the graph of each quadratic function. Give results to the nearest hundredth.*

47. $y = 2x^2 - x + 1$

48. $y = x^2 + 5x - 6$

49. $y = 7 + x - x^2$

50. $y = 2x^2 - 3x + 2$

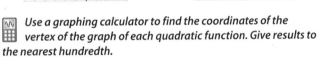 *Use a graphing calculator to solve each equation. If a result is not exact, give the result to the nearest hundredth.*

51. $x^2 + x - 6 = 0$

52. $2x^2 - 5x - 3 = 0$

53. $0.5x^2 - 0.7x - 3 = 0$

54. $2x^2 - 0.5x - 2 = 0$

55. The equation $y - 2 = (x - 5)^2$ represents a quadratic function whose graph is a parabola. Find its vertex.

56. Show that $y = ax^2$, where $a \neq 0$, represents a quadratic function whose vertex is at the origin.

APPLICATIONS   *Solve each application problem. Use a graphing calculator if necessary.* See Examples 9–11. (Objective 8)

57. Ballistics   If a ball is thrown straight up with an initial velocity of 48 feet per second, its height s after t seconds is given by the equation $s = 48t - 16t^2$. Find the maximum height attained by the ball and the time it takes for the ball to reach that height.

58. Ballistics   From the top of the building, a ball is thrown straight up with an initial velocity of 32 feet per second. The equation $s = -16t^2 + 32t + 48$ gives the height s of the ball t seconds after it is thrown. Find the maximum height reached by the ball and the time it takes for the ball to hit the ground.   (*Hint:* Let $s = 0$ and solve for t.)

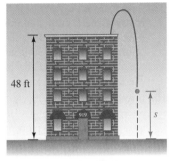

48 ft

59. Maximizing area   Find the dimensions of the rectangle of maximum area that can be constructed with 200 feet of fencing. Find the maximum area.

60. Fencing a field   A farmer wants to fence in three sides of a rectangular field with 1,000 feet of fencing. The other side of the rectangle will be a river. If the enclosed area is to be maximum, find the dimensions of the field.

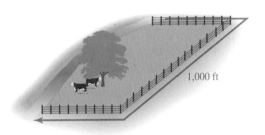

1,000 ft

61. Finding the variance   If p is the chance that a person sampled at random has high blood pressure, $1 - p$ is the chance that the person doesn't. If 50 people are sampled at random, the variance of the sample will be $50p(1 - p)$. What two values of p will give a variance of 9.375?

62. Finding the variance   If p is the chance that a person sampled at random smokes, then $1 - p$ is the chance that the person doesn't. If 75 people are sampled at random, the variance of the sample will be $75p(1 - p)$. What two values of p will give a variance of 12?

63. Police investigations   A police officer seals off the scene of a car collision using a roll of yellow police tape that is 300 feet long. What dimensions should be used to seal off the maximum rectangular area around the collision? What is the maximum area?

64. Operating costs The cost C in dollars of operating a certain concrete-cutting machine is related to the number of minutes n the machine is run by the function

$$C(n) = 2.2n^2 - 66n + 655$$

For what number of minutes is the cost of running the machine a minimum? What is the minimum cost?

65. Water usage The height (in feet) of the water level in a reservoir over a 1-year period is modeled by the function

$$H(t) = 3.3t^2 - 59.4t + 281.3$$

How low did the water level get that year?

66. School enrollment The total annual enrollment (in millions) in U.S. elementary and secondary schools for the years 1975–1996 is given by the function

$$E(x) = 0.058x^2 - 1.162x + 50.604$$

For this period, what was the lowest enrollment?

67. Maximizing revenue The revenue R received for selling x stereos is given by the equation

$$R = -\frac{x^2}{1,000} + 10x$$

Find the number of stereos that must be sold to obtain the maximum revenue.

68. Maximizing revenue In Exercise 67, find the maximum revenue.

69. Maximizing revenue The revenue received for selling x radios is given by the formula

$$R = -\frac{x^2}{728} + 9x$$

How many radios must be sold to obtain the maximum revenue? Find the maximum revenue.

70. Maximizing revenue The revenue received for selling x stereos is given by the formula

$$R = -\frac{x^2}{5} + 80x - 1,000$$

How many stereos must be sold to obtain the maximum revenue? Find the maximum revenue.

71. Maximizing revenue When priced at $30 each, a toy has annual sales of 4,000 units. The manufacturer estimates that each $1 increase in cost will decrease sales by 100 units. Find the unit price that will maximize total revenue. (*Hint:* Total revenue = price · the number of units sold.)

72. Maximizing revenue When priced at $57, one type of camera has annual sales of 525 units. For each $1 the camera is reduced in price, management expects to sell an additional 75 cameras. Find the unit price that will maximize total revenue. (*Hint:* Total revenue = price · the number of units sold.)

WRITING ABOUT MATH

73. The graph of $y = ax^2 + bx + c$ $(a \neq 0)$ passes the vertical line test. Explain why this shows that the equation defines a function.

74. The graph of $x = y^2 - 2y$ is a parabola. Explain why its graph does not represent a function.

SOMETHING TO THINK ABOUT

75. Can you use a graphing calculator to find solutions of the equation $x^2 + x + 1 = 0$? What is the problem? How do you interpret the result?

76. Complete the square on x in the equation $y = ax^2 + bx + c$ and show that the vertex of the parabolic graph is the point with coordinates of

$$\left(-\frac{b}{2a}, \frac{4ac - b^2}{4a}\right)$$

SECTION 10.5
Quadratic and Other Nonlinear Inequalities

Objectives

1. Solve a quadratic inequality.
2. Solve a rational inequality.
3. Graph a nonlinear inequality in two variables.

Vocabulary

quadratic inequality	critical values	critical points

Getting Ready

Factor each trinomial.

1. $x^2 + 2x - 15$

2. $x^2 - 3x + 2$

We have previously solved linear inequalities. We will now discuss how to solve quadratic and rational inequalities.

1 Solve a quadratic inequality.

Quadratic inequalities in one variable, say x, are inequalities that can be written in one of the following forms, where $a \neq 0$:

$$ax^2 + bx + c < 0 \qquad ax^2 + bx + c > 0$$
$$ax^2 + bx + c \leq 0 \qquad ax^2 + bx + c \geq 0$$

To solve one of these inequalities, we must find its solution set. For example, to solve

$$x^2 + x - 6 < 0$$

we must find the values of x that make the inequality true. To find these values, we can factor the trinomial to obtain

$$(x + 3)(x - 2) < 0$$

Since the product of $x + 3$ and $x - 2$ is to be less than 0, the values of the factors must be opposite in sign. This will happen when one of the factors is positive and the other is negative.

To keep track of the sign of $x + 3$, we can construct the following graph.

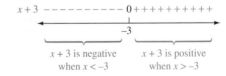

To keep track of the sign of $x - 2$, we can construct the following graph.

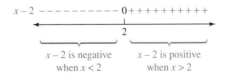

We can merge these graphs as shown in Figure 10-19 and note where the signs of the factors are opposite. This occurs in the interval $(-3, 2)$. Therefore, the product $(x + 3)(x - 2)$ will be less than 0 when

$$-3 < x < 2$$

The graph of the solution set is shown on the number line in the figure.

```
x + 3   ----0+++++++++|++++++
x - 2   ----|---------0++++++
        ←——————|—————————|——————→
              -3         2
```

Figure 10-19

Another way to solve the inequality $x^2 + x - 6 < 0$ is to solve its related quadratic equation $x^2 + x - 6 = 0$. The solutions to this equation are sometimes called **critical values** and they establish points on the number line, called **critical points.**

$$x^2 + x - 6 = 0$$
$$(x + 3)(x - 2) = 0$$
$$x + 3 = 0 \quad \text{or} \quad x - 2 = 0$$
$$x = -3 \quad | \quad x = 2$$

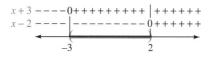

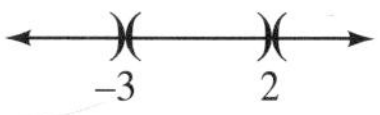

The graphs of these critical values establish the three intervals shown on the number line. To determine which intervals are solutions, we test a number in each interval and see whether it satisfies the inequality.

Interval	Test value	Inequality $x^2 + x - 6 < 0$	Result
$(-\infty, -3)$	-6	$(-6)^2 - (-6) - 6 \overset{?}{<} 0$ $36 < 0$ false	The numbers in this interval are not solutions.
$(-3, 2)$	0	$(0)^2 - (0) - 6 \overset{?}{<} 0$ $-6 < 0$ true	The numbers in this interval are solutions.
$(2, \infty)$	5	$(5)^2 - (5) - 6 \overset{?}{<} 0$ $14 < 0$ false	The numbers in this interval are not solutions.

Table 10-1

Figure 10-20

The solution set is the interval $(-3, 2)$, as shown in Figure 10-20.

EXAMPLE 1   Solve: $x^2 + 2x - 3 \geq 0$.

Solution   **Method 1**   We can factor the trinomial to get $(x - 1)(x + 3)$ and construct the sign chart shown in Figure 10-21.

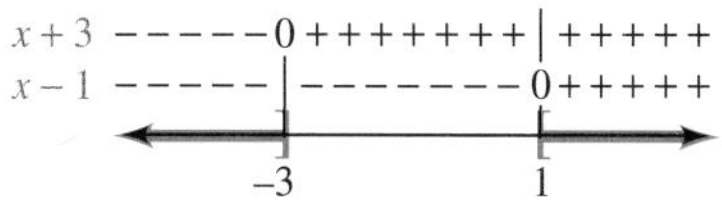

```
x + 3   -----0+++++++|+++++
x - 1   -----|-------0+++++
        ←——————|—————————|——————→
              -3        1
```

Figure 10-21

- $x - 1$ is 0 when $x = 1$, is positive when $x > 1$, and is negative when $x < 1$.
- $x + 3$ is 0 when $x = -3$, is positive when $x > -3$, and is negative when $x < -3$.

The product of $x - 1$ and $x + 3$ will be greater than 0 when the signs of the binomial factors are the same. This occurs in the intervals $(-\infty, -3)$ and $(1, \infty)$. The numbers -3 and 1 are also included, because they make the product equal to 0. Thus, the solution set is the union of two intervals

$$(-\infty, -3] \cup [1, \infty)$$

The graph of the solution set is shown on the number line in Figure 10-21.

Method 2   We can obtain the same result by solving the related quadratic equation $x^2 + 2x - 3 = 0$ and establishing critical points on the number line.

$$x^2 + 2x - 3 = 0$$
$$(x + 3)(x - 1) = 0$$
$$x + 3 = 0 \quad \text{or} \quad x - 1 = 0$$
$$x = -3 \quad\quad\quad x = 1$$

The graphs of these critical values establish the three intervals shown on the number line. To determine which intervals are solutions, we test a number in each interval and see whether it satisfies the inequality.

Interval	Test value	Inequality $x^2 + 2x - 3 \geq 0$	Result
$(-\infty, -3)$	-5	$(-5)^2 + 2(-5) - 3 \overset{?}{\geq} 0$ $12 \geq 0$ true	The numbers in this interval are solutions.
$(-3, 1)$	0	$(0)^2 + 2(0) - 3 \overset{?}{\geq} 0$ $-3 \geq 0$ false	The numbers in this interval are not solutions.
$(1, \infty)$	4	$(4)^2 + 2(4) - 3 \overset{?}{\geq} 0$ $21 \geq 0$ true	The numbers in this interval are solutions.

Table 10-2

From the table, we see that numbers in the intervals $(-\infty, -3)$ and $(1, \infty)$ satisfy the inequality. Because the quadratic inequality contains an $\geq$ symbol, the critical values of $x = -3$ and $x = 1$ also satisfy the inequality. Thus, the solution set is the union of two intervals: $(-\infty, -3] \cup [1, \infty)$, as shown in Figure 10-22.

Figure 10-22

⇨ **SELF CHECK 1**   Solve $x^2 + 2x - 15 > 0$ and graph its solution set.

2   **Solve a rational inequality.**

Making a sign chart is useful for solving many inequalities that are neither linear nor quadratic.

EXAMPLE 2   Solve: $\dfrac{1}{x} < 6.$

Solution   We subtract 6 from both sides to make the right side equal to 0, find a common denominator, and add the fractions:

$$\frac{1}{x} < 6$$

$$\frac{1}{x} - 6 < 0 \quad \text{Subtract 6 from both sides.}$$

$$\frac{1}{x} - \frac{6x}{x} < 0 \qquad \text{Write each fraction with the same denominator.}$$

$$\frac{1 - 6x}{x} < 0 \qquad \text{Subtract the numerators and keep the common denominator.}$$

To use Method 1, we make a sign chart, as in Figure 10-23.

- The denominator x is 0 when $x = 0$, is positive when $x > 0$, and is negative when $x < 0$.
- The numerator $1 - 6x$ is 0 when $x = \frac{1}{6}$, is positive when $x < \frac{1}{6}$, and is negative when $x > \frac{1}{6}$.

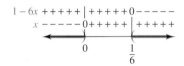

Figure 10-23

The fraction $\frac{1 - 6x}{x}$ will be less than 0 when the numerator and denominator are opposite in sign. This occurs in the union of two intervals:

$$(-\infty, 0) \cup \left(\frac{1}{6}, \infty\right)$$

The graph of this union is shown in Figure 10-23.

To solve this inequality by Method 2, we can find the critical values by finding the values of x that make the numerator of $\frac{1 - 6x}{x}$ equal to 0 and the values of x that make the denominator equal to 0. The critical values are the numbers $\frac{1}{6}$ and 0 and the solution is $(-\infty, 0) \cup \left(\frac{1}{6}, \infty\right)$.

COMMENT   Since we don't know whether x is positive, 0, or negative, multiplying both sides of the inequality $\frac{1}{x} < 6$ by x is a three-case situation:

- If $x > 0$, then $1 < 6x$.
- If $x = 0$, then the fraction $\frac{1}{x}$ is undefined.
- If $x < 0$, then $1 > 6x$.

If you multiply both sides by x and solve $1 < 6x$, you are only considering one case and will get only part of the answer.

▷ **SELF CHECK 2**   Solve: $\frac{3}{x} > 5$.

EXAMPLE 3   Solve: $\dfrac{x^2 - 3x + 2}{x - 3} \geq 0$.

Solution   We write the fraction with the numerator in factored form.

$$\frac{(x - 2)(x - 1)}{x - 3} \geq 0$$

To keep track of the signs of the binomials, we construct the sign chart shown in Figure 10-24. The fraction will be positive in the intervals where all factors are positive, or where two factors are negative. The numbers 1 and 2 are included, because they make the numerator (and thus the fraction) equal to 0. The number 3 is not included, because it gives a 0 in the denominator.

The solution is the union of two intervals $[1, 2] \cup (3, \infty)$. The graph appears in Figure 10-24.

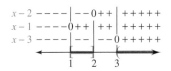

Figure 10-24

To solve this inequality by Method 2, we can find the critical values by finding the values of x that make the numerator of $\frac{(x-2)(x-1)}{x-3}$ equal to 0 and the values of x that make the denominator equal to 0. The critical values are the numbers 1, 2, and 3 and the solution is $[1, 2] \cup (3, \infty)$.

⇨ SELF CHECK 3   Solve: $\dfrac{x+2}{x^2-2x-3} > 0$ and graph the solution set.

EXAMPLE 4   Solve: $\dfrac{3}{x-1} < \dfrac{2}{x}$.

Solution   We subtract $\frac{2}{x}$ from both sides to get 0 on the right side and proceed as follows:

$$\frac{3}{x-1} < \frac{2}{x}$$

$$\frac{3}{x-1} - \frac{2}{x} < 0 \qquad \text{Subtract } \tfrac{2}{x} \text{ from both sides.}$$

$$\frac{3x}{(x-1)x} - \frac{2(x-1)}{x(x-1)} < 0 \qquad \text{Write each fraction with the same denominator.}$$

$$\frac{3x-2x+2}{x(x-1)} < 0 \qquad \text{Keep the denominator and subtract the numerators.}$$

$$\frac{x+2}{x(x-1)} < 0 \qquad \text{Combine like terms.}$$

We can keep track of the signs of the three factors with the sign chart shown in Figure 10-25. The fraction will be negative in the intervals with either one or three negative factors. The numbers 0 and 1 are not included, because they give a 0 in the denominator, and the number -2 is not included, because it does not satisfy the inequality.

The solution is the union of two intervals $(-\infty, -2) \cup (0, 1)$, as shown in Figure 10-25.

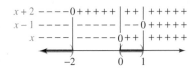

Figure 10-25

To solve this inequality by Method 2, we can find the critical values by finding the values of x that make the numerator of $\frac{x+2}{x(x-1)}$ equal to 0 and the values of x that make the denominator equal to 0. The critical values are the numbers -2, 0, and 1 and the solution is $(-\infty, -2) \cup (0, 1)$.

➡ **SELF CHECK 4**   Solve $\frac{2}{x+1} > \frac{1}{x}$ and graph the solution set.

ACCENT ON TECHNOLOGY

Solving Inequalities

To approximate the solutions of $x^2 + 2x - 3 \geq 0$ (Example 1) by graphing, we can use window settings of $[-10, 10]$ for x and $[-10, 10]$ for y and graph the quadratic function $y = x^2 + 2x - 3$, as in Figure 10-26. The solutions of the inequality will be those numbers x for which the graph of $y = x^2 + 2x - 3$ lies above or on the x-axis. We can trace to find that this interval is $(-\infty, -3] \cup [1, \infty)$.

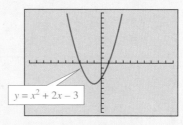

Figure 10-26

To approximate the solutions of $\frac{3}{x-1} < \frac{2}{x}$ (Example 4), we first write the inequality in the form

$$\frac{3}{x-1} - \frac{2}{x} < 0$$

Then we use window settings of $[-5, 5]$ for x and $[-3, 3]$ for y and graph the function $y = \frac{3}{x-1} - \frac{2}{x}$, as in Figure 10-27(a). The solutions of the inequality will be those numbers x for which the graph lies below the x-axis.

We can trace to see that the graph is below the x-axis when x is less than -2. Since we cannot see the graph in the interval $0 < x < 1$, we redraw the graph using window settings of $[-1, 2]$ for x and $[-25, 10]$ for y. See Figure 10-27(b).

We can now see that the graph is below the x-axis in the interval $(0, 1)$. Thus, the solution of the inequality is the union of two intervals:

$$(-\infty, -2) \cup (0, 1)$$

COMMENT Graphing calculators cannot determine whether a critical value is included in a solution set. You must make that determination yourself.

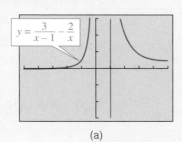

(a)

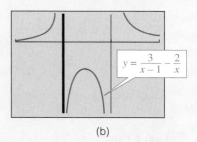

(b)

Figure 10-27

3 **Graph a nonlinear inequality in two variables.**

We now consider the graphs of nonlinear inequalities in two variables.

EXAMPLE 5 Graph: $y < -x^2 + 4$.

Solution The graph of $y = -x^2 + 4$ is the parabolic boundary separating the region representing $y < -x^2 + 4$ and the region representing $y > -x^2 + 4$.

We graph $y = -x^2 + 4$ as a dashed parabola, because there is no equality symbol in the original inequality. Since the coordinates of the origin satisfy the inequality $y < -x^2 + 4$, the point $(0, 0)$ is in the graph. The complete graph is shown in Figure 10-28.

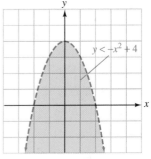

Figure 10-28

SELF CHECK 5 Graph: $y \geq -x^2 + 4$.

EXAMPLE 6 Graph: $x \leq |y|$.

Solution We first graph $x = |y|$ as in Figure 10-29(a), using a solid line because the symbol in the inequality is $\leq$. Since the origin is on the graph, we cannot use it as a test point. However, another point, such as $(1, 0)$, will do. We substitute 1 for x and 0 for y into the inequality to get

$$x \leq |y|$$
$$1 \leq |0|$$
$$1 \leq 0$$

Since $1 \leq 0$ is a false statement, the point $(1, 0)$ does not satisfy the inequality and is not part of the graph. Thus, the graph of $x \leq |y|$ is to the left of the boundary.

The complete graph is shown in Figure 10-29(b).

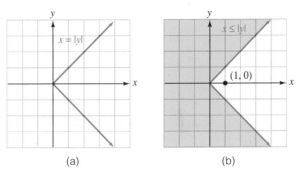

(a) (b)

Figure 10-29

SELF CHECK 6 Graph: $x \geq -|y|$.

⇨ **SELF CHECK ANSWERS**

1. $(-\infty, -5) \cup (3, \infty)$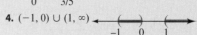

2. $\left(0, \frac{3}{5}\right)$

3. $(-2, -1) \cup (3, \infty)$

4. $(-1, 0) \cup (1, \infty)$

5.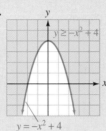

6.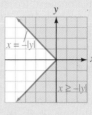

NOW TRY THIS

Find the domain of each of the following.

1. $f(x) = \sqrt{x - 6}$

2. $y \geq x^2 - 5x - 6$

3. $h(x) = \sqrt{x^2 - 5x - 6}$

4. $k(x) = \dfrac{3x - 5}{\sqrt{x^2 - 5x - 6}}$

10.5 EXERCISES

WARM-UPS

Determine where x − 2 is

1. 0   **2.** positive

3. negative

Determine where x + 3 is

4. 0   **5.** positive

6. negative

Multiply both sides of the equation $\frac{1}{x} < 2$ by x when x is

7. positive   **8.** negative

REVIEW

Write each expression as an equation.

9. y varies directly with x.

10. y varies inversely with t.

11. t varies jointly with x and y.

12. d varies directly with t but inversely with u^2.

Find the slope of the graph of each equation.

13. $y = 3x - 4$ **14.** $\dfrac{2x - y}{5} = 8$

VOCABULARY AND CONCEPTS   *Fill in the blanks.*

15. When $x > 3$, the binomial $x - 3$ is _____ than zero.

16. When $x < 3$, the binomial $x - 3$ is ____ than zero.

17. The expression $x^2 + 9x + 18 \leq 0$ is an example of a _____ inequality.

18. The expression $\dfrac{x + 3}{x - 2} > 0$ is an example of a _____ inequality.

19. If $x = 0$, the fraction $\frac{1}{x}$ is _____.

20. To solve $x^2 + 2x - 3 < 0$, we can find the solutions of the related equation $x^2 + 2x - 3 = 0$. The solutions are called _____. They establish points on a number line that separate the line into _____.

21. To keep track of the signs of factors in a product or quotient, we can use a ____ chart.

22. The inequality $|x + 3| < 0$ will be graphed with a _____ line.

GUIDED PRACTICE

Solve each inequality. Give each result in interval notation and graph the solution set. **See Example 1. (Objective 1)**

23. $x^2 - 5x + 4 < 0$

24. $x^2 - 3x - 4 > 0$

25. $x^2 - 8x + 15 > 0$

26. $x^2 + 2x - 8 < 0$

27. $x^2 + x - 12 \le 0$

28. $x^2 + 7x + 12 \ge 0$

29. $x^2 + 2x \ge 15$

30. $x^2 - 8x \le -15$

31. $x^2 + 8x < -16$

32. $x^2 + 6x \ge -9$

33. $x^2 \ge 9$

34. $x^2 \ge 16$

Solve each inequality. Give each result in interval notation and graph the solution set. **See Example 2. (Objective 2)**

35. $\dfrac{1}{x} < 2$

36. $\dfrac{1}{x} > 3$

37. $\dfrac{4}{x} \ge 2$

38. $-\dfrac{6}{x} < 12$

Solve each inequality. Give each result in interval notation and graph the solution set. **See Example 3. (Objective 2)**

39. $\dfrac{x^2 - x - 12}{x - 1} < 0$

40. $\dfrac{x^2 + x - 6}{x - 4} \ge 0$

41. $\dfrac{x^2 + x - 20}{x + 2} \ge 0$

42. $\dfrac{x^2 - 10x + 25}{x + 5} < 0$

43. $\dfrac{x^2 - 4x + 4}{x + 4} < 0$

44. $\dfrac{2x^2 - 5x + 2}{x + 2} > 0$

45. $\dfrac{6x^2 - 5x + 1}{2x + 1} > 0$

46. $\dfrac{6x^2 + 11x + 3}{3x - 1} < 0$

Solve each inequality. Give each result in interval notation and graph the solution set. **See Example 4. (Objective 2)**

47. $\dfrac{3}{x - 2} < \dfrac{4}{x}$

48. $\dfrac{-6}{x + 1} \ge \dfrac{1}{x}$

49. $\dfrac{-5}{x + 2} \ge \dfrac{4}{2 - x}$

50. $\dfrac{-6}{x - 3} < \dfrac{5}{3 - x}$

51. $\dfrac{7}{x - 3} \ge \dfrac{2}{x + 4}$

52. $\dfrac{-5}{x - 4} < \dfrac{3}{x + 1}$

53. $(x + 2)^2 > 0$

54. $(x - 3)^2 < 0$

Graph each inequality. **See Example 5. (Objective 3)**

55. $y < x^2 + 1$

56. $y > x^2 - 3$

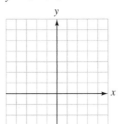

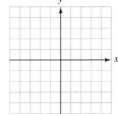

57. $y \le x^2 + 5x + 6$

58. $y \ge x^2 + 5x + 4$

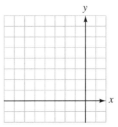

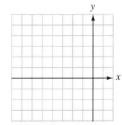

59. $y \geq (x - 1)^2$

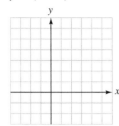

60. $y \leq (x + 2)^2$

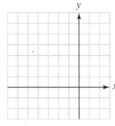

61. $-x^2 - y + 6 > -x$

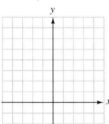

62. $y > (x + 3)(x - 2)$

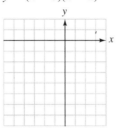

Graph each inequality. **See Example 6. (Objective 3)**

63. $y < |x + 4|$

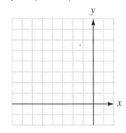

64. $y \geq |x - 3|$

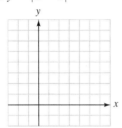

65. $y \leq -|x| + 2$

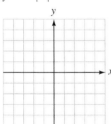

66. $y > |x| - 2$

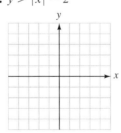

ADDITIONAL PRACTICE

Solve each inequality. Give each result in interval notation and graph the solution set.

67. $2x^2 - 50 < 0$

68. $3x^2 - 243 < 0$

69. $-\dfrac{5}{x} < 3$

70. $\dfrac{4}{x} \geq 8$

71. $\dfrac{x}{x + 4} \leq \dfrac{1}{x + 1}$

72. $\dfrac{x}{x + 9} \geq \dfrac{1}{x + 1}$

73. $\dfrac{x}{x + 16} > \dfrac{1}{x + 1}$

74. $\dfrac{x}{x + 25} < \dfrac{1}{x + 1}$

Use a graphing calculator to solve each inequality. Give the answer in interval notation.

75. $x^2 - 2x - 3 < 0$

76. $x^2 + x - 6 > 0$

77. $\dfrac{x + 3}{x - 2} > 0$

78. $\dfrac{3}{x} < 2$

WRITING ABOUT MATH

79. Explain why $(x - 4)(x + 5)$ will be positive only when the signs of $x - 4$ and $x + 5$ are the same.

80. Explain how to find the graph of $y \geq x^2$.

SOMETHING TO THINK ABOUT

81. Under what conditions will the fraction $\dfrac{(x - 1)(x + 4)}{(x + 2)(x + 1)}$ be positive?

82. Under what conditions will the fraction $\dfrac{(x - 1)(x + 4)}{(x + 2)(x + 1)}$ be negative?

SECTION 10.6 Algebra and Composition of Functions

Objectives

1. Find the sum, difference, product, and quotient of two functions.
2. Find the composition of two functions.
3. Find the difference quotient of a function.
4. Solve an application problem requiring the composition of two functions.

Vocabulary

composition   identity function   difference quotient
composite functions

Getting Ready

Assume that $P(x) = 2x + 1$ and $Q(x) = x - 2$. Find each expression.

1. $P(x) + Q(x)$ 2. $P(x) - Q(x)$

3. $P(x) \cdot Q(x)$ 4. $\dfrac{P(x)}{Q(x)}$

Throughout the text, we have talked about functions. In this section, we will show how to add, subtract, multiply, and divide them. We also will show how to find the composition of two functions.

1 **Find the sum, difference, product, and quotient of two functions.**

We now consider how functions can be added, subtracted, multiplied, and divided.

Operations on Functions

If the domains and ranges of functions f and g are subsets of the real numbers,

The *sum* of f and g, denoted as $f + g$, is defined by
$$(f + g)(x) = f(x) + g(x)$$
The *difference* of f and g, denoted as $f - g$, is defined by
$$(f - g)(x) = f(x) - g(x)$$
The *product* of f and g, denoted as $f \cdot g$, is defined by
$$(f \cdot g)(x) = f(x)g(x)$$
The *quotient* of f and g, denoted as f/g, is defined by
$$(f/g)(x) = \frac{f(x)}{g(x)} \quad (g(x) \neq 0)$$

The domain of each of these functions is the set of real numbers x that are in the domain of both f and g. In the case of the quotient, there is the further restriction that $g(x) \neq 0$.

EXAMPLE 1   Let $f(x) = 2x^2 + 1$ and $g(x) = 5x - 3$. Find each function and its domain.
a. $f + g$ **b.** $f - g$

Solution   **a.** $(f + g)(x) = f(x) + g(x)$
$$= (2x^2 + 1) + (5x - 3)$$
$$= 2x^2 + 5x - 2$$

The domain of $f + g$ is the set of real numbers that are in the domain of both f and g. Since the domain of both f and g is the interval $(-\infty, \infty)$, the domain of $f + g$ is also the interval $(-\infty, \infty)$.

b. $(f - g)(x) = f(x) - g(x)$
$$= (2x^2 + 1) - (5x - 3)$$
$$= 2x^2 + 1 - 5x + 3 \qquad \text{Remove parentheses.}$$
$$= 2x^2 - 5x + 4 \qquad \text{Combine like terms.}$$

Since the domain of both f and g is $(-\infty, \infty)$, the domain of $f - g$ is also the interval $(-\infty, \infty)$.

SELF CHECK 1   Let $f(x) = 3x - 2$ and $g(x) = 2x^2 + 3x$. Find each function and its domain.
a. $f + g$ **b.** $f - g$

EXAMPLE 2   Let $f(x) = 2x^2 + 1$ and $g(x) = 5x - 3$. Find each function and its domain.
a. $f \cdot g$ **b.** f/g

Solution   **a.** $(f \cdot g)(x) = f(x)g(x)$
$$= (2x^2 + 1)(5x - 3)$$
$$= 10x^3 - 6x^2 + 5x - 3 \qquad \text{Multiply.}$$

The domain of $f \cdot g$ is the set of real numbers that are in the domain of both f and g. Since the domain of both f and g is the interval $(-\infty, \infty)$, the domain of $f \cdot g$ is also the interval $(-\infty, \infty)$.

b. $(f/g)(x) = \dfrac{f(x)}{g(x)}$
$$= \dfrac{2x^2 + 1}{5x - 3}$$

Since the denominator of the fraction cannot be 0, $x \neq \frac{3}{5}$. The domain of f/g is the union of two intervals $\left(-\infty, \frac{3}{5}\right) \cup \left(\frac{3}{5}, \infty\right)$.

SELF CHECK 2   Let $f(x) = 2x^2 - 3$ and $g(x) = x - 1$. Find each function and its domain.
a. $f \cdot g$ **b.** f/g

2   **Find the composition of two functions.**

We have seen that a function can be represented by a machine: We put in a number from the domain, and a number from the range comes out. For example, if we put the number

2 into the machine shown in Figure 10-30(a), the number $f(2) = 5(2) - 2 = 8$ comes out. In general, if we put x into the machine shown in Figure 10-30(b), the value $f(x)$ comes out.

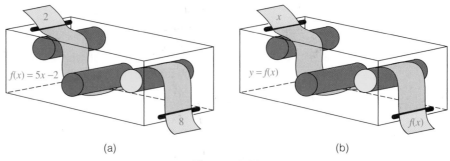

(a)   (b)

Figure 10-30

Often one quantity is a function of a second quantity that depends, in turn, on a third quantity. For example, the cost of a car trip is a function of the gasoline consumed. The amount of gasoline consumed, in turn, is a function of the number of miles driven. Such chains of dependence can be analyzed mathematically as **compositions of functions.**

The function machines shown in Figure 10-31 illustrate the composition of functions f and g. When we put a number x into the function g, $g(x)$ comes out. The value $g(x)$ goes into function f, which transforms $g(x)$ into $f(g(x))$. This two-step process defines a new function, called a **composite function.** If the function machines for g and f were connected to make a single machine, that machine would be named $f \circ g$, read as "f composition g."

To be in the domain of the composite function $f \circ g$, a number x has to be in the domain of g. Also, the output of g must be in the domain of f. Thus, the domain of $f \circ g$ consists of those numbers x that are in the domain of g, and for which $g(x)$ is in the domain of f.

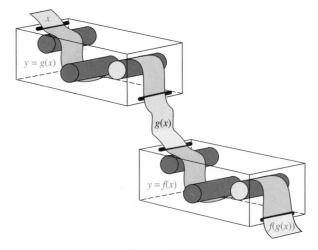

Figure 10-31

Composite Functions

The **composite function** $f \circ g$ is defined by

$$(f \circ g)(x) = f(g(x))$$

COMMENT Note that in this example, $(f \circ g)(x) \neq (g \circ f)(x)$. This shows that the composition of functions is not commutative.

For example, if $f(x) = 4x - 5$ and $g(x) = 3x + 2$, then

$$(f \circ g)(x) = f(g(x)) \qquad\qquad (g \circ f)(x) = g(f(x))$$
$$\qquad = f(3x + 2) \qquad\qquad\qquad = g(4x - 5)$$
$$\qquad = 4(3x + 2) - 5 \qquad\qquad = 3(4x - 5) + 2$$
$$\qquad = 12x + 8 - 5 \qquad\qquad\quad = 12x - 15 + 2$$
$$\qquad = 12x + 3 \qquad\qquad\qquad\; = 12x - 13$$

EXAMPLE 3 Let $f(x) = 2x + 1$ and $g(x) = x - 4$. Find:
a. $(f \circ g)(9)$ **b.** $(f \circ g)(x)$ **c.** $(g \circ f)(-2)$.

Solution **a.** $(f \circ g)(9)$ means $f(g(9))$. In Figure 10-32(a), function g receives the number 9, subtracts 4, and releases the number $g(9) = 5$. The 5 then goes into the f function, which doubles 5 and adds 1. The final result, 11, is the output of the composite function $f \circ g$:

$$(f \circ g)(9) = f(g(9)) = f(5) = 2(5) + 1 = 11$$

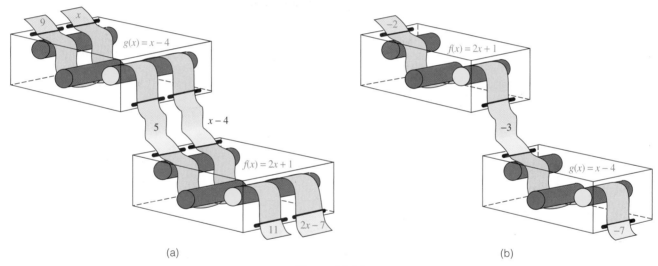

(a)   (b)

Figure 10-32

b. $(f \circ g)(x)$ means $f(g(x))$. In Figure 10-32(a), function g receives the number x, subtracts 4, and releases the number $x - 4$. The $x - 4$ then goes into the f function, which doubles $x - 4$ and adds 1. The final result, $2x - 7$, is the output of the composite function $f \circ g$.

$$(f \circ g)(x) = f(g(x)) = f(x - 4) = 2(x - 4) + 1 = 2x - 7$$

c. $(g \circ f)(-2)$ means $g(f(-2))$. In Figure 10-32(b), function f receives the number -2, doubles it and adds 1, and releases -3 into the g function. Function g subtracts 4 from -3 and releases a final result of -7. Thus,

$$(g \circ f)(-2) = g(f(-2)) = g(-3) = -3 - 4 = -7$$

SELF CHECK 3 Let $f(x) = 3x + 2$ and $g(x) = 9x - 5$. Find
a. $(f \circ g)(2)$ **b.** $(g \circ f)(x)$ **c.** $(g \circ f)(-4)$.

Recall that in the real number system, 0 is called the *additive identity* because $0 + x = x$ and 1 is called the *multiplicative identity* because $1 \cdot x = x$. There is an identity for functions as well. The **identity function** is defined by the equation $I(x) = x$. Under this function, the value that corresponds to any real number x is x itself. If f is any function, the composition of f with the identity function is the function f:

$$(f \circ I)(x) = (I \circ f)(x) = f(x)$$

We can show this as follows:

$(f \circ I)(x)$ means $f(I(x))$. Because $I(x) = x$, we have

$$(f \circ I)(x) = f(I(x)) = f(x)$$

$(I \circ f)(x)$ means $I(f(x))$. Because I passes any number through unchanged, we have $I(f(x)) = f(x)$ and

$$(I \circ f)(x) = I(f(x)) = f(x)$$

3 ### Find the difference quotient of a function.

An important function in calculus, called the **difference quotient,** represents the slope of a line that passes through two given points on the graph of a function. The difference quotient is defined as follows:

$$\frac{f(x + h) - f(x)}{h}$$

EXAMPLE 4 If $f(x) = x^2 - 4$, evaluate the difference quotient.

Solution First, we evaluate $f(x + h)$.

$$f(x) = x^2 - 4$$
$$f(x + h) = (x + h)^2 - 4 \qquad \text{Substitute } x + h \text{ for } h.$$
$$= x^2 + 2xh + h^2 - 4 \qquad (x + h)^2 = x^2 + 2hx + h^2$$

Then we note that $f(x) = x^2 - 4$. We can now substitute the values of $f(x + h)$ and $f(x)$ into the difference quotient and simplify.

$$\frac{f(x + h) - f(x)}{h} = \frac{(x^2 + 2xh + h^2 - 4) - (x^2 - 4)}{h}$$

$$= \frac{x^2 + 2xh + h^2 - 4 - x^2 + 4}{h} \qquad \text{Remove parentheses.}$$

$$= \frac{2xh + h^2}{h} \qquad \text{Combine like terms.}$$

$$= \frac{h(2x + h)}{h} \qquad \text{Factor out } h \text{ in the numerator.}$$

$$= 2x + h \qquad \text{Divide out } h; \frac{h}{h} = 1.$$

The difference quotient for this function simplifies as $2x + h$.

⇨ **SELF CHECK 4** If $f(x) = 3x^2 - 4$, evaluate the difference quotient.

4 **Solve an application problem requiring the composition of two functions.**

EXAMPLE 5   **TEMPERATURE CHANGE**   A laboratory sample is removed from a cooler at a temperature of 15° Fahrenheit. Technicians are warming the sample at a controlled rate of 3° F per hour. Express the sample's Celsius temperature as a function of the time, t (in hours), since it was removed from refrigeration.

Solution   The temperature of the sample is 15° F when $t = 0$. Because it warms at 3° F per hour, it warms $3t°$ after t hours. The Fahrenheit temperature after t hours is given by the function

$$F(t) = 3t + 15$$

The Celsius temperature is a function of the Fahrenheit temperature, given by the formula

$$C(F) = \frac{5}{9}(F - 32)$$

To express the sample's Celsius temperature as a function of time, we find the composition function $C \circ F$.

$$(C \circ F)(t) = C(F(t))$$

$$= \frac{5}{9}(F(t) - 32)$$

$$= \frac{5}{9}[(3t + 15) - 32] \quad \text{Substitute } 3t + 15 \text{ for } F(t).$$

$$= \frac{5}{9}(3t - 17) \quad\quad\quad \text{Simplify.}$$

$$= \frac{15}{9}t - \frac{85}{9}$$

$$= \frac{5}{3}t - \frac{85}{9}$$

⇨ **SELF CHECK ANSWERS**   **1. a.** $2x^2 + 6x - 2, (-\infty, \infty)$ **b.** $-2x^2 - 2, (-\infty, \infty)$ **2. a.** $2x^3 - 2x^2 - 3x + 3, (-\infty, \infty)$
b. $\frac{2x^2 - 3}{x - 1}, (-\infty, 1) \cup (1, \infty)$ **3. a.** 41   **b.** $27x + 13$ **c.** -95 **4.** $6x + 3h$

NOW TRY THIS

Given $f(x) = 3x - 2$ and $g(x) = x^2 - 5x + 1$, find:

1. $(g \circ f)(-1)$

2. $(g \circ f)(x)$

3. $(f \circ f)(x)$

10.6 EXERCISES

Assume no denominators are 0.

WARM-UPS   *If f(x) = 2x, g(x) = 3x, and h(x) = 4x, find:*

1. $f + g$
2. $h - g$
3. $f \cdot h$
4. g/f
5. h/f
6. $g \cdot h$
7. $(f \circ h)(x)$
8. $(f \circ g)(x)$

REVIEW   *Simplify each expression.*

9. $\dfrac{3x^2 + x - 14}{4 - x^2}$

10. $\dfrac{2x^3 + 14x^2}{3 + 2x - x^2} \cdot \dfrac{x^2 - 3x}{x}$

11. $\dfrac{8 + 2x - x^2}{12 + x - 3x^2} \div \dfrac{3x^2 + 5x - 2}{3x - 1}$

12. $\dfrac{x - 1}{1 + \dfrac{x}{x - 2}}$

VOCABULARY AND CONCEPTS   *Fill in the blanks.*

13. $(f + g)(x) =$ _____
14. $(f - g)(x) =$ _____
15. $(f \cdot g)(x) =$ _____

16. $(f/g)(x) =$ _____ $(g(x) \neq 0)$

17. In Exercises 13–15, the domain of each function is the set of real numbers x that are in the _____ of both f and g.
18. The _____ of functions f and g is denoted by $(f \circ g)(x)$ or $f \circ g$.
19. $(f \circ g)(x) =$ _____
20. If I is the identity function, then $(f \circ I)(x) =$ ____.
21. If I is the identity function, then $(I \circ f)(x) =$ ____.
22. The difference quotient is defined as _____.

GUIDED PRACTICE

Let f(x) = 3x and g(x) = 4x. Find each function and its domain.
See Examples 1–2. (Objective 1)

23. $f + g$
24. $f - g$
25. $f \cdot g$
26. f/g
27. $g - f$
28. $g + f$
29. g/f
30. $g \cdot f$

Let f(x) = 2x + 1 and g(x) = x − 3. Find each function and its domain. See Examples 1–2. (Objective 1)

31. $f + g$
32. $f - g$

33. $f \cdot g$
34. f/g

35. $g - f$
36. $g + f$
37. g/f
38. $g \cdot f$

Let f(x) = 2x + 1 and g(x) = x² − 1. Find each value.
See Example 3. (Objective 2)

39. $(f \circ g)(2)$
40. $(g \circ f)(2)$
41. $(g \circ f)(-3)$
42. $(f \circ g)(-3)$
43. $(f \circ g)(0)$
44. $(g \circ f)(0)$
45. $(f \circ g)\left(\dfrac{1}{2}\right)$
46. $(g \circ f)\left(\dfrac{1}{3}\right)$
47. $(f \circ g)(x)$
48. $(g \circ f)(x)$
49. $(g \circ f)(2x)$
50. $(f \circ g)(2x)$

Find $\dfrac{f(x + h) - f(x)}{h}$. See Example 4. (Objective 3)

51. $f(x) = 2x + 3$
52. $f(x) = 3x - 5$
53. $f(x) = x^2$
54. $f(x) = x^2 - 1$
55. $f(x) = 2x^2 - 1$
56. $f(x) = 3x^2$
57. $f(x) = x^2 + x$
58. $f(x) = x^2 - x$
59. $f(x) = x^2 + 3x - 4$
60. $f(x) = x^2 - 4x + 3$
61. $f(x) = 2x^2 + 3x - 7$
62. $f(x) = 3x^2 - 2x + 4$

ADDITIONAL PRACTICE

Let f(x) = 3x − 2 and g(x) = 2x² + 1. Find each function and its domain.

63. $f - g$
64. $f + g$
65. f/g
66. $f \cdot g$

Let f(x) = x² − 1 and g(x) = x² − 4. Find each function and its domain.

67. $f - g$
68. $f + g$
69. g/f
70. $g \cdot f$

Let f(x) = 3x − 2 and g(x) = x² + x. Find each value.

71. $(f \circ g)(4)$
72. $(g \circ f)(4)$

73. $(g \circ f)(-3)$ **74.** $(f \circ g)(-3)$

75. $(g \circ f)(0)$ **76.** $(f \circ g)(0)$

77. $(g \circ f)(x)$ **78.** $(f \circ g)(x)$

Find $\dfrac{f(x) - f(a)}{x - a}$ $(x \neq a)$.

79. $f(x) = 2x + 3$ **80.** $f(x) = 3x - 5$

81. $f(x) = x^2$ **82.** $f(x) = x^2 - 1$

83. $f(x) = 2x^2 - 1$ **84.** $f(x) = 3x^2$

85. $f(x) = x^2 + x$ **86.** $f(x) = x^2 - x$

87. $f(x) = x^2 + 3x - 4$ **88.** $f(x) = x^2 - 4x + 3$

89. $f(x) = 2x^2 + 3x - 7$ **90.** $f(x) = 3x^2 - 2x + 4$

91. If $f(x) = x + 1$ and $g(x) = 2x - 5$, show that $(f \circ g)(x) \neq (g \circ f)(x)$.

92. If $f(x) = x^2 + 1$ and $g(x) = 3x^2 - 2$, show that $(f \circ g)(x) \neq (g \circ f)(x)$.

93. If $f(x) = x^2 + 2x - 3$, find $f(a)$, $f(h)$, and $f(a + h)$. Then show that $f(a + h) \neq f(a) + f(h)$.

94. If $g(x) = 2x^2 + 10$, find $g(a)$, $g(h)$, and $g(a + h)$. Then show that $g(a + h) \neq g(a) + g(h)$.

95. If $f(x) = x^3 - 1$, find $\dfrac{f(x + h) - f(x)}{h}$.

96. If $f(x) = x^3 + 2$, find $\dfrac{f(x + h) - f(x)}{h}$.

APPLICATIONS *Solve each application problem.* See Example 5. (Objective 4)

97. Alloys A molten alloy must be cooled slowly to control crystallization. When removed from the furnace, its temperature is 2,700° F, and it will be cooled at 200° F per hour. Express the Celsius temperature as a function of the number of hours t since cooling began.

98. Weather forecasting A high-pressure area promises increasingly warmer weather for the next 48 hours. The temperature is now 34° Celsius and will rise 1° every 6 hours. Express the Fahrenheit temperature as a function of the number of hours from now.

WRITING ABOUT MATH

99. Explain how to find the domain of f/g.

100. Explain why the difference quotient represents the slope of a line passing through $(x, f(x))$ and $(x + h, f(x + h))$.

SOMETHING TO THINK ABOUT

101. Is composition of functions associative? Choose functions f, g, and h and determine whether $[f \circ (g \circ h)](x) = [(f \circ g) \circ h](x)$.

102. Choose functions f, g, and h and determine whether $f \circ (g + h) = f \circ g + f \circ h$.

SECTION 10.7   Inverses of Functions

Objectives

1. Determine whether a function is one-to-one.
2. Apply the horizontal line test to determine if the graph of a function is one-to-one.
3. Find the inverse of a function.

Vocabulary

one-to-one function   horizontal line test   inverse function

Solve each equation for y.

1. $x = 3y + 2$

2. $x = \dfrac{3}{2}y + 5$

We already know that real numbers have inverses. For example, the additive inverse of 3 is -3, because $3 + (-3) = 0$. The multiplicative inverse of 3 is $\frac{1}{3}$, because $3\left(\frac{1}{3}\right) = 1$. In a similar way, functions have inverses. After discussing one-to-one functions, we will learn how to find the inverse of a function.

1 **Determine whether a function is one-to-one.**

Recall that for each input into a function, there is a single output. For some functions, different inputs have the same output, as shown in Figure 10-33(a). For other functions, different inputs have different outputs, as shown in Figure 10-33(b).

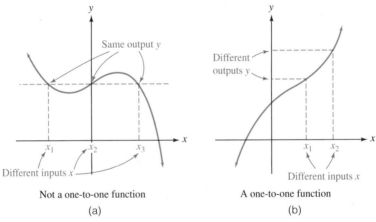

Not a one-to-one function
(a)

A one-to-one function
(b)

Figure 10-33

When every output of a function corresponds to exactly one input, we say that the function is *one-to-one*.

One-to-One Functions

A function is called **one-to-one** if each input value of x in the domain determines a different output value of y in the range.

EXAMPLE 1 Determine whether **a.** $f(x) = x^2$ and **b.** $f(x) = x^3$ are one-to-one.

Solution **a.** The function $f(x) = x^2$ is not one-to-one, because different input values x can determine the same output value y. For example, inputs of 3 and -3 produce the same output value of 9.

$$f(3) = 3^2 = 9 \qquad \text{and} \qquad f(-3) = (-3)^2 = 9$$

b. The function $f(x) = x^3$ is one-to-one, because different input values x determine different output values of y for all x. This is because different numbers have different cubes.

⇨ **SELF CHECK 1**   Determine whether $f(x) = 2x + 3$ is one-to-one.

2   **Apply the horizontal line test to determine if the graph of a function is one-to-one.**

A **horizontal line test** can be used to determine whether the graph of a function represents a one-to-one function. If every horizontal line that intersects the graph of a function does so only once, the function is one-to-one. Otherwise, the function is not one-to-one. See Figure 10-34.

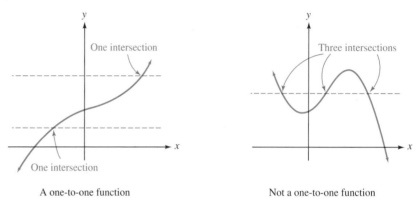

A one-to-one function   Not a one-to-one function

Figure 10-34

EXAMPLE 2   The graphs in Figure 10-35 represent functions. Use the horizontal line test to determine whether the graphs represent one-to-one functions.

Solution   **a.** Because many horizontal lines intersect the graph shown in Figure 10-35(a) twice, the graph does not represent a one-to-one function.

b. Because each horizontal line that intersects the graph in Figure 10-35(b) does so exactly once, the graph does represent a one-to-one function.

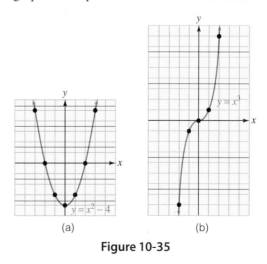

(a)   (b)

Figure 10-35

⇨ **SELF CHECK 2** Does the following graph represent a one-to-one function?

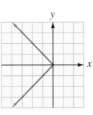

COMMENT Use the vertical line test to determine whether a graph represents a function. If it does, use the horizontal line test to determine whether the function is one-to-one.

3 **Find the inverse of a function.**

The function defined by $C = \frac{5}{9}(F - 32)$ is the formula that we use to convert degrees Fahrenheit to degrees Celsius. If we substitute a Fahrenheit reading into the formula, a Celsius reading comes out. For example, if we substitute 41° for F we obtain a Celsius reading of 5°:

$$C = \frac{5}{9}(F - 32)$$

$$= \frac{5}{9}(41 - 32) \quad \text{Substitute 41 for } F.$$

$$= \frac{5}{9}(9)$$

$$= 5$$

If we want to find a Fahrenheit reading from a Celsius reading, we need a formula into which we can substitute a Celsius reading and have a Fahrenheit reading come out. Such a formula is $F = \frac{9}{5}C + 32$, which takes the Celsius reading of 5° and turns it back into a Fahrenheit reading of 41°.

$$F = \frac{9}{5}C + 32$$

$$= \frac{9}{5}(5) + 32 \quad \text{Substitute 5 for } C.$$

$$= 41$$

The functions defined by these two formulas do opposite things. The first turns 41° F into 5° Celsius, and the second turns 5° Celsius back into 41° F. For this reason, we say that the functions are *inverses* of each other.

If f is the function determined by the table shown in Figure 10-36(a), it turns the number 1 into 10, 2 into 20, and 3 into 30. Since the inverse of f must turn 10 back into 1, 20 back into 2, and 30 back into 3, it consists of the ordered pairs shown in Figure 10-36(b) on the next page.

Function f

x	y
1	10
2	20
3	30

↑   ↑
Domain Range
(a)

Inverse of f

x	y
10	1
20	2
30	3

↑   ↑
Domain Range
(b)

Note that the inverse of f is also a function.

Figure 10-36

We note that the domain of f and the range of its inverse is $\{1, 2, 3\}$. The range of f and the domain of its inverse is $\{10, 20, 30\}$.

This example suggests that to form the inverse of a function f, we simply interchange the coordinates of each ordered pair that determines f. When the inverse of a function is also a function, we call it f *inverse* and denote it with the symbol f^{-1}.

COMMENT   The symbol $f^{-1}(x)$ is read as "the inverse of $f(x)$" or just "f inverse." The -1 in the notation $f^{-1}(x)$ is not an exponent. Remember that $f^{-1}(x) \neq \frac{1}{f(x)}$.

Finding the Inverse of a One-to-One Function

If a function is one-to-one, we find its inverse as follows:

1. Replace $f(x)$ with y, if necessary.

2. Interchange the variables x and y.

3. Solve the resulting equation for y.

4. This equation is $y = f^{-1}(x)$.

EXAMPLE 3   If $f(x) = 4x + 2$, find the inverse of f and determine whether it is a function.

Solution   To find the inverse, we replace $f(x)$ with y and interchange the positions of x and y.

$$f(x) = 4x + 2$$
$$y = 4x + 2 \qquad \text{Replace } f(x) \text{ with } y.$$
$$x = 4y + 2 \qquad \text{Interchange the variables } x \text{ and } y.$$

Then we solve the equation for y.

$$x = 4y + 2$$
$$x - 2 = 4y \qquad \text{Subtract 2 from both sides.}$$
$$y = \frac{x - 2}{4} \qquad \text{Divide both sides by 4 and write } y \text{ on the left side.}$$

Because each input x that is substituted into the resulting equation gives one output y, the inverse of f is a function. Expressing the inverse in function notation, we have

$$f^{-1}(x) = \frac{x - 2}{4}$$

SELF CHECK 3   If $f(x) = -5x - 3$, find the inverse of f and determine whether it is a function.

COMMENT   If the inverse of a function is also a function, we usually write the inverse function using function notation.

To emphasize an important relationship between a function and its inverse, we substitute some number x, such as $x = 3$, into the function $f(x) = 4x + 2$ of Example 3. The corresponding value of y produced is

$$f(3) = 4(3) + 2 = 14$$

If we substitute 14 into the inverse function, f^{-1}, the corresponding value of y that is produced is

$$f^{-1}(14) = \frac{14 - 2}{4} = 3$$

Thus, the function f turns 3 into 14, and the inverse function f^{-1} turns 14 back into 3. In general, *the composition of a function and its inverse is the identity function.*

To prove that $f(x) = 4x + 2$ and $f^{-1}(x) = \frac{x - 2}{4}$ are inverse functions, we must show that their composition (in both directions) is the identity function:

$$(f \circ f^{-1})(x) = f(f^{-1}(x)) \qquad\qquad (f^{-1} \circ f)(x) = f^{-1}(f(x))$$

$$= f\left(\frac{x - 2}{4}\right) \qquad\qquad\qquad\qquad = f^{-1}(4x + 2)$$

$$= 4\left(\frac{x - 2}{4}\right) + 2 \qquad\qquad\qquad = \frac{4x + 2 - 2}{4}$$

$$= x - 2 + 2 \qquad\qquad\qquad\qquad = \frac{4x}{4}$$

$$= x \qquad\qquad\qquad\qquad\qquad\qquad = x$$

Thus, $(f \circ f^{-1})(x) = (f^{-1} \circ f)(x) = x$, which is the identity function $I(x)$.

EXAMPLE 4   The set of all pairs (x, y) determined by $3x + 2y = 6$ is a function. Find its inverse function, and graph the function and its inverse on one coordinate system.

Solution   To find the inverse function of $3x + 2y = 6$, we interchange x and y to obtain

$$3y + 2x = 6$$

and then solve the equation for y.

$$3y + 2x = 6$$
$$3y = -2x + 6 \qquad \text{Subtract } 2x \text{ from both sides.}$$
$$y = -\frac{2}{3}x + 2 \qquad \text{Divide both sides by 3.}$$

Since the resulting equation represents a function, we can write it in inverse function notation as

$$f^{-1}(x) = -\frac{2}{3}x + 2$$

The graphs of $3x + 2y = 6$ and $f^{-1}(x) = -\frac{2}{3}x + 2$ appear in Figure 10-37.

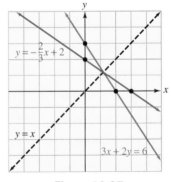

Figure 10-37

⇨ **SELF CHECK 4**   Find the inverse of the function defined by $2x - 3y = 6$. Graph the function and its inverse on one coordinate system.

In Example 4, the graph of $3x + 2y = 6$ and $f^{-1}(x) = -\frac{2}{3}x + 2$ are symmetric about the line $y = x$. In general, *any function and its inverse are symmetric about the line $y = x$*, because when the coordinates (a, b) satisfy an equation, the coordinates (b, a) will satisfy its inverse.

In each example so far, the inverse of a function has been another function. This is not always true, as the following example will show.

EXAMPLE 5   Find the inverse of the function determined by $f(x) = x^2$.

Solution

$y = x^2$ Replace $f(x)$ with y.

$x = y^2$ Interchange x and y.

$y = \pm\sqrt{x}$ Use the square-root property and write y on the left side.

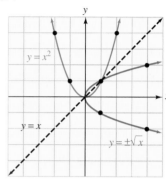

When the inverse $y = \pm\sqrt{x}$ is graphed as in Figure 10-38, we see that the graph does not pass the vertical line test. Thus, it is not a function.

The graph of $y = x^2$ is also shown in the figure. As expected, the graphs of $y = x^2$ and $y = \pm\sqrt{x}$ are symmetric about the line $y = x$.

Figure 10-38

➡ **SELF CHECK 5**   Find the inverse of the function determined by $f(x) = 4x^2$.

EXAMPLE 6   Find the inverse of $f(x) = x^3$.

Solution   To find the inverse, we proceed as follows:

$y = x^3$ Replace $f(x)$ with y.

$x = y^3$ Interchange the variables x and y.

$\sqrt[3]{x} = y$ Take the cube root of both sides.

We note that to each number x there corresponds one real cube root. Thus, $y = \sqrt[3]{x}$ represents a function. In function notation, we have

$f^{-1}(x) = \sqrt[3]{x}$

➡ **SELF CHECK 6**   Find the inverse of $f(x) = x^5$.

If a function is not one-to-one, we often can make it a one-to-one function by restricting its domain.

EXAMPLE 7   Find the inverse of $f(x) = x^2$ $(x \geq 0)$. Then determine whether the inverse is a function. Graph the function and its inverse.

Solution   The inverse of the function $f(x) = x^2$ with $x \geq 0$ is

$y = x^2$ with $x \geq 0$ Replace $f(x)$ with y.

$x = y^2$ with $y \geq 0$ Interchange the variables x and y.

$y = \pm\sqrt{x}$ with $y \geq 0$ Solve for y and write y on the left side.

Considering the restriction $y \geq 0$, the equation can be written more simply as

$$y = \sqrt{x} \qquad \text{This is the inverse of } f(x) = x^2.$$

In this equation, each number x gives only one value of y. Thus, the inverse is a function, which we can write as

$$f^{-1}(x) = \sqrt{x}$$

The graphs of the two functions appear in Figure 10-39. The line $y = x$ is included so that we can see that the graphs are symmetric about the line $y = x$.

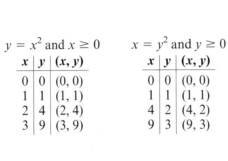

$y = x^2$ and $x \geq 0$			$x = y^2$ and $y \geq 0$		
x	y	(x, y)	x	y	(x, y)
0	0	(0, 0)	0	0	(0, 0)
1	1	(1, 1)	1	1	(1, 1)
2	4	(2, 4)	4	2	(4, 2)
3	9	(3, 9)	9	3	(9, 3)

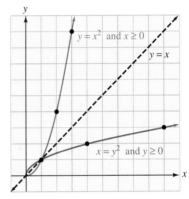

Figure 10-39

⇨ **SELF CHECK 7** Find the inverse of $f(x) = x^2 - 8$ $(x \geq 0)$. Graph the function and its inverse.

⇨ **SELF CHECK ANSWERS**

1. yes **2.** no **3.** $f^{-1}(x) = -\frac{1}{5}x - \frac{3}{5}$; yes **4.** $f^{-1}(x) = \frac{3}{2}x + 3$

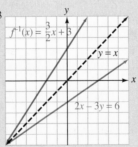

5. $y = \pm\frac{\sqrt{x}}{2}$ **6.** $f^{-1}(x) = \sqrt[5]{x}$

7. $f^{-1}(x) = \sqrt{x + 8}$

NOW TRY THIS

1. Find the inverse of $f(x) = \frac{1}{x}$.

2. Given $f(x) = \frac{5x + 1}{3x - 2}$, find $f^{-1}(x)$.

10.7 EXERCISES

WARM-UPS

Find the inverse of each set of ordered pairs.

1. $\{(1, 2), (2, 3), (5, 10)\}$
2. $\{(1, 1), (2, 8), (4, 64)\}$

Find the inverse function of each linear function.

3. $y = \frac{1}{2}x$
4. $y = 2x$

Determine whether each function is one-to-one.

5. $y = x^2 - 2$
6. $y = x^3$

REVIEW   *Write each complex number in $a + bi$ form or find each value.*

7. $3 - \sqrt{-64}$
8. $(2 - 3i) + (4 + 5i)$

9. $(3 + 4i)(2 - 3i)$
10. $\frac{6 + 7i}{3 - 4i}$

11. $|6 - 8i|$
12. $\left| \frac{2 + i}{3 - i} \right|$

VOCABULARY AND CONCEPTS   *Fill in the blanks.*

13. A function is called _____ if each input determines a different output.
14. If every _____ line that intersects the graph of a function does so only once, the function is one-to-one.
15. If a one-to-one function turns an input of 2 into an output of 5, the inverse function will turn 5 into __.
16. The symbol $f^{-1}(x)$ is read as _____ or _____.
17. $(f \circ f^{-1})(x) = (f^{-1} \circ f)(x) =$ __.
18. The graphs of a function and its inverse are symmetrical about the line _____.

GUIDED PRACTICE

Determine whether each function is one-to-one. **See Example 1.** (Objective 1)

19. $f(x) = 2x$
20. $f(x) = |x|$

21. $f(x) = x^4$
22. $f(x) = x^3 + 1$

Each graph represents a function. Use the horizontal line test to decide whether the function is one-to-one. **See Example 2.** (Objective 2)

23.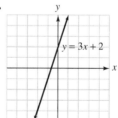

$y = 3x + 2$

24.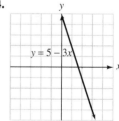

$y = 5 - 3x$

25.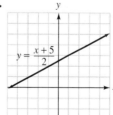

$y = \frac{x + 5}{2}$

26.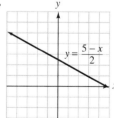

$y = \frac{5 - x}{2}$

27.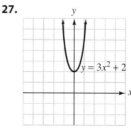

$y = 3x^2 + 2$

28.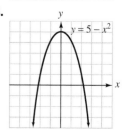

$y = 5 - x^2$

29.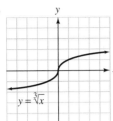

30.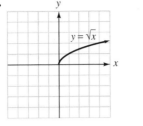

Find the inverse of each set of ordered pairs (x, y) and determine whether the inverse is a function. (Objective 3)

31. $\{(3, 2), (2, 1), (1, 0)\}$

32. $\{(4, 1), (5, 1), (6, 1), (7, 1)\}$

33. $\{(1, 2), (2, 3), (1, 3), (1, 5)\}$

34. $\{(-1, -1), (0, 0), (1, 1), (2, 2)\}$

Find the inverse of each function and express it in the form $y = f^{-1}(x)$. Verify each result by showing that $(f \circ f^{-1})(x) = (f^{-1} \circ f)(x) = x$. See Example 3. (Objective 3)

35. $f(x) = 3x + 1$

36. $y + 1 = 5x$

37. $x + 4 = 5y$

38. $x = 3y + 1$

39. $f(x) = \dfrac{x - 4}{5}$

40. $f(x) = \dfrac{2x + 6}{3}$

41. $4x - 5y = 20$

42. $3x + 5y = 15$

Find the inverse of each function. Then graph the function and its inverse on one coordinate system. Draw the line of symmetry on the graph. See Example 4. (Objective 3)

43. $y = 4x + 3$

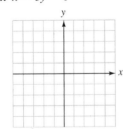

44. $x = 3y - 1$

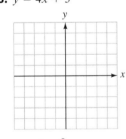

45. $x = \dfrac{y - 2}{3}$

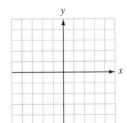

46. $y = \dfrac{x + 3}{4}$

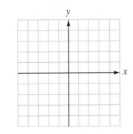

47. $3x - y = 5$

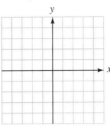

48. $2x + 3y = 9$

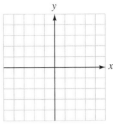

49. $3(x + y) = 2x + 4$

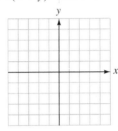

50. $-4(y - 1) + x = 2$

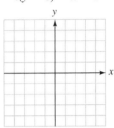

Find the inverse of each function and determine whether it is a function. If it is a function, express it in function notation. See Examples 5–6. (Objective 3)

51. $y = x^2 + 4$

52. $y = x^2 + 5$

53. $y = x^3$

54. $xy = 4$

Graph each equation and its inverse on one set of coordinate axes. Find the axis of symmetry. See Example 7. (Objective 3)

55. $y = x^2 + 1$

56. $y = \dfrac{1}{4}x^2 - 3$

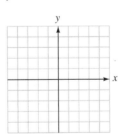

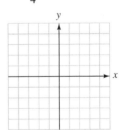

57. $y = \sqrt{x}$

58. $y = |x|$

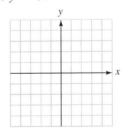

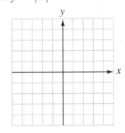

ADDITIONAL PRACTICE *Find the inverse of each function. Do not rationalize denominators.*

59. $\{(1, 1), (2, 4), (3, 9), (4, 16)\}$

60. $\{(1, 1), (2, 1), (3, 1), (4, 1)\}$

61. $y = |x|$

62. $y = \sqrt[3]{x}$

63. $f(x) = 2x^3 - 3$

64. $f(x) = \dfrac{3}{x^3} - 1$

WRITING ABOUT MATH

65. Explain the purpose of the vertical line test.

66. Explain the purpose of the horizontal line test.

SOMETHING TO THINK ABOUT

67. Find the inverse of $y = \dfrac{x + 1}{x - 1}$.

68. Using the functions of Exercise 67, show that $(f \circ f^{-1})(x) = x$.

PROJECTS

Project 1

Ballistics is the study of how projectiles fly. The general formula for the height above the ground of an object thrown straight up or down is given by the function

$$h(t) = -16t^2 + v_0 t + h_0$$

where h is the object's height (in feet) above the ground t seconds after it is thrown. The initial velocity v_0 is the velocity with which the object is thrown, measured in feet per second. The initial height h_0 is the object's height (in feet) above the ground when it is thrown. (If $v_0 > 0$, the object is thrown upward; if $v_0 < 0$, the object is thrown downward.)

This formula takes into account the force of gravity, but disregards the force of air resistance. It is much more accurate for a smooth, dense ball than for a crumpled piece of paper.

One act in the Bungling Brothers Circus is Amazing Glendo's cannonball-catching act. A cannon fires a ball vertically into the air; Glendo, standing on a platform above the cannon, uses his catlike reflexes to catch the ball as it passes by on its way toward the roof of the big top. As the balls fly past, they are within Glendo's reach only during a two-foot interval of their upward path.

As an investigator for the company that insures the circus, you have been asked to find answers to the following questions. The answers will determine whether or not Bungling Brothers' insurance policy will be renewed.

a. In the first part of the act, cannonballs are fired from the end of a six-foot cannon with an initial velocity of 80 feet per second. Glendo catches one ball between 40 and 42 feet above the ground. Then he lowers his platform and catches another ball between 25 and 27 feet above the ground.

    i. Show that if Glendo missed a cannonball, it would hit the roof of the 56-foot-tall big top. How long would it take for a ball to hit the big top? To prevent this from happening, a special net near the roof catches and holds any missed cannonballs.

    ii. Find (to the nearest thousandth of a second) how long the cannonballs are within Glendo's reach for each of his catches. Which catch is easier? Why does your answer make sense? Your company is willing to insure against injuries to Glendo if he has at least 0.025 second to make each catch. Should the insurance be offered?

b. For Glendo's grand finale, the special net at the roof of the big top is removed, making Glendo's catch more significant to the people in the audience, who worry that if Glendo misses, the tent will collapse around them. To make it even more dramatic, Glendo's arms are tied to restrict his reach to a one-foot interval of the ball's flight, and he stands on a platform just under the peak of the big top, so that his catch is made at the very last instant (between 54 and 55 feet above the ground). For this part of the act, however, Glendo has the cannon charged with less gunpowder, so that the muzzle velocity of the cannon is 56 feet per second. Show work to prove that Glendo's big finale is in fact his easiest catch, and that even if he misses, the big top is never in any danger of collapsing, so insurance should be offered against injury to the audience.

Project 2

The center of Sterlington is the intersection of Main Street (running east–west) and Due North Road (running north–south). The recreation area for the townspeople is Robin Park, a few blocks from there. The park is bounded on the south by Main Street and on every other side by Parabolic Boulevard, named for its distinctive shape. In fact, if Main Street and Due North Road were used as the axes of a rectangular coordinate system, Parabolic

Boulevard would have the equation $y = -(x - 4)^2 + 5$, where each unit on the axes is 100 yards.

The city council has recently begun to consider whether or not to put two walkways through the park. (See Illustration 1.) The walkways would run from two points on Main Street and converge at the northernmost point of the park, dividing the area of the park exactly into thirds.

The city council is pleased with the esthetics of this arrangement but needs to know two important facts.

a. For planning purposes, they need to know exactly where on Main Street the walkways would begin.

b. In order to budget for the construction, they need to know how long the walkways will be.

Provide answers for the city council, along with explanations and work to show that your answers are correct. You will need to use the formula shown in Illustration 2, due to Archimedes (287–212 B.C.), for the area under a parabola but above a line perpendicular to the axis of symmetry of the parabola.

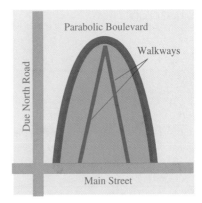

Illustration 1

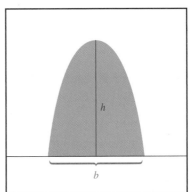

Shaded area $= \dfrac{2}{3} \cdot b \cdot h$

Illustration 2

Chapter 10 REVIEW

SECTION 10.1 Solving Quadratic Equations Using the Square-Root Property and by Completing the Square

DEFINITIONS AND CONCEPTS	EXAMPLES
Square-root property: The equation $x^2 = c$ has two solutions: $\quad x = \sqrt{c} \quad$ and $\quad x = -\sqrt{c}$	To solve $x^2 - 28 = 0$, proceed as follows: $\qquad x^2 = 28 \qquad\qquad$ Add 28 to both sides. $x = \sqrt{28} \quad$ or $\quad x = -\sqrt{28} \quad$ Use the square-root property. $x = 2\sqrt{7} \quad \mid \quad x = -2\sqrt{7} \qquad \sqrt{28} = \sqrt{4}\sqrt{7} = 2\sqrt{7}$ The solutions are $2\sqrt{7}$ and $-2\sqrt{7}$, or $\pm 2\sqrt{7}$.
Completing the square: **1.** Make sure that the coefficient of x^2 is 1. If not, make it 1 by dividing both sides of the equation by the coefficient of x^2.	To solve $2x^2 - 12x + 24 = 0$, we first make the coefficient of x^2 equal to 1 by dividing both sides by 2. **1.** $\dfrac{2x^2}{2} - \dfrac{12x}{2} + \dfrac{24}{2} = \dfrac{0}{2} \qquad$ Divide both sides by 2. $\qquad x^2 - 6x + 12 = 0 \qquad$ Simplify.

2. If necessary, get the constant term on the right side of the equal sign.

3. Complete the square:
   a. Find one-half of the coefficient of x and square it.
   b. Add the square to both sides of the equation.

4. Factor the trinomial square on one side of the equation and combine like terms on the other side.

5. Solve the resulting equation by using the square-root property.

2. $x^2 - 6x = -12$ Subtract 12 from both sides.

3. Since $\left[\frac{1}{2}(-6)\right]^2 = (-3)^2 = 9$, we complete the square by adding 9 to both sides.

$$x^2 - 6x + 9 = -12 + 9$$

4. $(x - 3)^2 = -3$ Factor the left side and combine terms on the right side.

5. $x - 3 = \sqrt{-3}$ or $x - 3 = -\sqrt{-3}$ Use the square-root property.

$x - 3 = \sqrt{3}i$ $\quad x - 3 = -\sqrt{3}i$ Simplify $\sqrt{-3}$.

$x = 3 + \sqrt{3}i$ $\quad x = 3 - \sqrt{3}i$ Add 3 to both sides.

The solutions are $3 \pm \sqrt{3}i$.

REVIEW EXERCISES
Solve each equation by factoring or by using the square-root property.
1. $12x^2 + x - 6 = 0$
2. $6x^2 + 17x + 5 = 0$
3. $15x^2 + 2x - 8 = 0$
4. $(x + 2)^2 = 36$

Solve each equation by completing the square.
5. $x^2 + 6x + 8 = 0$
6. $2x^2 - 9x + 7 = 0$
7. $2x^2 - x - 5 = 0$

SECTION 10.2   Solving Quadratic Equations by the Quadratic Formula

DEFINITIONS AND CONCEPTS

Quadratic formula:
The solutions of

$$ax^2 + bx + c = 0 \quad (a \neq 0)$$

are given by the formula

$$x = \frac{-b \pm \sqrt{b^2 - 4ac}}{2a}$$

EXAMPLES

To solve $2x^2 - 5x + 4 = 0$, note that in the equation $a = 2$, $b = -5$, and $c = 4$, and substitute these values into the quadratic formula.

$$x = \frac{-b \pm \sqrt{b^2 - 4ac}}{2a}$$

$$= \frac{-(-5) \pm \sqrt{(-5)^2 - 4(2)(4)}}{2(2)}$$ Substitute the values.

$$= \frac{5 \pm \sqrt{25 - 32}}{4}$$ Simplify.

$$= \frac{5 \pm \sqrt{-7}}{4}$$ Add.

$$= \frac{5 \pm i\sqrt{7}}{4}$$ $\sqrt{-7} = i\sqrt{7}$

The solutions are $\frac{5}{4} \pm \frac{\sqrt{7}}{4}i$.

REVIEW EXERCISES
Solve each equation by using the quadratic formula.
8. $x^2 - 8x - 9 = 0$
9. $x^2 - 10x = 0$
12. $2x^2 - x - 2 = 0$
13. $x^2 + x + 2 = 0$
10. $2x^2 + 13x - 7 = 0$
11. $3x^2 + 20x - 7 = 0$

14. Dimensions of a rectangle A rectangle is 2 centimeters longer than it is wide. If both the length and width are doubled, its area is increased by 72 square centimeters. Find the dimensions of the original rectangle.

15. Dimensions of a rectangle A rectangle is 1 foot longer than it is wide. If the length is tripled and the width is doubled, its area is increased by 30 square feet. Find the dimensions of the original rectangle.

16. Ballistics If a rocket is launched straight up into the air with an initial velocity of 112 feet per second, its height after t seconds is given by the formula $h = 112t - 16t^2$, where h represents the height of the rocket in feet. After launch, how long will it be before it hits the ground?

17. Ballistics What is the maximum height of the rocket discussed in Exercise 16?

SECTION 10.3 The Discriminant and Equations That Can Be Written in Quadratic Form

DEFINITIONS AND CONCEPTS	EXAMPLES

The discriminant: If a, b, and c are real numbers and a is not 0,
 If $b^2 - 4ac > 0$, the equation $ax^2 + bx + c = 0$ has two unequal solutions.
 	
 If $b^2 - 4ac = 0$, the equation $ax^2 + bx + c = 0$ has two equal solutions (called a *double root*).
 	
 If $b^2 - 4ac < 0$, the equation $ax^2 + bx + c = 0$ has two solutions that are complex conjugates.
 	
 If a, b, and c are rational numbers and the discriminant:
 	
   is a perfect square greater than 0, there are two unequal rational solutions.
 	
   is positive but not a perfect square, the solutions are irrational and unequal.
	To determine the type of solutions for the equation $x^2 - x + 9 = 0$, we calculate the discriminant.
	
	 $$b^2 - 4ac = (-1)^2 - 4(1)(9) \quad a = 1, b = -1, \text{ and } c = 9.$$ $$= 1 - 36$$ $$= -35$$
	 Since $b^2 - 4ac < 0$, the solutions are complex conjugates.
	
	 To determine the type of solutions for the equation $2x^2 + 4x - 5 = 0$, we calculate the discriminant.
	
	 $$b^2 - 4ac = 4^2 - 4(2)(-5) \quad a = 2, b = 4, \text{ and } c = -5.$$ $$= 16 + 40$$ $$= 56$$
	 Since $b^2 - 4ac > 0$, the solutions are unequal and irrational.

Solving equations quadratic in form: Use u substitution when necessary.	To solve the equation $x^4 - 3x^2 - 4 = 0$, we can proceed as follows: $$x^4 - 3x^2 - 4 = 0$$ $$(x^2)^2 - 3(x^2) - 4 = 0$$ $$u^2 - 3u - 4 = 0 \quad \text{Substitute } u \text{ for } x^2.$$ $$(u - 4)(u + 1) = 0 \quad \text{Factor } u^2 - 5u + 4.$$ $$u - 4 = 0 \quad \text{or} \quad u + 1 = 0 \quad \text{Set each factor equal to 0.}$$ $$u = 4 \quad | \quad u = -1$$ Since $x^2 = u$, it follows that $x^2 = 4$ or $x^2 = -1$. Thus, $$x^2 = 4 \qquad \text{or} \qquad x^2 = -1$$ $$x = 2 \quad \text{or} \quad x = -2 \quad | \quad x = i \quad \text{or} \quad x = -i$$
Verifying solutions: If r_1 and r_2 are solutions of $ax^2 + bx + c = 0$ ($a \neq 0$), then $$r_1 + r_2 = -\frac{b}{a} \quad \text{and} \quad r_1 r_2 = \frac{c}{a}$$	To verify that $\frac{5}{3}$ and 2 are the solutions of $3x^2 - 11x + 10 = 0$, make the following calculations: $$-\frac{b}{a} = -\frac{-11}{3} = \frac{11}{3} \quad \text{and} \quad \frac{c}{a} = \frac{10}{3}$$ Since $\frac{5}{3} + 2 = \frac{5}{3} + \frac{6}{3} = \frac{11}{3}$ and $\frac{5}{3}(2) = \frac{5}{3} \cdot \frac{2}{1} = \frac{10}{3}$, $\frac{5}{3}$ and 2 are the solutions of $3x^2 - 11x + 10 = 0$.

REVIEW EXERCISES

Use the discriminant to determine what types of solutions exist for each equation.

18. $3x^2 + 4x - 3 = 0$

19. $4x^2 - 5x + 7 = 0$

20. Find the values of k that will make the solutions of $(k - 8)x^2 + (k + 16)x = -49$ equal.

21. Find the values of k such that the solutions of $3x^2 + 4x = k + 1$ will be real numbers.

Solve each equation.

22. $x - 13x^{1/2} + 12 = 0$

23. $a^{2/3} + a^{1/3} - 6 = 0$

24. $\dfrac{1}{x + 1} - \dfrac{1}{x} = -\dfrac{1}{x + 1}$

25. $\dfrac{6}{x + 2} + \dfrac{6}{x + 1} = 5$

26. Find the sum of the solutions of the equation $3x^2 - 14x + 3 = 0$.

27. Find the product of the solutions of the equation $3x^2 - 14x + 3 = 0$.

SECTION 10.4 Graphs of Quadratic Functions

DEFINITIONS AND CONCEPTS	EXAMPLES
Graphing quadratic functions: If f is a function and k and h positive numbers, then: The graph of $f(x) + k$ is identical to the graph of $f(x)$, except that it is translated k units upward. The graph of $f(x) - k$ is identical to the graph of $f(x)$, except that it is translated k units downward. The graph of $f(x - h)$ is identical to the graph of $f(x)$, except that it is translated h units to the right. The graph of $f(x + h)$ is identical to the graph of $f(x)$, except that it is translated h units to the left.	Graph each of the following: **a.** $f(x) = 4x^2$ **b.** $f(x) = 4x^2 - 3$ **c.** $f(x) = 4(x - 3)^2$ 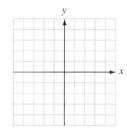 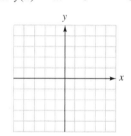 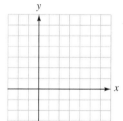
Finding the vertex of a parabola: If $a \neq 0$, the graph of $y = a(x - h)^2 + k$ is a parabola with vertex at (h, k). It opens upward when $a > 0$ and downward when $a < 0$.	The vertex of the graph of $y = 2(x - 3)^2 - 5$ is $(3, -5)$. Since $2 > 0$, the graph will open upward.
The coordinates of the vertex of the graph of $$f(x) = ax^2 + bc + c \quad (a \neq 0)$$ are $\left(-\dfrac{b}{2a}, f\left(-\dfrac{b}{2a}\right)\right)$. The axis of symmetry is $x = -\dfrac{b}{2a}$.	Find the axis of symmetry and the vertex of the graph of $f(x) = 2x^2 - 4x - 5$. $$x\text{-coordinate} = -\frac{b}{2a} = -\frac{-4}{2(2)} = -\frac{-4}{4} = \frac{4}{4} = 1$$ The axis of symmetry is $x = 1$. To find the y-coordinate of the vertex, substitute 1 for x in $f(x) = 2x^2 - 4x - 5$. $$f(x) = 2x^2 - 4x - 5$$ $$f(1) = 2(1)^2 - 4(1) - 5$$ $$= 2 - 4 - 5$$ $$= -7$$ The vertex is $(1, -7)$.

REVIEW EXERCISES
Graph each function and give the coordinates of the vertex of the
resulting parabola.

28. $y = 2x^2 - 3$

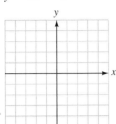

29. $y = -2x^2 - 1$

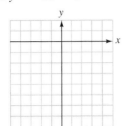

30. $y = -4(x - 2)^2 + 1$

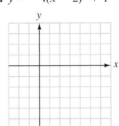

31. $y = 5x^2 + 10x - 1$

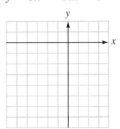

32. Find the vertex of the graph of $f(x) = 3x^2 - 12x - 5$.

SECTION 10.5   Quadratic and Other Nonlinear Inequalities

DEFINITIONS AND CONCEPTS	EXAMPLES
Solving quadratic inequalities: To solve a quadratic inequality in one variable, make a sign chart and determine which intervals are solutions.	To solve $x^2 - 2x - 8 > 0$, factor the trinomial to get $(x - 4)(x + 2)$ and construct the chart shown below. The critical values will occur at 4 and -2.  $x - 4$ is positive when $x > 4$, and is negative when $x < 4$. $x + 2$ is positive when $x > -2$, and is negative when $x < -2$. The product of $x - 4$ and $x + 2$ will be greater than 0 when the signs of the binomial factors are the same. This occurs in the intervals $(-\infty, -2)$ and $(4, \infty)$. The numbers -2 and 4 are not included, because equality is not indicated in the original inequality. Thus, the solution set in interval notation is $\quad (-\infty, -2) \cup (4, \infty)$ The graph of the solution set is shown on the number line below.
Graphing rational inequalities: To solve inequalities with rational expressions, get 0 on the right side, add the fractions, and then factor the numerator and denominator. Use a sign chart to determine the solution.	To solve $\frac{1}{x} \geq -4$, add 4 to both sides to make the right side equal to 0 and proceed as follows: $\quad \dfrac{1}{x} + 4 \geq 0$ $\quad \dfrac{1}{x} + \dfrac{4x}{x} \geq 0 \quad$ Write each fraction with a common denominator. $\quad \dfrac{1 + 4x}{x} \geq 0 \quad$ Add. Finally, make a sign chart, as shown. 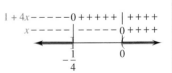

The denominator x is undefined when $x = 0$, positive when $x > 0$, and negative when $x < 0$. The numerator $1 + 4x$ is 0 when $x = -\frac{1}{4}$, positive when $x > -\frac{1}{4}$, and negative when $x < -\frac{1}{4}$. The critical values occur when the numerator or denominator is 0: 0 and $-\frac{1}{4}$.

The fraction $\frac{1 + 4x}{x}$ will be greater than or equal to 0 when the numerator and denominator are the same sign and when the numerator is 0. This occurs in the interval

$$\left(-\infty, -\frac{1}{4}\right] \cup (0, \infty)$$

The graph of this interval is shown.

Graphing nonlinear inequalities in two variables:
To graph a nonlinear inequality, first graph the equation. Then determine which region represents the graph of the inequality.

To graph $x > |y|$, first graph $x = |y|$ as in the illustration below using a dashed line, because equality is not indicated in the original inequality.

Since the origin is on the graph, we cannot use it as a test point. We select another point, such as $(1, 0)$. We substitute 1 for x and 0 for y into the inequality to get

$$x > |y|$$
$$1 > |0|$$
$$1 > 0$$

Since $1 > 0$ is a true statement, the point $(1, 0)$ satisfies the inequality and is part of the graph. Thus, the graph of $x > |y|$ is to the right of the boundary.

The complete graph is shown.

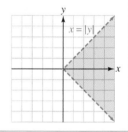

REVIEW EXERCISES

Solve each inequality. Give each result in interval notation and graph the solution set.

33. $x^2 + 2x - 35 > 0$

34. $x^2 + 7x - 18 < 0$

35. $\dfrac{3}{x} \le 5$

36. $\dfrac{2x^2 - x - 28}{x - 1} > 0$

 Use a graphing calculator to solve each inequality. Compare the results with Review Exercises 33–36.

37. $x^2 + 2x - 35 > 0$

38. $x^2 + 7x - 18 < 0$

39. $\dfrac{3}{x} \le 5$

40. $\dfrac{2x^2 - x - 28}{x - 1} > 0$

Graph each inequality.

41. $y < \dfrac{1}{2}x^2 - 1$

42. $y \ge -|x|$

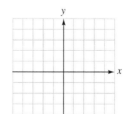

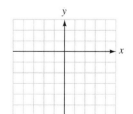

SECTION 10.6 Algebra and Composition of Functions

DEFINITIONS AND CONCEPTS	EXAMPLES
Operations with functions: $$(f + g)(x) = f(x) + g(x)$$ $$(f - g)(x) = f(x) - g(x)$$ $$(f \cdot g)(x) = f(x)g(x)$$ $$(f/g)(x) = \frac{f(x)}{g(x)} \quad (g(x) \neq 0)$$	Given $f(x) = 6x - 2$ and $g(x) = x^2 + 4$, find **a.** $f + g$ **b.** $f - g$ **c.** $f \cdot g$ **d.** f/g **a.** $f + g = f(x) + g(x)$ $\quad\quad = (6x - 2) + (x^2 + 4)$ $\quad\quad = x^2 + 6x + 2$ Combine like terms. **b.** $f - g = (6x - 2) - (x^2 + 4)$ $\quad\quad = 6x - 2 - x^2 - 4$ Remove parentheses. $\quad\quad = -x^2 + 6x - 6$ Combine like terms. **c.** $f \cdot g = (6x - 2)(x^2 + 4)$ $\quad\quad = 6x^3 + 24x - 2x^2 - 8$ Multiply. $\quad\quad = 6x^3 - 2x^2 + 24x - 8$ Write exponents in descending order. **d.** $f/g = \dfrac{6x - 2}{x^2 + 4}$
Composition of functions: $$(f \circ g)(x) = f(g(x))$$	Let $f(x) = 5x - 4$ and $g(x) = x^2 + 2$. Find **a.** $(f \circ g)(x)$ **b.** $(g \circ f)(x)$ **a.** $(f \circ g)(x)$ means $f(g(x))$. $\quad f(g(x)) = f(x^2 + 2)$ $\quad\quad\quad = 5(x^2 + 2) - 4$ Substitute $x^2 + x$ for x. $\quad\quad\quad = 5x^2 + 10 - 4$ Multiply. $\quad\quad\quad = 5x^2 + 6$ Add. **b.** $(g \circ f)(x)$ means $g(f(x))$. $\quad g(f(x)) = g(5x - 4)$ $\quad\quad\quad = (5x - 4)^2 + 2$ Substitute $5x - 4$ for x. $\quad\quad\quad = 25x^2 - 40x + 16 + 2$ Square the binomial. $\quad\quad\quad = 25x^2 - 40x + 18$ Add.
The difference quotient: The difference quotient is defined as follows: $$\frac{f(x + h) - f(x)}{h}$$	To evaluate the difference quotient for $f(x) = x^2 + 2x - 6$, first evaluate $f(x + h)$. $\quad f(x) = x^2 + 2x - 6$ $\quad f(x + h) = (x + h)^2 + 2(x + h) - 6$ Substitute $x + h$ for h. $\quad\quad\quad = x^2 + 2xh + h^2 + 2x + 2h - 6$ $(x + h)^2 = x^2 + 2hx + h^2$

Now substitute the values of $f(x + h)$ and $f(x)$ into the difference quotient and simplify.

$$\frac{f(x + h) - f(x)}{h}$$

$$= \frac{(x^2 + 2xh + h^2 + 2x + 2h - 6) - (x^2 + 2x - 6)}{h}$$

$$= \frac{x^2 + 2xh + h^2 + 2x + 2h - 6 - x^2 - 2x + 6}{h} \quad \text{Remove parentheses.}$$

$$= \frac{2xh + h^2 + 2h}{h} \quad \text{Combine like terms.}$$

$$= \frac{h(2x + h + 2)}{h} \quad \text{Factor out } h \text{ in the numerator.}$$

$$= 2x + h + 2 \quad \text{Divide out } h.$$

The difference quotient for this function is $2x + h + 2$.

REVIEW EXERCISES

Let $f(x) = 2x$ and $g(x) = x + 1$. Find each function or value.

43. $f + g$ 　　　　　 **44.** $f - g$ 　　　　　 **47.** $(f \circ g)(2)$ 　　　 **48.** $(g \circ f)(-1)$

　　　　　　　　　　　　　　　　　　　　　 49. $(f \circ g)(x)$ 　　　 **50.** $(g \circ f)(x)$

45. $f \cdot g$ 　　　　　 **46.** f/g

SECTION 10.7   Inverses of Functions

DEFINITIONS AND CONCEPTS	EXAMPLES

Horizontal line test:
If every horizontal line that intersects the graph of a function does so only once, the function is one-to-one.

Determine if the graph of each function is one-to-one.

a.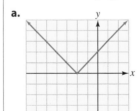

not one-to-one

b.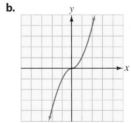

one-to-one

a. The function is not one-to-one because a horizontal line will cross its graph more than once.
b. The function is one-to-one because any horizontal line will cross its graph no more than once.

Finding the inverse of a one-to-one function:
If a function is one-to-one, we find its inverse as follows:

1. Replace $f(x)$ with y, if necessary.
2. Interchange the variables x and y.
3. Solve the resulting equation for y.
4. If the equation is a function, write the equation in function notation.

To find the inverse of $f(x) = x^3 - 5$, we proceed as follows:

$$y = x^3 - 5 \quad \text{Replace } f(x) \text{ with } y.$$
$$x = y^3 - 5 \quad \text{Interchange the variables } x \text{ and } y.$$
$$x + 5 = y^3 \quad \text{Add 5 to both sides.}$$
$$\sqrt[3]{x + 5} = y \quad \text{Take the cube root of both sides.}$$

Because there corresponds one real cube root for each x, $y = \sqrt[3]{x + 5}$ represents a function. In function notation, we describe the inverse as

$$f^{-1}(x) = \sqrt[3]{x + 5}$$

REVIEW EXERCISES

Graph each function and use the horizontal line test to decide whether the function is one-to-one.

51. $f(x) = 2(x - 3)$

52. $f(x) = x(2x - 3)$

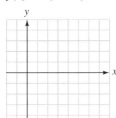

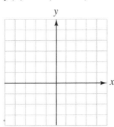

53. $f(x) = -3(x - 2)^2 + 5$

54. $f(x) = |x|$

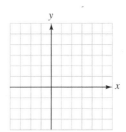

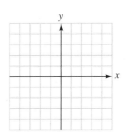

Find the inverse of each function. Do not rationalize the result.

55. $f(x) = 6x - 3$

56. $f(x) = 4x + 5$

57. $y = 2x^2 - 1$ $(x \geq 0)$

58. $y = |x|$

Chapter 10   TEST

Solve each equation by factoring.

1. $x^2 + 3x - 18 = 0$

2. $x(6x + 19) = -15$

Determine what number must be added to each binomial to make it a perfect square.

3. $x^2 + 24x$

4. $x^2 - 50x$

Solve each equation by completing the square.

5. $x^2 + 4x + 1 = 0$

6. $x^2 - 5x - 3 = 0$

Solve each equation by the quadratic formula.

7. $2x^2 + 5x + 1 = 0$

8. $x^2 - x + 3 = 0$

9. Determine whether the solutions of $3x^2 + 5x + 17 = 0$ are real or nonreal numbers.

10. For what value(s) of k are the solutions of $4x^2 - 2kx + k - 1 = 0$ equal?

11. One leg of a right triangle is 14 inches longer than the other, and the hypotenuse is 26 inches. Find the length of the shorter leg.

12. Solve: $2y - 3y^{1/2} + 1 = 0$.

13. Graph $f(x) = \frac{1}{2}x^2 - 4$ and give the coordinates of its vertex.

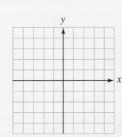

14. Find the vertex of the graph of $f(x) = -2x^2 + 8x - 7$.

15. Graph: $y \leq -x^2 + 3$.

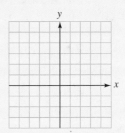

Solve each inequality and graph the solution set.

16. $x^2 - 2x - 8 > 0$

17. $\dfrac{x - 2}{} \leq 0$

Let f(x) = 4x and g(x) = x − 1. Find each function.

18. $g + f$

19. $f - g$

20. $g \cdot f$

21. g/f

Let f(x) = 4x and g(x) = x − 1. Find each value.

22. $(g \circ f)(1)$

23. $(f \circ g)(0)$

24. $(f \circ g)(-1)$

25. $(g \circ f)(-2)$

Let f(x) = 4x and g(x) = x − 1. Find each function.

26. $(f \circ g)(x)$ **27.** $(g \circ f)(x)$

Find the inverse of each function. Do not rationalize the result.

28. $3x + 2y = 12$ **29.** $y = 3x^2 + 4 \quad (x \le 0)$

Cumulative Review Exercises

Find the domain and range of each function.

1. $f(x) = 2x^2 - 3$

2. $f(x) = -|x - 4|$

Write the equation of the line with the given properties.

3. $m = 3$, passing through $(-2, -4)$

4. parallel to the graph of $2x + 3y = 6$ and passing through $(0, -2)$

Perform each operation.

5. $(2a^2 + 4a - 7) - 2(3a^2 - 4a)$

6. $(3x + 2)(2x - 3)$

Factor each expression completely using only integers.

7. $x^4 - 16y^4$

8. $15x^2 - 2x - 8$

Solve each equation.

9. $x^2 - 5x - 6 = 0$ **10.** $6a^3 - 2a = a^2$

Simplify each expression. Assume that all variables represent positive numbers.

11. $\sqrt{25x^4}$ **12.** $\sqrt{48t^3}$

13. $\sqrt[3]{-27x^3}$ **14.** $\sqrt[3]{\dfrac{128x^4}{2x}}$

15. $8^{-1/3}$ **16.** $64^{2/3}$

17. $\dfrac{y^{2/3}y^{5/3}}{y^{1/3}}$ **18.** $\dfrac{x^{5/3}x^{1/2}}{x^{3/4}}$

Graph each function and give the domain and the range.

19. $f(x) = \sqrt{x - 2}$ **20.** $f(x) = -\sqrt{x + 2}$

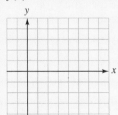

Perform the operations.

21. $(x^{2/3} - x^{1/3})(x^{2/3} + x^{1/3})$

22. $(x^{-1/2} + x^{1/2})^2$

Simplify each statement. Assume no division by 0.

23. $\sqrt{50} - \sqrt{8} + \sqrt{32}$

24. $-3\sqrt[4]{32} - 2\sqrt[4]{162} + 5\sqrt[4]{48}$

25. $3\sqrt{2}\left(2\sqrt{3} - 4\sqrt{12}\right)$ **26.** $\dfrac{5}{\sqrt[3]{x}}$

27. $\dfrac{\sqrt{x} + 2}{\sqrt{x} - 1}$ **28.** $\sqrt[6]{x^3 y^3}$

Solve each equation.

29. $5\sqrt{x + 2} = x + 8$ **30.** $\sqrt{x} + \sqrt{x + 2} = 2$

31. Find the length of the hypotenuse of the right triangle shown in Illustration 1.

32. Find the length of the hypotenuse of the right triangle shown in Illustration 2.

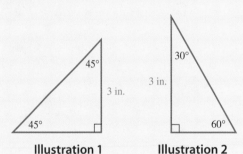

Illustration 1   **Illustration 2**

33. Find the distance between $(-2, 6)$ and $(4, 14)$.

34. What number must be added to $x^2 + 6x$ to make a perfect trinomial square?

35. Use the method of completing the square to solve $2x^2 + x - 3 = 0$.

36. Use the quadratic formula to solve $3x^2 + 4x - 1 = 0$.

37. Graph $f(x) = \frac{1}{2}x^2 + 5$ and find the coordinates of its vertex.

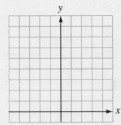

38. Graph $y \leq -x^2 + 3$ and find the coordinates of its vertex.

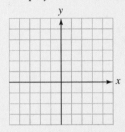

Write each expression as a real number or as a complex number in $a + bi$ form.

39. $(3 + 5i) + (4 - 3i)$

40. $(7 - 4i) - (12 + 3i)$

41. $(2 - 3i)(2 + 3i)$

42. $(3 + i)(3 - 3i)$

43. $(3 - 2i) - (4 + i)^2$

44. $\dfrac{5}{3 - i}$

45. $|3 + 2i|$

46. $|5 - 6i|$

47. For what values of k will the solutions of $2x^2 + 4x = k$ be equal?

48. Solve: $a - 7a^{1/2} + 12 = 0$.

Solve each inequality and graph the solution set on the number line.

49. $x^2 - x - 6 > 0$

50. $x^2 - x - 6 \leq 0$

Let $f(x) = 3x^2 + 2$ and $g(x) = 2x - 1$. Find each value or composite function.

51. $f(-1)$

52. $(g \circ f)(2)$

53. $(f \circ g)(x)$

54. $(g \circ f)(x)$

Find the inverse of each function.

55. $f(x) = 3x + 2$

56. $f(x) = x^3 + 4$

Exponential and Logarithmic Functions

©Shutterstock.com/Alistair Scott

Careers and Mathematics

PEST-CONTROL WORKERS

Few people welcome roaches, rats, mice, spiders, termites, fleas, ants, and bees into their homes. It is the job of pest-control workers to locate, identify, destroy, control, and repel these pests.
Of the 70,000 pest-control workers that held jobs in 2006, 85 percent were employed in services related to the building industry, primarily in states with warmer climates. About 9 percent are self-employed.
Both federal and state laws require pest-control workers to be certified.

Job Outlook:
Employment of pest-control workers is expected to grow 15 percent between 2006 and 2016, which is faster than the average for all occupations.

Hourly Earnings:
$10.79–$16.76.

For More Information:
http://www.bls.gov/oco/ocos254.htm

For a Sample Application:
See Problem 87 in Section 11.6.

In this chapter ▶

In this chapter, we will discuss two functions that are important in many applications of mathematics. Exponential functions are used to compute compound interest, find radioactive decay, and model population growth. Logarithmic functions are used to measure acidity of solutions, drug dosage, gain of an amplifier, magnitude of earthquakes, and safe noise levels in factories.

1. Simplify an expression containing irrational exponents.
2. Graph an exponential function.
3. Graph a translation of an exponential function.
4. Evaluate an application problem containing an exponential function.

exponential function   compound interest   periodic interest rate
increasing function   future value   compounding period
decreasing function

Find each value.

1. 2^3 **2.** $25^{1/2}$ **3.** 5^{-2} **4.** $\left(\dfrac{3}{2}\right)^{-3}$

The graph in Figure 11-1 shows the balance in an investment account in which $10,000 was invested in 2000 at 9% annual interest, compounded monthly. The graph shows that in the year 2010, the value of the account will be approximately $25,000, and in the year 2030, the value will be approximately $147,000. The curve shown in Figure 11-1 is the graph of a function called an *exponential function,* the topic of this section.

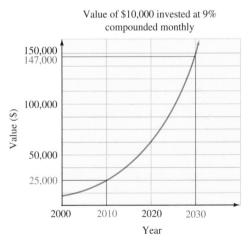

Value of $10,000 invested at 9% compounded monthly

Figure 11-1

1   Simplify an expression containing irrational exponents.

We have discussed expressions of the form b^x, where x is a rational number.

$8^{1/2}$ means "the square root of 8."

$5^{1/3}$ means "the cube root of 5."

$3^{-2/5} = \dfrac{1}{3^{2/5}}$ means "the reciprocal of the fifth root of 3^2."

To give meaning to b^x when x is an irrational number, we consider the expression

$5^{\sqrt{2}}$ where $\sqrt{2}$ is the irrational number 1.414213562. . .

Each number in the following list is defined, because each exponent is a rational number.

$$5^{1.4},\ 5^{1.41},\ 5^{1.414},\ 5^{1.4142},\ 5^{1.41421},\ \ldots$$

Since the exponents are getting closer to $\sqrt{2}$, the numbers in this list are successively better approximations of $5^{\sqrt{2}}$. We can use a calculator to obtain a very good approximation.

ACCENT ON TECHNOLOGY

Evaluating Exponential Expressions

To approximate the value of $5^{\sqrt{2}}$ with a scientific calculator, we enter these numbers and press these keys:

5 $\boxed{y^x}$ 2 $\boxed{\sqrt{\ }}$ $\boxed{=}$

The display will read **9.738517742** .

With a graphing calculator, we enter these numbers and press these keys:

5 $\boxed{\wedge}$ $\boxed{\sqrt{\ }}$ 2 $\boxed{)}$ $\boxed{\text{ENTER}}$

The display will read **5^$\sqrt{\ }$ (2)** .

9.738517742

In general, if b is positive and x is a real number, b^x represents a positive number. It can be shown that all of the rules of exponents hold true for irrational exponents.

EXAMPLE 1 Use the rules of exponents to simplify: **a.** $\left(5^{\sqrt{2}}\right)^{\sqrt{2}}$ **b.** $b^{\sqrt{3}} \cdot b^{\sqrt{12}}$.

Solution **a.** $\left(5^{\sqrt{2}}\right)^{\sqrt{2}} = 5^{\sqrt{2}\sqrt{2}}$ Keep the base and multiply the exponents.

$\qquad = 5^2$ $\sqrt{2}\sqrt{2} = \sqrt{4} = 2$

$\qquad = 25$

b. $b^{\sqrt{3}} \cdot b^{\sqrt{12}} = b^{\sqrt{3}+\sqrt{12}}$ Keep the base and add the exponents.

$\qquad = b^{\sqrt{3}+2\sqrt{3}}$ $\sqrt{12} = \sqrt{4}\sqrt{3} = 2\sqrt{3}$

$\qquad = b^{3\sqrt{3}}$ $\sqrt{3} + 2\sqrt{3} = 3\sqrt{3}$

SELF CHECK 1 Simplify: **a.** $\left(3^{\sqrt{2}}\right)^{\sqrt{8}}$ **b.** $b^{\sqrt{2}} \cdot b^{\sqrt{18}}$.

2 **Graph an exponential function.**

If $b > 0$ and $b \neq 1$, the function $f(x) = b^x$ is called an *exponential function*. Since x can be any real number, its domain is the set of real numbers. This is the interval $(-\infty, \infty)$. Since b is positive, the value of $f(x)$ is positive and the range is the set of positive numbers. This is the interval $(0, \infty)$.

Since $b \neq 1$, an exponential function cannot be the constant function $f(x) = 1^x$, in which $f(x) = 1$ for every real number x.

Exponential Functions

An **exponential function with base b** is defined by the equation

$$f(x) = b^x \quad (b > 0, b \neq 1, \text{ and } x \text{ is a real number})$$

The **domain of any exponential function** is the interval $(-\infty, \infty)$. The **range** is the interval $(0, \infty)$.

Since the domain and range of $f(x) = b^x$ are subsets of the real numbers, we can graph exponential functions on a rectangular coordinate system.

EXAMPLE 2 Graph: $f(x) = 2^x$.

Solution To graph $f(x) = 2^x$, we find several points (x, y) whose coordinates satisfy the equation, plot the points, and join them with a smooth curve, as shown in Figure 11-2.

$f(x) = 2^x$

x	$f(x)$	$(x, f(x))$
-1	$\frac{1}{2}$	$\left(-1, \frac{1}{2}\right)$
0	1	$(0, 1)$
1	2	$(1, 2)$
2	4	$(2, 4)$
3	8	$(3, 8)$

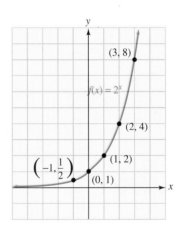

Figure 11-2

By looking at the graph, we can verify that the domain is the interval $(-\infty, \infty)$ and that the range is the interval $(0, \infty)$.

Note that as x decreases, the values of $f(x)$ decrease and approach 0, but will never be 0. Thus, the x-axis is the horizontal asymptote of the graph.

Also note that the graph of $f(x) = 2^x$ passes through the points $(0, 1)$ and $(1, 2)$.

➪ **SELF CHECK 2** Graph: $f(x) = 4^x$.

In Example 2, the values of $f(x)$ increase as the values of x increase. When the graph of a function rises as we move to the right, we call the function an **increasing function.** When $b > 1$, the larger the value of b, the steeper the curve.

EXAMPLE 3 Graph: $f(x) = \left(\frac{1}{2}\right)^x$.

Solution We find and plot pairs (x, y) that satisfy the equation. The graph of $f(x) = \left(\frac{1}{2}\right)^x$ appears in Figure 11-3.

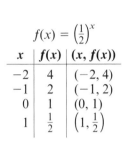

$$f(x) = \left(\frac{1}{2}\right)^x$$

x	$f(x)$	$(x, f(x))$
-2	4	$(-2, 4)$
-1	2	$(-1, 2)$
0	1	$(0, 1)$
1	$\frac{1}{2}$	$\left(1, \frac{1}{2}\right)$

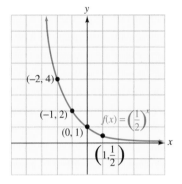

Figure 11-3

By looking at the graph, we can see that the domain is the interval $(-\infty, \infty)$ and that the range is the interval $(0, \infty)$.

In this case, as x increases, the values of $f(x)$ decrease and approach 0. The x-axis is a horizontal asymptote. Note that the graph of $f(x) = \left(\frac{1}{2}\right)^x$ passes through the points $(0, 1)$ and $\left(1, \frac{1}{2}\right)$.

SELF CHECK 3 Graph: $f(x) = \left(\frac{1}{4}\right)^x$.

In Example 3, the values of $f(x)$ decrease as the values of x increase. When the graph of a function drops as we move to the right, we call the function a **decreasing function.** When $0 < b < 1$, the smaller the value of b, the steeper the curve.

Examples 2 and 3 illustrate the following properties of exponential functions.

Properties of Exponential Functions

The **domain** of the exponential function $y = f(x) = b^x$ is the interval $(-\infty, \infty)$.

The **range** is the interval $(0, \infty)$.

The graph has a y-intercept of $(0, 1)$.

The x-axis is an asymptote of the graph.

The graph of $f(x) = b^x$ passes through the point $(1, b)$.

If $b > 1$, then $f(x) = b^x$ is an **increasing function.**

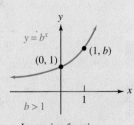

Increasing function

If $0 < b < 1$, then $f(x) = b^x$ is a **decreasing function.**

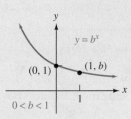

Decreasing function

EXAMPLE 4   From the graph of $f(x) = b^x$ shown in Figure 11-4, find the value of b.

Solution   We first note that the graph passes through $(0, 1)$. Since the point $(2, 9)$ is on the graph, we substitute 9 for y and 2 for x in the equation $y = b^x$ to get

$$y = b^x$$
$$9 = b^2$$
$$3 = b \qquad \text{Because 3 is the positive number whose square is 9.}$$

The base b is 3.

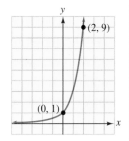

Figure 11-4

SELF CHECK 4   From the graph of $f(x) = b^x$ shown to the right, find the value of b.

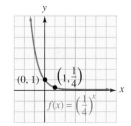

An exponential function with base b is either increasing (for $b > 1$) or decreasing ($0 < b < 1$). Since different real numbers x determine different values of b^x, exponential functions are one-to-one.

The exponential function defined by

$$f(x) = b^x \quad \text{where } b > 0 \text{ and } b \neq 1$$

is one-to-one. Thus,

1. If $b^r = b^s$, then $r = s$.
2. If $r \neq s$, then $b^r \neq b^s$.

To use a graphing calculator to graph $f(x) = \left(\frac{2}{3}\right)^x$ and $f(x) = \left(\frac{3}{2}\right)^x$, we enter the right sides of the equations. The screen will show the following equations.

$$\backslash Y_1 = (2/3)^\wedge X$$
$$\backslash Y_2 = (3/2)^\wedge X$$

If we use window settings of $[-10, 10]$ for x and $[-2, 10]$ for y and press **GRAPH** , we will obtain the graph shown in Figure 11-5.

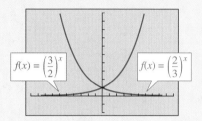

Figure 11-5

The graph of $f(x) = \left(\frac{2}{3}\right)^x$ passes through the points $(0, 1)$ and $\left(1, \frac{2}{3}\right)$. Since $\frac{2}{3} < 1$, the function is decreasing.

The graph of $f(x) = \left(\frac{3}{2}\right)^x$ passes through the points $(0, 1)$ and $\left(1, \frac{3}{2}\right)$. Since $\frac{3}{2} > 1$, the function is increasing.

Since both graphs pass the horizontal line test, each function is one-to-one.

3   Graph a translation of an exponential function.

We have seen that when $k > 0$ the graph of

$y = f(x) + k$ is the graph of $y = f(x)$ translated k units upward.
$y = f(x) - k$ is the graph of $y = f(x)$ translated k units downward.
$y = f(x - k)$ is the graph of $y = f(x)$ translated k units to the right.
$y = f(x + k)$ is the graph of $y = f(x)$ translated k units to the left.

EXAMPLE 5   On one set of axes, graph $f(x) = 2^x$ and $f(x) = 2^x + 3$.

Solution   The graph of $f(x) = 2^x + 3$ is identical to the graph of $f(x) = 2^x$, except that it is translated 3 units upward. (See Figure 11-6.)

	$f(x) = 2^x$	
x	$f(x)$	$(x, f(x))$
-4	$\frac{1}{16}$	$\left(-4, \frac{1}{16}\right)$
0	1	$(0, 1)$
2	4	$(2, 4)$

	$f(x) = 2^x + 3$	
x	$f(x)$	$(x, f(x))$
-4	$3\frac{1}{16}$	$\left(-4, 3\frac{1}{16}\right)$
0	4	$(0, 4)$
2	7	$(2, 7)$

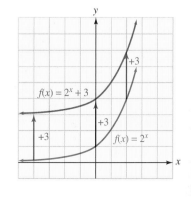

Figure 11-6

⇨ **SELF CHECK 5**   On one set of axes, graph $f(x) = 4^x$ and $f(x) = 4^x - 3$.

EXAMPLE 6   On one set of axes, graph $f(x) = 2^x$ and $f(x) = 2^{x+3}$.

Solution   The graph of $f(x) = 2^{x+3}$ is identical to the graph of $f(x) = 2^x$, except that it is translated 3 units to the left. (See Figure 11-7.)

$f(x) = 2^x$

x	$f(x)$	$(x, f(x))$
0	1	$(0, 1)$
2	4	$(2, 4)$
4	16	$(4, 16)$

$f(x) = 2^{x+3}$

x	$f(x)$	$(x, f(x))$
0	8	$(0, 8)$
−1	4	$(-1, 4)$
−2	2	$(-2, 2)$

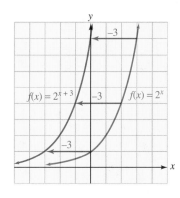

Figure 11-7

⇨ **SELF CHECK 6**   On one set of axes, graph $f(x) = 4^x$ and $f(x) = 4^{x-3}$.

The graphs of $f(x) = kb^x$ and $f(x) = b^{kx}$ are vertical and horizontal stretchings, respectively, of the graph of $f(x) = b^x$. To graph these functions, we can plot several points and join them with a smooth curve or use a graphing calculator.

ACCENT ON TECHNOLOGY

Graphing Exponential Functions

To use a graphing calculator to graph the exponential function $f(x) = 3(2^{x/3})$, we enter the right side of the equation. The display will show the equation

$$\backslash Y_1 = 3(2^{\wedge}(X/3))$$

If we use window settings of $[-10, 10]$ for x and $[-2, 18]$ for y and press **GRAPH**, we will obtain the graph shown in Figure 11-8.

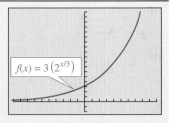

Figure 11-8

---

4   **Evaluate an application problem containing an exponential function.**

EXAMPLE 7   **CELL PHONE GROWTH**   In the decade from 1990 to 2000, the U.S. cellular telephone industry experienced exponential growth. The exponential function $S(n) = 5.74(1.39)^n$ approximates the number of cellular telephone subscribers in millions from 1990 to 2000, where n is the number of years since 1990.
a. How many subscribers were there at the beginning of the decade?
b. How many subscribers were there at the end of the decade?

Solution   **a.** To find the number of subscribers in 1990, we substitute 0 for n in the function and find $S(0)$.

$$S(n) = 5.74(1.39)^n$$
$$S(0) = 5.74(1.39)^0 \quad \text{Substitute 0 for } n.$$
$$= 5.74 \cdot 1 \quad (1.39)^0 = 1$$
$$= 5.74$$

In 1990, there were approximately 5.74 million cellular telephone subscribers in the U.S.

b. To find the number of subscribers in 2000, we substitute 10 for n in the function and find $S(10)$.

$$S(n) = 5.74(1.39)^n$$
$$S(10) = 5.74(1.39)^{10} \quad \text{Substitute 10 for } n.$$
$$\approx 154.5467565 \quad \text{Use a calculator to find an approximation.}$$

In 2000, there were approximately 154.55 million cellular telephone subscribers.

If we deposit $\$P$ in an account paying an annual simple interest rate r, we can find the amount A in the account at the end of t years by using the formula $A = P + Prt$ or $A = P(1 + rt)$.

Suppose that we deposit $\$500$ in an account that pays interest every six months. Then $P = 500$, and after six months $\left(\frac{1}{2} \text{ year}\right)$, the amount in the account will be

$$A = 500(1 + rt)$$
$$= 500\left(1 + r \cdot \frac{1}{2}\right) \quad \text{Substitute } \tfrac{1}{2} \text{ for } t.$$
$$= 500\left(1 + \frac{r}{2}\right)$$

The account will begin the second six-month period with a value of $\$500\left(1 + \frac{r}{2}\right)$. After the second six-month period, the amount will be

$$A = P(1 + rt)$$
$$A = \left[500\left(1 + \frac{r}{2}\right)\right]\left(1 + r \cdot \frac{1}{2}\right) \quad \text{Substitute } 500\left(1 + \tfrac{r}{2}\right) \text{ for } P \text{ and } \tfrac{1}{2} \text{ for } t.$$
$$= 500\left(1 + \frac{r}{2}\right)\left(1 + \frac{r}{2}\right)$$
$$= 500\left(1 + \frac{r}{2}\right)^2$$

At the end of the third six-month period, the amount in the account will be

$$A = 500\left(1 + \frac{r}{2}\right)^3$$

In this discussion, the earned interest is deposited back in the account and also earns interest. When this is the case, we say that the account is earning **compound interest.**

Formula for Compound Interest

If $P is deposited in an account and interest is paid k times a year at an annual rate r, the amount A in the account after t years is given by

$$A = P\left(1 + \frac{r}{k}\right)^{kt}$$

EXAMPLE 8

SAVING FOR COLLEGE To save for college, parents invest $12,000 for their newborn child in a mutual fund that should average a 10% annual return. If the quarterly interest is reinvested, how much will be available in 18 years?

Solution We substitute 12,000 for P, 0.10 for r, and 18 for t into the formula for compound interest and find A. Since interest is paid quarterly, $k = 4$.

$$A = P\left(1 + \frac{r}{k}\right)^{kt}$$
$$A = 12{,}000\left(1 + \frac{0.10}{4}\right)^{4(18)}$$
$$= 12{,}000(1 + 0.025)^{72}$$
$$= 12{,}000(1.025)^{72}$$
$$\approx 71{,}006.74 \qquad \text{Use a calculator.}$$

In 18 years, the account will be worth $71,006.74.

SELF CHECK 8 How much would be available if the parents invest $20,000?

In business applications, the initial amount of money deposited is the **present value** (PV). The amount to which the money will grow is called the **future value** (FV). The interest rate used for each compounding period is the **periodic interest rate** (i), and the number of times interest is compounded is the number of **compounding periods** (n). Using these definitions, we have an alternate formula for compound interest.

Formula for Future Value

$$FV = PV(1 + i)^n \quad \text{where } i = \frac{r}{k} \text{ and } n = kt$$

This alternate formula appears on business calculators. To use this formula to solve Example 8, we proceed as follows:

$$FV = PV(1 + i)^n$$
$$FV = 12{,}000(1 + 0.025)^{72} \qquad i = \tfrac{0.10}{4} = 0.025 \text{ and } n = 4(18) = 72.$$
$$\approx 71{,}006.74$$

ACCENT ON TECHNOLOGY

Solving Investment Problems

Suppose $1 is deposited in an account earning 6% annual interest, compounded monthly. To use a graphing calculator to estimate how much money will be in the account in 100 years, we can substitute 1 for P, 0.06 for r, and 12 for k into the formula

(continued)

$$A = P\left(1 + \frac{r}{k}\right)^{kt}$$

$$A = 1\left(1 + \frac{0.06}{12}\right)^{12t}$$

and simplify to get

$$A = (1.005)^{12t}$$

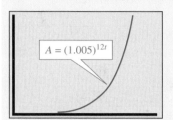

$A = (1.005)^{12t}$

Figure 11-9

We now graph $A = (1.005)^{12t}$ using window settings of $[0, 120]$ for t and $[0, 400]$ for A to obtain the graph shown in Figure 11-9. We can then trace and zoom to estimate that $1 grows to be approximately $397 in 100 years. From the graph, we can see that the money grows slowly in the early years and rapidly in the later years.

We can use the VALUE feature under the CALC menu to determine that exactly $397.44 will be in the account in 100 years.

SELF CHECK ANSWERS

1. a. 81 **b.** $b^{4\sqrt{2}}$ **2.** **3.** **4.** $\frac{1}{4}$

5. **6.** **8.** $118,344.56

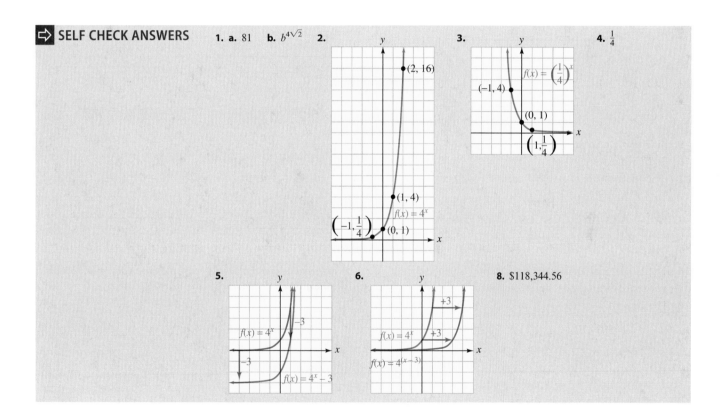

NOW TRY THIS

1. If you were given $1 on May 1, $2 on May 2, $4 on May 3, $8 on May 4, and double the previous day's earnings each day after, how much would you earn on
   a. May 10?
   b. May 15?
   c. May 21?

Try to find an equation to model this problem.

11.1 EXERCISES

WARM-UPS

If x = 2, evaluate each expression.

1. 2^x

2. 5^x

3. $2(3^x)$

4. 3^{x-1}

If x = −2, evaluate each expression.

5. 2^x

6. 5^x

7. $2(3^x)$

8. 3^{x-1}

REVIEW *In the illustration, lines r and s are parallel.*

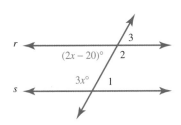

9. Find the value of x.

10. Find the measure of $\angle 1$.

11. Find the measure of $\angle 2$.

12. Find the measure of $\angle 3$.

VOCABULARY AND CONCEPTS *Fill in the blanks.*

13. If $b > 0$ and $b \neq 1$, $y = f(x) = b^x$ is called an _____ function.

14. The _____ of an exponential function is $(-\infty, \infty)$.

15. The range of an exponential function is the interval _____.

16. The graph of $y = f(x) = 3^x$ passes through the points $(0, \underline{\ })$ and $(1, \underline{\ })$.

17. If $b > 1$, then $y = f(x) = b^x$ is an _____ function.

18. If $0 < b < 1$, then $y = f(x) = b^x$ is a _____ function.

19. The formula for compound interest is $A =$ _____.

20. An alternate formula for compound interest is $FV =$ _____, where PV stands for present value, i stands for the _____, and n stands for the number of _____.

GUIDED PRACTICE

Find each value to four decimal places. (Objective 1)

21. $2^{\sqrt{2}}$

22. $7^{\sqrt{2}}$

23. $5^{\sqrt{5}}$

24. $6^{\sqrt{3}}$

Simplify and give the exact value of each expression. See Example 1. (Objective 1)

25. $\left(2^{\sqrt{3}}\right)^{\sqrt{3}}$

26. $3^{\sqrt{2}}3^{\sqrt{18}}$

27. $7^{\sqrt{3}}7^{\sqrt{12}}$

28. $\left(3^{\sqrt{5}}\right)^{\sqrt{5}}$

Graph each exponential function. Check your work with a graphing calculator. See Examples 2–3. (Objective 2)

29. $f(x) = 3^x$

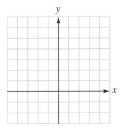

30. $f(x) = 5^x$

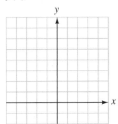

31. $f(x) = \left(\dfrac{1}{3}\right)^x$

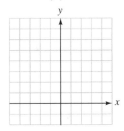

32. $f(x) = \left(\dfrac{1}{5}\right)^x$

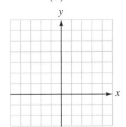

Find the value of b that would cause the graph of $y = b^x$ to look like the graph indicated. See Example 4. (Objective 2)

33.

34.

35.

36.

Graph each exponential function. Check your work with a graphing calculator. See Examples 5–6. (Objective 3)

37. $f(x) = 3^x - 2$

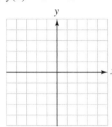

38. $f(x) = 2^x + 1$

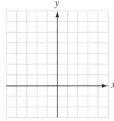

39. $f(x) = 3^{x-1}$

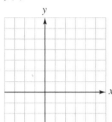

40. $f(x) = 2^{x+1}$

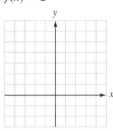

ADDITIONAL PRACTICE

Find the value of b that would cause the graph of $y = b^x$ *to look like the graph indicated.*

41.

42.

Use a graphing calculator to graph each function. Determine whether the function is an increasing or a decreasing function.

43. $f(x) = \dfrac{1}{2}(3^{x/2})$

44. $f(x) = -3(2^{x/3})$

45. $f(x) = 2(3^{-x/2})$

46. $f(x) = -\dfrac{1}{4}(2^{-x/2})$

APPLICATIONS

Evaluate each application. See Examples 7–8. (Objective 4)

47. Cell phone usage Refer to Example 7 and find the number of cell phone users in 1995.

48. Cell phone usage Refer to Example 7 and find the number of cell phone users in 1998.

49. Radioactive decay A radioactive material decays according to the formula $A = A_0\left(\dfrac{2}{3}\right)^t$, where A_0 is the initial amount present and t is measured in years. Find an expression for the amount present in 5 years.

50. Bacteria cultures A colony of 6 million bacteria is growing in a culture medium. (See the illustration.) The population P after t hours is given by the formula $P = (6 \times 10^6)(2.3)^t$. Find the population after 4 hours.

Assume that there are no deposits or withdrawals.

51. Compound interest An initial deposit of $10,000 earns 8% interest, compounded quarterly. How much will be in the account after 10 years?

52. Compound interest An initial deposit of $10,000 earns 8% interest, compounded monthly. How much will be in the account after 10 years?

53. Comparing interest rates How much more interest could $1,000 earn in 5 years, compounded quarterly, if the annual interest rate were $5\frac{1}{2}\%$ instead of 5%?

54. Comparing savings plans Which institution in the two ads provides the better investment?

Fidelity Savings & Loan
Earn 5.25%
compounded monthly

Union Trust
Money Market Account
paying 5.35%
compounded annually

55. Compound interest If $1 had been invested on July 4, 1776, at 5% interest, compounded annually, what would it be worth on July 4, 2076?

56. Frequency of compounding $10,000 is invested in each of two accounts, both paying 6% annual interest. In the first account, interest compounds quarterly, and in the second account, interest compounds daily. Find the difference between the accounts after 20 years.

57. Discharging a battery The charge remaining in a battery decreases as the battery discharges. The charge C (in coulombs) after t days is given by the formula $C = (3 \times 10^{-4})(0.7)^t$. Find the charge after 5 days.

58. Town population The population of North Rivers is decreasing exponentially according to the formula $P = 3,745(0.93)^t$, where t is measured in years from the present date. Find the population in 6 years, 9 months.

59. Salvage value A small business purchases a computer for $4,700. It is expected that its value each year will be 75% of its value in the preceding year. If the business disposes of the computer after 5 years, find its salvage value (the value after 5 years).

60. Louisiana Purchase In 1803, the United States acquired territory from France in the Louisiana Purchase. The country doubled its territory by adding 827,000 square miles of land for $15 million. If the value of the land has appreciated at the rate of 6% each year, what would one square mile of land be worth in 2023?

WRITING ABOUT MATH

61. If the world population is increasing exponentially, why is there cause for concern?

62. How do the graphs of $y = b^x$ differ when $b > 1$ and $0 < b < 1$?

SOMETHING TO THINK ABOUT

63. In the definition of the exponential function, b could not equal 0. Why not?

64. In the definition of the exponential function, b could not be negative. Why not?

SECTION 11.2
Base-*e* Exponential Functions

Objectives

1 Compute the continuously compounded interest of an investment given the principal, rate, and duration.

2 Graph an exponential function.

3 Solve an application problem involving exponential growth or decay.

Vocabulary

compound interest   annual growth rate   exponential function

Getting Ready

Evaluate $\left(1 + \frac{1}{n}\right)^n$ *for the following values. Round each answer to the nearest hundredth.*

1. $n = 1$ **2.** $n = 2$ **3.** $n = 4$ **4.** $n = 10$

In this section, we will discuss special exponential functions with a base of e, an important number with a value of approximately 2.72.

1 **Compute the continuously compounded interest of an investment given the principal, rate, and duration.**

If a bank pays interest twice a year, we say that interest is *compounded semiannually.* If it pays interest four times a year, we say that interest is *compounded quarterly.* If it pays interest continuously (infinitely many times in a year), we say that interest is *compounded continuously.*

To develop the formula for continuous **compound interest,** we start with the formula

$$A = P\left(1 + \frac{r}{k}\right)^{kt} \qquad \text{This is the formula for compound interest.}$$

and substitute *rn* for *k.* Since *r* and *k* are positive numbers, so is *n.*

$$A = P\left(1 + \frac{r}{rn}\right)^{rnt}$$

We can then simplify the fraction $\frac{r}{rn}$ and use the commutative property of multiplication to change the order of the exponents.

$$A = P\left(1 + \frac{1}{n}\right)^{nrt}$$

Finally, we can use a property of exponents to write this formula as

$$(1) \qquad A = P\left[\left(1 + \frac{1}{n}\right)^{n}\right]^{rt} \qquad \text{Use the property } a^{mn} = (a^m)^n.$$

To find the value of $\left(1 + \frac{1}{n}\right)^{n}$, we use a calculator to evaluate it for several values of *n*, as shown in Table 11-1.

n	$\left(1 + \dfrac{1}{n}\right)^{n}$
1	2
2	2.25
4	2.44140625 . . .
12	2.61303529 . . .
365	2.71456748 . . .
1,000	2.71692393 . . .
100,000	2.71826823 . . .
1,000,000	2.71828046 . . .

Table 11-1

**Leonhard Euler
(1707–1783)**

Euler first used the letter *i* to represent $\sqrt{-1}$, the letter *e* for the base of natural logarithms, and the symbol Σ for summation. Euler was one of the most prolific mathematicians of all time, contributing to almost all areas of mathematics. Much of his work was accomplished after he became blind.

The results suggest that as *n* gets larger, the value of $\left(1 + \frac{1}{n}\right)^{n}$ approaches an irrational number with a value of 2.71828. . . . This number is called *e*, which has the following approximate value.

$$e \approx 2.718281828459$$

In continuous compound interest, *k* (the number of compoundings) is infinitely large. Since *k*, *r*, and *n* are all positive and *k* = *rn*, as *k* gets very large (approaches infinity), then so does *n*. Therefore, we can replace $\left(1 + \frac{1}{n}\right)^{n}$ in Equation 1 with *e* to get

$$A = Pe^{rt}$$

Formula for Exponential Growth	If a quantity P increases or decreases at an annual rate r, compounded continuously, then the amount A after t years is given by $$A = Pe^{rt}$$

If time is measured in years, then r is called the **annual growth rate.** If r is negative, the "growth" represents a decrease, commonly referred to as *decay.*

To compute the amount to which \$12,000 will grow if invested for 18 years at 10% annual interest, compounded continuously, we substitute 12,000 for P, 0.10 for r, and 18 for t in the formula for exponential growth:

$$
\begin{aligned}
A &= Pe^{rt} \\
&= 12{,}000e^{0.10(18)} \\
&= 12{,}000e^{1.8} \\
&\approx 72{,}595.76957 \quad \text{Use a calculator.}
\end{aligned}
$$

After 18 years, the account will contain \$72,595.77. This is \$1,589.03 more than the result in Example 8 in the previous section, where interest was compounded quarterly.

EXAMPLE 1 **CONTINUOUS COMPOUND INTEREST** If \$25,000 accumulates interest at an annual rate of 8%, compounded continuously, find the balance in the account in 50 years.

Solution We substitute 25,000 for P, 0.08 for r, and 50 for t.

$$
\begin{aligned}
A &= Pe^{rt} \\
A &= 25{,}000e^{(0.08)(50)} \\
&= 25{,}000e^{4} \\
&\approx 1{,}364{,}953.751 \quad \text{Use a calculator.}
\end{aligned}
$$

In 50 years, the balance will be \$1,364,953.75—over one million dollars.

⇨ **SELF CHECK 1** Find the balance in 60 years.

The exponential function $f(x) = e^x$ is so important that it is often called the **exponential function.**

2 **Graph an exponential function.**

To graph the exponential function $f(x) = e^x$, we plot several points and join them with a smooth curve, as shown in Figure 11-10.

$$f(x) = e^x$$

x	$f(x)$	$(x, f(x))$
-2	0.1	$(-2, 0.1)$
-1	0.4	$(-1, 0.4)$
0	1	$(0, 1)$
1	2.7	$(1, 2.7)$
2	7.4	$(2, 7.4)$

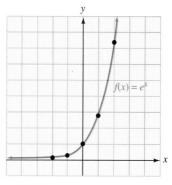

Figure 11-10

ACCENT ON TECHNOLOGY

Translations of the Exponential Function

Figure 11-11(a) shows the graphs of $f(x) = e^x$, $f(x) = e^x + 5$, and $f(x) = e^x - 3$. To graph these functions with window settings of $[-3, 6]$ for x and $[-5, 15]$ for y, we enter the right sides of the equations after the symbols $Y_1 =$, $Y_2 =$, and $Y_3 =$. The display will show

$$Y_1 = e^\wedge(x)$$
$$Y_2 = e^\wedge(x) + 5$$
$$Y_3 = e^\wedge(x) - 3$$

After graphing these functions, we can see that the graph of $f(x) = e^x + 5$ is 5 units above the graph of $f(x) = e^x$, and that the graph of $f(x) = e^x - 3$ is 3 units below the graph of $f(x) = e^x$.

Figure 11-11(b) shows the calculator graphs of $f(x) = e^x$, $f(x) = e^{x+5}$, and $f(x) = e^{x-3}$. To graph these functions with window settings of $[-7, 10]$ for x and $[-5, 15]$ for y, we enter the right sides of the equations after the symbols $Y_1 =$, $Y_2 =$, $Y_3 =$. The display will show

$$Y_1 = e^\wedge(x)$$
$$Y_2 = e^\wedge(x + 5)$$
$$Y_3 = e^\wedge(x - 3)$$

After graphing these functions, we can see that the graph of $f(x) = e^{x+5}$ is 5 units to the left of the graph of $f(x) = e^x$, and that the graph of $f(x) = e^{x-3}$ is 3 units to the right of the graph of $f(x) = e^x$.

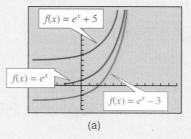

(a)

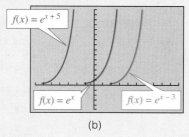

(b)

Figure 11-11

Figure 11-12 shows the calculator graph of $f(x) = 3e^{-x/2}$. To graph this function with window settings of $[-7, 10]$ for x and $[-5, 15]$ for y, we enter the right side of the equation after the symbol $Y_1 =$. The display will show the equation

$$Y_1 = 3(e^{\wedge}(-x/2))$$

Explain why the graph has a y-intercept of $(0, 3)$.

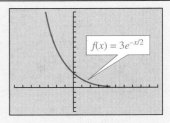

Figure 11-12

3 Solve an application problem involving exponential growth or decay.

An equation based on the exponential function provides a model for population growth. In the Malthusian model for population growth, the future or past population of a colony is related to the present population by the formula $A = Pe^{rt}$.

EXAMPLE 2 **CITY PLANNING** The population of a city is currently 15,000, but changing economic conditions are causing the population to decrease by 2% each year. If this trend continues, find the population in 30 years.

Solution Since the population is decreasing by 2% each year, the annual growth rate is -2%, or -0.02. We can substitute -0.02 for r, 30 for t, and 15,000 for P in the formula for exponential growth and find A.

$$A = Pe^{rt}$$
$$A = 15,000e^{-0.02(30)}$$
$$= 15,000e^{-0.6}$$
$$\approx 8,232.174541$$

In 30 years, city planners expect a population of approximately 8,232.

SELF CHECK 2 Find the population in 50 years.

The English economist Thomas Robert Malthus (1766–1834) pioneered in population study. He believed that poverty and starvation were unavoidable, because the human population tends to grow exponentially, but the food supply tends to grow linearly.

EXAMPLE 3 **POPULATION GROWTH** Suppose that a country with a population of 1,000 people is growing exponentially according to the formula

$$P = 1,000e^{0.02t}$$

where t is in years. Furthermore, assume that the food supply measured in adequate food per day per person is growing linearly according to the formula

$$y = 30.625x + 2,000$$

where x is in years. In how many years will the population outstrip the food supply?

Solution   We can use a graphing calculator, with window settings of [0, 100] for *x* and [0, 10,000] for *y*. After graphing the functions, we obtain Figure 11-13(a). If we trace, as in Figure 11-13(b), we can find the point where the two graphs intersect. From the graph, we can see that the food supply will be adequate for about 71 years. At that time, the population of approximately 4,160 people will have problems.

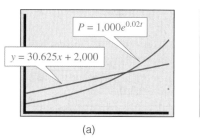
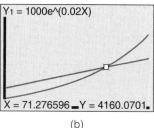

(a)   (b)

Figure 11-13

If we use the INTERSECT feature in the CALC menu, we will find that the food supply will be adequate for about 71.7 years when the population will be about 4,196.

⇨ SELF CHECK 3   Suppose that the population grows at a 3% rate. For how many years will the food supply be adequate?

The atomic structure of a radioactive material changes as the material emits radiation. The amount of radioactive material that is present decays exponentially according to the following formula.

Radioactive Decay Formula

The amount A of radioactive material present at a time t is given by the formula

$$A = A_0 e^{kt}$$

where A_0 is the amount that was present at $t = 0$ and k is a negative number.

EXAMPLE 4   **RADIOACTIVE DECAY**   The radioactive material radon-22 decays according to the formula $A = A_0 e^{-0.181t}$, where t is expressed in days. How much radon-22 will be left if a sample of 100 grams decays for 20 days?

Solution   To find the number of grams of radon-22 that will be left, we substitute 100 for A_0 and 20 for t and simplify.

COMMENT Note that the radioactive decay formula is the same as the formula for exponential growth, except for the variables.

$A = A_0 e^{-0.181t}$

$A = 100 e^{-0.181(20)}$

$\quad = 100 e^{-3.62}$ $\quad -0.181 \cdot 20 = -3.62$

$\quad \approx 100(0.0267826765)$ $e^{-3.62} \approx 0.0267826765$

$\quad \approx 2.678267649$ Multiply.

To the nearest hundredth, 2.68 grams of radon-22 will be left in 20 days.

⇨ SELF CHECK 4   To the nearest hundredth, how much radon-22 will be left in 30 days?

⇨ SELF CHECK ANSWERS   **1.** $3,037,760.44   **2.** approximately 5,518   **3.** about 38 years   **4.** 0.44 gram

---

NOW TRY THIS

Give all answers to the nearest milligram (mg).

The half-life of Ibuprofen is approximately 1.8 hours. This translates to $k \approx -0.39$. (We will learn how to compute this value in Section 11.6.)

1. If a woman takes two 200mg tablets, how many mg of Ibuprofen are in her system 4 hours after taking the medication?

2. If she takes 2 more tablets 4 hours after taking the first dose, how many mg are in her system 6 hours after the first dose?

3. If she doesn't take any more medication, how many mg are in her system 12 hours after the first dose?   18 hours?

11.2 EXERCISES

WARM-UPS

Use a calculator to find each value to the nearest hundredth.

1. e^0 **2.** e^1

3. e^2 **4.** e^3

Fill in the blanks.

5. The graph of $f(x) = e^x + 2$ is __ units above the graph of $f(x) = e^x$.

6. The graph of $f(x) = e^{(x-2)}$ is __ units to the right of the graph of $f(x) = e^x$.

REVIEW   *Simplify each expression. Assume that all variables represent positive numbers.*

7. $\sqrt{240x^5}$ **8.** $\sqrt[3]{-125x^5y^4}$

9. $4\sqrt{48y^3} - 3y\sqrt{12y}$ **10.** $\sqrt[4]{48z^5} + \sqrt[4]{768z^5}$

VOCABULARY AND CONCEPTS   *Fill in the blanks.*

11. To two decimal places, the value of e is _____.

12. The formula for continuous compound interest is $A =$ _____.

13. Since $e > 1$, the base-e exponential function is a(n) _____ function.

14. The graph of the exponential function $y = e^x$ passes through the points $(0, 1)$ and _____.

15. The Malthusian population growth formula is _____.

16. The Malthusian theory is pessimistic, because _____ grows exponentially, but food supplies grow _____.

GUIDED PRACTICE

Graph each function. Check your work with a graphing calculator. Compare each graph to the graph of $f(x) = e^x$. (Objective 2)

17. $f(x) = e^x + 1$

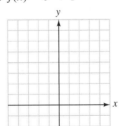

18. $f(x) = e^x - 2$

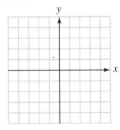

19. $f(x) = e^{x+3}$

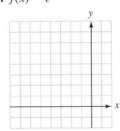

20. $f(x) = e^{x-5}$

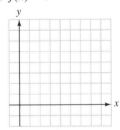

21. $f(x) = -e^x$

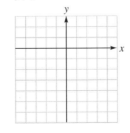

22. $f(x) = -e^x + 1$

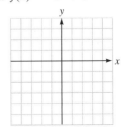

23. $f(x) = 2e^x$

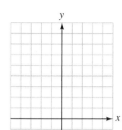

24. $f(x) = \dfrac{1}{2}e^x$

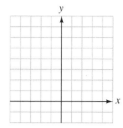

Determine whether the graph of f(x) = e^x could look like the graph shown here. (Objective 2)

25.

26.

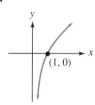

27.

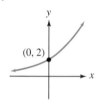

28.

APPLICATIONS

Use a calculator to help solve each problem. Assume that there are no deposits or withdrawals. See Example 1. (Objective 1)

29. Continuous compound interest   An investment of $5,000 earns 6% interest, compounded continuously. What will the investment be worth in 12 years?

30. Continuous compound interest   An investment of $6,000 earns 7% interest, compounded continuously. What will the investment be worth in 35 years?

31. Determining the initial deposit   An account now contains $12,000 and has been accumulating 7% annual interest, compounded continuously, for 9 years. Find the initial deposit.

32. Determining a previous balance   An account now contains $8,000 and has been accumulating 8% annual interest, compounded continuously. How much was in the account 6 years ago?

Use a calculator to help solve each problem. See Example 2. (Objective 3)

33. World population growth   Earth's population is approximately 6 billion people and is growing at an annual rate of 1.9%. Assuming a Malthusian growth model, find the world population in 30 years.

34. World population growth   Earth's population is approximately 6 billion people and is growing at an annual rate of 1.9%. Assuming a Malthusian growth model, find the world population in 40 years.

35. World population growth   Assuming a Malthusian growth model and an annual growth rate of 1.9%, by what factor will Earth's current population increase in 50 years? (See Exercise 33.)

36. Population growth   The growth of a population is modeled by

$$P = 173e^{0.03t}$$

How large will the population be when $t = 30$?

Use a calculator to help solve each problem. See Example 3. (Objective 3)

37. In Example 3, suppose that better farming methods change the formula for food growth to $y = 31x + 2,000$. How long will the food supply be adequate?

38. In Example 3, suppose that a birth-control program changed the formula for population growth to $P = 1,000e^{0.01t}$. How long will the food supply be adequate?

Use a calculator to help solve each problem. Round each answer to the nearest hundredth. See Example 4. (Objective 3)

39. Radioactive decay   The radioactive material iodine-131 decays according to the formula $A = A_0e^{-0.087t}$, where t is expressed in days. To the nearest hundredth, how much iodine-131 will be left if a sample of 50 grams decays for 30 days?

40. Radioactive decay   The radioactive material strontium-89 decays according to the formula $A = A_0e^{-0.013t}$, where t is expressed in days. To the nearest hundredth, how much strontium-89 will be left if a sample of 25 grams decays for 45 days?

41. Radioactive decay   The radioactive material tin-126 decays according to the formula $A = A_0e^{-0.00000693t}$, where t is expressed in years. To the nearest hundredth, how much tin-126 will be left if a sample of 2,500 grams decays for 100 years?

42. Radioactive decay   The radioactive material plutonium-239 decays according to the formula $A = A_0e^{-0.0000284t}$, where t is expressed in years. To the nearest hundredth, how much plutonium-239 will be left if a sample of 75 grams decays for 50,000 years?

Use a graphing calculator to solve each problem.

43. Comparison of compounding methods   An initial deposit of $5,000 grows at an annual rate of 8.5% for 5 years. Compare the final balances resulting from continuous compounding and annual compounding.

44. Comparison of compounding methods An initial deposit of $30,000 grows at an annual rate of 8% for 20 years. Compare the final balances resulting from continuous compounding and annual compounding.

45. Population decline The decline of a population is modeled by

$$P = 8,000e^{-0.008t}$$

How large will the population be when $t = 20$?

46. Epidemics The spread of foot and mouth disease through a herd of cattle can be modeled by the formula

$$P = P_0e^{0.27t} \quad (t \text{ is in days})$$

If a rancher does not act quickly to treat two cases, how many cattle will have the disease in 10 days?

47. Medicine The concentration, x, of a certain drug in an organ after t minutes is given by $x = 0.08(1 - e^{-0.1t})$. Find the concentration of the drug after 30 minutes.

48. Medicine Refer to Exercise 47. Find the initial concentration of the drug.

49. Skydiving Before her parachute opens, a skydiver's velocity v in meters per second is given by $v = 50(1 - e^{-0.2t})$. Find the initial velocity.

50. Skydiving Refer to Exercise 49 and find the velocity after 20 seconds.

51. Free-falling objects After t seconds, a certain falling object has a velocity v given by $v = 50(1 - e^{-0.3t})$. Which is falling faster after 2 seconds, this object or the skydiver in Exercise 49?

52. Alcohol absorption In one individual, the blood alcohol level t minutes after drinking two shots of whiskey is given by $P = 0.3(1 - e^{-0.05t})$. Find the blood alcohol level after 15 minutes.

53. Depreciation A camping trailer originally purchased for $4,570 is continuously losing value at the rate of 6% per year. Find its value when it is $6\frac{1}{2}$ years old.

54. Depreciation A boat purchased for $7,500 has been continuously decreasing in value at the rate of 2% each year. It is now 8 years, 3 months old. Find its value.

WRITING ABOUT MATH

55. Explain why the graph of $f(x) = e^x - 5$ is 5 units below the graph of $f(x) = e^x$.

56. Explain why the graph of $f(x) = e^{(x+5)}$ is 5 units to the left of the graph of $f(x) = e^x$.

SOMETHING TO THINK ABOUT

57. The value of e can be calculated to any degree of accuracy by adding the first several terms of the following list:

$$1, 1, \frac{1}{2}, \frac{1}{2 \cdot 3}, \frac{1}{2 \cdot 3 \cdot 4}, \frac{1}{2 \cdot 3 \cdot 4 \cdot 5}, \cdots$$

The more terms that are added, the closer the sum will be to e. Add the first six numbers in the preceding list. To how many decimal places is the sum accurate?

58. Graph the function defined by the equation

$$y = f(x) = \frac{e^x + e^{-x}}{2}$$

from $x = -2$ to $x = 2$. The graph will look like a parabola, but it is not. The graph, called a **catenary,** is important in the design of power distribution networks, because it represents the shape of a uniform flexible cable whose ends are suspended from the same height. The function is called the **hyperbolic cosine function.**

59. If $e^{t+5} = ke^t$, find k.

60. If $e^{5t} = k^t$, find k.

SECTION 11.3 Logarithmic Functions

Objectives

1. Write a logarithmic function as an exponential function and write an exponential function as a logarithmic function.
2. Graph a logarithmic function.
3. Graph a vertical and horizontal translation of a logarithmic function.
4. Evaluate a common logarithm.
5. Solve an application problem involving a logarithm.

Vocabulary

logarithmic function
logarithm

common logarithm
decibel

Richter scale

Getting Ready

Find each value.

1. 7^0　　　　　　**2.** 5^2　　　　　　**3.** 5^{-2}　　　　　　**4.** $16^{1/2}$

In this section, we consider the inverse function of an exponential function $f(x) = b^x$. The inverse function is called a *logarithmic function*. These functions can be used to solve application problems from fields such as electronics, seismology, and business.

1 Write a logarithmic function as an exponential function and write an exponential function as a logarithmic function.

Since the exponential function $y = b^x$ is one-to-one, it has an inverse function defined by the equation $x = b^y$. To express this inverse function in the form $y = f^{-1}(x)$, we must solve the equation $x = b^y$ for y. To do this, we need the following definition.

Logarithmic Functions

If $b > 0$ and $b \neq 1$, the **logarithmic function with base** b is defined by

$$y = \log_b x \quad \text{if and only if} \quad x = b^y$$

The **domain of the logarithmic function** is the interval $(0, \infty)$. The **range** is the interval $(-\infty, \infty)$.

COMMENT Since the domain of the logarithmic function is the set of positive numbers, the logarithm of 0 or the logarithm of a negative number is not defined in the real-number system.

Since the function $y = \log_b x$ is the inverse of the one-to-one exponential function $y = b^x$, the logarithmic function is also one-to-one.

The previous definition guarantees that any pair (x, y) that satisfies the equation $y = \log_b x$ also satisfies the equation $x = b^y$.

$\log_4 1 = 0$	because	$1 = 4^0$
$\log_5 25 = 2$	because	$25 = 5^2$
$\log_5 \dfrac{1}{25} = -2$	because	$\dfrac{1}{25} = 5^{-2}$
$\log_{16} 4 = \dfrac{1}{2}$	because	$4 = 16^{1/2}$
$\log_2 8 = -3$	because	$\dfrac{1}{8} = 2^{-3}$
$\log_b x = y$	because	$x = b^y$

COMMENT Since $b^y = x$ is equivalent to $y = \log_b x$, then $b^{\log_b x} = x$ by substitution.

In each of these examples, the **logarithm** of a number is an exponent. In fact,

$\log_b x$ **is the exponent to which b is raised to get x.**

In equation form, we write

$$b^{\log_b x} = x$$

EXAMPLE 1 Find y in each equation: **a.** $\log_6 1 = y$ **b.** $\log_3 27 = y$ **c.** $\log_5 \frac{1}{5} = y$.

Solution **a.** We can change the equation $\log_6 1 = y$ into the equivalent exponential equation $6^y = 1$. Since $6^0 = 1$, it follows that $y = 0$. Thus,

$$\log_6 1 = 0$$

b. $\log_3 27 = y$ is equivalent to $3^y = 27$. Since $3^3 = 27$, it follows that $3^y = 3^3$, and $y = 3$. Thus,

$$\log_3 27 = 3$$

c. $\log_5 \frac{1}{5} = y$ is equivalent to $5^y = \frac{1}{5}$. Since $5^{-1} = \frac{1}{5}$, it follows that $5^y = 5^{-1}$, and $y = -1$. Thus,

$$\log_5 \frac{1}{5} = -1$$

⇨ **SELF CHECK 1** Find y: **a.** $\log_3 9 = y$ **b.** $\log_2 64 = y$ **c.** $\log_5 \frac{1}{125} = y$.

EXAMPLE 2 Find x in each equation: **a.** $\log_3 81 = x$ **b.** $\log_x 125 = 3$ **c.** $\log_4 x = 3$.

Solution **a.** $\log_3 81 = x$ is equivalent to $3^x = 81$. Because $3^4 = 81$, it follows that $3^x = 3^4$. Thus, $x = 4$.

b. $\log_x 125 = 3$ is equivalent to $x^3 = 125$. Because $5^3 = 125$, it follows that $x^3 = 5^3$. Thus, $x = 5$.

c. $\log_4 x = 3$ is equivalent to $4^3 = x$. Because $4^3 = 64$, it follows that $x = 64$.

⇨ **SELF CHECK 2** Find x: **a.** $\log_2 32 = x$ **b.** $\log_x 8 = 3$ **c.** $\log_5 x = 2$.

EXAMPLE 3 Find x in each equation.
a. $\log_{1/3} x = 2$ **b.** $\log_{1/3} x = -2$ **c.** $\log_{1/3} \frac{1}{27} = x$

Solution **a.** $\log_{1/3} x = 2$ is equivalent to $\left(\frac{1}{3}\right)^2 = x$. Thus, $x = \frac{1}{9}$.

b. $\log_{1/3} x = -2$ is equivalent to $\left(\frac{1}{3}\right)^{-2} = x$. Thus,

$$x = \left(\frac{1}{3}\right)^{-2} = 3^2 = 9$$

c. $\log_{1/3} \frac{1}{27} = x$ is equivalent to $\left(\frac{1}{3}\right)^x = \frac{1}{27}$. Because $\left(\frac{1}{3}\right)^3 = \frac{1}{27}$, it follows that $x = 3$.

⇨ **SELF CHECK 3** Find x: **a.** $\log_{1/4} x = 3$ **b.** $\log_{1/4} x = -2$.

2 **Graph a logarithmic function.**

To graph the logarithmic function $y = \log_2 x$, we calculate and plot several points with coordinates (x, y) that satisfy the equation $x = 2^y$. After joining these points with a smooth curve, we have the graph shown in Figure 11-14(a).

To graph $y = \log_{1/2} x$, we calculate and plot several points with coordinates (x, y) that satisfy the equation $x = \left(\frac{1}{2}\right)^y$. After joining these points with a smooth curve, we have the graph shown in Figure 11-14(b).

$y = \log_2 x$

x	y	(x, y)
$\frac{1}{4}$	-2	$\left(\frac{1}{4}, -2\right)$
$\frac{1}{2}$	-1	$\left(\frac{1}{2}, -1\right)$
1	0	$(1, 0)$
2	1	$(2, 1)$
4	2	$(4, 2)$
8	3	$(8, 3)$

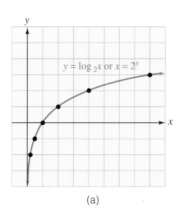

$y = \log_{1/2} x$

x	y	(x, y)
$\frac{1}{4}$	2	$\left(\frac{1}{4}, 2\right)$
$\frac{1}{2}$	1	$\left(\frac{1}{2}, 1\right)$
1	0	$(1, 0)$
2	-1	$(2, -1)$
4	-2	$(4, -2)$
8	-3	$(8, -3)$

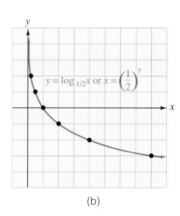

(a)   (b)

Figure 11-14

The graphs of all logarithmic functions are similar to those in Figure 11-15. If $b > 1$, the logarithmic function is increasing, as in Figure 11-15(a). If $0 < b < 1$, the logarithmic function is decreasing, as in Figure 11-15(b).

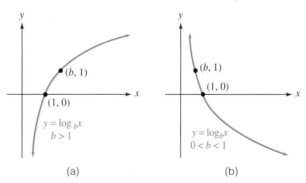

(a)   (b)

Figure 11-15

The graph of $f(x) = \log_b x$ has the following properties.

1. It passes through the point $(1, 0)$.

2. It passes through the point $(b, 1)$.

3. The y-axis is an asymptote.

4. The domain is $(0, \infty)$ and the range is $(-\infty, \infty)$.

The exponential and logarithmic functions are inverses of each other and, therefore, have symmetry about the line $y = x$. The graphs $y = \log_b x$ and $y = b^x$ are shown in Figure 11-16(a) when $b > 1$, and in Figure 11-16(b) when $0 < b < 1$.

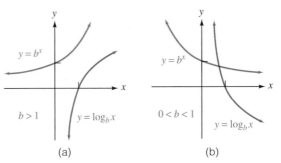

Figure 11-16

3 **Graph a vertical and horizontal translation of a logarithmic function.**

The graphs of many functions involving logarithms are translations of the basic logarithmic graphs.

EXAMPLE 4   Graph the function defined by $f(x) = 3 + \log_2 x$.

Solution   The graph of $f(x) = 3 + \log_2 x$ is identical to the graph of $f(x) = \log_2 x$, except that it is translated 3 units upward. (See Figure 11-17.)

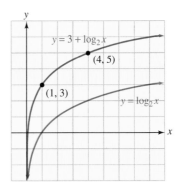

Figure 11-17

➡ **SELF CHECK 4**   Graph: $f(x) = \log_3 x - 2$.

EXAMPLE 5   Graph: $f(x) = \log_{1/2} (x - 1)$.

Solution   The graph of $f(x) = \log_{1/2} (x - 1)$ is identical to the graph of $f(x) = \log_{1/2} x$, except that it is translated 1 unit to the right. (See Figure 11-18.)

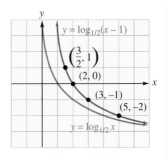

Figure 11-18

➡ **SELF CHECK 5**   Graph: $f(x) = \log_{1/3} (x + 2)$.

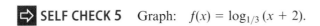

Graphing calculators can graph logarithmic functions directly only if the base of the logarithmic function is 10 or e. To use a calculator to graph $f(x) = -2 + \log_{10}\left(\frac{1}{2}x\right)$, we enter the right side of the equation after the symbol $Y_1 =$. The display will show the equation

$$Y_1 = -2 + \log(1/2*x)$$

If we use window settings of $[-1, 5]$ for x and $[-4, 1]$ for y and press GRAPH , we will obtain the graph shown in Figure 11-19.

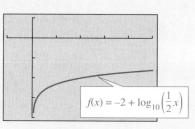

$f(x) = -2 + \log_{10}\left(\frac{1}{2}x\right)$

Figure 11-19

4 ### Evaluate a common logarithm.

For computational purposes and in many applications, we will use base-10 logarithms (also called **common logarithms**). When the base b is not indicated in the notation $\log x$, we assume that $b = 10$:

$$\log x \quad \text{means} \quad \log_{10} x$$

Because base-10 logarithms appear so often, it is a good idea to become familiar with the following base-10 logarithms:

$$\log_{10} \frac{1}{100} = -2 \quad \text{because} \quad 10^{-2} = \frac{1}{100}$$

$$\log_{10} \frac{1}{10} = -1 \quad \text{because} \quad 10^{-1} = \frac{1}{10}$$

$$\log_{10} 1 = 0 \quad \text{because} \quad 10^0 = 1$$

$$\log_{10} 10 = 1 \quad \text{because} \quad 10^1 = 10$$

$$\log_{10} 100 = 2 \quad \text{because} \quad 10^2 = 100$$

$$\log_{10} 1{,}000 = 3 \quad \text{because} \quad 10^3 = 1{,}000$$

In general, we have

$$\log_{10} 10^x = x$$

Before calculators, extensive tables provided logarithms of numbers. Today, logarithms are easy to find with a calculator. For example, to find $\log 32.58$ with a scientific calculator, we enter these numbers and press these keys:

32.58 **LOG**

The display will read 1.51295108 . To four decimal places, $\log 32.58 = 1.5130$.

To use a graphing calculator, we enter these numbers and press these keys:

LOG 32.58 **ENTER**

The display will read LOG (32.58)   .

                                         1.51295108

To four decimal places, $\log 32.58 = 1.5130$.

EXAMPLE 6 Find x in the equation $\log x = 0.3568$. Round to four decimal places.

Solution The equation $\log x = 0.3568$ is equivalent to $10^{0.3568} = x$. To find x with a calculator, we can enter these numbers and press these keys:

Scientific Calculator   *Graphing Calculator*

10 y^x 0.3568 =   10 ^ 0.3568 **ENTER**

Either way, the display will read **2.274049951**. To four decimal places,

$$x = 2.2740$$

⇨ **SELF CHECK 6** Solve: $\log x = 2.7$. Round to four decimal places.

5 Solve an application problem involving a logarithm.

Common logarithms are used in electrical engineering to express the voltage gain (or loss) of an electronic device such as an amplifier. The unit of gain (or loss), called the **decibel,** is defined by a logarithmic relation.

Decibel Voltage Gain   If E_O is the output voltage of a device and E_I is the input voltage, the decibel voltage gain is given by

$$\text{dB gain} = 20 \log \frac{E_O}{E_I}$$

EXAMPLE 7 **FINDING dB GAIN** If the input to an amplifier is 0.4 volt and the output is 50 volts, find the decibel voltage gain of the amplifier.

Solution We can find the decibel voltage gain by substituting 0.4 for E_I and 50 for E_O into the formula for dB gain:

$$\text{dB gain} = 20 \log \frac{E_O}{E_I}$$

$$\text{dB gain} = 20 \log \frac{50}{0.4}$$

$$= 20 \log 125$$

$$\approx 42 \qquad \text{Use a calculator.}$$

The amplifier provides a 42-decibel voltage gain.

In seismology, the study of earthquakes, common logarithms are used to measure the magnitude (ground motion) of earthquakes on the **Richter scale.** The magnitude of an earthquake is given by the following logarithmic function.

Richter Scale

If R is the magnitude of an earthquake, A is the amplitude (measured in micrometers), and P is the period (the time of one oscillation of Earth's surface, measured in seconds), then

$$R = \log \frac{A}{P}$$

EXAMPLE 8 **MEASURING EARTHQUAKES** Find the measure on the Richter scale of an earthquake with an amplitude of 10,000 micrometers (1 centimeter) and a period of 0.1 second.

Solution We substitute 10,000 for A and 0.1 for P in the Richter scale formula and simplify:

$$R = \log \frac{A}{P}$$
$$R = \log \frac{10,000}{0.1}$$
$$= \log 100,000$$
$$= 5$$

The earthquake measures 5 on the Richter scale.

SELF CHECK ANSWERS   **1. a.** 2   **b.** 6   **c.** -3 **2. a.** 5   **b.** 2   **c.** 25   **3. a.** $\frac{1}{64}$ **b.** 16

4. **5.** **6.** 501.1872

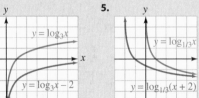

NOW TRY THIS

In 1989, an earthquake measuring 7.1 on the Richter scale rocked San Francisco.

1. Write a logarithmic equation to describe the earthquake.

2. Write the equation in exponential form.

In 1964, an earthquake measuring 9.1 on the Richter scale devastated Juneau, Alaska.

3. Write the equation in exponential form.

4. Given that each earthquake had the same period, the amplitude in Juneau was how many times greater than that in San Francisco?

Source: http://pubs.usgs.gov/gip/earthq1/measure.html

11.3 EXERCISES

WARM-UPS *Find the value of x in each equation.*

1. $\log_2 8 = x$

2. $\log_3 9 = x$

3. $\log_x 125 = 3$

4. $\log_x 8 = 3$

5. $\log_4 16 = x$

6. $\log_x 32 = 5$

7. $\log_{1/2} x = 2$

8. $\log_9 3 = x$

9. $\log_x \dfrac{1}{4} = -2$

REVIEW *Solve each equation.*

10. $\sqrt[3]{6x + 4} = 4$

11. $\sqrt{3x - 4} = \sqrt{-7x + 2}$

12. $\sqrt{a + 1} - 1 = 3a$

13. $3 - \sqrt{t - 3} = \sqrt{t}$

VOCABULARY AND CONCEPTS *Fill in the blanks.*

14. The equation $y = \log_b x$ is equivalent to _____.

15. The domain of the logarithmic function is the interval _____.

16. The _____ of the logarithmic function is the interval $(-\infty, \infty)$.

17. $b^{\log_b x} = $ __.

18. Because an exponential function is one-to-one, it has an _____ function that is called a _____ function.

19. $\text{Log}_b x$ is the _____ to which b is raised to get x.

20. The y-axis is an _____ to the graph of $f(x) = \log_b x$.

21. The graph of $f(x) = \log_b x$ passes through the points _____ and _____.

22. A logarithm with a base of 10 is called a _____ logarithm and $\log_{10} 10^x = $ __.

23. The decibel voltage gain is found using the equation dB gain = _____.

24. The magnitude of an earthquake is measured by the formula $R = $ _____.

GUIDED PRACTICE

Write each equation in exponential form. (Objective 1)

25. $\log_3 27 = 3$

26. $\log_8 8 = 1$

27. $\log_{1/2} \dfrac{1}{4} = 2$

28. $\log_{1/5} 1 = 0$

29. $\log_4 \dfrac{1}{64} = -3$

30. $\log_6 \dfrac{1}{36} = -2$

31. $\log_{1/2} \dfrac{1}{8} = 3$

32. $\log_{1/5} 25 = -2$

Write each equation in logarithmic form. (Objective 1)

33. $6^2 = 36$

34. $10^3 = 1,000$

35. $5^{-2} = \dfrac{1}{25}$

36. $3^{-3} = \dfrac{1}{27}$

37. $\left(\dfrac{1}{2}\right)^{-5} = 32$

38. $\left(\dfrac{1}{3}\right)^{-3} = 27$

39. $x^y = z$

40. $m^n = p$

Find each value of x. See Example 1. (Objective 1)

41. $\log_7 x = 2$

42. $\log_5 x = 0$

43. $\log_6 x = 1$

44. $\log_2 x = 4$

45. $\log_{25} x = \dfrac{1}{2}$

46. $\log_4 x = \dfrac{1}{2}$

47. $\log_5 x = -2$

48. $\log_{27} x = -\dfrac{1}{3}$

Find each value of x. See Example 2. (Objective 1)

49. $\log_x 5^3 = 3$

50. $\log_x 5 = 1$

51. $\log_x \dfrac{9}{4} = 2$

52. $\log_x \dfrac{\sqrt{3}}{3} = \dfrac{1}{2}$

Find each value of x. See Example 3. (Objective 1)

53. $\log_2 16 = x$

54. $\log_3 9 = x$

55. $\log_4 16 = x$

56. $\log_6 216 = x$

57. $\log_{1/2} \dfrac{1}{8} = x$

58. $\log_{1/3} \dfrac{1}{81} = x$

59. $\log_9 3 = x$

60. $\log_{125} 5 = x$

Graph each function. Determine whether each function is an increasing or decreasing function. (Objective 2)

61. $f(x) = \log_3 x$

62. $f(x) = \log_{1/3} x$

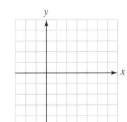

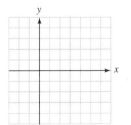

63. $f(x) = \log_{1/2} x$

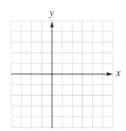

64. $f(x) = \log_4 x$

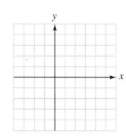

Graph each pair of inverse functions on a single coordinate system. (Objective 2)

65. $f(x) = 2^x$

$g(x) = \log_2 x$

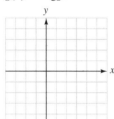

66. $f(x) = \left(\dfrac{1}{2}\right)^x$

$g(x) = \log_{1/2} x$

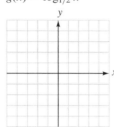

67. $f(x) = \left(\dfrac{1}{4}\right)^x$

$g(x) = \log_{1/4} x$

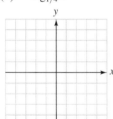

68. $f(x) = 4^x$

$g(x) = \log_4 x$

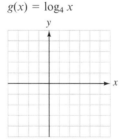

Graph each function. See Examples 4–5. (Objective 3)

69. $f(x) = 3 + \log_3 x$

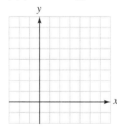

70. $f(x) = \log_{1/3} x - 1$

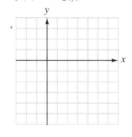

71. $f(x) = \log_{1/2}(x - 2)$

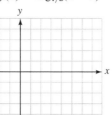

72. $f(x) = \log_4(x + 2)$

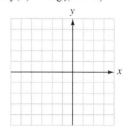

Use a calculator to find each value. Give answers to four decimal places. (Objective 4)

73. $\log 8.25$

74. $\log 0.77$

75. $\log 0.00867$

76. $\log 375.876$

Use a calculator to find each value of y. If an answer is not exact, give the answer to two decimal places. (Objective 4)

77. $\log y = 4.24$

78. $\log y = 0.926$

79. $\log y = -3.71$

80. $\log y = -0.28$

ADDITIONAL PRACTICE

Find each value of x.

81. $\log_{36} x = -\dfrac{1}{2}$

82. $\log_{27} x = -\dfrac{1}{3}$

83. $\log_{1/2} 8 = x$

84. $\log_{1/2} 16 = x$

85. $\log_{100} \dfrac{1}{1,000} = x$

86. $\log_{5/2} \dfrac{4}{25} = x$

87. $\log_{27} 9 = x$

88. $\log_{12} x = 0$

89. $\log_{2\sqrt{2}} x = 2$

90. $\log_4 8 = x$

91. $\log_x \dfrac{1}{64} = -3$

92. $\log_x \dfrac{1}{100} = -2$

93. $2^{\log_2 4} = x$

94. $3^{\log_3 5} = x$

95. $x^{\log_4 6} = 6$

96. $x^{\log_3 8} = 8$

97. $\log 10^3 = x$

98. $\log 10^{-2} = x$

99. $10^{\log x} = 100$

100. $10^{\log x} = \dfrac{1}{10}$

Use a calculator to find each value of y. If an answer is not exact, give the answer to two decimal places.

101. $\log y = 1.4023$

102. $\log y = 2.6490$

103. $\log y = \log 8$

104. $\log y = \log 7$

Find the value of b, if any, that would cause the graph of $f(x) = \log_b x$ to look like the graph indicated.

105.

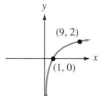

106.

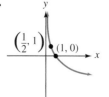

107.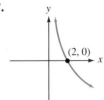

108.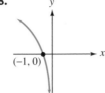

APPLICATIONS

 *Use a calculator to help solve each problem. If an answer is not exact, round to the nearest tenth.* **See Example 6.**
(Objective 5)

109. Finding the gain of an amplifier Find the dB gain of an amplifier if the input voltage is 0.71 volt when the output voltage is 20 volts.

110. Finding the gain of an amplifier Find the dB gain of an amplifier if the output voltage is 2.8 volts when the input voltage is 0.05 volt.

111. dB gain of an amplifier Find the dB gain of the amplifier.

112. dB gain of an amplifier An amplifier produces an output of 80 volts when driven by an input of 0.12 volts. Find the amplifier's dB gain.

 *Use a calculator to help solve each problem. If an answer is not exact, round to the nearest tenth.* **See Example 7.**
(Objective 6)

113. Earthquakes An earthquake has an amplitude of 5,000 micrometers and a period of 0.2 second. Find its measure on the Richter scale.

114. Earthquakes The period of an earthquake with amplitude of 80,000 micrometers is 0.08 second. Find its measure on the Richter scale.

115. Earthquakes An earthquake has a period of $\frac{1}{4}$ second and an amplitude of 2,500 micrometers. Find its measure on the Richter scale.

116. Earthquakes By what factor must the amplitude of an earthquake change to increase its magnitude by 1 point on the Richter scale? Assume that the period remains constant.

 *Use a calculator to help solve each problem. If an answer is not exact, round to the nearest tenth.*

117. Depreciation Business equipment is often depreciated using the double declining-balance method. In this method, a piece of equipment with a life expectancy of N years, costing $\$C$, will depreciate to a value of $\$V$ in n years, where n is given by the formula

$$n = \frac{\log V - \log C}{\log\left(1 - \dfrac{2}{N}\right)}$$

A computer that cost $17,000 has a life expectancy of 5 years. If it has depreciated to a value of $2,000, how old is it?

118. Depreciation See Exercise 117. A printer worth $470 when new had a life expectancy of 12 years. If it is now worth $189, how old is it?

119. Time for money to grow If $\$P$ is invested at the end of each year in an annuity earning annual interest at a rate r, the amount in the account will be $\$A$ after n years, where

$$n = \frac{\log\left(\dfrac{Ar}{P} + 1\right)}{\log(1 + r)}$$

If $1,000 is invested each year in an annuity earning 12% annual interest, how long will it take for the account to be worth $20,000?

120. Time for money to grow If $5,000 is invested each year in an annuity earning 8% annual interest, how long will it take for the account to be worth $50,000? (See Exercise 119.)

WRITING ABOUT MATH

121. Describe the appearance of the graph of $y = f(x) = \log_b x$ when $0 < b < 1$ and when $b > 1$.

122. Explain why it is impossible to find the logarithm of a negative number.

SOMETHING TO THINK ABOUT

123. Graph $f(x) = -\log_3 x$. How does the graph compare to the graph of $f(x) = \log_3 x$?

124. Find a logarithmic function that passes through the points $(1, 0)$ and $(5, 1)$.

125. Explain why an earthquake measuring 7 on the Richter scale is much worse than an earthquake measuring 6.

SECTION
11.4

Natural Logarithms

Objectives

1 Evaluate a natural logarithm.
2 Solve a logarithmic equation.
3 Graph a natural logarithmic function.
4 Solve an application problem involving a natural logarithm.

Vocabulary

natural logarithm

Getting Ready

Evaluate each expression.

1. $\log_4 16$ **2.** $\log_2 \frac{1}{8}$ **3.** $\log_5 5$ **4.** $\log_7 1$

In this section, we will discuss special logarithmic functions with a base of e. They play an important role in advanced mathematics courses.

1 Evaluate a natural logarithm.

We have seen the importance of base-e exponential functions in mathematical models of events in nature. Base-e logarithms are just as important. They are called **natural logarithms** or **Napierian logarithms,** after John Napier (1550–1617), and usually are written as ln x, rather than $\log_e x$:

> ln x means $\log_e x$

As with all logarithmic functions, the domain of $f(x) = \ln x$ is the interval $(0, \infty)$, and the range is the interval $(-\infty, \infty)$.

We have seen that the logarithm of a number is an exponent. For natural logarithms,

> ln x **is the exponent to which e is raised to get x.**

In equation form, we write

> $e^{\ln x} = x$

To find the base-e logarithms of numbers, we can use a calculator.

ACCENT ON TECHNOLOGY

Evaluating Logarithms

To use a scientific calculator to find the value of ln 9.87, we enter these numbers and press these keys:

9.87 **LN**

The display will read **2.289499853** . To four decimal places, ln 9.87 = 2.2895.
To use a graphing calculator, we enter

LN 9.87 **)** **ENTER**

The display will read
ln (9.87)
                2.289499853

EXAMPLE 1 Use a calculator to find each value: **a.** ln 17.32   **b.** ln (log 0.05).

Solution **a.** We can enter these numbers and press these keys:

Scientific Calculator   *Graphing Calculator*
17.32 **LN**   **LN** 17.32 **)** **ENTER**

Either way, the result is 2.851861903.

b. We can enter these numbers and press these keys:

Scientific Calculator   *Graphing Calculator*
0.05 **LOG** **LN**   **LN** **(** **LOG** 0.05 **)** **)** **ENTER**

Either way, we obtain an error, because log 0.05 is a negative number. Because the domain of $f(x) = \ln x$ is $(0, \infty)$, we cannot take the logarithm of a negative number.

➡ **SELF CHECK 1** Find each value to four decimal places.
a. $\ln \pi$ **b.** $\ln \left(\log \frac{1}{2}\right)$

2 Solve a logarithmic equation.

EXAMPLE 2 Find the value of x to four decimal places.
a. $\ln x = 1.335$ **b.** $\ln x = \log 5.5$

Solution **a.** The equation $\ln x = 1.335$ is equivalent to $e^{1.335} = x$. To use a scientific calculator to find x, we enter these numbers and press these keys:

1.335 e^x

The display will read 3.799995946. To four decimal places,

$x = 3.8000$

b. The equation $\ln x = \log 5.5$ is equivalent to $e^{\log 5.5} = x$. To use a scientific calculator to find x, we press these keys:

5.5 **LOG** e^x

The display will read 2.096695826. To four decimal places,

$$x = 2.0967$$

⇨ **SELF CHECK 2** Find the value of x to four decimal places.
 a. $\ln x = 2.5437$ **b.** $\log x = \ln 5$

---

3 **Graph a natural logarithmic function.**

The equation $y = \ln x$ is equivalent to the equation $x = e^y$. To graph $f(x) = \ln x$, we can plot points that satisfy the equation $x = e^y$ and join them with a smooth curve, as shown in Figure 11-20(a). Figure 11-20(b) shows the calculator graph.

**John Napier
(1550–1617)**

Napier is famous for his work with natural logarithms. In fact, natural logarithms are often called *Napierian logarithms*. He also invented a device, called *Napier's rods*, that did multiplications mechanically. His device was a forerunner of modern-day computers.

$f(x) = \ln x$

x	y	$(x, f(x))$
$\dfrac{1}{e} \approx 0.4$	-1	$(0.4, -1)$
1	0	$(1, 0)$
$e \approx 2.7$	1	$(2.7, 1)$
$e^2 \approx 7.4$	2	$(7.4, 2)$

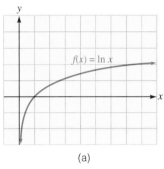

(a)

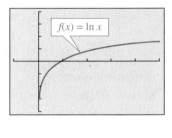

(b)

Figure 11-20

ACCENT ON TECHNOLOGY

Graphing Logarithmic Functions

Many graphs of logarithmic functions involve translations of the graph of $f(x) = \ln x$. For example, Figure 11-21 shows calculator graphs of the functions $f(x) = \ln x$, $f(x) = \ln x + 2$, and $f(x) = \ln x - 3$.

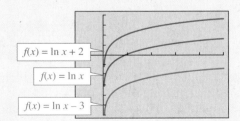

The graph of $f(x) = \ln x + 2$ is 2 units above the graph of $f(x) = \ln x$.

The graph of $f(x) = \ln x - 3$ is 3 units below the graph of $f(x) = \ln x$.

Figure 11-21

Figure 11-22 shows the calculator graphs of the functions $f(x) = \ln x$, $f(x) = \ln (x - 2)$, and $f(x) = \ln (x + 2)$.

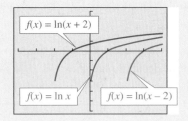

The graph of $f(x) = \ln(x - 2)$ is 2 units to the right of the graph of $f(x) = \ln x$.

The graph of $f(x) = \ln(x + 2)$ is 2 units to the left of the graph of $f(x) = \ln x$.

Figure 11-22

Natural logarithms have many applications.

4 **Solve an application problem involving a natural logarithm.**

If a population grows exponentially at a certain annual rate, the time required for the population to double is called the *doubling time*.

EXAMPLE 3 **DOUBLING TIME** If the Earth's population continues to grow at the approximate rate of 2% per year, how long will it take for its population to double?

Solution In Section 11.2, we learned that the formula for population growth is $A = Pe^{rt}$, where P is the population at time $t = 0$, A is the population after t years, and r is the annual rate of growth, compounded continuously. Since we want to find out how long it takes for the population to double, we can substitute $2P$ for A and 0.02 for r in the formula and proceed as follows.

$$A = Pe^{rt}$$
$$2P = Pe^{0.02t} \qquad \text{Substitute } 2P \text{ for } A \text{ and } 0.02 \text{ for } r.$$
$$2 = e^{0.02t} \qquad \text{Divide both sides by } P.$$
$$\ln 2 = 0.02t \qquad \ln 2 \text{ is the exponent to which } e \text{ is raised to get } 2.$$
$$34.65735903 \approx t \qquad \text{Divide both sides by } 0.02 \text{ and simplify.}$$

The population will double in about 35 years.

SELF CHECK 3 If the world population's annual growth rate could be reduced to 1.5% per year, what would be the doubling time? Give the result to the nearest year.

By solving the formula $A = Pe^{rt}$ for t, we can obtain a simpler formula for finding the doubling time.

$$A = Pe^{rt}$$
$$2P = Pe^{rt} \qquad \text{Substitute } 2P \text{ for } A.$$
$$2 = e^{rt} \qquad \text{Divide both sides by } P.$$
$$\ln 2 = rt \qquad \ln 2 \text{ is the exponent to which } e \text{ is raised to get } 2.$$
$$\frac{\ln 2}{r} = t \qquad \text{Divide both sides by } r.$$

This result gives a specific formula for finding the doubling time.

| **Formula for Doubling Time** | If r is the annual rate (compounded continuously) and t is the time required for a population to double, then

$$t = \frac{\ln 2}{r}$$ |

EXAMPLE 4   **DOUBLING TIME**   How long will it take $1,000 to double at an annual rate of 8%, compounded continuously?

Solution   We can substitute 0.08 for r and simplify:

$$t = \frac{\ln 2}{r}$$

COMMENT   To find the doubling time, you can use either the method in Example 3 or the method in Example 4.

$$t = \frac{\ln 2}{0.08}$$

$$\approx 8.664339757$$

It will take about $8\frac{2}{3}$ years for the money to double.

SELF CHECK 4   How long will it take at 9%, compounded continuously?

SELF CHECK ANSWERS   **1. a.** 1.1447   **b.** no value   **2. a.** 12.7267   **b.** 40.6853   **3.** 46 years   **4.** about 7.7 years

NOW TRY THIS

Between 2000 and 2007, McKinney, TX, was ranked overall as the fastest growing city in the United States.

1. The population more than doubled from 54,369 to 115,620 during this period. To the nearest tenth, what was the average growth rate?

2. If the growth rate slowed to half that of problem 1 and was estimated to remain there for the next 10 years, project the population in 2015.

3. Discuss with another student (or in a group) the difficulties a city might face with such a growth rate.

11.4 EXERCISES

WARM-UPS

1. Write $y = \ln x$ as an exponential equation.

2. Write $e^a = b$ as a logarithmic equation.

3. Write the formula for doubling time.

REVIEW

Write the equation of the required line.

4. Parallel to $y = 5x + 8$ and passing through the origin

5. Having a slope of 9 and a y-intercept of $(0, 5)$

6. Passing through the point (3, 2) and perpendicular to the line $y = \frac{2}{3}x - 12$

7. Parallel to the line $3x + 2y = 9$ and passing through the point $(-3, 5)$

8. Vertical line through the point (5, 3)

9. Horizontal line through the point (2, 5)

Simplify each expression. Assume no denominators are 0.

10. $\dfrac{2x + 3}{4x^2 - 9}$

11. $\dfrac{x + 1}{x} + \dfrac{x - 1}{x + 1}$

12. $\dfrac{x^2 + 3x + 2}{3x + 12} \cdot \dfrac{x + 4}{x^2 - 4}$

13. $\dfrac{1 + \frac{y}{x}}{\frac{y}{x} - 1}$

VOCABULARY AND CONCEPTS   *Fill in the blanks.*

14. The expression ln x means _____ and is called a _____ logarithm.

15. The domain of the function $f(x) = \ln x$ is the interval _____ and the range is the interval _____.

16. The graph of $y = f(x) = \ln x$ has the _____ as an asymptote.

17. In the expression log x, the base is understood to be ___.

18. In the expression ln x, the base is understood to be ___.

19. If a population grows exponentially at a rate r, the time it will take the population to double is given by the formula $t = \dfrac{\quad}{\quad}$.

20. The logarithm of a negative number is _____.

GUIDED PRACTICE

 *Use a calculator to find each value, if possible. Express all answers to four decimal places. See Example 1. (Objective 1)*

21. ln 25.25

22. ln 0.523

23. ln 9.89

24. ln 0.00725

25. log (ln 2)

26. ln (log 28.8)

27. ln (log 0.5)

28. log (ln 0.2)

Use a calculator to find y, if possible. Express all answers to four decimal places. See Example 2. (Objective 2)

29. ln y = 2.3015

30. ln y = 1.548

31. ln y = 3.17

32. ln y = 0.837

33. ln y = −4.72

34. ln y = −0.48

35. log y = ln 6

36. ln y = log 5

Use a graphing calculator to graph each function. (Objective 3)

37. $y = -\ln x$

38. $y = \ln x^2$

39. $y = \ln (-x)$

40. $y = \ln\left(\dfrac{1}{2}x\right)$

Determine whether the graph could represent the graph of $y = \ln x$.

41.

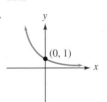

42.

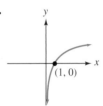

43.

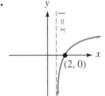

44.

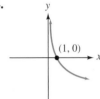

APPLICATIONS

 *Use a calculator to solve each problem. Round each answer to the nearest tenth. See Examples 3–4. (Objective 4)*

45. Population growth   See the ad. How long will it take the population of River City to double?

> **River City**
> *A growing community*
> • 6 parks   • 12% annual growth
> • 10 churches   • Low crime rate

46. Population growth   A population growing at an annual rate r will triple in a time t given by the formula

$$t = \dfrac{\ln 3}{r}$$

How long will it take the population of a town growing at the rate of 12% per year to triple?

47. Doubling money   How long will it take $1,000 to double if it is invested at an annual rate of 5%, compounded continuously?

48. Tripling money   Find the length of time for $25,000 to triple if invested at 6% annual interest, compounded continuously. (See Exercise 46.)

49. Making Jell-O After the contents of a package of Jell-O are combined with boiling water, the mixture is placed in a refrigerator whose temperature remains a constant 38° F. Estimate the number of hours t that it will take for the Jell-O to cool to 50° F using the formula

$$t = -\frac{1}{0.9} \ln \frac{50 - T_r}{200 - T_r}$$

where T_r is the temperature of the refrigerator.

50. Forensic medicine To estimate the number of hours t that a murder victim had been dead, a coroner used the formula

$$t = \frac{1}{0.25} \ln \frac{98.6 - T_s}{82 - T_s}$$

where T_s is the temperature of the surroundings where the body was found. If the crime took place in an apartment where the thermostat was set at 72° F, approximately how long ago did the murder occur?

WRITING ABOUT MATH

51. The time it takes money to double at an annual rate r, compounded continuously, is given by the formula $t = (\ln 2)/r$. Explain why money doubles more quickly as the rate increases.

52. The time it takes money to triple at an annual rate r, compounded continuously, is given by the formula $t = (\ln 3)/r$. Explain why money triples less quickly as the rate decreases.

SOMETHING TO THINK ABOUT

53. Use the formula $P = P_0 e^{rt}$ to verify that P will be three times as large as P_0 when $t = \frac{\ln 3}{r}$.

54. Use the formula $P = P_0 e^{rt}$ to verify that P will be four times as large as P_0 when $t = \frac{\ln 4}{r}$.

55. Find a formula to find how long it will take a sum of money to become five times as large.

56. Use a graphing calculator to graph

$$f(x) = \frac{1}{1 + e^{-2x}}$$

and discuss the graph.

SECTION 11.5 Properties of Logarithms

Objectives

1 Simplify a logarithmic expression by applying a property of logarithms.
2 Expand a logarithmic expression.
3 Write a logarithmic expression as a single logarithm.
4 Evaluate a logarithm by applying properties of logarithms.
5 Apply the change-of-base formula.
6 Solve an application problem using one or more logarithmic properties.

Vocabulary

change-of-base formula

Getting Ready

Simplify each expression. Assume $x \neq 0$.

1. $x^m x^n$ **2.** x^0 **3.** $(x^m)^n$ **4.** $\dfrac{x^m}{x^n}$

In this section, we will consider many properties of logarithms. We will then use these properties to solve application problems.

1   **Simplify a logarithmic expression by applying a property of logarithms.**

Since logarithms are exponents, the properties of exponents have counterparts in the theory of logarithms. We begin with four basic properties.

Properties of Logarithms

If b is a positive number and $b \neq 1$, then

1. $\log_b 1 = 0$ **2.** $\log_b b = 1$

3. $\log_b b^x = x$ **4.** $b^{\log_b x} = x$ $(x > 0)$

Properties 1 through 4 follow directly from the definition of a logarithm.

1. $\log_b 1 = 0$, because $b^0 = 1$.
2. $\log_b b = 1$, because $b^1 = b$.
3. $\log_b b^x = x$, because $b^x = b^x$.
4. $b^{\log_b x} = x$, because $\log_b x$ is the exponent to which b is raised to get x.

Properties 3 and 4 also indicate that the composition of the exponential and logarithmic functions with the same base (in both directions) is the identity function. This is expected, because the exponential and logarithmic functions with the same base are inverse functions.

EXAMPLE 1   Simplify each expression: **a.** $\log_5 1$ **b.** $\log_3 3$ **c.** $\log_7 7^3$ **d.** $b^{\log_b 7}$.

Solution   **a.** By Property 1, $\log_5 1 = 0$, because $5^0 = 1$.
     b. By Property 2, $\log_3 3 = 1$, because $3^1 = 3$.
     c. By Property 3, $\log_7 7^3 = 3$, because $7^3 = 7^3$.
     d. By Property 4, $b^{\log_b 7} = 7$, because $\log_b 7$ is the power to which b is raised to get 7.

▷ **SELF CHECK 1**   Simplify: **a.** $\log_4 1$ **b.** $\log_5 5$ **c.** $\log_2 2^4$ **d.** $5^{\log_5 2}$.

The next two properties state that

The logarithm of a product is the sum of the logarithms.

The logarithm of a quotient is the difference of the logarithms.

The Product and Quotient Properties of Logarithms	If M, N, and b are positive numbers and $b \neq 1$, then
	5. $\log_b MN = \log_b M + \log_b N$ **6.** $\log_b \dfrac{M}{N} = \log_b M - \log_b N$

Proof   To prove the product property of logarithms, we let $x = \log_b M$ and $y = \log_b N$. We use the definition of logarithms to write each equation in exponential form.

$$M = b^x \quad \text{and} \quad N = b^y$$

Then $MN = b^x b^y$ and a property of exponents gives

$$MN = b^{x+y} \qquad b^x b^y = b^{x+y}\text{: Keep the base and add the exponents.}$$

We write this exponential equation in logarithmic form as

$$\log_b MN = x + y$$

Substituting the values of x and y completes the proof.

$$\log_b MN = \log_b M + \log_b N$$

The proof of the quotient property of logarithms is similar.

COMMENT   By the product property of logarithms, the logarithm of a *product* is equal to the *sum* of the logarithms. The logarithm of a sum or a difference usually does not simplify. In general,

$$\log_b(M + N) = \log_b M + \log_b N$$
$$\log_b(M - N) = \log_b M - \log_b N$$

By the quotient property of logarithms, the logarithm of a *quotient* is equal to the *difference* of the logarithms. The logarithm of a quotient is not the quotient of the logarithms:

$$\log_b \frac{M}{N} = \frac{\log_b M}{\log_b N}$$

ACCENT ON TECHNOLOGY

Verifying Properties of Logarithms

We can use a calculator to illustrate the product property of logarithms by showing that

$$\ln[(3.7)(15.9)] = \ln 3.7 + \ln 15.9$$

We calculate the left and right sides of the equation separately and compare the results. To use a calculator to find $\ln[(3.7)(15.9)]$, we enter these numbers and press these keys:

3.7 $\times$ 15.9 $=$ **LN**   Using a scientific calculator

LN 3.7 $\times$ 15.9 **)** **ENTER**   Using a graphing calculator

The display will read **4.074651929** .

To find $\ln 3.7 + \ln 15.9$, we enter these numbers and press these keys:

3.7 **LN** $+$ 15.9 **LN** $=$ Using a scientific calculator

LN 3.7 **)** $+$ **LN** 15.9 **)** **ENTER**   Using a graphing calculator

The display will read **4.074651929** . Since the left and right sides are equal, the equation is true.

The power rule of logarithms states that

The logarithm of an expression to a power is the power times the logarithm of the expression.

The Power Rule of Logarithms	If M, p, and b are positive numbers and $b \neq 1$, then **7.** $\log_b M^p = p \log_b M$

Proof To prove the power rule, we let $x = \log_b M$, write the expression in exponential form, and raise both sides to the pth power:

$$M = b^x$$
$$(M)^p = (b^x)^p \qquad \text{Raise both sides to the } p\text{th power.}$$
$$M^p = b^{px} \qquad \text{Keep the base and multiply the exponents.}$$

Using the definition of logarithms gives

$$\log_b M^p = px$$

Substituting the value for x completes the proof.

$$\log_b M^p = p \log_b M$$

The logarithmic property of equality states that

If the logarithms of two numbers are equal, the numbers are equal.

The Logarithmic Property of Equality	If M, p, and b are positive numbers and $b \neq 1$, then **8.** If $\log_b x = \log_b y$, then $x = y$.

The logarithmic property of equality follows from the fact that the logarithmic function is a one-to-one function. It will be important in the next section when we solve logarithmic equations.

2 **Expand a logarithmic expression.**

We can use the properties of logarithms to write a logarithm as the sum or difference of several logarithms.

EXAMPLE 2 Assume that b, x, y, and z are positive numbers and $b \neq 1$. Write each expression in terms of the logarithms of x, y, and z.

a. $\log_b xyz$ **b.** $\log_b \dfrac{xy}{z}$

Solution **a.** $\log_b xyz = \log_b(xy)z$

$$= \log_b(xy) + \log_b z \qquad \text{The log of a product is the sum of the logs.}$$
$$= \log_b x + \log_b y + \log_b z \qquad \text{The log of a product is the sum of the logs.}$$

b. $\log_b \dfrac{xy}{z} = \log_b(xy) - \log_b z$ The log of a quotient is the difference of the logs.

$\qquad\qquad = (\log_b x + \log_b y) - \log_b z$ The log of a product is the sum of the logs.

$\qquad\qquad = \log_b x + \log_b y - \log_b z$ Remove parentheses.

▷ **SELF CHECK 2**   Write $\log_b \dfrac{x}{yz}$ in terms of the logarithms of x, y, and z.

EXAMPLE 3   Assume that b, x, y, and z are positive numbers and $b \neq 1$. Write each expression in terms of the logarithms of x, y, and z.

     a. $\log_b(x^2 y^3 z)$ **b.** $\log_b \dfrac{\sqrt{x}}{y^3 z}$

Solution   **a.** $\log_b(x^2 y^3 z) = \log_b x^2 + \log_b y^3 + \log_b z$ The log of a product is the sum of the logs.

$\qquad\qquad\qquad\quad = 2\log_b x + 3\log_b y + \log_b z$ The log of an expression to a power is the power times the log of the expression.

     b. $\log_b \dfrac{\sqrt{x}}{y^3 z} = \log_b \sqrt{x} - \log_b(y^3 z)$ The log of a quotient is the difference of the logs.

$\qquad\qquad\quad = \log_b x^{1/2} - (\log_b y^3 + \log_b z)$ $\sqrt{x} = x^{1/2}$. The log of a product is the sum of the logs.

$\qquad\qquad\quad = \dfrac{1}{2}\log_b x - (3\log_b y + \log_b z)$ The log of a power is the power times the log.

$\qquad\qquad\quad = \dfrac{1}{2}\log_b x - 3\log_b y - \log_b z$ Use the distributive property to remove parentheses.

▷ **SELF CHECK 3**   Write $\log_b \sqrt[4]{\dfrac{x^3 y}{z}}$ in terms of the logarithms of x, y, and z.

---

3   **Write a logarithmic expression as a single logarithm.**

We can use the properties of logarithms to combine several logarithms into one logarithm.

EXAMPLE 4   Assume that b, x, y, and z are positive numbers and $b \neq 1$. Write each expression as one logarithm.

     a. $3\log_b x + \dfrac{1}{2}\log_b y$ **b.** $\dfrac{1}{2}\log_b(x - 2) - \log_b y + 3\log_b z$

Solution   **a.** $3\log_b x + \dfrac{1}{2}\log_b y = \log_b x^3 + \log_b y^{1/2}$ A power times a log is the log of the power.

$\qquad\qquad\qquad\qquad\quad = \log_b(x^3 y^{1/2})$ The sum of two logs is the log of a product.

$\qquad\qquad\qquad\qquad\quad = \log_b\left(x^3 \sqrt{y}\right)$ $y^{1/2} = \sqrt{y}$

     b. $\dfrac{1}{2}\log_b(x - 2) - \log_b y + 3\log_b z$

$\qquad\quad = \log_b(x - 2)^{1/2} - \log_b y + \log_b z^3$ A power times a log is the log of the power.

$$= \log_b \frac{(x-2)^{1/2}}{y} + \log_b z^3$$

The difference of two logs is the log of the quotient.

$$= \log_b \frac{z^3 \sqrt{x-2}}{y}$$

The sum of two logs is the log of a product.

⇨ **SELF CHECK 4**   Write the expression as one logarithm:
$2 \log_b x + \frac{1}{2} \log_b y - 2 \log_b(x-y)$.

We summarize the properties of logarithms as follows.

Properties of Logarithms	If b, M, and N are positive numbers and $b \neq 1$, then

1. $\log_b 1 = 0$ **2.** $\log_b b = 1$

3. $\log_b b^x = x$ **4.** $b^{\log_b x} = x$

5. $\log_b MN = \log_b M + \log_b N$ **6.** $\log_b \dfrac{M}{N} = \log_b M - \log_b N$

7. $\log_b M^p = p \log_b M$ **8.** If $\log_b x = \log_b y$, then $x = y$.

4 **Evaluate a logarithm by applying properties of logarithms.**

EXAMPLE 5   Given that $\log 2 \approx 0.3010$ and $\log 3 \approx 0.4771$, find approximations for
a. $\log 6$ **b.** $\log 9$ **c.** $\log 18$ **d.** $\log 2.5$ without using a calculator.

Solution   **a.** $\log 6 = \log(2 \cdot 3)$

$= \log 2 + \log 3$ The log of a product is the sum of the logs.

$\approx 0.3010 + 0.4771$ Substitute the value of each logarithm.

≈ 0.7781

b. $\log 9 = \log(3^2)$

$= 2 \log 3$ The log of a power is the power times the log.

$\approx 2(0.4771)$ Substitute the value of $\log 3$.

≈ 0.9542

c. $\log 18 = \log(2 \cdot 3^2)$

$= \log 2 + \log 3^2$ The log of a product is the sum of the logs.

$= \log 2 + 2 \log 3$ The log of a power is the power times the log.

$\approx 0.3010 + 2(0.4771)$

≈ 1.2552

d. $\log 2.5 = \log\left(\dfrac{5}{2}\right)$

$= \log 5 - \log 2$ The log of a quotient is the difference of the logs.

$= \log \dfrac{10}{2} - \log 2$ Write 5 as $\frac{10}{2}$.

$$= \log 10 - \log 2 - \log 2 \qquad \text{The log of a quotient is the difference of the logs.}$$
$$= 1 - 2 \log 2 \qquad \log_{10} 10 = 1$$
$$\approx 1 - 2(0.3010)$$
$$\approx 0.3980$$

SELF CHECK 5   Use the values given in Example 5 and approximate
a. log 1.5   **b.** log 0.2.

5 Apply the change-of-base formula.

If we know the base-*a* logarithm of a number, we can find its logarithm to some other
base *b* with a formula called the **change-of-base formula.**

Change-of-Base Formula

If *a*, *b*, and *x* are real numbers, $b > 0$, and $b \neq 1$, then

$$\log_b x = \frac{\log_a x}{\log_a b}$$

Proof   To prove this formula, we begin with the equation $\log_b x = y$.

$$y = \log_b x$$
$$x = b^y \qquad \text{Change the equation from logarithmic to exponential form.}$$
$$\log_a x = \log_a b^y \qquad \text{Take the base-}a\text{ logarithm of both sides.}$$
$$\log_a x = y \log_a b \qquad \text{The log of a power is the power times the log.}$$
$$y = \frac{\log_a x}{\log_a b} \qquad \text{Divide both sides by } \log_a b.$$
$$\log_b x = \frac{\log_a x}{\log_a b} \qquad \text{Refer to the first equation and substitute } \log_b x \text{ for } y.$$

If we know logarithms to base *a* (for example, $a = 10$), we can find the logarithm of *x*
to a new base *b*. We simply divide the base-*a* logarithm of *x* by the base-*a* logarithm of *b*.

EXAMPLE 6   Find $\log_4 9$ using base-10 logarithms.

Solution   We can substitute 4 for *b*, 10 for *a*, and 9 for *x* into the change-of-base formula:

COMMENT $\frac{\log_a x}{\log_a b}$ means that
one logarithm is to be divided
by the other. They are not to
be subtracted.

$$\log_b x = \frac{\log_a x}{\log_a b}$$
$$\log_4 9 = \frac{\log_{10} 9}{\log_{10} 4}$$
$$\approx 1.584962501$$

To four decimal places, $\log_4 9 = 1.5850$.

SELF CHECK 6   Find $\log_5 3$ to four decimal places using base-10 logarithms.

COMMENT   It does not matter what base you choose when applying the change-of-base formula. You could use base-e (natural logarithm) and obtain the same result. In the example above, $\log_4 9 = \frac{\ln 9}{\ln 4} \approx 1.584962501$.

6   Solve an application problem using one or more logarithmic properties.

Common logarithms are used to express the acidity of solutions. The more acidic a solution, the greater the concentration of hydrogen ions. This concentration is indicated indirectly by the **pH scale,** or **hydrogen ion index.** The pH of a solution is defined by the following equation.

pH of a Solution	If $[H^+]$ is the hydrogen ion concentration in gram-ions per liter, then
	$$pH = -\log [H^+]$$

EXAMPLE 7   **FINDING THE pH OF A SOLUTION**   Find the pH of pure water, which has a hydrogen ion concentration of 10^{-7} gram-ions per liter.

Solution   Since pure water has approximately 10^{-7} gram-ions per liter, its pH is

$$pH = -\log [H^+]$$
$$pH = -\log 10^{-7}$$
$$= -(-7)\log 10 \qquad \text{The log of a power is the power times the log.}$$
$$= -(-7)(1) \qquad \log 10 = 1$$
$$= 7$$

EXAMPLE 8   **FINDING THE HYDROGEN-ION CONCENTRATION**   Find the hydrogen-ion concentration of seawater if its pH is 8.5.

Solution   To find its hydrogen-ion concentration, we substitute 8.5 for the pH and find $[H^+]$.

$$8.5 = -\log [H^+]$$
$$-8.5 = \log [H^+] \qquad \text{Multiply both sides by } -1.$$
$$[H^+] = 10^{-8.5} \qquad \text{Change the equation to exponential form.}$$

We can use a calculator to find that

$$[H^+] \approx 3.2 \times 10^{-9} \text{ gram-ions per liter}$$

In physiology, experiments suggest that the relationship between the loudness and the intensity of sound is a logarithmic one known as the **Weber–Fechner law.**

Weber–Fechner Law	If L is the apparent loudness of a sound, I is the actual intensity, and k is a constant, then
	$$L = k \ln I$$

EXAMPLE 9 **WEBER–FECHNER LAW** Find the increase in intensity that will cause the apparent loudness of a sound to double.

Solution If the original loudness L_O is caused by an actual intensity I_O, then

(1) $L_O = k \ln I_O$

To double the apparent loudness, we multiply both sides of Equation 1 by 2 and use the power rule of logarithms:

$$2\, L_O = 2\, k \ln I_O$$
$$= k \ln (I_O)^2$$

To double the loudness of a sound, the intensity must be squared.

➡ **SELF CHECK 9** What decrease in intensity will cause a sound to be half as loud?

➡ **SELF CHECK ANSWERS**   **1. a.** 0   **b.** 1   **c.** 4   **d.** 2   **2.** $\log_b x - \log_b y - \log_b z$ **3.** $\frac{1}{4}(3 \log_b x + \log_b y - \log_b z)$
4. $\log_b \frac{x^2\sqrt{y}}{(x-y)^2}$ **5. a.** 0.1761   **b.** −0.6990   **6.** 0.6826   **9.** the square root of the intensity

NOW TRY THIS

Evaluate.

1. $\log 5 + \log 20$ **2.** $\log_3 24 - \log_3 8$

3. $7 \log_2 \frac{1}{2} - \log_2 \frac{1}{8}$

11.5 EXERCISES

WARM-UPS   *Find the value of x in each equation.*

1. $\log_3 9 = x$

2. $\log_x 5 = 1$

3. $\log_7 x = 3$

4. $\log_2 x = -2$

5. $\log_4 x = \dfrac{1}{2}$

6. $\log_x 4 = 2$

7. $\log_{1/2} x = 2$

8. $\log_9 3 = x$

9. $\log_x \dfrac{1}{4} = -2$

REVIEW   *Consider the line that passes through (−2, 3) and (4, −4).*

10. Find the slope of the line.

11. Find the distance between the points.

12. Find the midpoint of the segment.

13. Write an equation of the line.

VOCABULARY AND CONCEPTS   *Fill in the blanks.*

14. $\log_b 1 =$ ___

15. $\log_b b =$ ___

16. $\log_b MN = \log_b \underline{\quad} + \log_b \underline{\quad}$

17. $b^{\log_b x} = \underline{\quad}$

18. If $\log_b x = \log_b y$, then $\underline{\quad} = \underline{\quad}$.

19. $\log_b \dfrac{M}{N} = \log_b M \underline{\quad} \log_b N$

20. $\log_b x^p = p \cdot \log_b \underline{\quad}$

21. $\log_b b^x = \underline{\quad}$

22. $\log_b (A + B) \underline{\quad} \log_b A + \log_b B$

23. $\log_b A + \log_b B \underline{\quad} \log_b AB$

24. The change-of-base formula states that $\log_b x = \underline{\quad\quad}$.

GUIDED PRACTICE

Simplify each expression. **See Example 1. (Objective 1)**

25. $\log_4 1 = \underline{\quad}$ **26.** $\log_4 4 = \underline{\quad}$

27. $\log_4 4^7 = \underline{\quad}$ **28.** $4^{\log_4 8} = \underline{\quad}$

29. $5^{\log_5 10} = \underline{\quad}$ **30.** $\log_5 5^2 = \underline{\quad}$

31. $\log_5 5 = \underline{\quad}$ **32.** $\log_5 1 = \underline{\quad}$

33. $\log_7 1 = \underline{\quad}$ **34.** $\log_9 9 = \underline{\quad}$

35. $\log_3 3^7 = \underline{\quad}$ **36.** $5^{\log_5 8} = \underline{\quad}$

37. $8^{\log_8 10} = \underline{\quad}$ **38.** $\log_4 4^2 = \underline{\quad}$

39. $\log_9 9 = \underline{\quad}$ **40.** $\log_3 1 = \underline{\quad}$

Use a calculator to verify each equation. **(Objective 1)**

41. $\log[(2.5)(3.7)] = \log 2.5 + \log 3.7$

42. $\ln \dfrac{11.3}{6.1} = \ln 11.3 - \ln 6.1$

43. $\ln (2.25)^4 = 4 \ln 2.25$

44. $\log 45.37 = \dfrac{\ln 45.37}{\ln 10}$

Assume that x, y, z, and b are positive numbers ($b \neq 1$). Use the properties of logarithms to write each expression in terms of the logarithms of x, y, and z. **See Examples 2–3. (Objective 2)**

45. $\log_b xyz$ **46.** $\log_b 4xz$

47. $\log_b \dfrac{2x}{y}$ **48.** $\log_b \dfrac{x}{yz}$

49. $\log_b x^3 y^2$ **50.** $\log_b xy^2 z^3$

51. $\log_b (xy)^{1/2}$

52. $\log_b x^3 y^{1/2}$

53. $\log_b x\sqrt{z}$

54. $\log_b \sqrt{xy}$

55. $\log_b \dfrac{\sqrt[3]{x}}{\sqrt[4]{yz}}$

56. $\log_b \sqrt[4]{\dfrac{x^3 y^2}{z^4}}$

Assume that x, y, z, and b are positive numbers ($b \neq 1$). Use the properties of logarithms to write each expression as the logarithm of a single quantity. **See Example 4. (Objective 3)**

57. $\log_b (x + 1) - \log_b x$

58. $\log_b x + \log_b (x + 2) - \log_b 8$

59. $2 \log_b x + \dfrac{1}{2} \log_b y$

60. $-2 \log_b x - 3 \log_b y + \log_b z$

61. $-3 \log_b x - 2 \log_b y + \dfrac{1}{2} \log_b z$

62. $3 \log_b (x + 1) - 2 \log_b (x + 2) + \log_b x$

63. $\log_b \left(\dfrac{x}{z} + x \right) - \log_b \left(\dfrac{y}{z} + y \right)$

64. $\log_b (xy + y^2) - \log_b (xz + yz) + \log_b z$

Assume that $\log 4 \approx 0.6021$, $\log 7 \approx 0.8451$, and $\log 9 \approx 0.9542$. Use these values and the properties of logarithms to approximate each value. Do not use a calculator. **See Example 5. (Objective 4)**

65. $\log 28$ **66.** $\log \dfrac{7}{4}$

67. $\log 2.25$ **68.** $\log 36$

69. $\log \dfrac{63}{4}$ **70.** $\log \dfrac{4}{63}$

71. $\log 252$ **72.** $\log 49$

73. $\log 112$ **74.** $\log 324$

75. $\log \dfrac{144}{49}$ **76.** $\log \dfrac{324}{63}$

Use a calculator and the change-of-base formula to find each logarithm to four decimal places. **See Example 6. (Objective 5)**

77. $\log_3 7$ **78.** $\log_7 3$

79. $\log_{1/3} 3$ **80.** $\log_{1/2} 6$

81. $\log_3 8$ **82.** $\log_5 10$

83. $\log_{\sqrt{2}} \sqrt{5}$ **84.** $\log_\pi e$

ADDITIONAL PRACTICE

Use a calculator to verify each equation.

85. $\log \sqrt{24.3} = \dfrac{1}{2} \log 24.3$ **86.** $\ln 8.75 = \dfrac{\log 8.75}{\log e}$

Determine whether each statement is true. If a statement is false, explain why.

87. $\log_b 0 = 1$

88. $\log_b (x + y) \neq \log_b x + \log_b y$

89. $\log_b xy = (\log_b x)(\log_b y)$

90. $\log_b ab = \log_b a + 1$

91. $\log_7 7^7 = 7$

92. $7^{\log_7 7} = 7$

93. $\dfrac{\log_b A}{\log_b B} = \log_b A - \log_b B$

94. $\log_b (A - B) = \dfrac{\log_b A}{\log_b B}$

95. $3 \log_b \sqrt[3]{a} = \log_b a$

96. $\dfrac{1}{3} \log_b a^3 = \log_b a$

97. $\log_b \dfrac{1}{a} = -\log_b a$

98. $\log_b 2 = \log_2 b$

APPLICATIONS   *Use a calculator to find each value.*
See Examples 7–9. (Objective 6)

99. **pH of a solution**   Find the pH of a solution with a hydrogen ion concentration of 1.7×10^{-5} gram-ions per liter.

100. **Hydrogen ion concentration**   Find the hydrogen ion concentration of a saturated solution of calcium hydroxide whose pH is 13.2.

101. **Aquariums**   To test for safe pH levels in a fresh-water aquarium, a test strip is compared with the scale shown in the illustration. Find the corresponding range in the hydrogen ion concentration.

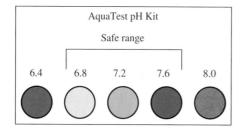

102. **pH of pickles**   The hydrogen ion concentration of sour pickles is 6.31×10^{-4}. Find the pH.

103. **Change in loudness**   If the intensity of a sound is doubled, find the apparent change in loudness.

104. **Change in loudness**   If the intensity of a sound is tripled, find the apparent change in loudness.

105. **Change in intensity**   What change in intensity of sound will cause an apparent tripling of the loudness?

106. **Change in intensity**   What increase in the intensity of a sound will cause the apparent loudness to be multiplied by 4?

WRITING ABOUT MATH

107. Explain why $\ln (\log 0.9)$ is undefined in the real-number system.

108. Explain why $\log_b (\ln 1)$ is undefined in the real-number system.

SOMETHING TO THINK ABOUT

109. Show that $\ln(e^x) = x$.

110. If $\log_b 3x = 1 + \log_b x$, find the value of x.

111. Show that $\log_{b^2} x = \dfrac{1}{2} \log_b x$.

112. Show that $e^{x \ln a} = a^x$.

Objectives

1 Solve an exponential equation.

2 Solve a logarithmic equation.

3 Solve an application problem involving an exponential or logarithmic equation.

Vocabulary

exponential equation   logarithmic equation   half-life

Getting Ready

Write each expression without using exponents.

1. $\log x^2$

2. $\log x^{1/2}$

3. $\log x^0$

4. $\log a^b + b \log a$

An **exponential equation** is an equation that contains a variable in one of its exponents. Some examples of exponential equations are

$$3^x = 5, \qquad 6^{x-3} = 2^x, \qquad \text{and} \qquad 3^{2x+1} - 10(3^x) + 3 = 0$$

A **logarithmic equation** is an equation with logarithmic expressions that contain a variable. Some examples of logarithmic equations are

$$\log(2x) = 25, \qquad \ln x - \ln(x - 12) = 24, \qquad \text{and} \qquad \log x = \log \frac{1}{x} + 4$$

In this section, we will learn how to solve many of these equations.

1 Solve an exponential equation.

EXAMPLE 1 Solve: $4^x = 7$.

Solution Since logarithms of equal numbers are equal, we can take the common or natural logarithm of both sides of the equation and obtain a new equation. For the sake of discussion, we will use the common logarithm. The power rule of logarithms then provides a way of moving the variable x from its position as an exponent to a position as a coefficient.

$$4^x = 7$$

$$\log(4^x) = \log(7) \qquad \text{Take the common logarithm of both sides.}$$

$$x \log 4 = \log 7 \qquad \text{The log of a power is the power times the log.}$$

$$(1) \qquad x = \frac{\log 7}{\log 4} \qquad \text{Divide both sides by log 4.}$$

$$\approx 1.403677461 \qquad \text{Use a calculator.}$$

To four decimal places, $x = 1.4037$.

SELF CHECK 1 Solve: $5^x = 4$. Give the result to four decimal places.

COMMENT A careless reading of Equation 1 leads to a common error. The right side of Equation 1 calls for a division, not a subtraction.

$$\frac{\log 7}{\log 4} \quad \text{means} \quad (\log 7) \div (\log 4)$$

It is the expression $\log\left(\frac{7}{4}\right)$ that means $\log 7 - \log 4$.

EXAMPLE 2 Solve: $73 = 1.6(1.03)^t$.

Solution We divide both sides by 1.6 to obtain

$$\frac{73}{1.6} = 1.03^t$$

and solve the equation as in Example 1.

$$1.03^t = \frac{73}{1.6}$$

$$\log(1.03^t) = \log\left(\frac{73}{1.6}\right) \qquad \text{Take the common logarithm of both sides.}$$

$$t \log 1.03 = \log \frac{73}{1.6} \qquad \text{The logarithm of a power is the power times the logarithm.}$$

$$t = \frac{\log \frac{73}{1.6}}{\log 1.03} \qquad \text{Divide both sides by } \log 1.03.$$

$$t \approx 129.2493444 \qquad \text{Use a calculator.}$$

To four decimal places, $t = 129.2493$.

SELF CHECK 2 Solve: $47 = 2.5(1.05)^t$. Give the result to the nearest tenth.

EXAMPLE 3 Solve: $6^{x-3} = 2^x$.

Solution

$$6^{x-3} = 2^x$$

$$\log(6^{x-3}) = \log(2^x) \qquad \text{Take the common logarithm of both sides.}$$

$$(x-3)\log 6 = x \log 2 \qquad \text{The log of a power is the power times the log.}$$

$$x \log 6 - 3 \log 6 = x \log 2 \qquad \text{Use the distributive property.}$$

$$x \log 6 - x \log 2 = 3 \log 6 \qquad \text{Add } 3 \log 6 \text{ and subtract } x \log 2 \text{ from both sides.}$$

$$x(\log 6 - \log 2) = 3 \log 6 \qquad \text{Factor out } x \text{ on the left side.}$$

$$x = \frac{3 \log 6}{\log 6 - \log 2} \qquad \text{Divide both sides by } \log 6 - \log 2.$$

$$x \approx 4.892789261 \qquad \text{Use a calculator.}$$

To four decimal places, $x = 4.8928$.

SELF CHECK 3 Solve to four decimal places: $5^{x-2} = 3^x$.

EXAMPLE 4 Solve: $2^{x^2+2x} = \frac{1}{2}$.

Solution Since $\frac{1}{2} = 2^{-1}$, we can write the equation in the form

$$2^{x^2+2x} = 2^{-1}$$

Since equal quantities with equal bases have equal exponents, we have

$$x^2 + 2x = -1$$
$$x^2 + 2x + 1 = 0 \qquad \text{Add 1 to both sides.}$$
$$(x + 1)(x + 1) = 0 \qquad \text{Factor the trinomial.}$$
$$x + 1 = 0 \quad \text{or} \quad x + 1 = 0 \qquad \text{Set each factor equal to 0.}$$
$$x = -1 \quad | \qquad x = -1 \qquad -1 \text{ is a double root.}$$

Verify that -1 satisfies the equation.

⇨ **SELF CHECK 4**   Solve: $3^{x^2 - 2x} = \frac{1}{3}$.

ACCENT ON TECHNOLOGY

Solving Exponential Equations

To use a graphing calculator to approximate the solutions of $2^{x^2+2x} = \frac{1}{2}$ (see Example 4), we can subtract $\frac{1}{2}$ from both sides of the equation to get

$$2^{x^2+2x} - \frac{1}{2} = 0$$

and graph the corresponding function

$$f(x) = 2^{x^2+2x} - \frac{1}{2}$$

If we use window settings of $[-4, 4]$ for x and $[-2, 6]$ for y, we obtain the graph shown in Figure 11-23(a).

Since the solutions of the equation are its x-intercepts, we can approximate the solutions by zooming in on the values of the x-intercepts, as in Figure 11-23(b). Since $x = -1$ is the only x-intercept, -1 is the only solution. In this case, we have found an exact solution.

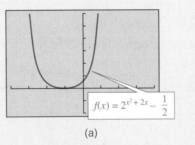

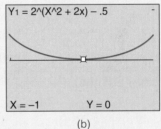

(a)   (b)

Figure 11-23

We also can find the solution by using the ZERO feature in the CALC menu.

---

2   **Solve a logarithmic equation.**

In each of the following examples, we use the properties of logarithms to change a logarithmic equation into an algebraic equation.

EXAMPLE 5   Solve: $\log_b(3x + 2) - \log_b(2x - 3) = 0$.

Solution $\log_b(3x + 2) - \log_b(2x - 3) = 0$
$$\log_b(3x + 2) = \log_b(2x - 3) \qquad \text{Add } \log_b(2x - 3) \text{ to both sides.}$$

$$3x + 2 = 2x - 3 \qquad \text{If } \log_b r = \log_b s, \text{ then } r = s.$$
$$x = -5 \qquad \text{Subtract } 2x \text{ and } 2 \text{ from both sides.}$$

COMMENT Example 5 illustrates that you must check the solutions of all logarithmic equations.

Check:
$$\log_b(3x + 2) - \log_b(2x - 3) = 0$$
$$\log_b[3(-5) + 2] - \log_b[2(-5) - 3] \overset{?}{=} 0$$
$$\log_b(-13) - \log_b(-13) \overset{?}{=} 0$$

Since the logarithm of a negative number does not exist, the apparent solution of -5 must be discarded. Since this equation has no solution, its solution set is $\varnothing$.

 SELF CHECK 5 Solve: $\log_b(5x + 2) - \log_b(7x - 2) = 0$.

EXAMPLE 6 Solve: $\log x + \log(x - 3) = 1$.

Solution
$$\log x + \log(x - 3) = 1$$
$$\log[x(x - 3)] = 1 \qquad \text{The sum of two logs is the log of a product.}$$
$$x(x - 3) = 10^1 \qquad \text{Use the definition of logarithms to change the equation to exponential form.}$$
$$x^2 - 3x - 10 = 0 \qquad \text{Remove parentheses and subtract 10 from both sides.}$$
$$(x + 2)(x - 5) = 0 \qquad \text{Factor the trinomial.}$$
$$x + 2 = 0 \quad \text{or} \quad x - 5 = 0 \qquad \text{Set each factor equal to 0.}$$
$$x = -2 \quad \mid \quad x = 5$$

Check: The number -2 is not a solution, because it does not satisfy the equation. (A negative number does not have a logarithm.) We will check the remaining number, 5.

$$\log x + \log(x - 3) = 1$$
$$\log 5 + \log(5 - 3) \overset{?}{=} 1 \qquad \text{Substitute 5 for } x.$$
$$\log 5 + \log 2 \overset{?}{=} 1$$
$$\log 10 \overset{?}{=} 1 \qquad \text{The sum of two logs is the log of a product.}$$
$$1 = 1 \qquad \log 10 = 1$$

Since 5 satisfies the equation, it is a solution.

 SELF CHECK 6 Solve: $\log x + \log(x + 3) = 1$.

EXAMPLE 7 Solve: $\dfrac{\log(5x - 6)}{\log x} = 2$.

Solution We can multiply both sides of the equation by $\log x$ to get

$$\log(5x - 6) = 2 \log x$$

and apply the power rule of logarithms to get

$$\log(5x - 6) = \log x^2$$

By Property 8 of logarithms, $5x - 6 = x^2$. Thus,

$$5x - 6 = x^2$$
$$0 = x^2 - 5x + 6$$
$$0 = (x - 3)(x - 2)$$
$$x - 3 = 0 \quad \text{or} \quad x - 2 = 0$$
$$x = 3 \quad | \quad x = 2$$

Verify that both 2 and 3 satisfy the equation.

⇨ **SELF CHECK 7**   Solve: $\dfrac{\log(5x + 6)}{\log x} = 2$.

ACCENT ON TECHNOLOGY

Solving Logarithmic Equations

To use a graphing calculator to approximate the solutions of $\log x + \log(x - 3) = 1$ (see Example 6), we can subtract 1 from both sides of the equation to get

$$\log x + \log(x - 3) - 1 = 0$$

and graph the corresponding function

$$f(x) = \log x + \log(x - 3) - 1$$

If we use window settings of $[0, 20]$ for x and $[-2, 2]$ for y, we obtain the graph shown in Figure 11-24. Since the solution of the equation is the x-intercept, we can find the solution by zooming in on the value of the x-intercept or by using the ZERO command. The solution is $x = 5$.

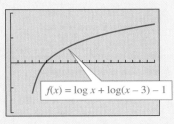

$f(x) = \log x + \log(x - 3) - 1$

Figure 11-24

3 **Solve an application problem involving an exponential or logarithmic equation.**

We have learned that the amount A of radiation present in a radioactive material decays exponentially according to the formula $A = A_0 e^{kt}$, where A_0 is the amount of radioactive material present at time $t = 0$, and k is a negative number.

Experiments have determined the time it takes for one-half of a sample of a radioactive element to decompose. That time is a constant, called the given material's **half-life.**

EXAMPLE 8   **HALF-LIFE OF RADON-22**   In Example 4 of Section 11.2, we learned that radon-22 decays according to the formula $A = A_0 e^{-0.181t}$, where t is expressed in days. Find the material's half-life.

Solution   At time $t = 0$, the amount of radioactive material is A_0. At the end of one half-life, the amount present will be $\frac{1}{2}A_0$. To find the material's half-life, we can substitute $\frac{1}{2}A_0$ for A in the formula and solve for t.

$$A = A_0 e^{-0.181t}$$

$$\frac{1}{2} A_0 = A_0 e^{-0.181t} \qquad \text{Substitute } \tfrac{1}{2} A_0 \text{ for } A.$$

$$\frac{1}{2} = e^{-0.181t} \qquad \text{Divide both sides by } A_0.$$

$$\ln\left(\frac{1}{2}\right) = \ln(e^{-0.181t}) \qquad \text{Take the natural logarithm of both sides.}$$

$$-0.6931471806 \approx -0.181t \ln e \qquad \text{Find } \ln \tfrac{1}{2}, \text{ and use the property } \ln M^p = p \ln M.$$

$$3.829542434 \approx t \qquad \text{Divide both sides by } -0.181 \text{ and note that } \ln e = 1.$$

To the nearest hundredth, the half-life of radon-22 is 3.83 days.

⇨ SELF CHECK 8 To the nearest hundredth, find the half-life of iodine-131 given that it decays according to the formula $A = A_0 e^{-0.087t}$ where t is expressed in days.

When a living organism dies, the oxygen/carbon dioxide cycle common to all living things stops and carbon-14, a radioactive isotope with a half-life of 5,700 years, is no longer absorbed. By measuring the amount of carbon-14 present in an ancient object, archaeologists can estimate the object's age.

EXAMPLE 9 **CARBON-14 DATING** How old is a wooden statue that retains one-third of its original carbon-14 content?

Solution The formula for radioactive decay is $A = A_0 e^{kt}$, where A_0 is the original amount of carbon-14 present, t is the age of the object, and k is a negative number. We can find k by using the fact that after 5,730 years, half of the original amount of carbon-14 will remain.

$$A = A_0 e^{kt}$$

$$\frac{1}{2} A_0 = A_0 e^{k(5,730)} \qquad \text{Substitute } \tfrac{1}{2} A_0 \text{ for } A \text{ and 5,730 for } t.$$

$$\frac{1}{2} = e^{5,730k} \qquad \text{Divide both sides by } A_0.$$

$$\ln\left(\frac{1}{2}\right) = \ln(e^{5,730k}) \qquad \text{Take the natural logarithm of both sides.}$$

$$-0.6931471806 \approx 5,730k \ln e \qquad \text{Find } \ln \tfrac{1}{2}, \text{ and use the property } \ln M^p = p \ln M.$$

$$-0.000120968094 \approx k \qquad \text{Divide both sides by 5,730 and note that } \ln e = 1.$$

Thus, the formula for radioactive decay for carbon-14 can be written as

$$A \approx A_0 e^{-0.000120968094t}$$

Since $\frac{1}{3}$ of the original carbon-14 still remains, we can proceed as follows:

$$A \approx A_0 e^{-0.000120968094t}$$

$$\frac{1}{3} A_0 \approx A_0 e^{-0.000120968094t} \qquad \text{Substitute } \tfrac{1}{3} A_0 \text{ for } A.$$

$$\frac{1}{3} \approx e^{-0.000120968094t} \qquad \text{Divide both sides by } A_0.$$

$$\ln\left(\frac{1}{3}\right) \approx \ln(e^{-0.000120968094t})$$ Take the natural logarithm of both sides.

$$-1.098612289 \approx (-0.000120968094t)\ln e$$ Find $\ln\frac{1}{3}$, and use the property $\ln M^p = p\ln M$.

$$9081.835155 \approx t$$ Divide both sides by -0.000120968094 and note that $\ln e = 1$.

To the nearest one hundred years, the statue is 9,100 years old.

➡ **SELF CHECK 9**   To the nearest hundred years, find the age of a statue that retains 25% of its original carbon-14 content.

Recall that when there is sufficient food and space, populations of living organisms tend to increase exponentially according to the Malthusian growth model.

Malthusian Growth Model

If P is the population at some time t, P_0 is the initial population at $t = 0$, and k is the rate of growth, then

$$P = P_0 e^{kt}$$

COMMENT   Note that this formula is the same as all exponential growth formulas, except for the variables.

EXAMPLE 10   **POPULATION GROWTH**   The bacteria in a laboratory culture increased from an initial population of 500 to 1,500 in 3 hours. How long will it take for the population to reach 10,000?

Solution   We substitute 500 for P_0, 1,500 for P, and 3 for t and simplify to find k:

$$P = P_0 e^{kt}$$

$$1{,}500 = 500(e^{k3})$$ Substitute 1,500 for P, 500 for P_0, and 3 for t.

$$3 = e^{3k}$$ Divide both sides by 500.

$$3k = \ln 3$$ Change the equation from exponential to logarithmic form.

$$k = \frac{\ln 3}{3}$$ Divide both sides by 3.

To find when the population will reach 10,000, we substitute 10,000 for P, 500 for P_0, and $\frac{\ln 3}{3}$ for k in the equation $P = P_0 e^{kt}$ and solve for t:

$$P = P_0 e^{kt}$$

$$10{,}000 = 500 e^{[(\ln 3)/3]t}$$

$$20 = e^{[(\ln 3)/3]t}$$ Divide both sides by 500.

$$\left(\frac{\ln 3}{3}\right)t = \ln 20$$ Change the equation to logarithmic form.

$$t = \frac{3\ln 20}{\ln 3}$$ Multiply both sides by $\frac{3}{\ln 3}$.

$$\approx 8.180499084$$ Use a calculator.

The culture will reach 10,000 bacteria in about 8 hours.

⇨ SELF CHECK 10   How long will it take to reach 20,000?

EXAMPLE 11   **GENERATION TIME**   If a medium is inoculated with a bacterial culture that contains 1,000 cells per milliliter, how many generations will pass by the time the culture has grown to a population of 1 million cells per milliliter?

Solution   During bacterial reproduction, the time required for a population to double is called the *generation time*. If b bacteria are introduced into a medium, then after the generation time of the organism has elapsed, there are $2b$ cells. After another generation, there are $2(2b)$, or $4b$ cells, and so on. After n generations, the number of cells present will be

(1) $B = b \cdot 2^n$

To find the number of generations that have passed while the population grows from b bacteria to B bacteria, we solve Equation 1 for n.

EVERYDAY CONNECTIONS   **U.S. Population Growth**

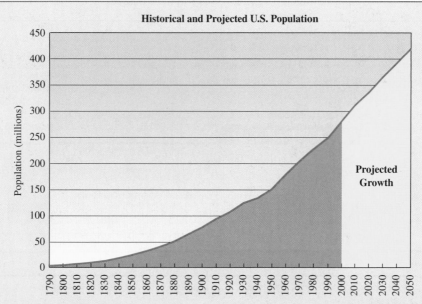

Historical and Projected U.S. Population

Source: http://txsdc.utsa.edu/txdata/apport/hist_a.php

Population growth in the United States can be modeled by an exponential function of the form $P(t) = P_0 \cdot e^{rt}$, where $P_0 =$ the initial population during a given time interval, and t represents the number of years in that time interval.

1. Given that the United States population was approximately 150 million in 1950 and approximately 200 million in 1970, determine the growth rate of the population during this time period.

2. Given that the United States population was 200 million in 1970 and approximately 280 million in 2000, determine the growth rate of the population during this time period.

3. Using the population growth rate from question 2, to the nearest year how long would it take for the United States population to double?

$$\log B = \log(b \cdot 2^n) \qquad \text{Take the common logarithm of both sides.}$$

$$\log B = \log b + n \log 2 \qquad \text{Apply the product and power rules of logarithms.}$$

$$\log B - \log b = n \log 2 \qquad \text{Subtract } \log b \text{ from both sides.}$$

$$n = \frac{1}{\log 2}(\log B - \log b) \qquad \text{Multiply both sides by } \tfrac{1}{\log 2}.$$

$$(2) \qquad n = \frac{1}{\log 2}\left(\log \frac{B}{b}\right) \qquad \text{Use the quotient rule of logarithms.}$$

Equation 2 is a formula that gives the number of generations that will pass as the population grows from b bacteria to B bacteria.

To find the number of generations that have passed while a population of 1,000 cells per milliliter has grown to a population of 1 million cells per milliliter, we substitute 1,000 for b and 1,000,000 for B in Equation 2 and solve for n.

$$n = \frac{1}{\log 2}\log \frac{1,000,000}{1,000}$$

$$= \frac{1}{\log 2}\log 1,000 \qquad \text{Simplify.}$$

$$\approx 3.321928095(3) \qquad \tfrac{1}{\log 2} \approx 3.321928095 \text{ and } \log 1,000 = 3.$$

$$\approx 9.965784285$$

Approximately 10 generations will have passed.

SELF CHECK ANSWERS   **1.** 0.8614   **2.** 60.1   **3.** 6.3013   **4.** 1, 1   **5.** 2   **6.** 2; -5 is extraneous   **7.** 6; -1 is extraneous
8. 8.00 days   **9.** about 11,500 years   **10.** about 10 hours

---

NOW TRY THIS

Given $f(x) = \log_3(x + 2) + \log_3 x$,

1. solve $f(x) = 1$.

2. solve $f(x) = 2$.

11.6 EXERCISES

WARM-UPS   *Solve each equation for x. Do not simplify answers.*

1. $3^x = 5$

2. $5^x = 3$

3. $2^{-x} = 7$

4. $6^{-x} = 1$

5. $\log 2x = \log (x + 2)$

6. $\log 2x = 0$

7. $\log x^4 = 4$

8. $\log \sqrt{x} = \dfrac{1}{2}$

REVIEW   *Solve each equation.*

9. $5x^2 - 25x = 0$

10. $4y^2 - 25 = 0$

11. $3p^2 + 10p = 8$ **12.** $4t^2 + 1 = -6t$

VOCABULARY AND CONCEPTS *Fill in the blanks.*

13. An equation with a variable as an exponent is called a(n) _____ equation.

14. An equation with a logarithmic expression that contains a variable is a(n) _____ equation.

15. The formula for carbon dating is $A =$ _____.

16. The _____ of a radioactive element is determined by how long it takes for half of a sample to decompose.

GUIDED PRACTICE

Solve each exponential equation. If an answer is not exact, give the answer to four decimal places. See Examples 1–2. (Objective 1)

17. $4^x = 5$ **18.** $7^x = 12$

19. $e^t = 50$ **20.** $e^{-t} = 0.25$

21. $2^x = 3^x$ **22.** $3^{2x} = 4^x$

23. $5 = 2.1(1.04)^t$ **24.** $61 = 1.5(1.02)^t$

Solve each exponential equation. If an answer is not exact, give the answer to four decimal places. See Example 3. (Objective 1)

25. $13^{x-1} = 2$ **26.** $5^{x+1} = 3$

27. $2^{x+1} = 3^x$ **28.** $5^{x-3} = 3^{2x}$

Solve each exponential equation. If an answer is not exact, give the answer to four decimal places. See Example 4. (Objective 1)

29. $2^{x^2-3x} = 16$ **30.** $3^{x^2-3x} = 81$

31. $3^{x^2+4x} = \dfrac{1}{81}$ **32.** $7^{x^2+3x} = \dfrac{1}{49}$

33. $7^{x^2} = 10$ **34.** $8^{x^2} = 11$

35. $8^{x^2} = 9^x$ **36.** $5^{x^2} = 2^{5x}$

Use a calculator to solve each equation, if possible. Give all answers to the nearest tenth. (Objective 1)

37. $2^{x+1} = 7$ **38.** $3^{x-1} = 2^x$

39. $2^{x^2-2x} - 8 = 0$ **40.** $3^x - 10 = 3^{-x}$

Solve each logarithmic equation. Check all solutions. See Example 5. (Objective 2)

41. $\log 2x = \log 4$

42. $\log 3x = \log 9$

43. $\log (3x + 1) = \log (x + 7)$

44. $\log (x^2 + 4x) = \log (x^2 + 16)$

45. $\log (3 - 2x) - \log (x + 24) = 0$

46. $\log (3x + 5) - \log (2x + 6) = 0$

47. $\log x^2 = 2$

48. $\log x^3 = 3$

Solve each logarithmic equation. Check all solutions. See Example 6. (Objective 2)

49. $\log x + \log (x - 48) = 2$

50. $\log x + \log (x + 9) = 1$

51. $\log x + \log (x - 15) = 2$

52. $\log x + \log (x + 21) = 2$

53. $\log (x + 90) = 3 - \log x$

54. $\log (x - 90) = 3 - \log x$

55. $\log (x - 6) - \log (x - 2) = \log \dfrac{5}{x}$

56. $\log (3 - 2x) - \log (x + 9) = 0$

Solve each logarithmic equation. Check all solutions. See Example 7. (Objective 2)

57. $\dfrac{\log (2x + 1)}{\log (x - 1)} = 2$

58. $\dfrac{\log (4x + 9)}{\log (2x - 3)} = 2$

59. $\dfrac{\log (3x + 4)}{\log x} = 2$

60. $\dfrac{\log (8x - 7)}{\log x} = 2$

Use a graphing calculator to solve each equation. If an answer is not exact, give all answers to the nearest tenth. (Objective 2)

61. $\log x + \log (x - 15) = 2$

62. $\log x + \log (x + 3) = 1$

63. $\ln(2x + 5) - \ln 3 = \ln(x - 1)$

64. $2 \log (x^2 + 4x) = 1$

ADDITIONAL PRACTICE *Solve each equation. If the answer is not exact, round to 4 decimal places.*

65. $4^{x+2} - 4^x = 15$ (*Hint:* $4^{x+2} = 4^x 4^2$.)

66. $3^{x+3} + 3^x = 84$ (*Hint:* $3^{x+3} = 3^x 3^3$.)

67. $\dfrac{\log (5x + 6)}{2} = \log x$

68. $\dfrac{1}{2} \log (4x + 5) = \log x$

69. $\log_3 x = \log_3 \left(\dfrac{1}{x}\right) + 4$

70. $\log_5(7 + x) + \log_5(8 - x) - \log_5 2 = 2$

71. $2(3^x) = 6^{2x}$

72. $2(3^{x+1}) = 3(2^{x-1})$

73. $\log x^2 = (\log x)^2$

74. $\log (\log x) = 1$

75. $2 \log_2 x = 3 + \log_2(x - 2)$

76. $2 \log_3 x - \log_3(x - 4) = 2 + \log_3 2$

77. $\log (7y + 1) = 2 \log (y + 3) - \log 2$

78. $2 \log (y + 2) = \log (y + 2) - \log 12$

79. $\log \dfrac{4x + 1}{2x + 9} = 0$

80. $\log \dfrac{2 - 5x}{2(x + 8)} = 0$

APPLICATIONS

Solve each application problem. **See Examples 8–11. (Objective 3)**

81. Half-life To the nearest day, find the half-life of strontium-89, given that it decays according to the formula $A = A_0 e^{-0.013t}$.

82. Half-life To the nearest thousand years, find the half-life of plutonium-239, given that it decays according to the formula $A = A_0 e^{-0.0000284t}$.

83. Radioactive decay In two years, 20% of a radioactive element decays. Find its half-life.

84. Tritium decay The half-life of tritium is 12.4 years. How long will it take for 25% of a sample of tritium to decompose?

85. Carbon-14 dating The bone fragment shown in the illustration contains 60% of the carbon-14 that it is assumed to have had initially. How old is it?

86. Carbon-14 dating Only 10% of the carbon-14 in a small wooden bowl remains. How old is the bowl?

87. Rodent control The rodent population in a city is currently estimated at 30,000. If it is expected to double every 5 years, when will the population reach 1 million?

88. Population growth The population of a city is expected to triple every 15 years. When can the city planners expect the present population of 140 persons to double?

89. Bacterial culture A bacterial culture doubles in size every 24 hours. By how much will it have increased in 36 hours?

90. Bacterial growth A bacterial culture grows according to the formula

$$P = P_0 a^t$$

If it takes 5 days for the culture to triple in size, how long will it take to double in size?

91. Medicine If a medium is inoculated with a bacterial culture containing 500 cells per milliliter, how many generations will have passed by the time the culture contains 5×10^6 cells per milliliter?

92. Medicine If a medium is inoculated with a bacterial culture containing 800 cells per milliliter, how many generations will have passed by the time the culture contains 6×10^7 cells per milliliter?

Solve each application problem.

93. Thorium decay An isotope of thorium, ^{227}Th, has a half-life of 18.4 days. How long will it take for 80% of the sample to decompose?

94. Lead decay An isotope of lead, ^{201}Pb, has a half-life of 8.4 hours. How many hours ago was there 30% more of the substance?

95. Compound interest If $500 is deposited in an account paying 8.5% annual interest, compounded semiannually, how long will it take for the account to increase to $800?

96. Continuous compound interest In Exercise 95, how long will it take if the interest is compounded continuously?

97. Compound interest If $1,300 is deposited in a savings account paying 9% interest, compounded quarterly, how long will it take the account to increase to $2,100?

98. Compound interest A sum of $5,000 deposited in an account grows to $7,000 in 5 years. Assuming annual compounding, what interest rate is being paid?

99. Rule of seventy A rule of thumb for finding how long it takes an investment to double is called the **rule of seventy.** To apply the rule, divide 70 by the interest rate written as a percent. At 5%, it takes $\frac{70}{5} = 14$ years to double an investment. At 7%, it takes $\frac{70}{7} = 10$ years. Explain why this formula works.

100. Oceanography The intensity I of a light a distance x meters beneath the surface of a lake decreases exponentially. From the illustration, find the depth at which the intensity will be 20%.

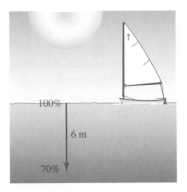

WRITING ABOUT MATH

101. Explain how to solve the equation $2^x = 7$.

102. Explain how to solve the equation $x^2 = 7$.

SOMETHING TO THINK ABOUT

103. Without solving the following equation, find the values of x that cannot be a solution:

$$\log(x - 3) - \log(x^2 + 2) = 0$$

104. Solve the equation $x^{\log x} = 10,000$.

PROJECTS

Project 1

When an object moves through air, it encounters air resistance. So far, all ballistics problems in this text have ignored air resistance. We now consider the case where an object's fall is affected by air resistance.

At relatively low velocities ($v < 200$ feet per second), the force resisting an object's motion is a constant multiple of the object's velocity:

Resisting force $= f_r = bv$

where b is a constant that depends on the size, shape, and texture of the object, and has units of kilograms per second. This is known as **Stokes' law of resistance.**

In a vacuum, the downward velocity of an object dropped with an initial velocity of 0 feet per second is

$v(t) = 32t$ (no air resistance)

t seconds after it is released. However, with air resistance, the velocity is given by the formula

$$v(t) = \frac{32m}{b}(1 - e^{-(b/m)t})$$

where m is the object's mass (in kilograms). There is also a formula for the distance an object falls (in feet) during the first t seconds after release, taking into account air resistance:

$$d(t) = \frac{32m}{b}t - \frac{32m^2}{b^2}(1 - e^{-(b/m)t})$$

Without air resistance, the formula would be

$$d(t) = 16t^2$$

a. Fearless Freda, a renowned skydiving daredevil, performs a practice dive from a hot-air balloon with an altitude of 5,000 feet. With her parachute on, Freda has a mass of 75 kg, so that $b = 15$ kg/sec. How far (to the nearest foot) will Freda fall in 5 seconds? Compare this with the answer you get by disregarding air resistance.

b. What downward velocity (to the nearest ft/sec) does Freda have after she has fallen for 2 seconds? For 5 seconds? Compare these answers with the answers you get by disregarding air resistance.

c. Find Freda's downward velocity after falling for 20, 22, and 25 seconds. (Without air resistance, Freda would hit the ground in less than 18 seconds.) Note

that Freda's velocity increases only slightly. This is because for a large enough velocity, the force of air resistance almost counteracts the force of gravity; after Freda has been falling for a few seconds, her velocity becomes nearly constant. The constant velocity that a falling object approaches is called the *terminal velocity.*

$$\text{Terminal velocity} = \frac{32m}{b}$$

Find Freda's terminal velocity for her practice dive.

d. In Freda's show, she dives from a hot-air balloon with an altitude of only 550 feet, and pulls her ripcord when her velocity is 100 feet per second. (She can't tell her speed, but she knows how long it takes to reach that speed.) It takes a fall of 80 more feet for the chute to open fully, but then the chute increases the force of air resistance, making $b = 80$. After that, Freda's velocity approaches the terminal velocity of an object with this new b-value.

To the nearest hundredth of a second, how long should Freda fall before she pulls the ripcord? To the nearest foot, how close is she to the ground when she pulls the ripcord? How close to the ground is she when the chute takes full effect? At what velocity will Freda hit the ground?

Project 2

If an object at temperature T_0 is surrounded by a constant temperature T_s (for instance, an oven or a large amount of fluid that has a constant temperature), the temperature of the object will change with time t according to the formula

$$T(t) = T_s + (T_0 - T_s)e^{-kt}$$

This is **Newton's law of cooling and warming.** The number k is a constant that depends on how well the object absorbs and dispels heat.

In the course of brewing "yo ho! grog," the dread pirates of Hancock Isle have learned that it is important that their rather disgusting, soupy mash be heated slowly to allow all of the ingredients a chance to add their particular offensiveness to the mixture. However, after the mixture has simmered for several hours, it is equally important that the grog be cooled very quickly, so that it retains its potency. The kegs of grog are then stored in a cool spring.

By trial and error, the pirates have learned that by placing the mash pot into a tub of boiling water (100° C), they can heat the mash in the correct amount of time. They have also learned that they can cool the grog to the temperature of the spring by placing it in ice caves for 1 hour.

With a thermometer, you find that the pirates heat the mash from 20° C to 95° C and then cool the grog from 95° C to 7° C. Calculate how long the pirates cook the mash, and how cold the ice caves are. Assume that $k = 0.5$, and t is measured in hours.

Chapter 11   REVIEW

SECTION 11.1   Exponential Functions

DEFINITIONS AND CONCEPTS	EXAMPLES
An exponential function with base b is defined by the equation $f(x) = b^x \quad (b > 0, b \neq 1)$	Graph $f(x) = 4^x$ and $f(x) = \left(\frac{1}{4}\right)^x$.
Increasing/decreasing functions: The graph of $f(x) = b^x$ is an increasing function if $b > 1$ and decreasing if $0 < b < 1$.	The graph of $f(x) = 4^x$ is an increasing function because as x gets larger, $f(x)$ also gets larger. The graph of $f(x) = \left(\frac{1}{4}\right)^x$ is a decreasing function because as x gets larger, $f(x)$ gets smaller.
Graphing translations: Graphing a translation of an exponential function follows the same rules as for polynomial functions.	Graph $f(x) = 4^x - 2$ and $f(x) = 4^{x-2}$. The graph of $f(x) = 4^x - 2$ is the same as the graph of $f(x) = 4^x$ but shifted 2 units down. The graph of $f(x) = 4^{x-2}$ is the same as the graph of $f(x) = 4^x$ but shifted 2 units to the right.

Compound interest:
The amount of money in an account with an initial deposit of P at an annual interest rate of $r\%$, compounded k times a year for t years, can be found using the formula $A = P\left(1 + \dfrac{r}{k}\right)^{kt}$.

To find the balance in an account after 3 years when \$5,000 is deposited at 6% interest, compounded quarterly, we note that

$$P = 5,000 \qquad r = 0.06 \qquad k = 4 \qquad t = 3$$

We can substitute these values into the formula for compound interest and proceed as follows:

$$A = P\left(1 + \frac{r}{k}\right)^{kt}$$
$$A = 5{,}000\left(1 + \frac{0.06}{4}\right)^{4(3)}$$
$$A = 5{,}000(1 + 0.015)^{12}$$
$$A = 5{,}000(1.015)^{12}$$
$$A \approx 5{,}978.090857 \qquad \text{Use a calculator.}$$

There will be \$5,978.09 in the account after 3 years.

REVIEW EXERCISES
Use properties of exponents to simplify.

1. $5^{\sqrt{2}} \cdot 5^{\sqrt{2}}$ **2.** $\left(2^{\sqrt{5}}\right)^{\sqrt{2}}$

Graph the function defined by each equation.

3. $y = 3^x$ **4.** $y = \left(\dfrac{1}{3}\right)^x$

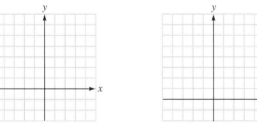

5. The graph of $f(x) = 6^x$ will pass through the points $(0, x)$ and $(1, y)$. Find x and y.

6. Give the domain and range of the function $f(x) = b^x$.

Graph each function by using a translation.

7. $f(x) = \left(\dfrac{1}{2}\right)^x - 2$ **8.** $f(x) = \left(\dfrac{1}{2}\right)^{x+2}$

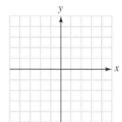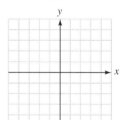

9. Savings How much will \$10,500 become if it earns 9% per year for 60 years, compounded quarterly?

SECTION 11.2   Base-*e* Exponential Functions

| **DEFINITIONS AND CONCEPTS** | **EXAMPLES** |

$$e \approx 2.71828182845904$$

Continuous compound interest:
The amount of money A in an account with an initial deposit of P at an annual interest rate of $r\%$, compounded continuously for t years, can be found using the formula

$$A = Pe^{rt}$$

To find the balance in an account after 3 years when \$5,000 is deposited at 6% interest, compounded continuously, we note that

$$P = 5,000 \qquad r = 0.06 \qquad t = 3$$

We can substitute these values into the formula $A = Pe^{rt}$ and simplify to obtain

$$A = Pe^{rt}$$
$$A = 5{,}000e^{0.06(3)}$$
$$A = 5{,}000e^{0.18}$$
$$A \approx 5{,}986.09 \qquad \text{Use a calculator.}$$

There will be \$5,986.09 in the account.

Malthusian population growth:

The same formula for continuous compound interest is used for population growth, where A is the new population, P is the previous population, r is the growth rate, and t is the number of years.

$$A = Pe^{rt}$$

To find the population of a town in 5 years with a current population of 4,000 and a growth rate of 1.5%, we note that

$$P = 4,000 \qquad r = 0.015 \qquad t = 5$$

We can substitute these values into the formula $A = Pe^{rt}$ to obtain

$$A = Pe^{rt}$$
$$A = 4,000e^{0.015(5)}$$
$$A = 4,000e^{0.075}$$
$$A \approx 4,311.54 \qquad \text{Use a calculator.}$$

There will be about 4,312 people in 5 years.

Radioactive decay:

The formula $A = A_0 e^{kt}$ can be used to determine the amount of material left (A) when an initial amount (A_0) has been decaying for t years at a rate of k. The value of k in this type of problem will be negative.

The radioactive material radon-22 decays with a rate of $k = -0.181t$, where t is in days. To find how much radon-22 will be left if a sample of 100 grams decays for 30 days, we can substitute the values into the radioactive decay formula and proceed as follows:

$$A = A_0 e^{kt}$$
$$A = 100e^{-0.181(30)}$$
$$A = 100e^{-5.43}$$
$$A \approx .4383095803 \qquad \text{Use a calculator.}$$

There will be approximately 0.44 grams remaining.

REVIEW EXERCISES

10. If $10,500 accumulates interest at an annual rate of 9%, compounded continuously, how much will be in the account in 60 years?

Graph each function.

11. $f(x) = e^x + 1$

12. $f(x) = e^{x-3}$

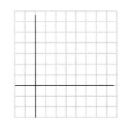

13. **U.S. population** The population of the United States is approximately 275,000,000 people. Find the population in 50 years if $k = 0.015$.

14. **Radioactive decay** The radioactive material strontium-90 decays according to the formula $A = A_0 e^{-0.0244t}$, where t is expressed in years. To the nearest hundredth, how much of the material will remain if a sample of 50 grams decays for 20 years?

SECTION 11.3 Logarithmic Functions

DEFINITIONS AND CONCEPTS	EXAMPLES
If $b > 0$ and $b \neq 1$, then $$y = \log_b x \quad \text{means} \quad x = b^y$$	$y = \log_3 27$ is equivalent to $27 = 3^y$. Since $\log_4 x = 2$ is equivalent to $x = 4^2$, we have $x = 16$. Since $\log_2 32 = x$ is equivalent to $32 = 2^x$ or $2^5 = 2^x$, we have $x = 5$. Since $\log_x 64 = 3$ is equivalent to $64 = x^3$ or $4^3 = x^3$, we have $x = 4$.

REVIEW EXERCISES

15. Give the domain and range of the logarithmic function $y = \log_b x$.

16. Explain why the functions $y = b^x$ and $y = \log_b x$ are called inverse functions.

Find each value.

17. $\log_3 9$

18. $\log_9 \dfrac{1}{3}$

19. $\log_\pi 1$

20. $\log_5 0.04$

21. $\log_a \sqrt{a}$

22. $\log_a \sqrt[3]{a}$

Find the value of x.

23. $\log_2 x = 5$

24. $\log_{\sqrt{3}} x = 4$

25. $\log_{\sqrt{3}} x = 6$

26. $\log_{0.1} 10 = x$

27. $\log_x 2 = -\dfrac{1}{3}$

28. $\log_x 32 = 5$

29. $\log_{0.25} x = -1$

30. $\log_{0.125} x = -\dfrac{1}{3}$

31. $\log_{\sqrt{2}} 32 = x$

32. $\log_{\sqrt{5}} x = -4$

33. $\log_{\sqrt{3}} 9\sqrt{3} = x$

34. $\log_{\sqrt{5}} 5\sqrt{5} = x$

Graph each function.

35. $f(x) = \log(x - 2)$

36. $f(x) = 3 + \log x$

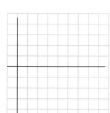

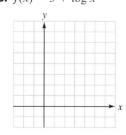

Graph each pair of equations on one set of coordinate axes.

37. $y = 4^x$ and $y = \log_4 x$

38. $y = \left(\dfrac{1}{3}\right)^x$ and $y = \log_{1/3} x$

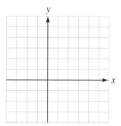

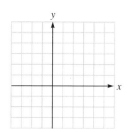

39. dB gain   An amplifier has an output of 18 volts when the input is 0.04 volt. Find the dB gain.

40. Earthquakes   An earthquake had a period of 0.3 second and an amplitude of 7,500 micrometers. Find its measure on the Richter scale.

SECTION 11.4   Natural Logarithms

DEFINITIONS AND CONCEPTS	EXAMPLES
$\ln x$ means $\log_e x$.	Use a calculator to evaluate $\ln 5.89$. $\ln 5.89 \approx 1.7732$
Population doubling time: $A = A_0 e^{kt}$ or $t = \dfrac{\ln 2}{r}$	To find the time it takes for the population of a colony to double if the growth rate is 1.5% per year, substitute 0.015 into the formula for doubling time: $t = \dfrac{\ln 2}{r}$ $t = \dfrac{\ln 2}{0.015}$ $t \approx 46.2098$ Use a calculator. The colony will double in population in about 46 years.

REVIEW EXERCISES

Use a calculator to find each value to four decimal places.

41. $\ln 452$

42. $\ln (\log 7.85)$

Find x.

43. $\ln x = 2.336$

44. $\ln x = \log 8.8$

Graph each function.

45. $f(x) = 1 + \ln x$

46. $f(x) = \ln(x + 1)$

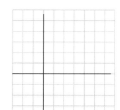

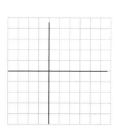

47. U.S. population   How long will it take the population of the United States to double if the growth rate is 3% per year?

SECTION 11.5   Properties of Logarithms

DEFINITIONS AND CONCEPTS	EXAMPLES
Properties of logarithms: If b is a positive number and $b \neq 1$, **1.** $\log_b 1 = 0$ **2.** $\log_b b = 1$ **3.** $\log_b b^x = x$ **4.** $b^{\log_b x} = x$ **5.** $\log_b MN = \log_b M + \log_b N$ **6.** $\log_b \dfrac{M}{N} = \log_b M - \log_b N$ **7.** $\log_b M^P = p \log_b M$ **8.** If $\log_b x = \log_b y$, then $x = y$.	**1.** $\log_b 1 = 0$ because $b^0 = 1$. **2.** $\log_b b = 1$ because $b^1 = b$. **3.** $\log_b b^x = x$ because $b^x = b^x$. **4.** $b^{\log_b x} = x$ because $b^y = x$ and $y = \log_b x$. **5.** $\log_5 xy = \log_5 x + \log_5 y$ **6.** $\log_5 \dfrac{x}{y} = \log_5 x - \log_5 y$ **7.** $\log_5 x^3 = 3 \log_5 x$ **8.** If $\log_3 x = \log_3 9$, then $x = 9$.
Change-of-base formula: $$\log_b y = \frac{\log_a y}{\log_a b}$$	To evaluate $\log_7 16$, substitute 7 and 16 into the change-of-base formula. $$\log_7 16 = \frac{\log_{10} 16}{\log_{10} 7} \approx 1.4248 \quad \text{Use a calculator.}$$ or $$\log_7 16 = \frac{\ln 16}{\ln 7} \approx 1.4248 \quad \text{Use a calculator.}$$

REVIEW EXERCISES

Simplify each expression.

48. $\log_7 1$ **49.** $\log_7 7$

50. $\log_7 7^3$ **51.** $7^{\log_7 4}$

Simplify each expression.

52. $\ln e^4$ **53.** $\ln 1$

54. $10^{\log_{10} 7}$ **55.** $e^{\ln 3}$

56. $\log_b b^4$ **57.** $\ln e^9$

Write each expression in terms of the logarithms of x, y, and z.

58. $\log_b \dfrac{x^2 y^3}{z^4}$

59. $\log_b \sqrt{\dfrac{x}{yz^2}}$

Write each expression as the logarithm of one quantity.

60. $3 \log_b x - 5 \log_b y + 7 \log_b z$

61. $\dfrac{1}{2} \log_b x + 3 \log_b y - 7 \log_b z$

Assume that $\log a = 0.6$, $\log b = 0.36$, and $\log c = 2.4$. Find the value of each expression.

62. $\log abc$ **63.** $\log a^2 b$

64. $\log \dfrac{ac}{b}$ **65.** $\log \dfrac{a^2}{c^3 b^2}$

66. To four decimal places, find $\log_5 17$.

67. pH of grapefruit   The pH of grapefruit juice is about 3.1. Find its hydrogen ion concentration.

68. Find the decrease in loudness if the intensity is cut in half.

SECTION 11.6   Exponential and Logarithmic Equations

DEFINITIONS AND CONCEPTS	EXAMPLES
Solving exponential and logarithmic equations: If the bases of an exponential equation are the same, set the exponents equal.	**1.** Solve each equation. **a.** $9^x = 3^{x-1}$ $\quad (3^2)^x = 3^{x-1}$ $\quad 3^{2x} = 3^{x-1}$ $\quad 2x = x - 1$ $\quad x = -1$
If the bases of an exponential equation are not the same, take the logarithms of both sides. Then use the properties of logarithms to solve for the variable.	**b.** $9^x = 5$ $\ln(9^x) = \ln 5$ Take the natural logarithm of both sides. $x \ln 9 = \ln 5$ The logarithm of a power is the power times the logarithm. $x = \dfrac{\ln 5}{\ln 9}$ Divide both sides by $\ln 9$. $x \approx .7325$ Use a calculator.
Use the properties of logarithms to combine multiple logarithms into a single logarithm.	**c.** $\log_2 (x + 1) + \log_2 (x - 1) = 3$ $\quad \log_2 [(x + 1)(x - 1)] = 3$ Write as a single logarithm. $\quad \log_2 (x^2 - 1) = 3$ Multiply inside the brackets. $\quad 2^3 = x^2 - 1$ Write as an exponential expression. $\quad 8 = x^2 - 1$ Simplify. $\quad 9 = x^2$ Add 1 to both sides. $\quad x = 3, -3$ Take the square root of both sides.
	Since 3 checks, it is a solution. Since -3 does not check, it is extraneous.

REVIEW EXERCISES

Solve each equation for x. If an answer is not exact, round to four decimal places.

69. $3^x = 7$

70. $5^{x+2} = 625$

71. $25 = 5.5(1.05)^t$

72. $4^{2t-1} = 64$

73. $2^x = 3^{x-1}$

74. $2^{x^2+4x} = \dfrac{1}{8}$

Solve each equation for x.

75. $\log x + \log(29 - x) = 2$

76. $\log_2 x + \log_2 (x - 2) = 3$

77. $\log_2 (x + 2) + \log_2 (x - 1) = 2$

78. $\dfrac{\log(7x - 12)}{\log x} = 2$

79. $\log x + \log(x - 5) = \log 6$

80. $\log 3 - \log(x - 1) = -1$

81. $e^{x \ln 2} = 9$

82. $\ln x = \ln(x - 1)$

83. $\ln x = \ln(x - 1) + 1$

84. $\ln x = \log_{10} x$ (*Hint:* Use the change-of-base formula.)

85. Carbon-14 dating   A wooden statue found in Egypt has a carbon-14 content that is two-thirds of that found in living wood. If the half-life of carbon-14 is 5,730 years, how old is the statue?

Chapter 11   TEST

Graph each function.

1. $f(x) = 2^x + 1$

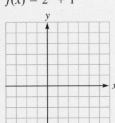

2. $f(x) = 2^{-x}$

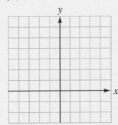

Solve each equation.

3. Radioactive decay   A radioactive material decays according to the formula $A = A_0(2)^{-t}$. How much of a 3-gram sample will be left in 6 years?

4. Investing   An initial deposit of $1,000 earns 6% interest, compounded twice a year. How much will be in the account in one year?

5. Graph the function $f(x) = e^x$.

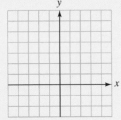

6. Investing   An account contains $2,000 and has been earning 8% interest, compounded continuously. How much will be in the account in 10 years?

Find the value of x.

7. $\log_4 16 = x$

8. $\log_x 81 = 4$

9. $\log_3 x = -3$

10. $\log_x 100 = 2$

11. $\log_{3/2} \dfrac{9}{4} = x$

12. $\log_{2/3} x = -3$

Graph each function.

13. $f(x) = -\log_3 x$

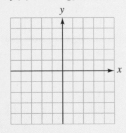

14. $f(x) = \ln x$

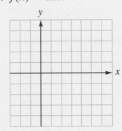

Write each expression in terms of the logarithms of a, b, and c.

15. $\log a^2 b c^3$

16. $\ln \sqrt{\dfrac{a}{b^2 c}}$

Write each expression as a logarithm of a single quantity.

17. $\dfrac{1}{2}\log(a + 2) + \log b - 3 \log c$

18. $\dfrac{1}{3}(\log a - 2 \log b) - \log c$

Assume that log 2 ≈ 0.3010 and log 3 ≈ 0.4771. Find each value. Do not use a calculator.

19. $\log 24$

20. $\log \dfrac{8}{3}$

Use the change-of-base formula to find each logarithm. Do not simplify the answer.

21. $\log_7 3$

22. $\log_\pi e$

Determine whether each statement is true. If a statement is not true, explain why.

23. $\log_a ab = 1 + \log_a b$

24. $\dfrac{\log a}{\log b} = \log a - \log b$

25. $\log a^{-3} = \dfrac{1}{3 \log a}$

26. $\ln(-x) = -\ln x$

27. Find the pH of a solution with a hydrogen ion concentration of 3.7×10^{-7}.   (*Hint:* pH $= -\log[\text{H}^+]$.)

28. Find the dB gain of an amplifier when $E_O = 60$ volts and $E_I = 0.3$ volt.   (*Hint:* dB gain $= 20 \log(E_O/E_I)$.)

Solve each equation. Do not simplify the logarithms.

29. $5^x = 3$

30. $3^{x-1} = 100^x$

Solve each equation.

31. $\log(5x + 2) = \log(2x + 5)$

32. $\log x + \log(x - 9) = 1$

Conic Sections and More Graphing

©Shutterstock.com/andrej pol

Careers and Mathematics

WATER TRANSPORTATION OCCUPATIONS

The movement of cargo and passengers between nations depends on workers in the water transportation occupations, also known on commercial ships as merchant mariners. They operate and maintain deep-sea merchant ships, tugboats, ferries, and excursion vessels.

Water transportation workers held more than 84,000 jobs in 2006. About 17 percent worked in inland waters, primarily the Mississippi River system, 23 percent worked on the deep seas and the Great Lakes, and another 24 percent were employed in harbor operations.

Job Outlook:
Employment in this industry is projected to grow 16 percent over the 2006–2016 decade. This is faster than average for all occupations.

Annual Earnings:
$30,630–$54,280

For More Information:
http://www.bls.gov/oco/ocos247.htm

For a Sample Application:
See Problem 38 in Section 12.3.

In this chapter ▶

We have seen that the graphs of linear functions are straight lines, and that the graphs of quadratic functions are parabolas. In this chapter, we will discuss some special curves, called conic sections. Then we will discuss piecewise-defined functions and step functions.

Objectives

1. Find the center and radius of a circle given an equation in standard and general form.
2. Write an equation of a circle in general form given the center and the radius.
3. Solve an application problem involving a circle.
4. Graph a parabola of the form $x = (y - k)^2 + h$.
5. Solve an application problem involving a parabola.

Vocabulary

conic section	radius of a circle	point circle
circle	standard form of the equation	general form of the equation
center of a circle	of a circle	of a circle

Getting Ready

Square each binomial.

1. $(x - 2)^2$ **2.** $(x + 4)^2$

What number must be added to each binomial to make it a perfect square trinomial?

3. $x^2 + 9x$ **4.** $x^2 - 12x$

In this chapter, we will introduce a group of curves, called *conic sections*.

The graphs of second-degree equations in *x* and *y* represent figures that were investigated in the 17th century by René Descartes (1596–1650) and Blaise Pascal (1623–1662). Descartes discovered that graphs of second-degree equations fall into one of several categories: a pair of lines, a point, a circle, a parabola, an ellipse, a hyperbola, or no graph at all. Because all of these graphs can be formed by the intersection of a plane and a right-circular cone, they are called **conic sections.** See Figure 12-1 on the next page.

In this first section, we will discuss the circle and extend the discussion of parabolas. In Section 12.2, we will discuss the ellipse, and in Section 12.3, we will discuss the hyperbola.

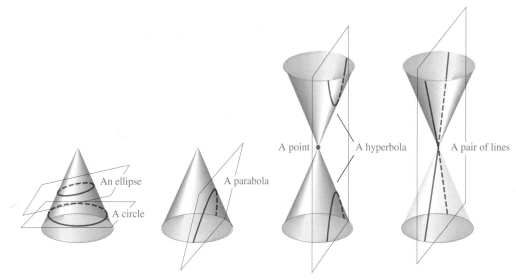

A point   A hyperbola   A pair of lines

An ellipse

A parabola

A circle

Figure 12-1

1 Find the center and radius of a circle given an equation in standard and general form.

A *circle* is one of the most common of the conic sections. Everyone knows about circular wheels and gears, pizza cutters, and Ferris wheels. Because of their importance, we will begin the study of conic sections with the circle.

Every conic section can be represented by a second-degree equation in x and y. To find the form of an equation of a circle, we use the following definition.

The Circle	A **circle** is the set of all points in a plane that are a fixed distance from a point, called its **center.** The fixed distance is the **radius** of the circle.

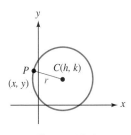

Figure 12-2

To develop the general equation of a circle, we must write the equation of a circle with a radius of r and with center at some point $C(h, k)$, as in Figure 12-2. This task is equivalent to finding all points $P(x, y)$ such that the length of line segment CP is r. We can use the distance formula to find r.

$$r = \sqrt{(x - h)^2 + (y - k)^2}$$

We then square both sides to obtain

$$(1) \quad r^2 = (x - h)^2 + (y - k)^2$$

Equation 1 is called the **standard form of the equation of a circle** with radius r and center at the point with coordinates (h, k).

Standard Form of the Equation of a Circle with Center at (h, k)	Any equation that can be written in the form $$(x - h)^2 + (y - k)^2 = r^2$$ has a graph that is a circle with radius r and center at point (h, k).

If $r = 0$, the graph reduces to a single point called a **point circle.** If $r^2 < 0$, a circle does not exist. If both coordinates of the center are 0, the center of the circle is the origin.

Standard Form of the Equation of a Circle with Center at (0, 0)	Any equation that can be written in the form $$x^2 + y^2 = r^2$$ has a graph that is a circle with radius r and center at the origin.

EXAMPLE 1 Find the center and the radius of each circle and then graph it.
a. $(x - 4)^2 + (y - 1)^2 = 9$ **b.** $x^2 + y^2 = 25$ **c.** $(x + 3)^2 + y^2 = 12$

Solution **a.** It is easy to determine the center and the radius of a circle when its equation is written in standard form.

$$(x - 4)^2 + (y - 1)^2 = 9$$

$h = 4, k = 1,$ and $r^2 = 9.$ Since the radius of a circle must be positive, $r = 3.$

$$(x - h)^2 + (y - k)^2 = r^2$$

The center of the circle is $(h, k) = (4, 1)$ and the radius is 3.

To plot four points on the circle, we move up, down, left, and right 3 units from the center, as shown in Figure 12-3(a). Then we draw a circle through the points to get the graph of $(x - 4)^2 + (y - 1)^2 = 9$, as shown in Figure 12-3(b).

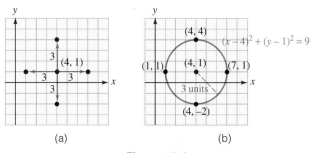

(a)   (b)

Figure 12-3

b. To verify that the center of the circle is the origin, we can write $x^2 + y^2 = 25$ in the following way:

$$(x - 0)^2 + (y - 0)^2 = 25$$

$h = 0, k = 0,$ and $r^2 = 25.$ Since the radius of a circle must be positive, $r = 5.$

$$h \qquad\quad k \quad\; r^2$$

This shows that the center of the circle is at $(0, 0)$ and the radius is 5.

To plot four points on the circle, we move up, down, left, and right 5 units from the center. Then we draw a circle through the points to get the graph of $x^2 + y^2 = 25$, as shown in Figure 12-4.

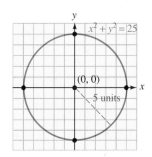

Figure 12-4

c. To determine h in the equation $(x + 3)^2 + y^2 = 12$, it is helpful to write $x + 3$ as $x - (-3)$.

Standard form requires
a minus symbol here.

↓

$$[x - (-3)]^2 + (y - 0)^2 = 12$$

↑   ↑   ↑ $h = -3, k = 0,$ and $r^2 = 12.$
h k r^2

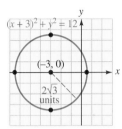

$(x + 3)^2 + y^2 = 12$

$(-3, 0)$

$2\sqrt{3}$ units

Figure 12-5

If $r^2 = 12$, by the square root property

$$r = \pm\sqrt{12} = \pm 2\sqrt{3}$$

Since the radius can't be negative, we get $r = 2\sqrt{3}$. The center of the circle is at $(-3, 0)$ and the radius is $2\sqrt{3}$.

To plot four points on the circle, we move up, down, left, and right $2\sqrt{3} \approx 3.5$ units from the center. Then we draw a circle through the points to get the graph of $(x + 3)^2 + y^2 = 12$, as shown in Figure 12-5.

⇨ **SELF CHECK 1**   Find the center and the radius of each circle and then graph it.
a. $(x - 3)^2 + (y + 4)^2 = 4$ **b.** $x^2 + y^2 = 8$

Another important form of the equation of a circle is called the *general form of the equation of a circle.*

General Form of the Equation of a Circle	The equation of any circle can be written in the form $$x^2 + y^2 + Dx + Ey + F = 0$$

EXAMPLE 2   Graph: $x^2 + y^2 - 4x + 2y - 20 = 0$.

Solution   Since the equation matches the general form of the equation of a circle, we know that its graph will be a circle. To find its center and radius, we must complete the square on both x and y and write the equation in standard form.

$x^2 + y^2 - 4x + 2y = 20$ Add 20 to both sides.
$x^2 - 4x + y^2 + 2y = 20$

To complete the square on x and y, add 4 and 1 to both sides.

$x^2 - 4x + 4 + y^2 + 2y + 1 = 20 + 4 + 1$
$(x - 2)^2 + (y + 1)^2 = 25$ Factor $x^2 - 4x + 4$ and $y^2 + 2y + 1$.
$(x - 2)^2 + [y - (-1)]^2 = 5^2$

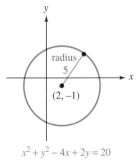

radius 5

$(2, -1)$

$x^2 + y^2 - 4x + 2y = 20$

Figure 12-6

We can now see that this result is the standard equation of a circle with a radius of 5 and center at $h = 2$ and $k = -1$. If we plot the center and draw a circle with a radius of 5 units, we will obtain the circle shown in Figure 12-6.

⇨ **SELF CHECK 2**   Write the equation $x^2 + y^2 + 2x - 4y - 11 = 0$ in standard form and graph it.

2   **Write an equation of a circle in general form given the center and the radius.**

EXAMPLE 3   Find the general form of the equation of the circle with radius 5 and center at (3, 2).

Solution   We substitute 5 for r, 3 for h, and 2 for k in the standard form of a circle and proceed as follows:

$$(x - h)^2 + (y - k)^2 = r^2$$
$$(x - 3)^2 + (y - 2)^2 = 5^2$$
$$x^2 - 6x + 9 + y^2 - 4y + 4 = 25 \quad (x - 3)^2 = x^2 - 6x + 9; (y - 2)^2 = y^2 - 4y + 4$$
$$x^2 + y^2 - 6x - 4y - 12 = 0 \quad \text{Subtract 25 from both sides and simplify.}$$

The general form of the equation is $x^2 + y^2 - 6x - 4y - 12 = 0$.

⇨ **SELF CHECK 3**   Find the general form of the equation of the circle with radius 6 and center at (2, 3).

ACCENT ON TECHNOLOGY

Graphing Circles

Since the graphs of circles fail the vertical line test, their equations do not represent functions. It is somewhat more difficult to use a graphing calculator to graph equations that are not functions. For example, to graph the circle described by $(x - 1)^2 + (y - 2)^2 = 4$, we must split the equation into two functions and graph each one separately. We begin by solving the equation for y.

$$(x - 1)^2 + (y - 2)^2 = 4$$
$$(y - 2)^2 = 4 - (x - 1)^2 \quad \text{Subtract } (x - 1)^2 \text{ from both sides.}$$
$$y - 2 = \pm\sqrt{4 - (x - 1)^2} \quad \text{Use the square-root property.}$$
$$y = 2 \pm \sqrt{4 - (x - 1)^2} \quad \text{Add 2 to both sides.}$$

This equation defines two functions. If we use window settings of $[-3, 5]$ for x and $[-3, 5]$ for y and graph the functions

$$y = 2 + \sqrt{4 - (x - 1)^2} \quad \text{and} \quad y = 2 - \sqrt{4 - (x - 1)^2}$$

we get the distorted circle shown in Figure 12-7(a). To get a better circle, graphing calculators have a squaring feature, ZSquare, that gives an equal unit distance on both the x- and y-axes. After using this feature, we get the circle shown in Figure 12-7(b).

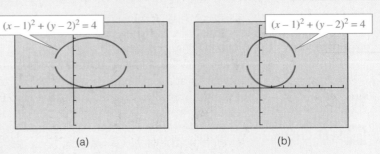

(a)   (b)

Figure 12-7

3 Solve an application problem involving a circle.

EXAMPLE 4 **TELEVISION TRANSLATORS**   The broadcast area of a television station is bounded by the circle $x^2 + y^2 = 3{,}600$, where x and y are measured in miles. A translator station picks up the signal and retransmits it from the center of a circular area bounded by $(x + 30)^2 + (y - 40)^2 = 1{,}600$. Find the location of the translator and the greatest distance from the main transmitter that the signal can be received.

Solution   The coverage of the television station is bounded by $x^2 + y^2 = 60^2$, a circle centered at the origin with a radius of 60 miles, as shown in Figure 12-8. Because the translator is at the center of the circle $(x + 30)^2 + (y - 40)^2 = 1{,}600$, it is located at $(-30, 40)$, a point 30 miles west and 40 miles north of the television station. The radius of the translator's coverage is $\sqrt{1{,}600}$, or 40 miles.

As shown in the figure, the greatest distance of reception is the sum of A, the distance from the translator to the TV station, and 40 miles, the radius of the translator's coverage.

To find A, we use the distance formula to find the distance between $(x_1, y_1) = (-30, 40)$ and the origin, $(x_2, y_2) = (0, 0)$.

$$A = \sqrt{(x_1 - x_2)^2 + (y_1 - y_2)^2}$$
$$A = \sqrt{(-30 - 0)^2 + (40 - 0)^2}$$
$$= \sqrt{(-30)^2 + 40^2}$$
$$= \sqrt{2{,}500}$$
$$= 50$$

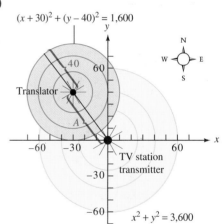

Figure 12-8

Since the translator is 50 miles from the TV station and it broadcasts the signal an additional 40 miles, the greatest reception distance is 50 + 40, or 90 miles.

4 Graph a parabola of the form $x = (y - k)^2 + h$.

Parabolas can be rotated to generate dish-shaped surfaces called *paraboloids*. Any light or sound placed at the *focus* of a paraboloid is reflected outward in parallel paths, as shown in Figure 12-9(a). This property makes parabolic surfaces ideal for flashlight and headlight reflectors. It also makes parabolic surfaces good antennas, because signals captured by such antennas are concentrated at the focus. Parabolic mirrors are capable of concentrating the rays of the Sun at a single point and thereby generating tremendous heat. This property is used in the design of solar furnaces.

Any object thrown upward and outward travels in a parabolic path, as shown in Figure 12-9(b). In architecture, many arches are parabolic in shape, because this gives strength. Cables that support suspension bridges hang in the form of a parabola. (See Figure 12-9(c).)

Parabolas

(a)

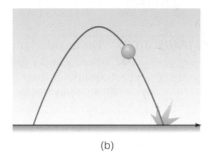
(b)

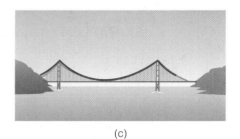
(c)

Figure 12-9

We have seen that equations of the form $y = a(x - h)^2 + k$, with $a \neq 0$, represent parabolas with the vertex at the point (h, k). They open upward when $a > 0$ and downward when $a < 0$.

Equations of the form $x = a(y - k)^2 + h$ $(a \neq 0)$, also represent parabolas with vertex at point (h, k). However, they open to the right when $a > 0$ and to the left when $a < 0$. Parabolas that open to the right or left do not represent functions, because their graphs fail the vertical line test.

Standard equations of many parabolas are summarized in the following table.

Equations of Parabolas	**Parabola opening**	**Vertex at origin**	**Vertex at (h, k)**
	Up	$y = ax^2$ $(a > 0)$	$y = a(x - h)^2 + k$ $(a > 0)$
	Down	$y = ax^2$ $(a < 0)$	$y = a(x - h)^2 + k$ $(a < 0)$
	Right	$x = ay^2$ $(a > 0)$	$x = a(y - k)^2 + h$ $(a > 0)$
	Left	$x = ay^2$ $(a < 0)$	$x = a(y - k)^2 + h$ $(a < 0)$

EXAMPLE 5   Graph: **a.** $x = \dfrac{1}{2}y^2$ **b.** $x = -2(y - 2)^2 + 3$.

Solution   **a.** We can make a table of ordered pairs that satisfy the equation, plot each pair, and draw the parabola, as in Figure 12-10(a). Because the equation is of the form $x = ay^2$ with $a > 0$, the parabola opens to the right and has its vertex at the origin.

b. We can make a table of ordered pairs that satisfy the equation, plot each pair, and draw the parabola, as in Figure 12-10(b). Because the equation is of the form $x = a(y - k)^2 + h$ $(a < 0)$, the parabola opens to the left and has its vertex at the point with coordinates (3, 2).

$x = \dfrac{1}{2}y^2$

x	y	(x, y)
0	0	$(0, 0)$
2	2	$(2, 2)$
2	-2	$(2, -2)$
8	4	$(8, 4)$
8	-4	$(8, -4)$

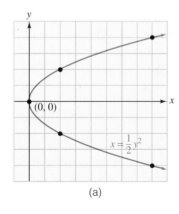
(a)

$x = -2(y - 2)^2 + 3$

x	y	(x, y)
-5	0	$(-5, 0)$
1	1	$(1, 1)$
3	2	$(3, 2)$
1	3	$(1, 3)$
-5	4	$(-5, 4)$

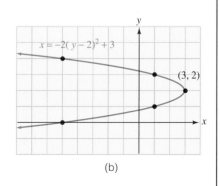
(b)

Figure 12-10

⇨ **SELF CHECK 5**   Graph: $x = \frac{1}{2}(y - 1)^2 - 2$.

The general forms of the equations of a parabola are as follows:

General Form of the Equation of a Parabola That Opens Upward or Downward	The general form of the equation of a parabola that opens upward or downward is $y = ax^2 + bx + c \quad (a \neq 0)$ If $a > 0$, the parabola opens upward. If $a < 0$, the parabola opens downward.
General Form of the Equation of a Parabola That Opens Left or Right	The general form of the equation of a parabola that opens to the left or to the right is $x = ay^2 + by + c \quad (a \neq 0)$ If $a > 0$, the parabola opens to the right. If $a < 0$, the parabola opens to the left.

EXAMPLE 6   Graph: $x = -2y^2 + 12y - 15$.

Solution   This equation is the general form of a parabola that opens left or right. Since $a = -2$ and $-2 < 0$, the parabola opens to the left. To find the coordinates of its vertex, we write the equation in standard form by completing the square on y.

$$x = -2y^2 + 12y - 15$$
$$= -2(y^2 - 6y) - 15 \qquad \text{Factor out } -2 \text{ from } -2y^2 + 12y.$$
$$= -2(y^2 - 6y + 9) - 15 + 18 \qquad \text{Subtract and add 18; } -2(9) = -18.$$
$$= -2(y - 3)^2 + 3$$

Because the equation is written in the form $x = a(y - k)^2 + h$, we can see that the parabola has its vertex at (3, 3). The graph is shown in Figure 12-11.

$x = -2y^2 + 12y - 15$

x	y	(x, y)
-5	1	$(-5, 1)$
1	2	$(1, 2)$
3	3	$(3, 3)$
1	4	$(1, 4)$
-5	5	$(-5, 5)$

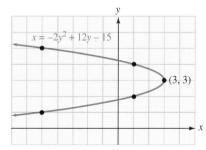

Figure 12-11

⇨ **SELF CHECK 6**   Graph: $x = 0.5y^2 - y - 1$.

COMMENT   To find the y-coordinate of the vertex for this horizontal parabola, we could just as well compute $-\frac{b}{2a}$. To find the x-coordinate, we could substitute the value of $-\frac{b}{2a}$ for y and find x.

5   **Solve an application problem involving a parabola.**

EXAMPLE 7   **GATEWAY ARCH**   The shape of the Gateway Arch in St. Louis is approximately a parabola 630 feet high and 630 feet wide, as shown in Figure 12-12(a). How high is the arch 100 feet from its foundation?

Solution   We place the parabola in a coordinate system as in Figure 12-12(b), with ground level on the x-axis and the vertex of the parabola at the point $(h, k) = (0, 630)$.

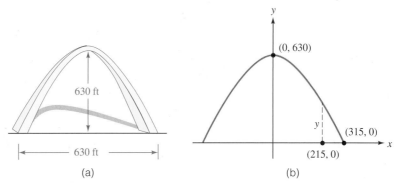

Figure 12-12

The equation of this downward-opening parabola has the form

$$y = a(x - h)^2 + k \qquad \text{With } a < 0.$$
$$= a(x - 0)^2 + 630 \qquad \text{Substitute } h = 0 \text{ and } k = 630.$$
$$= ax^2 + 630 \qquad \text{Simplify.}$$

Because the Gateway Arch is 630 feet wide at its base, the parabola passes through the point $\left(\frac{630}{2}, 0\right)$, or $(315, 0)$. To find a in the equation of the parabola, we proceed as follows:

$$y = ax^2 + 630$$
$$0 = a(315)^2 + 630 \qquad \text{Substitute 315 for } x \text{ and 0 for } y.$$
$$\frac{-630}{315^2} = a \qquad \text{Subtract 630 from both sides and divide both sides by } 315^2.$$
$$-\frac{2}{315} = a \qquad \text{Simplify; } \frac{-630}{315^2} = \frac{-2}{315}.$$

The equation of the parabola that approximates the shape of the Gateway Arch is

$$y = -\frac{2}{315}x^2 + 630$$

To find the height of the arch at a point 100 feet from its foundation, we substitute $315 - 100$, or 215, for x in the equation of the parabola and solve for y.

$$y = -\frac{2}{315}x^2 + 630$$
$$= -\frac{2}{315}(215)^2 + 630$$
$$= 336.5079365$$

At a point 100 feet from the foundation, the height of the arch is about 337 feet.

⇨ SELF CHECK ANSWERS

1. a. $(3, -4)$, 2

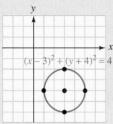

$(x - 3)^2 + (y + 4)^2 = 4$

b. $(0, 0)$, $2\sqrt{2}$

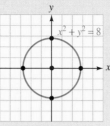

$x^2 + y^2 = 8$

2. $(x + 1)^2 + (y - 2)^2 = 16$

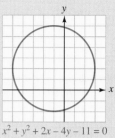

$x^2 + y^2 + 2x - 4y - 11 = 0$

3. $x^2 + y^2 - 4x - 6y - 23 = 0$

5.

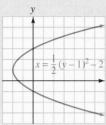

$x = \frac{1}{2}(y - 1)^2 - 2$

6.

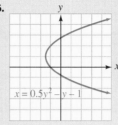

$x = 0.5y^2 - y - 1$

NOW TRY THIS

1. The equation $4y^2 + (4x - 1)y + x^2 - 5x - 3 = 0$ is an equation for a parabola that is neither vertical nor horizontal. Use the quadratic formula to solve for y and then graph the equation with a calculator. (*Hint:* $a = 4$, $b = 4x - 1$, and $c = x^2 - 5x - 3$.)

12.1 EXERCISES

WARM-UPS

Find the center and the radius of each circle.

1. $x^2 + y^2 = 144$

2. $x^2 + y^2 = 121$

3. $(x - 2)^2 + y^2 = 16$

4. $x^2 + (y + 1)^2 = 9$

Determine whether the graph of each parabola opens up or down or left or right.

5. $y = -3x^2 - 2$

6. $y = 7x^2 - 5$

7. $x = -3y^2$

8. $x = (y - 3)^2$

REVIEW   *Solve each equation.*

9. $|3x - 4| = 11$

10. $\left| \dfrac{4 - 3x}{5} \right| = 12$

11. $|3x + 4| = |5x - 2|$

12. $|6 - 4x| = |x + 2|$

VOCABULARY AND CONCEPTS   *Fill in the blanks.*

13. A _____ section is determined by the intersection of a plane and a right-circular cone.

14. A _____ is the set of all points in a _____ that are a fixed distance from a given point. The fixed distance is called the _____ and the point is called the _____.

15. The equation of the circle $x^2 + (y - 3)^2 = 16$ is in _____ form with the center at _____ and a radius __.

16. The graph of the equation $x^2 + y^2 = 0$ is a _____.

17. The equation $x^2 + y^2 - 10x - 8y - 8 = 0$ is an equation of a _____ written in _____ form.

18. The graph of $y = ax^2$ $(a > 0)$ is a _____ with vertex at the _____ that opens _____.

19. The graph of $x = a(y - 2)^2 + 3$ $(a > 0)$ is a _____ with vertex at _____ that opens to the _____.

20. The graph of $x = a(y - 1)^2 - 3$ $(a < 0)$ is a _____ with vertex at _____ that opens to the ____.

GUIDED PRACTICE

Graph each equation and find the center and radius of the resulting circle. **See Example 1. (Objective 1)**

21. $x^2 + y^2 = 9$

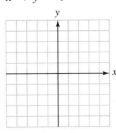

22. $x^2 + y^2 = 16$

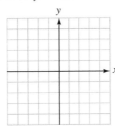

23. $(x - 2)^2 + y^2 = 9$

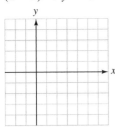

24. $x^2 + (y - 3)^2 = 4$

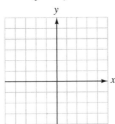

25. $(x - 2)^2 + (y - 4)^2 = 4$

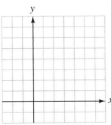

26. $(x - 3)^2 + (y - 2)^2 = 4$

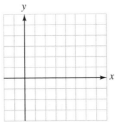

27. $(x + 3)^2 + (y - 1)^2 = 16$

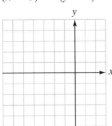

28. $(x - 1)^2 + (y + 4)^2 = 9$

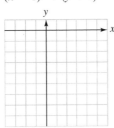

Graph each circle. Give the coordinates of the center and find the radius. **See Example 2. (Objective 1)**

29. $x^2 + y^2 + 2x - 8 = 0$

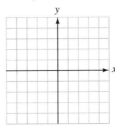

30. $x^2 + y^2 - 4y = 12$

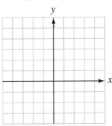

31. $9x^2 + 9y^2 - 12y = 5$

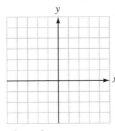

32. $4x^2 + 4y^2 + 4y = 15$

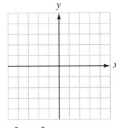

33. $x^2 + y^2 - 2x + 4y = -1$

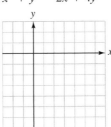

34. $x^2 + y^2 + 4x + 2y = 4$

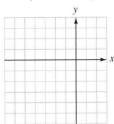

35. $x^2 + y^2 + 6x - 4y = -12$

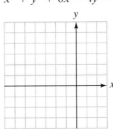

36. $x^2 + y^2 + 8x + 2y = -13$

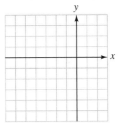

Write the equation of the circle with the following properties in standard form and in general form. **See Example 3. (Objective 2)**

37. Center at origin; radius 1

38. Center at origin; radius 4

39. Center at (6, 8); radius 5

40. Center at (5, 3); radius 2

41. Center at (−2, 6); radius 12

42. Center at (5, −4); radius 6

43. Center at the origin; diameter $2\sqrt{2}$

44. Center at the origin; diameter $8\sqrt{3}$

Find the vertex of each parabola and graph it. **See Examples 5–6.**
(Objective 4)

45. $x = y^2$

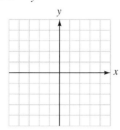

46. $x = -y^2 + 1$

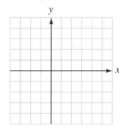

47. $x = -\dfrac{1}{4}y^2$

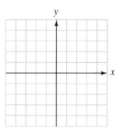

48. $x = 4y^2$

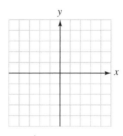

49. $y^2 + 4x - 6y = -1$

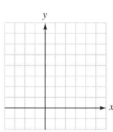

50. $x = \dfrac{1}{2}y^2 + 2y$

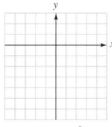

51. $y = 2(x - 1)^2 + 3$

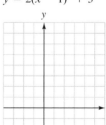

52. $y = -2(x + 1)^2 + 2$

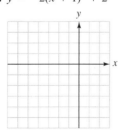

ADDITIONAL PRACTICE

Graph each equation.

53. $x^2 + (y + 3)^2 = 1$

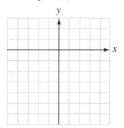

54. $(x + 4)^2 + y^2 = 1$

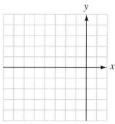

55. $y = x^2 + 4x + 5$

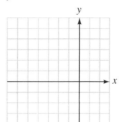

56. $y = -x^2 - 2x + 3$

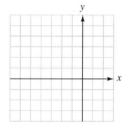

57. $y = -x^2 - x + 1$

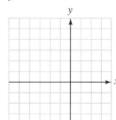

58. $x^2 - 2y - 2x = -7$

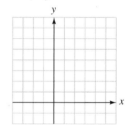

Use a graphing calculator to graph each equation.

59. $3x^2 + 3y^2 = 16$

60. $2x^2 + 2y^2 = 9$

61. $(x + 1)^2 + y^2 = 16$

62. $x^2 + (y - 2)^2 = 4$

63. $x = 2y^2$

64. $x = y^2 - 4$

65. $x^2 - 2x + y = 6$

66. $x = -2(y - 1)^2 + 2$

APPLICATIONS   *Solve each application.* **See Examples 4 and 7.**
(Objectives 3 and 5)

67. Meshing gears   For design purposes, the large gear is the circle $x^2 + y^2 = 16$. The smaller gear is a circle centered at $(7, 0)$ and tangent to the larger circle. Find the equation of the smaller gear.

68. Width of a walkway   The following walkway is bounded by the two circles $x^2 + y^2 = 2,500$ and $(x - 10)^2 + y^2 = 900$, measured in feet. Find the largest and the smallest width of the walkway.

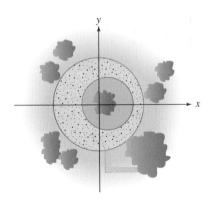

69. Broadcast ranges   Radio stations applying for licensing may not use the same frequency if their broadcast areas overlap. One station's coverage is bounded by $x^2 + y^2 - 8x - 20y + 16 = 0$, and the other's by $x^2 + y^2 + 2x + 4y - 11 = 0$. May they be licensed for the same frequency?

70. Highway design   Engineers want to join two sections of highway with a curve that is one-quarter of a circle as shown in the illustration. The equation of the circle is $x^2 + y^2 - 16x - 20y + 155 = 0$, where distances are measured in kilometers. Find the locations (relative to the center of town) of the intersections of the highway with State and with Main.

71. Projectiles   The cannonball in the illustration follows the parabolic trajectory $y = 30x - x^2$. Where does it land?

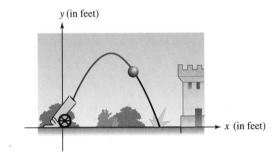

72. Projectiles   In Exercise 71, how high does the cannonball rise?

73. Path of a comet   If the path of a comet is given by the equation $2y^2 - 9x = 18$, how far is it from the Sun at the vertex of the orbit? Distances are measured in astronomical units (AU).

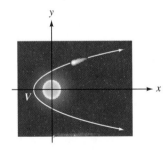

74. Satellite antennas   The cross section of the satellite antenna is a parabola given by the equation $y = \frac{1}{16}x^2$, with distances measured in feet. If the dish is 8 feet wide, how deep is it?

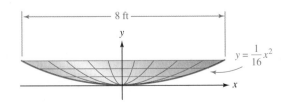

WRITING ABOUT MATH

75. Explain how to decide from its equation whether the graph of a parabola opens up, down, right, or left.

76. From the equation of a circle, explain how to determine the radius and the coordinates of the center.

SOMETHING TO THINK ABOUT

77. From the values of a, h, and k, explain how to determine the number of x-intercepts of the graph of $y = a(x - h)^2 + k$.

78. Under what conditions will the graph of $x = a(y - k)^2 + h$ have no y-intercepts?

SECTION 12.2 The Ellipse

Objectives

1 Graph an ellipse given an equation in standard form.
2 Graph an ellipse given an equation in general form.
3 Solve an application problem involving an ellipse.

Vocabulary

ellipse   eccentricity   major axis
focus   vertices   minor axis
foci

Getting Ready

Solve each equation for the indicated variable $(a \neq 0, b \neq 0)$.

1. $\dfrac{y^2}{b^2} = 1$ for y **2.** $\dfrac{x^2}{a^2} = 1$ for x

---

A third conic section is an oval-shaped curve called an *ellipse*. Ellipses can be nearly round or they can be long and narrow. In this section, we will learn how to construct ellipses and how to graph equations that represent them.

Ellipses have optical and acoustical properties that are useful in architecture and engineering. For example, many arches are portions of an ellipse, because the shape is pleasing to the eye. (See Figure 12-13(a).) The planets and many comets have elliptical orbits. (See Figure 12-13(b).) Gears are often cut into elliptical shapes to provide nonuniform motion. (See Figure 12-13(c).)

Ellipses

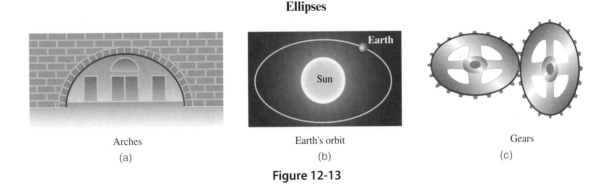

Arches
(a)

Earth's orbit
(b)

Gears
(c)

Figure 12-13

1 Graph an ellipse given an equation in standard form.

The Ellipse

An **ellipse** is the set of all points P in the plane the sum of whose distances from two fixed points is a constant. See Figure 12-14, in which $d_1 + d_2$ is a constant.

Each of the two points is called a **focus.** Midway between the **foci** is the *center* of the ellipse.

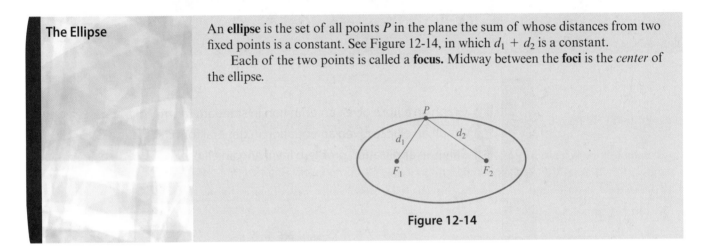

Figure 12-14

We can construct an ellipse by placing two thumbtacks fairly close together, as in Figure 12-15. We then tie each end of a piece of string to a thumbtack, catch the loop with the point of a pencil, and, while keeping the string taut, draw the ellipse.

Figure 12-15

Using this method, we can construct an ellipse of any specific size. For example, to construct an ellipse that is 10 inches wide and 6 inches high, we must find the length of string to use and the distance between thumbtacks.

To do this, we will let a represent the distance between the center and vertex V, as shown in Figure 12-16(a) on the next page. We will also let c represent the distance between the center of the ellipse and either focus. When the pencil is at vertex V, the length of the string is $c + a + (a - c)$, or just $2a$. Because $2a$ is the 10 inch width of the ellipse, the string needs to be 10 inches long. The distance $2a$ is constant for any point on the ellipse, including point B shown in Figure 12-16(b).

Sir Isaac Newton (1642–1727)

Newton was an English scientist and mathematician. Because he was not a good farmer, he went to Cambridge University to become a preacher. When he had to leave Cambridge because of the plague, he made some of his most important discoveries. He is best known in mathematics for developing calculus and in physics for discovering the laws of motion. Newton probably contributed more to science and mathematics than anyone else in history.

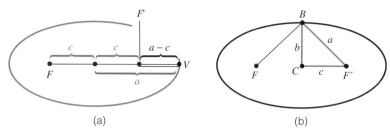

(a)   (b)

Figure 12-16

From right triangle BCF' in Figure 12-16(b) and the Pythagorean theorem, we can find c as follows:

$$a^2 = b^2 + c^2 \qquad \text{or} \qquad c = \sqrt{a^2 - b^2}$$

Since distance b is one-half of the height of the ellipse, $b = 3$. Since $2a = 10$, $a = 5$. We can now substitute $a = 5$ and $b = 3$ into the formula to find c:

$$c = \sqrt{5^2 - 3^2}$$
$$= \sqrt{25 - 9}$$
$$= \sqrt{16}$$
$$= 4$$

Since $c = 4$, the distance between the thumbtacks must be 8 inches. We can construct the ellipse by tying a 10 inch string to thumbtacks that are 8 inches apart.

To graph ellipses, we can make a table of ordered pairs that satisfy the equation, plot them, and join the points with a smooth curve.

EXAMPLE 1   Graph: $\dfrac{x^2}{36} + \dfrac{y^2}{9} = 1$.

Solution   We note that the equation can be written in the form

$$\frac{x^2}{6^2} + \frac{y^2}{3^2} = 1 \qquad 36 = 6^2 \text{ and } 9 = 3^2.$$

After making a table of ordered pairs that satisfy the equation, plotting each of them, and joining the points with a curve, we obtain the ellipse shown in Figure 12-17.

We note that the center of the ellipse is the origin, the ellipse intersects the x-axis at points $(6, 0)$ and $(-6, 0)$, and the ellipse intersects the y-axis at points $(0, 3)$ and $(0, -3)$.

$$\frac{x^2}{36} + \frac{y^2}{9} = 1$$

x	y	(x, y)
-6	0	$(-6, 0)$
-4	± 2.2	$(-4, \pm 2.2)$
-2	± 2.8	$(-2, \pm 2.8)$
0	± 3	$(0, \pm 3)$
2	± 2.8	$(2, \pm 2.8)$
4	± 2.2	$(4, \pm 2.2)$
6	0	$(6, 0)$

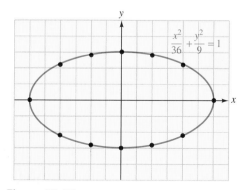

Figure 12-17

⇨ **SELF CHECK 1**   Graph: $\dfrac{x^2}{4} + \dfrac{y^2}{16} = 1$.

Example 1 illustrates that the graph of

$$\frac{x^2}{a^2} + \frac{y^2}{b^2} = 1$$

is an ellipse centered at the origin. To find the x-intercepts of the graph, we can let $y = 0$ and solve for x.

$$\frac{x^2}{a^2} + \frac{0^2}{b^2} = 1$$

$$\frac{x^2}{a^2} + 0 = 1$$

$$x^2 = a^2$$

$$x = a \quad \text{or} \quad x = -a$$

The x-intercepts are $(a, 0)$ and $(-a, 0)$.

To find the y-intercepts, we let $x = 0$ and solve for y.

$$\frac{0^2}{a^2} + \frac{y^2}{b^2} = 1$$

$$0 + \frac{y^2}{b^2} = 1$$

$$y^2 = b^2$$

$$y = b \quad \text{or} \quad y = -b$$

The y-intercepts are $(0, b)$ and $(0, -b)$.

In general, we have the following results.

Equations of an Ellipse Centered at the Origin

The equation of an ellipse centered at the origin, with x-intercepts at $V_1(a, 0)$ and $V_2(-a, 0)$ and with y-intercepts of $(0, b)$ and $(0, -b)$, is

$$\frac{x^2}{a^2} + \frac{y^2}{b^2} = 1 \quad (a > b > 0) \quad \text{See Figure 12-18(a) on the next page.}$$

The equation of an ellipse centered at the origin, with y-intercepts at $V_1(0, a)$ and $V_2(0, -a)$ and x-intercepts of $(b, 0)$ and $(-b, 0)$, is

$$\frac{x^2}{b^2} + \frac{y^2}{a^2} = 1 \quad (a > b > 0) \quad \text{See Figure 12-18(b).}$$

In Figure 12-18, the points V_1 and V_2 are the **vertices** of the ellipse, the midpoint of segment V_1V_2 is the *center* of the ellipse, and the distance between the center and either vertex is a. The segment V_1V_2 is called the **major axis,** and the segment joining either $(0, b)$ and $(0, -b)$ or $(b, 0)$ and $(-b, 0)$ is called the **minor axis.**

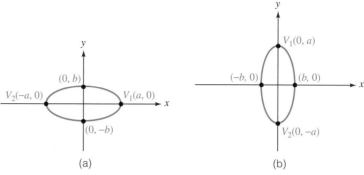

Figure 12-18

The equations for ellipses centered at (h, k) are as follows.

Standard Equation of a Horizontal Ellipse Centered at (h, k)	The equation of a horizontal ellipse centered at (h, k), with major axis parallel to the x-axis, is $$(1)\quad \frac{(x - h)^2}{a^2} + \frac{(y - k)^2}{b^2} = 1 \quad (a > b > 0)$$
Standard Equation of a Vertical Ellipse Centered at (h, k)	The equation of a vertical ellipse centered at (h, k), with major axis parallel to the y-axis, is $$(2)\quad \frac{(x - h)^2}{b^2} + \frac{(y - k)^2}{a^2} = 1 \quad (a > b > 0)$$

EVERYDAY CONNECTIONS   Eccentricity of an Ellipse

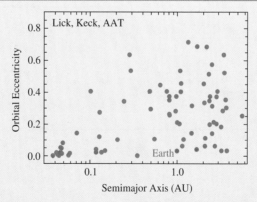

Source: Eccentricity vs. semimajor axis for extrasolar planets. The 75 planets shown were found in a Doppler survey of 1,300 FGKM main sequence stars using the Lick, Keck, and AAT telescopes. The survey was carried out by the California-Carnegie planet search team. http://exoplanets.org/newsframe.html

In Figure 12-16(a) on page 859, the ratio of c to a is called the **eccentricity** of the ellipse. We can use the eccentricity of an ellipse to judge its shape. If the eccen-

tricity is close to 1, the ellipse is relatively flat. If it is close to 0, the ellipse is more circular. Specifically, the eccentricity of a true circle equals 0.

Use the data plot above to estimate how many of the 75 planets shown follow orbits that are true circles.

COMMENT To determine whether an ellipse is horizontal or vertical, look at the denominators in its standard equation. If the largest denominator is associated with the *x*-term, the ellipse will be horizontal. If the largest denominator is associated with the *y*-term, the ellipse will be vertical.

EXAMPLE 2   Graph: $25(x - 2)^2 + 16(y + 3)^2 = 400$.

Solution   We first write the equation in standard form.

$$25(x - 2)^2 + 16(y + 3)^2 = 400$$

$$\frac{25(x - 2)^2}{400} + \frac{16(y + 3)^2}{400} = \frac{400}{400} \qquad \text{Divide both sides by 400.}$$

$$\frac{(x - 2)^2}{16} + \frac{(y + 3)^2}{25} = 1 \qquad \text{Simplify each fraction.}$$

$$\frac{(x - 2)^2}{4^2} + \frac{[y - (-3)]^2}{5^2} = 1 \quad (5 > 4)$$

This is the equation of a vertical ellipse centered at $(h, k) = (2, -3)$ with major axis parallel to the *y*-axis and with $b = 4$ and $a = 5$. We first plot the center, as shown in Figure 12-19. Since *a* is the distance from the center to a vertex, we can locate the vertices by counting 5 units above and 5 units below the center. The vertices are at points $(2, 2)$ and $(2, -8)$.

Since $b = 4$, we can locate two more points on the ellipse by counting 4 units to the left and 4 units to the right of the center. The points $(-2, -3)$ and $(6, -3)$ are also on the graph.

Using these four points as guides, we can draw the ellipse.

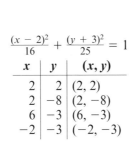

$$\frac{(x - 2)^2}{16} + \frac{(y + 3)^2}{25} = 1$$

x	y	(x, y)
2	2	(2, 2)
2	-8	(2, -8)
6	-3	(6, -3)
-2	-3	(-2, -3)

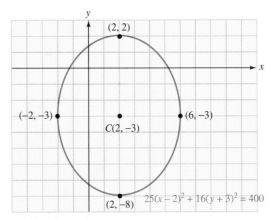

Figure 12-19

⇨ **SELF CHECK 2**   Graph: $16(x - 1)^2 + 9(y + 2)^2 = 144$.

ACCENT ON TECHNOLOGY

Graphing Ellipses

To use a graphing calculator to graph

$$\frac{(x + 2)^2}{4} + \frac{(y - 1)^2}{25} = 1$$

(continued)

we first clear the fractions by multiplying both sides by 100 and solving for y.

$$25(x + 2)^2 + 4(y - 1)^2 = 100$$
Multiply both sides by 100.

$$4(y - 1)^2 = 100 - 25(x + 2)^2$$
Subtract $25(x + 2)^2$ from both sides.

$$(y - 1)^2 = \frac{100 - 25(x + 2)^2}{4}$$
Divide both sides by 4.

$$y - 1 = \pm \frac{\sqrt{100 - 25(x + 2)^2}}{2}$$
Use the square-root property.

$$y = 1 \pm \frac{\sqrt{100 - 25(x + 2)^2}}{2}$$
Add 1 to both sides.

If we use window settings $[-6, 6]$ for x and $[-6, 6]$ for y and graph the functions

$$y = 1 + \frac{\sqrt{100 - 25(x + 2)^2}}{2} \qquad \text{and} \qquad y = 1 - \frac{\sqrt{100 - 25(x + 2)^2}}{2}$$

we will obtain the ellipse shown in Figure 12-20.

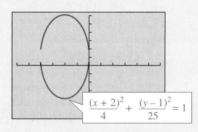

$$\frac{(x + 2)^2}{4} + \frac{(y - 1)^2}{25} = 1$$

Figure 12-20

Another important form of the equation of an ellipse is called the *general form*.

General Form of the Equation of an Ellipse	The equation of any ellipse can be written in the form $$Ax^2 + Cy^2 + Dx + Ey + F = 0$$

We can use completing the square to write the general form of the equation of an ellipse.

2   Graph an ellipse given an equation in general form.

EXAMPLE 3   Write $4x^2 + 9y^2 - 16x - 18y - 11 = 0$ in standard form to show that the equation represents an ellipse. Then graph the equation.

Solution   We write the equation in standard form by completing the square on x and y:

$$4x^2 + 9y^2 - 16x - 18y - 11 = 0$$

$$4x^2 + 9y^2 - 16x - 18y = 11 \qquad \text{Add 11 to both sides.}$$

$$4x^2 - 16x + 9y^2 - 18y = 11 \qquad \text{Use the commutative property to rearrange terms.}$$

$$4(x^2 - 4x) + 9(y^2 - 2y) = 11$$

Factor 4 from $4x^2 - 16x$ and factor 9 from $9y^2 - 18y$ to get coefficients of 1 for the squared terms.

$$4(x^2 - 4x + 4) + 9(y^2 - 2y + 1) = 11 + 16 + 9$$

Complete the square to make $x^2 - 4x$ and $y^2 - 2y$ perfect trinomial squares. Since $16 + 9$ is added to the left side, add $16 + 9$ to the right side.

$$4(x - 2)^2 + 9(y - 1)^2 = 36$$

Factor $x^2 - 4x + 4$ and $y^2 - 2y + 1$.

$$\frac{(x - 2)^2}{9} + \frac{(y - 1)^2}{4} = 1$$

Divide both sides by 36.

Since this equation matches Equation 1 on page 861, it represents an ellipse with $h = 2$, $k = 1$, $a = 3$, and $b = 2$. Its graph is shown in Figure 12-21.

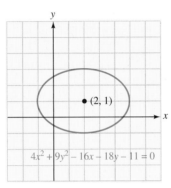

Figure 12-21

SELF CHECK 3   Graph: $4x^2 - 8x + 9y^2 - 36y = -4$.

COMMENT   To distinguish between an equation of an ellipse and an equation of a circle, look at the coefficients of the squared terms. If the coefficients are the same, the equation is the equation of a circle. If the coefficients are different, but both positive, the equation is the equation of an ellipse.

3   Solve an application problem involving an ellipse.

EXAMPLE 4   **LANDSCAPE DESIGN**   A landscape architect is designing an elliptical pool that will fit in the center of a 20-by-30-foot rectangular garden, leaving at least 5 feet of space on all sides. Find the equation of the ellipse.

Solution   We place the rectangular garden in a coordinate system, as in Figure 12-22 on the next page. To maintain 5 feet of clearance at the ends of the ellipse, the vertices must be the points $V_1(10, 0)$ and $V_2(-10, 0)$. Similarly, the y-intercepts are the points $(0, 5)$ and $(0, -5)$.

The equation of the ellipse has the form

$$\frac{x^2}{a^2} + \frac{y^2}{b^2} = 1$$

with $a = 10$ and $b = 5$. Thus, the equation of the boundary of the pool is

$$\frac{x^2}{100} + \frac{y^2}{25} = 1$$

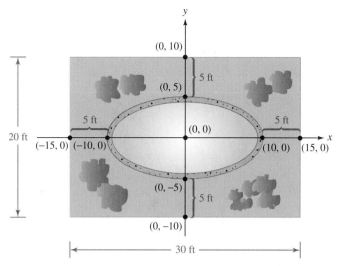

Figure 12-22

⇨ **SELF CHECK ANSWERS**

1.

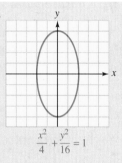

$$\frac{x^2}{4} + \frac{y^2}{16} = 1$$

2.

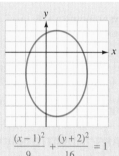

$$\frac{(x-1)^2}{9} + \frac{(y+2)^2}{16} = 1$$

3.

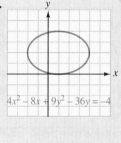

$$4x^2 - 8x + 9y^2 - 36y = -4$$

NOW TRY THIS

1. If the vertices of an ellipse are (5, −1) and (5, 5) and the endpoints of the minor axis are (3, 2) and (7, 2), find the equation.

2. The eccentricity of an ellipse is $\frac{c}{a}$. If the eccentricity is $\frac{2}{3}$, $a = 3$, and the center is located at (4, −1), find the equation of the horizontal ellipse.

12.2 EXERCISES

WARM-UPS

Find the x- and y-intercepts of each ellipse.

1. $\frac{x^2}{9} + \frac{y^2}{16} = 1$

2. $\frac{x^2}{25} + \frac{y^2}{36} = 1$

Find the center of each ellipse.

3. $\frac{(x-2)^2}{9} + \frac{y^2}{16} = 1$

4. $\frac{x^2}{25} + \frac{(y+1)^2}{36} = 1$

REVIEW

Find each product.

5. $3x^{-2}y^2(4x^2 + 3y^{-2})$

6. $(2a^{-2} - b^{-2})(2a^{-2} + b^{-2})$

Write each expression without using negative exponents.

7. $\dfrac{x^{-2} + y^{-2}}{x^{-2} - y^{-2}}$

8. $\dfrac{2x^{-3} - 2y^{-3}}{4x^{-3} + 4y^{-3}}$

VOCABULARY AND CONCEPTS   *Fill in the blanks.*

9. An _____ is the set of all points in a plane the ____ of whose distances from two fixed points is a constant.

10. The fixed points in Exercise 9 are the ____ of the ellipse.

11. The midpoint of the line segment joining the foci of an ellipse is called the _____ of the ellipse.

12. The graph of $\dfrac{x^2}{a^2} + \dfrac{y^2}{b^2} = 1$ $(a > b > 0)$ has vertices at _____, y-intercepts at _____, and eccentricity of __.

13. The center of the ellipse with an equation of $\dfrac{x^2}{a^2} + \dfrac{y^2}{b^2} = 1$ is ____ with the _____ having a length of $2a$ and the minor axis having a length of ___.

14. The center of the ellipse with an equation of $\dfrac{(x - h)^2}{a^2} + \dfrac{(y - k)^2}{b^2} = 1$ is the point _____.

GUIDED PRACTICE

Graph each equation. See Example 1. (Objective 1)

15. $\dfrac{x^2}{4} + \dfrac{y^2}{9} = 1$

16. $x^2 + \dfrac{y^2}{9} = 1$

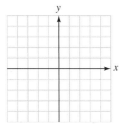

17. $\dfrac{x^2}{9} + \dfrac{y^2}{16} = 1$

18. $\dfrac{x^2}{25} + \dfrac{y^2}{36} = 1$

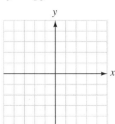

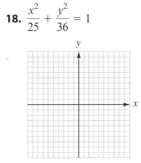

19. $\dfrac{(x - 2)^2}{16} + \dfrac{y^2}{25} = 1$

20. $\dfrac{x^2}{25} + \dfrac{(y + 1)^2}{36} = 1$

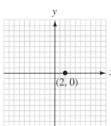

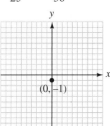

21. $\dfrac{(x - 2)^2}{9} + \dfrac{(y - 1)^2}{4} = 1$

22. $\dfrac{(x - 1)^2}{9} + \dfrac{(y - 3)^2}{4} = 1$

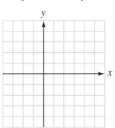

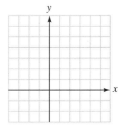

Graph each equation. See Example 2. (Objective 1)

23. $x^2 + 9y^2 = 9$

24. $25x^2 + 9y^2 = 225$

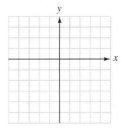

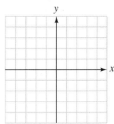

25. $16x^2 + 4y^2 = 64$

26. $4x^2 + 9y^2 = 36$

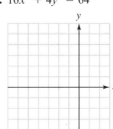

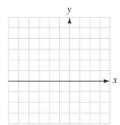

27. $(x + 1)^2 + 4(y + 2)^2 = 4$

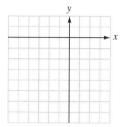

28. $9(x - 5)^2 + (y + 2)^2 = 9$

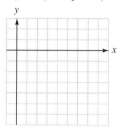

29. $25(x + 1)^2 + 9y^2 = 225$

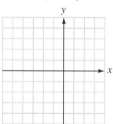

30. $4(x - 6)^2 + 25(y - 3)^2 = 100$

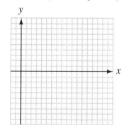

Write each equation in standard form and graph it. **See Example 3.** (Objective 2)

31. $x^2 + 4y^2 - 4x + 8y + 4 = 0$

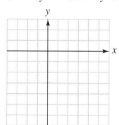

32. $x^2 + 4y^2 - 2x - 16y = -13$

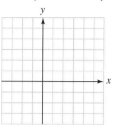

33. $9x^2 + 4y^2 - 18x + 16y = 11$

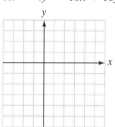

34. $16x^2 + 25y^2 - 160x - 200y + 400 = 0$

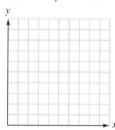

ADDITIONAL PRACTICE *Use a graphing calculator to graph each equation.*

35. $\dfrac{x^2}{9} + \dfrac{y^2}{4} = 1$ **36.** $x^2 + 16y^2 = 16$

37. $\dfrac{x^2}{4} + \dfrac{(y - 1)^2}{9} = 1$ **38.** $\dfrac{(x + 1)^2}{9} + \dfrac{(y - 2)^2}{4} = 1$

APPLICATIONS See Example 4. (Objective 3)

39. Fitness equipment With elliptical cross-training equipment, the feet move through the natural elliptical pattern that one experiences when walking, jogging, or running. Write the equation of the elliptical pattern shown on the next page.

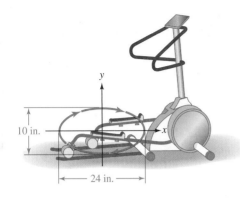

40. Pool tables Find the equation of the outer edge of the elliptical pool table shown below. Assume the red ball is at the focus.

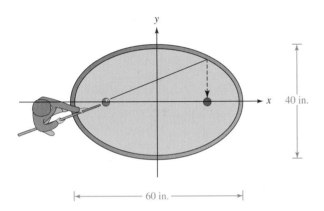

41. Designing an underpass The arch of the underpass is half of an ellipse. Find the equation of the arch.

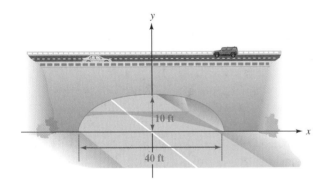

42. Calculating clearance Find the height of the elliptical arch in Exercise 41 at a point 10 feet from the center of the roadway.

43. Area of an ellipse The area A of the ellipse

$$\frac{x^2}{a^2} + \frac{y^2}{b^2} = 1$$

is given by $A = \pi ab$. Find the area of the ellipse $9x^2 + 16y^2 = 144$.

44. Area of a track The elliptical track is bounded by the ellipses $4x^2 + 9y^2 = 576$ and $9x^2 + 25y^2 = 900$. Find the area of the track. (See Exercise 43.)

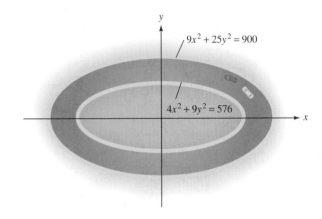

WRITING ABOUT MATH

45. Explain how to find the x- and the y-intercepts of the graph of the ellipse

$$\frac{x^2}{a^2} + \frac{y^2}{b^2} = 1$$

46. Explain the relationship between the center, focus, and vertex of an ellipse.

SOMETHING TO THINK ABOUT

47. What happens to the graph of $\frac{x^2}{a^2} + \frac{y^2}{b^2} = 1$ when $a = b$?

48. Explain why the graph of $x^2 - 2x + y^2 + 4y + 20 = 0$ does not exist.

SECTION
12.3

The Hyperbola

Objectives

1. Graph a hyperbola given an equation in standard form.
2. Graph a hyperbola given an equation in general form.
3. Graph a hyperbola of the form $xy = k$.
4. Solve an application problem involving a hyperbola.

Vocabulary

hyperbola center fundamental rectangle
focus (foci) vertices

Getting Ready

Find the value of y when $\frac{x^2}{25} - \frac{y^2}{9} = 1$ and x is the given value. Give each result to the nearest tenth.

1. $x = 6$ **2.** $x = -7$

The last conic section, the *hyperbola,* is a curve with two branches. In this section, we will see how to graph equations that represent hyperbolas.

Hyperbolas are the basis of a navigational system known as LORAN (LOng RAnge Navigation). (See Figure 12-23.) They are also used to find the source of a distress signal, are the basis for the design of hypoid gears, and describe the paths of some comets.

Hyperbola

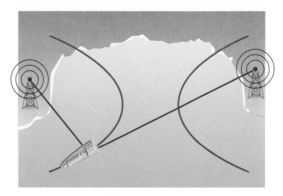

Figure 12-23

① **Graph a hyperbola given an equation in standard form.**

The Hyperbola

A **hyperbola** is the set of all points P in the plane for which the difference of the distances of each point from two fixed points is a constant. See Figure 12-24, in which $d_1 - d_2$ is a constant.

Each of the two points is called a **focus.** Midway between the foci is the **center** of the hyperbola.

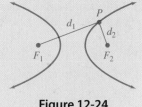

Figure 12-24

The graph of the equation

$$\frac{x^2}{25} - \frac{y^2}{9} = 1$$

is a hyperbola. To graph the equation, we make a table of ordered pairs that satisfy the equation, plot each pair, and join the points with a smooth curve as in Figure 12-25.

$$\frac{x^2}{25} - \frac{y^2}{9} = 1$$

x	y	(x, y)
-7	± 2.9	$(-7, \pm 2.9)$
-6	± 2.0	$(-6, \pm 2.0)$
-5	0	$(-5, 0)$
5	0	$(5, 0)$
6	± 2.0	$(6, \pm 2.0)$
7	± 2.9	$(7, \pm 2.9)$

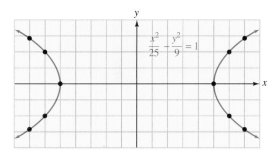

Figure 12-25

This graph is centered at the origin and intersects the x-axis at $(5, 0)$ and $(-5, 0)$. We also note that the graph does not intersect the y-axis.

It is possible to draw a hyperbola without plotting points. For example, if we want to graph the hyperbola with an equation of

$$\frac{x^2}{a^2} - \frac{y^2}{b^2} = 1$$

we first look at the x- and y-intercepts. To find the x-intercepts, we let $y = 0$ and solve for x:

$$\frac{x^2}{a^2} - \frac{0^2}{b^2} = 1$$

$$x^2 = a^2$$

$$x = \pm a$$

Thus, the hyperbola crosses the x-axis at the points $V_1(a, 0)$ and $V_2(-a, 0)$, called the **vertices** of the hyperbola. See Figure 12-26.

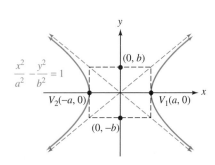

Figure 12-26

To attempt to find the y-intercepts, we let $x = 0$ and solve for y:

$$\frac{0^2}{a^2} - \frac{y^2}{b^2} = 1$$
$$y^2 = -b^2$$
$$y = \pm\sqrt{-b^2}$$

Since b^2 is always positive, $\sqrt{-b^2}$ is an imaginary number. This means that the hyperbola does not cross the y-axis.

If we construct a rectangle, called the **fundamental rectangle,** whose sides pass horizontally through $\pm b$ on the y-axis and vertically through $\pm a$ on the x-axis, the extended diagonals of the rectangle will be asymptotes of the hyperbola.

Equation of a Hyperbola Centered at the Origin with Vertices on the x-Axis

Any equation that can be written in the form

$$\frac{x^2}{a^2} - \frac{y^2}{b^2} = 1$$

has a graph that is a hyperbola centered at the origin, as in Figure 12-27. The x-intercepts are the vertices $V_1(a, 0)$ and $V_2(-a, 0)$. There are no y-intercepts.

The asymptotes of the hyperbola are the extended diagonals of the rectangle shown in the figure.

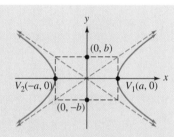

Figure 12-27

The branches of the hyperbola in previous discussions open to the left and to the right. It is possible for hyperbolas to have different orientations with respect to the x- and y-axes. For example, the branches of a hyperbola can open upward and downward. In that case, the following equation applies.

Equation of a Hyperbola Centered at the Origin with Vertices on the y-Axis

Any equation that can be written in the form

$$\frac{y^2}{a^2} - \frac{x^2}{b^2} = 1$$

has a graph that is a hyperbola centered at the origin, as in Figure 12-28. The y-intercepts are the vertices $V_1(0, a)$ and $V_2(0, -a)$. There are no x-intercepts.

The asymptotes of the hyperbola are the extended diagonals of the rectangle shown in the figure.

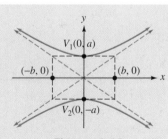

Figure 12-28

COMMENT To determine whether a hyperbola opens horizontally, as in Figure 12-27, or vertically, as in Figure 12-28, we can look at the signs of the terms. If the term containing x^2 is positive, the hyperbola will open horizontally. If the term containing y^2 is positive, the hyperbola will open vertically.

EXAMPLE 1   Graph: $9y^2 - 4x^2 = 36$.

Solution   To write the equation in standard form, we divide both sides by 36 to obtain

$$\frac{9y^2}{36} - \frac{4x^2}{36} = 1$$

$$\frac{y^2}{4} - \frac{x^2}{9} = 1 \qquad \text{Simplify each fraction.}$$

Because the term containing y^2 is positive, the hyperbola will open vertically. We can find the y-intercepts of the graph by letting $x = 0$ and solving for y:

$$\frac{y^2}{4} - \frac{0^2}{9} = 1$$

$$y^2 = 4$$

Thus, $y = \pm 2$, and the vertices of the hyperbola are $V_1(0, 2)$ and $V_2(0, -2)$. (See Figure 12-29.)

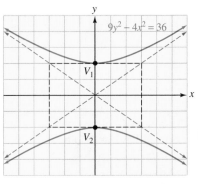

Figure 12-29

Since $\pm \sqrt{9} = \pm 3$, we can use the points $(3, 0)$ and $(-3, 0)$ on the x-axis to help draw the fundamental rectangle. We then draw its extended diagonals and sketch the hyperbola.

⇨ **SELF CHECK 1**   Graph: $9x^2 - 4y^2 = 36$.

ACCENT ON TECHNOLOGY

Graphing Hyperbolas

To graph $\frac{x^2}{9} - \frac{y^2}{16} = 1$ using a graphing calculator, we follow the same procedure that we used for circles and ellipses. To write the equation as two functions, we solve for y to get $y = \pm \dfrac{\sqrt{16x^2 - 144}}{3}$. Then we graph the following two functions in a square window setting to get the graph of the hyperbola shown in Figure 12-30.

$$y = \frac{\sqrt{16x^2 - 144}}{3} \qquad \text{and} \qquad y = -\frac{\sqrt{16x^2 - 144}}{3}$$

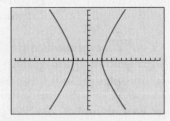

Figure 12-30

If a hyperbola is centered at a point with coordinates (h, k), the equations on the next page apply.

Equations of Hyperbolas Centered at (h, k)

Any equation that can be written in the form

$$\frac{(x-h)^2}{a^2} - \frac{(y-k)^2}{b^2} = 1$$

is a hyperbola centered at (h, k) that opens left and right.

Any equation of the form

$$\frac{(y-k)^2}{a^2} - \frac{(x-h)^2}{b^2} = 1$$

is a hyperbola centered at (h, k) that opens up and down.

EXAMPLE 2 Graph: $\dfrac{(x-3)^2}{16} - \dfrac{(y+1)^2}{4} = 1.$

Solution We write the equation in the form

$$\frac{(x-3)^2}{16} - \frac{[y-(-1)]^2}{4} = 1$$

to see that its graph will be a hyperbola centered at the point $(h, k) = (3, -1)$. Its vertices are located at $a = 4$ units to the right and left of center, at $(7, -1)$ and $(-1, -1)$. Since $b = 2$, we can count 2 units above and below center to locate points $(3, 1)$ and $(3, -3)$. With these points, we can draw the fundamental rectangle along with its extended diagonals. We can then sketch the hyperbola, as shown in Figure 12-31.

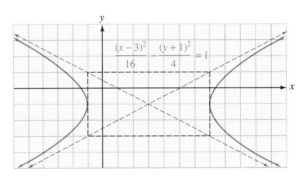

Figure 12-31

⇨ **SELF CHECK 2** Graph: $\dfrac{(x+2)^2}{9} - \dfrac{(y-1)^2}{4} = 1.$

2 **Graph a hyperbola given an equation in general form.**

Another important form of the equation of a hyperbola is called the *general form*.

General Form of the Equation of a Hyperbola

The equation of any hyperbola can be written in the form

$$Ax^2 - Cy^2 + Dx + Ey + F = 0$$

EXAMPLE 3   Write the equation $x^2 - y^2 - 2x + 4y - 12 = 0$ in standard form to show that the equation represents a hyperbola. Then graph it.

Solution   We proceed as follows.

$$x^2 - y^2 - 2x + 4y - 12 = 0$$

$$x^2 - y^2 - 2x + 4y = 12 \qquad \text{Add 12 to both sides.}$$

$$x^2 - 2x - y^2 + 4y = 12 \qquad \text{Use the commutative property to group the } x \text{ terms and } y \text{ terms.}$$

$$x^2 - 2x - (y^2 - 4y) = 12 \qquad \text{Factor } -1 \text{ from } -y^2 + 4y.$$

We then complete the square on x and y to make $x^2 - 2x$ and $y^2 - 4y$ perfect trinomial squares.

$$x^2 - 2x + 1 - (y^2 - 4y + 4) = 12 + 1 - 4$$

We then factor $x^2 - 2x + 1$ and $y^2 - 4y + 4$ to get

$$(x - 1)^2 - (y - 2)^2 = 9$$

$$\frac{(x - 1)^2}{9} - \frac{(y - 2)^2}{9} = 1 \qquad \text{Divide both sides by 9.}$$

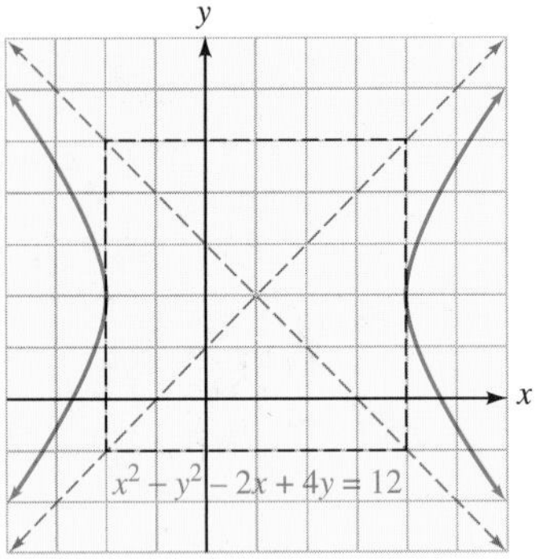

This is the equation of a hyperbola centered at $(1, 2)$. Its graph is shown in Figure 12-32.

Figure 12-32

The figure shows a hyperbola labeled $x^2 - y^2 - 2x + 4y = 12$ with asymptotes.

➡ **SELF CHECK 3**   Graph: $x^2 - 4y^2 + 2x - 8y = 7$.

3   **Graph a hyperbola of the form $xy = k$.**

There is a special type of hyperbola (also centered at the origin) that does not intersect either the x- or the y-axis. These hyperbolas have equations of the form $xy = k$, where $k \neq 0$.

EXAMPLE 4   Graph: $xy = -8$.

Solution   We make a table of ordered pairs, plot each pair, and join the points with a smooth curve to obtain the hyperbola in Figure 12-33.

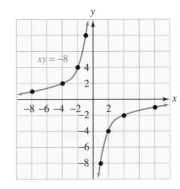

$xy = -8$		
x	y	(x, y)
1	-8	$(1, -8)$
2	-4	$(2, -4)$
4	-2	$(4, -2)$
8	-1	$(8, -1)$
-1	8	$(-1, 8)$
-2	4	$(-2, 4)$
-4	2	$(-4, 2)$
-8	1	$(-8, 1)$

Figure 12-33

➡ **SELF CHECK 4**   Graph: $xy = 6$.

The result in Example 4 illustrates the following general equation.

Equations of Hyperbolas of the Form $xy = k$	Any equation of the form $xy = k$, where $k \neq 0$, has a graph that is a hyperbola that does not intersect either the x-axis or the y-axis.

4   **Solve an application problem involving a hyperbola.**

EXAMPLE 5   **ATOMIC STRUCTURE**   In an experiment that led to the discovery of the atomic structure of matter, Lord Rutherford (1871–1937) shot high-energy alpha particles toward a thin sheet of gold. Because many were reflected, Rutherford showed the existence of

EVERYDAY CONNECTIONS   **Focus on Conics**

Satellite dishes and flashlight reflectors are familiar examples of a conic's ability to reflect a beam of light or to concentrate incoming satellite signals at one point. That property is shown in the following illustration.

An ellipse has two foci, the points marked in the following illustration. Any light or signal that starts at one focus will be reflected to the other. This property is the basis of whispering galleries, where a person standing at one focus can clearly hear another person speaking at the other focus.

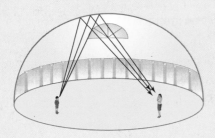

The focal property of the ellipse is also used in *lithotripsy*, a medical procedure for treating kidney stones. The patient is placed in an elliptical tank of water with the kidney stone at one focus. Shock waves from a small controlled explosion at the other focus are concentrated on the stone, pulverizing it.

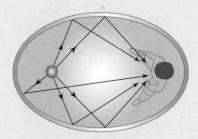

The hyperbola also has two foci, the two points labeled F in the following illustration. As in the ellipse, light aimed at one focus is reflected toward the other. Hyperbolic mirrors are used in some reflecting telescopes.

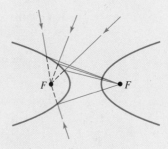

the nucleus of a gold atom. The alpha particle in Figure 12-34 is repelled by the nucleus at the origin; it travels along the hyperbolic path given by $4x^2 - y^2 = 16$. How close does the particle come to the nucleus?

Solution   To find the distance from the nucleus at the origin, we must find the coordinates of the vertex V. To do so, we write the equation of the particle's path in standard form:

$$4x^2 - y^2 = 16$$

$$\frac{4x^2}{16} - \frac{y^2}{16} = \frac{16}{16} \qquad \text{Divide both sides by 16.}$$

$$\frac{x^2}{4} - \frac{y^2}{16} = 1 \qquad \text{Simplify.}$$

$$\frac{x^2}{2^2} - \frac{y^2}{4^2} = 1 \qquad \text{Write 4 as } 2^2 \text{ and 16 as } 4^2.$$

This equation is in the form

$$\frac{x^2}{a^2} - \frac{y^2}{b^2} = 1$$

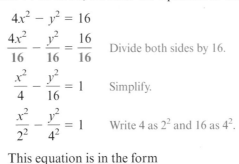

Figure 12-34

with $a = 2$. Thus, the vertex of the path is $(2, 0)$. The particle is never closer than 2 units from the nucleus.

⇨ **SELF CHECK ANSWERS**

1.
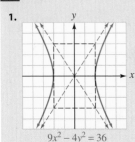
$9x^2 - 4y^2 = 36$

2.
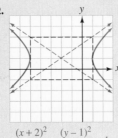
$\dfrac{(x+2)^2}{9} - \dfrac{(y-1)^2}{4} = 1$

3.
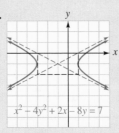
$x^2 - 4y^2 + 2x - 8y = 7$

4.
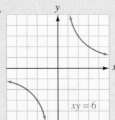
$xy = 6$

NOW TRY THIS

Given the equation $\frac{x^2}{a^2} - \frac{y^2}{b^2} = 1$, the equations for the asymptotes are $y = \frac{b}{a}x$, and $y = -\frac{b}{a}x$.

1. Find the equations for the asymptotes for the hyperbola described by the equation $\frac{x^2}{25} - \frac{y^2}{9} = 1$.

2. Find the equations for the asymptotes for the hyperbola described by the equation $\frac{y^2}{4} - \frac{x^2}{9} = 1$.

3. Find the equations for the asymptotes for the hyperbola described by the equation $\frac{(x+2)^2}{9} - \frac{(y-1)^2}{4} = 1$.

12.3 EXERCISES

WARM-UPS *Find the x- or y-intercepts of each hyperbola.*

1. $\dfrac{x^2}{9} - \dfrac{y^2}{16} = 1$ **2.** $\dfrac{x^2}{25} - \dfrac{y^2}{36} = 1$

REVIEW *Factor each expression.*

3. $-6x^4 + 9x^3 - 6x^2$

4. $4a^2 - b^2$

5. $15a^2 - 4ab - 4b^2$

6. $8p^3 - 27q^3$

VOCABULARY AND CONCEPTS *Fill in the blanks.*

7. A _____ is the set of all points in a plane for which the _____ of the distances from two fixed points is a constant.

8. The fixed points in Exercise 7 are the _____ of the hyperbola.

9. The midpoint of the line segment joining the foci of a hyperbola is called the _____ of the hyperbola.

10. To graph a hyperbola, we locate its center and vertices, sketch the _____, and sketch the asymptotes.

11. The hyperbolic graph of $\dfrac{x^2}{a^2} - \dfrac{y^2}{b^2} = 1$ has x-intercepts of _____. There are no _____.

12. The center of the hyperbola with an equation of $\dfrac{x^2}{a^2} - \dfrac{y^2}{b^2} = 1$ is the point _____. The center of the hyperbola with an equation of $\dfrac{(x-h)^2}{a^2} - \dfrac{(y-k)^2}{b^2} = 1$ is the point _____.

GUIDED PRACTICE

Graph each hyperbola. See Examples 1–2. (Objective 1)

13. $\dfrac{x^2}{9} - \dfrac{y^2}{4} = 1$ **14.** $\dfrac{x^2}{4} - \dfrac{y^2}{4} = 1$

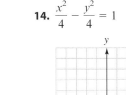

15. $\dfrac{y^2}{4} - \dfrac{x^2}{9} = 1$ **16.** $\dfrac{y^2}{4} - \dfrac{x^2}{64} = 1$

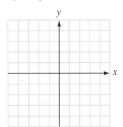
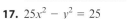
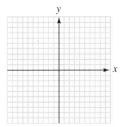

17. $25x^2 - y^2 = 25$ **18.** $9x^2 - 4y^2 = 36$

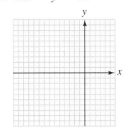
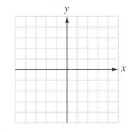

19. $\dfrac{(x-2)^2}{9} - \dfrac{y^2}{16} = 1$ **20.** $\dfrac{(x+2)^2}{16} - \dfrac{(y-3)^2}{25} = 1$

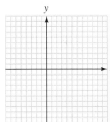
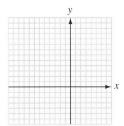

21. $\dfrac{(y+1)^2}{1} - \dfrac{(x-2)^2}{4} = 1$ **22.** $\dfrac{(y-2)^2}{4} - \dfrac{(x+1)^2}{1} = 1$

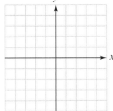
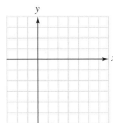
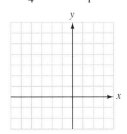

23. $4(x + 3)^2 - (y - 1)^2 = 4$

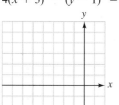

24. $(x + 5)^2 - 16y^2 = 16$

Write each equation in standard form and graph it. See Example 3. (Objective 2)

25. $4x^2 - y^2 + 8x - 4y = 4$

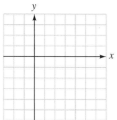

26. $x^2 - 9y^2 - 4x - 54y = 86$

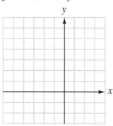

27. $4y^2 - x^2 + 8y + 4x = 4$

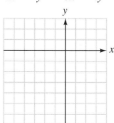

28. $y^2 - 4x^2 - 4y - 8x = 4$

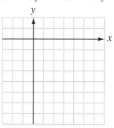

Graph each hyperbola. See Example 4. (Objective 3)

29. $xy = 8$

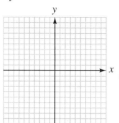

30. $xy = -10$

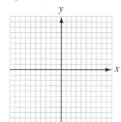

31. $xy = -12$

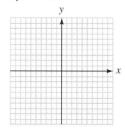

32. $xy = 6$

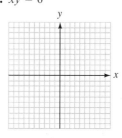

ADDITIONAL PRACTICE *Use a graphing calculator to graph each equation.*

33. $\dfrac{x^2}{9} - \dfrac{y^2}{4} = 1$

34. $y^2 - 16x^2 = 16$

35. $\dfrac{x^2}{4} - \dfrac{(y - 1)^2}{9} = 1$

36. $\dfrac{(y + 1)^2}{9} - \dfrac{(x - 2)^2}{4} = 1$

APPLICATIONS See Example 5. (Objective 4)

37. Alpha particles The particle in the illustration approaches the nucleus at the origin along the path $9y^2 - x^2 = 81$. How close does the particle come to the nucleus?

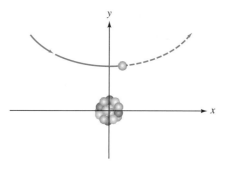

38. LORAN By determining the difference of the distances between the ship and two land-based radio transmitters, the LORAN system places the ship on the hyperbola $x^2 - 4y^2 = 576$. If the ship is also 5 miles out to sea, find its coordinates.

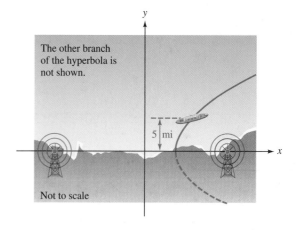

The other branch of the hyperbola is not shown.

5 mi

Not to scale

39. Sonic boom The position of the sonic boom caused by faster-than-sound aircraft is the hyperbola $y^2 - x^2 = 25$ in the coordinate system shown on the next page. How wide is the hyperbola 5 units from its vertex?

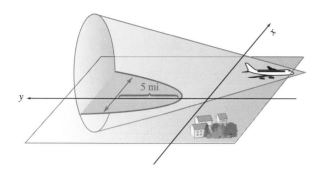

40. Electrostatic repulsion Two similarly charged particles are shot together for an almost head-on collision, as shown in the illustration. They repel each other and travel the two branches of the hyperbola given by $x^2 - 4y^2 = 4$. How close do they get?

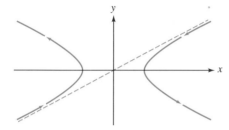

WRITING ABOUT MATH

41. Explain how to find the x- and the y-intercepts of the graph of the hyperbola

$$\frac{x^2}{a^2} - \frac{y^2}{b^2} = 1$$

42. Explain why the graph of the hyperbola

$$\frac{x^2}{a^2} - \frac{y^2}{b^2} = 1$$

has no y-intercept.

SOMETHING TO THINK ABOUT

43. Describe the fundamental rectangle of

$$\frac{x^2}{a^2} - \frac{y^2}{b^2} = 1$$

when $a = b$.

44. The hyperbolas $x^2 - y^2 = 1$ and $y^2 - x^2 = 1$ are called **conjugate hyperbolas.** Graph both on the same axes. What do they have in common?

SECTION
12.4

Piecewise-Defined Functions and the Greatest Integer Function

Objectives

1 Graph a piecewise-defined function and determine the open intervals over which the function is increasing, decreasing, and constant.

2 Graph the greatest integer function.

Vocabulary

piecewise-defined function   greatest integer function   step function

1. Is $f(x) = x^2$ positive or negative when $x > 0$?
2. Is $f(x) = -x^2$ positive or negative when $x > 0$?
3. What is the largest integer that is less than 98.6?
4. What is the largest integer that is less than -2.7?

Some functions are defined by using different equations for different parts of their domains. Such functions are called **piecewise-defined functions.**

1 **Graph a piecewise-defined function and determine the open intervals over which the function is increasing, decreasing, and constant.**

A simple piecewise-defined function is the absolute value function, $f(x) = |x|$, which can be written in the form

$$f(x) = \begin{cases} x \text{ when } x \geq 0 \\ -x \text{ when } x < 0 \end{cases}$$

When x is in the interval $[0, \infty)$, we use the function $f(x) = x$ to evaluate $|x|$. However, when x is in the interval $(-\infty, 0)$, we use the function $f(x) = -x$ to evaluate $|x|$. The graph of the absolute value function is shown in Figure 12-35.

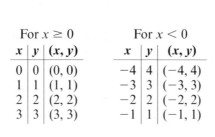

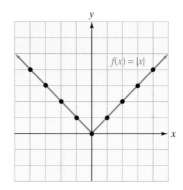

Figure 12-35

If the values of $f(x)$ increase as x increases on an open interval, we say that the function is *increasing on the interval* (see Figure 12-36(a)) on the next page. If the values of $f(x)$ decrease as x increases on an open interval, we say that the function is *decreasing on the interval* (see Figure 12-36(b)). If the values of $f(x)$ remain constant as x increases on an open interval, we say that the function is *constant on the interval* (see Figure 12-36(c)).

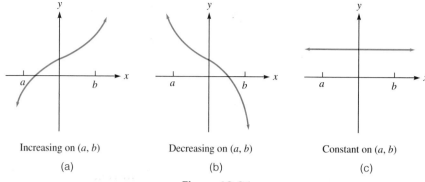

Increasing on (a, b)	Decreasing on (a, b)	Constant on (a, b)
(a)	(b)	(c)

Figure 12-36

The absolute value function, shown in Figure 12-35, is decreasing on the interval $(-\infty, 0)$ and is increasing on the interval $(0, \infty)$.

EXAMPLE 1   Graph the piecewise-defined function given by

$$f(x) = \begin{cases} x^2 \text{ when } x \le 0 \\ x \text{ when } 0 < x < 2 \\ -1 \text{ when } x \ge 2 \end{cases}$$

and determine where the function is increasing, decreasing, and constant.

Solution   For each number x, we decide which of the three equations will be used to find the corresponding value of y:

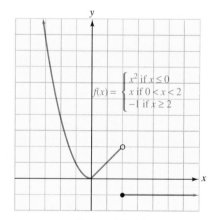

- For numbers $x \le 0$, $f(x)$ is determined by $f(x) = x^2$, and the graph is the left half of a parabola. See Figure 12-37. Since the values of $f(x)$ decrease on this graph as x increases, the function is decreasing on the interval $(-\infty, 0)$.

- For numbers $0 < x < 2$, $f(x)$ is determined by $f(x) = x$, and the graph is part of a line. Since the values of $f(x)$ increase on this graph as x increases, the function is increasing on the interval $(0, 2)$.

- For numbers $x \ge 2$, $f(x)$ is the constant -1, and the graph is part of a horizontal line. Since the values of $f(x)$ remain constant on this line, the function is constant on the interval $(2, \infty)$.

Figure 12-37

The use of solid and open circles on the graph indicates that $f(x) = -1$ when $x = 2$.

Since every number x determines one value y, the domain of this function is the interval $(-\infty, \infty)$. The range is $\{-1\} \cup [0, \infty)$.

In set-builder notation, the range is $\{y \mid y = -1 \text{ and } y \ge 0\}$.

SELF CHECK 1   Graph: $f(x) = \begin{cases} 2x \text{ when } x \le 0 \\ \frac{1}{2}x \text{ when } x > 0 \end{cases}$.

2 Graph the greatest integer function.

The **greatest integer function** is important in computer applications. It is a function determined by the equation

$$f(x) = [x] \qquad \text{Read as "}y\text{ equals the greatest integer in }x\text{."}$$

where the value of y that corresponds to x is the greatest integer that is less than or equal to x. For example,

$$[4.7] = 4, \quad \left[2\frac{1}{2}\right] = 2, \quad [\pi] = 3, \quad [-3.7] = -4, \quad [-5.7] = -6$$

COMMENT   One way to help determine the greatest integer is to visualize the number on a number line. The integer directly to the left of the number is the greatest integer.

EXAMPLE 2   Graph: $f(x) = [x]$.

Solution   We list several intervals and the corresponding values of the greatest integer function:

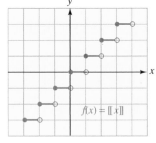

Figure 12-38

$[0, 1)$ $y = [x] = 0$ For numbers from 0 to 1, not including 1, the greatest integer in the interval is 0.

$[1, 2)$ $y = [x] = 1$ For numbers from 1 to 2, not including 2, the greatest integer in the interval is 1.

$[2, 3)$ $y = [x] = 2$ For numbers from 2 to 3, not including 3, the greatest integer in the interval is 2.

In each interval, the values of y are constant, but they jump by 1 at integer values of x. The graph is shown in Figure 12-38. From the graph, we see that the domain is $(-\infty, \infty)$, and the range is the set of integers $\{ \ldots , -3, -2, -1, 0, 1, 2, 3, \ldots \}$.

Since the greatest integer function is made up of a series of horizontal line segments, it is an example of a group of functions called **step functions**.

SELF CHECK 2   Graph: $f(x) = [x] + 1$.

EXAMPLE 3   **PRINTING STATIONERY**   To print stationery, a printer charges $10 for setup charges, plus $20 for each box. Any portion of a box counts as a full box. Graph this step function.

Solution   If we order stationery and cancel the order before it is printed, the cost will be $10. Thus, the ordered pair (0, 10) will be on the graph.

If we purchase 1 box, the cost will be $10 for setup plus $20 for printing, for a total cost of $30. Thus, the ordered pair (1, 30) will be on the graph.

The cost of $1\frac{1}{2}$ boxes will be the same as the cost of 2 boxes, or $50. Thus, the ordered pairs (1.5, 50) and (2, 50) will be on the graph. The complete graph is shown in Figure 12-39.

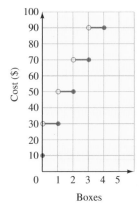

Figure 12-39

SELF CHECK 3   How much will $3\frac{1}{2}$ boxes cost?

➡️ **SELF CHECK ANSWERS**

1.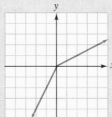
2.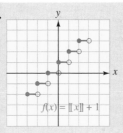
3. $90

NOW TRY THIS

1. Graph the piecewise-defined function.

$$f(x) = \begin{cases} -x^2 \text{ if } x < 1 \\ |x| \text{ if } 1 \le x < 4 \\ x - 1 \text{ if } x \ge 4 \end{cases}$$

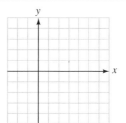

12.4 EXERCISES

WARM-UPS   *Determine whether each function is increasing, decreasing, or constant on the interval* $(-2, 3)$.

1.

2.

3.

4.

REVIEW   *Find the value of x. Assume that lines r and s are parallel.*

5.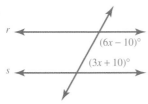

6.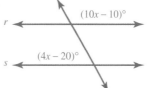

VOCABULARY AND CONCEPTS   *Fill in the blanks.*

7. Piecewise-defined functions are defined by using different functions for different parts of their _____.

8. When the values $f(x)$ increase as the values of x increase over an interval, we say that the function is an _____ function over that interval.

9. In a _____ function, the values of _____ are the same.

10. When the values of $f(x)$ decrease as the values of x _____ over an interval, we say that the function is a decreasing function over that interval.

11. When the graph of a function contains a series of horizontal line segments, the function is called a _____ function.

12. The function that gives the largest integer that is less than or equal to a number x is called the _____ function.

GUIDED PRACTICE

Give the intervals on which each function is increasing, decreasing, or constant. (Objective 1)

13.

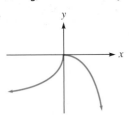

14.

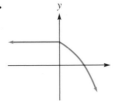

15.

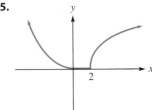

16

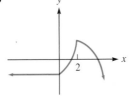

Graph each function and give the intervals on which f is increasing, decreasing, or constant. See Example 1. (Objective 1)

17. $f(x) = \begin{cases} -1 \text{ when } x \le 0 \\ x \text{ when } x > 0 \end{cases}$

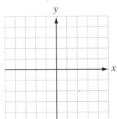

18. $f(x) = \begin{cases} -2 \text{ if } x \le 0 \\ x^2 \text{ if } x > 0 \end{cases}$

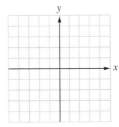

19. $f(x) = \begin{cases} -x \text{ if } x \le 0 \\ x \text{ if } 0 < x < 2 \\ -x \text{ if } x \ge 2 \end{cases}$

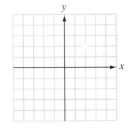

20. $f(x) = \begin{cases} -x \text{ if } x < 0 \\ x^2 \text{ if } 0 \le x \le 1 \\ 1 \text{ if } x > 1 \end{cases}$

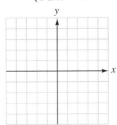

Graph each function. See Example 2. (Objective 1)

21. $f(x) = -[x]$

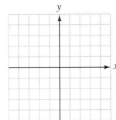

22. $f(x) = [x] + 2$

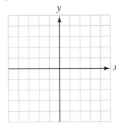

23. $f(x) = 2[x]$

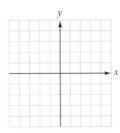

24. $f(x) = \left[\!\left[\dfrac{1}{2}x \right]\!\right]$

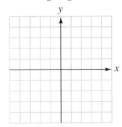

ADDITIONAL PRACTICE

25. Signum function   Computer programmers use a function denoted by $f(x) = \text{sgn } x$ that is defined in the following way:

$$f(x) = \begin{cases} -1 \text{ if } x < 0 \\ 0 \text{ if } x = 0 \\ 1 \text{ if } x > 0 \end{cases}$$

Graph this function.

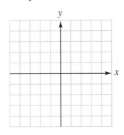

26. Heaviside unit step function   This function, used in calculus, is defined by

$$f(x) = \begin{cases} 1 \text{ if } x > 0 \\ 0 \text{ if } x < 0 \end{cases}$$

Graph this function.

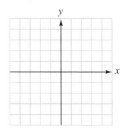

APPLICATIONS   See Example 3. (Objective 2)

27. Renting a jet ski   A marina charges $20 to rent a jet ski for 1 hour, plus $5 for every extra hour (or portion of an hour). In the illustration, graph the ordered pairs (h, c), where h represents the number of hours and c represents the cost. Find the cost if the ski is used for 2.5 hours.

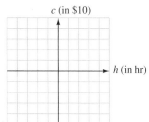

28. Riding in a taxi   A cab company charges $3 for a trip up to 1 mile, and $2 for every extra mile (or portion of a mile). In the illustration, graph the ordered pairs (m, c), where m represents the number of miles traveled and c represents the cost. Find the cost to ride $10\frac{1}{4}$ miles.

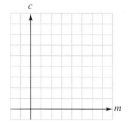

29. Information access   Computer access to international data network A costs $10 per day plus $8 per hour or fraction of an hour. Network B charges $15 per day, but only $6 per hour or fraction of an hour. For each network, graph the ordered pairs (t, C), where t represents the connect time and C represents the total cost. Find the minimum daily usage at which it would be more economical to use network B.

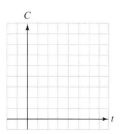

30. Royalties   A publisher has agreed to pay the author of a novel 7% royalties on sales of the first 50,000 copies and 10% on sales thereafter. If the book sells for $10, express the royalty income I as a function of s, the number of copies sold, and graph the function.   (*Hint:* When sales are into the second 50,000 copies, how much was earned on the first 50,000?)

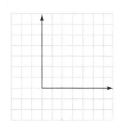

WRITING ABOUT MATH

31. Explain how to decide whether a function is increasing on the interval (a, b).

32. Describe the greatest integer function.

SOMETHING TO THINK ABOUT

33. Find a piecewise-defined function that is increasing on the interval $(-\infty, -2)$ and decreasing on the interval $(-2, \infty)$.

34. Find a piecewise-defined function that is constant on the interval $(-\infty, 0)$, increasing on the interval $(0, 5)$, and decreasing on the interval $(5, \infty)$.

PROJECTS

The zillionaire G. I. Luvmoney is known for his love of flowers. On his estate, he recently set aside a circular plot of land with a radius of 100 yards to be made into a flower garden. He has hired your landscape design firm to do the job. If Luvmoney is satisfied, he will hire your firm to do more lucrative jobs. Here is Luvmoney's plan.

The center of the circular plot of land is to be the origin of a rectangular coordinate system. You are to make 100 circles, all centered at the origin, with radii of 1 yard, 2 yards, 3 yards, and so on up to the outermost circle, which will have a radius of 100 yards. Inside the innermost circle, he wants a fountain with a circular walkway around it. In the ring between the first and second circle, he wants to plant his favorite kind of flower, in the next ring his second favorite, and so on, until you reach the edge of the circular plot. Luvmoney provides you with a list ranking his 99 favorite flowers.

The first thing he wants to know is the area of each ring, so that he will know how many of each plant to order. Then he wants a simple formula that will give the area of any ring just by substituting in the number of the ring.

He also wants a walkway to go through the garden in the form of a hyperbolic path, following the equation

$$x^2 - \frac{y^2}{9} = 1$$

Luvmoney wants to know the x- and y-coordinates of the points where the path will intersect the circles, so that those points can be marked with stakes to keep gardeners from planting flowers where the walkway will later be built. He wants a formula (or two) that will enable him to put in the number of a circle and get out the intersection points.

Finally, although cost has no importance for Luvmoney, his accountants will want an estimate of the total cost of all of the flowers.

You go back to your office with Luvmoney's list. You find that because the areas of the rings grow from the inside of the garden to the outside, and because of Luvmoney's ranking of flowers, a strange thing happens. The first ring of flowers will cost \$360, and the flowers in every ring after that will cost 110% as much as the flowers in the previous ring. That is, the second ring of flowers will cost \$360(1.1) = \$396, the third will cost \$435.60, and so on.

Answer all of Luvmoney's questions, and show work that will convince him that you are right.

Chapter 12   REVIEW

SECTION 12.1   The Circle and the Parabola

DEFINITIONS AND CONCEPTS	EXAMPLES
Equations of a circle: **Standard forms:** $\quad x^2 + y^2 = r^2$ $\qquad$ center $(0, 0)$, radius r	To graph a circle, we need to know the center and the radius. Graph each circle. **a.** $x^2 + y^2 = 25$ $\qquad C(0, 0)$ $\qquad$ From the formula $\qquad r^2 = 25$ $\qquad$ From the formula $\qquad r = 5$ The center is $(0, 0)$ and the radius is 5 units.

$(x - h)^2 + (y - k)^2 = r^2$
center (h, k), radius r

b. $(x - 3)^2 + (y + 4)^2 = 16$

$(x - 3)^2 + [y - (-4)]^2 = 16$ Write in standard form.

$C(3, -4)$ Comparing to the formula, $h = 3$ and $k = -4$.

$r^2 = 16$ Comparing to the formula

$r = 4$ Take the positive square root of 16.

The center is at $(3, -4)$ and the radius is 4 units.

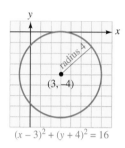

$(x - 3)^2 + (y + 4)^2 = 16$

General form:

$x^2 + y^2 + Dx + Ey + F = 0$

c. $x^2 + y^2 + 2x + 6y + 6 = 0$

To write the equation in standard form, we can complete the square on both x and y.

$x^2 + y^2 + 2x + 6y = -6$ Subtract 6 from both sides.

$x^2 + 2x + y^2 + 6y = -6$ Rearrange the terms.

$x^2 + 2x + 1 + y^2 + 6y + 9 = -6$ Complete the square on x and y.

$(x + 1)^2 + (y + 3)^2 = 4$ Factor and simplify.

$[x - (-1)]^2 + [y - (-3)]^2 = 4$ Write in standard form.

Comparing to the standard form, we see that $C(-1, -3)$, $r^2 = 4$, and $r = 2$.

The center is at $(-1, -3)$ with a radius of 2 units.

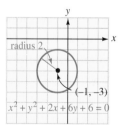

$x^2 + y^2 + 2x + 6y + 6 = 0$

Equations of parabolas:

Parabola opening	Vertex at origin	
Up	$y = ax^2$	$(a > 0)$
Down	$y = ax^2$	$(a < 0)$
Right	$x = ay^2$	$(a > 0)$
Left	$x = ay^2$	$(a < 0)$

Parabola opening	Vertex at (h, k)	
Up	$y = a(x - h)^2 + k$	$(a > 0)$
Down	$y = a(x - h)^2 + k$	$(a < 0)$
Right	$x = a(y - k)^2 + h$	$(a > 0)$
Left	$x = a(y - k)^2 + h$	$(a < 0)$

Graph each parabola.

a. $x = y^2$

The parabola is horizontal and opens to the right because $a > 0$. To obtain the graph, we can plot several points and connect them with a smooth curve.

$$x = y^2$$

x	y	(x, y)
0	0	$(0, 0)$
4	2	$(4, 2)$
4	-2	$(4, -2)$
9	3	$(9, 3)$
9	-3	$(9, -3)$

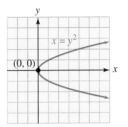

b. $x = -2(y - 1)^2 + 3$

The parabola is horizontal and opens to the left because $a < 0$. To obtain the graph, we can plot several points and connect them with a smooth curve.

$$x = -2(y - 1)^2 + 3$$

x	y	(x, y)
1	0	$(1, 0)$
1	2	$(1, 2)$
3	1	$(3, 1)$
-5	-1	$(-5, -1)$
-5	3	$(3, 1)$

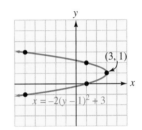

REVIEW EXERCISES

Graph each equation.

1. $(x - 1)^2 + (y + 2)^2 = 9$

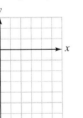

2. $x^2 + y^2 = 16$

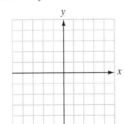

Graph each equation.

4. $x = -3(y - 2)^2 + 5$

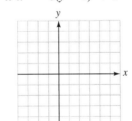

5. $x = 2(y + 1)^2 - 2$

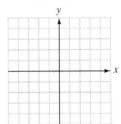

3. Write the equation in standard form and graph it.

$$x^2 + y^2 + 4x - 2y = 4$$

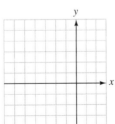

SECTION 12.2   The Ellipse

DEFINITIONS AND CONCEPTS	EXAMPLES

DEFINITIONS AND CONCEPTS

Equations of an ellipse:

Standard forms:

Center at $(0, 0)$

$$\frac{x^2}{a^2} + \frac{y^2}{b^2} = 1 \quad (a > b > 0)$$

$$\frac{x^2}{b^2} + \frac{y^2}{a^2} = 1 \quad (a > b > 0)$$

Center at (h, k)

$$\frac{(x - h)^2}{a^2} + \frac{(y - k)^2}{b^2} = 1$$

$$\frac{(x - h)^2}{b^2} + \frac{(y - k)^2}{a^2} = 1$$

In either case,
The length of the major axis is $2a$.
The length of the minor axis is $2b$.

General form:

$$Ax^2 + Cy^2 + Dx + Ey + F = 0$$

EXAMPLES

To graph an ellipse, we need to know the center and the endpoints of the major and minor axes.

Graph each ellipse:

a. $\dfrac{x^2}{9} + \dfrac{y^2}{16} = 1$

Comparing to the formula, the center is $(0, 0)$ and

$$a^2 = 16 \qquad b^2 = 9$$
$$a = 4 \qquad b = 3$$

The ellipse will be vertical because the larger denominator is associated with the y-term. The endpoints of the major axis will be 4 units above and below the center, $(0, 4)$ and $(0, -4)$. The endpoints of the minor axis will be 3 units to the left and right of center, $(3, 0)$ and $(-3, 0)$.

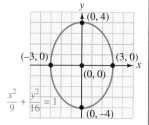

b. $\dfrac{(x - 3)^2}{9} + \dfrac{(y - 4)^2}{4} = 1$

From the formula, the center is $(3, 4)$ and

$$a^2 = 9 \qquad b^2 = 4$$
$$a = 3 \qquad b = 2$$

The ellipse will be horizontal because the larger denominator is associated with the x-term. The endpoints of the major axis will be 3 units to the left and right of the center, $(6, 4)$ and $(0, 4)$. The endpoints of the minor axis will be 2 units above and below the center, $(3, 6)$ and $(3, 2)$.

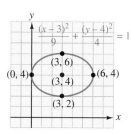

To find the standard equation of the ellipse with equation $4x^2 + y^2 - 8x - 2y - 11 = 0$, proceed as follows:

$4x^2 + y^2 - 8x - 2y = 11$	Add 11 to both sides.
$4x^2 - 8x + y^2 - 2y = 11$	Rearrange terms.
$4(x^2 - 2x) + y^2 - 2y = 11$	Factor to get a coefficient of 1 for the term involving x-squared.
$4(x^2 - 2x + 1) + (y^2 - 2y + 1) = 11 + 4 + 1$	Complete the square on both x and y.
$4(x - 1)^2 + (y - 1)^2 = 16$	Factor and simplify.
$\dfrac{(x - 1)^2}{4} + \dfrac{(y - 1)^2}{16} = 1$	Divide both sides by 16.

REVIEW EXERCISES
Graph each ellipse.

6. $9x^2 + 16y^2 = 144$

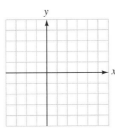

7. $\dfrac{(x-2)^2}{4} + \dfrac{(y-1)^2}{9} = 1$

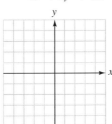

8. Write the equation in standard form and graph it.

$$4x^2 + 9y^2 + 8x - 18y = 23$$

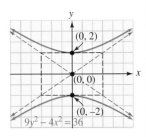

SECTION 12.3   The Hyperbola

DEFINITIONS AND CONCEPTS	EXAMPLES

Equations of a hyperbola:
 	
Standard forms:
  Center at $(0, 0)$
 	
  $\dfrac{x^2}{a^2} - \dfrac{y^2}{b^2} = 1$
 	
  $\dfrac{y^2}{a^2} - \dfrac{x^2}{b^2} = 1$
	To graph a hyperbola, we need to know where it is centered, the coordinates of the vertices, and the location of the asymptotes.
	
	Graph $9y^2 - 4x^2 = 36$.
	
	$\dfrac{9y^2}{36} - \dfrac{4x^2}{36} = 1$ Write the equation in standard form.
	
	$\dfrac{y^2}{4} - \dfrac{x^2}{9} = 1$ Simplify each fraction.

From the previous equation, we can determine that $a = 2$ and $b = 3$. Because the y-term is positive, the hyperbola will be vertical and the vertices of the hyperbola are $V_1(0, 2)$ and $V_2(0, -2)$.

Since $b = 3$, we can use the points $(3, 0)$ and $(-3, 0)$ on the x-axis to help draw the fundamental rectangle. We then draw its extended diagonals and sketch the hyperbola.

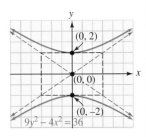

Center at (h, k)

$\dfrac{(x-k)^2}{a^2} - \dfrac{(y-h)^2}{b^2} = 1$ opens left or right

$\dfrac{(y-k)^2}{a^2} - \dfrac{(x-h)^2}{b^2} = 1$ opens up or down

Graph: $\dfrac{(x-3)^2}{4} - \dfrac{(y+1)^2}{4} = 1$.

From the equation, we see that the hyperbola is centered at $(3, -1)$. Its vertices are located 2 units to the right and left of center, at $(5, -1)$ and $(1, -1)$. Since $b = 2$, we can count 2 units above and below center to locate points $(3, -3)$ and $(3, 1)$. With these points, we can draw the fundamental rectangle along with its extended diagonals. Then we can sketch the hyperbola.

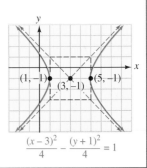

REVIEW EXERCISES
Graph each hyperbola.

9. $9x^2 - y^2 = -9$

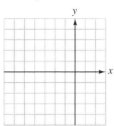

10. $xy = 9$

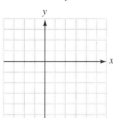

12. Write the equation in standard form and graph it.

$$9x^2 - 4y^2 - 18x - 8y = 31$$

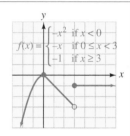

11. Write the equation $4x^2 - 2y^2 + 8x - 8y = 8$ in standard form and determine whether its graph will be an ellipse or a hyperbola.

SECTION 12.4   Piecewise-Defined Functions and the Greatest Integer Function

DEFINITIONS AND CONCEPTS	EXAMPLES
Piecewise-defined functions: A piecewise-defined function is a function that has different rules for different intervals of x. **Increasing and decreasing functions:** A function is increasing on the interval (a, b) if the values of $f(x)$ increase as x increases from a to b. A function is decreasing on the interval (a, b) if the values of $f(x)$ decrease as x increases from a to b. A function is constant on the interval (a, b) if the value of $f(x)$ is constant as x increases from a to b.	Graph the function $$f(x) = \begin{cases} -x^2 & \text{if } x < 0 \\ -x & \text{if } 0 \le x < 3 \\ -1 & \text{if } x \ge 3 \end{cases}$$ and determine where the function is increasing, decreasing, and constant. For each number x, we decide which of the three equations will be used to find the corresponding value of y: • For numbers $x < 0$, $f(x)$ is determined by $f(x) = -x^2$, and the graph is the left half of a parabola. Since the values of $f(x)$ increase on this graph as x increases, the function is increasing on the interval $(-\infty, 0)$. • For numbers $0 < x < 3$, $f(x)$ is determined by $f(x) = -x$, and the graph is part of a line. Since the values of $f(x)$ decrease on this graph as x increases, the function is decreasing on the interval $(0, 3)$. • For numbers $x \ge 3$, $f(x)$ is the constant -1, and the graph is part of a horizontal line. Since the values of $f(x)$ remain constant on this line, the function is constant on the interval $(3, \infty)$.
Greatest integer function: The function $f(x) = [x]$ describes the greatest integer function. To find the greatest integer, visualize the number on a number line and the integer directly to the left is the greatest integer.	Graph: $f(x) = [x] - 1$. We list several intervals and the corresponding values of the greatest integer function: [0, 1) $f(x) = [x] - 1$ For numbers from 0 to 1, not including 1, the greatest integer in the interval is 0 and then we subtract 1 and graph -1 in the interval. [1, 2) $f(x) = [x] - 1$ For numbers from 1 to 2, not including 2, the greatest integer in the interval is 1 and then we subtract 1 and graph 0 in the interval. [2, 3) $f(x) = [x] - 1$ For numbers from 2 to 3, not including 3, the greatest integer in the interval is 0 and then we subtract 1 and graph 1 in the interval.

REVIEW EXERCISES

13. Determine when the function is increasing, decreasing, or constant.

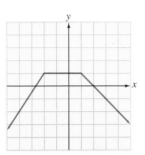

Graph each function.

14. $f(x) = \begin{cases} x \text{ if } x \le 1 \\ -x^2 \text{ if } x > 1 \end{cases}$

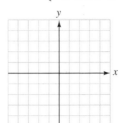

15. $f(x) = 3\lfloor x \rfloor$

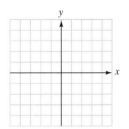

Chapter 12   TEST

1. Find the center and the radius of the circle
$(x - 2)^2 + (y + 3)^2 = 4$.

2. Find the center and the radius of the circle
$x^2 + y^2 + 4x - 6y = 3$.

Graph each equation.

3. $(x + 1)^2 + (y - 2)^2 = 9$

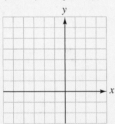

4. $x = (y - 2)^2 - 1$

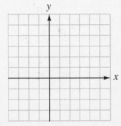

5. $9x^2 + 4y^2 = 36$

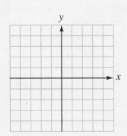

6. $\dfrac{(x - 2)^2}{9} - y^2 = 1$

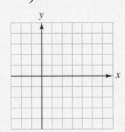

Write each equation in standard form and graph the equation.

7. $4x^2 + y^2 - 24x + 2y = -33$

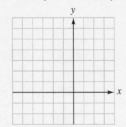

8. $x^2 - 9y^2 + 2x + 36y = 44$

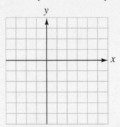

9. Determine where the function is increasing, decreasing, or constant.

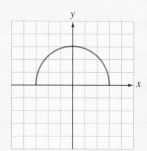

10. Graph: $f(x) = \begin{cases} -x^2, \text{ when } x < 0 \\ -x, \text{ when } x \geq 0 \end{cases}$.

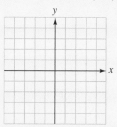

Cumulative Review Exercises

Perform the operations.

1. $(4x - 3y)(3x + y)$

2. $(a^n + 1)(a^n - 3)$

Simplify each fraction. Assume no division by zero.

3. $\dfrac{5a - 10}{a^2 - 4a + 4}$

4. $\dfrac{a^4 - 5a^2 + 4}{a^2 + 3a + 2}$

Perform the operations and simplify the result. Assume no division by zero.

5. $\dfrac{a^2 - a - 6}{a^2 - 4} \div \dfrac{a^2 - 9}{a^2 + a - 6}$

6. $\dfrac{2}{a - 2} + \dfrac{3}{a + 2} - \dfrac{a - 1}{a^2 - 4}$

Determine whether the graphs of the linear equations are parallel, perpendicular, or neither.

7. $3x - 4y = 12, y = \dfrac{3}{4}x - 5$

8. $y = 3x + 4, x = -3y + 4$

Write the equation of each line with the following properties.

9. $m = -2$, passing through $(0, 5)$

10. Passing through $(8, -5)$ and $(-5, 4)$

Graph each inequality.

11. $2x - 3y < 6$

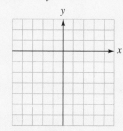

12. $y \geq x^2 - 4$

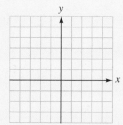

Simplify each expression.

13. $\sqrt{98} + \sqrt{8} - \sqrt{32}$

14. $12\sqrt[3]{648x^4} + 3\sqrt[3]{81x^4}$

Solve each equation.

15. $\sqrt{3a + 1} = a - 1$

16. $\sqrt{x + 3} - \sqrt{3} = \sqrt{x}$

17. $6a^2 + 5a - 6 = 0$

18. $3x^2 + 8x - 1 = 0$

19. If $f(x) = x^2 - 2$ and $g(x) = 2x + 1$, find $(f \circ g)(x)$.

20. Find the inverse function of $y = 2x^3 - 1$.

21. Graph $y = \left(\dfrac{1}{2}\right)^x$.

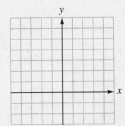

22. Write $y = \log_2 x$ as an exponential equation.

Solve each equation.

23. $2^{x+2} = 3^x$

24. $2 \log 5 + \log x - \log 4 = 2$

Graph each equation.

25. $x^2 + (y + 1)^2 = 9$

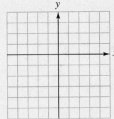

26. $x^2 - 9(y + 1)^2 = 9$

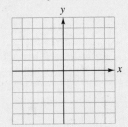

More Systems of Equations and Inequalities

©Shutterstock.com/Natalia D.

Careers and Mathematics

ELECTRONICS ENGINEERS

All engineers apply the principles of science and mathematics to develop economical solutions to technical problems. Electronics engineers are responsible for a wide range of technologies from portable music players to global positioning systems (GPS). They design, develop, test, and supervise the manufacture of electronic equipment such as broadcast and communications systems, and many work in areas closely related to computers. In 2006, engineers held about 1.5 million jobs. Of these, 138,000 jobs were held by electronics engineers.

Job Outlook:
Engineering jobs are expected to grow by 11 percent over the 2006–2016 decade. This is about as fast as the average for all occupations.

Annual Earnings:
$55,292–$75,982

For More Information:
http://www.bls.gov/oco/ocos027.htm

For a Sample Application:
See Problem 75 in Section 13.1.

In this chapter ▶

In this chapter, we will review the basic methods used for solving systems of two equations and two inequalities, each with two variables. We will then extend the discussion to include solving systems of three equations in three variables. Finally, we will solve systems of equations and inequalities that contain second-degree polynomials.

Objectives

1. Solve a system of two linear equations by graphing.
2. Solve a system of two linear equations by substitution.
3. Solve a system of two linear equations by elimination (addition).
4. Solve an application problem by setting up and solving a system of two linear equations.
5. Solve a system of two linear inequalities.

Vocabulary

consistent system of equations   inconsistent system   dependent equations
independent equations

Getting Ready

Evaluate the function $f(x) = 3x + 2$ for the following values of x.

1. $x = 0$ **2.** $x = 1$ **3.** $x = -2$ **4.** $x = -\dfrac{5}{3}$

In this section, we will review three methods used for solving systems of two linear equations, each with two variables.

 Solve a system of two linear equations by graphing.

Follow these steps to solve a system of two equations in two variables by graphing.

Solving Systems of Equations by Graphing

1. On a single set of coordinate axes, graph each equation.
2. Find the coordinates of the point (or points) where the graphs intersect. These coordinates give the solution of the system.
3. Check the solution in both of the original equations.
4. If the graphs have no point in common, the system has no solution.

EXAMPLE 1   Solve the system by graphing: $\begin{cases} x + 2y = 4 \\ 2x - y = 3 \end{cases}$.

Solution   We graph both equations on a single set of coordinate axes, as shown in Figure 13-1.

Although infinitely many pairs (x, y) satisfy $x + 2y = 4$ and infinitely many pairs (x, y) satisfy $2x - y = 3$, only the coordinates of the point where the graphs intersect satisfy both equations simultaneously. Since the intersection point has coordinates of $(2, 1)$, the solution is the pair $(2, 1)$, or $x = 2$ and $y = 1$.

To check the solution, we substitute 2 for x and 1 for y in each equation and verify that $(2, 1)$ satisfies each equation.

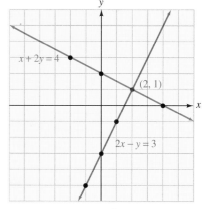

$x + 2y = 4$

x	y	(x, y)
4	0	$(4, 0)$
0	2	$(0, 2)$
-2	3	$(-2, 3)$

$2x - y = 3$

x	y	(x, y)
1	-1	$(1, -1)$
0	-3	$(0, -3)$
-1	-5	$(-1, -5)$

Figure 13-1

⇨ **SELF CHECK 1**   Solve by graphing: $\begin{cases} 2x + y = 0 \\ x - 2y = 5 \end{cases}$.

When a system of equations (as in Example 1) has a solution, the system is a *consistent system of equations*. A system with no solution is an *inconsistent system*.

EXAMPLE 2   Solve the system by graphing: $\begin{cases} 2x + 3y = 6 \\ 4x + 6y = 24 \end{cases}$.

Solution   We graph both equations on the same set of coordinate axes, as shown in Figure 13-2. Since the lines do not intersect, the system does not have a solution and its solution set is $\varnothing$. It is an inconsistent system.

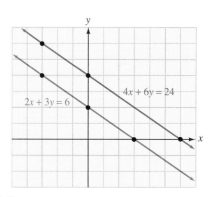

$2x + 3y = 6$

x	y	(x, y)
3	0	$(3, 0)$
0	2	$(0, 2)$
-3	4	$(-3, 4)$

$4x + 6y = 24$

x	y	(x, y)
6	0	$(6, 0)$
0	4	$(0, 4)$
-3	6	$(-3, 6)$

Figure 13-2

⇨ **SELF CHECK 2**   Solve by graphing: $\begin{cases} 2x - 5y = 15 \\ y = \frac{2}{5}x - 2 \end{cases}$.

When the equations of a system have different graphs (as in Examples 1 and 2), the equations are *independent equations.* Two equations with the same graph are *dependent equations.*

EXAMPLE 3 Solve the system by graphing: $\begin{cases} 2y - x = 4 \\ 2x + 8 = 4y \end{cases}$.

Solution We graph each equation on the same set of coordinate axes, as shown in Figure 13-3. Since the graphs coincide, the system has infinitely many solutions. Any pair (x, y) that satisfies one equation satisfies the other also.

From the tables shown in the figure, we see that $(-4, 0)$ and $(0, 2)$ are solutions. We can find infinitely many more solutions by finding additional pairs (x, y) that satisfy either equation.

Because the two equations have the same graph, they are dependent equations.

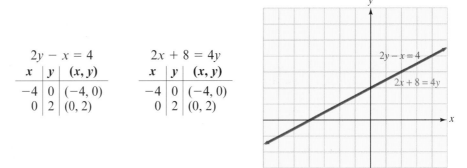

$2y - x = 4$

x	y	(x, y)
-4	0	(-4, 0)
0	2	(0, 2)

$2x + 8 = 4y$

x	y	(x, y)
-4	0	(-4, 0)
0	2	(0, 2)

Figure 13-3

To describe these solutions, we can solve either equation for y. If we choose the first equation, we have

$$2y - x = 4$$
$$2y = x + 4$$
$$y = \frac{x + 4}{2}$$

Because $\frac{x + 4}{2}$ is equal to y, every solution (x, y) of the previous system will have the form $\left(x, \frac{x + 4}{2}\right)$.

⇨ SELF CHECK 3 Solve by graphing: $\begin{cases} x - 3y = 12 \\ y = \frac{1}{3}x - 4 \end{cases}$.

When we graph two linear equations in two variables, the following possibilities can occur.

If the lines are different and intersect, the equations are independent and the system is consistent. *One solution exists.*

 If the lines are different and parallel, the equations are independent and the system is inconsistent. *No solution exists.*

 If the lines coincide, the equations are dependent and the system is consistent. *Infinitely many solutions exist.*

To solve more difficult systems such as

$$\begin{cases} \frac{3}{2}x - y = \frac{5}{2} \\ x + \frac{1}{2}y = 4 \end{cases}$$

we multiply both sides of the first equation by 2 and both sides of the second equation by 2 to eliminate the fractions:

$$\begin{cases} 3x - 2y = 5 \\ 2x + y = 8 \end{cases}$$

This new system is equivalent to the first. If we graph each equation in the new system, as in Figure 13-4, we see that the coordinates of the point where the two lines intersect are (3, 2).

$3x - 2y = 5$

x	y	(x, y)
0	$-\frac{5}{2}$	$\left(0, -\frac{5}{2}\right)$
$\frac{5}{3}$	0	$\left(\frac{5}{3}, 0\right)$

$2x + y = 8$

x	y	(x, y)
4	0	$(4, 0)$
1	6	$(1, 6)$

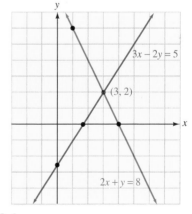

Figure 13-4

ACCENT ON TECHNOLOGY

Solving Systems of Equations

With a graphing calculator, we can obtain very good approximations of the solutions of a system of two linear equations in two variables. For example, to solve

$$\begin{cases} 3x + 2y = 12 \\ 2x - 3y = 12 \end{cases}$$

(continued)

with a graphing calculator, we must solve each equation for y to get the following equivalent system:

$$\begin{cases} y = -\frac{3}{2}x + 6 \\ y = \frac{2}{3}x - 4 \end{cases}$$

If we use window settings of $[-10, 10]$ for x and $[-10, 10]$ for y, the graphs of the equations will look like those in Figure 13-5(a). If we zoom in on the intersection point of the two lines as in Figure 13-5(b) and trace, we will find the approximate solution shown in the figure. To get better results, we can do more zooms.

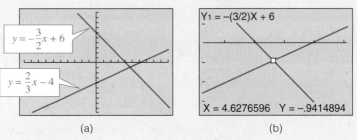

(a) (b)

Figure 13-5

We can also solve this system using the intersect command found in the CALC menu on a TI-84 graphing calculator. To use this method, we graph each equation as shown in Figure 13-5(a). Then we open the CALC menu and select "5: intersect" to obtain Figure 13-6(a). Next, we select a point on the first curve by pressing **ENTER**, select a point on the second curve by pressing **ENTER**, and press **ENTER** again to obtain Figure 13-6(b). From the figure, we see that the solution is approximately $(4.6153846, -0.9230769)$.

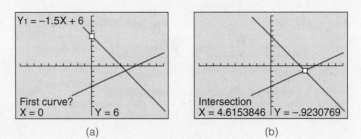

(a) (b)

Figure 13-6

Verify that the exact solution is $x = \frac{60}{13}$ and $y = -\frac{12}{13}$.

2 **Solve a system of two linear equations by substitution.**

Use the following steps to solve a system of two equations in two variables by substitution.

Solving Systems of Equations by Substitution

1. If necessary, solve one equation for one of its variables, preferably a variable with a coefficient of 1.
2. Substitute the resulting expression for the variable obtained in Step 1 into the other equation and solve that equation.
3. Find the value of the other variable by substituting the value of the variable found in Step 2 into any equation containing both variables.
4. State the solution.
5. Check the solution in both of the original equations.

EXAMPLE 4   Solve the system using substitution: $\begin{cases} \frac{4}{3}x + \frac{1}{2}y = -\frac{2}{3} \\ \frac{1}{2}x + \frac{2}{3}y = \frac{5}{3} \end{cases}$.

Solution   First we find an equivalent system without fractions by multiplying both sides of each equation by 6, the LCD of 2 and 3.

$$\begin{aligned} (1) \\ (2) \end{aligned} \quad \begin{cases} 8x + 3y = -4 \\ 3x + 4y = 10 \end{cases}$$

Because no variable in either equation has a coefficient of 1, it is impossible to avoid fractions when solving for a variable. We solve Equation 2 for x.

$$3x + 4y = 10$$
$$3x = -4y + 10 \qquad \text{Subtract } 4y \text{ from both sides.}$$
$$(3) \qquad x = -\frac{4}{3}y + \frac{10}{3} \qquad \text{Divide both sides by 3.}$$

We then substitute $-\frac{4}{3}y + \frac{10}{3}$ for x in Equation 1 and solve for y.

$$8x + 3y = -4$$
$$8\left(-\frac{4}{3}y + \frac{10}{3}\right) + 3y = -4 \qquad \text{Substitute } -\frac{4}{3}y + \frac{10}{3} \text{ for } x.$$
$$-\frac{32}{3}y + \frac{80}{3} + 3y = -4 \qquad \text{Use the distributive property to remove parentheses.}$$
$$-32y + 80 + 9y = -12 \qquad \text{Multiply both sides by 3.}$$
$$-23y = -92 \qquad \text{Combine like terms and subtract 80 from both sides.}$$
$$y = 4 \qquad \text{Divide both sides by } -23.$$

We can find x by substituting 4 for y in Equation 3 and simplifying:

$$x = -\frac{4}{3}y + \frac{10}{3}$$
$$= -\frac{4}{3}(4) + \frac{10}{3} \qquad \text{Substitute 4 for } y.$$
$$= -\frac{6}{3} \qquad\qquad -\frac{16}{3} + \frac{10}{3} = -\frac{6}{3}$$
$$= -2$$

The solution is the ordered pair $(-2, 4)$. Verify that this solution checks.

⇨ **SELF CHECK 4** Solve using substitution: $\begin{cases} \frac{3}{2}x + \frac{1}{3}y = -5 \\ \frac{1}{2}x - \frac{2}{3}y = -4 \end{cases}.$

3 **Solve a system of two linear equations by elimination (addition).**

In the elimination (or addition) method, we combine the equations of the system in a way that will eliminate terms involving one of the variables.

Solving Systems of Equations by Elimination (Addition)

1. If necessary, write both equations of the system in general form.

2. If necessary, multiply the terms of one or both of the equations by constants chosen to make the coefficients of one of the variables differ only in sign.

3. Add the equations and solve the resulting equation, if possible.

4. Substitute the value obtained in Step 3 into either of the original equations and solve for the remaining variable.

5. State the solution obtained in Steps 3 and 4.

6. Check the solution in both of the original equations.

EXAMPLE 5 Solve the system by elimination: $\begin{cases} \frac{4}{3}x + \frac{1}{2}y = -\frac{2}{3} \\ \frac{1}{2}x + \frac{2}{3}y = \frac{5}{3} \end{cases}.$

Solution This is the system in Example 4. To solve it by elimination, we find an equivalent system with no fractions by multiplying both sides of each equation by 6 to obtain

(1) $\begin{cases} 8x + 3y = -4 \\ 3x + 4y = 10 \end{cases}$
(2)

We can solve for x by eliminating the terms involving y. To do so, we multiply both sides of Equation 1 by 4 and both sides of Equation 2 by -3 to get

$$\begin{cases} 32x + 12y = -16 \\ -9x - 12y = -30 \end{cases}$$

When these equations are added, the y-terms are eliminated and the result is

$$23x = -46$$
$$x = -2 \qquad \text{Divide both sides by 23.}$$

To find y, we substitute -2 for x in either Equation 1 or Equation 2. If we substitute -2 for x in Equation 2, we get

$$3x + 4y = 10$$
$$3(-2) + 4y = 10 \qquad \text{Substitute } -2 \text{ for } x.$$
$$-6 + 4y = 10 \qquad \text{Simplify.}$$
$$4y = 16 \qquad \text{Add 6 to both sides.}$$
$$y = 4 \qquad \text{Divide both sides by 4.}$$

The solution is $(-2, 4)$.

⇨ **SELF CHECK 5** Solve by elimination: $\begin{cases} \frac{2}{3}x - \frac{2}{5}y = 10 \\ \frac{1}{2}x + \frac{2}{3}y = -7 \end{cases}$.

EXAMPLE 6 Solve the system: $\begin{cases} y = 2x + 4 \\ 8x - 4y = 7 \end{cases}$.

Solution Because the first equation is already solved for y, we use the substitution method.

$$8x - 4y = 7$$
$$8x - 4(2x + 4) = 7 \quad \text{Substitute } 2x + 4 \text{ for } y.$$

We then solve this equation for x:

$$8x - 8x - 16 = 7 \quad \text{Use the distributive property to remove parentheses.}$$
$$-16 = 7 \quad \text{Combine like terms.}$$

This impossible result shows that the equations in the system are independent, but that the system is inconsistent. Since the system has no solution, its solution set is $\varnothing$. If the equations of this system were graphed, the lines would be parallel.

⇨ **SELF CHECK 6** Solve: $\begin{cases} 4x - 8y = 9 \\ y = \frac{1}{2}x - \frac{8}{9} \end{cases}$.

EXAMPLE 7 Solve the system: $\begin{cases} 4x + 6y = 12 \\ -2x - 3y = -6 \end{cases}$.

Solution Since the equations are written in general form, we use the elimination (addition) method. To eliminate the x-terms when adding the equations, we multiply both sides of the second equation by 2 to obtain

$$\begin{cases} 4x + 6y = 12 \\ -4x - 6y = -12 \end{cases}$$

After adding the left and right sides, we get

$$0x + 0y = 0$$
$$0 = 0$$

Here, both the x- and y-terms are eliminated. The true statement $0 = 0$ shows that the equations in this system are dependent and that the system is consistent.

Note that the equations of the system are equivalent, because when the second equation is multiplied by -2, it becomes the first equation. The line graphs of these equations would coincide.

To write a general solution, we will solve for y in terms of x in the first equation.

$$4x + 6y = 12$$
$$6y = -4x + 12$$
$$y = \frac{-4x + 12}{6}$$
$$y = -\frac{2}{3}x + 2$$

Since any ordered pair that satisfies one of the equations also satisfies the other, there are infinitely many solutions (x, y) of the form $\left(x, -\frac{2}{3}x + 2\right)$.

⇨ **SELF CHECK 7**   Solve: $\begin{cases} 2(x + y) - y = 12 \\ y = -2x + 12 \end{cases}$.

4   **Solve an application problem by setting up and solving a system of two linear equations.**

EXAMPLE 8   **RETAIL SALES**   A store advertises two types of cell phones, one selling for $67 and the other for $100. If the receipts from the sale of 36 phones totaled $2,940, how many of each type were sold?

Analyze the problem   We can let x represent the number of phones sold for $67 and let y represent the number of phones sold for $100.

Form two equations   Because a total of 36 phones were sold, we can form the equation

The number of lower-priced phones	plus	the number of higher-priced phones	equals	the total number of phones.
x	$+$	y	$=$	36

We know that the receipts for the sale of x of the $67 phones will be $67x$ and that the receipts for the sale of y of the $100 phones will be $100y$. Since the sum of these receipts is $2,940, the second equation is

The value of the lower-priced phones	plus	the value of the higher-priced phones	equals	the total receipts.
$67x$	$+$	$100y$	$=$	2,940

Solve the system   To find out how many of each type of phone were sold, we must solve the system

$$\begin{aligned} (1) \\ (2) \end{aligned} \quad \begin{cases} x + y = 36 \\ 67x + 100y = 2,940 \end{cases}$$

To solve using the elimination method, we multiply both sides of Equation 1 by -100, add the resulting equation to Equation 2, and solve for x:

$$\begin{array}{r} -100x - 100y = -3,600 \\ \underline{67x + 100y = 2,940} \\ -33x = -600 \\ x = 20 \end{array}$$ Divide both sides by -33.

To find y, we substitute 20 for x in Equation 1 and solve for y:

$x + y = 36$

$20 + y = 36$ Substitute 20 for x.

$y = 16$ Subtract 20 from both sides.

State the conclusion   The store sold 20 of the $67 phones and 16 of the $100 phones.

Check the result   If 20 of one type were sold and 16 of the other type were sold, a total of 36 phones were sold.

Since the value of the lower-priced phones is 20($67) = $1,340 and the value of the higher-priced phones is 16($100) = $1,600, the total receipts are $2,940.

5 Solve a system of two linear inequalities.

We now review the graphing method of solving systems of two linear inequalities in two variables. Recall that the solutions are usually the intersection of half-planes.

EXAMPLE 9   Graph the solution set of the system: $\begin{cases} x + y \leq 1 \\ 2x - y > 2 \end{cases}$.

Solution   On one set of coordinate axes, we graph each inequality as shown in Figure 13-7.

The graph of $x + y \leq 1$ includes the line graph of the equation $x + y = 1$ and all points below it. Since the edge is included, we draw it as a solid line.

The graph of $2x - y > 2$ contains the points below the graph of the equation $2x - y = 2$. Since the edge is not included, we draw it as a dashed line.

The area where the half-planes intersect represents the solution of the system of inequalities, because any point in that region has coordinates that will satisfy both inequalities.

$x + y = 1$		
x	y	(x, y)
0	1	$(0, 1)$
1	0	$(1, 0)$

$2x - y = 2$		
x	y	(x, y)
0	-2	$(0, -2)$
1	0	$(1, 0)$

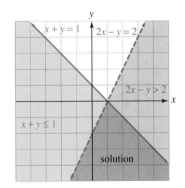

Figure 13-7

SELF CHECK ANSWERS

1. 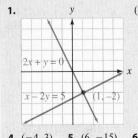 $(1, -2)$ **2.** $\varnothing$ 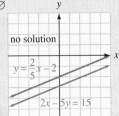   **3.** 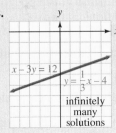 infinitely many solutions of the form, $\left(x, \frac{1}{3}x - 4\right)$

4. $(-4, 3)$ **5.** $(6, -15)$ **6.** $\varnothing$ **7.** infinitely many solutions of the form, $(x, -2x + 12)$

NOW TRY THIS

1. Use substitution to solve $\begin{cases} t = r + 1 \\ r + s + t = 0. \\ r + s = -2 \end{cases}$

2. $\begin{cases} x - y > 0 \\ y \leq x + 2 \end{cases}$

3. $\begin{cases} 4x - 3y \leq -4 \\ y < \frac{4}{3}x - \frac{5}{2} \end{cases}$

4. $\begin{cases} y \leq x^2 - 6x + 7 \\ x - y < 3 \end{cases}$

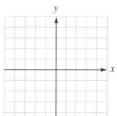

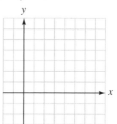

13.1 EXERCISES

WARM-UPS

Determine whether each system has one solution, no solution, or infinitely many solutions.

1. $\begin{cases} y = 2x \\ y = 2x + 5 \end{cases}$

2. $\begin{cases} y = 2x \\ y - x = x \end{cases}$

3. $\begin{cases} y = 2x \\ y = -2x \end{cases}$

4. $\begin{cases} y = 2x + 1 \\ 2x = y \end{cases}$

Solve each system for x.

5. $\begin{cases} y = 2x \\ x + y = 6 \end{cases}$

6. $\begin{cases} y = -x \\ 2x + y = 4 \end{cases}$

7. $\begin{cases} x - y = 6 \\ x + y = 2 \end{cases}$

8. $\begin{cases} x + y = 4 \\ 2x - y = 5 \end{cases}$

REVIEW

Simplify each expression. Write all answers without using negative exponents. Assume no variable is 0.

9. $(a^2a^3)^2(a^4a^2)^2$

10. $\left(\dfrac{a^2b^3c^4d}{ab^2c^3d^4}\right)^{-3}$

11. $\left(\dfrac{-3x^3y^4}{x^{-5}y^3}\right)^{-4}$

12. $\dfrac{3t^0 - 4t^0 + 5}{5t^0 + 2t^0}$

Solve each formula for the given variable.

13. $A = p + prt$ for r

14. $A = p + prt$ for p

15. $\dfrac{1}{r} = \dfrac{1}{r_1} + \dfrac{1}{r_2}$ for r

16. $\dfrac{1}{r} = \dfrac{1}{r_1} + \dfrac{1}{r_2}$ for r_1

VOCABULARY AND CONCEPTS *Fill in the blanks.*

17. When a system of equations has a solution, it is called a _____ system of equations.

18. When a system of equations has no solution, it is called an _____ system of equations.

19. When the equations of a system have different graphs, the equations are called _____ equations.

20. Two equations with the same graph are called _____ equations.

GUIDED PRACTICE

Solve each system by graphing. Check your graphs with a graphing calculator, if possible. See Examples 1–3. (Objective 1)

21. $\begin{cases} x - y = 4 \\ 2x + y = 5 \end{cases}$

22. $\begin{cases} 2x + y = 1 \\ x - 2y = -7 \end{cases}$

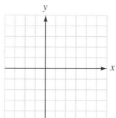

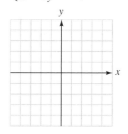

23. $\begin{cases} x = 13 - 4y \\ 3x = 4 + 2y \end{cases}$

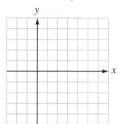

24. $\begin{cases} 3x = 7 - 2y \\ 2x = 2 + 4y \end{cases}$

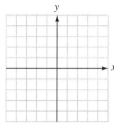

25. $\begin{cases} 2x + 3y = 0 \\ 2x + y = 4 \end{cases}$

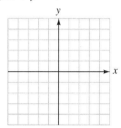

26. $\begin{cases} 3x - 2y = 0 \\ 2x + 3y = 0 \end{cases}$

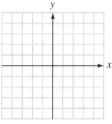

27. $\begin{cases} x = 3 - 2y \\ 2x + 4y = 6 \end{cases}$

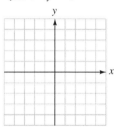

28. $\begin{cases} 3x = 5 - 2y \\ 3x + 2y = 7 \end{cases}$

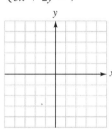

Solve each system by substitution. See Example 4. (Objective 2)

29. $\begin{cases} y = x \\ x + y = 4 \end{cases}$

30. $\begin{cases} 2x - 3y = -10 \\ y = x + 2 \end{cases}$

31. $\begin{cases} x - y = 2 \\ 2x + y = 13 \end{cases}$

32. $\begin{cases} x - y = -4 \\ 3x - 2y = -5 \end{cases}$

33. $\begin{cases} x + 2y = 6 \\ 3x - y = -10 \end{cases}$

34. $\begin{cases} 2x - y = -21 \\ 4x + 5y = 7 \end{cases}$

35. $\begin{cases} 3x = 2y - 4 \\ 6x - 4y = -4 \end{cases}$

36. $\begin{cases} 8x = 4y + 10 \\ 4x - 2y = 5 \end{cases}$

Solve each system by elimination. See Examples 5–7. (Objective 3)

37. $\begin{cases} x - y = 3 \\ x + y = 7 \end{cases}$

38. $\begin{cases} x + y = 1 \\ x - y = 7 \end{cases}$

39. $\begin{cases} 2x + y = -10 \\ 2x - y = -6 \end{cases}$

40. $\begin{cases} x + 2y = -9 \\ x - 2y = -1 \end{cases}$

41. $\begin{cases} 8x - 4y = 16 \\ 2x - 4 = y \end{cases}$

42. $\begin{cases} 2y - 3x = -13 \\ 3x - 17 = 4y \end{cases}$

43. $\begin{cases} x = \frac{3}{2}y + 5 \\ 2x - 3y = 8 \end{cases}$

44. $\begin{cases} x = \frac{2}{3}y \\ y = 4x + 5 \end{cases}$

Graph the solution set of each system of inequalities. See Example 9. (Objective 5)

45. $\begin{cases} y < 3x + 2 \\ y < -2x + 3 \end{cases}$

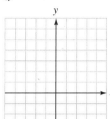

46. $\begin{cases} y \le x - 2 \\ y \ge 2x + 1 \end{cases}$

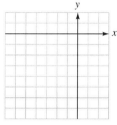

47. $\begin{cases} 3x + 2y > 6 \\ x + 3y \le 2 \end{cases}$

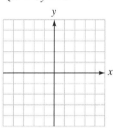

48. $\begin{cases} 3x + y \le 1 \\ -x + 2y \ge 6 \end{cases}$

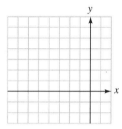

ADDITIONAL PRACTICE

Solve using any method.

49. $\begin{cases} y = 3 \\ x = 2 \end{cases}$

50. $\begin{cases} 2x + 3y = -15 \\ 2x + y = -9 \end{cases}$

51. $\begin{cases} x = \frac{11 - 2y}{3} \\ y = \frac{11 - 6x}{4} \end{cases}$

52. $\begin{cases} x = \frac{1 - 3y}{4} \\ y = \frac{12 + 3x}{2} \end{cases}$

53. $\begin{cases} \frac{5}{2}x + y = \frac{1}{2} \\ 2x - \frac{3}{2}y = 5 \end{cases}$

54. $\begin{cases} \frac{5}{2}x + 3y = 6 \\ y = \frac{24 - 10x}{12} \end{cases}$

55. $\begin{cases} 3x - 4y = 9 \\ x + 2y = 8 \end{cases}$

56. $\begin{cases} 3x - 2y = -10 \\ 6x + 5y = 25 \end{cases}$

57. $\begin{cases} 2x + 2y = -1 \\ 3x + 4y = 0 \end{cases}$

58. $\begin{cases} 5x + 3y = -7 \\ 3x - 3y = 7 \end{cases}$

59. $\begin{cases} 2x + 3y = 8 \\ 3x - 2y = -1 \end{cases}$

60. $\begin{cases} 5x - 2y = 19 \\ 3x + 4y = 1 \end{cases}$

61. $\begin{cases} 4x + 9y = 8 \\ 2x - 6y = -3 \end{cases}$

62. $\begin{cases} 4x + 6y = 5 \\ 8x - 9y = 3 \end{cases}$

63. $\begin{cases} \dfrac{x}{2} + \dfrac{y}{2} = 6 \\ \dfrac{x}{2} - \dfrac{y}{2} = -2 \end{cases}$

64. $\begin{cases} \dfrac{x}{2} - \dfrac{y}{3} = -4 \\ \dfrac{x}{2} + \dfrac{y}{9} = 0 \end{cases}$

65. $\begin{cases} \dfrac{3}{4}x + \dfrac{2}{3}y = 7 \\ \dfrac{3}{5}x - \dfrac{1}{2}y = 18 \end{cases}$

66. $\begin{cases} \dfrac{2}{3}x - \dfrac{1}{4}y = -8 \\ \dfrac{1}{2}x - \dfrac{3}{8}y = -9 \end{cases}$

 Use a graphing calculator to solve each system. Give each answer to the nearest hundredth.

67. $\begin{cases} y = 3.2x - 1.5 \\ y = -2.7x - 3.7 \end{cases}$

68. $\begin{cases} y = -0.45x + 5 \\ y = 5.55x - 13.7 \end{cases}$

69. $\begin{cases} 1.7x + 2.3y = 3.2 \\ y = 0.25x + 8.95 \end{cases}$

70. $\begin{cases} 2.75x = 12.9y - 3.79 \\ 7.1x - y = 35.76 \end{cases}$

APPLICATIONS *Use two variables to solve each problem.*
See Example 8. (Objective 4)

71. Retailing The cost of manufacturing one type of camera and the revenue from the sale of those cameras are shown in the illustration.

a. From the illustration, find the cost of manufacturing 15,000 cameras.

b. From the illustration, find the revenue obtained by selling 20,000 cameras.

c. For what number of cameras will the revenue equal the cost?

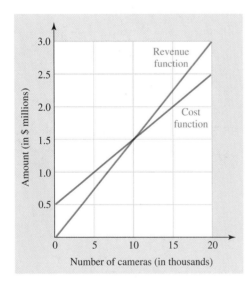

72. Food service

a. Estimate the point of intersection of the two graphs shown in the illustration. Express your answer in the form (year, number of meals).

b. What information about dining out does the point of intersection give?

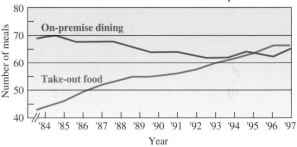

Number of Take-Out and On-Premise Meals Purchased at Commercial Restaurants Per Person Annually

73. Merchandising A pair of shoes and a sweater cost $98. If the sweater cost $16 more than the shoes, how much did the sweater cost?

74. Merchandising A sporting goods salesperson sells 2 fishing reels and 5 rods for $270. The next day, the salesperson sells 4 reels and 2 rods for $220. How much does each cost?

75. Electronics Two resistors in the following voltage divider circuit have a total resistance of 1,375 ohms. To provide the required voltage, R_1 must be 125 ohms greater than R_2. Find both resistances.

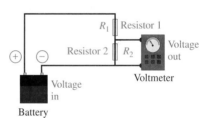

76. Stowing baggage A small aircraft can carry 950 pounds of baggage, distributed between two storage compartments. On one flight, the plane is fully loaded, with 150 pounds more baggage in one compartment than the other. How much is stowed in each compartment?

77. Geometry The rectangular field in the following illustration is surrounded by 72 meters of fencing. If the field is partitioned as shown, a total of 88 meters of fencing is required. Find the dimensions of the field.

78. Geometry In a right triangle, one acute angle is 15° greater than two times the other acute angle. Find the difference between the angles.

WRITING ABOUT MATH

79. Determine which method you would use to solve the following system. Why?

$$\begin{cases} y = 3x + 1 \\ 3x + 2y = 12 \end{cases}$$

80. Determine which method you would use to solve the following system. Why?

$$\begin{cases} 2x + 4y = 9 \\ 3x - 5y = 20 \end{cases}$$

81. When graphing a system of linear inequalities, explain how to decide which region to shade.

82. Explain how a system of two linear inequalities might have no solution.

SOMETHING TO THINK ABOUT

83. Under what conditions will a system of two equations in two variables be inconsistent?

84. Under what conditions will the equations of a system of two equations in two variables be dependent?

85. The solution of a system of inequalities in two variables is *bounded* if it is possible to draw a circle around it. Can the non-empty solution of a system of two linear inequalities be bounded?

86. The solution of $\begin{cases} y \geq |x| \\ y \leq k \end{cases}$ has an area of 25. Find k.

SECTION 13.2
Solving Systems of Three Linear Equations in Three Variables

Objectives

1. Solve a system of three linear equations in three variables.
2. Identify an inconsistent system.
3. Identify a dependent system and express the solution as an ordered triple in terms of one of the variables.
4. Solve an application problem by setting up and solving a system of three linear equations in three variables.

Vocabulary

plane

Getting Ready

Determine whether the equation $x + 2y + 3z = 6$ is satisfied by the following values.

1. $(1, 1, 1)$ **2.** $(-2, 1, 2)$
3. $(2, -2, -1)$ **4.** $(2, 2, 0)$

We now extend the definition of a linear equation to include equations of the form $ax + by + cz = d$. The solution of a system of three linear equations with three variables is an ordered triple of numbers. For example, the solution of the system

$$\begin{cases} 2x + 3y + 4z = 20 \\ 3x + 4y + 2z = 17 \\ 3x + 2y + 3z = 16 \end{cases}$$

is the ordered triple $(1, 2, 3)$, since each equation is satisfied if $x = 1$, $y = 2$, and $z = 3$.

$$2x + 3y + 4z = 20 \qquad 3x + 4y + 2z = 17 \qquad 3x + 2y + 3z = 16$$
$$2(1) + 3(2) + 4(3) \stackrel{?}{=} 20 \qquad 3(1) + 4(2) + 2(3) \stackrel{?}{=} 17 \qquad 3(1) + 2(2) + 3(3) \stackrel{?}{=} 16$$
$$2 + 6 + 12 \stackrel{?}{=} 20 \qquad 3 + 8 + 6 \stackrel{?}{=} 17 \qquad 3 + 4 + 9 \stackrel{?}{=} 16$$
$$20 = 20 \qquad 17 = 17 \qquad 16 = 16$$

The graph of an equation of the form $ax + by + cz = d$ is a flat surface called a **plane.** A system of three linear equations in three variables is consistent or inconsistent, depending on how the three planes corresponding to the three equations intersect. Figure 13-8 illustrates some of the possibilities.

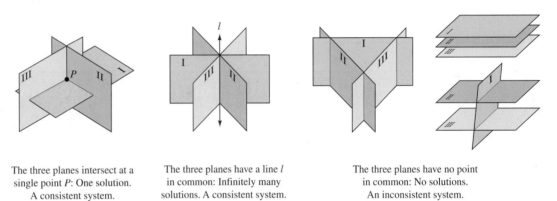

The three planes intersect at a single point P: One solution. A consistent system.	The three planes have a line l in common: Infinitely many solutions. A consistent system.	The three planes have no point in common: No solutions. An inconsistent system.
(a)	(b)	(c)

Figure 13-8

 Solve a system of three linear equations in three variables.

To solve a system of three linear equations in three variables, we follow these steps.

Solving Three Equations in Three Variables

1. Pick any two equations and eliminate a variable.

2. Pick a different pair of equations and eliminate the same variable.

3. Solve the resulting pair of two equations in two variables.

4. To find the value of the third variable, substitute the values of the two variables found in Step 3 into any equation containing all three variables and solve the equation.

5. Check the solution in all three of the original equations.

EXAMPLE 1 Solve the system: $\begin{cases} 2x + y + 4z = 12 \\ x + 2y + 2z = 9 \\ 3x - 3y - 2z = 1 \end{cases}$.

Solution   We are given the system

(1) $\begin{cases} 2x + y + 4z = 12 \\ x + 2y + 2z = 9 \\ 3x - 3y - 2z = 1 \end{cases}$
(2)
(3)

If we pick Equations 2 and 3 and add them, the variable z is eliminated:

(2) $x + 2y + 2z =\ \ 9$
(3) $\underline{3x - 3y - 2z =\ \ 1}$
(4) $4x -\ \ y\ \ \ \ \ \ \ = 10$

We now pick a different pair of equations (Equations 1 and 3) and eliminate z again. If each side of Equation 3 is multiplied by 2 and the resulting equation is added to Equation 1, z is again eliminated:

(1) $2x +\ \ y + 4z = 12$
         $\underline{6x - 6y - 4z =\ \ 2}$
(5) $8x - 5y\ \ \ \ \ \ \ = 14$

Equations 4 and 5 form a system of two equations in two variables:

(4) $\begin{cases} 4x - y = 10 \\ 8x - 5y = 14 \end{cases}$
(5)

To solve this system, we multiply Equation 4 by -5 and add the resulting equation to Equation 5 to eliminate y:

         $-20x + 5y = -50$
(5) $\underline{\ \ \ 8x - 5y =\ \ \ 14}$
         $-12x\ \ \ \ \ \ \ = -36$
              $x = 3$ Divide both sides by -12.

To find y, we substitute 3 for x in any equation containing only x and y (such as Equation 5) and solve for y:

(5) $8x - 5y = 14$
         $8(3) - 5y = 14$ Substitute 3 for x.
         $24 - 5y = 14$ Simplify.
         $-5y = -10$ Subtract 24 from both sides.
         $y = 2$ Divide both sides by -5.

To find z, we substitute 3 for x and 2 for y in an equation containing x, y, and z (such as Equation 1) and solve for z:

(1) $2x + y + 4z = 12$
         $2(3) + 2 + 4z = 12$ Substitute 3 for x and 2 for y.
         $8 + 4z = 12$ Simplify.
         $4z = 4$ Subtract 8 from both sides.
         $z = 1$ Divide both sides by 4.

The solution of the system is $(x, y, z) = (3, 2, 1)$. Verify that these values satisfy each equation in the original system.

⇨ **SELF CHECK 1**   Solve the system: $\begin{cases} 2x + y + 4z = 16 \\ x + 2y + 2z = 11 \\ 3x - 3y - 2z = -9 \end{cases}$.

2 **Identify an inconsistent system.**

The next example has no solution.

EXAMPLE 2   Solve the system: $\begin{cases} 2x + y - 3z = -3 \\ 3x - 2y + 4z = 2 \\ 4x + 2y - 6z = -7 \end{cases}$.

Solution   We are given the system of equations

(1) $\begin{cases} 2x + y - 3z = -3 \\ (2) \quad 3x - 2y + 4z = 2 \\ (3) \quad 4x + 2y - 6z = -7 \end{cases}$

We can multiply Equation 1 by 2 and add the resulting equation to Equation 2 to eliminate y.

$$4x + 2y - 6z = -6$$
(2) $\underline{3x - 2y + 4z = 2}$
(4) $7x - 2z = -4$

We now add Equations 2 and 3 to again eliminate y.

(2) $3x - 2y + 4z = 2$
(3) $\underline{4x + 2y - 6z = -7}$
(5) $7x - 2z = -5$

Equations 4 and 5 form the system

(4) $\begin{cases} 7x - 2z = -4 \\ (5) \quad 7x - 2z = -5 \end{cases}$

Since $7x - 2z$ cannot equal both -4 and -5, this system is inconsistent; it has no solution. Its solution set is $\varnothing$.

⇨ **SELF CHECK 2**   Solve the system: $\begin{cases} 2x + y - 3z = 8 \\ 3x - 2y + 4z = 10 \\ 4x + 2y - 6z = -5 \end{cases}$.

3 **Identify a dependent system and express the solution as an ordered triple in terms of one of the variables.**

When the equations in a system of two equations in two variables were dependent, the system had infinitely many solutions. This is not always true for systems of three equations in three variables. In fact, a system can have dependent equations and still be inconsistent. Figure 13-9 illustrates the different possibilities.

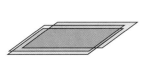

When three planes coincide, the equations are dependent, and there are infinitely many solutions.

(a)

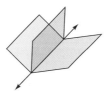

When three planes intersect in a common line, the equations are dependent, and there are infinitely many solutions.

(b)

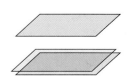

When two planes coincide and are parallel to a third plane, the system is inconsistent, and there are no solutions.

(c)

Figure 13-9

EXAMPLE 3 Solve the system: $\begin{cases} 3x - 2y + z = -1 \\ 2x + y - z = 5 \\ 5x - y = 4 \end{cases}$.

Solution We can add the first two equations to get

$$3x - 2y + z = -1$$
$$\underline{2x + \;\; y - z = \;\;\; 5}$$
(1) $\;\;\; 5x - \;\; y \;\;\;\;\;\;\; = \;\;\; 4$

Since Equation 1 is the same as the third equation of the system, the equations of the system are dependent, and there will be infinitely many solutions. From a graphical perspective, the equations represent three planes that intersect in a common line, as shown in Figure 13-9(b).

To write the general solution to this system, we can solve Equation 1 for y to get

$5x - y = 4$

$-y = -5x + 4$ Subtract $5x$ from both sides.

$\;\;\; y = 5x - 4$ Multiply both sides by -1.

We then can substitute $5x - 4$ for y in the first equation of the system and solve for z to get

$\;\;\;\;\;\;\;\;\; 3x - 2y + z = -1$

$\;\;\;\; 3x - 2(\mathbf{5x - 4}) + z = -1$ Substitute $5x - 4$ for y.

$\;\;\;\; 3x - 10x + 8 + z = -1$ Use the distributive property to remove parentheses.

$\;\;\;\;\;\;\;\;\; -7x + 8 + z = -1$ Combine like terms.

$\;\;\;\;\;\;\;\;\;\;\;\;\;\;\;\;\;\; z = 7x - 9$ Add $7x$ and -8 to both sides.

COMMENT The solution in Example 3 is called a *general* solution. If we had eliminated different variables, we could have expressed the general solution in terms of y or in terms of z.

Since we have found the values of y and z in terms of x, every solution to the system has the form $(x, 5x - 4, 7x - 9)$, where x can be any real number. For example,

If $x = 1$, a solution is $(1, 1, -2)$. $5(1) - 4 = 1$, and $7(1) - 9 = -2$.

If $x = 2$, a solution is $(2, 6, 5)$. $5(2) - 4 = 6$, and $7(2) - 9 = 5$.

If $x = 3$, a solution is $(3, 11, 12)$. $5(3) - 4 = 11$, and $7(3) - 9 = 12$.

This system has infinitely many solutions.

⇨ **SELF CHECK 3**   Solve the system: $\begin{cases} 3x + 2y + z = -1 \\ 2x - y - z = 5 \\ 5x + y = 4 \end{cases}$.

4   **Solve an application problem by setting up and solving a system of three linear equations in three variables.**

EXAMPLE 4   **MANUFACTURING HAMMERS**   A company makes three types of hammers—good, better, and best. The cost of making each type of hammer is $4, $6, and $7, respectively, and the hammers sell for $6, $9, and $12. Each day, the cost of making 100 hammers is $520, and the daily revenue from their sale is $810. How many of each type are manufactured?

Analyze the problem   We need to know the number of each type of hammer manufactured, so we will let x represent the number of good hammers, y represent the number of better hammers, and z represent the number of best hammers.

Form three equations   Since x represents the number of good hammers, y represents the number of better hammers, and z represents the number of best hammers, we know that

The total number of hammers is $x + y + z$.
The cost of making good hammers is $4x$ ($4 times x hammers).
The cost of making better hammers is $6y$ ($6 times y hammers).
The cost of making best hammers is $7z$ ($7 times z hammers).
The revenue received by selling good hammers is $6x$ ($6 times x hammers).
The revenue received by selling better hammers is $9y$ ($9 times y hammers).
The revenue received by selling best hammers is $12z$ ($12 times z hammers).

The information leads to three equations:

The number of good hammers	plus	the number of better hammers	plus	the number of best hammers	equals	the total number of hammers.
x	$+$	y	$+$	z	$=$	100

The cost of making good hammers	plus	the cost of making better hammers	plus	the cost of making best hammers	equals	the total cost.
$4x$	$+$	$6y$	$+$	$7z$	$=$	520

The revenue from the good hammers	plus	the revenue from the better hammers	plus	the revenue from the best hammers	equals	the total revenue.
$6x$	$+$	$9y$	$+$	$12z$	$=$	810

Solve the system   These three equations give the following system:

$$\begin{align} (1) \\ (2) \\ (3) \end{align} \quad \begin{cases} x + y + z = 100 \\ 4x + 6y + 7z = 520 \\ 6x + 9y + 12z = 810 \end{cases}$$

that we can solve as follows:

If we multiply Equation 1 by -7 and add the result to Equation 2, we obtain

$$-7x - 7y - 7z = -700$$
$$\underline{4x + 6y + 7z = 520}$$
$$(4) \quad -3x - y = -180$$

If we multiply Equation 1 by -12 and add the result to Equation 3, we obtain

$$-12x - 12y - 12z = -1{,}200$$
$$\underline{6x + 9y + 12z = \phantom{-1{,}}810}$$
$$(5) \quad -6x - 3y = \phantom{-1{,}}-390$$

If we multiply Equation 4 by -3 and add it to Equation 5, we obtain

$$9x + 3y = 540$$
$$\underline{-6x - 3y = -390}$$
$$3x = 150$$
$$x = 50 \qquad \text{Divide both sides by 3.}$$

To find y, we substitute 50 for x in Equation 4:

$$-3x - y = -180$$
$$-3(\mathbf{50}) - y = -180 \qquad \text{Substitute 50 for } x.$$
$$-y = -30 \qquad \text{Add 150 to both sides.}$$
$$y = 30 \qquad \text{Divide both sides by } -1.$$

To find z, we substitute 50 for x and 30 for y in Equation 1:

$$x + y + z = 100$$
$$\mathbf{50} + \mathbf{30} + z = 100$$
$$z = 20 \qquad \text{Subtract 80 from both sides.}$$

State the conclusion Each day, the company makes 50 good hammers, 30 better hammers, and 20 best hammers.

Check the result Check the solution in each equation in the original system.

EXAMPLE 5 **CURVE FITTING** The equation of the parabola shown in Figure 13-10 is of the form $y = ax^2 + bx + c$. Find the equation of the parabola.

Solution Since the parabola passes through the points shown in the figure, each pair of coordinates satisfies the equation $y = ax^2 + bx + c$. If we substitute the x- and y-values of each point into the equation and simplify, we obtain the following system.

$$(1) \quad \begin{cases} a - b + c = 5 \\ (2) \quad a + b + c = 1 \\ (3) \quad 4a + 2b + c = 2 \end{cases}$$

If we add Equations 1 and 2, we obtain $2a + 2c = 6$. If we multiply Equation 1 by 2 and add the result to Equation 3, we get $6a + 3c = 12$. We can then divide both sides of $2a + 2c = 6$ by 2 and divide both sides of $6a + 3c = 12$ by 3 to get the system

$$(4) \quad \begin{cases} a + c = 3 \\ (5) \quad 2a + c = 4 \end{cases}$$

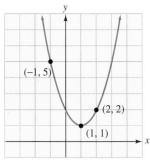

(−1, 5)

(2, 2)

(1, 1)

Figure 13-10

If we multiply Equation 4 by -1 and add the result to Equation 5, we get $a = 1$. To find c, we can substitute 1 for a in Equation 4 and find that $c = 2$. To find b, we can substitute 1 for a and 2 for c in Equation 2 and find that $b = -2$.

After we substitute these values of a, b, and c into the equation $y = ax^2 + bx + c$ we have the equation of the parabola.

$$y = ax^2 + bx + c$$
$$y = 1x^2 + (-2)x + 2$$
$$y = x^2 - 2x + 2$$

SELF CHECK ANSWERS   **1.** $(1, 2, 3)$ **2.** $\varnothing$ **3.** infinitely many solutions of the form $(x, 4 - 5x, -9 + 7x)$

NOW TRY THIS

1. The manager of a coffee bar wants to mix some Peruvian Organic coffee worth \$15 per pound with some Colombian coffee worth \$10 per pound and Indian Malabar coffee worth \$18 per pound to get 50 pounds of a blend that he can sell for \$17.50 per pound. He wants to use 10 fewer pounds of the Indian Malabar than Peruvian Organic. How many pounds of each should he use? (*Hint:* This problem is based on the formula $V = np$, where V represents value, n represents the number of pounds, and p represents the price per pound.)

13.2 EXERCISES

WARM-UPS   *Is the ordered triple a solution of the system?*

1. $(1, 1, 1)$; $\begin{cases} 2x + y - 3z = 0 \\ 3x - 2y + 4z = 5 \\ 4x + 2y - 6z = 0 \end{cases}$

2. $(2, 0, 1)$; $\begin{cases} 3x + 2y - z = 5 \\ 2x - 3y + 2z = 4 \\ 4x - 2y + 3z = 10 \end{cases}$

REVIEW

Consider the line passing through $(-2, -4)$ and $(3, 5)$.

3. Find the slope of the line.

4. Write the equation of the line in general form.

Find each value if $f(x) = 2x^2 + 1$.

5. $f(0)$

6. $f(-2)$

7. $f(s)$

8. $f(2t)$

VOCABULARY AND CONCEPTS

Fill in the blanks.

9. The graph of the equation $2x + 3y + 4z = 5$ is a flat surface called a _____.

10. When three planes coincide, the equations of the system are _____, and there are _____ many solutions.

11. When three planes intersect in a line, the system will have _____ many solutions.

12. When three planes are parallel, the system will have ____ solutions.

Determine whether the ordered triple is a solution of the given system.

13. $(2, 1, 1)$, $\begin{cases} x - y + z = 2 \\ 2x + y - z = 4 \\ 2x - 3y + z = 2 \end{cases}$

14. $(-3, 2, -1)$, $\begin{cases} 2x + 2y + 3z = -1 \\ 3x + y - z = -6 \\ x + y + 2z = 1 \end{cases}$

GUIDED PRACTICE

Solve each system. **See Example 1. (Objective 1)**

15. $\begin{cases} x + y + z = 4 \\ 2x + y - z = 1 \\ 2x - 3y + z = 1 \end{cases}$

16. $\begin{cases} x + y + z = 4 \\ x - y + z = 2 \\ x - y - z = 0 \end{cases}$

17. $\begin{cases} 2x + 2y + 3z = 10 \\ 3x + y - z = 0 \\ x + y + 2z = 6 \end{cases}$

18. $\begin{cases} x - y + z = 4 \\ x + 2y - z = -1 \\ x + y - 3z = -2 \end{cases}$

19. $\begin{cases} 4x + 3z = 4 \\ 2y - 6z = -1 \\ 8x + 4y + 3z = 9 \end{cases}$

20. $\begin{cases} 2x + 3y + 2z = 1 \\ 2x - 3y + 2z = -1 \\ 4x + 3y - 2z = 4 \end{cases}$

Solve each system. **See Example 2. (Objective 2)**

21. $\begin{cases} 2a + 3b + c = 2 \\ 4a + 6b + 2c = 5 \\ a - 2b + c = 3 \end{cases}$

22. $\begin{cases} 2x + y - z = 1 \\ x + 2y + 2z = 2 \\ 4x + 5y + 3z = 3 \end{cases}$

Solve each system. **See Example 3. (Objective 3)**

23. $\begin{cases} x - 2y + 3z = 9 \\ -x + 3y = -4 \\ 2x - 5y + 3z = 13 \end{cases}$

24. $\begin{cases} 7x - 2y - z = 1 \\ 9x - 6y + z = 7 \\ x - 2y + z = 3 \end{cases}$

ADDITIONAL PRACTICE   *Solve each system.*

25. $\begin{cases} a + b + 2c = 7 \\ a + 2b + c = 8 \\ 2a + b + c = 9 \end{cases}$

26. $\begin{cases} 3x - y - 2z = 12 \\ x + y + 6z = 8 \\ 2x - 2y - z = 11 \end{cases}$

27. $\begin{cases} x + \frac{1}{3}y + z = 13 \\ \frac{1}{2}x - y + \frac{1}{3}z = -2 \\ x + \frac{1}{2}y - \frac{1}{3}z = 2 \end{cases}$

28. $\begin{cases} x - \frac{1}{5}y - z = 9 \\ \frac{1}{4}x + \frac{1}{5}y - \frac{1}{2}z = 5 \\ 2x + y + \frac{1}{6}z = 12 \end{cases}$

29. $\begin{cases} x - 3y + z = 1 \\ 2x - y - 2z = 2 \\ x + 2y - 3z = -1 \end{cases}$

30. $\begin{cases} 2x + y - 3z = 5 \\ x - 2y + 4z = 9 \\ 4x + 2y - 6z = 1 \end{cases}$

31. $\begin{cases} 2x + 3y + 4z = 6 \\ 2x - 3y - 4z = -4 \\ 4x + 6y + 8z = 12 \end{cases}$

32. $\begin{cases} x - 3y + 4z = 2 \\ 2x + y + 2z = 3 \\ 4x - 5y + 10z = 7 \end{cases}$

APPLICATIONS

Set up a system of three linear equations to solve each problem.
See Examples 4–5. (Objective 4)

33. Integer problem   The sum of three integers is 18. The third integer is four times the second, and the second integer is 6 more than the first. Find the integers.

34. Integer problem   The sum of three integers is 48. If the first integer is doubled, the sum is 60. If the second integer is doubled, the sum is 63. Find the integers.

35. Geometry   The sum of the angles in any triangle is 180°. In triangle ABC, $\angle A$ is 100° less than the sum of $\angle B$ and $\angle C$, and $\angle C$ is 40° less than twice $\angle B$. Find the measure of each angle.

36. Geometry   The sum of the angles of any four-sided figure is 360°. In the quadrilateral, $\angle A = \angle B$, $\angle C$ is 20° greater than $\angle A$, and $\angle D = 40°$. Find the measure of each angle.

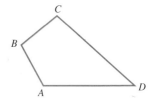

37. Nutritional planning   One unit of each of three foods contains the nutrients shown in the table. How many units of each must be used to provide exactly 11 grams of fat, 6 grams of carbohydrates, and 10 grams of protein?

Food	Fat	Carbohydrates	Protein
A	1	1	2
B	2	1	1
C	2	1	2

38. Nutritional planning   One unit of each of three foods contains the nutrients shown in the table. How many units of each must be used to provide exactly 14 grams of fat, 9 grams of carbohydrates, and 9 grams of protein?

Food	Fat	Carbohydrates	Protein
A	2	1	2
B	3	2	1
C	1	1	2

39. Making statues   An artist makes three types of ceramic statues at a monthly cost of $650 for 180 statues. The manufacturing costs for the three types are $5, $4, and $3. If the statues sell for $20, $12, and $9, respectively, how many of each type should be made to produce $2,100 in monthly revenue?

40. Manufacturing footballs   A factory manufactures three types of footballs at a monthly cost of $2,425 for 1,125 footballs. The manufacturing costs for the three types of footballs are $4, $3, and $2. These footballs sell for $16, $12, and $10, respectively. How many of each type are manufactured if the monthly profit is $9,275? (*Hint:* Profit = income − cost.)

41. Concert tickets   Tickets for a concert cost $5, $3, and $2. Twice as many $5 tickets were sold as $2 tickets. The receipts for 750 tickets were $2,625. How many of each price ticket were sold?

42. Mixing nuts   The owner of a candy store mixed some peanuts worth $3 per pound, some cashews worth $9 per pound, and some Brazil nuts worth $9 per pound to get 50 pounds of a mixture that would sell for $6 per pound. She used 15 fewer pounds of cashews than peanuts. How many pounds of each did she use?

43. Chainsaw sculpting   A north woods sculptor carves three types of statues with a chainsaw. The times required for carving, sanding, and painting a totem pole, a bear, and a deer are shown in the table. How many of each should be produced to use all available labor hours?

	Totem pole	Bear	Deer	Time available
Carving	2 hours	2 hours	1 hour	14 hours
Sanding	1 hour	2 hours	2 hours	15 hours
Painting	3 hours	2 hours	2 hours	21 hours

44. Making clothing   A clothing manufacturer makes coats, shirts, and slacks. The times required for cutting, sewing, and packaging each item are shown in the table. How many of each should be made to use all available labor hours?

	Coats	Shirts	Slacks	Time available
Cutting	20 min	15 min	10 min	115 hr
Sewing	60 min	30 min	24 min	280 hr
Packaging	5 min	12 min	6 min	65 hr

45. Earth's atmosphere   Use the information in the graph to determine what percent of Earth's atmosphere is nitrogen, is oxygen, and is other gases.

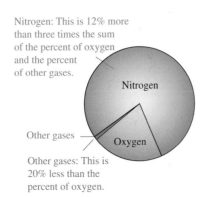

Nitrogen: This is 12% more than three times the sum of the percent of oxygen and the percent of other gases.

Other gases: This is 20% less than the percent of oxygen.

46. NFL records   Jerry Rice, who played with the San Francisco 49ers and the Oakland Raiders, holds the all-time record for touchdown passes caught. Here are interesting facts about this feat.

- He caught 30 more TD passes from Steve Young than he did from Joe Montana.
- He caught 39 more TD passes from Joe Montana than he did from Rich Gannon.
- He caught a total of 156 TD passes from Young, Montana, and Gannon.

Determine the number of touchdown passes Rice has caught from Young, from Montana, and from Gannon as of 2003.

47. Curve fitting   Find the equation of the parabola shown in the illustration.

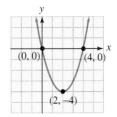

48. Curve fitting   Find the equation of the parabola shown in the illustration.

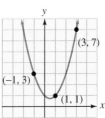

The equation of a circle is of the form $x^2 + y^2 + cx + dy + e = 0$.

49. Curve fitting   Find the equation of the circle shown in the illustration.

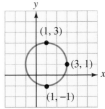

50. Curve fitting   Find the equation of the circle shown in the illustration.

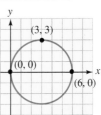

WRITING ABOUT MATH

51. What makes a system of three equations in three variables inconsistent?

52. What makes the equations of a system of three equations in three variables dependent?

SOMETHING TO THINK ABOUT

53. Solve the system:

$$\begin{cases} x + y + z + w = 3 \\ x - y - z - w = -1 \\ x + y - z - w = 1 \\ x + y - z + w = 3 \end{cases}$$

54. Solve the system:

$$\begin{cases} 2x + y + z + w = 3 \\ x - 2y - z + w = -3 \\ x - y - 2z - w = -3 \\ x + y - z + 2w = 4 \end{cases}$$

SECTION 13.3 — Solving Systems of Linear Equations Using Matrices

Objectives

1. Solve a system of linear equations with the same number of equations as variables using Gaussian elimination.

2. Solve a system with more linear equations than variables using row operations on a matrix.

3. Solve a system with fewer linear equations than variables using row operations on a matrix.

Vocabulary

matrix	augmented matrix	triangular form of a matrix
element of a matrix	coefficient matrix	back substitution
square matrix	Gaussian elimination	

Getting Ready

Multiply the first row by 2 and add the result to the second row.

1. $\begin{matrix} 2 & 3 & 5 \\ 1 & 2 & 3 \end{matrix}$

2. $\begin{matrix} -1 & 0 & 4 \\ 2 & 3 & -1 \end{matrix}$

Multiply the first row by -1 and add the result to the second row.

3. $\begin{matrix} 2 & 3 & 5 \\ 1 & 2 & 3 \end{matrix}$

4. $\begin{matrix} -1 & 0 & 4 \\ 2 & 3 & -1 \end{matrix}$

In this section, we will discuss a streamlined method used for solving systems of linear equations. This method involves the use of *matrices.*

1 Solve a system of linear equations with the same number of equations as variables using Gaussian elimination.

Another method of solving systems of equations involves rectangular arrays of numbers called *matrices.*

| **Matrix** | A **matrix** is any rectangular array of numbers. |

Arthur Cayley
(1821–1895)
Cayley taught mathematics at Cambridge University. When he refused to take religious vows, he was fired and became a lawyer. After 14 years, he returned to mathematics and to Cambridge. Cayley was a major force in developing the theory of matrices.

Some examples of matrices are

$$A = \begin{bmatrix} 1 & 2 & 3 \\ 4 & 5 & 6 \end{bmatrix} \qquad B = \begin{bmatrix} 1 & 2 \\ 3 & 4 \\ 5 & 6 \end{bmatrix} \qquad C = \begin{bmatrix} 2 & 4 & 6 \\ 8 & 10 & 12 \\ 14 & 16 & 18 \end{bmatrix}$$

The numbers in each matrix are called **elements.** Because matrix A has two rows and three columns, it is called a 2×3 matrix (read "2 by 3" matrix). Matrix B is a 3×2 matrix, because the matrix has three rows and two columns. Matrix C is a 3×3 matrix (three rows and three columns).

Any matrix with the same number of rows and columns, like matrix C, is called a **square matrix.**

To show how to use matrices to solve systems of linear equations, we consider the system

$$\begin{cases} x - 2y - z = 6 \\ 2x + 2y - z = 1 \\ -x - y + 2z = 1 \end{cases}$$

which can be represented by the following matrix, called an **augmented matrix:**

$$\begin{bmatrix} 1 & -2 & -1 & \vdots & 6 \\ 2 & 2 & -1 & \vdots & 1 \\ -1 & -1 & 2 & \vdots & 1 \end{bmatrix}$$

The first three columns of the augmented matrix form a 3×3 matrix called a **coefficient matrix.** It is determined by the coefficients of x, y, and z in the equations of the system. The 3×1 matrix to the right of the dashed line is determined by the constants in the equations.

Coefficient matrix

$$\begin{bmatrix} 1 & -2 & 1 \\ 2 & 2 & -1 \\ -1 & -1 & 2 \end{bmatrix}$$

Column of constants

$$\begin{bmatrix} 6 \\ 1 \\ 1 \end{bmatrix}$$

Each row of the augmented matrix represents one equation of the system:

$$\begin{bmatrix} 1 & -2 & -1 & \vdots & 6 \\ 2 & 2 & -1 & \vdots & 1 \\ -1 & -1 & 2 & \vdots & 1 \end{bmatrix} \quad \begin{matrix} \leftrightarrow \\ \leftrightarrow \\ \leftrightarrow \end{matrix} \quad \begin{cases} x - 2y - z = 6 \\ 2x + 2y - z = 1 \\ -x - y + 2z = 1 \end{cases}$$

To solve a 3×3 system of equations by **Gaussian elimination,** we transform an augmented matrix into the following matrix that has all 0's below its main diagonal, which is formed by the elements a, e, and h.

$$\begin{bmatrix} a & b & c & \vdots & d \\ 0 & e & f & \vdots & g \\ 0 & 0 & h & \vdots & i \end{bmatrix} \qquad (a, b, c, \ldots, i \text{ are real numbers})$$

We often can write a matrix in this form, called **triangular form,** by using the following operations.

Elementary Row Operations	**1.** Any two rows of a matrix can be interchanged.
	2. Any row of a matrix can be multiplied by a nonzero constant.
	3. Any row of a matrix can be changed by adding a nonzero constant multiple of another row to it.

- A type 1 row operation corresponds to interchanging two equations of a system.
- A type 2 row operation corresponds to multiplying both sides of an equation by a nonzero constant.
- A type 3 row operation corresponds to adding a nonzero multiple of one equation to another.

None of these operations will change the solution of the given system of equations.

After we have written the matrix in triangular form, we can solve the corresponding system of equations by a process called **back substitution,** as shown in Example 1.

EXAMPLE 1 Solve the system using matrices: $\begin{cases} x - 2y - z = 6 \\ 2x + 2y - z = 1 \\ -x - y + 2z = 1 \end{cases}$.

Solution We can represent the system with the following augmented matrix:

$$\left[\begin{array}{ccc|c} 1 & -2 & -1 & 6 \\ 2 & 2 & -1 & 1 \\ -1 & -1 & 2 & 1 \end{array} \right]$$

To get 0's under the 1 in the first column, we multiply row 1 of the augmented matrix by -2 and add it to row 2 to get a new row 2. We then multiply row 1 by 1 and add it to row 3 to get a new row 3.

$$\left[\begin{array}{ccc|c} 1 & -2 & -1 & 6 \\ 0 & 6 & 1 & -11 \\ 0 & -3 & 1 & 7 \end{array} \right]$$

To get a 0 under the 6 in the second column of the previous matrix, we multiply row 2 by $\frac{1}{2}$ and add it to row 3.

$$\left[\begin{array}{ccc|c} 1 & -2 & 1 & 6 \\ 0 & 6 & 1 & -11 \\ 0 & 0 & \frac{3}{2} & \frac{3}{2} \end{array} \right]$$

Finally, to clear the fraction in the third row, third column, we multiply row 3 by $\frac{2}{3}$, which is the reciprocal of $\frac{3}{2}$.

$$\left[\begin{array}{ccc|c} 1 & -2 & 1 & 6 \\ 0 & 6 & 1 & -11 \\ 0 & 0 & 1 & 1 \end{array} \right]$$

The final matrix represents the system of equations

$$\begin{aligned} (1) \\ (2) \\ (3) \end{aligned} \quad \begin{cases} x - 2y - z = 6 \\ 0x + 6y + z = -11 \\ 0x + 0y + z = 1 \end{cases}$$

From Equation 3, we can see that $z = 1$. To find y, we substitute 1 for z in Equation 2 and solve for y.

$$(2) \qquad 6y + z = -11$$

$$6y + 1 = -11 \qquad \text{Substitute 1 for } z.$$

$$6y = -12 \qquad \text{Subtract 1 from both sides.}$$

$$y = -2 \qquad \text{Divide both sides by 6.}$$

Thus, $y = -2$. To find x, we substitute 1 for z and -2 for y in Equation 1 and solve for x:

$$(1) \qquad x - 2y - z = 6$$

$$x - 2(-2) - 1 = 6 \qquad \text{Substitute 1 for } z \text{ and } -2 \text{ for } y.$$

$$x + 3 = 6 \qquad \text{Simplify.}$$

$$x = 3 \qquad \text{Subtract 3 from both sides.}$$

Thus, $x = 3$. The solution of the given system is $(3, -2, 1)$. Verify that this ordered triple satisfies each equation of the original system.

SELF CHECK 1 Solve the system using matrices: $\begin{cases} x - 2y - z = 2 \\ 2x + 2y - z = -5. \\ -x - y + 2z = 7 \end{cases}$

2 Solve a system with more linear equations than variables using row operations on a matrix.

We can use matrices to solve systems that have more equations than variables.

EXAMPLE 2 Solve the system using matrices: $\begin{cases} x + y = -1 \\ 2x - y = 7 \\ -x + 2y = -8 \end{cases}$.

Solution This system can be represented by the following augmented matrix:

$$\left[\begin{array}{cc|c} 1 & 1 & -1 \\ 2 & -1 & 7 \\ -1 & 2 & -8 \end{array} \right]$$

To get 0's under the 1 in the first column, we multiply row 1 by -2 and add it to row 2. Then we can multiply row 1 by 1 and add it to row 3.

$$\left[\begin{array}{cc|c} 1 & 1 & -1 \\ 0 & -3 & 9 \\ 0 & 3 & -9 \end{array} \right]$$

To get a 0 under the -3 in the second column, we can multiply row 2 by 1 and add it to row 3.

$$\left[\begin{array}{cc|c} 1 & 1 & -1 \\ 0 & -3 & 9 \\ 0 & 0 & 0 \end{array} \right]$$

Finally, to get a 1 in the second row, second column, we multiply row 2 by $-\frac{1}{3}$.

$$\begin{bmatrix} 1 & 1 & \vdots & -1 \\ 0 & 1 & \vdots & -3 \\ 0 & 0 & \vdots & 0 \end{bmatrix}$$

The final matrix represents the system

$$\begin{cases} x + y = -1 \\ 0x + y = -3 \\ 0x + 0y = 0 \end{cases}$$

The third equation can be discarded, because $0x + 0y = 0$ for all x and y. From the second equation, we can read that $y = -3$. To find x, we substitute -3 for y in the first equation and solve for x:

$$x + y = -1$$
$$x + (-3) = -1 \qquad \text{Substitute } -3 \text{ for } y.$$
$$x = 2 \qquad \text{Add 3 to both sides.}$$

The solution is $(2, -3)$. Verify that this solution satisfies all three equations of the original system.

➡ **SELF CHECK 2**   Solve the system using matrices: $\begin{cases} x + y = 1 \\ 2x - y = 8 \\ -x + 2y = -7 \end{cases}$.

If the last row of the final matrix in Example 2 had been of the form $0x + 0y = k$, where $k \neq 0$, the system would not have a solution. No values of x and y could make the expression $0x + 0y$ equal to a nonzero constant k.

3   **Solve a system with fewer linear equations than variables using row operations on a matrix.**

We also can solve many systems that have more variables than equations.

EXAMPLE 3   Solve the system using matrices: $\begin{cases} x + y - 2z = -1 \\ 2x - y + z = -3 \end{cases}$.

Solution   This system can be represented by the following augmented matrix.

$$\begin{bmatrix} 1 & 1 & -2 & \vdots & -1 \\ 2 & -1 & 1 & \vdots & -3 \end{bmatrix}$$

To get a 0 under the 1 in the first column, we multiply row 1 by -2 and add it to row 2.

$$\begin{bmatrix} 1 & 1 & -2 & \vdots & -1 \\ 0 & -3 & 5 & \vdots & -1 \end{bmatrix}$$

Then to get a 1 in the second row, second column, we multiply row 2 by $-\frac{1}{3}$.

$$\begin{bmatrix} 1 & 1 & -2 & \vdots & -1 \\ 0 & 1 & -\frac{5}{3} & \vdots & \frac{1}{3} \end{bmatrix}$$

The final matrix represents the system

$$\begin{cases} x + y - 2z = -1 \\ y - \frac{5}{3}z = \frac{1}{3} \end{cases}$$

We add $\frac{5}{3}z$ to both sides of the second equation to obtain

$$y = \frac{1}{3} + \frac{5}{3}z$$

We have not found a specific value for y. However, we have found y in terms of z.

To find a value of x in terms of z, we substitute $\frac{1}{3} + \frac{5}{3}z$ for y in the first equation and simplify to get

$$x + y - 2z = -1$$

$$x + \frac{1}{3} + \frac{5}{3}z - 2z = -1 \qquad \text{Substitute } \frac{1}{3} + \frac{5}{3}z \text{ for } y.$$

$$x + \frac{1}{3} - \frac{1}{3}z = -1 \qquad \text{Combine like terms.}$$

$$x - \frac{1}{3}z = -\frac{4}{3} \qquad \text{Subtract } \frac{1}{3} \text{ from both sides.}$$

$$x = -\frac{4}{3} + \frac{1}{3}z \qquad \text{Add } \frac{1}{3}z \text{ to both sides.}$$

A solution of this system must have the form

$$\left(-\frac{4}{3} + \frac{1}{3}z, \ \frac{1}{3} + \frac{5}{3}z, \ z \right) \qquad \text{This solution is a general solution of the system.}$$

for all real values of z. This system has infinitely many solutions, a different one for each value of z. For example,

- If $z = 0$, the corresponding solution is $\left(-\frac{4}{3}, \frac{1}{3}, 0 \right)$.
- If $z = 1$, the corresponding solution is $(-1, 2, 1)$.

Verify that both of these solutions satisfy each equation of the original system.

⇨ SELF CHECK 3   Solve the system using matrices: $\begin{cases} x + y - 2z = 11 \\ 2x - y + z = -2 \end{cases}$.

EVERYDAY CONNECTIONS   Staffing

Matrices with the same number of rows and columns can be added. We simply add their corresponding elements. For example,

$$\begin{bmatrix} 2 & 3 & -4 \\ -1 & 2 & 5 \end{bmatrix} + \begin{bmatrix} 3 & -1 & 0 \\ 4 & 3 & 2 \end{bmatrix}$$

$$= \begin{bmatrix} 2+3 & 3+(-1) & -4+0 \\ -1+4 & 2+3 & 5+2 \end{bmatrix}$$

$$= \begin{bmatrix} 5 & 2 & -4 \\ 3 & 5 & 7 \end{bmatrix}$$

To multiply a matrix by a constant, we multiply each element of the matrix by the constant. For example,

$$5 \cdot \begin{bmatrix} 2 & 3 & -4 \\ -1 & 2 & 5 \end{bmatrix}$$

$$= \begin{bmatrix} 5\cdot 2 & 5\cdot 3 & 5\cdot(-4) \\ 5\cdot(-1) & 5\cdot 2 & 5\cdot 5 \end{bmatrix}$$

$$= \begin{bmatrix} 10 & 15 & -20 \\ -5 & 10 & 25 \end{bmatrix}$$

Since matrices provide a good way to store information in computers, they often are used in applied problems. For example, suppose there are 66 security officers employed at either the downtown office or the suburban office:

Downtown Office		
	Male	**Female**
Day shift	12	18
Night shift	3	0

Suburban Office		
	Male	**Female**
Day shift	14	12
Night shift	5	2

The information about the employees is contained in the following matrices.

$$D = \begin{bmatrix} 12 & 18 \\ 3 & 0 \end{bmatrix} \quad \text{and} \quad S = \begin{bmatrix} 14 & 12 \\ 5 & 2 \end{bmatrix}$$

The entry in the first row-first column in matrix D gives the information that 12 males work the day shift at the downtown office. Company management can add the matrices D and S to find corporate-wide totals:

$$D + S = \begin{bmatrix} 12 & 18 \\ 3 & 0 \end{bmatrix} + \begin{bmatrix} 14 & 12 \\ 5 & 2 \end{bmatrix}$$

$$= \begin{bmatrix} 26 & 30 \\ 8 & 2 \end{bmatrix}$$

We interpret the total to mean:

	Male	Female
Day shift	26	30
Night shift	8	2

If one-third of the force in each category at the downtown location retires, the downtown staff would be reduced to $\frac{2}{3}D$ people. We can compute $\frac{2}{3}D$ by multiplying each entry by $\frac{2}{3}$.

$$\frac{2}{3}D = \frac{2}{3}\begin{bmatrix} 12 & 18 \\ 3 & 0 \end{bmatrix}$$

$$= \begin{bmatrix} 8 & 12 \\ 2 & 0 \end{bmatrix}$$

After retirements, downtown staff would be

	Male	Female
Day shift	8	12
Night shift	2	0

SELF CHECK ANSWERS   **1.** $(1, -2, 3)$ **2.** $(3, -2)$ **3.** infinitely many solutions of the form $\left(3 + \frac{1}{3}z, 8 + \frac{5}{3}z, z\right)$

NOW TRY THIS

1. A toy company builds authentic models of a compact car, a sedan, and a truck. The times required for preparation, assembly, and post-production are given below. Use matrices to help determine how many of each should be made in order to use all available labor hours.

	Compact	Sedan	Truck	Total labor hours
Preparation	1 hr	1 hr	2 hrs	60 hrs
Assembly	2 hrs	3 hrs	4 hrs	130 hrs
Post-production	2 hrs	2 hrs	3 hrs	100 hrs

13.3 EXERCISES

WARM-UPS

Consider the system $\begin{cases} 3x + 2y = 8 \\ 4x - 3y = 6 \end{cases}$.

1. Find the coefficient matrix.   **2.** Find the augmented matrix.

Determine whether each matrix is in triangular form.

3. $\begin{bmatrix} 4 & 1 & 5 \\ 0 & 2 & 7 \\ 0 & 0 & 4 \end{bmatrix}$ **4.** $\begin{bmatrix} 8 & 5 & 2 \\ 0 & 4 & 5 \\ 0 & 7 & 0 \end{bmatrix}$

REVIEW   Write each number in scientific notation.

5. 93,000,000   **6.** 0.00045
7. 63×10^3 **8.** 0.33×10^3

VOCABULARY AND CONCEPTS

Fill in the blanks.

9. A _____ is a rectangular array of numbers.
10. The numbers in a matrix are called its _____.
11. A 3×4 matrix has __ rows and 4 _____.
12. A _____ matrix has the same number of rows as columns.
13. An _____ matrix of a system of equations includes the _____ matrix and the column of constants.
14. If a matrix has all 0's below its main diagonal, it is written in _____ form.
15. A _____ row operation corresponds to interchanging two equations in a system of equations.
16. A type 2 row operation corresponds to _____ both sides of an equation by a nonzero constant.
17. A type 3 row operation corresponds to adding a _____ multiple of one equation to another.
18. In the Gaussian method of solving systems of equations, we transform the _____ matrix into triangular form and finish the solution by using _____ substitution.

Use a row operation on the first matrix to find the missing number in the second matrix.

19. $\begin{bmatrix} 2 & 1 & 1 \\ 5 & 4 & 1 \end{bmatrix}$
$\begin{bmatrix} 2 & 1 & 1 \\ 3 & 3 & \blacksquare \end{bmatrix}$

20. $\begin{bmatrix} -1 & 3 & 2 \\ 1 & -2 & 3 \end{bmatrix}$
$\begin{bmatrix} -1 & 3 & 2 \\ \blacksquare & 1 & 5 \end{bmatrix}$

21. $\begin{bmatrix} 3 & -2 & 1 \\ -1 & 2 & 4 \end{bmatrix}$
$\begin{bmatrix} 3 & -2 & 1 \\ -2 & 4 & \blacksquare \end{bmatrix}$

22. $\begin{bmatrix} 2 & 1 & -3 \\ 2 & 6 & 1 \end{bmatrix}$
$\begin{bmatrix} 6 & 3 & \blacksquare \\ 2 & 6 & 1 \end{bmatrix}$

GUIDED PRACTICE

Use matrices to solve each system of equations. See Example 1. (Objective 1)

23. $\begin{cases} x + y = 2 \\ x - y = 0 \end{cases}$ **24.** $\begin{cases} x + y = 3 \\ x - y = -1 \end{cases}$

25. $\begin{cases} x + 2y = -4 \\ 2x + y = 1 \end{cases}$ **26.** $\begin{cases} 2x - 3y = 16 \\ -4x + y = -22 \end{cases}$

27. $\begin{cases} x + y + z = 6 \\ x + 2y + z = 8 \\ x + y + 2z = 9 \end{cases}$ **28.** $\begin{cases} x - y + z = 2 \\ x + 2y - z = 6 \\ 2x - y - z = 3 \end{cases}$

29. $\begin{cases} 2x + y + 3z = 3 \\ -2x - y + z = 5 \\ 4x - 2y + 2z = 2 \end{cases}$ **30.** $\begin{cases} 3x + 2y + z = 8 \\ 6x - y + 2z = 16 \\ -9x + y - z = -20 \end{cases}$

31. $\begin{cases} x + 2y + 2z = 2 \\ 2x + y - z = 1 \\ 4x + 5y + 3z = 3 \end{cases}$ **32.** $\begin{cases} x + 2y - z = 3 \\ 2x - y + 2z = 6 \\ x - 3y + 3z = 4 \end{cases}$

Use matrices to solve each system of equations. See Example 2. (Objective 2)

33. $\begin{cases} x + y = 3 \\ 3x - y = 1 \\ 2x + y = 4 \end{cases}$ **34.** $\begin{cases} x - y = -5 \\ 2x + 3y = 5 \\ x + y = 1 \end{cases}$

35. $\begin{cases} 2x - y = 4 \\ x + 3y = 2 \\ -x - 4y = -2 \end{cases}$ **36.** $\begin{cases} 3x - 2y = 5 \\ x + 2y = 7 \\ -3x - y = -11 \end{cases}$

37. $\begin{cases} 2x + y = 7 \\ x - y = 2 \\ -x + 3y = -2 \end{cases}$ **38.** $\begin{cases} 3x - y = 2 \\ -6x + 3y = 0 \\ -x + 2y = -4 \end{cases}$

Use matrices to solve each system of equations. Give a general solution. See Example 3. (Objective 3)

39. $\begin{cases} x + 2y + 3z = -2 \\ -x - y - 2z = 4 \end{cases}$ **40.** $\begin{cases} 2x - 4y + 3z = 6 \\ -4x + 6y + 4z = -6 \end{cases}$

41. $\begin{cases} x - y = 1 \\ y + z = 1 \\ x + z = 2 \end{cases}$ **42.** $\begin{cases} x + z = 1 \\ x + y = 2 \\ 2x + y + z = 3 \end{cases}$

ADDITIONAL PRACTICE

Use matrices to solve each system of equations.

43. $\begin{cases} 3x + 4y = -12 \\ 9x - 2y = 6 \end{cases}$

44. $\begin{cases} 5x - 4y = 10 \\ x - 7y = 2 \end{cases}$

45. $\begin{cases} 5a = 24 + 2b \\ 5b = 3a + 16 \end{cases}$

46. $\begin{cases} 3m = 2n + 16 \\ 2m = -5n - 2 \end{cases}$

47. $\begin{cases} 3a + b - 3c = 5 \\ a - 2b + 4c = 10 \\ a + b + c = 13 \end{cases}$

48. $\begin{cases} 2a + b - 3c = -1 \\ 3a - 2b - c = -5 \\ a - 3b - 2c = -12 \end{cases}$

49. $\begin{cases} x + 3y = 7 \\ x + y = 3 \\ 3x + y = 5 \end{cases}$

50. $\begin{cases} x + y = 3 \\ x - 2y = -3 \\ x - y = 1 \end{cases}$

51. $\begin{cases} 5x - 2y = 4 \\ 2x - 4y = -8 \end{cases}$

52. $\begin{cases} 2x - y = -1 \\ x - 2y = 1 \end{cases}$

53. $\begin{cases} 2x + y = -4 \\ 6x + 3y = 1 \end{cases}$

54. $\begin{cases} x - 5y = 7 \\ -2x + 10y = 9 \end{cases}$

55. $\begin{cases} 3x - 2y + 4z = 4 \\ x + y + z = 3 \\ 6x - 2y - 3z = 10 \end{cases}$

56. $\begin{cases} 2x + 3y - z = -8 \\ x - y - z = -2 \\ -4x + 3y + z = 6 \end{cases}$

57. $\begin{cases} 3x - y = 9 \\ -6x + 2y = -18 \end{cases}$

58. $\begin{cases} x - y = 1 \\ -3x + 3y = -3 \end{cases}$

59. $\begin{cases} x + y + z = 6 \\ x - y + z = 2 \end{cases}$

60. $\begin{cases} x - y = 0 \\ y + z = 3 \\ x + z = 3 \end{cases}$

61. $\begin{cases} x + 2y + z = 1 \\ 2x - y + 2z = 2 \\ 3x + y + 3z = 3 \end{cases}$

62. $\begin{cases} x - 2y + 3z = 9 \\ -x + 3y = -4 \\ 2x - 5y + 3z = 13 \end{cases}$

Remember these facts from geometry. Then solve each problem using two variables.

  Two angles whose measures add up to 90° are complementary.
  Two angles whose measures add up to 180° are supplementary.
  The sum of the measures of the interior angles in a triangle is 180°.

63. Geometry One angle is 46° larger than its complement. Find the measure of each angle.

64. Geometry One angle is 28° larger than its supplement. Find the measure of each angle.

65. Geometry In the triangle in the next column, $\angle B$ is 25° more than $\angle A$, and $\angle C$ is 5° less than twice $\angle A$. Find the measure of each angle in the triangle.

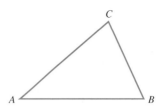

66. Geometry In the triangle below, $\angle A$ is 10° less than $\angle B$, and $\angle B$ is 10° less than $\angle C$. Find the measure of each angle in the triangle.

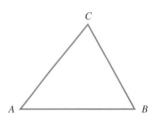

Remember that the equation of a parabola is of the form $y = ax^2 + bx + c$.

67. Curve fitting Find the equation of the parabola passing through the points $(0, 1)$, $(1, 2)$, and $(-1, 4)$.

68. Curve fitting Find the equation of the parabola passing through the points $(0, 1)$, $(1, 1)$, and $(-1, -1)$.

APPLICATIONS

69. Physical therapy After an elbow injury, a volleyball player has restricted movement of her arm. Her range of motion (the measure of $\angle 1$) is 28° less than the measure of $\angle 2$. Find the measure of each angle.

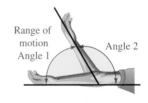

70. Cats and dogs In 2003, there were approximately 135 million dogs and cats in the U.S. If there were 15 million more cats than dogs, how many dogs and cats were there?

71. Piggy banks When a child breaks open her piggy bank, she finds a total of 64 coins, consisting of nickels, dimes, and quarters. The total value of the coins is $6. If the nickels were dimes, and the dimes were nickels, the value of the coins would be $5. How many nickels, dimes, and quarters were in the piggy bank?

72. Theater seating The illustration shows the cash receipts and the ticket prices from two sold-out performances of a play. Find the number of seats in each of the three sections of the 800-seat theater.

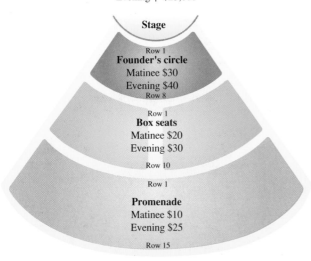

Sunday Ticket Receipts

Matinee	$13,000
Evening	$23,000

WRITING ABOUT MATH

73. Explain how to check the solution of a system of equations.

74. Explain how to perform a type 3 row operation.

SOMETHING TO THINK ABOUT

75. If the system represented by

$$\begin{bmatrix} 1 & 1 & 0 & \vert & 1 \\ 0 & 0 & 1 & \vert & 2 \\ 0 & 0 & 0 & \vert & k \end{bmatrix}$$

has no solution, what do you know about k?

76. Is it possible for a system with fewer equations than variables to have no solution? Illustrate.

SECTION 13.4 Solving Systems of Linear Equations Using Determinants

Objectives

1 Find the determinant of a 2 × 2 and a 3 × 3 matrix without a calculator.

2 Solve a system of linear equations using Cramer's rule.

Vocabulary

determinant   minors   Cramer's rule

Getting Ready

Find each value.

1. $3(-4) - 2(5)$

2. $5(2) - 3(-4)$

3. $2(2 - 5) - 3(5 - 2) + 2(4 - 3)$

4. $-3(5 - 2) + 2(3 + 1) - 2(5 + 1)$

We now discuss a final method for solving systems of linear equations. This method involves *determinants,* an idea related to the concept of matrices.

1 **Find the determinant of a 2 × 2 and a 3 × 3 matrix without a calculator.**

If a matrix A has the same number of rows as columns, it is called a *square matrix.* To each square matrix A, there is associated a number called its *determinant,* represented by the symbol $|A|$.

Value of a 2 × 2 Determinant	If a, b, c, and d are real numbers, the **determinant** of the matrix $\begin{bmatrix} a & b \\ c & d \end{bmatrix}$ is $$\begin{vmatrix} a & b \\ c & d \end{vmatrix} = ad - bc$$

COMMENT Note that if A is a matrix, $|A|$ represents the determinant of A. If A is a number, $|A|$ represents the absolute value of A.

The determinant of a 2 × 2 matrix is the number that is equal to the product of the numbers on the major diagonal

$$\begin{vmatrix} a & b \\ c & d \end{vmatrix}$$

minus the product of the numbers on the other diagonal

$$\begin{vmatrix} a & b \\ c & d \end{vmatrix}$$

EXAMPLE 1 Evaluate the determinants: **a.** $\begin{vmatrix} 3 & 2 \\ 6 & 9 \end{vmatrix}$ **b.** $\begin{vmatrix} -5 & \frac{1}{2} \\ -1 & 0 \end{vmatrix}$.

Solution **a.** $\begin{vmatrix} 3 & 2 \\ 6 & 9 \end{vmatrix} = 3(9) - 2(6)$

$= 27 - 12$

$= 15$

b. $\begin{vmatrix} -5 & \frac{1}{2} \\ -1 & 0 \end{vmatrix} = -5(0) - \frac{1}{2}(-1)$

$= 0 + \frac{1}{2}$

$= \frac{1}{2}$

➡ SELF CHECK 1 Evaluate: $\begin{vmatrix} 4 & -3 \\ 2 & 1 \end{vmatrix}$.

A 3 × 3 determinant can be evaluated by expanding by **minors.**

Value of a 3 × 3 Determinant	$$\begin{vmatrix} a_1 & b_1 & c_1 \\ a_2 & b_2 & c_2 \\ a_3 & b_3 & c_3 \end{vmatrix} = a_1 \underset{\text{Minor of } a_1}{\begin{vmatrix} b_2 & c_2 \\ b_3 & c_3 \end{vmatrix}} - b_1 \underset{\text{Minor of } b_1}{\begin{vmatrix} a_2 & c_2 \\ a_3 & c_3 \end{vmatrix}} + c_1 \underset{\text{Minor of } c_1}{\begin{vmatrix} a_2 & b_2 \\ a_3 & b_3 \end{vmatrix}}$$

To find the minor of a_1, we find the determinant formed by crossing out the elements of the matrix that are in the same row and column as a_1:

$$\begin{vmatrix} a_1 & b_1 & c_1 \\ a_2 & b_2 & c_2 \\ a_3 & b_3 & c_3 \end{vmatrix} \qquad \text{The minor of } a_1 \text{ is } \begin{vmatrix} b_2 & c_2 \\ b_3 & c_3 \end{vmatrix}.$$

To find the minor of b_1, we cross out the elements of the matrix that are in the same row and column as b_1:

$$\begin{vmatrix} a_1 & b_1 & c_1 \\ a_2 & b_2 & c_2 \\ a_3 & b_3 & c_3 \end{vmatrix} \qquad \text{The minor of } b_1 \text{ is } \begin{vmatrix} a_2 & c_2 \\ a_3 & c_3 \end{vmatrix}.$$

To find the minor of c_1, we cross out the elements of the matrix that are in the same row and column as c_1:

$$\begin{vmatrix} a_1 & b_1 & c_1 \\ a_2 & b_2 & c_2 \\ a_3 & b_3 & c_3 \end{vmatrix} \qquad \text{The minor of } c_1 \text{ is } \begin{vmatrix} a_2 & b_2 \\ a_3 & b_3 \end{vmatrix}.$$

EXAMPLE 2   Evaluate the determinant: $\begin{vmatrix} 1 & 3 & -2 \\ 2 & 1 & 3 \\ 1 & 2 & 3 \end{vmatrix}$.

Solution

$$
\begin{array}{ccc}
\text{Minor} & \text{Minor} & \text{Minor} \\
\text{of } 1 & \text{of } 3 & \text{of } -2 \\
\downarrow & \downarrow & \downarrow
\end{array}
$$

$$\begin{vmatrix} 1 & 3 & -2 \\ 2 & 1 & 3 \\ 1 & 2 & 3 \end{vmatrix} = 1 \begin{vmatrix} 1 & 3 \\ 2 & 3 \end{vmatrix} - 3 \begin{vmatrix} 2 & 3 \\ 1 & 3 \end{vmatrix} + (-2) \begin{vmatrix} 2 & 1 \\ 1 & 2 \end{vmatrix}$$

$$= 1(3 - 6) - 3(6 - 3) - 2(4 - 1)$$

$$= -3 - 9 - 6$$

$$= -18$$

⇨ **SELF CHECK 2**   Evaluate: $\begin{vmatrix} 2 & -1 & 3 \\ 1 & 2 & -2 \\ 3 & 1 & 1 \end{vmatrix}$.

We can evaluate a 3×3 determinant by expanding it along any row or column. To determine the signs between the terms of the expansion of a 3×3 determinant, we use the following array of signs.

Array of Signs for a 3×3 Determinant		
+	−	+
−	+	−
+	−	+

The pattern above holds true for any square matrix.

PERSPECTIVE   Lewis Carroll

One of the more amusing historical anecdotes concerning matrices and determinants involves the English mathematician Charles Dodgson, also known as Lewis Carroll. The anecdote describes how England's Queen Victoria so enjoyed reading Carroll's book *Alice in Wonderland* that she requested a copy of his next publication. To her great surprise, she

received an autographed copy of a mathematics text titled *An Elementary Treatise on Determinants.* The story was repeated as fact so often that Carroll finally included an explicit disclaimer in his book *Symbolic Logic,* insisting that the incident never actually occurred.

Source: http://mathworld.wolfram.com/Determinant.html

Evaluate each determinant.

1. $\begin{vmatrix} 3 & 4 \\ 2 & 1 \end{vmatrix}$

2. $\begin{vmatrix} 3 & 4 & 2 \\ 1 & -1 & 5 \\ 1 & 2 & -2 \end{vmatrix}$

EXAMPLE 3   Evaluate $\begin{vmatrix} 1 & 3 & -2 \\ 2 & 1 & 3 \\ 1 & 2 & 3 \end{vmatrix}$ by expanding on the middle column.

Solution   This is the determinant of Example 2. To expand it along the middle column, we use the signs of the middle column of the array of signs:

$$\begin{vmatrix} 1 & 3 & -2 \\ 2 & 1 & 3 \\ 1 & 2 & 3 \end{vmatrix} = -3\begin{vmatrix} 2 & 3 \\ 1 & 3 \end{vmatrix} + 1\begin{vmatrix} 1 & -2 \\ 1 & 3 \end{vmatrix} - 2\begin{vmatrix} 1 & -2 \\ 2 & 3 \end{vmatrix}$$

$$= -3(6 - 3) + 1[3 - (-2)] - 2[3 - (-4)]$$

$$= -3(3) + 1(5) - 2(7)$$

$$= -9 + 5 - 14$$

$$= -18$$

As expected, we get the same value as in Example 2.

⇨ SELF CHECK 3   Evaluate: $\begin{vmatrix} 2 & -1 & 3 \\ 1 & 2 & 2 \\ 3 & 1 & 1 \end{vmatrix}$.

---

2   **Solve a system of linear equations using Cramer's rule.**

The method of using determinants to solve systems of equations is called **Cramer's rule,** named after the 18th-century mathematician Gabriel Cramer. To develop Cramer's rule, we consider the system

$$\begin{cases} ax + by = e \\ cx + dy = f \end{cases}$$

where x and y are variables and a, b, c, d, e, and f are constants.

ACCENT ON TECHNOLOGY

Evaluating Determinants

To use a graphing calculator to evaluate the determinant in Example 3, we first enter the matrix by pressing the **MATRIX** key, selecting EDIT, and pressing the **ENTER** key. We then enter the dimensions and the elements of the matrix to get Figure 13-11(a). We then press **2ND QUIT** to clear the screen. We then press **MATRIX**, select MATH, and press 1 to get Figure 13-11(b). Next, press **MATRIX**, select NAMES, and press 1 to get Figure 13-11(c). To get the value of the determinant, we now press **ENTER** to get Figure 13-11(d), which shows that the value of the determinant is -18.

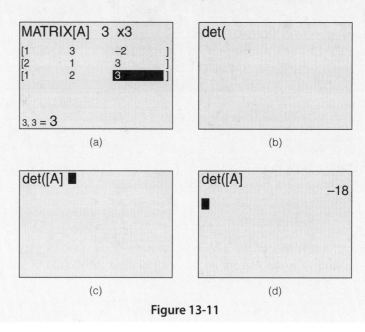

Figure 13-11

If we multiply both sides of the first equation by d and multiply both sides of the second equation by $-b$, we can add the equations and eliminate y:

$$\begin{aligned} adx + bdy &= ed \\ -bcx - bdy &= -bf \\ \hline adx - bcx &= ed - bf \end{aligned}$$

To solve for x, we use the distributive property to write $adx - bcx$ as $(ad - bc)x$ on the left side and divide each side by $ad - bc$:

$$(ad - bc)x = ed - bf$$

$$x = \frac{ed - bf}{ad - bc} \quad (ad - bc) \neq 0$$

We can find y in a similar manner. After eliminating the variable x, we get

$$y = \frac{af - ec}{ad - bc} \quad (ad - bc) \neq 0$$

Determinants provide an easy way of remembering these formulas. Note that the denominator for both x and y is

$$\begin{vmatrix} a & b \\ c & d \end{vmatrix} = ad - bc$$

Gabriel Cramer (1704–1752)

Although other mathematicians had worked with determinants, it was the work of Cramer that popularized them.

The numerators can be expressed as determinants also:

$$x = \frac{ed - bf}{ad - bc} = \frac{\begin{vmatrix} e & b \\ f & d \end{vmatrix}}{\begin{vmatrix} a & b \\ c & d \end{vmatrix}} \quad \text{and} \quad x = \frac{af - ec}{ad - bc} = \frac{\begin{vmatrix} a & e \\ c & f \end{vmatrix}}{\begin{vmatrix} a & b \\ c & d \end{vmatrix}}$$

If we compare these formulas with the original system

$$\begin{cases} ax + by = e \\ cx + dy = f \end{cases}$$

we note that in the expressions for x and y above, the denominator determinant is formed by using the coefficients a, b, c, and d of the variables in the equations. The numerator determinants are the same as the denominator determinant, except that the column of coefficients of the variable for which we are solving is replaced with the column of constants e and f.

Cramer's Rule for Two Equations in Two Variables

The solution of the system $\begin{cases} ax + by = e \\ cx + dy = f \end{cases}$ is given by

$$x = \frac{D_x}{D} \quad \text{and} \quad y = \frac{D_y}{D}$$

where $D = \begin{vmatrix} a & b \\ c & d \end{vmatrix}$, $D_x = \begin{vmatrix} e & b \\ f & d \end{vmatrix}$, and $D_y = \begin{vmatrix} a & e \\ c & f \end{vmatrix}$.

If $D \neq 0$, the system is consistent and the equations are independent.

If $D = 0$ and D_x or D_y is nonzero, the system is inconsistent.

If every determinant is 0, the system is consistent but the equations are dependent.

EXAMPLE 4 Use Cramer's rule to solve $\begin{cases} 4x - 3y = 6 \\ -2x + 5y = 4 \end{cases}$.

Solution The value of x is the quotient of two determinants. The denominator determinant is made up of the coefficients of x and y:

$$D = \begin{vmatrix} 4 & -3 \\ -2 & 5 \end{vmatrix}$$

To solve for x, we form the numerator determinant from the denominator determinant by replacing its first column (the coefficients of x) with the column of constants (6 and 4).

To solve for y, we form the numerator determinant from the denominator determinant by replacing the second column (the coefficients of y) with the column of constants (6 and 4).

To find the values of x and y, we evaluate each determinant:

$$x = \frac{D_x}{D} = \frac{\begin{vmatrix} 6 & -3 \\ 4 & 5 \end{vmatrix}}{\begin{vmatrix} 4 & -3 \\ -2 & 5 \end{vmatrix}} = \frac{6(5) - (-3)(4)}{4(5) - (-3)(-2)} = \frac{30 + 12}{20 - 6} = \frac{42}{14} = 3$$

$$y = \frac{D_y}{D} = \frac{\begin{vmatrix} 4 & 6 \\ -2 & 4 \end{vmatrix}}{\begin{vmatrix} 4 & -3 \\ -2 & 5 \end{vmatrix}} = \frac{4(4) - 6(-2)}{4(5) - (-3)(-2)} = \frac{16 + 12}{20 - 6} = \frac{28}{14} = 2$$

The solution of this system is (3, 2). Verify that $x = 3$ and $y = 2$ satisfy each equation in the given system.

⇨ **SELF CHECK 4**   Solve the system: $\begin{cases} 2x - 3y = -16 \\ 3x + 5y = 14 \end{cases}$.

EXAMPLE 5   Use Cramer's rule to solve $\begin{cases} 7x = 8 - 4y \\ 2y = 3 - \frac{7}{2}x \end{cases}$.

Solution   We multiply both sides of the second equation by 2 to eliminate the fraction and write the system in the form

$$\begin{cases} 7x + 4y = 8 \\ 7x + 4y = 6 \end{cases}$$

When we attempt to use Cramer's rule to solve this system for x, we obtain

$$x = \frac{D_x}{D} = \frac{\begin{vmatrix} 8 & 4 \\ 6 & 4 \end{vmatrix}}{\begin{vmatrix} 7 & 4 \\ 7 & 4 \end{vmatrix}} = \frac{8}{0} \quad \text{which is undefined}$$

This system is inconsistent because the denominator determinant is 0 and the numerator determinant is not 0. Since this system has no solution, its solution set is ∅.

We can see directly from the system that it is inconsistent. For any values of x and y, it is impossible that 7 times x plus 4 times y could be both 8 and 6.

⇨ **SELF CHECK 5**   Solve the system: $\begin{cases} 3x = 8 - 4y \\ y = \frac{5}{2} - \frac{3}{4}x \end{cases}$.

EXAMPLE 6   Use Cramer's rule to solve $\begin{cases} y = -3x + 1 \\ 6x + 2y = 2 \end{cases}$.

Solution   We first write the system in the form

$$\begin{cases} 3x + y = 1 \\ 6x + 2y = 2 \end{cases}$$

When we attempt to use Cramer's rule to solve this system for x, we obtain

$$x = \frac{D_x}{D} = \frac{\begin{vmatrix} 1 & 1 \\ 2 & 2 \end{vmatrix}}{\begin{vmatrix} 3 & 1 \\ 6 & 2 \end{vmatrix}} = \frac{0}{0} \quad \text{which is indeterminate.}$$

When we attempt to use Cramer's rule to solve this system for y, we obtain

$$y = \frac{D_y}{D} = \frac{\begin{vmatrix} 3 & 1 \\ 6 & 2 \end{vmatrix}}{\begin{vmatrix} 3 & 1 \\ 6 & 2 \end{vmatrix}} = \frac{0}{0} \quad \text{which is indeterminate}$$

This system is consistent and its equations are dependent because every determinant is 0. Every solution of one equation is also a solution of the other. The solution is the general ordered pair $(x, -3x + 1)$.

 **SELF CHECK 6**   Solve the system: $\begin{cases} y = 2x - 5 \\ 10x - 5y = 25 \end{cases}$.

Cramer's Rule for Three Equations in Three Variables

The solution of the system $\begin{cases} ax + by + cz = j \\ dx + ey + fz = k \\ gx + hy + iz = l \end{cases}$ is given by

$$x = \frac{D_x}{D}, \quad y = \frac{D_y}{D}, \quad \text{and} \quad z = \frac{D_z}{D}$$

where

$$D = \begin{vmatrix} a & b & c \\ d & e & f \\ g & h & i \end{vmatrix} \qquad D_x = \begin{vmatrix} j & b & c \\ k & e & f \\ l & h & i \end{vmatrix}$$

$$D_y = \begin{vmatrix} a & j & c \\ d & k & f \\ g & l & i \end{vmatrix} \qquad D_z = \begin{vmatrix} a & b & j \\ d & e & k \\ g & h & l \end{vmatrix}$$

If $D \neq 0$, the system is consistent and the equations are independent.

If $D = 0$ and D_x or D_y or D_z is nonzero, the system is inconsistent.

If every determinant is 0, the system is consistent but the equations are dependent.

EXAMPLE 7   Use Cramer's rule to solve $\begin{cases} 2x + y + 4z = 12 \\ x + 2y + 2z = 9 \\ 3x - 3y - 2z = 1 \end{cases}$.

Solution   The denominator determinant is the determinant formed by the coefficients of the variables. To form the numerator determinants, we substitute the column of constants for the coefficients of the variable to be found. We form the quotients for x, y, and z and evaluate the determinants:

$$x = \frac{D_x}{D} = \frac{\begin{vmatrix} 12 & 1 & 4 \\ 9 & 2 & 2 \\ 1 & -3 & -2 \end{vmatrix}}{\begin{vmatrix} 2 & 1 & 4 \\ 1 & 2 & 2 \\ 3 & -3 & -2 \end{vmatrix}} = \frac{12 \begin{vmatrix} 2 & 2 \\ -3 & -2 \end{vmatrix} - 1 \begin{vmatrix} 9 & 2 \\ 1 & -2 \end{vmatrix} + 4 \begin{vmatrix} 9 & 2 \\ 1 & -3 \end{vmatrix}}{2 \begin{vmatrix} 2 & 2 \\ -3 & -2 \end{vmatrix} - 1 \begin{vmatrix} 1 & 2 \\ 3 & -2 \end{vmatrix} + 4 \begin{vmatrix} 1 & 2 \\ 3 & -3 \end{vmatrix}} = \frac{12(2) - (-20) + 4(-29)}{2(2) - (-8) + 4(-9)} = \frac{-72}{-24} = 3$$

$$y = \frac{D_y}{D} = \frac{\begin{vmatrix} 2 & 12 & 4 \\ 1 & 9 & 2 \\ 3 & 1 & -2 \end{vmatrix}}{\begin{vmatrix} 2 & 1 & 4 \\ 1 & 2 & 2 \\ 3 & -3 & -2 \end{vmatrix}} = \frac{2\begin{vmatrix} 9 & 2 \\ 1 & -2 \end{vmatrix} - 12\begin{vmatrix} 1 & 2 \\ 3 & -2 \end{vmatrix} + 4\begin{vmatrix} 1 & 9 \\ 3 & 1 \end{vmatrix}}{-24} = \frac{2(-20) - 12(-8) + 4(-26)}{-24} = \frac{-48}{-24} = 2$$

$$z = \frac{D_z}{D} = \frac{\begin{vmatrix} 2 & 1 & 12 \\ 1 & 2 & 9 \\ 3 & -3 & 1 \end{vmatrix}}{\begin{vmatrix} 2 & 1 & 4 \\ 1 & 2 & 2 \\ 3 & -3 & -2 \end{vmatrix}} = \frac{2\begin{vmatrix} 2 & 9 \\ -3 & 1 \end{vmatrix} - 1\begin{vmatrix} 1 & 9 \\ 3 & 1 \end{vmatrix} + 12\begin{vmatrix} 1 & 2 \\ 3 & -3 \end{vmatrix}}{-24} = \frac{2(29) - 1(-26) + 12(-9)}{-24} = \frac{-24}{-24} = 1$$

The solution of this system is (3, 2, 1).

⇨ **SELF CHECK 7**   Solve the system: $\begin{cases} x + y + 2z = 6 \\ 2x - y + z = 9 \\ x + y - 2z = -6 \end{cases}$.

⇨ **SELF CHECK ANSWERS**   **1.** 10   **2.** 0   **3.** −20   **4.** (−2, 4)   **5.** ∅   **6.** (x, 2x − 5)   **7.** (2, −2, 3)

NOW TRY THIS

Solve for x.

1. $\begin{vmatrix} x & 2 \\ x & 3 \end{vmatrix} = 4$

2. $\begin{vmatrix} 2x & 3 \\ -5x & -3 \end{vmatrix} = 10(x - 1)$

3. $\begin{vmatrix} x + 4 & 3 \\ 2x - 5 & 2 \end{vmatrix} = 2x + 5$

4. $\begin{vmatrix} 2 & x & -1 \\ 1 & 2x & 4 \\ -4 & x & 1 \end{vmatrix} = 30$

13.4 EXERCISES

WARM-UPS

Evaluate each determinant.

1. $\begin{vmatrix} 2 & 1 \\ 1 & 1 \end{vmatrix}$

2. $\begin{vmatrix} 0 & 2 \\ 1 & 1 \end{vmatrix}$

3. $\begin{vmatrix} 0 & 1 \\ 0 & 1 \end{vmatrix}$

When using Cramer's rule to solve the system $\begin{cases} x + 2y = 5 \\ 2x - y = 4 \end{cases}$,

4. Set up the denominator determinant for x.

5. Set up the numerator determinant for x.

6. Set up the numerator determinant for y.

REVIEW *Solve each equation.*

7. $3(x + 2) - (2 - x) = x - 5$

8. $\frac{3}{7}x = 2(x + 11)$

9. $\frac{5}{3}(5x + 6) - 10 = 0$

10. $5 - 3(2x - 1) = 2(4 + 3x) - 24$

VOCABULARY AND CONCEPTS *Fill in the blanks.*

11. A determinant is a _____ that is associated with a _____ matrix.

12. The value of $\begin{vmatrix} a & b \\ c & d \end{vmatrix}$ is _____.

13. The minor of b_1 in $\begin{vmatrix} a_1 & b_1 & c_1 \\ a_2 & b_2 & c_2 \\ a_3 & b_3 & c_3 \end{vmatrix}$ is _____.

14. We can evaluate a determinant by expanding it along any _____ or _____.

15. The method of solving a system of linear equations using determinants is called _____.

16. The set up for the denominator determinant for the value of x in the system $\begin{cases} 3x + 4y = 7 \\ 2x - 3y = 5 \end{cases}$ is _____.

17. If $D \neq 0$, then the system is _____ and the equations are _____.

18. If the denominator determinant for y in a system of equations is zero, the equations of the system are _____ or the system is _____.

GUIDED PRACTICE

Evaluate each determinant. See Example 1. (Objective 1)

19. $\begin{vmatrix} 2 & 3 \\ -2 & 1 \end{vmatrix}$

20. $\begin{vmatrix} 3 & -2 \\ -2 & 4 \end{vmatrix}$

21. $\begin{vmatrix} -1 & 2 \\ 3 & -4 \end{vmatrix}$

22. $\begin{vmatrix} -1 & -2 \\ -3 & -4 \end{vmatrix}$

Evaluate each determinant. See Examples 2–3. (Objective 1)

23. $\begin{vmatrix} 1 & 0 & 1 \\ 0 & 1 & 0 \\ 1 & 1 & 1 \end{vmatrix}$

24. $\begin{vmatrix} 1 & 2 & 0 \\ 0 & 1 & 2 \\ 0 & 0 & 1 \end{vmatrix}$

25. $\begin{vmatrix} -1 & 2 & 1 \\ 2 & 1 & -3 \\ 1 & 1 & 1 \end{vmatrix}$

26. $\begin{vmatrix} 1 & 2 & 3 \\ 1 & 2 & 3 \\ 1 & 2 & 3 \end{vmatrix}$

27. $\begin{vmatrix} 1 & -2 & 3 \\ -2 & 1 & 1 \\ -3 & -2 & 1 \end{vmatrix}$

28. $\begin{vmatrix} 1 & 1 & 2 \\ 2 & 1 & -2 \\ 3 & 1 & 3 \end{vmatrix}$

29. $\begin{vmatrix} 1 & 2 & 3 \\ 4 & 5 & 6 \\ 7 & 8 & 9 \end{vmatrix}$

30. $\begin{vmatrix} 1 & 4 & 7 \\ 2 & 5 & 8 \\ 3 & 6 & 9 \end{vmatrix}$

Use Cramer's rule to solve each system, if possible. If the equations of the system are dependent, give a general solution. See Examples 4–6. (Objective 2)

31. $\begin{cases} 2x + y = 1 \\ x - 2y = -7 \end{cases}$

32. $\begin{cases} 3x - y = -3 \\ 2x + y = -7 \end{cases}$

33. $\begin{cases} x + y = 6 \\ x - y = 2 \end{cases}$

34. $\begin{cases} x - y = 4 \\ 2x + y = 5 \end{cases}$

35. $\begin{cases} 5x = 3y - 7 \\ y = \dfrac{5x - 7}{3} \end{cases}$

36. $\begin{cases} y = \dfrac{11 - 3x}{2} \\ x = \dfrac{11 - 4y}{6} \end{cases}$

37. $\begin{cases} 2x + 3y = 9 \\ y = -\dfrac{2}{3}x + 3 \end{cases}$

38. $\begin{cases} x = \dfrac{12 - 6y}{5} \\ y = \dfrac{24 - 10x}{12} \end{cases}$

Use Cramer's rule to solve each system, if possible. If the equations of the system are dependent, give a general solution. See Example 7. (Objective 2)

39. $\begin{cases} x + y + z = 4 \\ x + y - z = 0 \\ x - y + z = 2 \end{cases}$

40. $\begin{cases} x + y + z = 4 \\ x - y + z = 2 \\ x - y - z = 0 \end{cases}$

41. $\begin{cases} x + y + 2z = 7 \\ x + 2y + z = 8 \\ 2x + y + z = 9 \end{cases}$

42. $\begin{cases} x + 2y + 2z = 10 \\ 2x + y + 2z = 9 \\ 2x + 2y + z = 1 \end{cases}$

43. $\begin{cases} 2x + y - z = 1 \\ x + 2y + 2z = 2 \\ 4x + 5y + 3z = 3 \end{cases}$

44. $\begin{cases} 2x - y + 4z + 2 = 0 \\ 5x + 8y + 7z = -8 \\ x + 3y + z + 3 = 0 \end{cases}$

45. $\begin{cases} 2x + 3y + 4z = 6 \\ 2x - 3y - 4z = -4 \\ 4x + 6y + 8z = 12 \end{cases}$

46. $\begin{cases} x - 3y + 4z - 2 = 0 \\ 2x + y + 2z - 3 = 0 \\ 4x - 5y + 10z - 7 = 0 \end{cases}$

ADDITIONAL PRACTICE

Evaluate each determinant.

47. $\begin{vmatrix} x & y \\ y & x \end{vmatrix}$

48. $\begin{vmatrix} x + y & y - x \\ x & y \end{vmatrix}$

49. $\begin{vmatrix} a & 2a & -a \\ 2 & -1 & 3 \\ 1 & 2 & -3 \end{vmatrix}$

50. $\begin{vmatrix} 1 & 2b & -3 \\ 2 & -b & 2 \\ 1 & 3b & 1 \end{vmatrix}$

51. $\begin{vmatrix} 1 & a & b \\ 1 & 2a & 2b \\ 1 & 3a & 3b \end{vmatrix}$

52. $\begin{vmatrix} a & b & c \\ 0 & b & c \\ 0 & 0 & c \end{vmatrix}$

 Use a graphing calculator to evaluate each determinant.

53. $\begin{bmatrix} 2 & -3 & 4 \\ -1 & 2 & 4 \\ 3 & -3 & 1 \end{bmatrix}$

54. $\begin{bmatrix} -3 & 2 & -5 \\ 3 & -2 & 6 \\ 1 & -3 & 4 \end{bmatrix}$

55. $\begin{bmatrix} 2 & 1 & -3 \\ -2 & 2 & 4 \\ 1 & -2 & 2 \end{bmatrix}$

56. $\begin{bmatrix} 4 & 2 & -3 \\ 2 & -5 & 6 \\ 2 & 5 & -2 \end{bmatrix}$

Use Cramer's rule to solve each system.

57. $\begin{cases} 2x + 3y = 0 \\ 4x - 6y = -4 \end{cases}$

58. $\begin{cases} 4x - 3y = -1 \\ 8x + 3y = 4 \end{cases}$

59. $\begin{cases} y = \dfrac{-2x + 1}{3} \\ 3x - 2y = 8 \end{cases}$

60. $\begin{cases} 2x + 3y = -1 \\ x = \dfrac{y - 9}{4} \end{cases}$

61. $\begin{cases} x = \dfrac{5y - 4}{2} \\ y = \dfrac{3x - 1}{5} \end{cases}$

62. $\begin{cases} y = \dfrac{1 - 5x}{2} \\ x = \dfrac{3y + 10}{4} \end{cases}$

63. $\begin{cases} 2x + y + z = 5 \\ x - 2y + 3z = 10 \\ x + y - 4z = -3 \end{cases}$

64. $\begin{cases} 3x + 2y - z = -8 \\ 2x - y + 7z = 10 \\ 2x + 2y - 3z = -10 \end{cases}$

65. $\begin{cases} 4x + 3z = 4 \\ 2y - 6z = -1 \\ 8x + 4y + 3z = 9 \end{cases}$

66. $\begin{cases} \frac{1}{2}x + y + z + \frac{3}{2} = 0 \\ x + \frac{1}{2}y + z - \frac{1}{2} = 0 \\ x + y + \frac{1}{2}z + \frac{1}{2} = 0 \end{cases}$

67. $\begin{cases} x + y = 1 \\ \frac{1}{2}y + z = \frac{5}{2} \\ x - z = -3 \end{cases}$

68. $\begin{cases} 3x + 4y + 14z = 7 \\ -\frac{1}{2}x - y + 2z = \frac{3}{2} \\ x + \frac{3}{2}y + \frac{5}{2}z = 1 \end{cases}$

Solve the equation.

69. $\begin{vmatrix} x & 1 \\ 3 & 2 \end{vmatrix} = 1$

70. $\begin{vmatrix} x & -x \\ 2 & -3 \end{vmatrix} = -5$

71. $\begin{vmatrix} x & -2 \\ 3 & 1 \end{vmatrix} = \begin{vmatrix} 4 & 2 \\ x & 3 \end{vmatrix}$

72. $\begin{vmatrix} x & 3 \\ x & 2 \end{vmatrix} = \begin{vmatrix} 3 & 2 \\ 1 & 1 \end{vmatrix}$

APPLICATIONS

73. Signaling A system of sending signals uses two flags held in various positions to represent letters of the alphabet. The illustration shows how the letter U is signaled. Find x and y, if y is to be 30° more than x.

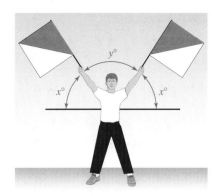

74. Inventories The table shows an end-of-the-year inventory report for a warehouse that supplies electronics stores. If the warehouse stocks two models of cordless telephones, one valued at $67 and the other at $100, how many of each model of phone did the warehouse have at the time of the inventory?

Item	Number	Merchandise value
Television	800	$1,005,450
Radios	200	$15,785
Cordless phones	360	$29,400

75. Investing A student wants to average a 6.6% return by investing $20,000 in the three stocks listed in the table. Because HiTech is considered to be a high-risk investment, he wants to invest three times as much in SaveTel and HiGas combined as he invests in HiTech. How much should he invest in each stock?

Stock	Rate of return
HiTech	10%
SaveTel	5%
HiGas	6%

76. Investing See the table. A woman wants to average a $7\frac{1}{3}\%$ return by investing $30,000 in three certificates of deposit. She wants to invest five times as much in the 8% CD as in the 6% CD. How much should she invest in each CD?

Type of CD	Rate of return
12 month	6%
24 month	7%
36 month	8%

WRITING ABOUT MATH

77. Explain how to find the minor of an element of a determinant.

78. Explain how to find x when solving a system of linear equations by Cramer's rule.

SOMETHING TO THINK ABOUT

79. Show that

$$\begin{vmatrix} x & y & 1 \\ -2 & 3 & 1 \\ 3 & 5 & 1 \end{vmatrix} = 0$$

is the equation of the line passing through $(-2, 3)$ and $(3, 5)$.

80. Show that

$$\frac{1}{2} \begin{vmatrix} 0 & 0 & 1 \\ 3 & 0 & 1 \\ 0 & 4 & 1 \end{vmatrix}$$

is the area of the triangle with vertices at $(0, 0)$, $(3, 0)$, and $(0, 4)$.

Determinants with more than 3 rows and 3 columns can be evaluated by expanding them by minors. The sign array for a 4×4 *determinant is*

$$\begin{matrix} + & - & + & - \\ - & + & - & + \\ + & - & + & - \\ - & + & - & + \end{matrix}$$

Evaluate each determinant.

81. $\begin{vmatrix} 1 & 0 & 2 & 1 \\ 2 & 1 & 1 & 3 \\ 1 & 1 & 1 & 1 \\ 2 & 1 & 1 & 1 \end{vmatrix}$

82. $\begin{vmatrix} 1 & 2 & -1 & 1 \\ -2 & 1 & 3 & -1 \\ 0 & 1 & 1 & 2 \\ 2 & 0 & 3 & 1 \end{vmatrix}$

SECTION 13.5
Solving Systems of Equations and Inequalities Containing One or More Second-Degree Terms

Objectives

1 Solve a system of equations containing one or more second-degree terms by graphing.

2 Solve a system of equations containing one or more second-degree terms by substitution.

3 Solve a system of equations containing one or more second-degree terms by elimination.

4 Solve a system of inequalities containing one or more second-degree terms.

Getting Ready

Add the left sides and the right sides of the following equations.

1. $3x^2 + 3y^2 = 12$
$\underline{4x^2 - 3y^2 = 32}$

2. $-12x^2 - 5y^2 = -17$
$\underline{12x^2 + 2y^2 = 25}$

We now discuss ways to solve systems of two equations in two variables where at least one of the equations is of second degree.

1 **Solve a system of equations containing one or more second-degree terms by graphing.**

EXAMPLE 1 Solve $\begin{cases} x^2 + y^2 = 25 \\ 2x + y = 10 \end{cases}$ by graphing.

Solution The graph of $x^2 + y^2 = 25$ is a circle with center at the origin and radius of 5. The graph of $2x + y = 10$ is a line. Depending on whether the line is a secant (intersecting the circle at two points) or a tangent (intersecting the circle at one point) or does not intersect the circle at all, there are two, one, or no solutions to the system, respectively.

After graphing the circle and the line, as shown in Figure 13-12, we see that there are two intersection points $(3, 4)$ and $(5, 0)$. These are the solutions of the system.

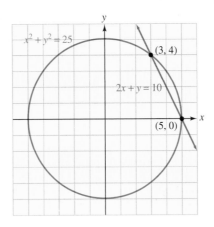

Figure 13-12

⇨ **SELF CHECK 1** Solve: $\begin{cases} x^2 + y^2 = 13 \\ y = -\frac{1}{5}x + \frac{13}{5} \end{cases}$.

ACCENT ON TECHNOLOGY

Solving Systems of Equations

To solve Example 1 with a graphing calculator, we graph the circle and the line on one set of coordinate axes (see Figure 13-13(a)). We then find approximations of the coordinates of the intersection points of the graphs (see Figure 13-13(b) and Figure 13-13(c)).

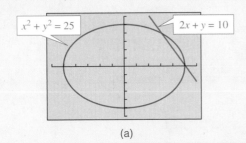

(a)

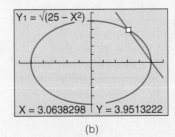

X = 3.0638298   Y = 3.9513222

(b)

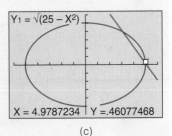

X = 4.9787234   Y = .46077468

(c)

Figure 13-13

We can find the exact answers by using the INTERSECT feature found in the CALC menu.

2 Solve a system of equations containing one or more second-degree terms by substitution.

Algebraic methods also can be used to solve systems of equations.

EXAMPLE 2 Solve using substitution: $\begin{cases} x^2 + y^2 = 25 \\ 2x + y = 10 \end{cases}$.

Solution This system has one second-degree equation and one first-degree equation. The first equation is the equation of a circle and the second equation is the equation of a line. Since a line can intersect a circle in 0, 1, or 2 points, this system can have 0, 1, or 2 solutions.

We can solve the system by substitution. Solving the linear equation for y gives

$$2x + y = 10$$
(1) $$y = -2x + 10$$

We can substitute $-2x + 10$ for y in the second-degree equation and solve the resulting quadratic equation for x:

$$x^2 + y^2 = 25$$
$$x^2 + (-2x + 10)^2 = 25$$
$$x^2 + 4x^2 - 40x + 100 = 25 \qquad (-2x + 10)(-2x + 10) = 4x^2 - 40x + 100$$
$$5x^2 - 40x + 75 = 0 \qquad \text{Combine like terms and subtract 25 from both sides.}$$
$$x^2 - 8x + 15 = 0 \qquad \text{Divide both sides by 5.}$$
$$(x - 5)(x - 3) = 0 \qquad \text{Factor } x^2 - 8x + 15.$$
$$x - 5 = 0 \quad \text{or} \quad x - 3 = 0 \qquad \text{Set each factor equal to 0.}$$
$$x = 5 \qquad \qquad x = 3$$

COMMENT Note that if we substitute 3 into the first equation, $x^2 + y^2 = 25$, we will get an ordered pair $(3, -4)$ that does not satisfy the other, $2x + y = 10$.

If we substitute 5 for x in Equation 1, we get $y = 0$. If we substitute 3 for x in Equation 1, we get $y = 4$. The two solutions are $(5, 0)$ and $(3, 4)$.

⇨ **SELF CHECK 2** Solve by substitution: $\begin{cases} x^2 + y^2 = 13 \\ y = -\frac{1}{5}x + \frac{13}{5} \end{cases}$.

EXAMPLE 3 Solve using substitution: $\begin{cases} 4x^2 + 9y^2 = 5 \\ y = x^2 \end{cases}$.

Solution This system has two second-degree equations. The first is the equation of an ellipse and the second is the equation of a parabola. Since an ellipse and a parabola can intersect in 0, 1, 2, 3, or 4 points, this system can have 0, 1, 2, 3, or 4 solutions.

We can solve this system by substitution.

$$4x^2 + 9y^2 = 5$$
$$4y + 9y^2 = 5 \qquad \text{Substitute } y \text{ for } x^2.$$
$$9y^2 + 4y - 5 = 0 \qquad \text{Subtract 5 from both sides.}$$
$$(9y - 5)(y + 1) = 0 \qquad \text{Factor } 9y^2 + 4y - 5.$$
$$9y - 5 = 0 \quad \text{or} \quad y + 1 = 0 \qquad \text{Set each factor equal to 0.}$$
$$y = \frac{5}{9} \qquad \qquad y = -1$$

Since $y = x^2$, the values of x are found by solving the equations

$$x^2 = \frac{5}{9} \quad \text{and} \quad x^2 = -1$$

Because $x^2 = -1$ has no real solutions, this possibility is discarded. The solutions of $x^2 = \frac{5}{9}$ are

$$x = \frac{\sqrt{5}}{3} \quad \text{or} \quad x = -\frac{\sqrt{5}}{3}$$

The solutions of the system are $\left(\frac{\sqrt{5}}{3}, \frac{5}{9} \right)$ and $\left(-\frac{\sqrt{5}}{3}, \frac{5}{9} \right)$.

⇨ **SELF CHECK 3**   Solve using substitution: $\begin{cases} x^2 + y^2 = 20 \\ y = x^2 \end{cases}$.

3   **Solve a system of equations containing one or more second-degree terms by elimination.**

EXAMPLE 4   Solve by elimination: $\begin{cases} 3x^2 + 2y^2 = 36 \\ 4x^2 - y^2 = 4 \end{cases}$.

Solution   This system has two second-degree equations. The first equation is the equation of an ellipse and the second equation is the equation of a hyperbola. Since an ellipse and a hyperbola can intersect in 0, 1, 2, 3, or 4 points, this system can have 0, 1, 2, 3, or 4 solutions.

Since both equations are in the form $ax^2 + by^2 = c$, we can solve the system by elimination. To do so, we can copy the first equation and multiply the second equation by 2 to obtain the equivalent system

$$\begin{cases} 3x^2 + 2y^2 = 36 \\ 8x^2 - 2y^2 = 8 \end{cases}$$

We add the equations to eliminate y and solve the resulting equation for x:

$$11x^2 = 44$$
$$x^2 = 4$$
$$x = 2 \quad \text{or} \quad x = -2$$

To find y, we substitute 2 for x and then -2 for x in the first equation and proceed as follows:

For x = 2	*For x = -2*
$3x^2 + 2y^2 = 36$	$3x^2 + 2y^2 = 36$
$3(2)^2 + 2y^2 = 36$	$3(-2)^2 + 2y^2 = 36$
$12 + 2y^2 = 36$	$12 + 2y^2 = 36$
$2y^2 = 24$	$2y^2 = 24$
$y^2 = 12$	$y^2 = 12$
$y = +\sqrt{12} \quad \text{or} \quad y = -\sqrt{12}$	$y = +\sqrt{12} \quad \text{or} \quad y = -\sqrt{12}$
$y = 2\sqrt{3} \quad \bigm| \quad y = -2\sqrt{3}$	$y = 2\sqrt{3} \quad \bigm| \quad y = -2\sqrt{3}$

The four solutions of this system are

$$\left(2, 2\sqrt{3}\right), \left(2, -2\sqrt{3}\right), \left(-2, 2\sqrt{3}\right), \quad \text{and} \quad \left(-2, -2\sqrt{3}\right)$$

⇨ **SELF CHECK 4**   Solve: $\begin{cases} x^2 + 4y^2 = 16 \\ x^2 - y^2 = 1 \end{cases}$.

4   Solve a system of inequalities containing one or more second-degree terms.

EXAMPLE 5   Graph the solution set of the system: $\begin{cases} y < x^2 \\ y > \dfrac{x^2}{4} - 2 \end{cases}$.

Solution   The graph of $y = x^2$ is the parabola shown in Figure 13-14, which opens upward and has its vertex at the origin. Because equality is not included, the parabola is drawn with a dashed line. The points with coordinates that satisfy the inequality $y < x^2$ are those points below the parabola.

The graph of $y > \dfrac{x^2}{4} - 2$ is a parabola opening upward, with vertex at $(0, -2)$. However, this time the points with coordinates that satisfy the inequality are those points above the parabola. Because equality is not included, the parabola is drawn with a dashed line.

The graph of the solution set of the system will be the area between the parabolas.

$y = x^2$

x	y	(x, y)
0	0	$(0, 0)$
1	1	$(1, 1)$
−1	1	$(−1, 1)$
2	4	$(2, 4)$
−2	4	$(−2, 4)$

$y = \dfrac{x^2}{4} - 2$

x	y	(x, y)
0	−2	$(0, -2)$
2	−1	$(2, -1)$
−2	−1	$(−2, -1)$
4	2	$(4, 2)$
−4	2	$(−4, 2)$

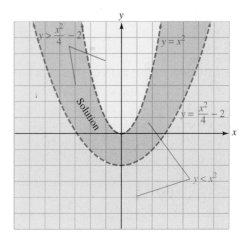

Figure 13-14

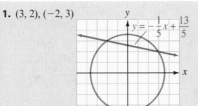

NOW TRY THIS

1. Solve by substitution. $\begin{cases} x^2 - y^2 = 4 \\ 9x^2 + 16y^2 = 144 \end{cases}$

13.5 EXERCISES

WARM-UPS   *Give the possible number of solutions of a system when the graphs of the equations are*

1. A line and a parabola   **2.** A line and a hyperbola

3. A circle and a parabola   **4.** A circle and a hyperbola

REVIEW   *Simplify each radical expression. Assume that all variables represent positive numbers.*

5. $\sqrt{200x^2} - 3\sqrt{98x^2}$

6. $a\sqrt{112a} - 5\sqrt{175a^3}$

7. $\dfrac{3t\sqrt{2t} - 2\sqrt{2t^3}}{\sqrt{18t} - \sqrt{2t}}$

8. $\sqrt[3]{\dfrac{x}{4}} + \sqrt[3]{\dfrac{x}{32}} - \sqrt[3]{\dfrac{x}{500}}$

VOCABULARY AND CONCEPTS   *Fill in the blanks.*

9. We can solve systems of equations by _____, elimination (addition), or _____.

10. A line can intersect an ellipse in at most ____ points.

11. A parabola can intersect an ellipse in at most ____ points.

12. An ellipse can intersect a hyperbola in at most ____ points.

GUIDED PRACTICE

Solve each system of equations by graphing. **See Example 1.** (Objective 1)

13. $\begin{cases} 8x^2 + 32y^2 = 256 \\ x = 2y \end{cases}$

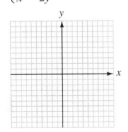

14. $\begin{cases} x^2 + y^2 = 2 \\ x + y = 2 \end{cases}$

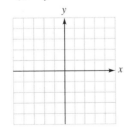

15. $\begin{cases} x^2 + y^2 = 10 \\ y = 3x^2 \end{cases}$

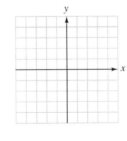

16. $\begin{cases} x^2 + y^2 = 5 \\ x + y = 3 \end{cases}$

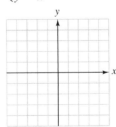

17. $\begin{cases} x^2 + y^2 = 25 \\ 12x^2 + 64y^2 = 768 \end{cases}$

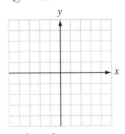

18. $\begin{cases} x^2 + y^2 = 13 \\ y = x^2 - 1 \end{cases}$

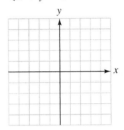

19. $\begin{cases} x^2 - 13 = -y^2 \\ y = 2x - 4 \end{cases}$

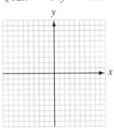

20. $\begin{cases} x^2 + y^2 = 20 \\ y = x^2 \end{cases}$

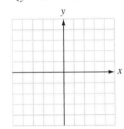

Solve each system by substitution. **See Examples 2–3.** (Objective 2)

21. $\begin{cases} 25x^2 + 9y^2 = 225 \\ 5x + 3y = 15 \end{cases}$

22. $\begin{cases} x^2 + y^2 = 20 \\ y = x^2 \end{cases}$

23. $\begin{cases} x^2 + y^2 = 2 \\ x + y = 2 \end{cases}$

24. $\begin{cases} x^2 + y^2 = 36 \\ 49x^2 + 36y^2 = 1,764 \end{cases}$

25. $\begin{cases} x^2 + y^2 = 5 \\ x + y = 3 \end{cases}$

26. $\begin{cases} x^2 - x - y = 2 \\ 4x - 3y = 0 \end{cases}$

27. $\begin{cases} x^2 + y^2 = 13 \\ y = x^2 - 1 \end{cases}$

28. $\begin{cases} x^2 + y^2 = 25 \\ 2x^2 - 3y^2 = 5 \end{cases}$

Solve each system by elimination. **See Example 4. (Objective 3)**

29. $\begin{cases} x^2 + y^2 = 30 \\ y = x^2 \end{cases}$

30. $\begin{cases} 9x^2 - 7y^2 = 81 \\ x^2 + y^2 = 9 \end{cases}$

31. $\begin{cases} x^2 + y^2 = 13 \\ x^2 - y^2 = 5 \end{cases}$

32. $\begin{cases} 2x^2 + y^2 = 6 \\ x^2 - y^2 = 3 \end{cases}$

33. $\begin{cases} y = x^2 - 4 \\ x^2 - y^2 = -16 \end{cases}$

34. $\begin{cases} 6x^2 + 8y^2 = 182 \\ 8x^2 - 3y^2 = 24 \end{cases}$

35. $\begin{cases} x^2 - y^2 = -5 \\ 3x^2 + 2y^2 = 30 \end{cases}$

36. $\begin{cases} x^2 + y^2 = 10 \\ 2x^2 - 3y^2 = 5 \end{cases}$

Graph the solution set of each system of inequalities. **See Example 5. (Objective 4)**

37. $\begin{cases} 2x - y > 4 \\ y < -x^2 + 2 \end{cases}$

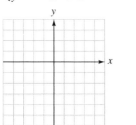

38. $\begin{cases} x \le y^2 \\ y \ge x \end{cases}$

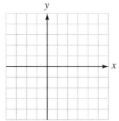

39. $\begin{cases} y > x^2 - 4 \\ y < -x^2 + 4 \end{cases}$

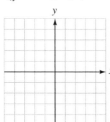

40. $\begin{cases} x \ge y^2 \\ y \ge x^2 \end{cases}$

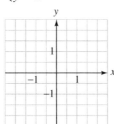

ADDITIONAL PRACTICE   *Solve using any method (including a graphing calculator).*

41. $\begin{cases} x^2 + y^2 = 5 \\ y = x + 1 \end{cases}$

42. $\begin{cases} x^2 - y^2 = -5 \\ 3x^2 + 2y^2 = 30 \end{cases}$

43. $\begin{cases} x^2 + y^2 = 20 \\ x^2 - y^2 = -12 \end{cases}$

44. $\begin{cases} xy = -\frac{9}{2} \\ 3x + 2y = 6 \end{cases}$

45. $\begin{cases} y^2 = 40 - x^2 \\ y = x^2 - 10 \end{cases}$

46. $\begin{cases} x^2 - 6x - y = -5 \\ x^2 - 6x + y = -5 \end{cases}$

47. $\begin{cases} \frac{1}{x} + \frac{2}{y} = 1 \\ \frac{2}{x} - \frac{1}{y} = \frac{1}{3} \end{cases}$

48. $\begin{cases} \frac{1}{x} + \frac{3}{y} = 4 \\ \frac{2}{x} - \frac{1}{y} = 7 \end{cases}$

49. $\begin{cases} 3y^2 = xy \\ 2x^2 + xy - 84 = 0 \end{cases}$

50. $\begin{cases} \frac{1}{x} + \frac{1}{y} = 5 \\ \frac{1}{x} - \frac{1}{y} = -3 \end{cases}$

51. $\begin{cases} xy = \frac{1}{6} \\ y + x = 5xy \end{cases}$

52. $\begin{cases} xy = \frac{1}{12} \\ y + x = 7xy \end{cases}$

APPLICATIONS   *Use a graphing calculator to help solve each application problem.*

53. Integer problem   The product of two integers is 32, and their sum is 12. Find the integers.

54. Number problem   The sum of the squares of two numbers is 221, and the sum of the numbers is 9. Find the numbers.

55. Geometry   The area of a rectangle is 63 square centimeters, and its perimeter is 32 centimeters. Find the dimensions of the rectangle.

56. Investing money   Grant receives $225 annual income from one investment. Jeff invested $500 more than Grant, but at an annual rate of 1% less. Jeff's annual income is $240. What is the amount and rate of Grant's investment?

57. Investing money   Carol receives $67.50 annual income from one investment. Juan invested $150 more than Carol at an annual rate of $1\frac{1}{2}$% more. Juan's annual income is $94.50. What is the amount and rate of Carol's investment?   (*Hint:* There are two answers.)

58. Artillery The shell fired from the base of the hill follows the parabolic path $y = -\frac{1}{6}x^2 + 2x$ with distances measured in miles. The hill has a slope of $\frac{1}{3}$. How far from the gun is the point of impact? (*Hint:* Find the coordinates of the point and then the distance.)

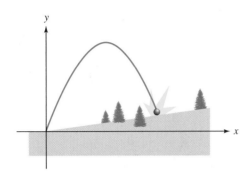

59. Driving rates Jim drove 306 miles. Jim's brother made the same trip at a speed 17 mph slower than Jim did and required an extra $1\frac{1}{2}$ hours. What was Jim's rate and time?

WRITING ABOUT MATH

60. Describe the benefits of the graphical method for solving a system of equations.

61. Describe the drawbacks of the graphical method.

SOMETHING TO THINK ABOUT

62. The graphs of the two independent equations of a system are parabolas. How many solutions might the system have?

63. The graphs of the two independent equations of a system are hyperbolas. How many solutions might the system have?

PROJECTS

Project 1

In this project, you will explore two of the many uses of determinants. In the first, you will discover that the equation of a line can be written as a determinant equation. If you are given the coordinates of two fixed points, you can use a determinant to write the equation of the line passing through them.

■ The equation of the line passing through the points $P(2, 3)$ and $Q(-1, 4)$ is

$$\begin{vmatrix} x & y & 1 \\ 2 & 3 & 1 \\ -1 & 4 & 1 \end{vmatrix} = 0$$

Verify this by expanding the determinant and graphing the resulting equation.

■ In general, the **two-point form** of the equation of the line passing through the points $P(x_1, y_1)$ and $Q(x_2, y_2)$ is

$$\begin{vmatrix} x & y & 1 \\ x_1 & y_1 & 1 \\ x_2 & y_2 & 1 \end{vmatrix} = 0$$

Find the equation of the line passing through $P(-4, 5)$ and $Q(1, -3)$.

■ Does this equation still work if the x-coordinates of the two points are equal? (For then the line would be vertical and therefore have no defined slope.)

As a second application, the formula for the area of a triangle can be written as a determinant.

■ The vertices of the triangle in Illustration 1 are $A(-3, -2)$, $B(4, -2)$, and $C(4, 4)$. Clearly, triangle ABC is a right triangle, and it is easy to find its area by the formula $A = \frac{1}{2}bh$. Show that the area is also given by

$$A = \frac{1}{2}\begin{vmatrix} -3 & -2 & 1 \\ 4 & -2 & 1 \\ 4 & 4 & 1 \end{vmatrix}$$

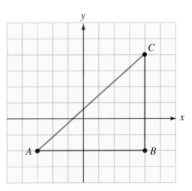

ILLUSTRATION 1

The formula works for any triangle, not just right triangles. The area of the triangle with vertices $A(x_1, y_1)$, $B(x_2, y_2)$, and $C(x_3, y_3)$ is

$$A = \frac{1}{2} \begin{vmatrix} x_1 & y_1 & 1 \\ x_2 & y_2 & 1 \\ x_3 & y_3 & 1 \end{vmatrix}$$

Project 2

Before recommending traffic controls for the intersection of the two one-way streets shown in Illustration 2, a traffic engineer places counters across the roads to record traffic flow. The illustration shows the number of vehicles passing each of the four counters during one hour. To find the number of vehicles passing straight through the intersection and the number that turn from one road to the other, refer to the illustration and assign the following variables.

Let L represent the number of vehicles turning left.

Let R represent the number of vehicles turning right.

Let N represent the number of vehicles headed north.

Let E represent the number of vehicles headed east.

Because the counter at A counts the total number of vehicles headed east and turning left, we have the equation

$L + E = 250$

From the data, explain why we can form the following system of equations:

$$\begin{aligned} L \quad\ + E &= 250 \\ R \qquad\quad &= 90 \\ R \quad + E &= 275 \\ R + N \qquad &= 340 \end{aligned}$$

Solve the system and interpret the results.

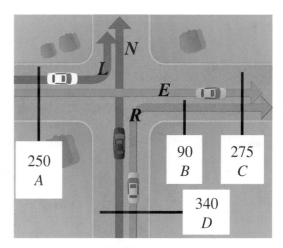

ILLUSTRATION 2

Exercise The intersection of Marsh Street and one-way Fleet Avenue has three counters to record the traffic, as shown in Illustration 3.

1. Find E, the number of vehicles passing through the intersection headed east.

2. Find S, the number of vehicles turning south.

3. Find N, the number of northbound vehicles turning east.

4. The traffic engineer suspects that the counters are in error. Why?

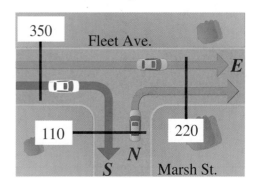

ILLUSTRATION 3

Chapter 13   REVIEW

SECTION 13.1   Solving Systems of Two Linear Equations or Inequalities in Two Variables

DEFINITIONS AND CONCEPTS	EXAMPLES
In a graph of two equations, each with two variables: If the lines are different and intersect, the equations are *independent* and the system is *consistent*. **One solution exists.** If the lines are different and parallel, the equations are *independent* and the system is *inconsistent*. **No solution exists.** If the lines coincide (are the same), the equations are *dependent* and the system is *consistent*. **Infinitely many solutions exist.**	Solve each system by graphing. **a.** $\begin{cases} x + y = 6 \\ x - y = 2 \end{cases}$ **b.** $\begin{cases} 2x + y = 6 \\ y = -2x - 3 \end{cases}$ 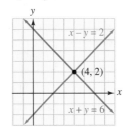 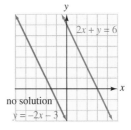 The solution is (4, 2). There are no solutions. **c.** $\begin{cases} x - 3y = 6 \\ y = \dfrac{1}{3}x - 2 \end{cases}$ 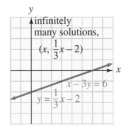 There are infinitely many solutions of the form $\left(x, \dfrac{1}{3}x - 2\right)$.
Strategy for solving a system by substitution: 1. If necessary, solve one equation for one of its variables. 2. Substitute the resulting expression for the variable obtained in Step 1 into the other equation and solve the equation. 3. Find the value of the other variable by substituting the value of the variable found in Step 2 into any equation containing both variables. 4. State the solution. 5. Check the solution in both of the original equations.	Solve by substitution: $\begin{cases} x = 3y - 9 \\ 2x - y = 2 \end{cases}$. Since the first equation is already solved for x, we will substitute its right side for x in the second equation. $2x - y = 2$ $2(3y - 9) - y = 2$ $6y - 18 - y = 2$ Remove parentheses. $5y - 18 = 2$ Combine like terms. $5y = 20$ Add 18 to both sides. $y = 4$ Divide both sides by 5. To find x, we can substitute 4 for y in the first equation. $x = 3(4) - 9$ $x = 3$ The solution is (3, 4).

Strategy for solving a system by elimination:

1. If necessary, write both equations of the system in general form.

2. If necessary, multiply the terms of one or both equations by constants chosen to make the coefficients of one of the variables differ only in sign.

3. Add the equations and solve the resulting equation, if possible.

4. Substitute the value obtained in Step 3 into either of the original equations and solve for the remaining variable.

5. State the solution obtained in Steps 3 and 4.

6. Check the solution in both of the original equations.

Solve by elimination: $\begin{cases} 2x - 3y = 8 \\ x + 2y = 4 \end{cases}$.

To eliminate x, we multiply the second equation by -2 and add the result to the first equation.

$$\begin{array}{rcl} 2x - 3y &=& 8 \\ -2x - 4y &=& -8 \\ \hline -7y &=& 0 \\ y &=& 0 \end{array}$$ Divide both sides by -7.

To find x, we can substitute 0 for y in the first equation.

$$\begin{aligned} 2x - 3y &= 8 \\ 2x - 3(0) &= 8 \quad \text{Substitute 0 for } y. \\ 2x &= 8 \quad \text{Simplify.} \\ x &= 4 \quad \text{Divide both sides by 2.} \end{aligned}$$

The solution is $(4, 0)$.

REVIEW EXERCISES

Solve each system by the graphing method.

1. $\begin{cases} 2x + y = 11 \\ -x + 2y = 7 \end{cases}$

2. $\begin{cases} 3x + 2y = 0 \\ 2x - 3y = -13 \end{cases}$

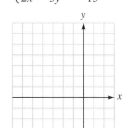

3. $\begin{cases} \frac{1}{2}x + \frac{1}{3}y = 2 \\ y = 6 - \frac{3}{2}x \end{cases}$

4. $\begin{cases} \frac{1}{3}x - \frac{1}{2}y = 1 \\ 6x - 9y = 2 \end{cases}$

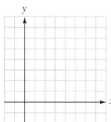

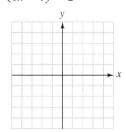

Solve each system by substitution.

5. $\begin{cases} y = x + 4 \\ 2x + 3y = 7 \end{cases}$

6. $\begin{cases} y = 2x + 5 \\ 3x - 5y = -4 \end{cases}$

7. $\begin{cases} x + 2y = 11 \\ 2x - y = 2 \end{cases}$

8. $\begin{cases} 2x + 3y = -2 \\ 3x + 5y = -2 \end{cases}$

Solve each system by addition.

9. $\begin{cases} x + y = 2 \\ 2x + 3y = -3 \end{cases}$

10. $\begin{cases} 3x + 2y = 1 \\ 2x - 3y = 5 \end{cases}$

11. $\begin{cases} x + \frac{1}{2}y = 7 \\ -2x = 3y - 6 \end{cases}$

12. $\begin{cases} y = \frac{x - 3}{2} \\ x = \frac{2y + 7}{2} \end{cases}$

SECTION 13.2   Solving Systems of Three Equations in Three Variables

DEFINITIONS AND CONCEPTS	EXAMPLES
Strategy for solving three linear equations in three variables: **1.** Pick any two equations and eliminate a variable.	To solve the system $\begin{cases} x + y + z = 4 \\ x - 2y - z = -9 \\ 2x - y + 2z = -1 \end{cases}$, we can add the first and second equations to obtain Equation 1: $x +\ y + z =\ \ \ 4$ $\underline{x - 2y - z = -9}$ $(1)\ \ 2x -\ y\ \ = -5$
2. Pick a different pair of equations and eliminate the same variable.	We now multiply the second equation by 2 and add it to the third equation to obtain Equation 2: $2x - 4y - 2z = -18$ $\underline{2x -\ y + 2z = -1}$ $(2)\ \ 4x - 5y\ \ \ \ \ = -19$
3. Solve the resulting pair of equations in two variables.	To solve the system $\begin{cases} 2x - y = -5 \\ 4x - 5y = -19 \end{cases}$, formed by Equations 1 and 2, we can multiply the first equation by -2 and add the result to the second equation to eliminate x. ${-4x} + 2y =\ \ \ \ 10$ $\underline{\ \ 4x - 5y = -19}$ $\ {-3y} = -9$ $\ y = 3 \qquad$ Divide both sides by -3. We can substitute 3 into either equation of the system to find x. $2x - y = -5 \qquad$ This is the first equation of the system. $2x - 3 = -5 \qquad$ Substitute 3 for y. $2x = -2 \qquad$ Add 3 to both sides. $x = -1 \qquad$ Divide both sides by 2.
4. To find the value of the third variable, substitute the values of the two variables found in Step 3 into any equation containing all three variables and solve the equation.	We now can substitute -1 for x and 3 for y into one of the equations in the original system and solve for z: $x + y + z = 4 \qquad$ This is the first equation of the original system. $-1 + 3 + z = 4 \qquad$ Substitute -1 for x and 3 for y. $2 + z = 4 \qquad$ Simplify. $z = 2 \qquad$ Subtract 2 from both sides.
5. Check the solution in all three of the original equations.	The solution is $(-1, 3, 2)$.

REVIEW EXERCISES

Solve each system.

13. $\begin{cases} x + y + z = 6 \\ x - y - z = -4 \\ -x + y - z = -2 \end{cases}$

14. $\begin{cases} 2x + 3y + z = -5 \\ -x + 2y - z = -6 \\ 3x + y + 2z = 4 \end{cases}$

SECTION 13.3 Solving Systems of Linear Equations Using Matrices

DEFINITIONS AND CONCEPTS	EXAMPLES
A **matrix** is any rectangular array of numbers. Systems of linear equations can be solved using matrices and the method of **Gaussian elimination** and back substitution.	To use matrices to solve the system $$\begin{cases} x + y + z = 4 \\ 2x - y + 2z = -1 \\ x - 2y - z = -9 \end{cases}$$ we can represent it with the following augmented matrix: $$\begin{bmatrix} 1 & 1 & 1 & \vdots & 4 \\ 2 & -1 & 2 & \vdots & -1 \\ 1 & -2 & -1 & \vdots & -9 \end{bmatrix}$$ To get 0's under the 1 in the first column, we multiply row 1 of the augmented matrix by -2 and add it to row 2 to get a new row 2. We then multiply row 1 by -1 and add it to row 3 to get a new row 3. $$\begin{bmatrix} 1 & 1 & 1 & \vdots & 4 \\ 0 & -3 & 0 & \vdots & -9 \\ 0 & -3 & -2 & \vdots & -13 \end{bmatrix}$$ To get a 0 under the -3 in the second column of the previous matrix, we multiply row 2 by -1 and add it to row 3. $$\begin{bmatrix} 1 & 1 & 1 & \vdots & 4 \\ 0 & -3 & 0 & \vdots & -9 \\ 0 & 0 & -2 & \vdots & -4 \end{bmatrix}$$ Finally, to obtain a 1 in the third row, third column, we multiply row 3 by $-\frac{1}{2}$. $$\begin{bmatrix} 1 & 1 & 1 & \vdots & 4 \\ 0 & -3 & 0 & \vdots & -9 \\ 0 & 0 & 1 & \vdots & 2 \end{bmatrix}$$ The final matrix represents the system $\begin{array}{l} (1) \\ (2) \\ (3) \end{array} \begin{cases} x + y + z = 4 \\ 0x - 3y + 0z = -9 \\ 0x + 0y + z = 2 \end{cases}$ From Equation 3, we see that $z = 2$. From Equation 2, we see that $y = 3$. To find x, we substitute 2 for z and 3 for y in Equation 1 and solve for x: $\begin{array}{ll} (1) \quad x + y + z = 4 & \\ \quad\quad x + 3 + 2 = 4 & \text{Substitute 2 for } z \text{ and 3 for } y. \\ \quad\quad\quad\quad x + 5 = 4 & \text{Simplify.} \\ \quad\quad\quad\quad\quad x = -1 & \text{Subtract 5 from both sides.} \end{array}$ Thus, $x = -1$. The solution of the given system is $(-1, 3, 2)$. Verify that this ordered triple satisfies each equation of the original system.

REVIEW EXERCISES

Solve each system by using matrices.

15. $\begin{cases} x + 2y = 4 \\ 2x - y = 3 \end{cases}$

16. $\begin{cases} x + y + z = 6 \\ 2x - y + z = 1 \\ 4x + y - z = 5 \end{cases}$

17. $\begin{cases} x + y = 3 \\ x - 2y = -3 \\ 2x + y = 4 \end{cases}$

18. $\begin{cases} x + 2y + z = 2 \\ 2x + 5y + 4z = 5 \end{cases}$

SECTION 13.4 Solving Systems of Linear Equations Using Determinants

DEFINITIONS AND CONCEPTS	EXAMPLES
A **determinant of a square matrix** is a number. $$\begin{vmatrix} a & b \\ c & d \end{vmatrix} = ad - bc$$ $$\begin{vmatrix} a_1 & b_1 & c_1 \\ a_2 & b_2 & c_2 \\ a_3 & b_3 & c_3 \end{vmatrix}$$ $$= a_1 \begin{vmatrix} b_2 & c_2 \\ b_3 & c_3 \end{vmatrix} - b_1 \begin{vmatrix} a_2 & c_2 \\ a_3 & c_3 \end{vmatrix} + c_1 \begin{vmatrix} a_2 & b_2 \\ a_3 & b_3 \end{vmatrix}$$	Find the determinant $\begin{vmatrix} 8 & -3 \\ 2 & -1 \end{vmatrix}$. $$\begin{vmatrix} 8 & -3 \\ 2 & -1 \end{vmatrix} = 8(-1) - (-3)(2)$$ $$= -8 + 6$$ $$= -2$$ To evaluate the determinant $\begin{vmatrix} 1 & 3 & -2 \\ 1 & -2 & -1 \\ 2 & -1 & 3 \end{vmatrix}$, we can expand by minors: $$\begin{array}{ccc} \text{Minor} & \text{Minor} & \text{Minor} \\ \text{of } 1 & \text{of } 3 & \text{of } -2 \\ \downarrow & \downarrow & \downarrow \end{array}$$ $$\begin{vmatrix} 1 & 3 & -2 \\ 1 & -2 & -1 \\ 2 & -1 & 3 \end{vmatrix} = 1\begin{vmatrix} -2 & -1 \\ -1 & 3 \end{vmatrix} - 3\begin{vmatrix} 1 & -1 \\ 2 & 3 \end{vmatrix} + (-2)\begin{vmatrix} 1 & -2 \\ 2 & -1 \end{vmatrix}$$ $$= 1(-6 - 1) - 3(3 + 2) - 2(-1 + 4)$$ $$= -7 - 15 - 6$$ $$= -28$$
Cramer's rule for two equations in two variables: The solution of the system $\begin{cases} ax + by = e \\ cx + dy = f \end{cases}$ is given by $$x = \frac{D_x}{D} = \frac{\begin{vmatrix} e & b \\ f & d \end{vmatrix}}{\begin{vmatrix} a & b \\ c & d \end{vmatrix}} \quad \text{and} \quad y = \frac{D_y}{D} = \frac{\begin{vmatrix} a & e \\ c & f \end{vmatrix}}{\begin{vmatrix} a & b \\ c & d \end{vmatrix}}$$ If $D \neq 0$, the system is consistent and the equations are independent. If $D = 0$ and D_x or D_y is nonzero, the system is inconsistent. If every determinant is 0, the system is consistent but the equations are dependent.	Solve using Cramer's rule: $\begin{cases} 2x - 4y = -14 \\ 3x + y = -7 \end{cases}$. $$x = \frac{D_x}{D} = \frac{\begin{vmatrix} -14 & -4 \\ -7 & 1 \end{vmatrix}}{\begin{vmatrix} 2 & -4 \\ 3 & 1 \end{vmatrix}} = \frac{-14 - 28}{2 - (-12)} = \frac{-42}{14} = -3$$ $$y = \frac{D_y}{D} = \frac{\begin{vmatrix} 2 & -14 \\ 3 & -7 \end{vmatrix}}{\begin{vmatrix} 2 & -4 \\ 3 & 1 \end{vmatrix}} = \frac{-14 - (-42)}{2 - (-12)} = \frac{28}{14} = 2$$ The solution is $(-3, 2)$.

Cramer's rule for three equations in three variables:

The solution of the system $\begin{cases} ax + by + cz = j \\ dx + ey + fz = k \\ gx + hy + iz = l \end{cases}$

is given by $x = \frac{D_x}{D}$, $y = \frac{D_y}{D}$, and $z = \frac{D_z}{D}$ where

$$D = \begin{vmatrix} a & b & c \\ d & e & f \\ g & h & i \end{vmatrix} \qquad D_x = \begin{vmatrix} j & b & c \\ k & e & f \\ l & h & i \end{vmatrix}$$

$$D_y = \begin{vmatrix} a & j & c \\ d & k & f \\ g & l & i \end{vmatrix} \qquad D_z = \begin{vmatrix} a & b & j \\ d & e & k \\ g & h & l \end{vmatrix}$$

If $D \neq 0$, the system is consistent and the equations are independent.

If $D = 0$ and D_x or D_y or D_z is nonzero, the system is inconsistent.

If every determinant is 0, the system is consistent but the equations are dependent.

To use Cramer's rule to solve $\begin{cases} x + y + z = 4 \\ 2x - y + 2z = -1 \\ x - 2y - z = -9 \end{cases}$, we can find D, D_x, D_y, and D_z and substitute these values into the formulas.

$$x = \frac{D_x}{D}, \qquad y = \frac{D_y}{D}, \qquad \text{and} \qquad z = \frac{D_z}{D}$$

After forming and evaluating the determinants, we will obtain

$$D = 6, \qquad D_x = -6, \qquad D_y = 18, \qquad \text{and} \qquad D_z = 12$$

and we have

$$x = \frac{D_x}{D} = \frac{-6}{6} = -1, \quad y = \frac{D_y}{D} = \frac{18}{6} = 3, \quad z = \frac{D_z}{D} = \frac{12}{6} = 2$$

The solution of this system is $(-1, 3, 2)$.

REVIEW EXERCISES

Evaluate each determinant.

19. $\begin{vmatrix} 2 & 3 \\ -4 & 3 \end{vmatrix}$

20. $\begin{vmatrix} -3 & -4 \\ 5 & -6 \end{vmatrix}$

21. $\begin{vmatrix} -1 & 2 & -1 \\ 2 & -1 & 3 \\ 1 & -2 & 2 \end{vmatrix}$

22. $\begin{vmatrix} 3 & -2 & 2 \\ 1 & -2 & -2 \\ 2 & 1 & -1 \end{vmatrix}$

Use Cramer's rule to solve each system.

23. $\begin{cases} 3x + 4y = 10 \\ 2x - 3y = 1 \end{cases}$

24. $\begin{cases} 2x - 5y = -17 \\ 3x + 2y = 3 \end{cases}$

25. $\begin{cases} x + 2y + z = 0 \\ 2x + y + z = 3 \\ x + y + 2z = 5 \end{cases}$

26. $\begin{cases} 2x + 3y + z = 2 \\ x + 3y + 2z = 7 \\ x - y - z = -7 \end{cases}$

SECTION 13.5   Solving Systems of Equations and Inequalities Containing One or More Second-Degree Terms

DEFINITIONS AND CONCEPTS	EXAMPLES

Solve by graphing:

To solve a system of equations by graphing, graph both equations. The coordinates of the intersection points of the graphs will be the solutions of the system.

Solve the system by graphing.

$$\begin{cases} x^2 + y^2 = 4 \\ x - y = 2 \end{cases}$$

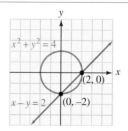

The equation $x^2 + y^2 = 4$ is that of a circle and $x - y = 2$ is that of a line. There is a possibility of zero, one, or two solutions.

After graphing the equations, we find that the two graphs intersect at the points $(2, 0)$, and $(0, -2)$. These are the solutions.

Solve by substitution:
Solve one equation for one variable, and substitute the result for the other variable.

Solve the system by substitution.

$$\begin{cases} x^2 + 9y^2 = 10 \\ y = x^2 \end{cases}$$

The equation $x^2 + 9y^2 = 10$ is that of an ellipse and $y = x^2$ is that of a parabola. We have the possibility of 0, 1, 2, 3, or 4 solutions. To find the solutions, proceed as follows:

$$x^2 + 9y^2 = 10$$
$$y + 9y^2 = 10 \qquad \text{Substitute } y \text{ for } x^2.$$
$$9y^2 + y - 10 = 0 \qquad \text{Subtract 10 from both sides.}$$
$$(9y + 10)(y - 1) = 0 \qquad \text{Factor } 9y^2 + y - 10.$$
$$9y + 10 = 0 \quad \text{or} \quad y - 1 = 0 \qquad \text{Set each factor equal to 0.}$$
$$y = -\frac{10}{9} \qquad\qquad y = 1$$

Since $y = x^2$, the values of x can be found by solving the equations

$$x^2 = -\frac{10}{9} \qquad \text{and} \qquad x^2 = 1$$

Because $x^2 = -\frac{10}{9}$ has no real solutions, this possibility is discarded. The solutions of $x^2 = 1$ are

$$x = 1 \qquad \text{or} \qquad x = -1$$

The solutions of the system are $(1, 1)$ and $(-1, 1)$.

Solve by elimination (addition):
To solve a system of equations by elimination, add the equations to eliminate one of the variables. Then solve the resulting equation for the other variable. Then substitute this value into one of the equations to find y.

Solve the system by elimination.

$$\begin{cases} 4x^2 - y^2 = 1 \\ 4x^2 + y^2 = 1 \end{cases}$$

The equation $4x^2 - y^2 = 1$ is that of a hyperbola and the equation $4x^2 + y^2 = 1$ is that of an ellipse. We have the possibility of 0, 1, 2, 3, or 4 solutions.

If we add the equations $\begin{cases} 4x^2 - y^2 = 1 \\ 4x^2 + y^2 = 1 \end{cases}$, we have

$$8x^2 = 2$$
$$x^2 = \frac{1}{4}$$
$$x = \frac{1}{2}, -\frac{1}{2}$$

After substituting each value of x for y in the first equation, we have

$$4\left(\frac{1}{2}\right)^2 - y^2 = 1 \qquad 4\left(-\frac{1}{2}\right)^2 - y^2 = 1$$
$$4\left(\frac{1}{4}\right) - y^2 = 1 \qquad 4\left(\frac{1}{4}\right) - y^2 = 1$$
$$1 - y^2 = 1 \qquad\qquad 1 - y^2 = 1$$
$$-y^2 = 0 \qquad\qquad -y^2 = 0$$
$$y = 0 \qquad\qquad\quad y = 0$$

The solutions are $\left(\frac{1}{2}, 0\right)$ and $\left(-\frac{1}{2}, 0\right)$.

Systems of inequalities are solved by graphing.

Solve: $\begin{cases} y \geq x^2 \\ y \leq -x^2 + 4 \end{cases}$.

The graph of $y = x^2$ is the parabola that opens upward and has its vertex at the origin. The points with coordinates that satisfy the inequality $y \geq x^2$ are those points above the parabola and include the points on the parabola.

The graph of $y \leq -x^2 + 4$ is a parabola opening downward, with vertex at $(0, 4)$. The points with coordinates that satisfy the inequality are those points below the parabola and include the points on the parabola. The graph of the solution set of the system is the area between the parabolas.

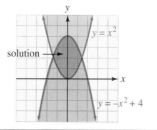

REVIEW EXERCISES
Solve each system of equations.

27. $\begin{cases} 3x^2 + y^2 = 52 \\ x^2 - y^2 = 12 \end{cases}$

28. $\begin{cases} \frac{x^2}{16} + \frac{y^2}{12} = 1 \\ x^2 - \frac{y^2}{3} = 1 \end{cases}$

29. Graph the solution set in the system $\begin{cases} y \geq x^2 - 4 \\ y < x + 3 \end{cases}$.

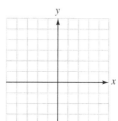

Chapter 13   TEST

1. Solve $\begin{cases} 2x + y = 5 \\ y = 2x - 3 \end{cases}$ by graphing.

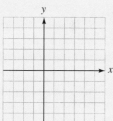

2. Use substitution to solve: $\begin{cases} 2x - 4y = 14 \\ x = -2y + 7 \end{cases}$.

3. Use elimination to solve: $\begin{cases} 2x + 3y = -5 \\ 3x - 2y = 12 \end{cases}$.

4. Use any method to solve: $\begin{cases} \frac{x}{2} - \frac{y}{4} = -4 \\ x + y = -2 \end{cases}$.

Consider the system $\begin{cases} 3(x + y) = x - 3 \\ -y = \frac{2x + 3}{3} \end{cases}$.

5. Are the equations of the system dependent or independent?

6. Is the system consistent or inconsistent?

Use an elementary row operation to find the missing number in the second matrix.

7. $\begin{bmatrix} 1 & 2 & -1 \\ 2 & -2 & 3 \end{bmatrix}, \begin{bmatrix} 1 & 2 & -1 \\ -1 & -8 & \boxed{} \end{bmatrix}$

8. $\begin{bmatrix} -1 & 3 & 6 \\ 3 & -2 & 4 \end{bmatrix}, \begin{bmatrix} -1 & 3 & 6 \\ 5 & -8 & \boxed{} \end{bmatrix}$

Consider the system $\begin{cases} x + y + z = 4 \\ x + y - z = 6 \\ 2x - 3y + z = -1 \end{cases}$.

9. Write the augmented matrix that represents the system.

10. Write the coefficient matrix that represents the system.

Use matrices to solve each system.

11. $\begin{cases} x + y = 4 \\ 2x - y = 2 \end{cases}$

12. $\begin{cases} x + y = 2 \\ x - y = -4 \\ 2x + y = 1 \end{cases}$

Evaluate each determinant.

13. $\begin{vmatrix} 2 & -3 \\ 4 & 5 \end{vmatrix}$

14. $\begin{vmatrix} -3 & -4 \\ -2 & 3 \end{vmatrix}$

15. $\begin{vmatrix} 1 & 2 & 0 \\ 2 & 0 & 3 \\ 1 & -2 & 2 \end{vmatrix}$

16. $\begin{vmatrix} 2 & -1 & 1 \\ 3 & 1 & 0 \\ 0 & 1 & 2 \end{vmatrix}$

Consider the system $\begin{cases} x - y = -6 \\ 3x + y = -6 \end{cases}$, *which is to be solved with Cramer's rule.*

17. When solving for x, what is the numerator determinant? **(Don't evaluate it.)**

18. When solving for y, what is the denominator determinant? **(Don't evaluate it.)**

19. Solve the system for x.

20. Solve the system for y.

Consider the system $\begin{cases} x + y + z = 4 \\ x + y - z = 6 \\ 2x - 3y + z = -1 \end{cases}$.

21. Solve for x. **22.** Solve for z.

Solve each system.

23. $\begin{cases} x^2 + y^2 = 5 \\ x^2 - y^2 = 3 \end{cases}$

24. $\begin{cases} x^2 + y^2 = 25 \\ 4x^2 - 9y = 0 \end{cases}$

25. Solve the system: $\begin{cases} y \geq x^2 \\ y < x + 3 \end{cases}$.

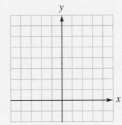

Linear Programming

Linear programming is a mathematical technique used to find the optimal allocation of resources in the military, business, telecommunications, and other fields. It got its start during World War II when it became necessary to move huge quantities of people, materials, and supplies as efficiently and economically as possible.

To solve linear programming problems, we maximize (or minimize) a function (called the **objective function**) subject to given conditions on its variables. These conditions (called **constraints**) are usually given as a system of linear inequalities. For example, suppose that the annual profit (in millions of dollars) earned by a business is given by the equation $P = y + 2x$ and that x and y are subject to the following constraints:

$$\begin{cases} 3x + y \leq 120 \\ x + y \leq 60 \\ x \geq 0 \\ y \geq 0 \end{cases}$$

To find the maximum profit P that can be earned by the business, we solve the system of inequalities as shown in Figure 6-19(a) and find the coordinates of each corner point of the region R. This region is often called a **feasibility region.** We can then write the profit equation

$$P = y + 2x \qquad \text{in the form} \qquad y = -2x + P$$

Charles Babbage

(1792–1871)

In 1823, Babbage built a steam-powered digital calculator, which he called a *difference engine*. Thought to be a crackpot by his London neighbors, Babbage was a visionary. His machine embodied principles still used in modern computers.

The equation $y = -2x + P$ is the equation of a set of parallel lines, each with a slope of -2 and a y-intercept of P. The graph of $y = -2x + P$ for three values of P is shown as red lines in Figure 6-19b. To find the red line that passes through region R and provides the maximum value of P, we locate the red line with the greatest y-intercept. Since line l has the greatest y-intercept and intersects region R at the corner point $(30, 30)$, the maximum value of P (subject to the given constraints) is

$$P = y + 2x$$
$$= 30 + 2(30)$$
$$= 90$$

Thus, the maximum profit P that can be earned is \$90 million. This profit occurs when $x = 30$ and $y = 30$.

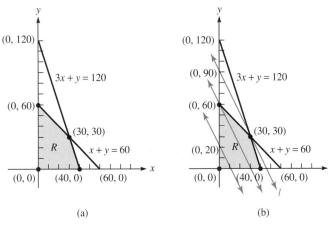

(a)   (b)

Figure 6-19

The preceding discussion illustrates the following important fact.

Maximum or Minimum of an Objective Function

If a linear function, subject to the constraints of a system of linear inequalities in two variables, attains a maximum or a minimum value, that value will occur at a corner point or along an entire edge of the region R that represents the solution of the system.

ACTIVE EXAMPLE 1

If $P = 2x + 3y$, find the maximum value of P subject to the following constraints:

$$\begin{cases} x + y \le 4 \\ 2x + y \le 6 \\ x \ge 0 \\ y \ge 0 \end{cases}$$

Solution

We solve the system of inequalities to find the feasibility region R shown in Figure 6-20. The coordinates of its corner points are $(0, 0)$, $(3, 0)$, $(0, 4)$, and $(2, 2)$.

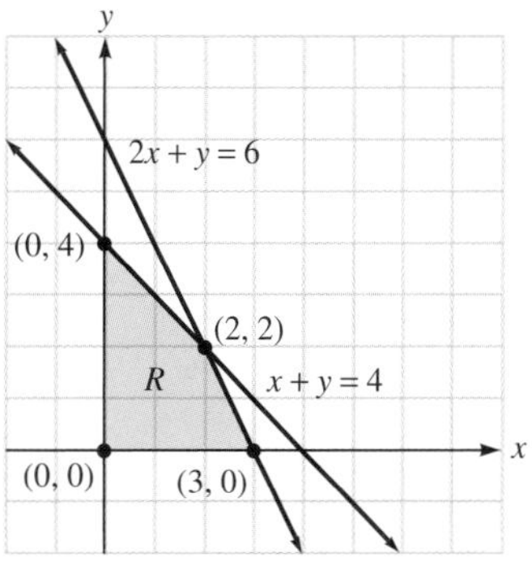

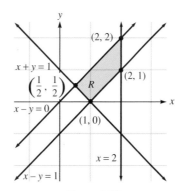

Figure 6-20

Since the maximum value of P will occur at a corner of R, we substitute the coordinates of each corner point into the objective function $P = 2x + 3y$ and find the one that gives the maximum value of P.

Point	$P = 2x + 3y$
$(0, 0)$	$P = 2(0) + 3(0) = 0$
$(3, 0)$	$P = 2(3) + 3(0) = 6$
$(2, 2)$	$P = 2(2) + 3(2) = 10$
$(0, 4)$	$P = 2(0) + 3(4) = 12$

The maximum value $P = 12$ occurs when $x = 0$ and $y = 4$.

Self Check Find the maximum value of $P = 4x + 3y$, subject to the constraints of Example 1. ■

ACTIVE EXAMPLE 2 If $P = 3x + 2y$, find the minimum value of P subject to the following constraints:

$$\begin{cases} x + y \geq 1 \\ x - y \leq 1 \\ x - y \geq 0 \\ x \leq 2 \end{cases}$$

Solution We refer to the feasibility region shown in Figure 6-21 with corner points at $\left(\frac{1}{2}, \frac{1}{2}\right)$, $(2, 2)$, $(2, 1)$, and $(1, 0)$.

Figure 6-21

Since the minimum value of P occurs at a corner point of region R, we substitute the coordinates of each corner point into the objective function $P = 3x + 2y$ and find the one that gives the minimum value of P.

Point	$P = 3x + 2y$
$\left(\frac{1}{2}, \frac{1}{2}\right)$	$P = 3\left(\frac{1}{2}\right) + 2\left(\frac{1}{2}\right) = \frac{5}{2}$
$(2, 2)$	$P = 3(2) + 2(2) = 10$
$(2, 1)$	$P = 3(2) + 2(1) = 8$
$(1, 0)$	$P = 3(1) + 2(0) = 3$

The minimum value $P = \frac{5}{2}$ occurs when $x = \frac{1}{2}$ and $y = \frac{1}{2}$.

Self Check Find the minimum value of $P = 2x + y$, subject to the constraints of Example 2.

Applications of Linear Programming

Linear programming problems can be very complex and involve hundreds of variables. In this section, we will consider a few simple problems. Since they involve only two variables, we can solve them using graphical methods.

ACTIVE EXAMPLE 3

COLLEGE
Algebra *f(x)* **Now**™
Go to academic.cengage.com/1pass
or your CD to practice this example.

An accountant prepares tax returns for individuals and for small businesses. On average, each individual return requires 3 hours of her time and 1 hour of computer time. Each business return requires 4 hours of her time and 2 hours of computer time. Because of other business considerations, her time is limited to 240 hours, and the computer time is limited to 100 hours. If she earns a profit of $80 on each individual return and a profit of $150 on each business return, how many returns of each type should she prepare to maximize her profit?

Solution First, we organize the given information into a table.

	Individual tax return	Business tax return	Time available
Accountant's time	3	4	240 hours
Computer time	1	2	100 hours
Profit	$80	$150	

Then we solve the problem using the following steps.

Find the objective function Suppose that x represents the number of individual returns to be completed and y represents the number of business returns to be completed. Since each of the x individual returns will earn an $80 profit, and each of the y business returns will earn a $150 profit, the total profit is given by the equation

$$P = 80x + 150y$$

Find the feasibility region
Since the number of individual returns and business returns cannot be negative, we know that $x \geq 0$ and $y \geq 0$.

Since each of the x individual returns will take 3 hours of her time, and each of the y business returns will take 4 hours of her time, the total number of hours she will work will be $(3x + 4y)$ hours. This amount must be less than or equal to her available time, which is 240 hours. Thus, the inequality $3x + 4y \leq 240$ is a constraint on the accountant's time.

Since each of the x individual returns will take 1 hour of computer time, and each of the y business returns will take 2 hours of computer time, the total number of hours of computer time will be $(x + 2y)$ hours. This amount must be less than or equal to the available computer time, which is 100 hours. Thus, the inequality $x + 2y \leq 100$ is a constraint on the computer time.

We have the following constraints on the values of x and y.

$$\begin{cases} x \geq 0 \\ y \geq 0 \\ 3x + 4y \leq 240 \\ x + 2y \leq 100 \end{cases}$$

The number of individual returns is nonnegative.
The number of business returns is nonnegative.
The accountant's time must be less than or equal to 240 hours.
The computer time must be less than or equal to 100 hours.

To find the feasibility region, we graph each of the constraints to find region R, as in Figure 6-22. The four corner points of this region have coordinates of $(0, 0)$, $(80, 0)$, $(40, 30)$, and $(0, 50)$.

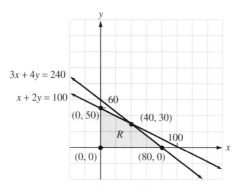

Figure 6-22

Find the maximum profit
To find the maximum profit, we substitute the coordinates of each corner point into the objective function $P = 80x + 150y$.

Point	$P = 80x + 150y$
$(0, 0)$	$P = 80(0) + 150(0) = 0$
$(80, 0)$	$P = 80(80) + 150(0) = 6,400$
$(40, 30)$	$P = 80(40) + 150(30) = 7,700$
$(0, 50)$	$P = 80(0) + 150(50) = 7,500$

From the table, we can see that the accountant will earn a maximum profit of $7,700 if she prepares 40 individual returns and 30 business returns. ◼

EXAMPLE 4 Vigortab and Robust are two diet supplements. Each Vigortab tablet costs 50¢ and contains 3 units of calcium, 20 units of vitamin C, and 40 units of iron. Each Robust tablet costs 60¢ and contains 4 units of calcium, 40 units of vitamin C, and 30 units of iron. At least 24 units of calcium, 200 units of vitamin C, and 120 units of iron are required for the daily needs of one patient. How many tablets of each supplement should be taken daily for a minimum cost? Find the daily minimum cost.

Solution First, we organize the given information into a table.

	Vigortab	Robust	Amount required
Calcium	3	4	24
Vitamin C	20	40	200
Iron	40	30	120
Cost	50¢	60¢	

Find the objective function We can let x represent the number of Vigortab tablets to be taken daily and y the corresponding number of Robust tablets. Because each of the x Vigortab tablets will cost 50¢, and each of the y Robust tablets will cost 60¢, the total cost will be given by the equation

$$C = 0.50x + 0.60y \quad \text{50¢ = \$0.50 and 60¢ = \$0.60.}$$

Find the feasibility region Since there are requirements for calcium, vitamin C, and iron, there is a constraint for each. Note that neither x nor y can be negative.

$$\begin{cases} 3x + 4y \geq 24 & \text{The amount of calcium must be greater than or equal to 24 units.} \\ 20x + 40y \geq 200 & \text{The amount of vitamin C must be greater than or equal to 200 units.} \\ 40x + 30y \geq 120 & \text{The amount of iron must be greater than or equal to 120 units.} \\ x \geq 0, y \geq 0 & \text{The number of tablets taken must be greater than or equal to 0.} \end{cases}$$

We graph the inequalities to find the feasibility region and the coordinates of its corner points, as in Figure 6-23.

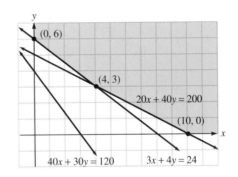

Figure 6-23

Find the minimum cost In this case, the feasibility region is not bounded on all sides. The coordinates of the corner points are $(0, 6)$, $(4, 3)$, and $(10, 0)$. To find the minimum cost, we substitute each pair of coordinates into the objective function.

Point	$C = 0.50x + 0.60y$
$(0, 6)$	$C = 0.50(0) + 0.60(6) = 3.60$
$(4, 3)$	$C = 0.50(4) + 0.60(3) = 3.80$
$(10, 0)$	$C = 0.50(10) + 0.60(0) = 5.00$

A minimum cost will occur if no Vigortab and 6 Robust tablets are taken daily. The minimum daily cost is $3.60. ∎

EXAMPLE 5   A television program director must schedule comedy skits and musical numbers for prime-time variety shows. Each comedy skit requires 2 hours of rehearsal time, costs $3,000, and brings in $20,000 from the show's sponsors. Each musical number requires 1 hour of rehearsal time, costs $6,000, and generates $12,000. If 250 hours are available for rehearsal, and $600,000 is budgeted for comedy and music, how many segments of each type should be produced to maximize income? Find the maximum income.

Solution   First, we organize the given information into a table.

	Comedy	Musical	Available
Rehearsal time (hours)	2	1	250
Cost (in $1,000s)	3	6	600
Generated income (in $1,000s)	20	12	

Find the objective function   We can let x represent the number of comedy skits and y the number of musical numbers to be scheduled. Since each of the x comedy skits generates $20 thousand, the income generated by the comedy skits is $20x$ thousand. The musical numbers produce $12y$ thousand. The objective function to be maximized is

$$V = 20x + 12y$$

Find the feasibility region   Since there are limits on rehearsal time and budget, there is a constraint for each. Note that neither x nor y can be negative.

$$\begin{cases} 2x + y \le 250 \\ 3x + 6y \le 600 \\ x \ge 0, y \ge 0 \end{cases}$$

The total rehearsal time must be less than or equal to 250 hours.
The total cost must be less than or equal to $600 thousand.
The numbers of skits and musical numbers must be greater than or equal to 0.

We graph the inequalities to find the feasibility region shown in Figure 6-24 and find the coordinates of each corner point.

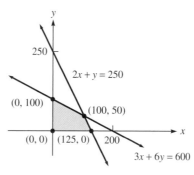

Figure 6-24

Find the maximum income   The coordinates of the corner points of the feasible region are (0, 0), (0, 100), (100, 50), and (125, 0). To find the maximum income, we substitute each pair of coordinates into the objective function.

Corner point	$V = 20x + 12y$
(0, 0)	$V = 20(0) + 12(0) = 0$
(0, 100)	$V = 20(0) + 12(100) = 1{,}200$
(100, 50)	$V = 20(100) + 12(50) = 2{,}600$
(125, 0)	$V = 20(125) + 12(0) = 2{,}500$

Maximum income will occur if 100 comedy skits and 50 musical numbers are scheduled. The maximum income will be 2,600 thousand dollars, or $2,600,000. ∎

Self Check Answers

1. 14   **2.** $\frac{3}{2}$

Exercises

VOCABULARY AND CONCEPTS Fill in the blanks.

1. In a linear program, the inequalities are called _____.

2. Ordered pairs that satisfy the constraints of a linear program are called _____ solutions.

3. The function to be maximized (or minimized) in a linear program is called the _____ function.

4. The objective function of a linear program attains a maximum (or minimum), subject to the constraints, at a _____ or along an ____ of the feasibility region.

PRACTICE Maximize P subject to the following constraints.

5. $P = 2x + 3y$
$$\begin{cases} x \geq 0 \\ y \geq 0 \\ x + y \leq 4 \end{cases}$$

6. $P = 3x + 2y$
$$\begin{cases} x \geq 0 \\ y \geq 0 \\ x + y \leq 4 \end{cases}$$

7. $P = y + \frac{1}{2}x$
$$\begin{cases} x \geq 0 \\ y \geq 0 \\ 2y - x \leq 1 \\ y - 2x \geq -2 \end{cases}$$

8. $P = 4y - x$
$$\begin{cases} x \leq 2 \\ y \geq 0 \\ x + y \geq 1 \\ 2y - x \leq 1 \end{cases}$$

9. $P = 2x + y$
$$\begin{cases} y \geq 0 \\ y - x \leq 2 \\ 2x + 3y \leq 6 \\ 3x + y \leq 3 \end{cases}$$

10. $P = x - 2y$
$$\begin{cases} x + y \leq 5 \\ y \leq 3 \\ x \leq 2 \\ x \geq 0 \\ y \geq 0 \end{cases}$$

11. $P = 3x - 2y$
$$\begin{cases} x \leq 1 \\ x \geq -1 \\ y - x \leq 1 \\ x - y \leq 1 \end{cases}$$

12. $P = x - y$
$$\begin{cases} 5x + 4y \leq 20 \\ y \leq 5 \\ x \geq 0 \\ y \geq 0 \end{cases}$$

Minimize P subject to the following constraints.

13. $P = 5x + 12y$
$$\begin{cases} x \geq 0 \\ y \geq 0 \\ x + y \leq 4 \end{cases}$$

14. $P = 3x + 6y$
$$\begin{cases} x \geq 0 \\ y \geq 0 \\ x + y \leq 4 \end{cases}$$

15. $P = 3y + x$
$$\begin{cases} x \geq 0 \\ y \geq 0 \\ 2y - x \leq 1 \\ y - 2x \geq -2 \end{cases}$$

16. $P = 5y + x$
$$\begin{cases} x \leq 2 \\ y \geq 0 \\ x + y \geq 1 \\ 2y - x \leq 1 \end{cases}$$

17. $P = 6x + 2y$
$$\begin{cases} y \geq 0 \\ y - x \leq 2 \\ 2x + 3y \leq 6 \\ 3x + y \leq 3 \end{cases}$$

18. $P = 2y - x$
$$\begin{cases} x \geq 0 \\ y \geq 0 \\ x + y \leq 5 \\ x + 2y \geq 2 \end{cases}$$

19. $P = 2x - 2y$
$$\begin{cases} x \leq 1 \\ x \geq -1 \\ y - x \leq 1 \\ x - y \leq 1 \end{cases}$$

20. $P = y - 2x$
$$\begin{cases} x + 2y \leq 4 \\ 2x + y \leq 4 \\ x + 2y \geq 2 \\ 2x + y \geq 2 \end{cases}$$

APPLICATIONS Write the objective function and the inequalities that describe the constraints in each problem. Graph the feasibility region, showing the corner points. Then find the maximum or minimum value of the objective function.

21. Making furniture   Two woodworkers, Tom and Carlos, get $100 for making a table and $80 for making a chair. On average, Tom must work 3 hours and Carlos 2 hours to make a chair. Tom must work 2 hours and Carlos 6 hours to make a table. If neither wishes to work more than 42 hours per week, how many tables and how many chairs should they make each week to maximize their income? Find the maximum income.

	Table	Chair	Time available
Income ($)	100	80	
Tom's time (hr)	2	3	42
Carlos's time (hr)	6	2	42

22. Making crafts   Two artists, Nina and Rob, make yard ornaments. They get $80 for each wooden snowman they make and $64 for each wooden Santa Claus. On average, Nina must work 4 hours and Rob 2 hours to make a snowman. Nina must work 3 hours and Rob 4 hours to make a Santa Claus. If neither wishes to work more than 20 hours per week, how many of each ornament should they make each week to maximize their income? Find the maximum income.

	Snowman	Santa Claus	Time available
Income ($)	80	64	
Nina's time (hr)	4	3	20
Rob's time (hr)	2	4	20

23. Inventories   An electronics store manager stocks from 20 to 30 IBM-compatible computers and from 30 to 50 Apple computers. There is room in the store to stock up to 60 computers. The manager receives a commission of $50 on the sale of each IBM-compatible computer and $40 on the sale of each Apple computer. If the manager can sell all of the computers, how many should she stock to maximize her commissions? Find the maximum commission.

Inventory	IBM	Apple
Minimum	20	30
Maximum	30	50
Commission	$50	$40

24. Diet problems   A diet requires at least 16 units of vitamin C and at least 34 units of vitamin B complex. Two food supplements are available that provide these nutrients in the amounts and costs shown in the table. How much of each should be used to minimize the cost?

Supplement	Vitamin C	Vitamin B	Cost
A	3 units/g	2 units/g	3¢/g
B	2 units/g	6 units/g	4¢/g

25. Production   Manufacturing VCRs and TVs requires the use of the electronics, assembly, and finishing departments of a factory, according to the following schedule:

	Hours for VCR	Hours for TV	Hours available per week
Electronics	3	4	180
Assembly	2	3	120
Finishing	2	1	60

Each VCR has a profit of $40, and each TV has a profit of $32. How many VCRs and TVs should be manufactured weekly to maximize profit? Find the maximum profit.

26. **Production problems** A company manufactures one type of computer chip that runs at 2.0 GHz and another that runs at 2.8 GHz. The company can make a maximum of 50 fast chips per day and a maximum of 100 slow chips per day. It takes 6 hours to make a fast chip and 3 hours to make a slow chip, and the company's employees can provide up to 360 hours of labor per day. If the company makes a profit of $20 on each 2.8-GHz chip and $27 on each 2.0-GHz chip, how many of each type should be manufactured to earn the maximum profit?

27. **Financial planning** A stockbroker has $200,000 to invest in stocks and bonds. She wants to invest at least $100,000 in stocks and at least $50,000 in bonds. If stocks have an annual yield of 9% and bonds have an annual yield of 7%, how much should she invest in each to maximize her income? Find the maximum return.

28. **Production** A small country exports soybeans and flowers. Soybeans require 8 workers per acre, flowers require 12 workers per acre, and 100,000 workers are available. Government contracts require that there be at least 3 times as many acres of soybeans as flowers planted. It costs $250 per acre to plant soybeans and $300 per acre to plant flowers, and there is a budget of $3 million. If the profit from soybeans is $1,600 per acre and the profit from flowers is $2,000 per acre, how many acres of each crop should be planted to maximize profit? Find the maximum profit.

29. **Band trips** A high school band trip will require renting buses and trucks to transport no fewer than 100 students and 18 or more large instruments. Each bus can accommodate 40 students plus three large instruments; it costs $350 to rent. Each truck can accommodate 10 students plus 6 large instruments and costs $200 to rent. How many of each type of vehicle should be rented for the cost to be minimum? Find the minimum cost.

30. **Making ice cream** An ice cream store sells two new flavors: Fantasy and Excess. Each barrel of Fantasy requires 4 pounds of nuts and 3 pounds of chocolate and has a profit of $500. Each barrel of Excess requires 4 pounds of nuts and 2 pounds of chocolate and has a profit of $400. There are 16 pounds of nuts and 18 pounds of chocolate in stock, and the owner does not want to buy more for this batch. How many barrels of each should be made for a maximum profit? Find the maximum profit.

DISCOVERY AND WRITING

31. Does the objective function attain a maximum at the corners of a region defined by nonlinear inequalities? Attempt to maximize $P(x) = x + y$ on the region.

$$\begin{cases} x \geq 0 \\ y \geq 0 \\ y \leq 4 - x^2 \end{cases}$$

and write a paragraph on your findings.

32. Attempt to minimize the objective function of Exercise 31.

REVIEW Write each matrix in reduced row echelon form. Problem 33 cannot be done with a calculator.

33. $\begin{bmatrix} 1 & 2 & 3 \\ 1 & -2 & 3 \\ 0 & 2 & -3 \\ 2 & 0 & 6 \end{bmatrix}$

34. $\begin{bmatrix} 1 & 3 & -2 & 1 \\ 3 & 9 & -3 & 2 \end{bmatrix}$

35. The matrix in Exercise 34 is the system matrix of a system of equations. Find the general solution of the system.

36. Find the inverse of $\begin{bmatrix} 7 & 2 & 5 \\ 3 & 1 & 2 \\ 3 & 1 & 3 \end{bmatrix}$.

Exercise 6.8   (page 515)

1.   constraints

3.   objective

5.

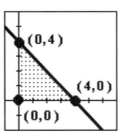

Point	$P = 2x + 3y$
$(0, 0)$	$= 2(0) + 3(0) = 0$
$(0, 4)$	$= 2(0) + 3(4) = 12$
$(4, 0)$	$= 2(4) + 3(0) = 8$

Max: $P = 12$ at $(0, 4)$

7.

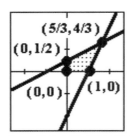

Point	$P = y + \frac{1}{2}x$
$(0, 0)$	$= 0 + \frac{1}{2}(0) = 0$
$\left(0, \frac{1}{2}\right)$	$= \frac{1}{2} + \frac{1}{2}(0) = \frac{1}{2}$
$\left(\frac{5}{3}, \frac{4}{3}\right)$	$= \frac{4}{3} + \frac{1}{2}\left(\frac{5}{3}\right) = \frac{13}{6}$
$(1, 0)$	$= 0 + \frac{1}{2}(1) = \frac{1}{2}$

Max: $P = \frac{13}{6}$ at $\left(\frac{5}{3}, \frac{4}{3}\right)$

9.

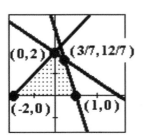

Point	$P = 2x + y$
$(-2, 0)$	$= 2(-2) + 0 = -4$
$(1, 0)$	$= 2(1) + 0 = 2$
$\left(\frac{3}{7}, \frac{12}{7}\right)$	$= 2\left(\frac{3}{7}\right) + \frac{12}{7} = \frac{18}{7}$
$(0, 2)$	$= 2(0) + 2 = 2$

Max: $P = \frac{18}{7}$ at $\left(\frac{3}{7}, \frac{12}{7}\right)$

11.

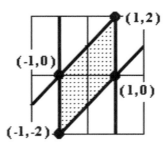

Point	$P = 3x - 2y$
$(1, 0)$	$= 3(1) - 2(0) = 3$
$(1, 2)$	$= 3(1) - 2(2) = -1$
$(-1, 0)$	$= 3(-1) - 2(0) = -3$
$(-1, -2)$	$= 3(-1) - 2(-2) = 1$

Max: $P = 3$ at $(1, 0)$

13.

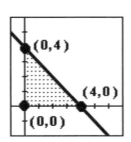

Point	$P = 5x + 12y$
$(0, 0)$	$= 5(0) + 12(0) = 0$
$(0, 4)$	$= 5(0) + 12(4) = 48$
$(4, 0)$	$= 5(4) + 12(0) = 20$

Min: $P = 0$ at $(0, 0)$

15.

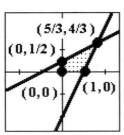

Point	$P = 3y + x$
$(0, 0)$	$= 3(0) + 0 = 0$
$(0, \frac{1}{2})$	$= 3(\frac{1}{2}) + 0 = \frac{3}{2}$
$(\frac{5}{3}, \frac{4}{3})$	$= 3(\frac{4}{3}) + \frac{5}{3} = \frac{17}{3}$
$(1, 0)$	$= 3(0) + 1 = 1$

Min: $P = 0$ at $(0, 0)$

17.

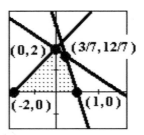

Point	$P = 6x + 2y$
$(-2, 0)$	$= 6(-2) + 2(0) = -12$
$(1, 0)$	$= 6(1) + 2(0) = 6$
$(\frac{3}{7}, \frac{12}{7})$	$= 6(\frac{3}{7}) + 2(\frac{12}{7}) = 6$
$(0, 2)$	$= 6(0) + 2(2) = 4$

Min: $P = -12$ at $(-2, 0)$

19.

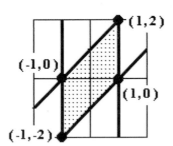

Point	$P = 2x - 2y$
$(1, 0)$	$= 2(1) - 2(0) = 2$
$(1, 2)$	$= 2(1) - 2(2) = -2$
$(-1, 0)$	$= 2(-1) - 2(0) = -2$
$(-1, -2)$	$= 2(-1) - 2(-2) = 2$

Min: $P = -2$ on the edge joining $(1, 2)$ and $(-1, 0)$

21. Let $x = $ # tables and $y = $ # chairs.

Maximize $P = 100x + 80y$

subject to $\begin{cases} 2x + 3y \le 42 \\ 6x + 2y \le 42 \\ x \ge 0, y \ge 0 \end{cases}$

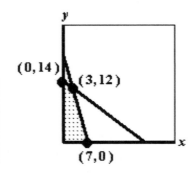

Point	$P = 100x + 80y$
$(7, 0)$	$= 100(7) + 80(0) = 700$
$(3, 12)$	$= 100(3) + 80(12) = 1260$
$(0, 14)$	$= 100(0) + 80(14) = 1120$
$(-1, -2)$	$= 2(-1) - 2(-2) = 2$

They should make 3 tables and 12 chairs, for a maximum profit of $1260.

23.   Let $x = $ # IBM and $y = $ # Macintosh.

Maximize $P = 50x + 40y$

subject to $\begin{cases} x + y \le 60 \\ 20 \le x \le 30 \\ 30 \le y \le 50 \end{cases}$

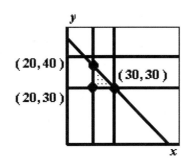

Point	$P = 50x + 40y$
$(20, 30)$	$= 50(20) + 40(30) = 2200$
$(30, 30)$	$= 50(30) + 40(30) = 2700$
$(20, 40)$	$= 50(20) + 40(40) = 2600$

She should stock 30 IBM and 30 Macintosh computers, for a maximum commission of $2700.

25.   Let $x = $ # VCRs and $y = $ # TVs.

Maximize $P = 40x + 32y$

subject to $\begin{cases} 3x + 4y \le 180 \\ 2x + 3y \le 120 \\ 2x + y \le 60 \\ x \ge 0, y \ge 0 \end{cases}$

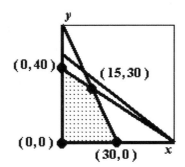

Point	$P = 40x + 32y$
$(0, 0)$	$= 40(0) + 32(0) = 0$
$(0, 40)$	$= 40(0) + 32(40) = 1280$
$(15, 30)$	$= 40(15) + 32(30) = 1560$
$(30, 0)$	$= 40(30) + 32(0) = 1200$

15 VCRs and 30 TVs should be made, for a maximum profit of $1560.

27.   Let $x = $ \$ in stocks and $y = $ \$ in bonds.

Maximize $P = 0.09x + 0.07y$

subject to $\begin{cases} x + y \le 200000 \\ x \ge 100000 \\ y \ge 50000 \end{cases}$

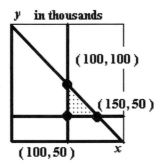

Point	$P = 0.09x + 0.07y$
$(100000, 50000)$	$= 12500$
$(150000, 50000)$	$= 17000$
$(100000, 100000)$	$= 16000$

She should invest $150,000 in stocks and $50,000 in bonds, for a maximum return of $17,000.

29. Let x = # buses and y = # trucks.

Minimize $P = 350x + 200y$

subject to $\begin{cases} 40x + 10y \geq 100 \\ 3x + 6y \geq 18 \\ x \geq 0, y \geq 0 \end{cases}$

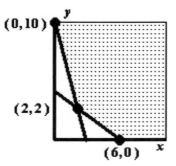

Point	$P = 350x + 200y$
$(0, 10)$	$= 350(0) + 200(10) = 2000$
$(2, 2)$	$= 350(2) + 200(2) = 1100$
$(6, 0)$	$= 350(6) + 200(0) = 2100$

2 buses and 2 trucks should be rented, for a minimum cost of $1100.

31. Answers may vary.

33.
$$\begin{bmatrix} 1 & 2 & 3 \\ 1 & -2 & 3 \\ 0 & 2 & -3 \\ 2 & 0 & 6 \end{bmatrix} \Rightarrow \begin{bmatrix} 1 & 2 & 3 \\ 0 & -4 & 0 \\ 0 & 2 & -3 \\ 0 & -4 & 0 \end{bmatrix} \Rightarrow \begin{bmatrix} 1 & 2 & 3 \\ 0 & 1 & 0 \\ 0 & 2 & -3 \\ 0 & 0 & 0 \end{bmatrix} \Rightarrow \begin{bmatrix} 1 & 0 & 3 \\ 0 & 1 & 0 \\ 0 & 0 & -3 \\ 0 & 0 & 0 \end{bmatrix} \Rightarrow \begin{bmatrix} 1 & 0 & 0 \\ 0 & 1 & 0 \\ 0 & 0 & 1 \\ 0 & 0 & 0 \end{bmatrix}$$
$$\begin{array}{ccccc} -R_1 + R_2 \Rightarrow R_2 & & -\frac{1}{4}R_2 \Rightarrow R_2 & -2R_2 + R_1 \Rightarrow R_1 & R_3 + R_1 \Rightarrow R_1 \\ -2R_1 + R_4 \Rightarrow R_4 & & -R_4 + R_2 \Rightarrow R_4 & -2R_2 + R_3 \Rightarrow R_3 & -\frac{1}{3}R_3 \Rightarrow R_3 \end{array}$$

35. $\left(\frac{1}{3} - 3y, y, -\frac{1}{3} \right)$

Glossary

absolute value The distance between a given number and 0 on a number line, usually denoted with $|\ \ |$

addition property of equality The property that states if a, b, and c are real numbers and $a = b$, then $a + c = b + c$

additive inverses A pair of numbers, a and b, are additive inverses if $a + b = 0$; also called **negatives** or **opposites**

algebraic expression A combination of variables, numbers, and arithmetic operations; an algebraic expression does not contain an equality or inequality symbol.

algebraic term An expression that is a constant, variable, or a product of constants and variables; for example, 37, xyz, and $32t$ are terms.

altitude The length of the perpendicular line from a vertex of a triangle to its opposite side

angle A geometric figure consisting of two rays emanating from a common point

annual growth rate The rate r that a quantity P increases or decreases within one year; the variable r in the exponential growth formula $A = Pe^{rt}$

area The amount of surface enclosed by a two-dimensional geometric figure

arithmetic means Numbers that are inserted between two elements in a sequence to form a new arithmetic sequence

arithmetic sequence A sequence in which each successive term is equal to the sum of the preceding term and a constant; written $a, a + d, a + 2d, a + 3d, \ldots$

arithmetic series The indicated sum of the terms of an arithmetic sequence

ascending powers of a variable An ordering of the terms of a polynomial, such that a given variable's exponents occur in increasing order.

associative properties The properties that state for real numbers a, b, and c, $(a + b) + c = a + (b + c)$ and $(ab)c = a(bc)$ *Note:* The associative property does not hold for subtraction or division.

augmented matrix A matrix representing a system of linear equations written in standard form, with columns consisting of the coefficients and a column of the constant terms of the equations

axis of symmetry The line that passes through the vertex of a parabola and divides it into two congruent halves

back substitution The process of finding the value of a second (or third, etc.) variable after finding the first by substituting the first into an equation of two variables and, if necessary, substituting both values into an equation of three values to find the third, etc.

base In the expression x^y, x is the base and y is the exponent. The base, x, will be used as a factor y times.

base angles of an isosceles triangle The two angles of an isosceles triangle opposite the two sides that are of the same length

binomial A polynomial with exactly two terms.

binomial theorem The theorem used to expand a binomial

Cartesian coordinate system A grid composed of a horizontal axis and a vertical axis that allows us to identify each point in a plane with a unique ordered pair of numbers; also called the **rectangular coordinate system**

Cartesian plane The set of all points in the Cartesian coordinate system.

center of a circle The point that is equidistant from all points on a circle

center of a hyperbola The midpoint of the segment joining the foci of a hyperbola

change-of-base formula A formula used to convert a logarithm from one base a to some other base b

circle The set of all points in a plane that are the same distance from a fixed point (center)

circumference The distance around a circle

closure properties The properties that state the sum, difference, product, or quotient of two real numbers is a real number.

coefficient matrix A matrix consisting of the coefficients of the variables in a system of linear equations

combinations The number of ways to choose k things from a set of n things if order is not important

common difference The constant difference between successive terms in an arithmetic sequence, that is, the number d in the formula $a_n = a_1 + (n - 1)d$

common logarithm A logarithm with a base of 10

common ratio The constant quotient of two successive terms in a geometric sequence, that is, the number r in the formula $a_n = a_1 r^n$

commutative properties The properties that state for real numbers a and b, $a + b = b + a$ and $ab = ba$. *Note:* The commutative property does not hold for subtraction and division.

complementary angles Two angles whose measures sum to 90°

completing the square The process of forming a trinomial square from a binomial of the form $x^2 + bx$

complex fraction A fraction that contains another fraction in its numerator and/or denominator

complex number The sum of a real number and an imaginary number

composite function A new function formed when one function is evaluated in terms of another, denoted by $(f \circ g)(x)$

composite numbers A natural number greater than 1 with factors other than 1 and itself

composition The process of using the output of one function as the input of another function

compound inequality A single statement representing the intersection or union of two inequalities

compounding periods The number of times per year interest is compounded is the number of compounding periods

compound interest The total interest earned on money deposited in an account where the interest for each compounding period is deposited back into the account, which increases the principle for the next compounding period

conditional equation A linear equation in one variable that has exactly one solution

conic section A graph that can be formed by the intersection of a plane and a right-circular cone

conjugate An expression that contains the same two terms as another but with opposite signs between them; for example, $a + \sqrt{b}$ and $a - \sqrt{b}$.

consistent system A system of equations with at least one solution

constant A term whose variable factor(s) have an exponent of 0

contradiction An equation that is false for all values of its variables; its solution set is $\varnothing$.

coordinate The number that corresponds to a given point on a number line.

Cramer's rule A method using determinants to solve systems of linear equations

critical points Given a quadratic or rational inequality, the points on the number line corresponding to its critical values

critical values Given a quadratic inequality in standard form, the solutions to the quadratic equation $ax^2 + bx + c = 0$; given a rational inequality in standard form, the values where the denominator is equal to zero and the numerator is equal to zero

cube root If $a = b^3$, then b is a cube root of a.

cube root function The function $f(x) = \sqrt[3]{x}$

cubic function A polynomial function whose equation is of third degree; alternately, a function whose equation is of the form $f(x) = ax^3 + bx^2 + cx + d$

cubic units The units given to a volume measurement

decibel A unit of measure that expresses the voltage gain (or loss) of an electronic device such as an amplifier

decreasing function A function whose value decreases as the independent value increases (graph drops as we move to the right)

degree A unit of measure for an angle

degree of a monomial The sum of the exponents of all variables in a monomial.

degree of a polynomial The largest degree of a polynomial's terms

denominator The expression below the bar of a fraction

dependent equations A system of equations that has infinitely many solutions

dependent variable The variable in an equation of two variables whose value is determined by the independent variable (usually y in an equation involving x and y)

descending powers of a variable An ordering of the terms of a polynomial such that a given variable's exponents occur in decreasing order.

determinant A calculated value from the elements in a square matrix: For a two-by-two matrix $\begin{bmatrix} a & b \\ c & d \end{bmatrix}$, the determinant is $ad - bc$. For a three-by-three determinant or larger, we use the method of expanding by minors.

diameter A line segment connecting two points on a circle and passing through the center; the length of such a line segment

difference The result of subtracting two expressions

difference of two cubes An expression of the form $a^3 - b^3$

difference of two squares An expression of the form $a^2 - b^2$

difference quotient The function defined by $\dfrac{f(x + h) - f(x)}{h}$

discriminant The part of the quadratic formula, $b^2 - 4ac$, used to determine the number and nature of solutions to the quadratic equation

distributive property The property that states for real numbers a, b, and c, $c(a + b) = ca + cb$ and $(a + b)c = ac + bc$.

dividend In a long division problem, the expression under the division symbol; in a fraction, the expression in the numerator

divisor In a long division problem, the expression in front of the division symbol; in a fraction, the expression in the denominator

double inequality Two inequalities written together to indicate a set of numbers that lie between two fixed values

doubly shaded region The area of a graph depicting the intersection of two half-planes

eccentricity A measure of the flatness of an ellipse

element of a matrix One of the numbers in a matrix

elimination (addition) An algebraic method for solving a system of equations where one variable is eliminated when the equations are added

ellipse The set of all points in a plane the sum of whose distances from two fixed points (foci) is a constant

ellipses A symbol consisting of three dots (...) meaning "and so forth" in the same manner

empty set A set that has no elements, denoted by the symbol $\varnothing$ or { }

equal ratios Two (or more) ratios that represent equal values

equation A statement indicating that two quantities are equal

equivalent equations Two equations that have the same solution set

equivalent fractions Two fractions with different denominators describing the same value; for example, $\frac{3}{11}$ and $\frac{6}{22}$ are equivalent fractions.

even integers The set of integers that can be divided exactly by 2; *Note:* 0 is an even integer.

even root If $b = \sqrt[n]{a}$, b is an even root if n is even.

event A situation that can have several different outcomes or a subset of the sample space of an experiment

exponent In the expression x^y, x is the base and y is the exponent. The exponent y states the number of times that the base x will be used as a factor.

exponential equation An equation that contains a variable in one of its exponents

exponential expression An expression of the form y^x, also called a **power of x**

exponential function A function of the form $f(x) = ab^x$

exponential function (natural) A function of the form $f(t) = Pe^{kt}$

extraneous solution A solution to an equation that does not result in a true statement when substituted for the variable in the original equation

extremes In the proportion $\frac{a}{b} = \frac{c}{d}$, the numbers a and d are called the extremes.

factorial For a natural number n, the product of all the natural numbers less than or equal to n (*Exception:* 0! is defined as 1.)

factoring The process of finding the individual factors of a product

factoring tree A visual representation of factors of a number, usually used as a tool to express the number in prime-factored form

factors of a number The natural numbers that divide a given number; for example, the factors of 12 are 1, 2, 3, 4, 6, and 12.

Fibonacci sequence The sequence 1, 1, 2, 3, 5, 8, ... with every successive term the sum of the two previous terms

finite sequence A sequence with a finite number of terms

foci of an ellipse The two fixed points used in the definition of the ellipse

foci of a hyperbola The two fixed points used in the definition of the hyperbola

FOIL method An acronym representing the order for multiplying the terms of two binomials

formula A literal equation in which the variables correspond to defined quantities

fundamental theorem of arithmetic The theorem that states there is exactly one prime factorization for any natural number greater than 1

future value The amount to which an invested amount of money will grow

Gaussian elimination A method of solving a system of linear equations by working with its associated augmented matrix

general form of the equation of a circle The equation of a circle written in the form $x^2 + y^2 + Dx + Ey + F = 0$

general form of a linear equation A linear equation written in the form $Ax + By = C$

geometric means Numbers that are inserted between two elements in a sequence to form a new geometric sequence

geometric sequence A sequence in which each successive term is equal to the product of the preceding term and a constant, written $a_1, a_1r, a_1r^2, a_1r^3, ...$

greatest common factor (GCF) The largest expression that is a factor of each of a group of expressions

greatest integer function The function whose output for a given x is the greatest integer that is less than or equal to x

grouping symbol A symbol (such as a radical sign or a fraction bar) or pair of symbols (such as parentheses or brackets) that indicate which operations should be computed before other operations

half-life The time it takes for one-half of a sample of a radioactive element to decompose

half-plane A subset of the coordinate plane consisting of all points on a given side of a boundary line

horizontal-line test A test used to determine if a given function is one-to-one: If every horizontal line that intersects the graph does so exactly once, then the graph represents a one-to-one function.

horizontal translation A graph that is the same shape as a given graph, except that it is shifted horizontally

hyperbola The set of all points in a plane the difference of whose distances from two fixed points (foci) is a constant

hypotenuse The longest side of a right triangle; the side opposite the 90° angle

identity An equation that is true for all values of its variables; its solution is $\mathbb{R}$.

identity elements The additive identity is 0, because for all real a, $a + 0 = 0 + a = a$. The multiplicative identity is 1, because for all real a, $a \cdot 1 = 1 \cdot a = a$.

identity function The function whose rule is $f(x) = x$

imaginary number The square root of a negative number

improper fraction A fraction whose numerator is greater than or equal to its denominator

inconsistent system A system of equations that has no solution; its solution set is $\varnothing$.

increasing function A function whose value increases as the independent variable increases (graph rises as we move to the right)

independent equations of a two-by-two system A system of two equations with two variables for which each equation's graph is different

independent variable The variable in an equation of two variables to which we assign input values (usually x in an equation involving x and y)

index If $b = \sqrt[n]{a}$, we say n is the index of the radical.

inequality A mathematical statement indicating that two quantities are not necessarily equal; most commonly a statement involving the symbols $<$, $\leq$, $>$, or $\geq$

inequality symbols A set of six symbols that are used to describe two expressions that are not equal:
$\approx$ "is approximately equal to"
$\neq$ "is not equal to"
$<$ "is less than"
$>$ "is greater than"
$\leq$ "is less than or equal to"
$\geq$ "is greater than or equal to"

infinite geometric series The sum of the terms of a geometric sequence for which $|r| < 1$

infinite sequence A sequence with infinitely many terms

input value A value substituted for the independent variable

integers The set of numbers given by $\{ \ldots, -4, -3, -2, -1, 0, 1, 2, 3, 4, \ldots \}$

integer square An integer that is the square of another integer

interval A set of all real numbers between two given real numbers a and b; it must be specified whether or not a and b are included in the interval.

inverse function The function, denoted by f^{-1}, obtained by reversing the coordinates of each ordered pair $(x, f(x))$; for example, if $f(2) = 3$, then $f^{-1}(3) = 2$.

irrational numbers The set of numbers that cannot be put in the form of a fraction with an integer numerator and nonzero integer denominator; can be expressed only as non-terminating, non-repeating decimals

isosceles triangle A triangle that has two sides of the same length

least (or lowest) common denominator The smallest expression that is exactly divisible by the denominators of a set of rational expressions

like radicals Radicals that have the same index and the same radicand

like signs Two numbers that are both positive or both negative

like terms Terms containing the same variables, each with the same exponents

linear equation in one variable An equation of the form $ax + b = c$, where a, b, and c are real numbers and $a \neq 0$

linear equation in two variables An equation of the form $Ax + By = C$, where A, B, and C are real numbers; A and B cannot both be 0.

linear function A function whose graph is a line; alternately, a function whose equation is of the form $f(x) = ax + b$

linear inequality A statement written in one of the following forms: $y > ax + b$, $y \geq ax + b$, $y < ax + b$, or $y \leq ax + b$

literal equation An equation with more than one variable, usually a formula

logarithm The exponent to which b is raised to get x, denoted by $\log_b x$

logarithmic equation An equation with logarithmic expressions that contain a variable

logarithmic function The function $f(x) = \log_b x$; $y = \log_b x$ if and only if $x = b^y$

lowest terms A fraction written in such a way so that no integer greater than 1 divides both its numerator and its denominator; also called **simplest form**

major axis of an ellipse The line segment joining the vertices of an ellipse

matrix A rectangular array of numbers

means In the proportion $\dfrac{a}{b} = \dfrac{c}{d}$, the numbers b and c are called the means.

minor A number associated with an element of a square matrix used to find a determinant of next lower order, by crossing out the elements of the matrix that are in the same row and column as the element

minor axis of an ellipse The line segment passing through the center of an ellipse perpendicular to the major axis

minuend The first expression in the difference of two expressions; for example, in the expression $(3x^2 + 2x - 5) - (4x^2 - x + 5)$, the expression $(3x^2 + 2x - 5)$ is the minuend.

mixed number A rational number expressed as an integer plus a proper fraction

monomial A polynomial with exactly one term

multiplication principle of events The method of determining the number of ways that one event can be followed by another

multiplication property of equality The property that states if a, b, and c are real numbers and $a = b$, then $ac = bc$.

multiplicative inverse Two numbers whose product is 1; also called **reciprocals**

natural logarithm A logarithm with a base of e

natural numbers The set of numbers given by {1, 2, 3, 4, 5, ... }; also called **positive integers**

negative numbers The set of numbers less than zero

negatives A pair of numbers, a and b, represented by points that lie on opposite sides of the origin and at equal distances from the origin. If a and b are negatives, $a + b = 0$. Also called **opposites** or **additive inverses**

number line A line that is used to represent real numbers or sets of real numbers

numerator The expression above the bar of a fraction

numerical coefficient The number factor of a term; for example, the numerical coefficient of $8ab$ is 8.

odd integers The set of integers that cannot be divided exactly by 2

odd root If $b = \sqrt[n]{a}$, b is an odd root if n is odd.

opposites A pair of numbers, a and b, represented by points that lie on opposite sides of the origin and at equal distances from the origin. If a and b are opposites, $a + b = 0$. Also called **negatives** or **additive inverses**

ordered pair A pair of real numbers, written as (x, y), that describes a unique point in the Cartesian plane

parabola The graph of a quadratic function

partial sum The sum of finitely many consecutive terms of a series, starting at the first term

Pascal's triangle A triangular array of numbers in which 1's begin and end each row, and each entry between the 1's is the sum of the closest pair of numbers in the line immediately above it; the first 4 rows of Pascal's triangle are

$$
\begin{array}{ccccccc}
 & & & 1 & & & \\
 & & 1 & & 1 & & \\
 & 1 & & 2 & & 1 & \\
1 & & 3 & & 3 & & 1
\end{array}
$$

percent The numerator of a fraction whose denominator is 100

perfect-square trinomial A trinomial of the form $a^2 + 2ab + b^2$ or of the form $a^2 - 2ab + b^2$

perimeter The distance around a non-circular geometric figure

periodic interest rate The interest rate used for each compounding period

permutations The number of ways to choose k things from a set of n things if order is important

perpendicular lines Two lines that meet at a 90° angle, two lines whose slopes are negative reciprocals of each other, or a horizontal line and a vertical line

piecewise-defined function A function defined by using different equations for different parts of its domain

plane The graph of an equation of the form $ax + by + cz = d$

point circle A circle with radius zero; a single point

point-slope form The equation of a line in the form $y - y_1 = m(x - x_1)$, where m is the slope and (x_1, y_1) is a point on the line

polynomial An algebraic expression that is a single term or the sum of several terms containing whole-number exponents on the variables

polynomial function A function whose equation is a polynomial, for example, $f(x) = x^2 - 3x + 6$

positive integers The set of numbers given by {1, 2, 3, 4, 5, ... }, that is, the set of integers that are greater than zero; also called the **natural numbers**

power of x An expression of the form x^y; also called an **exponential expression**

power rule The rule that states if x, y, and n are real numbers and $x = y$, then $x^n = y^n$

prime-factored form A natural number written as the product of factors that are prime numbers

prime number A natural number greater than 1 that can be divided exactly only by 1 and itself

prime polynomial A polynomial that does not factor over the rational numbers

principal square root The positive square root of a number

probability A measure of likelihood of an event

product The result of multiplying two or more expressions

proper fraction A fraction whose numerator is less than its denominator

proportion A statement that two ratios are equal

Pythagorean theorem If the length of the hypotenuse of a right triangle is c and the lengths of the two legs are a and b, then $a^2 + b^2 = c^2$.

quadrants The four regions in the Cartesian plane, formed by the x- and y-axes.

quadratic formula A formula that gives the solutions to the general quadratic equation; $x = \dfrac{-b \pm \sqrt{b^2 - 4ac}}{2a}$ $(a \neq 0)$

quadratic function A polynomial function whose equation in one variable is of second degree; alternately, a function whose equation is of the form $f(x) = ax^2 + bx + c$ $(a \neq 0)$

quadratic inequality An inequality involving a quadratic polynomial in one variable

quotient The result of dividing two expressions

radical sign The symbol used to represent the root of a number

radicand The expression under a radical sign

radius A segment drawn from the center of a circle to a point on the circle; the length of such a line segment

rate A ratio used to compare two quantities of different units

ratio The comparison of two numbers by their indicated quotient

rationalizing the denominator The process of simplifying a fraction so that there are no radicals in the denominator

rationalizing the numerator The process of simplifying a fraction so that there are no radicals in the numerator

rational numbers The set of fractions that have an integer numerator and a nonzero integer denominator; alternately, any terminating or repeating decimal

real numbers The set that contains the rational numbers and the irrational numbers

reciprocal One number is the reciprocal of another if their product is 1; for example, $\frac{3}{11}$ is the reciprocal of $\frac{11}{3}$. Also called **multiplicative inverses**

rectangular coordinate system A grid that allows us to identify each point in a plane with a unique pair of numbers; also called the **Cartesian coordinate system**

remainder The computation of $x \div y$ will yield an expression of the form $q + \frac{r}{y}$. The quantity r is called the remainder.

repeating decimal A decimal expression of a fraction that eventually falls into an infinitely repeating pattern

Richter scale A unit of measure that expresses magnitude (ground motion) of an earthquake

right angle An angle whose measure is 90°

root A number that makes an equation true when substituted for its variable; if there are several variables, then the set of numbers that make the equation true; also called a **solution**

sample space The set of all possible outcomes for an experiment

scientific notation The representation of a given number as the product of a number between 1 and 10 (1 is included), and an integer power of ten, for example, 6.02×10^{23}

sequence An ordered set of numbers that are defined by the position (1st, 2nd, 3rd, etc.) they hold

set A collection of objects whose members are listed or defined within braces

set-builder notation A method of describing a set that uses a variable (or variables) to represent the elements and a rule to determine the possible values of the variable; for example, we can describe the natural numbers as $\{x \mid x$ is an integer and $x > 0\}$.

similar triangles Two triangles that have the same shape, that is, two triangles whose corresponding angles have the same measure

simplest form The form of a fraction where no expression other than 1 divides both its numerator and its denominator

simplify (a fraction) To put a fraction into its simplest form

simultaneous solution Values for the variables in a system of equations that satisfy all of the equations

slope-intercept form The equation of the line in the form $y = mx + b$ where m is the slope and b is the y-coordinate of the y-intercept.

solution/solution set A number that makes an equation true when substituted for its variable; if there are several variables, then the numbers that make the equation true; also called a **root**

solution of an inequality The numbers that make a given inequality true

square matrix A matrix with the same number of rows as columns

square root If $a = b^2$, then b is a square root of a.

square root function The function $f(x) = \sqrt{x}$

square-root property The property that states the equation $x^2 = c$ has two solutions: $\sqrt{c}$ and $-\sqrt{c}$

square units The units given to an area measurement

standard deviation A measure of how closely a set of data is grouped about its mean

standard form of the equation of a circle The equation of a circle written in the form $(x - h)^2 + (y - k)^2 = r^2$, where (h, k) is the center and r is the radius

standard notation The representation of a given number as an integer part, followed by a decimal, for example, 212.3337012

step function A function whose graph is a series of horizontal line segments

straight angle An angle whose measure is 180°

subset A set, all of whose elements are included in a different set; for example, the set $\{1, 3, 5\}$ is a subset of the set $\{1, 2, 3, 4, 5\}$.

subtrahend The second expression in the difference of two expressions; for example, in the expression $(3x^2 + 2x - 5) - (4x^2 - x + 5)$, the expression $(4x^2 - x + 5)$ is the subtrahend.

sum The result of adding two expressions

summation notation A shorthand notation for indicating the sum of a number of consecutive terms in a series, denoted by Σ

sum of two squares An expression of the form $a^2 + b^2$

supplementary angles Two angles whose measures sum to 180°

system of equations Two or more equations that are solved simultaneously

term An expression that is a number, a variable, or a product of numbers and variables; for example, 37, xyz, and $3x$ are terms.

terminating decimal A decimal expression for a fraction that contains a finite number of decimal places

tree diagram A way of visually representing all the possible outcomes of an event

triangular form of a matrix A matrix with all zeros below its main diagonal

trinomial A polynomial with exactly three terms.

unit cost The ratio of an item's cost to its quantity

unlike signs Two numbers have unlike signs if one is positive and one is negative.

unlike terms Terms that are not like terms

variables Letters that are used to represent unknown numbers

vertex The lowest point of a parabola that opens up, or the highest point of a parabola that opens down

vertex angle of an isosceles triangle The angle in an isosceles triangle formed by the two sides that are of the same length

vertical translation A graph that is the same shape as a given graph, only shifted vertically

vertices of a hyperbola The endpoints of the transverse axis, the axis that passes through the foci

vertices of an ellipse The endpoints of the major axis

volume The amount of space enclosed by a three-dimensional geometric solid

whole numbers The set of numbers given by $\{0, 1, 2, 3, 4, 5, \dots\}$, that is, the set of integers that are greater than or equal to zero

x-coordinate The first number in the Cartesian coordinates of a point.

x-intercept The point $(a, 0)$ where a graph intersects the x-axis.

y-coordinate The second number in the Cartesian coordinates of a point.

y-intercept The point $(0, b)$ where a graph intersects the y-axis.

zero-factor property The property of real numbers that if the product of two quantities is 0, then at least one of those quantities must be equal to 0.

There are several ways that a graph can exhibit symmetry about the coordinate axes and the origin. It is often easier to draw graphs of equations if we first find the x- and y-intercepts and find any of the following symmetries of the graph:

1. **y-axis symmetry:** If the point $(-x, y)$ lies on a graph whenever the point (x, y) does, as in Figure I-1(a), we say that the graph is **symmetric about the y-axis.**

2. **Symmetry about the origin:** If the point $(-x, -y)$ lies on the graph whenever the point (x, y) does, as in Figure I-1(b), we say that the graph is **symmetric about the origin.**

3. **x-axis symmetry:** If the point $(x, -y)$ lies on the graph whenever the point (x, y) does, as in Figure I-1(c), we say that the graph is **symmetric about the x-axis.**

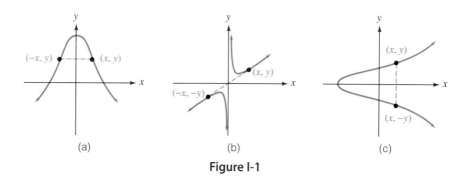

(a)　　　　　(b)　　　　　(c)

Figure I-1

Tests for Symmetry for Graphs in x and y

- To test a graph for y-axis symmetry, replace x with $-x$. If the new equation is equivalent to the original equation, the graph is symmetric about the y-axis. Symmetry about the y-axis will occur whenever x appears with only even exponents.

- To test a graph for symmetry about the origin, replace x with $-x$ and y with $-y$. If the resulting equation is equivalent to the original equation, the graph is symmetric about the origin.

- To test a graph for x-axis symmetry, replace y with $-y$. If the resulting equation is equivalent to the original equation, the graph is symmetric about the x-axis. The only function that is symmetric about the x-axis is $f(x) = 0$.

EXAMPLE 1   Find the intercepts and the symmetries of the graph of $y = f(x) = x^3 - 9x$. Then graph the function.

Solution   ***x*-intercepts:**   To find the *x*-intercepts, we let $y = 0$ and solve for *x*:

$$y = x^3 - 9x$$
$$0 = x^3 - 9x \qquad \text{Substitute 0 for } y.$$
$$0 = x(x^2 - 9) \qquad \text{Factor out } x.$$
$$0 = x(x + 3)(x - 3) \qquad \text{Factor } x^2 - 9.$$
$$x = 0 \quad \text{or} \quad x + 3 = 0 \quad \text{or} \quad x - 3 = 0 \qquad \text{Set each factor equal to 0.}$$
$$x = -3 \qquad\qquad x = 3$$

Since the *x*-coordinates of the *x*-intercepts are 0, −3, and 3, the graph intersects the *x*-axis at $(0, 0)$, $(-3, 0)$, and $(3, 0)$.

***y*-intercepts:**   To find the *y*-intercepts, we let $x = 0$ and solve for *y*.

$$y = x^3 - 9x$$
$$y = 0^3 - 9(0) \qquad \text{Substitute 0 for } x.$$
$$y = 0$$

Since the *y*-coordinate of the *y*-intercept is 0, the graph intersects the *y*-axis at $(0, 0)$.

Symmetry: We test for symmetry about the *y*-axis by replacing *x* with −*x*, simplifying, and comparing the result to the original equation.

(1) $y = x^3 - 9x$ This is the original equation.
       $y = (-x)^3 - 9(-x)$ Replace *x* with −*x*.
(2) $y = -x^3 + 9x$ Simplify.

Because Equation 2 is not equivalent to Equation 1, the graph is not symmetric about the *y*-axis.
   We test for symmetry about the origin by replacing *x* with −*x* and *y* with −*y*, respectively, and comparing the result to the original equation.

(1) $y = x^3 - 9x$ This is the original equation.
       $-y = (-x)^3 - 9(-x)$ Replace *x* with −*x*, and *y* with −*y*.
       $-y = -x^3 + 9x$ Simplify.
(3) $y = x^3 - 9x$ Multiply both sides by −1 to solve for *y*.

Because Equation 3 is equivalent to Equation 1, the graph is symmetric about the origin. Because the equation is the equation of a nonzero function, there is no symmetry about the *x*-axis.
   To graph the equation, we plot the *x*-intercepts of $(-3, 0)$, $(0, 0)$, and $(3, 0)$ and the *y*-intercept of $(0, 0)$. We also plot other points for positive values of *x* and use the symmetry about the origin to draw the rest of the graph, as in Figure I-2(a). (Note that the scale on the *x*-axis is different from the scale on the *y*-axis.)
   If we graph the equation with a graphing calculator, with window settings of $[-10, 10]$ for *x* and $[-10, 10]$ for *y*, we will obtain the graph shown in Figure I-2(b).
   From the graph, we can see that the domain is the interval $(-\infty, \infty)$, and the range is the interval $(-\infty, \infty)$.

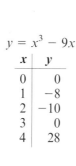

$y = x^3 - 9x$

x	y
0	0
1	−8
2	−10
3	0
4	28

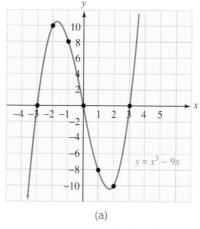

(a)

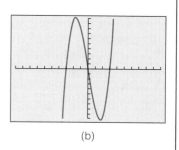

(b)

Figure I-2

EXAMPLE 2   Graph the function $y = f(x) = |x| - 2$.

Solution   **x-intercepts:**   To find the x-intercepts, we let $y = 0$ and solve for x:

$$y = |x| - 2$$
$$0 = |x| - 2$$
$$2 = |x|$$
$$x = -2 \quad \text{or} \quad x = 2$$

Since −2 and 2 are solutions, the points $(-2, 0)$ and $(2, 0)$ are the x-intercepts, and the graph passes through $(-2, 0)$ and $(2, 0)$.

y-intercepts: To find the y-intercepts, we let $x = 0$ and solve for y:

$$y = |x| - 2$$
$$y = |0| - 2$$
$$y = -2$$

Since $y = -2$, $(0, -2)$ is the y-intercept, and the graph passes through the point $(0, -2)$.

Symmetry: To test for y-axis symmetry, we replace x with $-x$.

(4) $y = |x| - 2$ This is the original equation.

$y = |-x| - 2$ Replace x with $-x$.

(5) $y = |x| - 2$ $|-x| = |x|$

Since Equation 5 is equivalent to Equation 4, the graph is symmetric about the y-axis. The graph has no other symmetries.

We plot the x- and y-intercepts and several other points (x, y), and use the y-axis symmetry to obtain the graph shown in Figure I-3(a) on the next page.

If we graph the equation with a graphing calculator, with window settings of $[-10, 10]$ for x and $[-10, 10]$ for y, we will obtain the graph shown in Figure I-3(b).

From the graph, we see that the domain is the interval $(-\infty, \infty)$, and the range is the interval $[-2, \infty)$.

$y = |x| - 2$

x	y
0	−2
1	−1
2	0
3	1
4	2

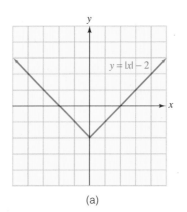

(a)

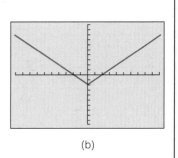

(b)

Figure I-3

I.1 EXERCISES

Find the symmetries of the graph of each equation. Do not draw the graph.

1. $y = x^2 - 1$ **2.** $y = x^3$

3. $y = x^5$ **4.** $y = x^4$

5. $y = -x^2 + 2$ **6.** $y = x^3 + 1$

7. $y = x^2 - x$ **8.** $y^2 = x + 7$

9. $y = -|x + 2|$ **10.** $y = |x| - 3$

11. $|y| = x$ **12.** $y = 2\sqrt{x}$

Graph each function and give its domain and range. Check each graph with a graphing calculator.

13. $f(x) = x^4 - 4$ **14.** $f(x) = \dfrac{1}{2}x^4 - 1$

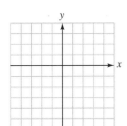 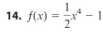

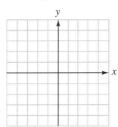

15. $f(x) = -x^3$ **16.** $f(x) = x^3 + 2$

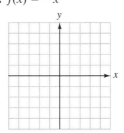 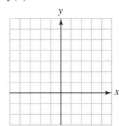

17. $f(x) = x^4 + x^2$ **18.** $f(x) = 3 - x^4$

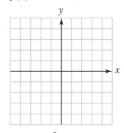 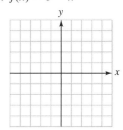

19. $f(x) = x^3 - x$ **20.** $f(x) = x^3 + x$

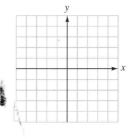 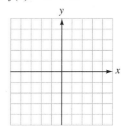

21. $f(x) = \dfrac{1}{2}|x| - 1$

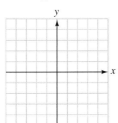

22. $f(x) = -|x| + 1$

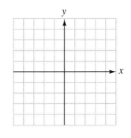

23. $f(x) = -|x + 2|$

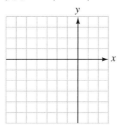

24. $f(x) = |x - 2|$

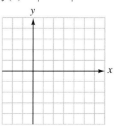

Table A   Powers and Roots

n	n^2	$\sqrt{n}$	n^3	$\sqrt[3]{n}$	n	n^2	$\sqrt{n}$	n^3	$\sqrt[3]{n}$
1	1	1.000	1	1.000	51	2,601	7.141	132,651	3.708
2	4	1.414	8	1.260	52	2,704	7.211	140,608	3.733
3	9	1.732	27	1.442	53	2,809	7.280	148,877	3.756
4	16	2.000	64	1.587	54	2,916	7.348	157,464	3.780
5	25	2.236	125	1.710	55	3,025	7.416	166,375	3.803
6	36	2.449	216	1.817	56	3,136	7.483	175,616	3.826
7	49	2.646	343	1.913	57	3,249	7.550	185,193	3.849
8	64	2.828	512	2.000	58	3,364	7.616	195,112	3.871
9	81	3.000	729	2.080	59	3,481	7.681	205,379	3.893
10	100	3.162	1,000	2.154	60	3,600	7.746	216,000	3.915
11	121	3.317	1,331	2.224	61	3,721	7.810	226,981	3.936
12	144	3.464	1,728	2.289	62	3,844	7.874	238,328	3.958
13	169	3.606	2,197	2.351	63	3,969	7.937	250,047	3.979
14	196	3.742	2,744	2.410	64	4,096	8.000	262,144	4.000
15	225	3.873	3,375	2.466	65	4,225	8.062	274,625	4.021
16	256	4.000	4,096	2.520	66	4,356	8.124	287,496	4.041
17	289	4.123	4,913	2.571	67	4,489	8.185	300,763	4.062
18	324	4.243	5,832	2.621	68	4,624	8.246	314,432	4.082
19	361	4.359	6,859	2.668	69	4,761	8.307	328,509	4.102
20	400	4.472	8,000	2.714	70	4,900	8.367	343,000	4.121
21	441	4.583	9,261	2.759	71	5,041	8.426	357,911	4.141
22	484	4.690	10,648	2.802	72	5,184	8.485	373,248	4.160
23	529	4.796	12,167	2.844	73	5,329	8.544	389,017	4.179
24	576	4.899	13,824	2.884	74	5,476	8.602	405,224	4.198
25	625	5.000	15,625	2.924	75	5,625	8.660	421,875	4.217
26	676	5.099	17,576	2.962	76	5,776	8.718	438,976	4.236
27	729	5.196	19,683	3.000	77	5,929	8.775	456,533	4.254
28	784	5.292	21,952	3.037	78	6,084	8.832	474,552	4.273
29	841	5.385	24,389	3.072	79	6,241	8.888	493,039	4.291
30	900	5.477	27,000	3.107	80	6,400	8.944	512,000	4.309
31	961	5.568	29,791	3.141	81	6,561	9.000	531,441	4.327
32	1,024	5.657	32,768	3.175	82	6,724	9.055	551,368	4.344
33	1,089	5.745	35,937	3.208	83	6,889	9.110	571,787	4.362
34	1,156	5.831	39,304	3.240	84	7,056	9.165	592,704	4.380
35	1,225	5.916	42,875	3.271	85	7,225	9.220	614,125	4.397
36	1,296	6.000	46,656	3.302	86	7,396	9.274	636,056	4.414
37	1,369	6.083	50,653	3.332	87	7,569	9.327	658,503	4.431
38	1,444	6.164	54,872	3.362	88	7,744	9.381	681,472	4.448
39	1,521	6.245	59,319	3.391	89	7,921	9.434	704,969	4.465
40	1,600	6.325	64,000	3.420	90	8,100	9.487	729,000	4.481
41	1,681	6.403	68,921	3.448	91	8,281	9.539	753,571	4.498
42	1,764	6.481	74,088	3.476	92	8,464	9.592	778,688	4.514
43	1,849	6.557	79,507	3.503	93	8,649	9.644	804,357	4.531
44	1,936	6.633	85,184	3.530	94	8,836	9.695	830,584	4.547
45	2,025	6.708	91,125	3.557	95	9,025	9.747	857,375	4.563
46	2,116	6.782	97,336	3.583	96	9,216	9.798	884,736	4.579
47	2,209	6.856	103,823	3.609	97	9,409	9.849	912,673	4.595
48	2,304	6.928	110,592	3.634	98	9,604	9.899	941,192	4.610
49	2,401	7.000	117,649	3.659	99	9,801	9.950	970,299	4.626
50	2,500	7.071	125,000	3.684	100	10,000	10.000	1,000,000	4.642

Table B *(continued)*

N	0	1	2	3	4	5	6	7	8	9
5.5	.7404	.7412	.7419	.7427	.7435	.7443	.7451	.7459	.7466	.7474
5.6	.7482	.7490	.7497	.7505	.7513	.7520	.7528	.7536	.7543	.7551
5.7	.7559	.7566	.7574	.7582	.7589	.7597	.7604	.7612	.7619	.7627
5.8	.7634	.7642	.7649	.7657	.7664	.7672	.7679	.7686	.7694	.7701
5.9	.7709	.7716	.7723	.7731	.7738	.7745	.7752	.7760	.7767	.7774
6.0	.7782	.7789	.7796	.7803	.7810	.7818	.7825	.7832	.7839	.7846
6.1	.7853	.7860	.7868	.7875	.7882	.7889	.7896	.7903	.7910	.7917
6.2	.7924	.7931	.7938	.7945	.7952	.7959	.7966	.7973	.7980	.7987
6.3	.7993	.8000	.8007	.8014	.8021	.8028	.8035	.8041	.8048	.8055
6.4	.8062	.8069	.8075	.8082	.8089	.8096	.8102	.8109	.8116	.8122
6.5	.8129	.8136	.8142	.8149	.8156	.8162	.8169	.8176	.8182	.8189
6.6	.8195	.8202	.8209	.8215	.8222	.8228	.8235	.8241	.8248	.8254
6.7	.8261	.8267	.8274	.8280	.8287	.8293	.8299	.8306	.8312	.8319
6.8	.8325	.8331	.8338	.8344	.8351	.8357	.8363	.8370	.8376	.8382
6.9	.8388	.8395	.8401	.8407	.8414	.8420	.8426	.8432	.8439	.8445
7.0	.8451	.8457	.8463	.8470	.8476	.8482	.8488	.8494	.8500	.8506
7.1	.8513	.8519	.8525	.8531	.8537	.8543	.8549	.8555	.8561	.8567
7.2	.8573	.8579	.8585	.8591	.8597	.8603	.8609	.8615	.8621	.8627
7.3	.8633	.8639	.8645	.8651	.8657	.8663	.8669	.8675	.8681	.8686
7.4	.8692	.8698	.8704	.8710	.8716	.8722	.8727	.8733	.8739	.8745
7.5	.8751	.8756	.8762	.8768	.8774	.8779	.8785	.8791	.8797	.8802
7.6	.8808	.8814	.8820	.8825	.8831	.8837	.8842	.8848	.8854	.8859
7.7	.8865	.8871	.8876	.8882	.8887	.8893	.8899	.8904	.8910	.8915
7.8	.8921	.8927	.8932	.8938	.8943	.8949	.8954	.8960	.8965	.8971
7.9	.8976	.8982	.8987	.8993	.8998	.9004	.9009	.9015	.9020	.9025
8.0	.9031	.9036	.9042	.9047	.9053	.9058	.9063	.9069	.9074	.9079
8.1	.9085	.9090	.9096	.9101	.9106	.9112	.9117	.9122	.9128	.9133
8.2	.9138	.9143	.9149	.9154	.9159	.9165	.9170	.9175	.9180	.9186
8.3	.9191	.9196	.9201	.9206	.9212	.9217	.9222	.9227	.9232	.9238
8.4	.9243	.9248	.9253	.9258	.9263	.9269	.9274	.9279	.9284	.9289
8.5	.9294	.9299	.9304	.9309	.9315	.9320	.9325	.9330	.9335	.9340
8.6	.9345	.9350	.9355	.9360	.9365	.9370	.9375	.9380	.9385	.9390
8.7	.9395	.9400	.9405	.9410	.9415	.9420	.9425	.9430	.9435	.9440
8.8	.9445	.9450	.9455	.9460	.9465	.9469	.9474	.9479	.9484	.9489
8.9	.9494	.9499	.9504	.9509	.9513	.9518	.9523	.9528	.9533	.9538
9.0	.9542	.9547	.9552	.9557	.9562	.9566	.9571	.9576	.9581	.9586
9.1	.9590	.9595	.9600	.9605	.9609	.9614	.9619	.9624	.9628	.9633
9.2	.9638	.9643	.9647	.9652	.9657	.9661	.9666	.9671	.9675	.9680
9.3	.9685	.9689	.9694	.9699	.9703	.9708	.9713	.9717	.9722	.9727
9.4	.9731	.9736	.9741	.9745	.9750	.9754	.9759	.9763	.9768	.9773
9.5	.9777	.9782	.9786	.9791	.9795	.9800	.9805	.9809	.9814	.9818
9.6	.9823	.9827	.9832	.9836	.9841	.9845	.9850	.9854	.9859	.9863
9.7	.9868	.9872	.9877	.9881	.9886	.9890	.9894	.9899	.9903	.9908
9.8	.9912	.9917	.9921	.9926	.9930	.9934	.9939	.9943	.9948	.9952
9.9	.9956	.9961	.9965	.9969	.9974	.9978	.9983	.9987	.9991	.9996

Table B Base-10 Logarithms

N	0	1	2	3	4	5	6	7	8	9
1.0	.0000	.0043	.0086	.0128	.0170	.0212	.0253	.0294	.0334	.0374
1.1	.0414	.0453	.0492	.0531	.0569	.0607	.0645	.0682	.0719	.0755
1.2	.0792	.0828	.0864	.0899	.0934	.0969	.1004	.1038	.1072	.1106
1.3	.1139	.1173	.1206	.1239	.1271	.1303	.1335	.1367	.1399	.1430
1.4	.1461	.1492	.1523	.1553	.1584	.1614	.1644	.1673	.1703	.1732
1.5	.1761	.1790	.1818	.1847	.1875	.1903	.1931	.1959	.1987	.2014
1.6	.2041	.2068	.2095	.2122	.2148	.2175	.2201	.2227	.2253	.2279
1.7	.2304	.2330	.2355	.2380	.2405	.2430	.2455	.2480	.2504	.2529
1.8	.2553	.2577	.2601	.2625	.2648	.2672	.2695	.2718	.2742	.2765
1.9	.2788	.2810	.2833	.2856	.2878	.2900	.2923	.2945	.2967	.2989
2.0	.3010	.3032	.3054	.3075	.3096	.3118	.3139	.3160	.3181	.3201
2.1	.3222	.3243	.3263	.3284	.3304	.3324	.3345	.3365	.3385	.3404
2.2	.3424	.3444	.3464	.3483	.3502	.3522	.3541	.3560	.3579	.3598
2.3	.3617	.3636	.3655	.3674	.3692	.3711	.3729	.3747	.3766	.3784
2.4	.3802	.3820	.3838	.3856	.3874	.3892	.3909	.3927	.3945	.3962
2.5	.3979	.3997	.4014	.4031	.4048	.4065	.4082	.4099	.4116	.4133
2.6	.4150	.4166	.4183	.4200	.4216	.4232	.4249	.4265	.4281	.4298
2.7	.4314	.4330	.4346	.4362	.4378	.4393	.4409	.4425	.4440	.4456
2.8	.4472	.4487	.4502	.4518	.4533	.4548	.4564	.4579	.4594	.4609
2.9	.4624	.4639	.4654	.4669	.4683	.4698	.4713	.4728	.4742	.4757
3.0	.4771	.4786	.4800	.4814	.4829	.4843	.4857	.4871	.4886	.4900
3.1	.4914	.4928	.4942	.4955	.4969	.4983	.4997	.5011	.5024	.5038
3.2	.5051	.5065	.5079	.5092	.5105	.5119	.5132	.5145	.5159	.5172
3.3	.5185	.5198	.5211	.5224	.5237	.5250	.5263	.5276	.5289	.5302
3.4	.5315	.5328	.5340	.5353	.5366	.5378	.5391	.5403	.5416	.5428
3.5	.5441	.5453	.5465	.5478	.5490	.5502	.5514	.5527	.5539	.5551
3.6	.5563	.5575	.5587	.5599	.5611	.5623	.5635	.5647	.5658	.5670
3.7	.5682	.5694	.5705	.5717	.5729	.5740	.5752	.5763	.5775	.5786
3.8	.5798	.5809	.5821	.5832	.5843	.5855	.5866	.5877	.5888	.5899
3.9	.5911	.5922	.5933	.5944	.5955	.5966	.5977	.5988	.5999	.6010
4.0	.6021	.6031	.6042	.6053	.6064	.6075	.6085	.6096	.6107	.6117
4.1	.6128	.6138	.6149	.6160	.6170	.6180	.6191	.6201	.6212	.6222
4.2	.6232	.6243	.6253	.6263	.6274	.6284	.6294	.6304	.6314	.6325
4.3	.6335	.6345	.6355	.6365	.6375	.6385	.6395	.6405	.6415	.6425
4.4	.6435	.6444	.6454	.6464	.6474	.6484	.6493	.6503	.6513	.6522
4.5	.6532	.6542	.6551	.6561	.6571	.6580	.6590	.6599	.6609	.6618
4.6	.6628	.6637	.6646	.6656	.6665	.6675	.6684	.6693	.6702	.6712
4.7	.6721	.6730	.6739	.6749	.6758	.6767	.6776	.6785	.6794	.6803
4.8	.6812	.6821	.6830	.6839	.6848	.6857	.6866	.6875	.6884	.6893
4.9	.6902	.6911	.6920	.6928	.6937	.6946	.6955	.6964	.6972	.6981
5.0	.6990	.6998	.7007	.7016	.7024	.7033	.7042	.7050	.7059	.7067
5.1	.7076	.7084	.7093	.7101	.7110	.7118	.7126	.7135	.7143	.7152
5.2	.7160	.7168	.7177	.7185	.7193	.7202	.7210	.7218	.7226	.7235
5.3	.7243	.7251	.7259	.7267	.7275	.7284	.7292	.7300	.7308	.7316
5.4	.7324	.7332	.7340	.7348	.7356	.7364	.7372	.7380	.7388	.7396

Table C   Base-e Logarithms

N	0	1	2	3	4	5	6	7	8	9
1.0	.0000	.0100	.0198	.0296	.0392	.0488	.0583	.0677	.0770	.0862
1.1	.0953	.1044	.1133	.1222	.1310	.1398	.1484	.1570	.1655	.1740
1.2	.1823	.1906	.1989	.2070	.2151	.2231	.2311	.2390	.2469	.2546
1.3	.2624	.2700	.2776	.2852	.2927	.3001	.3075	.3148	.3221	.3293
1.4	.3365	.3436	.3507	.3577	.3646	.3716	.3784	.3853	.3920	.3988
1.5	.4055	.4121	.4187	.4253	.4318	.4383	.4447	.4511	.4574	.4637
1.6	.4700	.4762	.4824	.4886	.4947	.5008	.5068	.5128	.5188	.5247
1.7	.5306	.5365	.5423	.5481	.5539	.5596	.5653	.5710	.5766	.5822
1.8	.5878	.5933	.5988	.6043	.6098	.6152	.6206	.6259	.6313	.6366
1.9	.6419	.6471	.6523	.6575	.6627	.6678	.6729	.6780	.6831	.6881
2.0	.6931	.6981	.7031	.7080	.7129	.7178	.7227	.7275	.7324	.7372
2.1	.7419	.7467	.7514	.7561	.7608	.7655	.7701	.7747	.7793	.7839
2.2	.7885	.7930	.7975	.8020	.8065	.8109	.8154	.8198	.8242	.8286
2.3	.8329	.8372	.8416	.8459	.8502	.8544	.8587	.8629	.8671	.8713
2.4	.8755	.8796	.8838	.8879	.8920	.8961	.9002	.9042	.9083	.9123
2.5	.9163	.9203	.9243	.9282	.9322	.9361	.9400	.9439	.9478	.9517
2.6	.9555	.9594	.9632	.9670	.9708	.9746	.9783	.9821	.9858	.9895
2.7	.9933	.9969	1.0006	.0043	.0080	.0116	.0152	.0188	.0225	.0260
2.8	1.0296	.0332	.0367	.0403	.0438	.0473	.0508	.0543	.0578	.0613
2.9	.0647	.0682	.0716	.0750	.0784	.0818	.0852	.0886	.0919	.0953
3.0	1.0986	.1019	.1053	.1086	.1119	.1151	.1184	.1217	.1249	.1282
3.1	.1314	.1346	.1378	.1410	.1442	.1474	.1506	.1537	.1569	.1600
3.2	.1632	.1663	.1694	.1725	.1756	.1787	.1817	.1848	.1878	.1909
3.3	.1939	.1969	.2000	.2030	.2060	.2090	.2119	.2149	.2179	.2208
3.4	.2238	.2267	.2296	.2326	.2355	.2384	.2413	.2442	.2470	.2499
3.5	1.2528	.2556	.2585	.2613	.2641	.2669	.2698	.2726	.2754	.2782
3.6	.2809	.2837	.2865	.2892	.2920	.2947	.2975	.3002	.3029	.3056
3.7	.3083	.3110	.3137	.3164	.3191	.3218	.3244	.3271	.3297	.3324
3.8	.3350	.3376	.3403	.3429	.3455	.3481	.3507	.3533	.3558	.3584
3.9	.3610	.3635	.3661	.3686	.3712	.3737	.3762	.3788	.3813	.3838
4.0	1.3863	.3888	.3913	.3938	.3962	.3987	.4012	.4036	.4061	.4085
4.1	.4110	.4134	.4159	.4183	.4207	.4231	.4255	.4279	.4303	.4327
4.2	.4351	.4375	.4398	.4422	.4446	.4469	.4493	.4516	.4540	.4563
4.3	.4586	.4609	.4633	.4656	.4679	.4702	.4725	.4748	.4770	.4793
4.4	.4816	.4839	.4861	.4884	.4907	.4929	.4951	.4974	.4996	.5019
4.5	1.5041	.5063	.5085	.5107	.5129	.5151	.5173	.5195	.5217	.5239
4.6	.5261	.5282	.5304	.5326	.5347	.5369	.5390	.5412	.5433	.5454
4.7	.5476	.5497	.5518	.5539	.5560	.5581	.5602	.5623	.5644	.5665
4.8	.5686	.5707	.5728	.5748	.5769	.5790	.5810	.5831	.5851	.5872
4.9	.5892	.5913	.5933	.5953	.5974	.5994	.6014	.6034	.6054	.6074
5.0	1.6094	.6114	.6134	.6154	.6174	.6194	.6214	.6233	.6253	.6273
5.1	.6292	.6312	.6332	.6351	.6371	.6390	.6409	.6429	.6448	.6467
5.2	.6487	.6506	.6525	.6544	.6563	.6582	.6601	.6620	.6639	.6658
5.3	.6677	.6696	.6715	.6734	.6752	.6771	.6790	.6808	.6827	.6845
5.4	.6864	.6882	.6901	.6919	.6938	.6956	.6974	.6993	.7011	.7029

Table C   (continued)

N	0	1	2	3	4	5	6	7	8	9
5.5	1.7047	.7066	.7084	.7102	.7120	.7138	.7156	.7174	.7192	.7210
5.6	.7228	.7246	.7263	.7281	.7299	.7317	.7334	.7352	.7370	.7387
5.7	.7405	.7422	.7440	.7457	.7475	.7492	.7509	.7527	.7544	.7561
5.8	.7579	.7596	.7613	.7630	.7647	.7664	.7681	.7699	.7716	.7733
5.9	.7750	.7766	.7783	.7800	.7817	.7834	.7851	.7867	.7884	.7901
6.0	1.7918	.7934	.7951	.7967	.7984	.8001	.8017	.8034	.8050	.8066
6.1	.8083	.8099	.8116	.8132	.8148	.8165	.8181	.8197	.8213	.8229
6.2	.8245	.8262	.8278	.8294	.8310	.8326	.8342	.8358	.8374	.8390
6.3	.8405	.8421	.8437	.8453	.8469	.8485	.8500	.8516	.8532	.8547
6.4	.8563	.8579	.8594	.8610	.8625	.8641	.8656	.8672	.8687	.8703
6.5	1.8718	.8733	.8749	.8764	.8779	.8795	.8810	.8825	.8840	.8856
6.6	.8871	.8886	.8901	.8916	.8931	.8946	.8961	.8976	.8991	.9006
6.7	.9021	.9036	.9051	.9066	.9081	.9095	.9110	.9125	.9140	.9155
6.8	.9169	.9184	.9199	.9213	.9228	.9242	.9257	.9272	.9286	.9301
6.9	.9315	.9330	.9344	.9359	.9373	.9387	.9402	.9416	.9430	.9445
7.0	1.9459	.9473	.9488	.9502	.9516	.9530	.9544	.9559	.9573	.9587
7.1	.9601	.9615	.9629	.9643	.9657	.9671	.9685	.9699	.9713	.9727
7.2	.9741	.9755	.9769	.9782	.9796	.9810	.9824	.9838	.9851	.9865
7.3	.9879	.9892	.9906	.9920	.9933	.9947	.9961	.9974	.9988	2.0001
7.4	2.0015	.0028	.0042	.0055	.0069	.0082	.0096	.0109	.0122	.0136
7.5	2.0149	.0162	.0176	.0189	.0202	.0215	.0229	.0242	.0255	.0268
7.6	.0281	.0295	.0308	.0321	.0334	.0347	.0360	.0373	.0386	.0399
7.7	.0412	.0425	.0438	.0451	.0464	.0477	.0490	.0503	.0516	.0528
7.8	.0541	.0554	.0567	.0580	.0592	.0605	.0618	.0631	.0643	.0656
7.9	.0669	.0681	.0694	.0707	.0719	.0732	.0744	.0757	.0769	.0782
8.0	2.0794	.0807	.0819	.0832	.0844	.0857	.0869	.0882	.0894	.0906
8.1	.0919	.0931	.0943	.0956	.0968	.0980	.0992	.1005	.1017	.1029
8.2	.1041	.1054	.1066	.1078	.1090	.1102	.1114	.1126	.1138	.1150
8.3	.1163	.1175	.1187	.1199	.1211	.1223	.1235	.1247	.1258	.1270
8.4	.1282	.1294	.1306	.1318	.1330	.1342	.1353	.1365	.1377	.1389
8.5	2.1401	.1412	.1424	.1436	.1448	.1459	.1471	.1483	.1494	.1506
8.6	.1518	.1529	.1541	.1552	.1564	.1576	.1587	.1599	.1610	.1622
8.7	.1633	.1645	.1656	.1668	.1679	.1691	.1702	.1713	.1725	.1736
8.8	.1748	.1759	.1770	.1782	.1793	.1804	.1815	.1827	.1838	.1849
8.9	.1861	.1872	.1883	.1894	.1905	.1917	.1928	.1939	.1950	.1961
9.0	2.1972	.1983	.1994	.2006	.2017	.2028	.2039	.2050	.2061	.2072
9.1	.2083	.2094	.2105	.2116	.2127	.2138	.2148	.2159	.2170	.2181
9.2	.2192	.2203	.2214	.2225	.2235	.2246	.2257	.2268	.2279	.2289
9.3	.2300	.2311	.2322	.2332	.2343	.2354	.2364	.2375	.2386	.2396
9.4	.2407	.2418	.2428	.2439	.2450	.2460	.2471	.2481	.2492	.2502
9.5	2.2513	.2523	.2534	.2544	.2555	.2565	.2576	.2586	.2597	.2607
9.6	.2618	.2628	.2638	.2649	.2659	.2670	.2680	.2690	.2701	.2711
9.7	.2721	.2732	.2742	.2752	.2762	.2773	.2783	.2793	.2803	.2814
9.8	.2824	.2834	.2844	.2854	.2865	.2875	.2885	.2895	.2905	.2915
9.9	.2925	.2935	.2946	.2956	.2966	.2976	.2986	.2996	.3006	.3016

Use the properties of logarithms and ln 10 ≈ 2.3026 to find logarithms of numbers less than 1 or greater than 10.

Getting Ready (page 2)

1. 1, 2, 3, etc. **2.** $\frac{1}{2}, \frac{2}{3}$, etc. **3.** $-3, -21$, etc.

Exercises 1.1 (page 10)

11. -15 **13.** set **15.** whole **17.** integers **19.** subset
21. rational **23.** real **25.** natural, prime **27.** odd
29. $<$ **31.** variables **33.** 7 **35.** parenthesis, open
37. absolute value **39.** 1, 2, 6, 9 **41.** 1, 2, 6, 9
43. $-3, -1, 0, 1, 2, 6, 9$ **45.** $-3, -\frac{1}{2}, -1, 0, 1, 2, \frac{5}{3}, \sqrt{7}, 3.25,$
$6, 9$ **47.** $-3, -1, 1, 9$ **49.** $6, 9$ **51.** $<$ **53.** $=$
55. $<$ **57.** $>$

59. ; 6, 6 **61.** ; 11, 11

63. ; 2, 2 **65.** ; 8, 8

67.

69. **71.**

73.

75. 36 **77.** 0 **79.** 230 **81.** 8 **83.** 9; natural, odd,
composite, and whole number **85.** 0; even integer, whole
number **87.** 24; natural, even, composite, and whole number
89. 3; natural, odd, prime, and whole number **91.** $=$
93. $=$ **95.** $<$ **97.** $>$ **99.** $=$ **101.** $7 > 3$
103. $8 \le 8$ **105.** $3 + 4 = 7$ **107.** $\sqrt{2} \approx 1.41$
109. $7 \ge 3$ **111.** $0 < 6$ **113.** $8 < 3 + 8$
115. $10 - 4 > 6 - 2$ **117.** $3 \cdot 4 > 2 \cdot 3$ **119.** $\frac{24}{6} > \frac{12}{4}$

121.

123.

125. **127.** 2

Getting Ready (page 13)

1. 250 **2.** 148 **3.** 16,606 **4.** 105

Exercises 1.2 (page 27)

1. $\frac{1}{2}$ **3.** $\frac{1}{2}$ **5.** $\frac{5}{12}$ **7.** $\frac{4}{9}$ **9.** $\frac{11}{9}$ **11.** $\frac{1}{6}$ **13.** 2.86
15. 0.5 **17.** 3.24 **19.** true **21.** false **23.** true
25. true **27.** $=$ **29.** $=$ **31.** numerator
33. undefined **35.** prime **37.** improper **39.** 1
41. multiply **43.** numerators, denominator **45.** least

common denominator, equivalent **47.** terminating, 2
49. divisor, dividend, quotient **51.** $2 \cdot 3 \cdot 5$ **53.** $2 \cdot 5 \cdot 7$
55. $\frac{1}{2}$ **57.** $\frac{3}{4}$ **59.** $\frac{4}{3}$ **61.** $\frac{9}{8}$ **63.** $\frac{3}{10}$ **65.** $\frac{8}{5}$ **67.** 10
69. $\frac{20}{3}$ **71.** $\frac{9}{10}$ **73.** $\frac{5}{8}$ **75.** 28 **77.** $\frac{1}{5}$ **79.** $\frac{6}{5}$ **81.** $\frac{1}{13}$
83. $\frac{5}{24}$ **85.** $\frac{22}{35}$ **87.** $5\frac{1}{5}$ **89.** $1\frac{2}{3}$ **91.** $1\frac{1}{4}$ **93.** $\frac{5}{9}$
95. 0.8, terminating **97.** $0.4\overline{09}$, repeating **99.** 158.65
101. 44.785 **103.** 44.88 **105.** 4.55 **107.** 587.27;
587.269 **109.** 6,025.40; 6,025.398 **111.** $\frac{3}{2}$ **113.** $\frac{1}{4}$
115. $\frac{1}{4}$ **117.** $\frac{14}{5}$ **119.** $\frac{19}{15}$ **121.** $\frac{17}{12}$ **123.** $\frac{9}{4}$ **125.** $\frac{29}{3}$
127. 350.49 **129.** 3,337.52 **131.** 10.02 **133.** 55.21
135. $31\frac{1}{6}$ acres **137.** $45\frac{1}{2}$ yd **139.** $68.45 million
141. $12,240 **143.** 13,475 **145.** $20,944,000
147. $1,764.23 **149.** $1,170 **151.** the high-capacity
boards **153.** 205,200 lb **155.** the high-efficiency furnace

Getting Ready (page 30)

1. 4 **2.** 9 **3.** 27 **4.** 8 **5.** $\frac{1}{4}$ **6.** $\frac{1}{27}$ **7.** $\frac{8}{125}$
8. $\frac{27}{1,000}$

Exercises 1.3 (page 38)

1. 32 **3.** 64 **5.** 24 **7.** 11 **9.** 16
11.
13. prime number **15.** exponent **17.** grouping
19. perimeter, circumference **21.** $P = 4s$; units
23. $P = 2l + 2w$; units **25.** $P = a + b + c$; units
27. $P = a + b + c + d$; units **29.** $C = \pi D$ or $C = 2\pi r$; units
31. $V = lwh$; cubic units **33.** $V = \frac{1}{3}Bh$; cubic units
35. $V = \frac{4}{3}\pi r^3$; cubic units **37.** $4 \cdot 4$; 16
39. $\left(\frac{1}{10}\right)\left(\frac{1}{10}\right)\left(\frac{1}{10}\right)\left(\frac{1}{10}\right); \frac{1}{10,000}$ **41.** $x \cdot x$ **43.** $3 \cdot z \cdot z \cdot z \cdot z$
45. $5t \cdot 5t$ **47.** $5 \cdot 2x \cdot 2x \cdot 2x$ **49.** 36 **51.** 1,000
53. 18 **55.** 216 **57.** 11 **59.** 3 **61.** 13 **63.** 16
65. 17 **67.** 8 **69.** $\frac{1}{144}$ **71.** 11 **73.** 1 **75.** 1
77. 16 in. **79.** 15 m **81.** 25 m^2 **83.** 60 ft^2
85. approx. 88 m **87.** approx. 1,386 ft^2 **89.** 6 cm^3
91. approx. 905 m^3 **93.** approx. 1,056 cm^3 **95.** 36
97. 28 **99.** 64 **101.** 2 **103.** 16 **105.** 21 **107.** 9
109. 8 **111.** $\frac{8}{9}$ **113.** 493.039 **115.** 640.09
117. $(3 \cdot 8) + (5 \cdot 3)$ **119.** $(3 \cdot 8 + 5) \cdot 3$
121. 40,764.51 ft^3 **123.** $121\frac{3}{5}$ m **125.** 480 ft^3 **127.** 8
131. bigger

Getting Ready (page 41)

1. 17.52 **2.** 2.94 **3.** 2 **4.** 1 **5.** 96 **6.** 382

Exercises 1.4 (page 48)

1. 5 **3.** 3 **5.** 4 **7.** 2 **9.** 20 **11.** 24 **13.** arrows
15. unlike **17.** subtract, greater **19.** add, opposite
21. 12 **23.** -10 **25.** $\frac{12}{35}$ **27.** 78 **29.** 2 **31.** 0.5
33. $\frac{5}{12}$ **35.** -14.97 **37.** 7 **39.** -1 **41.** 4 **43.** -7
45. 1 **47.** 2.2 **49.** 4 **51.** 12 **53.** 5 **55.** $\frac{1}{2}$ **57.** 4
59. -7 **61.** 10 **63.** 0 **65.** 8 **67.** 1 **69.** 3
71. 2.45 **73.** -0.41 **75.** -7.08 **77.** -2 **79.** -7
81. -8 **83.** 3 **85.** 1.3 **87.** $-8\frac{3}{4}$ **89.** -4.2 **91.** -6
93. $-\frac{29}{30}$ **95.** $175 **97.** $+9$ **99.** $-4°$ **101.** 2,000 yr
103. 1,325 m **105.** 4,000 ft **107.** $5°$ **109.** 12,187
111. 700 **113.** $422.66 **115.** $83,425.57

Getting Ready (page 50)

1. 56 **2.** 54 **3.** 72 **4.** 63 **5.** 9 **6.** 6 **7.** 8 **8.** 8

Exercises 1.5 (page 56)

1. -3 **3.** 24 **5.** -2 **7.** -9 **9.** -9 **11.** 1,125 lb
13. -45 **15.** positive **17.** positive **19.** positive
21. a **23.** 0 **25.** 48 **27.** 56 **29.** -144 **31.** 448
33. -24 **35.** 4 **37.** -64 **39.** 72 **41.** 5 **43.** -3
45. -8 **47.** 16 **49.** -16 **51.** 2 **53.** -4 **55.** 2
57. -4 **59.** -20 **61.** -6 **63.** -30 **65.** 2 **67.** 1
69. 0 **71.** undefined **73.** 9 **75.** 88 **77.** 1 **79.** -8
81. -96 **83.** -420 **85.** 49 **87.** -9 **89.** 5 **91.** 9
93. 5 **95.** 7 **97.** 20 **99.** $-\frac{11}{12}$ **101.** $-\frac{1}{6}$ **103.** $-\frac{7}{36}$
105. $-\frac{1}{36}$ **107.** $(2)(+3) = +6$
109. $(-350)(15) = -\$5,250$ **111.** $(+23)(-120) = -2,760$
113. $\frac{-18}{-3} = +6$ **115. a.** $-\$2,400 **b.** $-\$969
c. $-\$1,044 **d.** $-\$4,413 **117.** 2-point loss per day
119. yes

Getting Ready (page 59)

1. sum **2.** product **3.** quotient **4.** difference
5. quotient **6.** difference **7.** product **8.** sum

Exercises 1.6 (page 64)

1. 1 **3.** -11 **5.** 16 **7.** -12 **9.** 532 **11.** $\frac{1}{2}$
13. sum **15.** multiplication **17.** algebraic **19.** term, coefficient **21.** $x + y$ **23.** $y - x$ **25.** xy **27.** $3xy$
29. $\frac{y}{x}$ **31.** $\frac{3z}{4x}$ **33.** 3 **35.** 30 **37.** $\frac{15}{2}$ **39.** -3
41. undefined **43.** 5 **45.** 1; 6 **47.** 3; -1 **49.** 4; 3
51. 3; -4 **53.** 4; 3 **55.** $z + \frac{x}{y}$ **57.** $z - xy$ **59.** $\frac{xy}{x + z}$
61. $\frac{x - 4}{3y}$ **63.** the quotient obtained when the sum of 3 and x
is divided by y **65.** the product of x, y, and the sum of x
and y **67.** the sum of x and 3 **69.** the quotient obtained
when x is divided by y **71.** the product of 2, x, and y

73. the quotient obtained when 5 is divided by the sum of x
and y **75.** $x + z$; 10 **77.** $y - z$; 2 **79.** $yz - 3$; 5
81. $\frac{xy}{z}$; 16 **83.** 19 and x **85.** x **87.** 3, x, y, and z
89. 17, x, and z **91.** 5, 1, and 8 **93.** x and y **95.** 75
97. x and y **99.** $c + 4$ **101. a.** $h - 20$ **b.** $c + 20$
103. $35,000n **105.** $500 - x$ **107.** $(3d + 5)$
109. 49,995,000

Getting Ready (page 67)

1. 17 **2.** 17 **3.** 38.6 **4.** 38.6 **5.** 56 **6.** 56 **7.** 0
8. 1 **9.** 777 **10.** 777

Exercises 1.7 (page 73)

7. $x + y^2 \geq z$ **9.** $\geq$ **11.** positive **13.** real **15.** a
17. $(b + c)$ **19.** ac **21.** a **23.** element, multiplication
25. $a, \frac{1}{a}$; multiplicative **27.** 10 **29.** -24 **31.** 144
33. 3 **35.** Both are 12. **37.** Both are 29. **39.** Both
are 60. **41.** Both are 175. **43.** $4x + 8$ **45.** $2z - 6$
47. $3x + 3y$ **49.** $x^2 + 3x$ **51.** $-ax - bx$
53. $-4x^2 - 4x - 8$ **55.** $-2, \frac{1}{2}$ **57.** $-\frac{1}{3}$, 3 **59.** 0, none
61. $\frac{5}{2}, -\frac{2}{5}$ **63.** $0.2, -5$ **65.** $-\frac{4}{3}, \frac{3}{4}$ **67.** $3x + 3 \cdot 2$
69. xy^2 **71.** $(y + x)z$ **73.** $x(yz)$ **75.** Both are 0.
77. Both are -6. **79.** $-5t - 10$ **81.** $-2ax + 2a^2$
83. comm. prop. of add. **85.** comm. prop. of mult.
87. distrib. prop. **89.** comm. prop. of add. **91.** identity
for mult. **93.** add. inverse **95.** add. identity prop.

Chapter Review (page 75)

1. 1, 2, 3, 4, 5 **2.** 2, 3, 5 **3.** 1, 3, 5 **4.** 4 **5.** $-6, 0, 5$
6. $-6, -\frac{2}{3}, 0, 2.6, 5$ **7.** 5 **8.** all of them
9. $-6, 0$ **10.** 5 **11.** $\sqrt{2}, \pi$ **12.** $-6, -\frac{2}{3}$ **13.** $<$
14. $<$ **15.** $=$ **16.** $>$ **17.** 8 **18.** -8
19.

20.

21.

22.

23. 11 **24.** 31 **25.** $\frac{5}{3}$ **26.** 11 **27.** $\frac{1}{3}$ **28.** $\frac{1}{3}$ **29.** 1
30. $\frac{5}{2}$ **31.** $\frac{4}{3}$ **32.** $\frac{1}{3}$ **33.** $\frac{10}{21}$ **34.** $\frac{73}{63}$ **35.** $\frac{11}{21}$ **36.** $\frac{2}{15}$
37. $8\frac{11}{12}$ **38.** $2\frac{11}{12}$ **39.** 48.61 **40.** 12.99 **41.** 18.55
42. 3.7 **43.** 4.70 **44.** 26.36 **45.** 3.57 **46.** 3.75
47. $66\frac{3}{4}$ acres **48.** 6.85 hr **49.** 57 **50.** 40.2 ft **51.** 81
52. $\frac{4}{9}$ **53.** 0.25 **54.** 33 **55.** 25 **56.** 49
57. $22\frac{3}{4}$ sq ft **58.** 15,133.6 ft^3 **59.** 32 **60.** 7 **61.** 6
62. 3 **63.** 98 **64.** 38 **65.** 3 **66.** 15 **67.** 58
68. 4 **69.** 7 **70.** 3 **71.** 22 **72.** 1 **73.** 15
74. -57 **75.** -6.5 **76.** $\frac{1}{2}$ **77.** -12 **78.** 16 **79.** 1.2
80. -3.54 **81.** 19 **82.** 1 **83.** -5 **84.** -7 **85.** $\frac{3}{2}$
86. 1 **87.** 1 **88.** $-\frac{1}{7}$ **89.** 12 **90.** 60 **91.** $\frac{1}{4}$
92. 1.3875 **93.** -35 **94.** -105 **95.** $-\frac{2}{3}$ **96.** -45.14

97. 5   **98.** 7   **99.** $\frac{7}{2}$ **100.** 6   **101.** -5 **102.** -2
103. 26   **104.** 7   **105.** 6   **106.** $\frac{3}{2}$ **107.** xz
108. $x + 2y$ **109.** $2(x + y)$ **110.** $x - yz$
111. the product of 3, x, and y **112.** 5 decreased by the product of y and z **113.** 5 less than the product of y and z
114. the sum of x, y, and z, divided by twice their product
115. -4 **116.** -1 **117.** -2 **118.** 5   **119.** 4
120. 6   **121.** -6 **122.** 3   **123.** 2   **124.** 6   **125.** -7
126. 39   **127.** 6   **128.** -2 **129.** 3   **130.** 7   **131.** 1
132. 9   **133.** closure prop. of add.   **134.** comm. prop. of mult.   **135.** assoc. prop. of add.   **136.** distrib. prop.
137. comm. prop. of add.   **138.** assoc. prop. of mult.
139. comm. prop. of add.   **140.** identity for mult.
141. add. inverse   **142.** identity for add.

Chapter 1 Test (page 82)

1. 31, 37, 41, 43, 47   **2.** 2
3.

4.

5. -23 **6.** 0   **7.** =   **8.** <
9. >   **10.** =   **11.** $\frac{13}{20}$ **12.** 1   **13.** $\frac{4}{5}$ **14.** $\frac{9}{2} = 4\frac{1}{2}$
15. -1 **16.** $-\frac{1}{13}$ **17.** 77.7   **18.** 301.57 ft^2 **19.** 64 cm^2
20. 1,539 in.^{3} **21.** -2 **22.** -14 **23.** -4 **24.** 12
25. 5   **26.** -23 **27.** $\frac{xy}{x + y}$ **28.** $5y - (x + y)$
29. $24x + 14y$ **30.** $\$(12a + 8b)$ **31.** 3   **32.** 4
33. $3x + 6$ **34.** $-pr + pt$ **35.** 0   **36.** 5   **37.** comm. prop. of mult.   **38.** distrib. prop.   **39.** comm. prop. of add.
40. mult. inverse prop.

Getting Ready (page 84)

1. -3 **2.** 7   **3.** x **4.** 1   **5.** $\frac{1}{x}$ **6.** 1   **7.** 4   **8.** 4
9. 3

Exercises 2.1 (page 95)

1. 20   **3.** 2   **5.** 1   **7.** 10   **9.** $\frac{22}{15}$ **11.** $\frac{25}{27}$ **13.** 14
15. -317 **17.** equation, expression   **19.** equivalent
21. equal   **23.** equal   **25.** regular price   **27.** 100
29. equation   **31.** expression   **33.** equation
35. expression   **37.** yes   **39.** no   **41.** yes   **43.** yes
45. yes   **47.** yes   **49.** 19   **51.** -8 **53.** 519   **55.** $\frac{1}{2}$
57. 6   **59.** -13 **61.** -4 **63.** $-\frac{7}{15}$ **65.** 25   **67.** 15
69. 1   **71.** $-\frac{3}{2}$ **73.** 3   **75.** -11 **77.** -9 **79.** 27
81. $\frac{1}{8}$ **83.** 98   **85.** 85   **87.** 4,912   **89.** \$9,345
91. \$90   **93.** 80   **95.** 19   **97.** 320   **99.** 380   **101.** 150
103. 20%   **105.** 3.3   **107.** -64 **109.** -28
111. -5.58 **113.** $\frac{5}{2}$ **115.** 74   **117.** -33 **119.** $-\frac{1}{3}$
121. $\frac{1}{14}$ **123.** $-\frac{1}{5}$ **125.** 5   **127.** -2 **129.** $-\frac{1}{2}$
131. 8%   **133.** 200%   **135.** \$270   **137.** 6%   **139.** \$260
141. 234   **143.** 55%   **145.** 2,760   **147.** 370
149. \$17,750   **151.** \$2.22   **153.** \$4.95   **155.** \$145,149
159. about 3.16

Getting Ready (page 98)

1. 22   **2.** 36   **3.** 5   **4.** $\frac{13}{2}$ **5.** -1 **6.** -1 **7.** $\frac{7}{9}$
8. $-\frac{19}{3}$

Exercises 2.2 (page 105)

1. add 7   **3.** add 3   **5.** multiply by 3   **7.** 3   **9.** 50 cm
11. 80.325 in.^{2} **13.** cost   **15.** percent   **17.** percent of increase   **19.** 1   **21.** -2 **23.** -1 **25.** 3   **27.** -54
29. -9 **31.** 3   **33.** -33 **35.** 28   **37.** 5   **39.** 10
41. $\frac{17}{5}$ **43.** 10   **45.** -4 **47.** 10   **49.** 4   **51.** 2
53. -0.7 **55.** -2 **57.** 2   **59.** -5 **61.** $\frac{3}{2}$ **63.** 20
65. $\frac{15}{4}$ **67.** $\frac{16}{5}$ **69.** 7   **71.** -8 **73.** $-\frac{2}{3}$ **75.** 0
77. 6   **79.** $\frac{3}{5}$ **81.** \$250   **83.** 7 days   **85.** \$50
87. 6% to 15%   **89.** 5   **91.** 3   **93.** 29 min   **95.** \$7,400
97. no chance; he needs 112   **101.** $\frac{7x + 4}{22} = \frac{1}{2}$

Getting Ready (page 107)

1. $3x + 4x$ **2.** $7x + 2x$ **3.** $8w - 3w$ **4.** $10y - 4y$
5. $7x$ **6.** $9x$ **7.** $5w$ **8.** $6y$

Exercises 2.3 (page 113)

1. $8x$ **3.** 0   **5.** 12   **7.** 3   **9.** 2   **11.** 0   **13.** 2
15. $\frac{13}{56}$ **17.** $\frac{48}{35}$ **19.** variables, like, unlike, numerical
21. identity, contradiction   **23.** $20x$ **25.** $3x^2$
27. unlike terms   **29.** $7x + 6$ **31.** $7z - 15$
33. $12x + 121$ **35.** $6y + 62$ **37.** $-2x + 7y$ **39.** -41
41. -3 **43.** -2 **45.** 3   **47.** 1   **49.** 1   **51.** 6
53. 35   **55.** -9 **57.** -20 **59.** 9   **61.** 16   **63.** 5
65. 4   **67.** identity, $\mathbb{R}$ **69.** contradiction, $\varnothing$
71. contradiction, $\varnothing$ **73.** identity, $\mathbb{R}$ **75.** expression, $2 + y$ **77.** equation, 8   **79.** expression, $5x + 7$
81. equation, -20 **83.** equation, $\mathbb{R}$ **85.** equation, $\frac{1}{3}$
87. equation, 2   **89.** expression, $5x + 24$ **91.** equation, -3 **93.** expression, $0.7m + 22.16$ **95.** equation, 1
97. equation, 0   **99.** 0.9   **105.** 0

Getting Ready (page 115)

1. 3   **2.** -5 **3.** r **4.** $-a$ **5.** 7   **6.** 12   **7.** d **8.** s

Exercises 2.4 (page 120)

1. $a = -\frac{c}{b}$ **3.** $b = ac$ **5.** $5x - 5y$ **7.** $-x - 13$
9. literal   **11.** isolate   **13.** subtract   **15.** $I = \frac{E}{R}$
17. $w = \frac{V}{lh}$ **19.** $A = K - 32$ **21.** $h = \frac{3V}{B}$ **23.** $h = \frac{3V}{\pi r^2}$
25. $x = 2y - 2$ **27.** $B = 8A - 4$ **29.** $B = \frac{2}{3}A - 5$ or $B = \frac{2A - 15}{3}$ **31.** $q = \frac{2p - hr}{h}$ or $q = \frac{2p}{h} - r$ **33.** $r = \frac{G}{2b} + 1$ or $r = \frac{G + 2b}{2b}$ **35.** $t = \frac{d}{r}$; $t = 3$ **37.** $c = P - a - b$; $c = 3$
39. $s = \frac{P}{4}$ **41.** $w = \frac{P - 2l}{2}$ **43.** $t = \frac{A - P}{Pr}$ **45.** $w = \frac{2gK}{v^2}$
47. $g = \frac{wv^2}{2K}$ **49.** $M = \frac{Fd^2}{Gm}$ **51.** $t = \frac{i}{pr}$; $t = 2$
53. $h = \frac{2K}{a + b}$; $h = 8$ **55.** $h = \frac{3V}{\pi r^2}$; $h = 3$ in.   **57.** $I = \frac{E}{R}$;

$I = 4$ amp   **59.** $R = \frac{P}{I^2}$; $R = 13.78$ ohms   **61.** $m = \frac{Fd^2}{GM}$
63. $D = \frac{L - 3.25r - 3.25R}{2}$; $D = 6$ ft   **65.** $C \approx 0.1304T$, about
13% of taxable income   **69.** 90,000,000,000 joules

Getting Ready (page 123)

1. $(x + x + 2)$ ft or $(2x + 2)$ ft   **2.** $(x + 3x)$ ft or $4x$ ft
3. $P = 2l + 2w$

Exercises 2.5 (page 128)

1. 70°   **3.** 20 ft   **5.** 200 cm^3 **7.** $7x - 6$ **9.** $-\frac{3}{2}$
11. $1,488   **13.** $2l + 2w$ **15.** vertex   **17.** degrees
19. straight   **21.** supplementary   **23.** 4 ft and 8 ft
25. 5 ft, 10 ft, 15 ft   **27.** 6 ft, 8 ft, 10 ft   **29.** 9,500 hardcovers, 104,500 paperbacks   **31.** 10°   **33.** 159°   **35.** 47°
37. 27°   **39.** 53°   **41.** 130°   **43.** 19 cm by 26 cm
45. 17 in. by 39 in.   **47.** 19 ft   **49.** 20°   **51.** $6,000
53. $4,500 at 9% and $19,500 at 14%   **55.** $3,750 in each
account   **57.** $5,000   **59.** 6% and 7%

Getting Ready (page 131)

1. 60 mi   **2.** 385 mi   **3.** 5.6 gal   **4.** 9 lbs

Exercises 2.6 (page 137)

1. $50h$ mi   **3.** 4.8 oz   **5.** -17 **7.** -1 **9.** -3 **11.** 6
13. $d = rt$ **15.** $v = pn$ **17.** 3 hr   **19.** 3.5 days
21. 6.5 hr   **23.** $\frac{2}{7}$ hr or approximately 17 min   **25.** 10 hr
27. 7.5 hr   **29.** 65 mph and 45 mph   **31.** 4 hr
33. 2.5 liters   **35.** 20 gal   **37.** 50 gal   **39.** 7.5 oz
41. 40 lb lemon drops and 60 lb jelly beans   **43.** $1.20
45. 80 lb   **47.** $5.60

Getting Ready (page 140)

1.   **2.**

3.   **4.**

Exercises 2.7 (page 145)

1. $x < 2$ **3.** $x \geq 2$ **5.** $x < 6$ **7.** $5x^2 - 2y^2$
9. $-x + 14$ **11.** is less than; is greater than   **13.** double
inequality   **15.** inequality   **17.** $x > 3$;

19. $x \leq -1$;

21. $x \leq 4$;

23. $x > -3$;

25. $x > -1$;

27. $x \geq 3$;

29. $x \geq -10$;

31. $x > -3$;

33. $x < -2$;

35. $x < -4$;

37. $x > 3$;

39. $x > -15$;

41. $7 < x < 10$;

43. $-9 < x \leq 3$;

45. $-10 \leq x \leq 0$;

47. $-4 < x < 1$;

49. $x \geq -2$;

51. $x \geq 2$;

53. $x \leq 20$;

55. $x > -7$;

57. $x \geq 4$;

59. $-5 < x < -2$;

61. $-6 \leq x \leq 10$;

63. $2 \leq x < 3$;

65. $-1 \leq x < 2$;

67. $-6 < x < 14$;

69. $s \geq 98$ **71.** $s \geq 17$ cm   **73.** $r \geq 27$ mpg
75. 0.1 mi $\leq x \leq 2.5$ mi   **77.** 3.3 mi $< x < 4.1$ mi
79. $66.2° < F < 71.6°$ **81.** 37.052 in. $< C < 38.308$ in.
83. 68.18 kg $< w < 86.36$ kg   **85.** 5 ft $< w < 9$ ft

Chapter Review (page 148)

1. yes   **2.** no   **3.** no   **4.** yes   **5.** yes   **6.** no   **7.** 1
8. 9   **9.** 16   **10.** 0   **11.** 4   **12.** -2 **13.** $105.40
14. $97.70   **15.** 5   **16.** -2 **17.** $\frac{1}{2}$ **18.** $\frac{3}{2}$ **19.** 18
20. -35 **21.** $-\frac{1}{2}$ **22.** 6   **23.** 245   **24.** 1,300
25. 37%   **26.** 12.5%   **27.** 3   **28.** 2   **29.** 1   **30.** 1
31. 1   **32.** -2 **33.** 2   **34.** 7   **35.** -2 **36.** -1
37. 5   **38.** 3   **39.** 13   **40.** -12 **41.** 5   **42.** 7
43. 8   **44.** 30   **45.** $\frac{15}{2}$ **46.** 44   **47.** $320   **48.** 6.5%
49. 96.4%   **50.** 53.8%   **51.** $14x$ **52.** $19a$ **53.** $5b$
54. $-2x$ **55.** $-2y$ **56.** unlike terms   **57.** $9x$
58. $6 - 7x$ **59.** $4y^2 - 6$ **60.** 4   **61.** 7   **62.** 13

63. -3 **64.** -41 **65.** 9 **66.** -7 **67.** 7 **68.** 4
69. -8 **70.** -18 **71.** identity, $\mathbb{R}$ **72.** contradiction, $\varnothing$
73. identity, $\mathbb{R}$ **74.** contradiction, $\varnothing$ **75.** $R = \dfrac{E}{I}$
76. $t = \dfrac{i}{pr}$ **77.** $R = \dfrac{P}{I^2}$ **78.** $r = \dfrac{d}{t}$ **79.** $h = \dfrac{V}{lw}$
80. $m = \dfrac{y - b}{x}$ **81.** $h = \dfrac{V}{\pi r^2}$ **82.** $r = \dfrac{a}{2\pi h}$ **83.** $G = \dfrac{Fd^2}{Mm}$
84. $m = \dfrac{RT}{PV}$ **85.** 5 ft from one end   **86.** $15°$ **87.** $45°$
88. $21°$ **89.** $111°$ **90.** 13 in.   **91.** \$16,000 at 7%, \$11,000
at 9%   **92.** 20 min   **93.** 2 hr   **94.** 7.5 hr
95. 24 liters   **96.** 1 liter   **97.** 10 lb of each

98.    **99.**
100.   **101.**
102.   **103.**
104.   **105.**
106. $6 \text{ ft} < l \le 20 \text{ ft}$

Chapter 2 Test (page 154)

1. solution   **2.** solution   **3.** not a solution   **4.** solution
5. -36 **6.** 47 **7.** -12 **8.** -7 **9.** -2 **10.** 1
11. 7 **12.** -3 **13.** $6x - 15$ **14.** $8x - 10$ **15.** -18
16. $-36x + 13$ **17.** -2 **18.** 0 **19.** $t = \dfrac{d}{r}$
20. $l = \dfrac{P - 2w}{2}$ **21.** $h = \dfrac{A}{2\pi r}$ **22.** $r = \dfrac{A - P}{Pt}$
23. $75°$ **24.** $75°$ **25.** \$6,000 at 6%, \$4,000 at 5%
26. $\frac{3}{5}$ hr or 36 min   **27.** $7\frac{1}{2}$ liters   **28.** 40 lbs
29.   **30.**
31.   **32.**

Cumulative Review Exercises (page 155)

1. integer, rational, real   **2.** rational, real
3.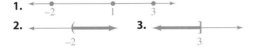
4.   **5.** 0 **6.** $\frac{10}{3}$ **7.** $8\frac{1}{10}$ **8.** 35.65
9. 0 **10.** -2 **11.** 16 **12.** 0 **13.** 24.75 **14.** $5{,}275$
15. 5 **16.** $37, y$ **17.** $-2x + 2y$ **18.** $x - 5$
19. $-2x^2 y^3$ **20.** $3x + 16$ **21.** 13 **22.** 41 **23.** $\frac{7}{4}$
24. $\mathbb{R}$ **25.** $h = \dfrac{2A}{b + B}$ **26.** $x = \dfrac{y - b}{m}$ **27.** \$22,814.56
28. \$900   **29.** \$12,650   **30.** 125 lb   **31.** no
32. 7.3 ft and 10.7 ft   **33.** 147 kwh   **34.** 85 ft   **35.** -9
36. 1 **37.** 280 **38.** -564
39.   **40.**

Getting Ready (page 158)

1.
2.   **3.**

4.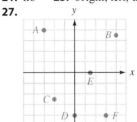

Exercises 3.1 (page 165)

3. IV   **5.** 12 **7.** 8 **9.** 7 **11.** -49 **13.** ordered pair
15. origin   **17.** rectangular, Cartesian   **19.** coordinates
21. no   **23.** origin, left, up   **25.** II
27. 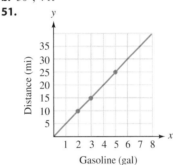   **29.** 3 or -3, 5 or -5, 4 or -4,
5 or -5, 3 or -3, 5 or -5, 4 or
-4 **31.** 10 minutes before the
workout, her heart rate was
60 beats per min.
33. 150 beats per min
35. approximately 5 min and
50 min after starting
37. 10 beats per min faster after cool-down   **39.** \$2   **41.** \$7
43. 44¢; 76¢   **45.** 32¢   **47.** Carbondale $\left(5\frac{1}{2}, \text{J}\right)$, Champaign
$(7, \text{D})$, Chicago $\left(8\frac{1}{2}, \text{B}\right)$, Peoria $\left(5\frac{3}{4}, \text{C}\right)$, Rockford $\left(5\frac{3}{4}, \text{A}\right)$,
Springfield $\left(4\frac{1}{2}, \text{E}\right)$, St. Louis $\left(4\frac{1}{4}, \text{H}\right)$ **49. a.** $60°$; 4 ft
b. $30°$; 4 ft

51.
a. 35 mi   **b.** 4 gal
c. 32.5 mi

Distance (mi) / Gasoline (gal)

53.
a. A 3-yr-old car is worth
\$7,000.   **b.** \$1,000
c. 6 yr

Value (\$1,000s) / Age of car (years)

Getting Ready (page 169)

1. 1 **2.** 5 **3.** -3 **4.** 2

Exercises 3.2 (page 180)

1. 3 **7.** -96 **9.** an expression   **11.** 1.25 **13.** 0.1
15. two   **17.** independent, dependent   **19.** linear
21. y-intercept   **23.** yes   **25.** no
27. $-3, -2, -5, -7$; $(0, -3), (1, -2), (-2, -5), (-4, -7)$
29. $0, -2, -6, 4$; $(0, 0), (1, -2), (3, -6), (-2, 4)$

31.
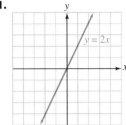

33.
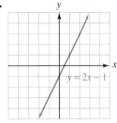

55.
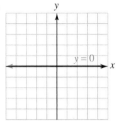

57.
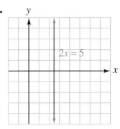

35.
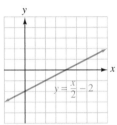

37.
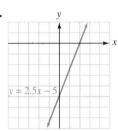

59.
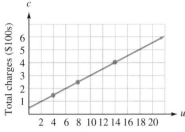

a. $c = 50 + 25u$ **b.** 150, 250, 400; (4, 150), (8, 250), (14, 400)
c. The service fee is $50.   **d.** $850

39.
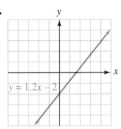

41.
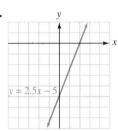

61.
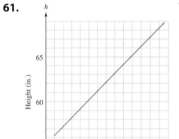

43.
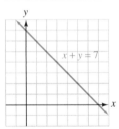

45.
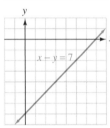

a. 56.2, 62.1, 64.0; (7, 56.2), (8.5, 62.1), (9, 64.0)   **b.** taller the
woman is   **c.** 58.1 in.   **69.** (6, 6)   **71.** $\left(-\frac{1}{2}, \frac{5}{2}\right)$ **73.** (7, 6)

Getting Ready (page 184)

1. -3 **2.** -2 **3.** 1   **4.** 6

Exercises 3.3 (page 192)

1. yes   **3.** no   **5.** 16   **7.** -18 **9.** system
11. independent   **13.** inconsistent; $\varnothing$ **15.** yes   **17.** yes
19. no   **21.** yes   **23.** no   **25.** no

47.
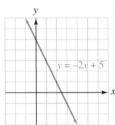

49.
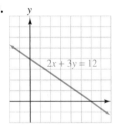

27.
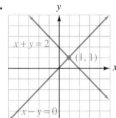

29.
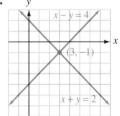

51.
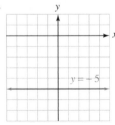

53.
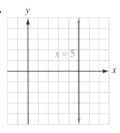

31.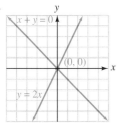

33.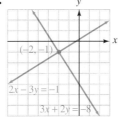

35. $\varnothing$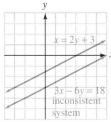

37. $\varnothing$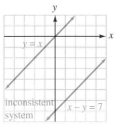

39.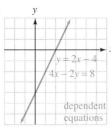

41.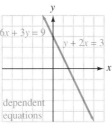

43.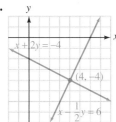

45.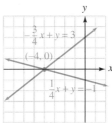

47.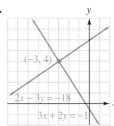

49.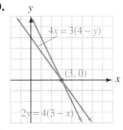

51.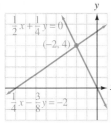

53.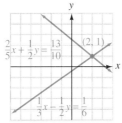

55. $(1, 3)$ **57.** $\left(\frac{2}{3}, -\frac{1}{3}\right)$ **59.** 1994; about 4,100

61. a. Houston, New Orleans, St. Augustine   **b.** St. Louis, Memphis, New Orleans   **c.** New Orleans   **63.** yes, $(2, 2)$

Getting Ready (page 196)

1. $6x + 4$ **2.** $-25 - 10x$ **3.** $2x - 4$ **4.** $3x - 12$

Exercises 3.4 (page 201)

1. $2z + 1$ **3.** $3t + 3$ **5.** 5   **7.** 12   **9.** 10
11. y, terms   **13.** $\varnothing$ **15.** infinitely many   **17.** $(2, 4)$
19. $(3, 0)$ **21.** $(-3, -1)$ **23.** $(3, -2)$ **25.** $(-1, 2)$
27. $(1, 1)$ **29.** $(4, -2)$ **31.** $(-2, 3)$ **33.** $(4, 2)$
35. $(-5, -5)$ **37.** $\varnothing$; inconsistent system   **39.** $\varnothing$; inconsistent system   **41.** dependent equations, $(x, 3x - 4)$
43. dependent equations, $\left(a, -\frac{a + 5}{2}\right)$ **45.** $\left(\frac{1}{2}, 3\right)$ **47.** $(3, 2)$
49. $(1, 4)$ **51.** $(-1, -1)$ **53.** $(-3, -1)$ **55.** $(-1, -3)$
57. $\left(\frac{1}{2}, \frac{1}{3}\right)$ **59.** $(-6, 4)$ **61.** $\left(\frac{1}{5}, 4\right)$ **63.** $(5, 5)$
65. $30°, 60°$

Getting Ready (page 203)

1. $5x = 10$ **2.** $y = 6$ **3.** $2x = 33$ **4.** $18y = 28$

Exercises 3.5 (page 208)

1. 1   **3.** 3   **5.** 4   **7.** 4   **9.** ⟵━━━┥
  2

11. coefficient   **13.** general   **15.** 15   **17.** $(1, 4)$
19. $(-2, 3)$ **21.** $(-1, 1)$ **23.** $(2, 5)$ **25.** $(2, 3)$
27. $(3, -2)$ **29.** $(2, 7)$ **31.** $\left(\frac{10}{3}, \frac{10}{3}\right)$ **33.** $(-2, 3)$
35. $(-5, 0)$ **37.** $(-1, 2)$ **39.** $(-1, -1)$ **41.** $(-1, 2)$
43. $(0, 1)$ **45.** $\varnothing$ **47.** $\varnothing$ **49.** infinitely many solutions of the form $\left(x, \frac{3x - 6}{4}\right)$ **51.** infinitely many solutions of the form $\left(x, \frac{x - 4}{2}\right)$ **53.** $(-3, 4)$ **55.** $(0, 8)$ **57.** $(2, -1)$
59. $\left(\frac{1}{2}, \frac{1}{3}\right)$ **61.** $\left(1, -\frac{5}{2}\right)$ **63.** $(-2, 3)$ **65.** $(2, 2)$
67. $x = 3, y = 2$ **71.** $(1, 4)$

Getting Ready (page 210)

1. $x + y$ **2.** $x - y$ **3.** xy **4.** $\frac{x}{y}$ **5.** $A = lw$
6. $P = 2l + 2w$

Exercises 3.6 (page 218)

1. $2x$ **3.** $2x + 3y$ **5.** $\$(3x + 2y)$
7. ⟵━━━━━━⟶
    4
9. ⟵━━(━━┥━⟶
   −1   2
11. $8^3 c$

13. $a^2 b^2$ **15.** variable   **17.** system   **19.** President: $400,000; Vice President: $192,600   **21.** $162,500   **23.** 10 ft, 15 ft   **25.** mitt: $29.50, glove: $21   **27.** 25 ft by 30 ft
29. 60 ft^2 **31.** 9.9 yr   **33.** 80+   **35.** $2,000   **37.** 250
39. 10 mph   **41.** 50 mph   **43.** 5 L of 40% solution, 10 L of 55% solution   **45.** 32 lb peanuts, 16 lb cashews   **47.** 32, 64
49. 8, 5   **51.** cleaner: $5.40, soaking solution: $6.20
53. 6,720 ft^2 **55.** $81\frac{2}{3}$ lb   **57.** 38,500 diabetes; 269,500 cancer   **59.** 3%   **61.** $800

Getting Ready (page 222)

1. below   **2.** above   **3.** below   **4.** on   **5.** on
6. above   **7.** below   **8.** above

Exercises 3.7 (page 230)

1. no **3.** yes **5.** no **7.** no **9.** 3 **11.** $t = \dfrac{A - P}{Pr}$

13. $7a - 15$ **15.** $-2a + 7b$ **17.** inequality

19. boundary **21.** inequalities **23.** doubly shaded

25. a. no **b.** yes **27. a.** yes **b.** no **c.** yes **d.** no

29. a. no **b.** yes **c.** yes **d.** yes

31.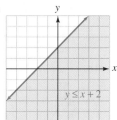

33.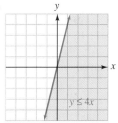

35.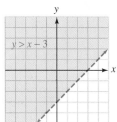

37.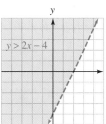

39.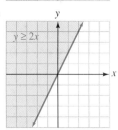

41.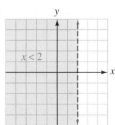

43.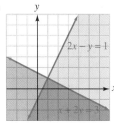

45.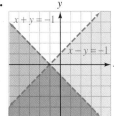

47.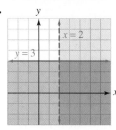

49.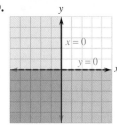

51. ∅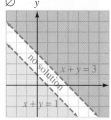

53. ∅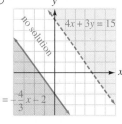

55.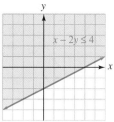

57.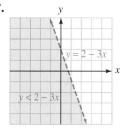

59.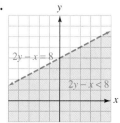

61.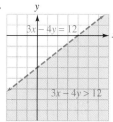

63.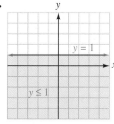

65.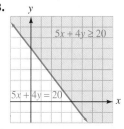

67.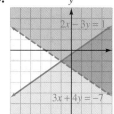

69.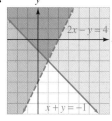

71.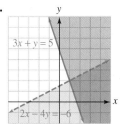

73.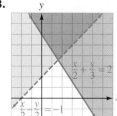

75. $(10, 10), (20, 10), (10, 20)$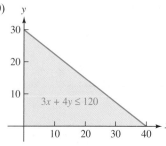

77. (50, 50), (30, 40), (40, 40)

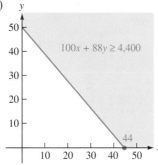

79. (80, 40), (80, 80), (120, 40)

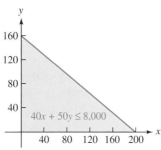

81.

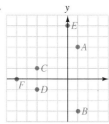

83.

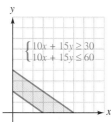

1 $10 CD and 2 $15 CDs;
4 $10 CDs and 1 $15 CD

2 desk chairs and 4 side chairs;
1 desk chair and 5 side chairs

Chapter Review (page 236)

1–6.

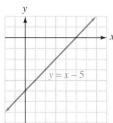

17.

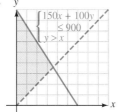

18.

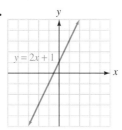

7. (3, 1)   **8.** (−4, 5)
9. (−3, −4)   **10.** (2, −3)
11. (0, 0)   **12.** (0, 4)
13. (−5, 0)   **14.** (0, −3)
15. no   **16.** yes

19.

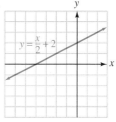

20.

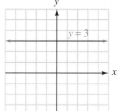

21.

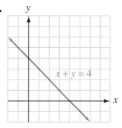

22.

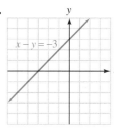

23.

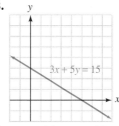

24.

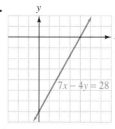

25. yes   **26.** no   **27.** yes   **28.** yes
29. (4, 3)   **30.** (−3, 0)

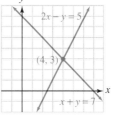

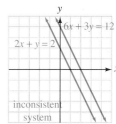

31. $\left(x, -\frac{1}{2}x + 1\right)$ **32.** $\varnothing$

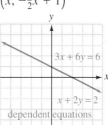

33. (−1, −2)   **34.** (−2, 5)   **35.** (1, −1)   **36.** (−2, 1)
37. (3, −5)   **38.** $\left(3, \frac{1}{2}\right)$ **39.** (−1, 7)   **40.** $\left(-\frac{1}{2}, \frac{7}{2}\right)$
41. (0, 9)   **42.** $\varnothing$ **43.** $\left(x, -3x + \frac{5}{3}\right)$ **44.** (0, 0)
45. 3, 15   **46.** 3 ft by 9 ft   **47.** 50¢   **48.** $66   **49.** $1.69
50. $750   **51.** 3 mph   **52.** 30 milliliters of 10% saline,
20 milliliters of 60% saline

53.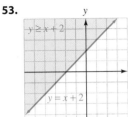

54.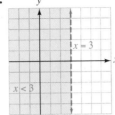

55.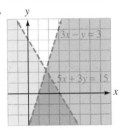

56.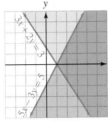

57.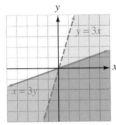

58.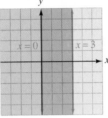

59. 3 shirts and 1 pair of pants, 1 shirt and 2 pairs of pants

Chapter 3 Test (page 243)

1.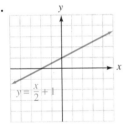

2.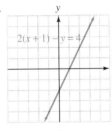

3.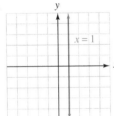

4.

5. yes   **6.** no

7.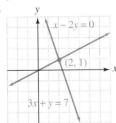

8.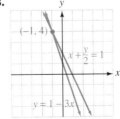

9. $(-3, -4)$ **10.** $(12, 10)$ **11.** $(2, 4)$ **12.** $(-3, 3)$

13. inconsistent   **14.** consistent   **15.** 65   **16.** 3 adult
17. \$4,000   **18.** 1 mph
19. 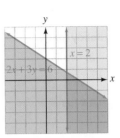   **20.**

Getting Ready (page 246)

1. 8   **2.** 9   **3.** 6   **4.** 6   **5.** 12   **6.** 32   **7.** 18   **8.** 3

Exercises 4.1 (page 252)

1. base x, exponent 3   **3.** base b, exponent c **5.** 36   **7.** 9
9.
11. the product of 3 and the sum of x and y **13.** $|2x| + 3$
15. base, -5, 3   **17.** $(3x)(3x)(3x)(3x)$ **19.** $y \cdot y \cdot y \cdot y \cdot y$
21. $x^n y^n$ **23.** a^{bc} **27.** base 4, exponent 3   **29.** base x,
exponent 5   **31.** base $2y$, exponent 3   **33.** base x,
exponent 4   **35.** base x, exponent 1   **37.** base x, exponent 3
39. 625   **41.** 13   **43.** 561   **45.** -725 **47.** $5 \cdot 5 \cdot 5$
49. $x \cdot x \cdot x \cdot x \cdot x \cdot x \cdot x$ **51.** $-4 \cdot x \cdot x \cdot x \cdot x$
53. $(3t)(3t)(3t)(3t)(3t)$ **55.** 2^3 **57.** x^4 **59.** $(2x)^3$
61. $-4t^4$ **63.** x^7 **65.** x^{10} **67.** a^{12} **69.** y^9 **71.** $12x^7$
73. $-4y^5$ **75.** 3^8 **77.** y^{15} **79.** x^{25} **81.** a^{27} **83.** x^{31}
85. r^{36} **87.** $x^3 y^3$ **89.** $r^6 s^4$ **91.** $16a^2 b^4$ **93.** $-8r^6 s^9 t^3$
95. $\frac{a^3}{b^3}$ **97.** $\frac{x^{10}}{y^{15}}$ **99.** x^2 **101.** y^4 **103.** $3a$ **105.** ab^4
107. t^3 **109.** $6x^9$ **111.** a^{21} **113.** $243z^{30}$ **115.** s^{33}
117. $\frac{-32a^5}{b^5}$ **119.** $\frac{b^6}{27a^3}$ **121.** $\frac{x^{12}y^{16}}{2}$ **123.** $\frac{y^3}{8}$ **125.** $-\frac{8r^3}{27}$
127. $\frac{10r^{13}s^3}{3}$ **129.** 2 ft   **131.** \$16,000   **133.** \$45,947.93

Getting Ready (page 255)

1. $\frac{1}{3}$ **2.** $\frac{1}{y}$ **3.** 1   **4.** $\frac{1}{xy}$

Exercises 4.2 (page 259)

1. $\frac{1}{2}$ **3.** 2   **5.** x **7.** 1   **9.** 2   **11.** $\frac{6}{5}$
13. $s = \frac{f(P - L)}{i}$ or $s = \frac{fP - fL}{i}$ **15.** $1, \frac{1}{x^n}$ **17.** $\frac{1}{8^2}$ **19.** 1
21. 2   **23.** 1   **25.** 1   **27.** $\frac{1}{625}$ **29.** $\frac{1}{x^2}$ **31.** $\frac{1}{16y^4}$
33. $-\frac{1}{125p^3}$ **35.** $\frac{1}{y^{12}}$ **37.** $\frac{3}{x^3}$ **39.** $\frac{1}{y}$ **41.** $\frac{1}{p^3}$ **43.** x^5
45. $\frac{5b^4}{a}$ **47.** $\frac{1}{a^{12}}$ **49.** $\frac{1}{a^{14}}$ **51.** $\frac{1}{9a^2 b^2}$ **53.** $\frac{c^{15}}{216a^9 b^3}$
55. x^{3m} **57.** $\frac{1}{x^{3n}}$ **59.** y^{2m+2} **61.** y^{2n+4} **63.** 8   **65.** 1
67. 1   **69.** 512   **71.** 1   **73.** -2 **75.** $\frac{1}{b^5}$ **77.** u^{5m}
79. x^{8n-12} **81.** y^{4n-8} **83.** y^m **85.** $\frac{1}{64t^3}$ **87.** $\frac{1}{a^3 b^6}$
89. $\frac{1}{x^4 y^2}$ **91.** $\frac{1}{r^6}$ **93.** y^5 **95.** 1   **97.** $\frac{1}{a^2 b^4}$ **99.** $\frac{1}{x^6 y^3}$
101. $\frac{1}{x^3}$ **103.** $\frac{1}{y^2}$ **105.** $a^8 b^{12}$ **107.** $-\frac{y^{10}}{32x^{15}}$ **109.** $\frac{1}{b^{14}}$
111. $\frac{256x^{28}}{81}$ **113.** $\frac{16y^{14}}{z^{10}}$ **115.** $\frac{x^{14}}{128y^{28}}$ **117.** $\frac{16u^4 v^8}{81}$

119. $\frac{1}{512}$ **121.** $\frac{17y^{27}z^5}{x^{35}}$ **123.** $\frac{1}{x^{3n}}$ **125.** \$6,678.04
127. \$3,183.76   **129.** \$9,875.85

Getting Ready (page 261)

1. 100   **2.** 1,000   **3.** 10   **4.** $\frac{1}{100}$ **5.** 500   **6.** 8,000
7. 30   **8.** $\frac{7}{100}$

Exercises 4.3 (page 266)

1. 3.72×10^2 **3.** 4.72×10^3 **5.** 3.72×10^{-1} **7.** 5
9. comm. prop. of add.   **11.** 6   **13.** scientific notation
15. 2.3×10^4 **17.** 1.7×10^6 **19.** 6.2×10^{-2}
21. 2.75×10^{-6} **23.** 4.25×10^3 **25.** 2.5×10^{-3}
27. 230   **29.** 812,000   **31.** 0.00115   **33.** 0.000976
35. 714,000   **37.** 30,000   **39.** 200,000   **41.** 0.000075
43. 5.1×10^{-6} **45.** 2.57×10^8 **47.** 4×10^{-22}
49. 25,000,000   **51.** 0.00051   **53.** 2.57×10^{13} mi
55. 114,000,000 mi   **57.** 6.22×10^{-3} mi
59. 1.9008×10^{11} ft   **61.** 1.09914×10^{13} gallons
63. 3.3×10^{-1} km/sec   **65.** x-rays, visible light, infrared
67. $1.5 \times 10^{-4}, 2.5 \times 10^{13}$

Getting Ready (page 268)

1. $2x^2y^3$ **2.** $3xy^3$ **3.** $2x^2 + 3y^2$ **4.** $x^3 + y^3$ **5.** $6x^3y^3$
6. $5x^2y^2z^4$ **7.** $5x^2y^2$ **8.** $x^3y^3z^3$

Exercises 4.4 (page 277)

9. 8   **11.** 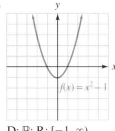   **13.** x^{18} **15.** y^9
17. algebraic   **19.** monomial; binomial; trinomial
21. sum   **23.** independent; dependent
25. quadratic, parabola   **27.** descending; 5   **29.** function
31. yes   **33.** no   **35.** binomial   **37.** trinomial
39. monomial   **41.** binomial   **43.** 4th   **45.** 3rd
47. 8th   **49.** 6th   **51.** 7   **53.** -8 **55.** -4 **57.** -5
59. $1, -2, -3, -2, 1$ **61.** $-6, 1, 2, 3, 10$ **63.** 1
65. $-\frac{3}{2}$ **67.** 5   **69.** $-\frac{22}{5}$
71.   **73.**

D: $\mathbb{R}$; R: $[-1, \infty)$ D: $\mathbb{R}$; R: $\mathbb{R}$
75. trinomial   **77.** none of these   **79.** binomial   **81.** 12th
83. 0th   **85.** 3   **87.** 11   **89.** 2.25   **91.** 64 ft
93. \$28,362   **95.** 63 ft

Getting Ready (page 280)

1. $5x$ **2.** $2y$ **3.** $25x$ **4.** $5z$ **5.** $12r$ **6.** not possible
7. 0   **8.** not possible

Exercises 4.5 (page 284)

1. $4x^3$ **3.** $2y$ **5.** $-2y^2$ **7.** $4x^2 + y$ **9.** -8 **11.** -9
13.   **15.** monomial
17. coefficients, variables   **19.** like terms   **21.** like terms,
$7y$ **23.** unlike terms   **25.** like terms, $13x^3$ **27.** like terms,
$8x^3y^2$ **29.** like terms, $65t^6$ **31.** unlike terms   **33.** $9y$
35. x **37.** $-4t^2$ **39.** $25x^2$ **41.** $-21a$ **43.** $16u^3$
45. $7x^5y^2$ **47.** $-8ab^2$ **49.** $7x + 4$ **51.** $7x - 7y + 2z$
53. $5x^2 + x + 11$ **55.** $-7x^3 - 7x^2 - x - 1$ **57.** $2a + 7$
59. $2a^2 + a - 3$ **61.** $5x^2 + 6x - 8$
63. $-x^3 + 6x^2 + x + 14$ **65.** $-19x - 4y$ **67.** $-2x^2 - 1$
69. $6x - 2$ **71.** $-5x^2 - 8x - 19$ **73.** $5x^2 - 25x - 20$
75. $4y^3 - 12y^2 + 8y + 8$ **77.** $14rst$ **79.** $-6a^2bc$
81. $15x^2$ **83.** $4x^2y^2$ **85.** $95x^8y^4$ **87.** $5x + 15$
89. $3x - 3y$ **91.** $7c^2 + 7c$ **93.** $2x^2y + xy + 13y^2$
95. $-12x^2y^2 - 13xy + 36y^2$ **97.** $3a^2b^2 - 6ab + b^2 - 6ab^2$
99. $-6x^2y^2 + 4xy^2z - 20xy^3 + 2y$ **101.** $6x^2 - 2x - 1$
103. $t^3 + 3t^2 + 6t - 5$ **105.** $-3x^2 + 5x - 7$
107. \$114,000   **109.** \$132,000   **111. a.** \$263,000
b. \$263,000   **113.** $y = -1,100x + 6,600$
115. $y = -2,800x + 15,800$ **119.** $6x + 3h - 10$ **121.** 49

Getting Ready (page 287)

1. $6x$ **2.** $3x^4$ **3.** $5x^3$ **4.** $8x^5$ **5.** $3x + 15$
6. $-2x - 10$ **7.** $4y - 12$ **8.** $-2y^2 + 6$

Exercises 4.6 (page 294)

1. $6x^3 - 2x^2$ **3.** $7x^2y + 7xy^2$ **5.** $x^2 + 5x + 6$
7. $2x^2 + 7x + 6$ **9.** $x^2 + 6x + 9$ **11.** distrib. prop.
13. comm. prop. of mult.   **15.** 0   **17.** monomial
19. special products   **21.** $6x^2$ **23.** $15x$ **25.** $12x^5$
27. $-10t^7$ **29.** $6x^5y^3$ **31.** $-24b^6$ **33.** $a^{10}b^{15}c^5$
35. $a^5b^4c^7$ **37.** $3x + 12$ **39.** $-4t - 28$ **41.** $3x^2 - 6x$
43. $-6x^4 + 2x^3$ **45.** $3x^2y + 3xy^2$ **47.** $6x^4 + 8x^3 - 14x^2$
49. $2x^7 - x^2$ **51.** $-6r^3t^2 + 2r^2t^3$ **53.** $a^2 + 9a + 20$
55. $3x^2 + 10x - 8$ **57.** $6a^2 + 2a - 20$ **59.** $6x^2 - 7x - 5$
61. $6s^2 + 7st - 3t^2$ **63.** $u^2 + 2tu + uv + 2tv$
65. $x^2 + xz + xy + yz$ **67.** $2x^2 - 6x - 8$
69. $3a^3 - 3ab^2$ **71.** $-6x^4y^4 - 6x^3y^5$ **73.** $5t^2 - 11t$
75. $x^2 + 10x + 25$ **77.** $x^2 - 8x + 16$ **79.** $4s^2 + 4s + 1$
81. $x^2 - 4xy + 4y^2$ **83.** $r^2 - 16$ **85.** $16x^2 - 25$
87. $2x^3 + 7x^2 + x - 1$ **89.** $4t^3 + 11t^2 + 18t + 9$
91. $4x^2 + 11x + 6$ **93.** $12x^2 + 14xy - 10y^2$ **95.** -3
97. -8 **99.** -1 **101.** 0   **103.** $x^{10}y^{15}$ **105.** $x^{15}y^6$
107. $-3x^4y^7z^8$ **109.** $2x^2 + 3x - 9$ **111.** $t^2 - 6t + 9$
113. $6x^2 - 7x - 5$ **115.** $-4r^2 - 20rs - 21s^2$
117. $4a^2 - 12ab + 9b^2$ **119.** $16x^2 - 25s^2$ **121.** $x^3 - 1$
123. $-3x^3 + 25x^2y - 56xy^2 + 16y^3$ **125.** $x^3 - 8y^3$
127. $x^2y + 3xy^2 + 2x^2$ **129.** $2x^2 + xy - y^2$ **131.** 4
133. $-12x$ **135.** $4x^2 - 5x - 11$ **137.** $3b^2 + 2b - 4$
139. 4 m   **141.** 90 ft

Getting Ready (page 297)

1. $2xy^2$ **2.** y **3.** $\frac{3xy}{2}$ **4.** $\frac{x}{y}$ **5.** xy **6.** 3

Exercises 4.7 (page 301)

1. $2x^2$ **3.** $5bc^2$ **5.** 1 **7.** binomial **9.** none of these

11. 2 **13.** $\frac{1}{3}$ **15.** $-\frac{5}{3}$ **17.** $\frac{3}{4}$ **19.** 1 **21.** $-\frac{1}{4}$ **23.** $\frac{42}{19}$

25. polynomial **27.** two **29.** $\frac{a}{b}$ **31.** $\frac{x}{z}$ **33.** $\frac{r^2}{s}$

35. $\frac{2x^2}{y}$ **37.** $-\frac{3u^3}{v^2}$ **39.** $\frac{2}{y} + \frac{3}{x}$ **41.** $\frac{x}{3} + \frac{2}{y}$ **43.** $\frac{1}{5y} - \frac{2}{5x}$

45. $\frac{1}{y^2} + \frac{2y}{x^2}$ **47.** $\frac{1}{y} - \frac{1}{2x} + \frac{2z}{xy}$ **49.** $3x^2y - 2x - \frac{1}{y}$

51. $5x - 6y + 1$ **53.** $3a - 2b$ **55.** $\frac{10x^2}{y} - 5x$

57. $-\frac{4x}{3} + \frac{3x^2}{2}$ **59.** $xy - 1$ **61.** 2 **63.** $\frac{4r}{y^2}$ **65.** $-\frac{13}{3rs}$

67. $\frac{x^4}{y^6}$ **69.** a^8b^8 **71.** $-\frac{3r}{s^9}$ **73.** $-\frac{x^3}{4y^3}$ **75.** $\frac{125}{8b^3}$ **77.** $\frac{xy^2}{3}$

79. a^8 **81.** z^3 **83.** $\frac{1}{81a^4b}$ **85.** $\frac{x}{y} - \frac{11}{6} + \frac{y}{2x}$ **87.** yes
89. yes

Getting Ready (page 304)

1. 13 **2.** 21 **3.** 19 **4.** 13

Exercises 4.8 (page 309)

1. $2 + \frac{3}{x}$ **3.** $2 + \frac{1}{x+1}$ **5.** x **7.** 21, 22, 24, 25, 26, 27, 28
9. 5 **11.** -5 **13.** $8x^2 - 6x + 1$ **15.** divisor, dividend
17. remainder **19.** $4x^3 - 2x^2 + 7x + 6$
21. $6x^4 - x^3 + 2x^2 + 9x$ **23.** $0x^3$ and $0x$ **25.** $x + 2$
27. $x + 2$ **29.** $x - 3$ **31.** $a + 5$ **33.** $3a - 2$
35. $b + 3$ **37.** $x + 1 + \frac{-1}{2x+3}$ **39.** $2x + 2 + \frac{-3}{2x+1}$
41. $a + b$ **43.** $2x - y$ **45.** $x - 3y$ **47.** $a + 2b$
49. $2x + 1$ **51.** $x - 7$ **53.** $x + 1$ **55.** $2x - 3$
57. $x - y$ **59.** $x^2 + 2x + 4$ **61.** $x^2 + xy + y^2$
63. $a^2 - 3a + 10 + \frac{-30}{a+3}$ **65.** $3x + 2y$ **67.** $x + 5y$
69. $x - 5y$ **71.** $x^2 + 2x - 1$ **73.** $2x^2 + 2x + 1$
75. $x^2 + xy + y^2$ **77.** $x^2 + 2x + 1$
79. $x^2 + 2x - 1 + \frac{6}{2x+3}$ **81.** $2x^2 + 8x + 14 + \frac{31}{x-2}$
83. $3y^2 + 6y - 9 + \frac{7}{2y+3}$

Chapter Review (page 311)

1. $(-3x)(-3x)(-3x)(-3x)$ **2.** $\left(\frac{1}{2}pq\right)\left(\frac{1}{2}pq\right)\left(\frac{1}{2}pq\right)$ **3.** 125

4. 243 **5.** 64 **6.** -64 **7.** 13 **8.** 25 **9.** x^5 **10.** x^9
11. y^{21} **12.** x^{42} **13.** a^3b^3 **14.** $81x^4$ **15.** b^{12}
16. $-y^2z^5$ **17.** $256s^3$ **18.** $-3y^6$ **19.** x^{15} **20.** $4x^4y^2$
21. x^4 **22.** $\frac{x^2}{y^2}$ **23.** $\frac{2y^2}{x^2}$ **24.** $5yz^4$ **25.** 1 **26.** 1

27. 9 **28.** $9x^4$ **29.** $\frac{1}{x^3}$ **30.** x **31.** y **32.** x^{10}

33. $\frac{1}{x^2}$ **34.** $\frac{a^6}{b^3}$ **35.** $\frac{1}{x^5}$ **36.** $\frac{1}{9z^2}$ **37.** 7.28×10^2

38. 9.37×10^3 **39.** 1.36×10^{-2} **40.** 9.42×10^{-3}
41. 7.73×10^0 **42.** 7.53×10^5 **43.** 1.8×10^{-4}
44. 6×10^4 **45.** 726,000 **46.** 0.000391 **47.** 2.68
48. 57.6 **49.** 7.39 **50.** 0.000437 **51.** 0.03 **52.** 160
53. 7th, monomial **54.** 2nd, binomial **55.** 5th, trinomial
56. 5th, binomial **57.** 11 **58.** 2 **59.** -4 **60.** 4
61. 402 **62.** 0 **63.** 82 **64.** 0.3405 **65.** -4 **66.** 21
67. 0 **68.** $-\frac{15}{4}$

69.
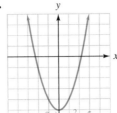
$y = f(x) = x^2 - 5$

70.
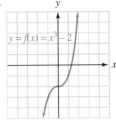
$y = f(x) = x^3 - 2$

71. $7x$ **72.** not possible **73.** $4x^2y^2$ **74.** x^2yz
75. $8x^2 - 6x$ **76.** $4a^2 + 4a - 6$ **77.** $5x^2 + 19x + 3$
78. $6x^3 + 8x^2 + 3x - 72$ **79.** $10x^3y^5$ **80.** x^7yz^5
81. $5x + 15$ **82.** $6x + 12$ **83.** $3x^4 - 5x^2$
84. $2y^4 + 10y^3$ **85.** $-x^2y^3 + x^3y^2$ **86.** $-3x^2y^2 + 3x^2y$
87. $x^2 + 5x + 6$ **88.** $2x^2 - x - 1$ **89.** $6a^2 - 6$
90. $6a^2 - 6$ **91.** $2a^2 - ab - b^2$ **92.** $6x^2 + xy - y^2$
93. $x^2 + 6x + 9$ **94.** $x^2 - 25$ **95.** $y^2 - 4$
96. $x^2 + 8x + 16$ **97.** $x^2 - 6x + 9$ **98.** $y^2 - 2y + 1$
99. $4y^2 + 4y + 1$ **100.** $y^4 - 1$ **101.** $3x^3 + 7x^2 + 5x + 1$
102. $8a^3 - 27$ **103.** 1 **104.** -1 **105.** 7 **106.** 5
107. 1 **108.** 0 **109.** $\frac{3}{2y} + \frac{3}{x}$ **110.** $2 - \frac{3}{y}$

111. $-3a - 4b + 5c$ **112.** $-\frac{x}{y} - \frac{y}{x}$ **113.** $x + 1 + \frac{3}{x+2}$

114. $x - 5$ **115.** $2x + 1$ **116.** $x + 5 + \frac{3}{3x-1}$

117. $3x^2 + 2x + 1 + \frac{2}{2x-1}$ **118.** $3x^2 - x - 4$

Chapter 4 Test (page 316)

1. $2x^3y^4$ **2.** 134 **3.** y^6 **4.** $6b^7$ **5.** $32x^{21}$ **6.** $8r^{18}$
7. 3 **8.** $\frac{2}{y^3}$ **9.** y^3 **10.** $\frac{64a^3}{b^3}$ **11.** 2.8×10^4
12. 2.5×10^{-3} **13.** 7,400 **14.** 0.000093 **15.** binomial
16. 10th degree **17.** 0

18.

$y = f(x) = x^2 + 2$

D: $\mathbb{R}$; R: $[2, \infty)$

19. $-7x + 2y$ **20.** $-3x + 6$
21. $5x^3 + 2x^2 + 2x - 5$
22. $-x^2 - 5x + 4$ **23.** $-4x^5y$
24. $3y^4 - 6y^3 + 9y^2$
25. $6x^2 - 7x - 20$
26. $2x^3 - 7x^2 + 14x - 12$
27. $\frac{y}{2x}$ **28.** $\frac{a}{4b} - \frac{b}{2a}$
29. $x - 2$ **30.** $\frac{1}{2}$

Cumulative Review Exercises (page 317)

1. 11 **2.** 71 **3.** $-\frac{11}{10}$ **4.** 7 **5.** 15 **6.** 4 **7.** -10
8. -6 **9.** ⟶ (number line, 2)

10. (number line, 2) **11.** (number line, -2, 5)

12. (number line, -2, 4) **13.** $r = \frac{A-p}{pt}$ **14.** $h = \frac{2A}{b}$

15. 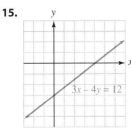   **16.**

17. -2 **18.** 13 **19.** -12 **20.** -1 **21.** y^{14} **22.** xy
23. $\dfrac{a^7}{b^6}$ **24.** x^2y^2 **25.** $x^2 + 4x - 14$ **26.** $6x^2 + 10x - 56$
27. $x^3 - 8$ **28.** $2x + 1$ **29.** 4.8×10^{18} m   **30.** 4 units
31. 879.6 square units   **32.** \$512

Getting Ready (page 320)

1. $5x + 15$ **2.** $7y - 56$ **3.** $3x^2 - 2x$ **4.** $5y^2 + 9y$
5. $3x + 3y + ax + ay$ **6.** $xy + x + 5y + 5$
7. $5x + 5 - yx - y$ **8.** $x^2 + 2x - yx - 2y$

Exercises 5.1 (page 327)

1. $2^2 \cdot 3^2$ **3.** 3^4 **5.** 3 **7.** $x + 3$ **9.** $5(3xy + 2)$
11. $(x + 3)(a - 3)$ **13.** 7 **15.** 11 **17.** prime-factored
19. largest   **21.** grouping   **23.** $2^2 \cdot 3$ **25.** $3 \cdot 5$
27. $2^3 \cdot 5$ **29.** $2 \cdot 7^2$ **31.** $3^2 \cdot 5^2$ **33.** $2^5 \cdot 3^2$ **35.** $5xy$
37. $6xy$ **39.** 4 **41.** r^2 **43.** $3(x + 2)$ **45.** $4(x - 2)$
47. $x(y - z)$ **49.** $t^2(t + 2)$ **51.** $a^2b^3z^2(az - 1)$
53. $8xy^2z^3(3xyz + 1)$ **55.** $3(x + y - 2z)$
57. $a(b + c - d)$ **59.** $2y(2y + 4 - x)$
61. $3r(4r - s + 3rs^2)$ **63.** $abx(1 - b + x)$
65. $2xyz^2(2xy - 3y + 6)$ **67.** $-(x + 2)$ **69.** $-(a + b)$
71. $-(2x - 5y)$ **73.** $-(2a - 3b)$ **75.** $-(3xy - 2z - 5w)$
77. $-(3ab + 5ac - 9bc)$ **79.** $-3xy(x + 2y)$
81. $-4a^2b^2(b - 3a)$ **83.** $-8a^3b^2(a^2 + b^2)$
85. $-2ab^2c(2ac - 7a + 5c)$ **87.** $(a + b)$ **89.** $(m - n)$
91. $(x + y)(2 + b)$ **93.** $(x - 3)(x - 2)$
95. $(y + 1)(x - 5)$ **97.** $(3t + 5)(3t + 4)$
99. $(x + y)(2 + a)$ **101.** $(p - q)(9 + m)$
103. $(a + b)(x - 1)$ **105.** $(a - b)(x - y)$ **107.** $4, x$
109. $r^2(r^2 + 1)$ **111.** $6uvw^2(2w - 3v)$
113. $7a^2b^2c^2(10a + 7bc - 3)$ **115.** $-(3m + 4n - 1)$
117. $-7ab(2a^5b^5 - 7ab^2 + 3)$
119. $-5a^2b^3c(1 - 3abc + 5a^2)$ **121.** $(r - 2s)(3 - x)$
123. $(a + b + c)(3x - 2y)$ **125.** $7xy(r + 2s - t)(2x - 3)$
127. $(x + 1)(x + 3 - y)$ **129.** $(x^2 - 2)(3x - y + 1)$
131. $3(c - 3d)(x + 2y)$ **133.** $(r + s)(x + y)$
135. $(2x + 3)(a + b)$ **137.** $(b + c)(2a + 3)$
139. $(v - 3w)(3t + u)$ **141.** $(3p + q)(3m - n)$
143. $x^2(a + b)(x + 2y)$ **145.** $4a(b + 3)(a - 2)$
147. $(x + y)(2x - 3)$ **149.** $(x^2 + 1)(x + 2)$
151. $y(x^2 - y)(x - 1)$ **153.** $(r - s)(2 + b)$
155. $(x + y)(a + b)$ **157.** $(a - b)(c - d)$
159. $r(r + s)(a - b)$ **161.** $(b + 1)(a + 3)$
163. $(r - s)(p - q)$

Getting Ready (page 330)

1. $a^2 - b^2$ **2.** $4r^2 - s^2$ **3.** $9x^2 - 4y^2$ **4.** $16x^4 - 9$

Exercises 5.2 (page 333)

1. $(x + 3)(x - 3)$ **3.** $(z + 2)(z - 2)$ **5.** $(5 + t)(5 - t)$
7. $(10 + y)(10 - y)$ **9.** $p = w\left(k - h - \dfrac{v^2}{2g}\right)$ **11.** difference
of two squares   **13.** prime   **15.** $(x - 3)$ **17.** $(2m - 3n)$
19. $(x + 4)(x - 4)$ **21.** $(y + 7)(y - 7)$
23. $(2y + 7)(2y - 7)$ **25.** $(3x + y)(3x - y)$
27. $(5t + 6u)(5t - 6u)$ **29.** $(4a + 5b)(4a - 5b)$
31. $8(x + 2y)(x - 2y)$ **33.** $2(a + 2y)(a - 2y)$
35. $3(r + 2s)(r - 2s)$ **37.** $x(x + y)(x - y)$
39. $(a^2 + 4)(a + 2)(a - 2)$ **41.** $(a^2 + b^2)(a + b)(a - b)$
43. $2(x^2 + y^2)(x + y)(x - y)$ **45.** $b(a^2 + b^2)(a + b)(a - b)$
47. $2y(x^2 + 16y^2)(x + 4y)(x - 4y)$ **49.** $(a + 3)^2(a - 3)$
51. $(a^2 + 2b)(a^2 - 2b)$ **53.** prime
55. $(7y + 15z^2)(7y - 15z^2)$ **57.** $(14x^2 + 13y)(14x^2 - 13y)$
59. $x(2a + 3b)(2a - 3b)$ **61.** $3m(m + n)(m - n)$
63. $x^2(2x + y)(2x - y)$ **65.** $2ab(a + 11b)(a - 11b)$
67. $(x^2 + 9)(x + 3)(x - 3)$
69. $(9r^2 + 16s^2)(3r + 4s)(3r - 4s)$
71. $(a^2 + b^4)(a + b^2)(a - b^2)$
73. $(x^4 + y^4)(x^2 + y^2)(x + y)(x - y)$
75. $3n(4m^2 + 9n^2)(2m + 3n)(2m - 3n)$
77. $2p^2q(p^4 + 4q^2)(p^2 + 2q)(p^2 - 2q)$ **79.** $2xy(x^8 + y^8)$
81. $a^2b^2(a^2 + b^2c^2)(a + bc)(a - bc)$
83. $a^2b^3(b^2 + 25)(b + 5)(b - 5)$
85. $3rs(9r^2 + 4s^2)(3r + 2s)(3r - 2s)$
87. $(4x - 4y + 3)(4x - 4y - 3)$ **89.** $(b + 5)(b - 5)(b - 2)$
91. $(a + 7)(a - 7)(a + 2)$ **93.** $3(m + n)(m - n)(m + a)$
95. $2(m + 4)(m - 4)(mn^2 + 4)$

Getting Ready (page 335)

1. $x^2 + 12x + 36$ **2.** $y^2 - 14y + 49$ **3.** $a^2 - 6a + 9$
4. $x^2 + 9x + 20$ **5.** $r^2 - 7r + 10$ **6.** $m^2 - 4m - 21$
7. $a^2 + ab - 12b^2$ **8.** $u^2 - 8uv + 15v^2$
9. $x^2 - 2xy - 24y^2$

Exercises 5.3 (page 343)

1. 4 **3.** $-, 3$ **5.** $6, 1$
7. $\quad$ **9.**
$\qquad 8 \qquad\qquad -3$
11. $\quad$ **13.**
$\qquad 17 \qquad\qquad -2 \quad 4$
15. $(x + y)^2$ **17.** $4, 2$ **19.** $y, 2y$ **21.** $(x + 2)(x + 1)$
23. $(z + 11)(z + 1)$ **25.** $(t - 7)(t - 2)$ **27.** $(p - 5)(p - 1)$
29. $(a + 8)(a - 2)$ **31.** $(s + 13)(s - 2)$
33. $(c + 5)(c - 1)$ **35.** $(t - 10)(t + 5)$
37. $(a - 5)(a + 1)$ **39.** $(y - 6)(y + 5)$
41. $(m + 5n)(m - 2n)$ **43.** $(a - 6b)(a + 2b)$
45. $(a + 9b)(a + b)$ **47.** $(m - 10n)(m - n)$
49. $-(x + 5)(x + 2)$ **51.** $-(y + 5)(y - 3)$
53. $-(t + 17)(t - 2)$ **55.** $-(r - 10)(r - 4)$ **57.** prime
59. prime   **61.** $2(x + 3)(x + 2)$ **63.** $3y(y - 6)(y - 1)$
65. $3(z - 4t)(z - t)$ **67.** $-4x(x + 3y)(x - 2y)$
69. $(x + 2 + y)(x + 2 - y)$ **71.** $(b - 3 + c)(b - 3 - c)$
73. $(x + 2)(x + 1)$ **75.** $(t - 7)(t - 2)$ **77.** $(a + 8)(a - 2)$
79. $(y - 6)(y + 5)$ **81.** $(x + 3)^2$ **83.** $(y - 4)^2$

85. $(u - 9)^2$ **87.** $(x + 2y)^2$ **89.** $(x - 4)(x - 1)$
91. $(y + 9)(y + 1)$ **93.** $-(r - 2s)(r + s)$
95. $(r + 3x)(r + x)$ **97.** $(a - 2b)(a - b)$
99. $-(a + 3b)(a + b)$ **101.** $-(x - 7y)(x + y)$
103. $3y(y + 1)^2$ **105.** $4y(x + 6)(x - 3)$ **107.** $(y + z)^2$
109. $(t + 10)^2$ **111.** $(r - 5s)^2$
113. $(a + b + 2)(a + b - 2)$ **115.** $(b + y + 2)(b - y - 2)$

Getting Ready (page 345)

1. $6x^2 + 7x + 2$ **2.** $6y^2 - 19y + 10$ **3.** $8t^2 + 6t - 9$
4. $4r^2 + 4r - 15$ **5.** $6m^2 - 13m + 6$ **6.** $16a^2 + 16a + 3$

Exercises 5.4 (page 352)

1. 2, 3   **3.** +, −   **5.** 3, 1   **7.** $n = \dfrac{l - f + d}{d}$
9. descending   **11.** opposites   **13.** 2   **15.** 2, 1   **17.** y, y
19. $(3a + 1)(a + 3)$ **21.** $(3a + 1)(a + 4)$
23. $(3b - 1)(2b - 1)$ **25.** $(2y - 1)(y - 3)$
27. $(5t + 3)(t + 2)$ **29.** $(8m - 3)(2m - 1)$
31. $(3a + 2)(a - 2)$ **33.** $(2x + 1)(x - 2)$
35. $(2m - 3)(m + 4)$ **37.** $(3y + 2)(2y - 1)$
39. $(2x + y)(x + y)$ **41.** $(3x - y)(x - y)$
43. $(2u + 3v)(u - v)$ **45.** $(2p + q)(3p - 2q)$
47. $2(3x + 2)(x - 5)$ **49.** $(2a - 5)(4a - 3)$
51. $(4x - 5y)(3x - 2y)$ **53.** $(5m + 2n)(2m - 5n)$
55. $(z + 3)(4z + 1)$ **57.** $(2x + 3)(2x + 1)$
59. $(2u - 3)(5u + 1)$ **61.** $(5y + 1)(2y - 1)$ **63.** $(3x - 2)^2$
65. $(5x + 3)^2$ **67.** $(2x + 3)^2$ **69.** $(3x + 2)^2$
71. $(2x + y + 4)(2x + y - 4)$
73. $(3 + a + 2b)(3 - a - 2b)$ **75.** $(4a - 3b)(a - 3b)$
77. $(2a + 3b)(a + b)$ **79.** $(3p - q)(2p + q)$ **81.** prime
83. $-(4y - 3)(3y - 4)$ **85.** prime   **87.** $(4x - y)^2$
89. $(2x + 3y)(2x + y)$ **91.** $2(2x - 1)(x + 3)$
93. $y(y + 12)(y + 1)$ **95.** $3x(2x + 1)(x - 3)$
97. $3r^3(5r - 2)(2r + 5)$ **99.** $4(a - 2b)(a + b)$
101. $4(2x + y)(x - 2y)$ **103.** $(2a - b)^2$
105. $-2mn(4m + 3n)(2m + n)$
107. $-2uv^3(7u - 3v)(2u - v)$
109. $(3p + 1 + q)(3p + 1 - q)$

Getting Ready (page 354)

1. $x^3 - 27$ **2.** $x^3 + 8$ **3.** $y^3 + 64$ **4.** $r^3 - 125$
5. $a^3 - b^3$ **6.** $a^3 + b^3$

Exercises 5.5 (page 358)

1. $(x - y)(x^2 + xy + y^2)$ **3.** $(a + 2)(a^2 - 2a + 4)$
5. $(1 + 2x)(1 - 2x + 4x^2)$ **7.** $(xy + 1)(x^2y^2 - xy + 1)$
9. 0.0000000000001 cm   **11.** sum of two cubes
13. $(x^2 - xy + y^2)$ **15.** $(y + 1)(y^2 - y + 1)$
17. $(2 + x)(4 - 2x + x^2)$ **19.** $(m + n)(m^2 - mn + n^2)$
21. $(2u + w)(4u^2 - 2uw + w^2)$ **23.** $(x - 2)(x^2 + 2x + 4)$
25. $(s - t)(s^2 + st + t^2)$ **27.** $(5p - q)(25p^2 + 5pq + q^2)$
29. $(3a - b)(9a^2 + 3ab + b^2)$ **31.** $2(x + 3)(x^2 - 3x + 9)$
33. $-(x - 6)(x^2 + 6x + 36)$
35. $8x(2m - n)(4m^2 + 2mn + n^2)$
37. $xy(x + 6y)(x^2 - 6xy + 36y^2)$
39. $(x + 1)(x^2 - x + 1)(x - 1)(x^2 + x + 1)$

41. $(x^2 + y)(x^4 - x^2y + y^2)(x^2 - y)(x^4 + x^2y + y^2)$
43. $(5 + b)(25 - 5b + b^2)$ **45.** $(3x + 5)(9x^2 - 15x + 25)$
47. $(4x + 3y)(16x^2 - 12xy + 9y^2)$
49. $(a + b^2)(a^2 - ab^2 + b^4)$ **51.** $(x - y^3)(x^2 + xy^3 + y^6)$
53. $4m^2n(m + 5n)(m^2 - 5mn + 25n^2)$
55. $8ab^4(3a - 5b)(9a^2 + 15ab + 25b^2)$
57. $xy^2(x^3 - y)(x^6 + x^3y + y^2)$
59. $3m^2n(2m - n)(4m^2 + 2mn + n^2)$
61. $(2a - b)(4a^2 + 2ab + b^2)(x + 4)$
63. $(a + b)(a^2 - ab + b^2)(x - y)$
65. $(x + y)(x^2 - xy + y^2)(x - y)$
67. $(y + 2)(y - 2)(z + 2)(z^2 - 2z + 4)$

Getting Ready (page 359)

1. $3ax(x + a)$ **2.** $(x + 3y)(x - 3y)$
3. $(x - 2)(x^2 + 2x + 4)$ **4.** $2(x + 2)(x - 2)$
5. $(x - 5)(x + 2)$ **6.** $(2x - 3)(3x - 2)$
7. $2(3x - 1)(x - 2)$ **8.** $(a + b)(x + y)(x - y)$

Exercises 5.6 (page 362)

1. common factor   **3.** sum of two cubes   **5.** none, prime
7. difference of two squares   **9.** $\frac{8}{3}$ **11.** 0   **13.** factors
15. binomials   **17.** $3(2x + 1)$ **19.** $(x - 7)(x + 1)$
21. $(3t - 1)(2t + 3)$ **23.** $(t - 1)^2$ **25.** $2(x + 4)(x - 4)$
27. prime   **29.** $-2x^2(x - 4)(x^2 + 4x + 16)$
31. $2t^2(3t - 5)(t + 4)$ **33.** prime   **35.** $a(6a - 1)(a + 6)$
37. $x^2(4 - 5x)^2$ **39.** $-3x(2x + 7)^2$
41. $8(x - 1)(x^2 + x + 1)(x + 1)(x^2 - x + 1)$
43. $-5x^2(x^3 - x - 5)$ **45.** prime   **47.** $2a(b + 6)(b - 2)$
49. $-4p^2q^3(2pq^4 + 1)$ **51.** $(2a - b + 3)(2a - b - 3)$
53. $(a + b)(a^2 - ab + b^2)$ **55.** $(y^2 - 2)(x + 1)(x - 1)$
57. $(a + b + y)(a + b - y)$ **59.** $(x - a)(a + b)(a - b)$
61. $(2p^2 - 3q^2)(4p^4 + 6p^2q^2 + 9q^4)$
63. $(5p - 4y)(25p^2 + 20py + 16y^2)$
65. $-x^2y^2z(16x^2 - 24x^3yz^3 + 15yz^6)$
67. $(9p^2 + 4q^2)(3p + 2q)(3p - 2q)$
69. $2(3x + 5y^2)(9x^2 - 15xy^2 + 25y^4)$
71. $(x + y)(x - y)(x + y)(x^2 - xy + y^2)$
73. $2(a + b)(a - b)(c + 2d)$

Getting Ready (page 363)

1. 1   **2.** 13   **3.** 3   **4.** 2

Exercises 5.7 (page 368)

1. 7, 8   **3.** 0, −7   **5.** 1, 1   **7.** u^9 **9.** $\frac{a}{b}$ **11.** quadratic
13. second   **15.** 2, −3   **17.** 4, −1   **19.** $\frac{5}{2}$, −2
21. 1, −2, 3   **23.** 0, 3   **25.** 0, $-\frac{7}{5}$ **27.** 0, 7   **29.** 0, $-\frac{8}{3}$
31. 5, −5   **33.** $\frac{2}{3}$, $-\frac{2}{3}$ **35.** 7, −7   **37.** $\frac{9}{2}$, $-\frac{9}{2}$ **39.** 12, 1
41. 5, −3   **43.** $\frac{1}{2}$, $-\frac{2}{3}$ **45.** $\frac{1}{2}$, 2   **47.** 1, −2, −3
49. 3, −3, −5   **51.** 0, −1, −2   **53.** 0, 9, −3
55. 0, −3, $-\frac{1}{3}$ **57.** 0, −3, −3   **59.** 0, 2   **61.** 0, $-\frac{1}{5}$
63. 7, −7   **65.** $\frac{1}{2}$, $-\frac{1}{2}$ **67.** −3, 7   **69.** 8, 1   **71.** −3, −5
73. −4, 2   **75.** $-\frac{3}{2}$, 1   **77.** $-\frac{1}{7}$, $-\frac{3}{2}$ **79.** 1, 5, $-\frac{3}{2}$

81. $9, -9, -2$ **83.** $-\frac{1}{3}, 3$ **85.** $\frac{2}{3}, -\frac{1}{5}$ **87.** $-\frac{3}{2}, \frac{2}{3}$
89. $\frac{1}{8}, 1$ **91.** $0, \frac{1}{5}, -\frac{3}{2}$

Getting Ready (page 370)

1. s^2 sq in.   **2.** $(2w + 4)$ cm   **3.** $x(x + 1)$
4. $w(w + 3)$ sq in.

Exercises 5.8 (page 373)

1. $A = lw$ **3.** $A = s^2$ **5.** $P = 2l + 2w$ **7.** -10
9. 675 cm^2 **11.** analyze   **13.** $5, 7$ or $-7, -5$ **15.** 9 or 1
17. 9 sec   **19.** $\frac{15}{4}$ sec and 10 sec   **21.** 2 sec   **23.** 21 ft
25. 4 m by 9 m   **27.** 48 ft   **29.** $b = 4$ in., $h = 18$ in.
31. 18 sq units   **33.** 1 m   **35.** 3 cm   **37.** 4 cm by 7 cm
39. 12   **41.** 841π sq m   **43.** 6, 16 ft

Chapter Review (page 377)

1. $5 \cdot 7$ **2.** $3^2 \cdot 5$ **3.** $2^5 \cdot 3$ **4.** $2 \cdot 3 \cdot 17$ **5.** $3 \cdot 29$
6. $3^2 \cdot 11$ **7.** $2 \cdot 5^2 \cdot 41$ **8.** 2^{12} **9.** $3(x + 3y)$
10. $5a(x^2 + 3)$ **11.** $7x(x + 2)$ **12.** $3x(x - 1)$
13. $2x(x^2 + 2x - 4)$ **14.** $a(x + y - z)$ **15.** $a(x + y - 1)$
16. $xyz(x + y)$ **17.** $(x + y)(a + b)$
18. $(x + y)(x + y + 1)$ **19.** $2x(x + 2)(x + 3)$
20. $3x(y + z)(1 - 3y - 3z)$ **21.** $(p + 3q)(3 + a)$
22. $(r - 2s)(a + 7)$ **23.** $(x + a)(x + b)$
24. $(y + 2)(x - 2)$ **25.** $(x + y)(a + b)$
26. $(x - 4)(x^2 + 3)$ **27.** $(x + 3)(x - 3)$
28. $(xy + 4)(xy - 4)$ **29.** $(x + 2 + y)(x + 2 - y)$
30. $(z + x + y)(z - x - y)$ **31.** $6y(x + 2y)(x - 2y)$
32. $(x + y + z)(x + y - z)$ **33.** $(x + 3)(x + 7)$
34. $(x - 3)(x + 7)$ **35.** $(x + 6)(x - 4)$
36. $(x - 6)(x + 2)$ **37.** $(2x + 1)(x - 3)$
38. $(3x + 1)(x - 5)$ **39.** $(2x + 3)(3x - 1)$
40. $3(2x - 1)(x + 1)$ **41.** $x(x + 3)(6x - 1)$
42. $x(4x + 3)(x - 2)$ **43.** $-2x(x + 2)(2x - 3)$
44. $-4a(a - 3b)(a + 2b)$ **45.** $(c - 3)(c^2 + 3c + 9)$
46. $(d + 2)(d^2 - 2d + 4)$ **47.** $2(x + 3)(x^2 - 3x + 9)$
48. $2ab(b - 1)(b^2 + b + 1)$ **49.** $y(3x - y)(x - 2)$
50. $5(x + 2)(x - 3y)$ **51.** $a(a + b)(2x + a)$
52. $(x + a + y)(x + a - y)$ **53.** $(x + 2)(x - 2 + b)$
54. $a(x + y)(x^2 - xy + y^2)(x - y)(x^2 + xy + y^2)$ **55.** $0, -2$
56. $0, 3$ **57.** $0, \frac{2}{3}$ **58.** $0, -5$ **59.** $3, -3$ **60.** $5, -5$
61. $3, 4$ **62.** $5, -3$ **63.** $-4, 6$ **64.** $2, 8$ **65.** $3, -\frac{1}{2}$
66. $1, -\frac{3}{2}$ **67.** $\frac{1}{2}, -\frac{1}{2}$ **68.** $\frac{2}{3}, -\frac{2}{3}$ **69.** $0, 3, 4$
70. $0, -2, -3$ **71.** $0, \frac{1}{2}, -3$ **72.** $0, -\frac{2}{3}, 1$ **73.** 5 and 7
74. $\frac{1}{3}$ **75.** 6 ft by 8 ft   **76.** 3 ft by 9 ft   **77.** 3 ft by 6 ft
78. 7 ft

Chapter 5 Test (page 381)

1. $2^2 \cdot 7^2$ **2.** $3 \cdot 37$ **3.** $5a(12b^2c^3 + 6a^2b^2c - 5)$
4. $3x(a + b)(x - 2y)$ **5.** $(x + y)(a + b)$ **6.** $(x + 5)(x - 5)$
7. $3(a + 3b)(a - 3b)$ **8.** $(4x^2 + 9y^2)(2x + 3y)(2x - 3y)$
9. $(x + 3)(x + 1)$ **10.** $(x - 11)(x + 2)$
11. $(x + 9y)(x + y)$ **12.** $6(x - 4y)(x - y)$

13. $(3x + 1)(x + 4)$ **14.** $(2a - 3)(a + 4)$
15. $(2x - y)(x + 2y)$ **16.** $(4x - 3)(3x - 4)$
17. $6(2a - 3b)(a + 2b)$ **18.** $(x - 4)(x^2 + 4x + 16)$
19. $8(3 + a)(9 - 3a + a^2)$
20. $z^3(x^3 - yz)(x^6 + x^3yz + y^2z^2)$ **21.** $0, -3$ **22.** $-1, -\frac{3}{2}$
23. $3, -3$ **24.** $3, -6$ **25.** $\frac{9}{5}, -\frac{1}{2}$ **26.** $-\frac{9}{10}, 1$ **27.** $\frac{1}{5}, -\frac{9}{2}$
28. $-\frac{1}{10}, 9$ **29.** 12 sec   **30.** 10 m

Getting Ready (page 383)

1. $\frac{3}{4}$ **2.** 2   **3.** $\frac{5}{11}$ **4.** $\frac{1}{2}$

Exercises 6.1 (page 390)

1. $\frac{2}{3}$ **3.** $\frac{z}{w}$ **5.** $\frac{x}{y}$ **7.** 1   **9.** $(a + b) + c = a + (b + c)$
11. 0   **13.** $\frac{5}{3}$ **15.** numerator   **17.** 0   **19.** negatives
21. $\frac{a}{b}$ **23.** factor, common   **25.** 2   **27.** $\frac{2}{3}$ **29.** $2, -1$
31. $\frac{3}{2}, -1$ **33.** $\frac{4}{5}$ **35.** $2x$ **37.** $-\frac{x}{3}$ **39.** in simplest form
41. $\frac{a}{3}$ **43.** $\frac{1}{3}$ **45.** 2   **47.** $\frac{x}{2}$ **49.** $\frac{x + 1}{x - 1}$ **51.** $\frac{x - 5}{x + 2}$
53. $\frac{2x}{x - 2}$ **55.** $a - 2$ **57.** $\frac{4}{3}$ **59.** $x + 1$ **61.** $\frac{x^2 - x + 1}{a + 1}$
63. $\frac{b + 2}{b + 1}$ **65.** -1 **67.** -1 **69.** $\frac{5}{a}$ **71.** $\frac{2}{z}$ **73.** $\frac{3x}{y}$
75. $\frac{x + 2}{x^2}$ **77.** $\frac{2}{x}$ **79.** $\frac{3}{x - 5}$ **81.** -1 **83.** $\frac{2}{3}$ **85.** $\frac{3}{x}$
87. $\frac{2(x + 2)}{x - 1}$ **89.** in simplest form   **91.** $\frac{3x}{5y}$ **93.** $\frac{x - 3}{5 - x}$ or
$-\frac{x - 3}{x - 5}$ **95.** $x + 1$ **97.** $\frac{y + 3}{x - 3}$

Getting Ready (page 392)

1. $\frac{2}{3}$ **2.** $\frac{14}{3}$ **3.** 3   **4.** 6   **5.** $\frac{5}{2}$ **6.** 1   **7.** $\frac{3}{4}$ **8.** 2

Exercises 6.2 (page 399)

1. $\frac{3}{2}$ **3.** 5   **5.** $\frac{1}{4}$ **7.** $-6x^5y^6z$ **9.** $\frac{1}{81y^4}$ **11.** $\frac{1}{x^m}$
13. $4y^3 + 4y^2 - 8y + 32$ **15.** numerator   **17.** numerators,
denominators   **19.** 1   **21.** divisor, multiply   **23.** $\frac{45}{91}$
25. $\frac{2y}{3}$ **27.** $\frac{4}{7}$ **29.** $-3y^2$ **31.** $\frac{b^3c}{a^4}$ **33.** $\frac{(z + 7)(z + 2)}{7z}$
35. $x + 2$ **37.** $\frac{1}{y}$ **39.** x **41.** $\frac{c^2}{ab}$ **43.** $\frac{5}{z + 2}$ **45.** z
47. $\frac{x + 1}{2(x - 2)}$ **49.** $\frac{1}{c - d}$ **51.** $\frac{2}{3}$ **53.** $\frac{3}{5}$ **55.** $\frac{2}{y}$ **57.** $\frac{2}{3x}$
59. $\frac{x + 2}{3}$ **61.** $\frac{y - 3}{y^3}$ **63.** $\frac{x - 2}{x - 3}$ **65.** $a + 2$ **67.** $\frac{x - 5}{2}$
69. $\frac{3}{x + 1}$ **71.** $\frac{9}{2x}$ **73.** $\frac{x}{36}$ **75.** $\frac{5}{3(x + 1)^2}$ **77.** $\frac{x + 2}{x - 2}$
79. $-\frac{3}{11}$ **81.** $\frac{5}{7}$ **83.** $\frac{3}{2y}$ **85.** 3   **87.** $\frac{14}{9}$ **89.** x^2y^2
91. $2xy^2$ **93.** $\frac{r^3t^4}{s}$ **95.** $\frac{6}{y}$ **97.** 6   **99.** $\frac{2x}{3}$ **101.** x
103. $\frac{x}{5}$ **105.** $\frac{2(z - 2)}{z}$ **107.** $\frac{(m - 2)(m - 3)}{2(m + 2)}$
109. $\frac{-(x - y)(x^2 + xy + y^2)}{(a + b)}$ **111.** 1   **113.** $x + 5$ **115.** 1
117. $-\frac{p}{m + n}$ **119.** $\frac{(x + 1)(x - 1)}{5(x - 3)}$ **121.** $\frac{2x(1 - x)}{5(x - 2)}$ **123.** $\frac{y^2}{3}$

Getting Ready (page 402)

1. $\frac{4}{5}$ **2.** 1   **3.** $\frac{7}{8}$ **4.** 2   **5.** $\frac{1}{9}$ **6.** $\frac{1}{2}$ **7.** $-\frac{2}{13}$ **8.** $\frac{13}{10}$

Exercises 6.3 (page 411)

1. equal   **3.** not equal   **5.** equal   **7.** equal   **9.** 7^2
11. $2^3 \cdot 17$ **13.** $2 \cdot 3 \cdot 17$ **15.** $2^4 \cdot 3^2$ **17.** LCD
19. numerators, common denominator   **21.** $\frac{2}{3}$ **23.** $\frac{1}{3}$
25. $\frac{4x}{y}$ **27.** 9   **29.** $-\frac{1}{8}$ **31.** $\frac{x}{y}$ **33.** $\frac{1}{y}$ **35.** 1   **37.** $\frac{4x}{3}$
39. $\frac{2(x+5)}{x-2}$ **41.** $\frac{125}{20}$ **43.** $\frac{8xy}{x^2 y}$ **45.** $\frac{3x(x+1)}{(x+1)^2}$
47. $\frac{2y(x+1)}{x^2+x}$ **49.** $\frac{z(z+1)}{z^2-1}$ **51.** $\frac{2(x+2)}{x^2+3x+2}$ **53.** $6x$
55. $18xy$ **57.** $(x-1)(x+1)$ **59.** $x(x+6)$ **61.** $\frac{7}{6}$
63. $\frac{5y}{9}$ **65.** $\frac{2xy+x-y}{xy}$ **67.** $\frac{2x^2+2}{(x-1)(x+1)}$ **69.** $\frac{x^2+7x+6}{2x^2}$
71. $\frac{2x^2-1}{x(x+1)}$ **73.** $-\frac{1}{6}$ **75.** $\frac{53x}{42}$ **77.** $\frac{x^2+4x+1}{x^2 y}$
79. $\frac{x+2}{x-2}$ **81.** $-\frac{2}{x-3}$ **83.** $\frac{2y+7}{y-1}$ **85.** $\frac{x}{x-2}$ **87.** $\frac{a+4}{a+2}$
89. $(x-3)(x+2)(x+3)$ **91.** $\frac{2}{y}$ **93.** $\frac{2y+6}{5z}$ **95.** $\frac{y}{x}$
97. $\frac{2x}{3y}$ **99.** $\frac{14y^2+10}{y^2}$ **101.** $\frac{4x-2y}{y+2}$ **103.** $\frac{-1}{(a+3)(a-3)}$

Getting Ready (page 414)

1. 4   **2.** -18 **3.** 7   **4.** -8 **5.** $3+3x$ **6.** $2-y$
7. $12x-2$ **8.** $3y+2x$

Exercises 6.4 (page 419)

1. $\frac{4}{3}$ **3.** $\frac{1}{4}$ **5.** t^9 **7.** $-2r^7$ **9.** $\frac{81}{256r^8}$ **11.** $\frac{r^{10}}{9}$
13. complex fraction   **15.** single, divide   **17.** $\frac{8}{9}$ **19.** $\frac{3}{8}$
21. $\frac{x^2}{y}$ **23.** $\frac{5t^2}{27}$ **25.** $\frac{5}{4}$ **27.** $\frac{5}{7}$ **29.** $\frac{1+3y}{3-2y}$ **31.** $\frac{1+x}{2+x}$
33. $\frac{3-x}{x-1}$ **35.** $\frac{a+4}{3}$ **37.** $\frac{1}{x+2}$ **39.** $\frac{1}{x+3}$ **41.** $\frac{xy}{y+x}$
43. $\frac{y}{x-2y}$ **45.** $\frac{3y+2x^2}{4y}$ **47.** $\frac{x^2}{(x-1)^2}$ **49.** $\frac{y}{x^2}$ **51.** $\frac{1+y^2}{1-y^2}$
53. $\frac{a^2-a+1}{a^2}$ **55.** 2   **57.** $\frac{x}{x-1}$ **59.** $\frac{7x+3}{-x-3}$ **61.** $\frac{x-2}{x+3}$
63. $\frac{m^2-3m-4}{m^2+5m-3}$ **65.** $\frac{2x(x-3)}{(4x-3)(x+2)}$ **67.** $\frac{(3x+1)(x-1)}{(x+1)^2}$
69. -1 **71.** $\frac{y-5}{y+5}$ **75.** $\frac{1}{2}, \frac{2}{3}, \frac{3}{5}, \frac{5}{8}$

Getting Ready (page 421)

1. $3x+1$ **2.** $8x-1$ **3.** $3+2x$ **4.** $y-6$ **5.** 19
6. $7x+6$ **7.** y **8.** $3x+5$

Exercises 6.5 (page 426)

1. Multiply by 10.   **3.** Multiply by 9.   **5.** $x(x+4)$
7. $(2x+3)(x-1)$ **9.** $(x^2+4)(x+2)(x-2)$
11. extraneous   **13.** LCD   **15.** xy **17.** 4   **19.** -20
21. 6   **23.** 60   **25.** -12 **27.** 0   **29.** -7 **31.** -1
33. $\varnothing$; -2 is extraneous   **35.** $\varnothing$; 5 is extraneous   **37.** 3
39. $\varnothing$, 0 is extraneous   **41.** 1   **43.** 5   **45.** 2   **47.** -3
49. 5   **51.** $\varnothing$; -2 is extraneous   **53.** 0   **55.** $-2, 1$
57. 1, 2   **59.** -4; 4 is extraneous   **61.** $a=\frac{b}{b-1}$
63. $b=\frac{ad}{d-c}$ **65.** 12   **67.** 0   **69.** -3 **71.** -1
73. 6   **75.** 3; -3 is extraneous   **77.** 1   **79.** $f=\frac{d_1 d_2}{d_1+d_2}$
83. 1, -1

Getting Ready (page 428)

1. $\frac{1}{5}$ **2.** $\$(0.05x)$ **3.** $\$\left(\frac{y}{0.05}\right)$ **4.** $\frac{y}{52}$ hr

Exercises 6.6 (page 432)

1. $i=pr$ **3.** $C=qd$ **5.** $-1, 6$ **7.** $-2, -3, -4$
9. 0, 0, 1   **11.** 2, -4 **15.** 2   **17.** 5   **19.** 30 min
21. $2\frac{2}{9}$ hr   **23.** heron, 20 mph; goose, 30 mph   **25.** 150 mph
27. 7% and 8%   **29.** 6%   **31.** $\frac{2}{3}$ and $\frac{3}{2}$ **33.** 8 hr
35. 4 mph   **37.** 30   **39.** 25 mph   **41.** 5   **43.** 44 mph
and 64 mph

Getting Ready (page 435)

1. $\frac{1}{2}$ **2.** $\frac{2}{3}$ **3.** $-\frac{4}{5}$ **4.** $-\frac{5}{9}$

Exercises 6.7 (page 439)

1. $\frac{5}{8}$ **3.** $\frac{1}{3}$ **5.** 17   **7.** 6   **9.** $2(x+3)$
11. $(2x+3)(x-2)$ **13.** quotient   **15.** equal   **19.** $\frac{5}{7}$
21. $\frac{1}{2}$ **23.** $\frac{2}{3}$ **25.** $\frac{2}{7}$ **27.** $\frac{1}{3}$ **29.** $\frac{1}{5}$ **31.** $\frac{3}{7}$ **33.** $\frac{3}{4}$
35. $\frac{1}{16}$ **37.** $\$1,825$ **39.** $\frac{22}{365}$ **41.** $\frac{\$53.55}{17\text{ gal}}$; \$3.15/gal
43. the 6-oz can   **45.** $\frac{\$337.50}{27\text{ hr}}$; \$12.50/hr   **47.** 65 mph
49. 7¢/oz   **51.** the truck   **53.** the second car
55. $\frac{11,880\text{ gal}}{27\text{ min}}$; 440 gal/min   **57.** \$8,725   **59.** $\frac{336}{1,745}$

Getting Ready (page 441)

1. 10   **2.** $\frac{7}{3}$ **3.** $\frac{20}{7}$ **4.** 5   **5.** $\frac{14}{3}$ **6.** 5   **7.** 21   **8.** $\frac{3}{2}$

Exercises 6.8 (page 449)

1. proportion   **3.** not a proportion   **5.** 90%   **7.** $\frac{1}{3}$
9. 480   **11.** \$73.50   **13.** proportion, ratios   **15.** means
17. similar   **19.** ad, bc **21.** triangle   **23.** no   **25.** yes
27. no   **29.** yes   **31.** yes   **33.** no   **35.** 4   **37.** 6
39. 0   **41.** -17 **43.** -3 **45.** 9   **47.** $-\frac{3}{2}$ **49.** $\frac{83}{2}$
51. -6 **53.** \$17   **55.** \$6.50   **57.** 24   **59.** about $4\frac{1}{4}$
61. 47   **63.** $7\frac{1}{2}$ gal   **65.** \$309   **67.** 65 ft 3 in.
69. 288 in. or 24 ft   **71.** not exactly, but close   **73.** 39 ft
75. $46\frac{7}{8}$ ft   **77.** 6,750 ft   **79.** 15,840 ft

Chapter Review (page 452)

1. 3, -3 **2.** 2, -3 **3.** $\frac{2}{5}$ **4.** $-\frac{2}{3}$ **5.** $-\frac{1}{3}$ **6.** $\frac{7}{3}$ **7.** $\frac{1}{2x}$
8. $\frac{5}{2x}$ **9.** $\frac{x}{x+1}$ **10.** $\frac{1}{x}$ **11.** 2   **12.** 1   **13.** -1
14. $\frac{x+7}{x+3}$ **15.** $\frac{x}{x-1}$ **16.** $\frac{a+2}{a+b}$ **17.** $\frac{3x}{y}$ **18.** $\frac{6}{x^2}$ **19.** 1
20. $\frac{2x}{x+1}$ **21.** $\frac{3y}{2}$ **22.** $\frac{1}{x}$ **23.** $x+2$ **24.** 1
25. $x+2$ **26.** 1   **27.** $\frac{2(x+1)}{x-7}$ **28.** $\frac{x^2+x-1}{x(x-1)}$
29. $\frac{x-7}{7x}$ **30.** $\frac{x-2}{x(x+1)}$ **31.** $\frac{x^2+4x-4}{2x^2}$ **32.** $\frac{x+1}{x}$
33. 0   **34.** $\frac{9}{4}$ **35.** $\frac{3}{2}$ **36.** $\frac{1+x}{1-x}$ **37.** $\frac{x(x+3)}{2x^2-1}$
38. x^2+3 **39.** $\frac{a(a+bc)}{b(b+ac)}$ **40.** 3   **41.** 1   **42.** 3

43. $4, -\frac{3}{2}$ **44.** -2 **45.** 0 **46.** $r_1 = \frac{rr_2}{r_2 - r}$

47. $T_1 = \frac{T_2}{1 - E}$ or $T_1 = \frac{-T_2}{E - 1}$ **48.** $R = \frac{HB}{B - H}$ or $R = \frac{-HB}{H - B}$

49. $9\frac{9}{19}$ hr **50.** $5\frac{5}{6}$ days **51.** 5 mph **52.** 40 mph **53.** $\frac{1}{2}$

54. $\frac{4}{5}$ **55.** $\frac{2}{3}$ **56.** $\frac{5}{6}$ **57.** $2.93/lb

58. 568.75 kwh per week **59.** no **60.** yes **61.** $\frac{9}{2}$

62. 0 **63.** 7 **64.** 1 **65.** 20 ft

Chapter 6 Test (page 459)

1. $\frac{8x}{9y}$ **2.** $\frac{x + 1}{2x + 3}$ **3.** 3 **4.** $\frac{5y^2}{4t}$ **5.** $\frac{x + 1}{3(x - 2)}$ **6.** $\frac{3t^2}{5y}$

7. $\frac{x^2}{3}$ **8.** $x + 2$ **9.** $\frac{10x - 1}{x - 1}$ **10.** $\frac{13}{2y + 3}$ **11.** $\frac{2x^2 + x + 1}{x(x + 1)}$

12. $\frac{2x + 6}{x - 2}$ **13.** $\frac{2x^3}{y^3}$ **14.** $\frac{x + y}{y - x}$ **15.** -5 **16.** 6 **17.** 4

18. $B = \frac{RH}{R - H}$ **19.** $3\frac{15}{16}$ hr **20.** 5 mph **21.** 8,050 ft

22. $\frac{2}{3}$ **23.** yes **24.** $\frac{2}{3}$ **25.** 45 ft

Cumulative Review Exercises (page 460)

1. x^7 **2.** x^{10} **3.** x^3 **4.** 1 **5.** $6x^3 - 2x - 1$

6. $2x^3 + 2x^2 + x - 1$ **7.** $13x^2 - 8x + 1$

8. $16x^2 - 24x + 2$ **9.** $-12x^5y^5$

10. $-35x^5 + 10x^4 + 10x^2$ **11.** $6x^2 + 14x + 4$

12. $15x^2 - 2xy - 8y^2$ **13.** $x + 4$ **14.** $x^2 + x + 1$

15. $3xy(x - 2y)$ **16.** $(a + b)(3 + x)$ **17.** $(a + b)(2 + b)$

18. $(5p^2 + 4q)(5p^2 - 4q)$ **19.** $(x - 12)(x + 1)$

20. $(x - 3y)(x + 2y)$ **21.** $(3a + 4)(2a - 5)$

22. $(4m + n)(2m - 3n)$ **23.** $(p - 3q)(p^2 + 3pq + 9q^2)$

24. $8(r + 2s)(r^2 - 2rs + 4s^2)$ **25.** 15 **26.** 4 **27.** $\frac{2}{3}, -\frac{1}{2}$

28. $0, 2$ **29.** $-1, -2$ **30.** $\frac{3}{2}, -4$

31. **32.**

33. **34.**

35. 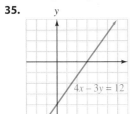 **36.**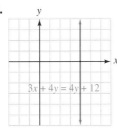

37. -3 **38.** 15 **39.** 5 **40.** $8x^2 - 3$ **41.** $\frac{x + 1}{x - 1}$

42. $\frac{x - 3}{x - 2}$ **43.** $\frac{(x - 2)^2}{x - 1}$ **44.** $\frac{(p + 2)(p - 3)}{3(p + 3)}$ **45.** 1

46. $\frac{2(x^2 + 1)}{(x + 1)(x - 1)}$ **47.** $\frac{-1}{2(a - 2)}$ **48.** $\frac{y + x}{y - x}$

Getting Ready (page 462)

1. 2 **2.** 8 **3.** 10 **4.** -7

Exercises 7.1 (page 472)

1. 1 **3.** $x < 2$ **5.** $x < -4$ **7.** $\frac{1}{t^{12}}$ **9.** 471 or more

11. equation **13.** multiplied, divided **15.** contradiction

17. is greater than **19.** half-open **21.** positive **23.** 6

25. 4 **27.** 2 **29.** 6 **31.** -4 **33.** -6 **35.** 24

37. 6 **39.** 0 **41.** -2 **43.** $\mathbb{R}$, identity

45. $\varnothing$, contradiction **47.** $B = \frac{3V}{h}$ **49.** $w = \frac{P - 2l}{2}$

51. $x = z\sigma + \mu$ **53.** $x = \frac{y - b}{m}$

55. $(2, \infty)$ **57.** $[-2, \infty)$

59. $\left(-\infty, -\frac{8}{5}\right)$

61. $[-36, \infty)$

63. $(-2, 5)$ **65.** $(8, 11)$

67. $[-4, 6)$ **69.** $\varnothing$

71. $(-\infty, 2) \cup (7, \infty)$

73. $(-\infty, 1)$ **75.** -11 **77.** $\mathbb{R}$, identity

79. $(-\infty, 1]$ **81.** $[2, \infty)$

83. $[-21, -3)$ **85.** $s = \frac{f(P - L)}{i}$

87. 12 m by 24 m **89.** 20 ft by 45 ft **91.** 7 ft, 15 ft

93. $p < 15 **95.** 18

Getting Ready (page 475)

1. 6 **2.** 5 **3.** $2 - x$ **4.** $\pi - 2$

Exercises 7.2 (page 480)

1. 5 **3.** -6 **5.** 8 or -8 **7.** 5 **9.** $\frac{3}{4}$ **11.** 6 **13.** x

15. 0 **17.** $a = -b$ **19.** 8 **21.** 12 **23.** -2 **25.** -30

27. 50 **29.** $4 - \pi$ **31.** $|2|$ **33.** $|5|$ **35.** $|-2|$

37. $-|4|$ **39.** $-|-7|$ **41.** $-x$ **43.** $8, -8$ **45.** $9, -3$

47. $4, -1$ **49.** $\frac{14}{3}, -6$ **51.** $0, -6$ **53.** $40, -20$ **55.** $\varnothing$

57. -8 **59.** $-2, -\frac{4}{5}$ **61.** $3, -1$ **63.** $0, -2$ **65.** 0

67. $8, -4$ **69.** $2, -\frac{1}{2}$ **71.** $\frac{20}{3}$ **73.** $\frac{4}{3}$ **75.** $\varnothing$

77. $-4, -28$ **79.** $-16.6, 16.2$

Getting Ready (page 481)

1. $x > 1$ **2.** $x > -2$ **3.** $x \le 7$

Exercises 7.3 (page 486)

1. $-8 < x < 8$ **3.** $x \le -4$ or $x \ge 4$ **5.** $-3 < x < 1$

7. $t = \frac{A - p}{pr}$ **9.** $l = \frac{P - 2w}{2}$ **11.** $-k < x < k$

13. $x < -k$ or $x > k$ **15.** $(-4, 4)$

17. $[-21, 3]$ **19.** $\left[-\frac{8}{3}, 4\right]$

21. $(-2, 5)$

23. $(-\infty, -1) \cup (1, \infty)$

25. $(-\infty, -12) \cup (36, \infty)$

27. $\left(-\infty, -\frac{16}{3}\right) \cup (4, \infty)$

29. $(-\infty, -2] \cup \left[\frac{10}{3}, \infty\right)$

31. $(-\infty, -24) \cup (-18, \infty)$

33. $(-\infty, -2) \cup (5, \infty)$

35. $\left(-\infty, -\frac{1}{5}\right) \cup \left(\frac{3}{5}, \infty\right)$

37. $(-\infty, -10) \cup (14, \infty)$

39. $(-\infty, \infty)$ **41.** $\varnothing$

43. $\left[-\frac{1}{2}, -\frac{1}{2}\right]$

45. $(-\infty, -4) \cup (-4, \infty)$

47. $(-\infty, -4] \cup [-1, \infty)$

49. $[-7, -7]$

51. $(-\infty, 25) \cup (25, \infty)$

53. $[1, 3]$

55. $(-\infty, \infty)$

57. $(-\infty, \infty)$

59. $(-6.6, 3.8)$ **61.** $(-\infty, -3.5) \cup (3.2, \infty)$
65. x and y must have different signs.

Getting Ready (page 488)

1. $6x^3y - 3x^2y^2$ **2.** $x^2 - 4$ **3.** $x^2 - x - 6$
4. $6x^2 + 7x - 3$ **5.** $x^3 - 27$ **6.** $x^3 + 8$

Getting Ready

1. $6x^2y - 3x^2y^2$

2. $x^2 - x - 6$

3. $2x^2y - 3x - 9$

4. $6a^2 + 7ab - 3b^2$

Orals

1. $3xy(y - 2x)$ **2.** $(x + 6)(x - 1)$

3. $(2x + 1)(x - 1)$ **4.** $(3a - b)(a - 2b)$

Exercises 7.4A

1. factored

3. greatest common factor

5. completely; prime

7. trinomial

9. lead; coefficient; 2

11. $6xy^2$

13. $9; 6; -9; -6$

15. Complete the key number table.

$$\text{Key number} = 12$$

Negative factors of 12	Sum of factors of 12
$-1(-12) = 12$	$-1 + (-12) = -13$
$-2(-6) = 12$	$-2 + (-6) = -8$
$-3(-4) = 12$	$-3 + (-4) = -7$

17. $5c^2d^4$

19. $3m; 3$

21. $2x(x - 3)$

23. $5x^2y(3 - 2y)$

25. $3z(9z^2 + 4z + 1)$

27. prime

29. $-(5xy - y + 4)$

31. $6s(4s^2 - 2st + t^2)$

33. $(x + y)(u + v)$

35. $-6ab(3a + 2b)$

37. $\frac{1}{5}x^2(3ax^2 + b - 4ax)$

39. $(a - b)(5 - t)$

41. $(m + n + p)(3 + x)$

43. $-7u^2v^3z^2(9uv^3z^7 - 4v^4 + 3uz^2)$

45. $2(x^2 + 1)^2(x^2 + 3)$

47. $r_1 = \frac{rr_2}{r_2 - r}$

49. $r = \frac{s^r_2 - a^r}{s - 1}$

51. $a^2 = \frac{b^2x^2}{b^2 - y^2}$

53. $(x + y)(a + b)$

55. $(x + y)(x + 1)$

57. $(a + b)(a - 4)$

59. $(x - y)(x - 4)$

61. $(a^2 + b)(x - 1)$

63. $(x + y)(x + y + z)$

65. $(1 - m)(1 - n)$

67. $(2x^2 + 1)(a - 4)$

69. $x(m + n)(p + q)$

71. $y(x + y)(x + y + 2z)$

73. $(x - 3)(x - 2)$

75. $(x - 2)(x - 5)$

77. prime

79. $(x + 5)(x - 6)$

81. $(a - 9)^2$

83. $(x + 3y)(x - 7y)$

85. $(s - 2t)(s - 8t)$

87. $3(x + 7)(x - 3)$

89. $-(a - 8)(a + 4)$

91. $-3a^2(x - 3)(x - 2)$

93. $(y^2 - 10)(y^2 - 3)$

95. $x^2(b^2 - 7)(b^2 - 5)$

97. $(3y + 2)(2y + 1)$

99. $(4a - 3)(2a + 3)$

101. $(3x - 4y)(2x + y)$

103. prime

105. $(2z + 3)(3z + 4)$

107. $(2y + 1)^2$

109. $-(3a + 2b)(a - b)$

111. $5(2a + 3b)^2$

113. $4h^4(8h - 1)(2h + 1)$

115. $(m + n)(6a - 5)(a + 3)$

117. $(x + a + 1)^2$

119. $(a + b + 4)(a + b - 6)$

121. $(7q - 7r + 2)(2q - 2r - 3)$

123. $x^2(x^n + x^{n+1})$

125. $(x^n + 1)^2$

127. $(x^{2n} + y^{2n})^2$

129. $pr^2\left(h_1 + \frac{1}{3}h_2\right)$

131. $x + 3$

133. Explain the error in the following solution.

Solve for r_1:

$$r_1 r_2 = rr_2 + rr_1$$
$$\frac{r_1 r_2}{r_2} = \frac{rr_2 + rr_1}{r_2}$$
$$r_1 = \frac{rr_2 + rr_1}{r_2}$$

135. \$4,900

Getting Ready

1. $x^2 - 4$

2. $4x^2 - 9y^2$

3. $x^3 - 27$

4. $(x^3 + 8)$

Orals

1. $(x + 1)(x - 1)$

2. $(2a + 3b)(2a - 3b)$

3. $(a + 2)(a^2 - 2a + 4)$

4. $(b - 3)(b^2 + 3b + 9)$

Exercises 7.4B

1. squares

3. 1, 4, 9, 16, 25, 36, 49, 64, 81, 100

5. a. $(x + 5)(x + 5) = x^2 + 10x + 25$

   b. $(x + 5)(x - 5) = x^2 - 25$

7. by the comm. property of mult.,
   $(9t - 4)(9t + 4) = (9t + 4)(9t - 4)$

9. $(p - q)$ **11.** pq

13. $(p^2 + pq + q^2)$

15. Answers may vary.

   a. $x^2 - 4$ **b.** $(x - 4)^2$

   c. $x^2 + 4$ **d.** $x^3 + 8$

   e. $(x + 8)^3$

17. $(x + 2)(x - 2)$

19. $(3y + 8)(3y - 8)$

21. prime

23. $(20 + c)(20 - c)$

25. $(25a + 13b^2)(25a - 13b^2)$

27. $(9a^2 + 7b)(9a^2 - 7b)$

29. $(6x^2y + 7z^2)(6x^2y - 7z^2)$

31. $(x + y + z)(x + y - z)$

33. $(a - b + c)(a - b - c)$

35. $(x^2 + y^2)(x + y)(x - y)$

37. $(16x^2y^2 + z^4)(4xy + z^2)(4xy - z^2)$

39. $\left(\dfrac{1}{6} + y^2\right)\left(\dfrac{1}{6} - y^2\right)$

41. $2(x + 12)(x - 12)$

43. $2x(x + 4)(x - 4)$

45. $5x(x + 5)(x - 5)$

47. $t^2(rs + x^2y)(rs - x^2y)$

49. $(a + b)(a - b + 1)$

51. $(a - b)(a + b + 2)$

53. $(2x + y)(1 + 2x - y)$

55. $(x - 4)(x + y)(x - y)$

57. $(x + 2 + y)(x + 2 - y)$

59. $(x + 1 + 3z)(x + 1 - 3z)$

61. $(c + 2a - b)(c - 2a + b)$

63. $(r + s)(r^2 - rs + s^2)$

65. $(x - 2y)(x^2 + 2xy + 4y^2)$

67. $(4a - 5b^2)(16a^2 + 20ab^2 + 25b^4)$

69. $(5xy^2 + 6z^3)(25x^2y^4 - 30xy^2z^3 + 36z^6)$

71. $(x^2 + y^2)(x^4 - x^2y^2 + y^4)$

73. $5(x + 5)(x^2 - 5x + 25)$

75. $4x^2(x - 4)(x^2 + 4x + 16)$

77. $2u^2(4v - t)(16v^2 + 4tv + t^2)$

79. $(a + b)(x + 3)(x^2 - 3x + 9)$

81. $(x^3 - y^4z^5)(x^6 + x^3y^4z^5 + y^8z^{10})$

83. $(a + b + 3)(a^2 + 2ab + b^2 - 3a - 3b + 9)$

85. $(y + 1)(y - 1)(y - 3)(y^2 + 3y + 9)$

87. $(x + 1)(x^2 - x + 1)(x - 1)(x^2 + x + 1)$

89. $(x^2 + y)(x^4 - x^2y + y^2)(x^2 - y)(x^4 + x^2y + y^2)$

91. $(a + 3)(a - 3)(a + 2)(a - 2)$

93. $(2x^n + 3y^n)(2x^n - 3y^n)$

95. $(a^b - c^b)(a^{2b} + a^bc^b + c^{2b})$

97. $(3x^n + y^n)(9x^{2n} - 3x^ny^n + y^{2n})$

99. $(x^{16} + y^{16})(x^8 + y^8)(x^4 + y^4)(x^2 + y^2)(x + y)(x - y)$

101. $\dfrac{4}{3}p(r_1 - r_2)(r_1^2 + r_1r_2 + r_2^2)$

103. Answers will vary.

105. 45 minutes for \$25

Exercises 7.5 (page 511)

1. $\frac{2}{3}$ **3.** $-\frac{5}{6}$ **5.** $\frac{x}{y}$ **7.** -1 **9.**

11. $w = \frac{P - 2l}{2}$ **13.** $2, -2, 3, -3$ **15.** $\frac{a}{b}$ **17.** $\frac{ad}{bc}$

19. $4x^2$ **21.** $-\frac{4y}{3x}$ **23.** $\frac{3y}{7(y - z)}$ **25.** 1 **27.** $\frac{-3(x + 2)}{x + 1}$

29. $x + 2$ **31.** $\frac{x + 1}{x + 3}$ **33.** $\frac{x + 4}{2(2x - 3)}$ **35.** $\frac{1}{x - y}$

37. $\frac{m - 2n}{n - 2m}$ **39.** $\frac{3(x - y)}{x + 2}$ **41.** $\frac{1}{x^2 + xy + y^2 - 1}$ **43.** $\frac{xy^2d}{c^3}$

45. $x + 1$ **47.** 1 **49.** $\frac{t - 1}{t + 1}$ **51.** $-\frac{x^{10}}{y^2}$ **53.** $\frac{x - 4}{x + 5}$

55. $\frac{(a + 7)^2(a - 5)}{12x^2}$ **57.** $x - 5$ **59.** $-\frac{x^7}{18y^4}$ **61.** $x^2(x + 3)$

63. $\frac{3x}{2}$ **65.** $\frac{x - 7}{x + 7}$ **67.** $\frac{x + 5}{x + 4}$ **69.** 3 **71.** 4

73. $\frac{6x}{(x - 3)(x - 2)}$ **75.** $\frac{10a + 4b}{21}$ **77.** $\frac{9a}{10}$ **79.** $\frac{17}{12x}$

81. $\frac{8x - 2}{(x + 2)(x - 4)}$ **83.** $\frac{x^2 + 1}{x}$ **85.** $\frac{-2(2a + 9)}{(a + 4)(a + 3)}$

87. $\frac{2x^2 + x}{(x + 3)(x + 2)(x - 2)}$ **89.** $\frac{-4x^2 + 14x + 54}{x(x + 3)(x - 3)}$

91. $\frac{x^2 - 5x - 5}{x - 5}$ **93.** $\frac{2}{x + 1}$ **95.** $\frac{2y}{3z}$ **97.** $-\frac{1}{y}$ **99.** $\frac{b + a}{b}$

101. $y - x$ **103.** $\frac{-1}{a + b}$ **105.** $\frac{x + 2}{x - 3}$ **107.** $\frac{y + x}{y - x}$

109. $\frac{x^2(xy^2 - 1)}{y^2(x^2y - 1)}$ **111.** $\frac{(b + a)(b - a)}{b(b - a - ab)}$ **113.** $\frac{3a^2 + 2a}{2a + 1}$

115. $-\frac{x + 3}{x + 2}$ **117.** $\frac{a + b}{(x - 3)(c + d)}$ **119.** $\frac{x + y}{x - y}$ **121.** -1

123. $-\frac{x + 1}{x + 3}$ **125.** $\frac{n + 2}{n + 1}$ **127.** 1   **129.** 2   **131.** $\frac{3x + 1}{x(x + 3)}$

133. $\frac{a - 1}{a + 1}$ **135.** xy **141.** yes   **143.** a, d

Getting Ready (page 515)

1. $x + 1$ with a remainder of 1, 1

2. $x + 3$ with a remainder of 9, 9

Exercises 7.6 (page 520)

1. 9   **3.** yes   **5.** 4   **7.** $12a^2 + 4a - 1$ **9.** $8x^2 + 2x + 4$

11. $x - r$ **13.** $P(r)$ **15.** $x + 2$ **17.** $x - 3$

19. $x - 7 + \frac{28}{x + 2}$ **21.** $3x^2 - x + 2$ **23.** $2x^2 + 4x + 3$

25. $x + 2$ **27.** $4x^2 + 2x - 1$ **29.** $6x^2 - x + 1 + \frac{3}{x + 1}$

31. -37 **33.** 23   **35.** -1 **37.** -1 **39.** -1 **41.** 18

43. 174   **45.** 2   **47.** yes   **49.** no   **51.** -8 **53.** 59

55. 44   **57.** $\frac{29}{32}$ **59.** $7.2x - 0.66 + \frac{0.368}{x - 0.2}$

61. $2.7x - 3.59 + \frac{0.903}{x + 1.7}$

63. $9x^2 - 513x + 29{,}241 + \frac{-1{,}666{,}762}{x + 57}$ **65.** 64   **69.** 1

Chapter Review (page 523)

1. 8   **2.** 7   **3.** 19   **4.** 8   **5.** $\mathbb{R}$ **6.** $\varnothing$ **7.** $h = \frac{3V}{\pi r^2}$

8. $x = \frac{6V}{ab} - y$ **9.** 5 ft from one end   **10.** 45 m²

11. $(-\infty, -24]$

12. $\left(-\infty, -\frac{51}{11}\right)$

13. $\left(-\frac{1}{3}, 2\right)$

14. $(2, \infty)$

15. $3, -\frac{11}{3}$ **16.** $\frac{26}{3}, -\frac{10}{3}$ **17.** $\frac{1}{5}, -5$ **18.** $-1, 1$

19. $(-5, -2)$

20. $\left(-\infty, \frac{4}{3}\right] \cup [4, \infty)$

21. $(-\infty, \infty)$ **22.** $\varnothing$

23. $4(x + 2)$

24. $5xy^2(xy - 2)$ **25.** $-4x^2y^3z^2(2z^2 + 3x^2)$

26. $3a^2b^4c^2(4a^4 + 5c^4)$ **27.** $(x + 2)(y + 4)$

28. $(a + b)(c + 3)$ **29.** $x^n(x^n + 1)$ **30.** $y^{2n}(1 - y^n)$

31. $(x^2 + 4)(x^2 + y)$ **32.** $(a^3 + c)(a^2 + b^2)$

33. $(z + 4)(z - 4)$ **34.** $(y + 11)(y - 11)$

35. $2(x^2 + 7)(x^2 - 7)$ **36.** $3x^2(x^2 + 10)(x^2 - 10)$

37. $(y + 20)(y + 1)$ **38.** $(z - 5)(z - 6)$

39. $-(x + 7)(x - 4)$ **40.** $-(y - 8)(y + 3)$

41. $y(y + 2)(y - 1)$ **42.** $2a^2(a + 3)(a - 1)$

43. $3(5x + y)(x - 4y)$ **44.** $5(6x + y)(x + 2y)$

45. $(x + 2 + 2p^2)(x + 2 - 2p^2)$ **46.** $(y + 2)(y + 1 + x)$

47. $(x + 7)(x^2 - 7x + 49)$ **48.** $(a - 5)(a^2 + 5a + 25)$

49. $8(y - 4)(y^2 + 4y + 16)$ **50.** $4y(x + 3z)(x^2 - 3xz + 9z^2)$

51. $\frac{31x}{72y}$ **52.** $\frac{x - 7}{x + 7}$ **53.** 1   **54.** 1   **55.** $\frac{5y - 3}{x - y}$

56. $\frac{6x - 7}{x^2 + 2}$ **57.** $\frac{5x + 13}{(x + 2)(x + 3)}$ **58.** $\frac{4x^2 + 9x + 12}{(x - 4)(x + 3)}$

59. $\frac{3x(x - 1)}{(x - 3)(x + 1)}$ **60.** 1   **61.** $\frac{5x^2 + 11x}{(x + 1)(x + 2)}$ **62.** $\frac{2(3x + 1)}{x - 3}$

63. $\frac{5x^2 + 23x + 4}{(x + 1)(x - 1)^2}$ **64.** $\frac{-x^4 - 4x^3 + 3x^2 + 18x + 16}{(x - 2)(x + 2)^2}$

65. $\frac{3y - 2x}{x^2y^2}$ **66.** $\frac{y + 2x}{2y - x}$ **67.** $\frac{2x + 1}{x + 1}$ **68.** $\frac{y - x}{y + x}$ **69.** 20

70. -1 **71.** yes   **72.** no

Chapter 7 Test (page 531)

1. -12 **2.** 6   **3.** $i = \frac{f(P - L)}{s}$ **4.** $a = \frac{180n - 360}{n}$

5. $13\frac{1}{3}$ ft   **6.** 36 cm²   **7.** $(-\infty, -5]$

8. $(-2, 16)$ **9.** $4, -7$ **10.** $4, -4$

11. $[-7, 1]$

12. $(-\infty, -9) \cup (13, \infty)$

13. $3xy(y + 2x)$ **14.** $3abc(4a^2b - abc + 2c^2)$

15. $(a - y)(x + y)$ **16.** $(x + y)(a + b - c)$

17. $(x + 7)(x - 7)$ **18.** $2(x + 4)(x - 4)$

19. $4(y^2 + 4)(y + 2)(y - 2)$ **20.** $(b + 5)(b^2 - 5b + 25)$

21. $(b - 3)(b^2 + 3b + 9)$ **22.** $3(u - 2)(u^2 + 2u + 4)$

23. $(x + 5)(x + 3)$ **24.** $(3b + 2)(2b - 1)$

25. $3(u + 2)(2u - 1)$ **26.** $(x + 3 + y)(x + 3 - y)$ **27.** $\frac{-2}{3xy}$

28. $\frac{2x + 1}{4}$ **29.** $\frac{xz}{y^4}$ **30.** 1   **31.** $\frac{(x + y)^2}{2}$

32. $\frac{2x + 3}{(x + 1)(x + 2)}$ **33.** $\frac{u^2}{2vw}$ **34.** $\frac{2x + y}{xy - 2}$ **35.** -7 **36.** 47

Getting Ready (page 533)

1. 1   **2.** 9   **3.** 5   **4.** 2

Exercises 8.1 (page 540)

1. $(3, 0), (0, 3)$ **3.** $(8, 0), (0, 2)$ **5.** $(4, 6)$

7.    **9.** $x(x - 1)$

11. $(x - 1)(x^2 + x + 1)$ **13.** origin   **15.** y-coordinate

17. x-axis   **19.** horizontal

21–28.   **29.** $(2, 4)$ **31.** $(-2, -1)$

33. $(4, 0)$ **35.** $(0, 0)$

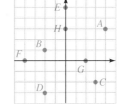

37.

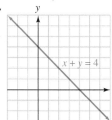

39.

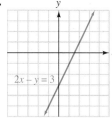

41.

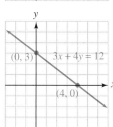

43.

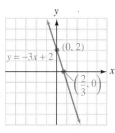

45.

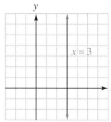

47.

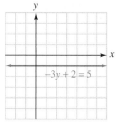

49. $(3, 4)$ **51.** $(9, 12)$ **53.** $\left(\frac{7}{2}, 6\right)$ **55.** $\left(\frac{1}{2}, -2\right)$

57.

59.

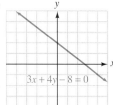

61. $(-4, 0)$ **63.** $\left(\frac{5a}{2}, 2b\right)$ **65.** $(a, 2b)$ **67.** $(4, 1)$
69. $162,500, $200,000   **71.** 200   **73.** 100 rpm
77. $a = 0, b > 0$

Getting Ready (page 543)

1. 1   **2.** -1 **3.** $\frac{13}{14}$ **4.** $\frac{3}{14}$

Exercises 8.2 (page 551)

1. 3   **3.** yes   **5.** yes   **7.** x^6 **9.** $x^{24}y^{12}$ **11.** $x^{16}y^2$
13. change   **15.** rise   **17.** horizontal   **19.** positive
21. perpendicular, reciprocals   **23.** 2   **25.** 3   **27.** -1
29. $-\frac{1}{3}$ **31.** 0   **33.** not defined   **35.** $-\frac{3}{2}$ **37.** $\frac{3}{4}$
39. $\frac{1}{2}$ **41.** 0   **43.** negative   **45.** positive
47. not defined   **49.** 0   **51.** perpendicular   **53.** neither
55. parallel   **57.** perpendicular   **59.** perpendicular
61. neither   **63.** parallel   **65.** same line   **67.** same line
69. not the same line   **71.** $x = 0$, no defined slope   **79.** $\frac{1}{4}$
81. $\frac{1}{25}, \frac{1}{10}, \frac{4}{25}$ **83.** $\frac{7}{500}$ of a degree increase per year
85. a. $\frac{2}{25}$ **b.** $\frac{1}{20}, \frac{1}{20}$ **87.** $525.13 per yr   **93.** -4

Getting Ready (page 554)

1. 14   **2.** $-\frac{5}{3}$ **3.** $y = 3x - 4$ **4.** $x = \frac{-By - 3}{A}$

Exercises 8.3 (page 564)

1. $y - 3 = 2(x - 2)$ **3.** $y = -3x + 5$ **5.** parallel   **7.** 6
9. -1 **11.** 20 oz   **13.** $y - y_1 = m(x - x_1)$
15. $Ax + By = C$ **17.** perpendicular   **19.** $y - 7 = 5x$
21. $y = -3(x - 2)$ **23.** $y = x$ **25.** $y = \frac{7}{3}x - 3$
27. $y = 3x + 17$ **29.** $y = -7x + 54$ **31.** $y = -4$
33. $y = -\frac{1}{2}x + 11$ **35.** $\frac{3}{2}, (0, -4)$ **37.** $-\frac{1}{3}, \left(0, -\frac{5}{6}\right)$
39. $1, (0, -1)$ **41.** $\frac{2}{3}, (0, 2)$

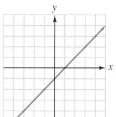

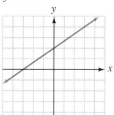

43. parallel   **45.** perpendicular   **47.** parallel
49. perpendicular   **51.** perpendicular   **53.** perpendicular
55. $y = 4x$ **57.** $y = 4x - 3$ **59.** $y = -\frac{1}{4}x$
61. $y = -\frac{1}{4}x + \frac{11}{2}$ **63.** $y = \frac{4}{5}x - \frac{26}{5}$ **65.** $y = -\frac{5}{4}x + 3$
67. perpendicular   **69.** parallel
71. $\frac{7}{2}, (0, 2)$ **73.** $-\frac{2}{3}, (0, 6)$

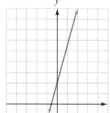

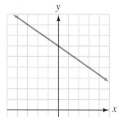

75. $y = \frac{2}{3}x + \frac{11}{3}$ **77.** $y = -\frac{7}{4}x + \frac{1}{2}$ **79.** $x = -2$
81. $x = 5$ **83.** $y = -\frac{A}{B}x + \frac{C}{B}$ **85.** $y = -2,298x + 19,984$
87. $y = 1,811,250x + 36,225,000$
89. $y = 50,000x + 250,000$ **91.** $y = -\frac{950}{3}x + 1,750$
93. $490   **95.** $154,000   **97.** $180   **107.** $a < 0, b > 0$

Getting Ready (page 568)

1. 1   **2.** 7   **3.** -20 **4.** $-\frac{11}{4}$

Exercises 8.4 (page 574)

1. yes   **3.** no   **5.** 3   **7.** -2 **9.** 2   **11.** relation
13. domain   **15.** 0   **17.** cannot   **19.** slope, y-intercept
21. y **23.** y **25.** D: $\{3, 5, -4, 0\}$, R: $\{-2, 0, -5\}$; yes
27. D: $\{-2, 6, 5\}$, R: $\{3, 8, 5, 4\}$; no   **29.** D: $(-\infty, 1]$;
R: $(-\infty, \infty)$; not a function   **31.** D: $(-\infty, \infty)$; R: $(-\infty, \infty)$;
a function   **33.** $9, -3, 0$ **35.** $3, -5, \frac{3}{2}$ **37.** 4, 9
39. 7, 26   **41.** 4, 4   **43.** 2, 2   **45.** $2w, 2w + 2$
47. $3w - 5, 3w - 2$ **49.** 12   **51.** $2b - 2a$
53. $\{-2, 4, 6\}$ **55.** $(-\infty, 4) \cup (4, \infty)$
57. $(-\infty, -3) \cup (-3, \infty)$ **59.** $(-\infty, \infty)$

61. D: $(-\infty, \infty)$;
R: $(-\infty, \infty)$

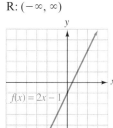

63. D: $(-\infty, \infty)$;
R: $(-\infty, \infty)$

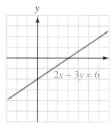

65. no   **67.** yes   **69.** 9, 16   **71.** 6, 15   **73.** 22, 2
75. 3, 11   **77.** $2b$ **79.** 1   **81.** 192
83. a. $I(h) = 0.10h + 50$ **b.** $61.50   **85.** 624 ft
87. 12 ft   **89.** 77°F   **93.** yes

Getting Ready (page 577)

1. 2, $(0, -3)$ **2.** -3, $(0, 4)$ **3.** 6, -9 **4.** 4, $\frac{5}{2}$

Exercises 8.5 (page 588)

5. 41, 43, 47   **7.** $a \cdot b = b \cdot a$ **9.** 1   **11.** squaring
13. absolute value   **15.** horizontal   **17.** 2, down
19. 4, to the left   **21.** rational

23.
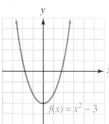

25.
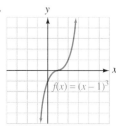

27.
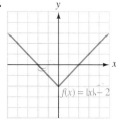

29.
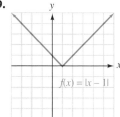

31.
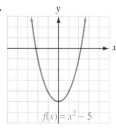

33.
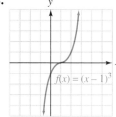

35.
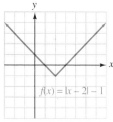

37.
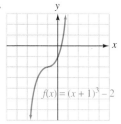

39.
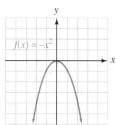

41.
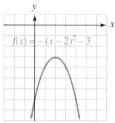

43. 20 hr   **45.** 12 hr
47. D: $(-\infty, 2) \cup (2, \infty)$; R: $(-\infty, 1) \cup (1, \infty)$
49. D: $(-\infty, -2) \cup (-2, 2) \cup (2, \infty)$; R: $(-\infty, \infty)$

51.

53.

55.

57.

59. $5,555.56   **61.** $50,000
63. $c = f(x) = 1.25x + 700$ **65.** $1,325
67. $1.95   **69.** $c = f(n) = 0.09n + 7.50$
71. $77.25   **73.** 9.75¢   **75.** $c = f(x) = 350x + 5,000$
77. $47,000

Getting Ready (page 591)

1. $\frac{3}{2}$ **2.** $\frac{10}{7}$ **3.** 4   **4.** 36

Exercises 8.6 (page 597)

1. 1   **3.** $a = kb$ **5.** $a = kbc$ **7.** x^{10} **9.** -1
11. 3.5×10^4 **13.** 0.0025   **15.** proportion   **17.** direct
19. rational   **21.** joint   **23.** direct   **25.** neither   **27.** 3
29. 5   **31.** -3 **33.** 5   **35.** $A = kp^2$ **37.** $v = \frac{k}{r^3}$
39. $B = kmn$ **41.** $P = \frac{ka^2}{j^3}$ **43.** L varies jointly with m
and n.   **45.** E varies jointly with a and the square of b.
47. X varies directly with the square of x and inversely with the
square of y.   **49.** R varies directly with L and inversely with
the square of d.   **51.** 4, -1 **53.** 2, -2 **55.** 39
57. $-\frac{5}{2}$, -1 **59.** 36π in.^{2} **61.** 432 mi   **63.** 25 days
65. 12 in.^{3} **67.** 85.3   **69.** 12   **71.** 26,437.5 gal
73. 3 ohms   **75.** 0.275 in.   **77.** 546 Kelvin

Chapter Review (page 601)

1.
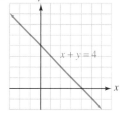

2.
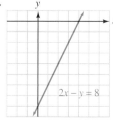

3.
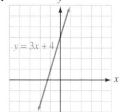

4.
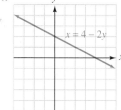

5.
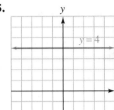

6.
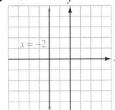

7.
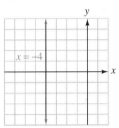

8.
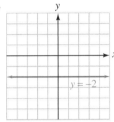

54.
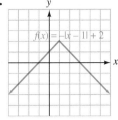

55.

56. **57.** **58.**

59. **60.** **61.**

62. D: $(-\infty, 2) \cup (2, \infty)$;
R: $(-\infty, 0) \cup (0, \infty)$
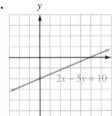

63. D: $(-\infty, -3) \cup (-3, \infty)$;
R: $(-\infty, 1) \cup (1, \infty)$

9. $\left(\frac{3}{2}, 8\right)$ **10.** 1   **11.** $\frac{14}{9}$ **12.** 5   **13.** $\frac{5}{11}$ **14.** 0

15. no defined slope   **16.** $\frac{2}{3}$ **17.** -2

18. no defined slope   **19.** 0   **20.** perpendicular

21. parallel   **22.** neither   **23.** perpendicular

24. \$21,666.67   **25.** $3x - y = -29$ **26.** $13x + 8y = 6$

27. $3x - 2y = 1$ **28.** $2x + 3y = -21$

29.
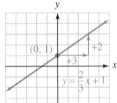

30. perpendicular

31. $y = -1,720x + 8,700$

32. yes   **33.** yes   **34.** no

35. no   **36.** -7 **37.** 60

38. 0   **39.** 17

40. D: $(-\infty, \infty)$; R:$(-\infty, \infty)$

41. D: $(-\infty, \infty)$; R: $(-\infty, \infty)$

42. D: $(-\infty, \infty)$; R: $[1, \infty)$

43. D: $(-\infty, 2) \cup (2, \infty)$; R: $(-\infty, 0) \cup (0, \infty)$

44. D: $(-\infty, 3) \cup (3, \infty)$; R: $(-\infty, 0) \cup (0, \infty)$

45. D: $(-\infty, \infty)$; R: $\{7\}$ **46.** a function   **47.** not a function

48. not a function   **49.** a function

50.
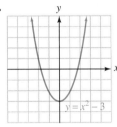

51.
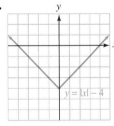

52.
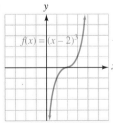

53.
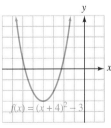

64. $\frac{13}{3}$ **65.** $-4, -12$ **66.** 2   **67.** 6   **68.** $\frac{1}{32}$ **69.** 16

Chapter 8 Test (page 608)

1.
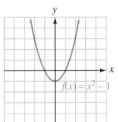

2. $\left(\frac{1}{2}, \frac{1}{2}\right)$

3. x-intercept $(3, 0)$, y-intercept $\left(0, -\frac{3}{5}\right)$ **4.** vertical   **5.** $\frac{1}{2}$

6. $\frac{2}{3}$ **7.** no defined slope

8. 0   **9.** $y = \frac{2}{3}x - \frac{23}{3}$

10. $8x - y = -22$

11. $m = -\frac{1}{3}, \left(0, -\frac{3}{2}\right)$

12. neither   **13.** perpendicular   **14.** $y = \frac{3}{2}x$

15. $y = \frac{3}{2}x + \frac{21}{2}$ **16.** no   **17.** D: $(-\infty, \infty)$; R: $[0, \infty)$

18. D: $(-\infty, \infty)$; R: $(-\infty, \infty)$ **19.** 10   **20.** -2

21. $3a + 1$ **22.** $x^2 - 2$ **23.** yes   **24.** no

25.
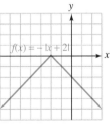

26.
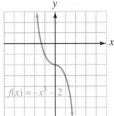

27. $6, -1$ **28.** $\frac{6}{5}$ **29.** $\frac{44}{3}$ **30.** yes

Cumulative Review Exercises (page 609)

1. $1, 2, 6, 7$ **2.** $0, 1, 2, 6, 7$ **3.** $-2, 0, 1, 2, \frac{13}{12}, 6, 7$

4. $\sqrt{5}, \pi$ **5.** -2 **6.** $-2, 0, 1, 2, \frac{13}{12}, 6, 7, \sqrt{5}, \pi$ **7.** $2, 7$

8. 6   **9.** $-2, 0, 2, 6$ **10.** $1, 7$

11.

12.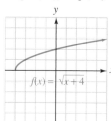

13. -2 **14.** -2

15. 22   **16.** -2 **17.** -4 **18.** -3 **19.** 4   **20.** -5
21. assoc. prop. of add.   **22.** distrib. prop.
23. comm. prop. of add.   **24.** assoc. prop. of mult.
25. x^8y^{12} **26.** c^2 **27.** $-\dfrac{b^3}{a^2}$ **28.** 1   **29.** 4.97×10^{-6}
30. 932,000,000

Getting Ready (page 611)

1. 0   **2.** 16   **3.** 16   **4.** -16 **5.** $\dfrac{8}{125}$ **6.** $\dfrac{81}{256}$
7. $49x^2y^2$ **8.** $343x^3y^3$

Exercises 9.1 (page 621)

1. 3   **3.** -2 **5.** $8|x|$ **7.** not real   **9.** $\dfrac{x+3}{x-4}$ **11.** 1
13. $\dfrac{3(m^2+2m-1)}{(m+1)(m-1)}$ **15.** $(5x^2)^2$, $6^2 = 36$ **17.** positive
19. 5, left   **21.** radical, index, radicand   **23.** $|x|$ **25.** x
27. even   **29.** $3x^2$ **31.** a^2+b^3 **33.** 11   **35.** -8
37. $\dfrac{1}{3}$ **39.** $-\dfrac{5}{7}$ **41.** not real   **43.** 0.4   **45.** $2|x|$
47. $3a^2$ **49.** $|t+5|$ **51.** $|a+3|$ **53.** 1   **55.** -5
57. $-\dfrac{2}{3}$ **59.** 0.4   **61.** $2a$ **63.** $-10pq$ **65.** 3   **67.** -3
69. -2 **71.** $\dfrac{2}{5}$ **73.** $\dfrac{1}{2}$ **75.** not real   **77.** $2|x|$ **79.** $2a$
81. $\dfrac{1}{2}|x|$ **83.** $|x^3|$ **85.** $-x$ **87.** $-3a^2$ **89.** 0   **91.** 4
93. 1   **95.** 0.5
97. D: $[-4, \infty)$, R: $[0, \infty)$ **99.** D: $(-\infty, \infty)$, R: $(-\infty, \infty)$

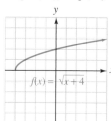
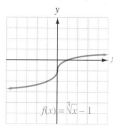

101. 4   **103.** not real   **105.** $5|b|$ **107.** $|t+12|$
109. $-\dfrac{1}{2}m^2n$ **111.** $0.2z^3$ **113.** $x+2$ **115.** $0.1x^2|y|$
117. 3.4641   **119.** 26.0624   **121.** 4.1231   **123.** 2.5539
125. 1.67   **127.** 11.8673   **129.** 3 units   **131.** 4 sec
133. about 7.4 amperes

Getting Ready (page 624)

1. 25   **2.** 169   **3.** 18   **4.** 11,236

Exercises 9.2 (page 629)

1. 5   **3.** 5   **5.** 4   **7.** $12x^2 - 14x - 10$
9. $15t^2 + 2ts - 8s^2$ **11.** hypotenuse   **13.** $a^2 + b^2 = c^2$
15. positive   **17.** 10 ft   **19.** 80 m   **21.** 48 in.   **23.** 3 mi
25. 5   **27.** 5   **29.** 13   **31.** 10   **33.** 10.2   **35.** 13.6
37. about 127 ft   **39.** about 135 ft   **41.** 9.9 cm   **47.** 13 ft
49. yes   **51.** 90 yd   **53.** 24 cm²   **55.** yes   **57.** no
59. 0.05 ft   **63.** about 25

Getting Ready (page 632)

1. x^7 **2.** a^{12} **3.** a^4 **4.** 1   **5.** $\dfrac{1}{x^4}$ **6.** x^3 **7.** $\dfrac{b^6}{c^9}$
8. a^{10}

Exercises 9.3 (page 638)

1. 2   **3.** 3   **5.** 8   **7.** $\dfrac{1}{2}$ **9.** $2x$ **11.** $x < 3$
13. $r > 28$ **15.** $1\frac{2}{3}$ pints   **17.** $a \cdot a \cdot a \cdot a$ **19.** a^{mn}
21. $\dfrac{a^n}{b^n}$ **23.** $\dfrac{1}{a^n}$, 0   **25.** $\left(\dfrac{b}{a}\right)^n$ **27.** $|x|$ **29.** $\sqrt[3]{7}$ **31.** $\sqrt[5]{8}$
33. $\sqrt[4]{3x}$ **35.** $\sqrt[4]{\frac{1}{2}x^3 y}$ **37.** $\sqrt[5]{4a^2b^3}$ **39.** $\sqrt{x^2+y^2}$
41. 2   **43.** 3   **45.** $\dfrac{1}{2}$ **47.** $\dfrac{1}{2}$ **49.** -2 **51.** not real
53. $11^{1/2}$ **55.** $(3a)^{1/4}$ **57.** $3a^{1/5}$ **59.** $\left(\dfrac{1}{7}abc\right)^{1/6}$
61. $\left(\dfrac{1}{2}mn\right)^{1/5}$ **63.** $(a^2-b^2)^{1/3}$ **65.** $5|x|$ **67.** $3x$
69. $|x+1|$ **71.** not real   **73.** 216   **75.** 27   **77.** 1,728
79. $\dfrac{1}{4}$ **81.** $\dfrac{1}{2}$ **83.** $\dfrac{1}{8}$ **85.** $\dfrac{1}{64x^3}$ **87.** $\dfrac{1}{9y^2}$ **89.** 8
91. $\dfrac{16}{81}$ **93.** $5^{8/9}$ **95.** $4^{3/5}$ **97.** $\dfrac{1}{36}$ **99.** $9^{1/5}$ **101.** $7^{1/2}$
103. $2^{2/3}$ **105.** a **107.** $a^{2/9}$ **109.** $y + y^2$
111. $x^2 - x + x^{3/5}$ **113.** $x - y$
115. $x^{4/3} + 2x^{2/3}y^{2/3} + y^{4/3}$ **117.** $\sqrt{p}$ **119.** $\sqrt{5b}$
121. 2   **123.** 2   **125.** 0   **127.** -3 **129.** $125x^6$
131. $\dfrac{4x^2}{9}$ **133.** $\dfrac{1}{4p^2}$ **135.** $-\dfrac{3}{2x}$ **137.** $a^{3/4}b^{1/2}$ **139.** $\dfrac{n^{2/5}}{m^{3/5}}$
141. $\dfrac{2x}{3}$ **143.** $\dfrac{1}{3}x$ **145.** $x^2 + 3x^3 - 4x^{4/3}$
147. $\dfrac{1}{x} - 2 + x$ **149.** 2.47   **151.** 1.01   **153.** 0.24
155. -1.32 **159.** yes

Getting Ready (page 641)

1. 15   **2.** 24   **3.** 5   **4.** 7   **5.** $4x^2$ **6.** $\dfrac{8}{11}x^3$ **7.** $3ab^3$
8. $-2a^4$

Exercises 9.4 (page 648)

1. 7   **3.** 3   **5.** $2\sqrt[3]{2}$ **7.** $7\sqrt{3}$ **9.** $5\sqrt[3]{9}$ **11.** $\dfrac{-15x^5}{y}$
13. $9t^2 + 12t + 4$ **15.** $3p + 4 + \dfrac{-5}{2p-5}$ **17.** $\sqrt[n]{a}\sqrt[n]{b}$
19. like   **21.** 6   **23.** t **25.** $5x$ **27.** 10   **29.** $7x$
31. $6b$ **33.** 2   **35.** $3a$ **37.** $2\sqrt{5}$ **39.** $-10\sqrt{2}$
41. $2\sqrt[3]{10}$ **43.** $-3\sqrt[3]{3}$ **45.** $2\sqrt[4]{2}$ **47.** $2\sqrt[5]{3}$ **49.** $\dfrac{\sqrt{7}}{3x}$
51. $\dfrac{a\sqrt[3]{7}}{4}$ **53.** $\dfrac{p\sqrt[4]{3}}{10q}$ **55.** $\dfrac{m^3\sqrt[5]{3}}{2n^2}$ **57.** $5x\sqrt{2}$ **59.** $4\sqrt{2b}$
61. $-4a\sqrt{7a}$ **63.** $5ab\sqrt{7b}$ **65.** $-10\sqrt{3xy}$
67. $-3x^2\sqrt[3]{2}$ **69.** $2x^4y\sqrt[3]{2}$ **71.** $\dfrac{z}{4x}$ **73.** $4\sqrt{3}$
75. $-\sqrt{2}$ **77.** $2\sqrt{2}$ **79.** $9\sqrt{6}$ **81.** $3\sqrt{2} + \sqrt{3}$
83. $3\sqrt[3]{3}$ **85.** $-\sqrt[3]{4}$ **87.** -10 **89.** $-11\sqrt[3]{2}$
91. $-x\sqrt[3]{3x^2}$ **93.** $8z\sqrt{y}$ **95.** $-7y^2\sqrt{y}$ **97.** 0
99. $b = 3$, $c = 3\sqrt{2}$ **101.** $a = \dfrac{2}{3}$, $c = \dfrac{2}{3}\sqrt{2}$
103. $b = 5\sqrt{2}$, $c = 10$ **105.** $a = 7$, $b = 7$
107. $b = 5\sqrt{3}$, $c = 10$ **109.** $a = 9$, $c = 18$
111. $a = 12$, $b = 12\sqrt{3}$ **113.** $a = \dfrac{15}{2}$, $b = \dfrac{15}{2}\sqrt{3}$
115. $10\sqrt{2x}$ **117.** $2x^3y\sqrt[4]{2}$ **119.** $\dfrac{\sqrt[4]{5x}}{2z}$ **121.** $-4\sqrt{2}$
123. 81   **125.** $94\sqrt[4]{3}$ **127.** $10\sqrt[4]{3}$ **129.** $9\sqrt[3]{5y}$
131. $9\sqrt[6]{12xyz}$ **133.** $4x\sqrt[5]{xy^2}$ **135.** $2x + 2$
137. $h = 2.83$, $x = 2.00$ **139.** $x = 8.66$, $h = 10.00$
141. $x = 4.69$, $y = 8.11$ **143.** $x = 12.11$, $y = 12.11$

145. $10\sqrt{3}$ mm, 17.32 mm **149.** If $a = 0$, then b can be any nonnegative real number. If $b = 0$, then a can be any nonnegative real number.

Getting Ready (page 651)

1. a^7 **2.** b^3 **3.** $a^2 - 2a$ **4.** $6b^3 + 9b^2$
5. $a^2 - 3a - 10$ **6.** $4a^2 - 9b^2$

Exercises 9.5 (page 658)

1. 3 **3.** $3\sqrt{3}$ **5.** $6 + 3\sqrt{2}$ **7.** $\frac{\sqrt{2}}{2}$ **9.** 1 **11.** $\frac{1}{3}$
13. $2, \sqrt{7}, \sqrt{5}$ **15.** $\sqrt{x} - 1$ **17.** conjugate **19.** 4
21. $5\sqrt{2}$ **23.** $6\sqrt{2}$ **25.** 5 **27.** $2\sqrt[3]{3}$ **29.** ab^2
31. $r\sqrt[3]{10s}$ **33.** $x^2(x + 3)$ **35.** $12\sqrt{5} - 15$
37. $12\sqrt{6} + 6\sqrt{14}$ **39.** $-1 - 2\sqrt{2}$
41. $8x - 14\sqrt{x} - 15$ **43.** $5z + 2\sqrt{15z} + 3$
45. $6a + 5\sqrt{3ab} - 3b$ **47.** $18r - 12\sqrt{2r} + 4$
49. $-6x - 12\sqrt{x} - 6$ **51.** $\frac{\sqrt{7}}{7}$ **53.** $\frac{\sqrt{6}}{3}$ **55.** $\frac{\sqrt{10}}{4}$
57. 2 **59.** $\frac{\sqrt[3]{4}}{2}$ **61.** $\frac{\sqrt[3]{6}}{3}$ **63.** $2\sqrt{2x}$ **65.** $\frac{\sqrt{5y}}{y}$
67. $\sqrt{2} + 1$ **69.** $\frac{3\sqrt{2} - \sqrt{10}}{4}$ **71.** $2 + \sqrt{3}$
73. $\frac{9 - 2\sqrt{14}}{5}$ **75.** $\frac{2(\sqrt{x} - 1)}{x - 1}$ **77.** $\frac{x(\sqrt{x} + 4)}{x - 16}$
79. $\frac{x - 2\sqrt{xy} + y}{x - y}$ **81.** $\frac{1}{\sqrt{3} - 1}$ **83.** $\frac{x - 9}{x(\sqrt{x} - 3)}$ **85.** 18
87. $5a\sqrt{b}$ **89.** $2a^2b^2\sqrt[3]{2}$ **91.** $3x(y + z)\sqrt[3]{4}$
93. $-8x\sqrt{10} + 6\sqrt{15x}$ **95.** $\sqrt[3]{3}$ **97.** $\frac{\sqrt[4]{4}}{2}$ **99.** $\frac{\sqrt[5]{2}}{2}$
101. $\frac{\sqrt[3]{2ab^2}}{b}$ **103.** $\sqrt{2z} + 1$ **105.** $\frac{x - y}{\sqrt{x}(\sqrt{x} - \sqrt{y})}$
107. $f/4$ **109.** $r = \frac{\sqrt{\pi A}}{\pi}$ **111.** $4\sqrt{2}$ cm
113. $2\sqrt{3}$ ft, $4\sqrt{3}$ ft **117.** $\frac{x - 9}{4(\sqrt{x} + 3)}$

Getting Ready (page 661)

1. a **2.** $5x$ **3.** $x + 4$ **4.** $y - 3$

Exercises 9.6 (page 667)

1. 7 **3.** 0 **5.** 17 **7.** 2 **9.** 6 **11.** $x^n = y^n$, power rule
13. square **15.** extraneous **17.** 2 **19.** 4 **21.** 4
23. $\frac{5}{2}, \frac{1}{2}$ **25.** 14; 6 is extraneous **27.** 4, 3
29. 2; 7 is extraneous **31.** $2, -1$ **33.** 0 **35.** 1 **37.** 16
39. 0; 4 is extraneous **41.** 1 **43.** 6; 0 is extraneous
45. 2; 142 is extraneous **47.** 0 **49.** 3; -1 is extraneous
51. $h = \frac{v^2}{2g}$ **53.** $l = \frac{8T^2}{\pi^2}$ **55.** $A = P(r + 1)^3$
57. $v^2 = c^2\left(1 - \frac{L_A^2}{L_B^2}\right)$ **59.** $1, -4$ **61.** 2; -8 is extraneous
63. -1; 1 is extraneous **65.** 1, 9 **67.** 2; -2 is extraneous
69. $\varnothing$; 6 is extraneous **71.** $\varnothing$; 8 is extraneous **73.** 2
75. 1 **77.** 2, -1 is extraneous **79.** 2,010 ft
81. about 29 mph **83.** 16% **85.** \$5 **87.** $R = \frac{8kl}{\pi r^4}$
91. 0, 4

Getting Ready (page 670)

1. $7x$ **2.** $-x + 10$ **3.** $12x^2 + 5x - 25$ **4.** $9x^2 - 25$

Exercises 9.7 (page 678)

1. $7i$ **3.** $10i$ **5.** $-i$ **7.** 1 **9.** 5 **11.** -1
13. 20 mph **15.** i **17.** $-i$ **19.** imaginary **21.** $\frac{\sqrt{a}}{\sqrt{b}}$
23. 5, 7 **25.** conjugates **27.** $3i$ **29.** $6i$ **31.** $i\sqrt{7}$
33. $2i\sqrt{2}$ **35.** yes **37.** no **39.** $8 - 2i$ **41.** $3 - 5i$
43. $15 + 7i$ **45.** $6 - 8i$ **47.** $3 + 6i$ **49.** $-25 - 25i$
51. $7 + i$ **53.** $14 - 8i$ **55.** $8 + \sqrt{2}i$ **57.** $3 + 4i$
59. $-5 + 12i$ **61.** $7 + 17i$ **63.** $-20 - 30i$ **65.** 61
67. $2 + i$ **69.** $\frac{1}{2} + \frac{5}{2}i$ **71.** $-\frac{42}{25} - \frac{6}{25}i$ **73.** $\frac{1}{4} + \frac{3}{4}i$
75. $\frac{5}{13} - \frac{12}{13}i$ **77.** $\frac{11}{10} + \frac{3}{10}i$ **79.** $\frac{1}{4} - \frac{\sqrt{15}}{4}i$
81. $-\frac{5}{169} + \frac{12}{169}i$ **83.** i **85.** $-i$ **87.** 1 **89.** i
91. $-1 - 3i$ **93.** $0 - i$ **95.** $0 + \frac{4}{5}i$ **97.** $\frac{1}{8} - 0i$
99. $0 + \frac{3}{5}i$ **101.** 10 **103.** 13 **105.** $\sqrt{74}$ **107.** 1
109. no **111.** $2 + 9i$ **113.** $-15 + 2\sqrt{3}i$ **115.** $5 + 5i$
117. $16 + 2i$ **119.** $\frac{3}{5} + \frac{4}{5}i$ **121.** $-\frac{6}{13} - \frac{9}{13}i$
127. $7 - 4i$ volts **129.** $1 - 3.4i$ **133.** $\frac{5}{3 + i}$

Chapter Review (page 681)

1. 7 **2.** -11 **3.** -6 **4.** 15 **5.** -3 **6.** -6 **7.** 5
8. -2 **9.** $5|x|$ **10.** $|x + 2|$ **11.** $3a^2b$ **12.** $4x^2|y|$
13.

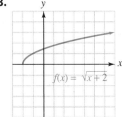

$f(x) = \sqrt{x + 2}$

14.

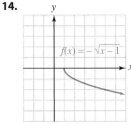

$f(x) = -\sqrt{x} - 1$

15.

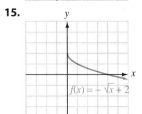

$f(x) = -\sqrt{x} + 2$

16.

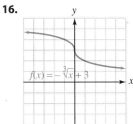

$f(x) = -\sqrt[3]{x} + 3$

17. 12 **18.** about 5.7 **19.** 3 mi **20.** 8.2 ft **21.** 88 yd
22. 16,000 yd, or about 9 mi **23.** 13 **24.** 2.83 units
25. 5 **26.** -6 **27.** 27 **28.** 64 **29.** -2 **30.** -4
31. $\frac{1}{4}$ **32.** $\frac{1}{2}$ **33.** $-16,807$ **34.** $\frac{1}{3,125}$ **35.** 8 **36.** $\frac{27}{8}$
37. $3xy^{1/3}$ **38.** $3xy^{1/2}$ **39.** $125x^{9/2}y^6$ **40.** $\frac{1}{4u^{4/3}v^2}$
41. $5^{3/4}$ **42.** $a^{5/7}$ **43.** $u - 1$ **44.** $v + v^2$
45. $x + 2x^{1/2}y^{1/2} + y$ **46.** $a^{4/3} - b^{4/3}$ **47.** $\sqrt[3]{5}$ **48.** $\sqrt{x}$
49. $\sqrt[3]{3ab^2}$ **50.** $\sqrt{5ab}$ **51.** $4\sqrt{15}$ **52.** $3\sqrt[3]{2}$
53. $2\sqrt[4]{2}$ **54.** $2\sqrt[5]{3}$ **55.** $2x\sqrt{2x}$ **56.** $3x^2y\sqrt{2y}$
57. $2xy\sqrt[3]{2x^2y}$ **58.** $3x^2y\sqrt[3]{2x}$ **59.** $4x$ **60.** $2x$

61. $\frac{\sqrt[3]{2a^2b}}{3x}$ **62.** $\frac{\sqrt{17xy}}{8a^2}$ **63.** $3\sqrt{2}$ **64.** $\sqrt{5}$ **65.** 0
66. $8\sqrt[4]{2}$ **67.** $29x\sqrt{2}$ **68.** $32a\sqrt{3a}$ **69.** $13\sqrt[3]{2}$
70. $-4x\sqrt[4]{2x}$ **71.** $7\sqrt{2}$ m **72.** $6\sqrt{3}$ cm, 18 cm
73. 7.07 in. **74.** 8.66 cm **75.** $6\sqrt{10}$ **76.** 72 **77.** $3x$
78. 3 **79.** $-2x$ **80.** $-20x^3y^3\sqrt{xy}$ **81.** $4 - 3\sqrt{2}$
82. $2 + 3\sqrt{2}$ **83.** $\sqrt{10} - \sqrt{5}$ **84.** $3 + \sqrt{6}$ **85.** 1
86. $5 + 2\sqrt{6}$ **87.** $x - y$ **88.** $6u + \sqrt{u} - 12$ **89.** $\frac{\sqrt{3}}{3}$
90. $\frac{\sqrt{15}}{5}$ **91.** $\frac{\sqrt{xy}}{y}$ **92.** $\frac{\sqrt[3]{u^2}}{u^2v^2}$ **93.** $2(\sqrt{2}+1)$
94. $\frac{\sqrt{6}+\sqrt{2}}{2}$ **95.** $2(\sqrt{x}-4)$ **96.** $\frac{a+2\sqrt{a}+1}{a-1}$
97. $\frac{3}{5\sqrt{3}}$ **98.** $\frac{1}{\sqrt{3}}$ **99.** $\frac{9-x}{2(3+\sqrt{x})}$ **100.** $\frac{a-b}{a+\sqrt{ab}}$
101. 22 **102.** 16, 9 **103.** 3, 9 **104.** $\frac{9}{16}$ **105.** 2
106. $0, -2$ **107.** $12 - 8i$ **108.** $2 - 68i$ **109.** $-96 + 3i$
110. $-2 - 2\sqrt{2}i$ **111.** $22 + 29i$ **112.** $-16 + 7i$
113. $-12 + 28\sqrt{3}i$ **114.** $118 + 10\sqrt{2}i$ **115.** $0 - \frac{3}{4}i$
116. $0 - \frac{2}{5}i$ **117.** $\frac{12}{5} - \frac{6}{5}i$ **118.** $\frac{21}{10} + \frac{7}{10}i$ **119.** $\frac{15}{17} + \frac{8}{17}i$
120. $\frac{4}{5} - \frac{3}{5}i$ **121.** $\frac{15}{29} - \frac{6}{29}i$ **122.** $\frac{1}{3} + \frac{1}{3}i$ **123.** 15
124. 26 **125.** 1 **126.** $-i$

Chapter 9 Test (page 689)

1. 7 **2.** 4 **3.** $2|x|$ **4.** $2x$
5. D: $[2, \infty)$, R: $[0, \infty)$ **6.** D: $(-\infty, \infty)$, R: $(-\infty, \infty)$

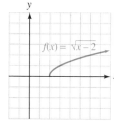

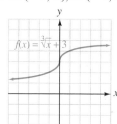

7. 28 in. **8.** 1.25 m **9.** 10 **10.** 25 **11.** 2 **12.** 9
13. $\frac{1}{216}$ **14.** $\frac{9}{4}$ **15.** $2^{4/3}$ **16.** $8xy$ **17.** $4\sqrt{3}$
18. $5xy^2\sqrt{10xy}$ **19.** $2x^5y\sqrt[3]{3}$ **20.** $\frac{1}{4a}$ **21.** $2|x|\sqrt{3}$
22. $2|x^3|\sqrt{2}$ **23.** $3x\sqrt[3]{3}$ **24.** $3x^2y^4\sqrt{2y}$ **25.** $-\sqrt{3}$
26. $14\sqrt[3]{5}$ **27.** $2y^2\sqrt{3y}$ **28.** $6z\sqrt[4]{3z}$
29. $-6x\sqrt{y} - 2xy^2$ **30.** $3 - 7\sqrt{6}$ **31.** $\frac{\sqrt{5}}{5}$
32. $\sqrt{3t} + 1$ **33.** $\frac{3}{\sqrt{21}}$ **34.** $\frac{a-b}{a-2\sqrt{ab}+b}$ **35.** 10
36. $\varnothing$; 4 is extraneous **37.** $-1 + 11i$ **38.** $4 - 7i$
39. $8 + 6i$ **40.** $-10 - 11i$ **41.** $0 - \frac{\sqrt{2}}{2}i$ **42.** $\frac{1}{2} + \frac{1}{2}i$

Getting Ready (page 692)

1. $(x + 5)(x - 5)$ **2.** $(b + 9)(b - 9)$ **3.** $(3x + 2)(2x - 1)$
4. $(2x - 3)(2x + 1)$

Exercises 10.1 (page 701)

1. ± 7 **3.** 4 **5.** $\frac{9}{4}$ **7.** 1 **9.** $t \le 4$
11. $x = \sqrt{c}, x = -\sqrt{c}$ **13.** positive or negative

15. $5, -5$ **17.** $0, -2$ **19.** $-2, -4$ **21.** $\frac{2}{3}, -\frac{5}{2}$ **23.** ± 6
25. $\pm\sqrt{5}$ **27.** $0, -2$ **29.** $2 \pm \sqrt{5}$ **31.** $\pm 4i$ **33.** $\pm\frac{9}{2}i$
35. $2, -4$ **37.** $2, 4$ **39.** $-1, -4$ **41.** $10, -1$
43. $-\frac{1}{3}, -\frac{3}{2}$ **45.** $\frac{5}{3}, -\frac{1}{2}$ **47.** $\frac{3}{4}, -\frac{3}{2}$ **49.** $1, -\frac{1}{2}$
51. $-\frac{7}{10} \pm \frac{\sqrt{29}}{10}$ **53.** $-1 \pm i$ **55.** $-4 \pm i\sqrt{2}$
57. $\frac{1}{3} \pm \frac{2\sqrt{2}}{3}i$ **59.** 6, 1 **61.** $\pm\frac{4\sqrt{3}}{3}$ **63.** 4, 10
65. $-5 \pm \sqrt{3}$ **67.** $2, \frac{1}{2}$ **69.** $1 \pm \frac{\sqrt{6}}{3}$ **71.** $\frac{1}{4} + \frac{3\sqrt{7}}{4}i$
73. $d = \frac{\sqrt{6h}}{2}$ **75.** $c = \frac{\sqrt{Em}}{m}$ **77.** $-\frac{1}{4} \pm \frac{\sqrt{41}}{4}$
79. $-\frac{1}{2} \pm \frac{\sqrt{13}}{2}$ **81.** 4 sec **83.** 72 mph **85.** 4%
87. width: $7\frac{1}{4}$ ft.; length: $13\frac{3}{4}$ ft **91.** $\frac{3}{4}$

Getting Ready (page 704)

1. $x^2 + 12x + 36, (x + 6)^2$ **2.** $x^2 - 7x + \frac{49}{4}, \left(x - \frac{7}{2}\right)^2$
3. 7 **4.** 8

Exercises 10.2 (page 709)

1. $3, -4, 7$ **3.** $y = \frac{-Ax + C}{B}$ **5.** $2\sqrt{6}$ **7.** $\sqrt{3}$
9. $3, -2, 6$ **11.** $-1, -2$ **13.** $-3, 5$ **15.** $-6, -6$
17. $-1, \frac{3}{2}$ **19.** $\frac{4}{3}, -\frac{2}{5}$ **21.** $-\frac{3}{2}, -\frac{1}{2}$ **23.** $\frac{1}{4}, -\frac{3}{4}$
25. $-\frac{1}{2} \pm \frac{\sqrt{5}}{10}$ **27.** $-1 \pm i$ **29.** $-\frac{1}{4} \pm \frac{\sqrt{7}}{4}i$
31. $\frac{2}{3} \pm \frac{\sqrt{2}}{3}i$ **33.** $\frac{1}{3} \pm \frac{2\sqrt{2}}{3}i$ **35.** $N = \frac{1 \pm \sqrt{1 + 8C}}{2}$
37. $x = \frac{k}{2} \pm \frac{\sqrt{k^2 - 4ay}}{2}$ **39.** $\frac{1}{2}, -\frac{1}{3}$ **41.** $-\frac{5}{2} \pm \frac{\sqrt{17}}{2}$
43. $\frac{3}{4} \pm \frac{\sqrt{17}}{4}$ **45.** $-\frac{1}{2} \pm \sqrt{5}$ **47.** $-\frac{1}{3} \pm \frac{\sqrt{5}}{3}i$
49. $8.98, -3.98$ **51.** $x^2 - 8x + 15 = 0$
53. $x^3 - x^2 - 14x + 24 = 0$ **55.** 8 ft by 12 ft **57.** 4 units
59. $\frac{4}{3}$ cm **61.** 16, 18 or $-16, -18$ **63.** 6, 7 or $-6, -7$
65. 30 mph **67.** $4.80 or $5.20 **69.** 4,000
71. 2.26 in. **73.** 1985 **75.** about 6.13×10^{-3} M
79. $\sqrt{2}, -3\sqrt{2}$ **81.** $i, 2i$

Getting Ready (page 712)

1. 17 **2.** -8

Exercises 10.3 (page 718)

1. -3 **3.** irrational and unequal **5.** no **7.** -2 **9.** $\frac{9}{5}$
11. $b^2 - 4ac$ **13.** rational, unequal **15.** rational, equal
17. complex conjugates **19.** irrational, unequal
21. rational, unequal **23.** 6, -6 **25.** 12, -12
27. $1, -1, 4, -4$ **29.** $1, -1, \sqrt{2}, -\sqrt{2}$
31. $1, -1, \sqrt{5}, -\sqrt{5}$ **33.** $1, -1, 2, -2$ **35.** 16, 4
37. $\frac{9}{4}$; 1 is extraneous **39.** 1; $\frac{9}{4}$ is extraneous
41. $\varnothing$; $\frac{4}{9}$ and 1 are both extraneous **43.** $-8, -27$
45. $-1, 27$ **47.** $-1, -4$ **49.** $4, -5$ **51.** 0, 2
53. $-1, -\frac{27}{13}$ **55.** $1, 1, -1, -1$ **57.** $-4, \frac{2}{3}$
59. $x = \pm\sqrt{r^2 - y^2}$ **61.** $y = \frac{-3x \pm \sqrt{9x^2 - 28x}}{2x}$

63. $\frac{2}{3}, -\frac{1}{4}$ **65.** $-\frac{5}{4} \pm \frac{\sqrt{17}}{4}$ **67.** $\frac{1}{3} \pm \frac{\sqrt{11}}{3}i$ **69.** $-1 \pm 2i$

71. yes **73.** $\frac{81}{16}$; 1 is extraneous **75.** $-\frac{8}{27}, 1$

77. $1, -1, 2\sqrt{3}, -2\sqrt{3}$ **79.** $2, -2, i\sqrt{7}, -i\sqrt{7}$ **81.** $\frac{3}{8}, 1$

83. $\frac{1}{27}, -1$ **85.** $1 \pm i$ **87.** $-\frac{5}{7}, 3$ **89.** $d = \pm\frac{\sqrt{kI}}{I}$

91. $\mu^2 = \frac{\Sigma x^2}{N} - \sigma^2$ **93.** 5 **95.** 12, -3 **97.** $k < -\frac{4}{3}$

101. no

Getting Ready (page 720)

1. -2 **2.** 2 **3.** 0 **4.** 8 **5.** 1 **6.** 4

Exercises 10.4 (page 732)

1. down **3.** up **5.** $(3, -1)$ **7.** 10 **9.** $3\frac{3}{5}$ hr

11. $f(x) = ax^2 + bx + c, a \neq 0$ **13.** maximum, minimum,
vertex **15.** upward **17.** to the right **19.** upward

21.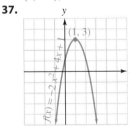

23.
y
$(0, 2)$ $f(x) = x^2 + 2$

25.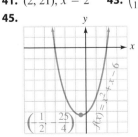
y
$(2, 0)$
$f(x) = -(x-2)^2$

27.
y
$(3, 2)$
$f(x) = (x-3)^2 + 2$

29. $(1, 2), x = 1$ **31.** $(-3, -4), x = -3$ **33.** $(0, 0), x = 0$
35. $(1, -2), x = 1$

37.
y
$(1, 3)$
$f(x) = -2x^2 + 4x + 1$

39.
y
$(2, -2)$
$f(x) = 3x^2 - 12x + 10$

41. $(2, 21), x = 2$ **43.** $\left(\frac{5}{12}, \frac{143}{24}\right), x = \frac{5}{12}$

45.
y
$\left(-\frac{1}{2}, -\frac{25}{4}\right)$
$f(x) = x^2 + x - 6$

47. $(0.25, 0.88)$ **49.** $(0.5, 7.25)$
51. $2, -3$ **53.** $-1.85, 3.25$
55. $(5, 2)$ **57.** 36 ft, 1.5 sec
59. 50 ft by 50 ft, 2,500 ft^2
61. 0.25 and 0.75 **63.** 75 ft by
75 ft, 5,625 ft^2 **65.** 14 ft
67. 5,000 **69.** 3,276, $14,742
71. $35

Getting Ready (page 736)

1. $(x + 5)(x - 3)$ **2.** $(x - 2)(x - 1)$

Exercises 10.5 (page 743)

1. $x = 2$ **3.** $x < 2$ **5.** $x > -3$ **7.** $1 < 2x$ **9.** $y = kx$
11. $t = kxy$ **13.** 3 **15.** greater **17.** quadratic
19. undefined **21.** sign

23. $(1, 4)$
25. $(-\infty, 3) \cup (5, \infty)$

27. $[-4, 3]$
29. $(-\infty, -5] \cup [3, \infty)$

31. $\varnothing$

33. $(-\infty, -3] \cup [3, \infty)$
35. $(-\infty, 0) \cup (1/2, \infty)$

37. $(0, 2]$
39. $(-\infty, -3) \cup (1, 4)$

41. $[-5, -2) \cup [4, \infty)$
43. $(-\infty, -4)$

45. $(-1/2, 1/3) \cup (1/2, \infty)$

47. $(0, 2) \cup (8, \infty)$
49. $(-\infty, -2) \cup (2, 18]$

51. $[-34/5, -4) \cup (3, \infty)$
53. $(-\infty, -2) \cup (-2, \infty)$

55.
y
$y = x^2 + 1$
$y < x^2 + 1$

57.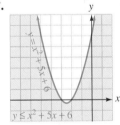
y
$y = x^2 + 5x + 6$
$y \leq x^2 + 5x + 6$

59.
y
$y = (x-1)^2$
$y \geq (x-1)^2$

61.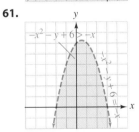
y
$-x^2 - y + 6 > -x$
$-x^2 - y + 6 = -x$

63.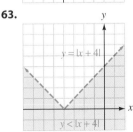
y
$y = |x + 4|$
$y < |x + 4|$

65.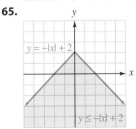
y
$y = -|x| + 2$
$y \leq -|x| + 2$

67.

(−5, 5)

69. (−∞, −5/3) ∪ (0, ∞)

71. (−4, −2] ∪ (−1, 2]

73. (−∞, −16) ∪ (−4, −1) ∪ (4, ∞)

75. (−1, 3)   **77.** (−∞, −3) ∪ (2, ∞)

81. when 4 factors are negative, 2 factors are negative, or no factors are negative

Getting Ready (page 746)

1. $3x − 1$ **2.** $x + 3$ **3.** $2x^2 − 3x − 2$ **4.** $\frac{2x + 1}{x − 2}$ $(x \neq 2)$

Exercises 10.6 (page 752)

1. $5x$ **3.** $8x^2$ **5.** 2   **7.** $8x$ **9.** $-\frac{3x + 7}{x + 2}$
11. $\frac{x − 4}{3x^2 − x − 12}$ **13.** $f(x) + g(x)$ **15.** $f(x)g(x)$
17. domain   **19.** $f(g(x))$ **21.** $f(x)$ **23.** $7x, (−∞, ∞)$
25. $12x^2, (−∞, ∞)$ **27.** $x, (−∞, ∞)$
29. $\frac{4}{3}, (−∞, 0) ∪ (0, ∞)$ **31.** $3x − 2, (−∞, ∞)$
33. $2x^2 − 5x − 3, (−∞, ∞)$ **35.** $−x − 4, (−∞, ∞)$
37. $\frac{x − 3}{2x + 1}, \left(−∞, −\frac{1}{2}\right) ∪ \left(−\frac{1}{2}, ∞\right)$ **39.** 7   **41.** 24   **43.** −1
45. $−\frac{1}{2}$ **47.** $2x^2 − 1$ **49.** $16x^2 + 8x$ **51.** 2
53. $2x + h$ **55.** $4x + 2h$ **57.** $2x + h + 1$
59. $2x + h + 3$ **61.** $4x + 2h + 3$ **63.** $−2x^2 + 3x − 3,$
$(−∞, ∞)$ **65.** $(3x − 2)/(2x^2 + 1), (−∞, ∞)$ **67.** $3, (−∞, ∞)$
69. $(x^2 − 4)/(x^2 − 1), (−∞, −1) ∪ (−1, 1) ∪ (1, ∞)$ **71.** 58
73. 110   **75.** 2   **77.** $9x^2 − 9x + 2$ **79.** 2   **81.** $x + a$
83. $2x + 2a$ **85.** $x + a + 1$ **87.** $x + a + 3$
89. $2x + 2a + 3$ **95.** $3x^2 + 3xh + h^2$
97. $C(t) = \frac{5}{9}(2,668 − 200t)$

Getting Ready (page 754)

1. $y = \frac{x − 2}{3}$ **2.** $y = \frac{2x − 10}{3}$

Exercises 10.7 (page 761)

1. {(2, 1), (3, 2), (10, 5)}   **3.** $f^{-1}(x) = 2x$ **5.** no
7. $3 − 8i$ **9.** $18 − i$ **11.** 10   **13.** one-to-one   **15.** 2
17. x **19.** yes   **21.** no

23.

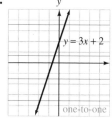

25.

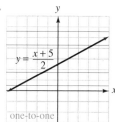

27.

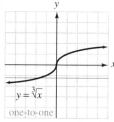

not one-to-one

29.

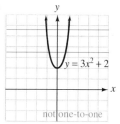

one-to-one

31. {(2, 3), (1, 2), (0, 1)}; yes   **33.** {(2, 1), (3, 2), (3, 1), (5, 1)};
no   **35.** $f^{-1}(x) = \frac{1}{3}x − \frac{1}{3}$ **37.** $f^{-1}(x) = 5x − 4$
39. $f^{-1}(x) = 5x + 4$ **41.** $f^{-1}(x) = \frac{5}{4}x + 5$

43.

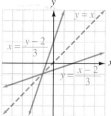

45.

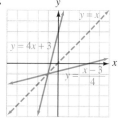

47.

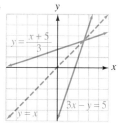

49.

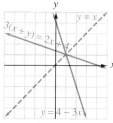

51. $y = \pm \sqrt{x − 4}$, no   **53.** $f^{-1}x = \sqrt[3]{x}$, yes

55.

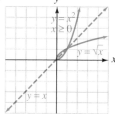

57.

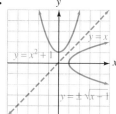

59. {(1, 1), (4, 2), (9, 3), (16, 4)}   **61.** $x = |y|$
63. $f^{-1}(x) = \sqrt[3]{\frac{x + 3}{2}}$ **67.** $f^{-1}(x) = \frac{x + 1}{x − 1}$

Chapter Review (page 764)

1. $\frac{2}{3}, −\frac{3}{4}$ **2.** $−\frac{1}{3}, −\frac{5}{2}$ **3.** $\frac{2}{3}, −\frac{4}{5}$ **4.** $4, −8$ **5.** $−4, −2$
6. $\frac{7}{2}, 1$ **7.** $\frac{1}{4} \pm \frac{\sqrt{41}}{4}$ **8.** $9, −1$ **9.** $0, 10$ **10.** $\frac{1}{2}, −7$
11. $−7, \frac{1}{3}$ **12.** $\frac{1}{4} \pm \frac{\sqrt{17}}{4}$ **13.** $−\frac{1}{2} \pm \frac{\sqrt{7}}{2}i$
14. 4 cm by 6 cm   **15.** 2 ft by 3 ft   **16.** 7 sec   **17.** 196 ft
18. irrational, unequal   **19.** complex conjugates
20. 12, 152   **21.** $k \geq −\frac{7}{3}$ **22.** 1, 144   **23.** 8, −27
24. 1   **25.** $1, −\frac{8}{5}$ **26.** $\frac{14}{3}$ **27.** 1

28.

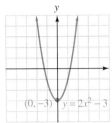

29.

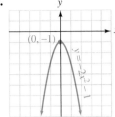

30.

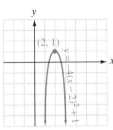

31.

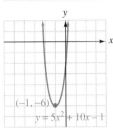

32. $(2, -17)$

33. $(-\infty, -7) \cup (5, \infty)$

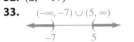

34. $(-9, 2)$

35. $(-\infty, 0) \cup [3/5, \infty)$

36. $(-7/2, 1) \cup (4, \infty)$

37. $x < -7$ or $x > 5$ **38.** $-9 < x < 2$

39. $x < 0$ or $x \geq \frac{3}{5}$ **40.** $-\frac{7}{2} < x < 1$ or $x > 4$

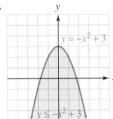

41.

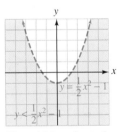

42.

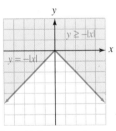

43. $(f + g)(x) = 3x + 1$ **44.** $(f - g)(x) = x - 1$
45. $(f \cdot g)(x) = 2x^2 + 2x$ **46.** $(f/g)(x) = \frac{2x}{x + 1}$ $(x \neq -1)$
47. 6   **48.** -1 **49.** $2(x + 1)$ **50.** $2x + 1$
51. yes   **52.** no

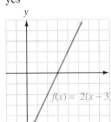

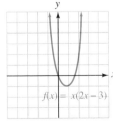

53. no

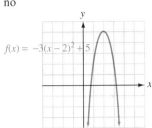

54. no

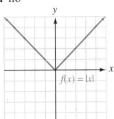

55. $f^{-1}(x) = \frac{x + 3}{6}$ **56.** $f^{-1}(x) = \frac{x - 5}{4}$
57. $y = \sqrt{\frac{x + 1}{2}}$ **58.** $x = |y|$

Chapter 10 Test (page 772)

1. $3, -6$ **2.** $-\frac{3}{2}, -\frac{5}{3}$ **3.** 144 **4.** 625 **5.** $-2 \pm \sqrt{3}$
6. $\frac{5}{2} \pm \frac{\sqrt{37}}{2}$ **7.** $-\frac{5}{4} \pm \frac{\sqrt{17}}{4}$ **8.** $\frac{1}{2} \pm \frac{\sqrt{11}}{2}i$ **9.** nonreal
10. 2 **11.** 10 in.   **12.** $1, \frac{1}{4}$
13.   **14.** $(2, 1)$

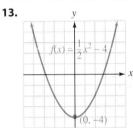

15.

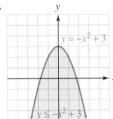

16. $(-\infty, -2) \cup (4, \infty)$

17. $(-3, 2]$

18. $(g + f)(x) = 5x - 1$
19. $(f - g)(x) = 3x + 1$

20. $(g \cdot f)(x) = 4x^2 - 4x$ **21.** $(g/f)(x) = \frac{x - 1}{4x}$ **22.** 3
23. -4 **24.** -8 **25.** -9 **26.** $4(x - 1)$ **27.** $4x - 1$
28. $y = \frac{12 - 2x}{3}$ **29.** $y = -\sqrt{\frac{x - 4}{3}}$

Cumulative Review Exercises (page 773)

1. D: $(-\infty, \infty)$; R: $[-3, \infty)$ **2.** D: $(-\infty, \infty)$; R: $(-\infty, 0]$
3. $y = 3x + 2$ **4.** $y = -\frac{2}{3}x - 2$ **5.** $-4a^2 + 12a - 7$
6. $6x^2 - 5x - 6$ **7.** $(x^2 + 4y^2)(x + 2y)(x - 2y)$
8. $(3x + 2)(5x - 4)$ **9.** $6, -1$ **10.** $0, \frac{2}{3}, -\frac{1}{2}$ **11.** $5x^2$
12. $4t\sqrt{3t}$ **13.** $-3x$ **14.** $4x$ **15.** $\frac{1}{2}$ **16.** 16 **17.** y^2
18. $x^{17/12}$

19.

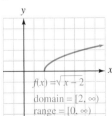

20.

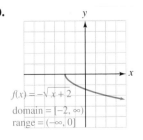

21. $x^{4/3} - x^{2/3}$ **22.** $\frac{1}{x} + 2 + x$ **23.** $7\sqrt{2}$

24. $-12\sqrt[4]{2} + 10\sqrt[4]{3}$ **25.** $-18\sqrt{6}$ **26.** $\frac{5\sqrt[3]{x^2}}{x}$

27. $\frac{x + 3\sqrt{x} + 2}{x - 1}$ **28.** $\sqrt{xy}$ **29.** $2, 7$ **30.** $\frac{1}{4}$

31. $3\sqrt{2}$ in. **32.** $2\sqrt{3}$ in. **33.** 10 **34.** 9

35. $1, -\frac{3}{2}$ **36.** $-\frac{2}{3} \pm \frac{\sqrt{7}}{3}$

37. 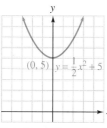 **38.**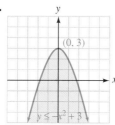

39. $7 + 2i$ **40.** $-5 - 7i$ **41.** 13 **42.** $12 - 6i$
43. $-12 - 10i$ **44.** $\frac{3}{2} + \frac{1}{2}i$ **45.** $\sqrt{13}$ **46.** $\sqrt{61}$
47. -2 **48.** $9, 16$
49. $(-\infty, -2) \cup (3, \infty)$ **50.** $[-2, 3]$

51. 5 **52.** 27 **53.** $12x^2 - 12x + 5$ **54.** $6x^2 + 3$
55. $f^{-1}(x) = \frac{x - 2}{3}$ **56.** $f^{-1}(x) = \sqrt[3]{x - 4}$

Getting Ready (page 776)

1. 8 **2.** 5 **3.** $\frac{1}{25}$ **4.** $\frac{8}{27}$

Exercises 11.1 (page 786)

1. 4 **3.** 18 **5.** $\frac{1}{4}$ **7.** $\frac{2}{9}$ **9.** 40 **11.** $120°$
13. exponential **15.** $(0, \infty)$ **17.** increasing
19. $P\left(1 + \frac{r}{k}\right)^{kt}$ **21.** 2.6651 **23.** 36.5548 **25.** 8

27. $7^{3\sqrt{3}}$

29. 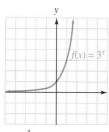 **31.**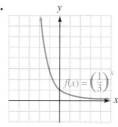

33. $b = \frac{1}{2}$ **35.** $b = 3$

37. 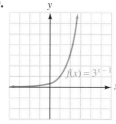 **39.**

41. $b = 2$

43. increasing function **45.** decreasing function

47. approximately 29.8 million
49. $\frac{32}{243} A_0$ **51.** $\$22,080.40$ **53.** $\$32.03$
55. $\$2,273,996.13$ **57.** 5.0421×10^{-5} coulombs
59. $\$1,115.33$

Getting Ready (page 788)

1. 2 **2.** 2.25 **3.** 2.44 **4.** 2.59

Exercises 11.2 (page 794)

1. 1 **3.** 7.39 **5.** 2 **7.** $4x^2\sqrt{15x}$ **9.** $10y\sqrt{3y}$
11. 2.72 **13.** increasing **15.** $A = Pe^{rt}$
17. 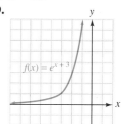 **19.**

21. 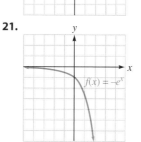 **23.**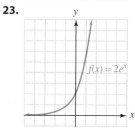

25. no **27.** no **29.** $\$10,272.17$ **31.** $\$6,391.10$
33. 10.6 billion **35.** 2.6 **37.** 72 yr **39.** 3.68 grams
41. $2,498.27$grams **43.** $\$7,518.28$ from annual compounding;
$\$7,647.95$ from continuous compounding **45.** $6,817$
47. 0.076 **49.** 0 mps **51.** this object **53.** $\$3,094.15$
57. 2 **59.** $k = e^5$

Getting Ready (page 797)

1. 1 **2.** 25 **3.** $\frac{1}{25}$ **4.** 4

Exercises 11.3 (page 804)

1. 3 **3.** 5 **5.** 2 **7.** $\frac{1}{4}$ **9.** 2 **11.** $\varnothing$; $\frac{3}{5}$ is extraneous
13. 4 **15.** $(0, \infty)$ **17.** x **19.** exponent
21. $(b, 1), (1, 0)$ **23.** $20 \log \frac{E_O}{E_I}$ **25.** $3^3 = 27$
27. $\left(\frac{1}{2}\right)^2 = \frac{1}{4}$ **29.** $4^{-3} = \frac{1}{64}$ **31.** $\left(\frac{1}{2}\right)^3 = \frac{1}{8}$
33. $\log_6 36 = 2$ **35.** $\log_5 \frac{1}{25} = -2$ **37.** $\log_{1/2} 32 = -5$
39. $\log_x z = y$ **41.** 49 **43.** 6 **45.** 5 **47.** $\frac{1}{25}$ **49.** 5
51. $\frac{3}{2}$ **53.** 4 **55.** 2 **57.** 3 **59.** $\frac{1}{2}$

61. increasing

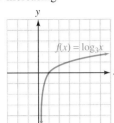

63. decreasing

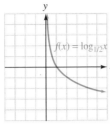

65.

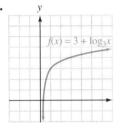

67.

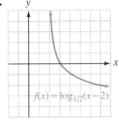

69.

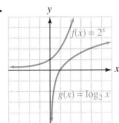

71.

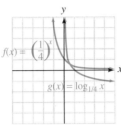

73. 0.9165   **75.** -2.0620 **77.** 17,378.01   **79.** 0.00
81. $\frac{1}{6}$ **83.** -3 **85.** $-\frac{3}{2}$ **87.** $\frac{2}{3}$ **89.** 8   **91.** 4   **93.** 4
95. 4   **97.** 3   **99.** 100   **101.** 25.25   **103.** 8
105. $b = 3$ **107.** no value of b **109.** 29.0 dB
111. 49.5 dB   **113.** 4.4   **115.** 4   **117.** 4.2 yr old
119. 10.8 yr

Getting Ready (page 807)

1. 2   **2.** -3 **3.** 1   **4.** 0

Exercises 11.4 (page 811)

1. $e^y = x$ **3.** $t = \frac{\ln 2}{r}$ **5.** $y = 9x + 5$ **7.** $y = -\frac{3}{2}x + \frac{1}{2}$
9. $y = 5$ **11.** $\frac{2x^2 + x + 1}{x(x + 1)}$ **13.** $\frac{x + y}{y - x}$ **15.** $(0, \infty), (-\infty, \infty)$
17. 10   **19.** $\frac{\ln 2}{r}$ **21.** 3.2288   **23.** 2.2915   **25.** -0.1592
27. no real value   **29.** 9.9892   **31.** 23.8075   **33.** 0.0089
35. 61.9098   **37.**   **39.**

41. no   **43.** no   **45.** 5.8 yr   **47.** 13.9 yr
49. about 2.9 hr

Getting Ready (page 814)

1. x^{m+n} **2.** 1   **3.** x^{mn} **4.** x^{m-n}

Exercises 11.5 (page 821)

1. 2   **3.** 343   **5.** 2   **7.** $\frac{1}{4}$ **9.** 2   **11.** $\sqrt{85}$
13. $y = -\frac{7}{6}x + \frac{2}{3}$ **15.** 1   **17.** x **19.** $-$ **21.** x

23. $=$ **25.** 0   **27.** 7   **29.** 10   **31.** 1   **33.** 0   **35.** 7
37. 10   **39.** 1   **45.** $\log_b x + \log_b y + \log_b z$
47. $\log_b 2 + \log_b x - \log_b y$ **49.** $3 \log_b x + 2 \log_b y$
51. $\frac{1}{2}(\log_b x + \log_b y)$ **53.** $\log_b x + \frac{1}{2}\log_b z$
55. $\frac{1}{3}\log_b x - \frac{1}{4}\log_b y - \frac{1}{4}\log_b z$ **57.** $\log_b \frac{x + 1}{x}$
59. $\log_b x^2 y^{1/2}$ **61.** $\log_b \frac{z^{1/2}}{x^3 y^2}$ **63.** $\log_b \frac{\frac{x}{z} + x}{\frac{y}{z} + y} = \log_b \frac{x}{y}$
65. 1.4472   **67.** 0.3521   **69.** 1.1972   **71.** 2.4014
73. 2.0493   **75.** 0.4682   **77.** 1.7712   **79.** -1.0000
81. 1.8928   **83.** 2.3219   **87.** false   **89.** false   **91.** true
93. false   **95.** true   **97.** true   **99.** 4.77
101. from 2.5119×10^{-8} to 1.585×10^{-7} **103.** It will
increase by $k \ln 2$.   **105.** The intensity must be cubed.

Getting Ready (page 824)

1. $2 \log x$ **2.** $\frac{1}{2}\log x$ **3.** 0   **4.** $2b \log a$

Exercises 11.6 (page 832)

1. $\frac{\log 5}{\log 3}$ **3.** $-\frac{\log 7}{\log 2}$ **5.** 2   **7.** 10   **9.** 0, 5   **11.** $\frac{2}{3}, -4$
13. exponential   **15.** $A_0 e^{-kt}$ **17.** 1.1610   **19.** 3.9120
21. 0   **23.** 22.1184   **25.** 1.2702   **27.** 1.7095   **29.** 4, -1
31. $-2, -2$ **33.** ± 1.0878 **35.** 0, 1.0566   **37.** 1.8
39. 3, -1 **41.** 2   **43.** 3   **45.** -7 **47.** 10, -10
49. 50; -2 is extraneous   **51.** 20; -5 is extraneous
53. 10; -100 is extraneous   **55.** 10; 1 is extraneous
57. 4; 0 is extraneous   **59.** 4; 1 is extraneous   **61.** 20
63. 8   **65.** 0   **67.** 6; -1 is extraneous
69. 9; -9 is extraneous   **71.** 0.2789   **73.** 100, 1   **75.** 4
77. 1, 7   **79.** 4   **81.** 53 days   **83.** 6.2 yr   **85.** about
4,200 yr   **87.** 25.3 yr   **89.** 2.828 times larger   **91.** 13.3
93. 42.7 days   **95.** 5.6 yr   **97.** 5.4 yr
99. because $\ln 2 \approx 0.7$ **103.** $x \leq 3$

Chapter Review (page 836)

1. $5^{2\sqrt{2}}$ **2.** $2^{\sqrt{10}}$
3.   **4.**

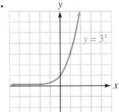

5. $x = 1, y = 6$ **6.** D: $(-\infty, \infty)$, R: $(0, \infty)$
7.   **8.**

9. \$2,189,703.45   **10.** \$2,324,767.37

11

1

1

32. $\frac{1}{25}$

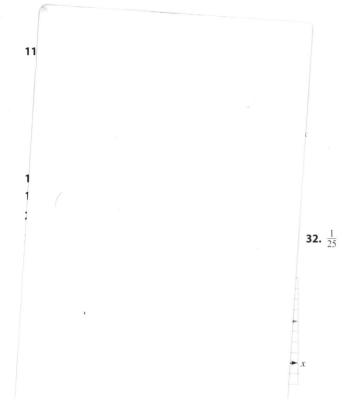

39. 53 dB   **40.** 4.4   **41.** 6.1137   **42.** -0.1111
43. 10.3398   **44.** 2.5715

45.   **46.**

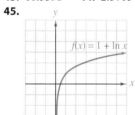 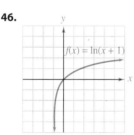

47. 23 yr   **48.** 0   **49.** 1   **50.** 3   **51.** 4   **52.** 4   **53.** 0
54. 7   **55.** 3   **56.** 4   **57.** 9
58. $2 \log_b x + 3 \log_b y - 4 \log_b z$
59. $\frac{1}{2}(\log_b x - \log_b y - 2 \log_b z)$ **60.** $\log_b \frac{x^3 z^7}{y^5}$
61. $\log_b \frac{y^3 \sqrt{x}}{z^7}$ **62.** 3.36   **63.** 1.56   **64.** 2.64
65. -6.72 **66.** 1.7604   **67.** about 7.94×10^{-4} gram-ions
per liter   **68.** $k \ln 2$ less   **69.** $\frac{\log 7}{\log 3} \approx 1.7712$ **70.** 2
71. 31.0335   **72.** 2   **73.** $\frac{\log 3}{\log 3 - \log 2} \approx 2.7095$
74. $-1, -3$ **75.** 25, 4   **76.** 4; -2 is extraneous
77. 2; -3 is extraneous   **78.** 4, 3   **79.** 6; -1 is extraneous
80. 31   **81.** $\frac{\ln 9}{\ln 2} \approx 3.1699$ **82.** $\varnothing$ **83.** $\frac{e}{e-1} \approx 1.5820$
84. 1   **85.** about 3,400 yr

Chapter 11 Test (page 842)

1.   **2.**

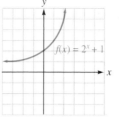 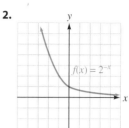

3. $\frac{3}{64}$ gram   **4.** $1,060.90   **5.**

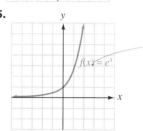

6. $4,451.08   **7.** 2   **8.** 3   **9.** $\frac{1}{27}$
10. 10   **11.** 2   **12.** $\frac{27}{8}$
13.   **14.**

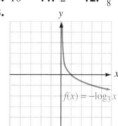 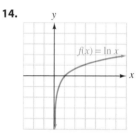

15. $2 \log a + \log b + 3 \log c$ **16.** $\frac{1}{2}(\ln a - 2 \ln b - \ln c)$
17. $\log \frac{b\sqrt{a+2}}{c^3}$ **18.** $\log \frac{\sqrt[3]{a}}{c\sqrt[3]{b^2}}$ **19.** 1.3801
20. 0.4259   **21.** $\frac{\log 3}{\log 7}$ or $\frac{\ln 3}{\ln 7}$ **22.** $\frac{\log e}{\log \pi}$ or $\frac{\ln e}{\ln \pi}$ **23.** true
24. false   **25.** false   **26.** false   **27.** 6.4   **28.** 46
29. $\frac{\log 3}{\log 5}$ **30.** $\frac{\log 3}{(\log 3) - 2}$ **31.** 1   **32.** 10; -1 is extraneous

Getting Ready (page 844)

1. $x^2 - 4x + 4$ **2.** $x^2 + 8x + 16$ **3.** $\frac{81}{4}$ **4.** 36

Exercises 12.1 (page 853)

1. $(0, 0)$, 12   **3.** $(2, 0)$, 4   **5.** down   **7.** left   **9.** 5, $-\frac{7}{3}$
11. 3, $-\frac{1}{4}$ **13.** conic   **15.** standard, $(0, 3)$, 4
17. circle, general   **19.** parabola, $(3, 2)$, right
21.   **23.**

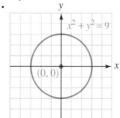 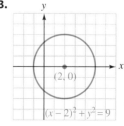

25.

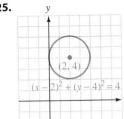

$(x - 2)^2 + (y - 4)^2 = 4$

27.

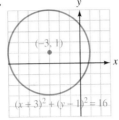

$(-3, 1)$

$(x + 3)^2 + (y - 1)^2 = 16$

29.

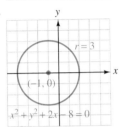

$r = 3$

$(-1, 0)$

$x^2 + y^2 + 2x - 8 = 0$

31.

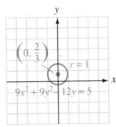

$\left(0, \dfrac{2}{3}\right)$

$r = 1$

$9x^2 + 9y^2 - 12y = 5$

33.

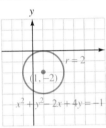

$r = 2$

$(1, -2)$

$x^2 + y^2 - 2x + 4y = -1$

35.

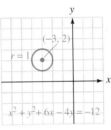

$(-3, 2)$

$r = 1$

$x^2 + y^2 + 6x - 4y = -12$

37. $x^2 + y^2 = 1, x^2 + y^2 - 1 = 0$
39. $(x - 6)^2 + (y - 8)^2 = 25, x^2 + y^2 - 12x - 16y + 75 = 0$
41. $(x + 2)^2 + (y - 6)^2 = 144, x^2 + y^2 + 4x - 12y - 104 = 0$
43. $x^2 + y^2 = 2, x^2 + y^2 - 2 = 0$

45.

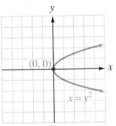

$(0, 0)$

$x = y^2$

47.

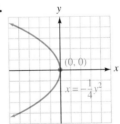

$(0, 0)$

$x = -\dfrac{1}{4}y^2$

49.

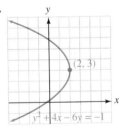

$(2, 3)$

$y^2 + 4x - 6y = -1$

51.

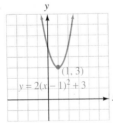

$(1, 3)$

$y = 2(x - 1)^2 + 3$

53.

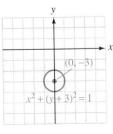

$(0, -3)$

$x^2 + (y + 3)^2 = 1$

55.

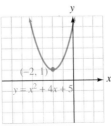

$(-2, 1)$

$y = x^2 + 4x + 5$

57.

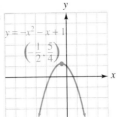

$y = -x^2 - x + 1$

$\left(-\dfrac{1}{2}, \dfrac{5}{4}\right)$

59.

61.

63.

65.

67. $(x - 7)^2 + y^2 = 9$ **69.** no   **71.** 30 ft away
73. 2 AU

Getting Ready (page 857)

1. $y = \pm b$ **2.** $x = \pm a$

Exercises 12.2 (page 865)

1. $(\pm 3, 0), (0, \pm 4)$ **3.** $(2, 0)$ **5.** $12y^2 + \dfrac{9}{x^2}$ **7.** $\dfrac{y^2 + x^2}{y^2 - x^2}$
9. ellipse, sum   **11.** center   **13.** $(0, 0)$, major axis, $2b$

15.

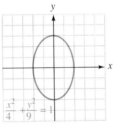

$\dfrac{x^2}{4} + \dfrac{y^2}{9} = 1$

17.

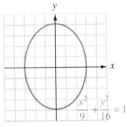

$\dfrac{x^2}{9} + \dfrac{y^2}{16} = 1$

19.

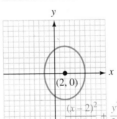

$(2, 0)$

$\dfrac{(x - 2)^2}{16} + \dfrac{y^2}{25} = 1$

21.

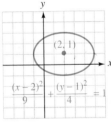

$(2, 1)$

$\dfrac{(x - 2)^2}{9} + \dfrac{(y - 1)^2}{4} = 1$

23.

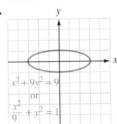

$x^2 + 9y^2 = 9$
or
$\dfrac{x^2}{9} + y^2 = 1$

25.

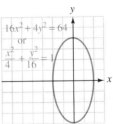

$16x^2 + 4y^2 = 64$
or
$\dfrac{x^2}{4} + \dfrac{y^2}{16} = 1$

27.

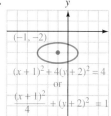

$(x+1)^2 + 4(y+2)^2 = 4$
or
$\dfrac{(x+1)^2}{4} + (y+2)^2 = 1$

29.

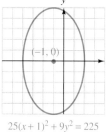

$25(x+1)^2 + 9y^2 = 225$
or
$\dfrac{(x+1)^2}{9} + \dfrac{y^2}{25} = 1$

21.

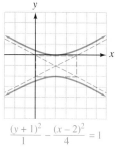

$\dfrac{(y+1)^2}{1} - \dfrac{(x-2)^2}{4} = 1$

23.

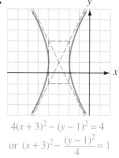

$4(x+3)^2 - (y-1)^2 = 4$
or $(x+3)^2 - \dfrac{(y-1)^2}{4} = 1$

31.

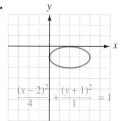

$\dfrac{(x-2)^2}{4} + \dfrac{(y+1)^2}{1} = 1$

33.

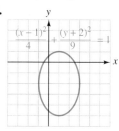

$\dfrac{(x-1)^2}{4} + \dfrac{(y+2)^2}{9} = 1$

25.

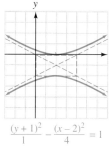

$\dfrac{(x+1)^2}{1} - \dfrac{(y+2)^2}{4} = 1$

27.

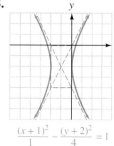

$\dfrac{(y+1)^2}{1} - \dfrac{(x-2)^2}{4} = 1$

35.   **37.**

29.

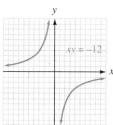

$xy = 8$

31.

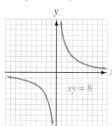

$xy = -12$

39. $\dfrac{x^2}{144} + \dfrac{y^2}{25} = 1$ **41.** $y = \dfrac{1}{2}\sqrt{400 - x^2}$ **43.** 12π sq. units

33.   **35.**

37. 3 units   **39.** $10\sqrt{3}$ units

Getting Ready (page 869)

1. $y = \pm 2.0$ **2.** $y = \pm 2.9$

Exercises 12.3 (page 877)

1. $(\pm 3, 0)$ **3.** $-3x^2(2x^2 - 3x + 2)$ **5.** $(5a + 2b)(3a - 2b)$
7. hyperbola, difference   **9.** center   **11.** $(\pm a, 0)$,
y-intercepts

Getting Ready (page 880)

1. positive   **2.** negative   **3.** 98   **4.** -3

Exercises 12.4 (page 883)

1. increasing   **3.** constant   **5.** 20   **7.** domains
9. constant, $f(x)$ **11.** step   **13.** increasing on $(-\infty, 0)$,
decreasing on $(0, \infty)$ **15.** decreasing on $(-\infty, 0)$,
constant on $(0, 2)$, increasing on $(2, \infty)$
17. constant on $(-\infty, 0)$,   **19.** decreasing on $(-\infty, 0)$,
    increasing on $(0, \infty)$ increasing on $(0, 2)$,
                                            decreasing on $(2, \infty)$

13.

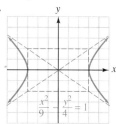

$\dfrac{x^2}{9} - \dfrac{y^2}{4} = 1$

15.

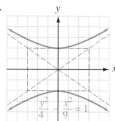

$\dfrac{y^2}{4} - \dfrac{x^2}{9} = 1$

17.

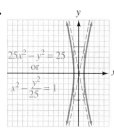

$25x^2 - y^2 = 25$
or
$x^2 - \dfrac{y^2}{25} = 1$

19.

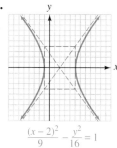

$\dfrac{(x-2)^2}{9} - \dfrac{y^2}{16} = 1$

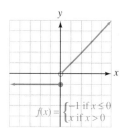

$f(x) = \begin{cases} -1 \text{ if } x \le 0 \\ x \text{ if } x > 0 \end{cases}$

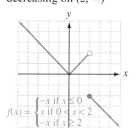

$f(x) = \begin{cases} -x \text{ if } x \le 0 \\ x \text{ if } 0 < x < 2 \\ -x \text{ if } x \ge 2 \end{cases}$

21.
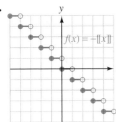
$f(x) = -[\![x]\!]$

23.
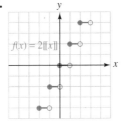
$f(x) = 2[\![x]\!]$

7.
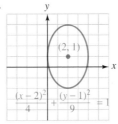
$(2, 1)$
$\dfrac{(x-2)^2}{4} + \dfrac{(y-1)^2}{9} = 1$

8.
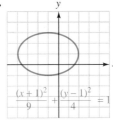
$\dfrac{(x+1)^2}{9} + \dfrac{(y-1)^2}{4} = 1$

25.
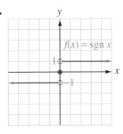
$f(x) = \text{sgn } x$

27. $30
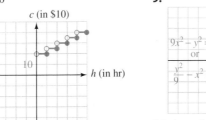
c (in $10)
h (in hr)

9.
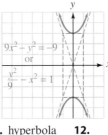
$9x^2 - y^2 = -9$
or
$\dfrac{y^2}{9} - x^2 = 1$

10.
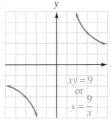
$xy = 9$
or
$y = \dfrac{9}{x}$

29. After 2 hours, network B is cheaper.
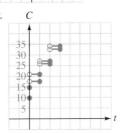
C

11. hyperbola

12.
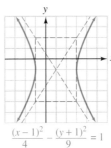
$\dfrac{(x-1)^2}{4} - \dfrac{(y+1)^2}{9} = 1$

13. increasing on $(-\infty, -2)$, constant on $(-2, 1)$, decreasing on $(1, \infty)$

Chapter Review (page 886)

1.
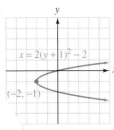
$(x-1)^2 + (y+2)^2 = 9$

2.
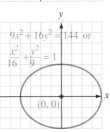
$(0, 0)$
$x^2 + y^2 = 16$

14.
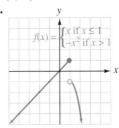
$f(x) = \begin{cases} x \text{ if } x \le 1 \\ -x^2 \text{ if } x > 1 \end{cases}$

15.
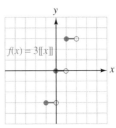
$f(x) = 3[\![x]\!]$

3.
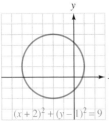
$(x+2)^2 + (y-1)^2 = 9$

4.
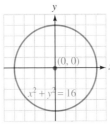
$(5, 2)$
$x = -3(y-2)^2 + 5$

Chapter 12 Test (page 892)

1. $(2, -3)$, 2   **2.** $(-2, 3)$, 4   **3.**
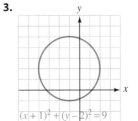
$(x+1)^2 + (y-2)^2 = 9$

5.
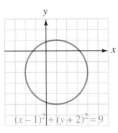
$x = 2(y+1)^2 - 2$
$(-2, -1)$

6.
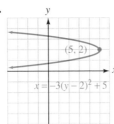
$9x^2 + 16y^2 = 144$ or
$\dfrac{x^2}{16} + \dfrac{y^2}{9} = 1$
$(0, 0)$

4.
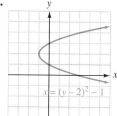
$x = (y - 2)^2 - 1$

5.
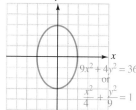
$9x^2 + 4y^2 = 36$
or
$\frac{x^2}{4} + \frac{y^2}{9} = 1$

6.
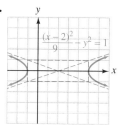
$\frac{(x-2)^2}{9} - y^2 = 1$

7.
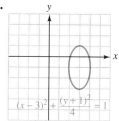
$(x - 3)^2 + \frac{(y+1)^2}{4} = 1$

8.
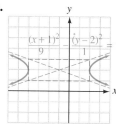
$\frac{(x+1)^2}{9} - \frac{(y-2)^2}{1} = 1$

9. increasing on $(-3, 0)$, decreasing on $(0, 3)$

10.
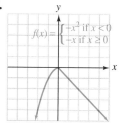
$f(x) = \begin{cases} -x^2 \text{ if } x < 0 \\ -x \text{ if } x \geq 0 \end{cases}$

Cumulative Review Exercises (page 893)

1. $12x^2 - 5xy - 3y^2$ **2.** $a^{2n} - 2a^n - 3$ **3.** $\frac{5}{a-2}$
4. $a^2 - 3a + 2$ **5.** 1   **6.** $\frac{4a-1}{(a+2)(a-2)}$ **7.** parallel
8. perpendicular   **9.** $y = -2x + 5$ **10.** $y = -\frac{9}{13}x + \frac{7}{13}$

11.
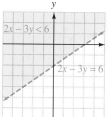
$2x - 3y < 6$
$2x - 3y = 6$

12.
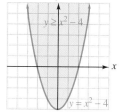
$y \geq x^2 - 4$
$y = x^2 - 4$

13. $5\sqrt{2}$ **14.** $81x\sqrt[3]{3x}$ **15.** 5; 0 is extraneous   **16.** 0
17. $\frac{2}{3}, -\frac{3}{2}$ **18.** $-\frac{4}{3} \pm \frac{\sqrt{19}}{3}$ **19.** $4x^2 + 4x - 1$
20. $f^{-1}(x) = \sqrt[3]{\frac{x+1}{2}} = \frac{\sqrt[3]{4x+4}}{2}$

21.
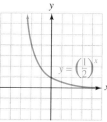
$y = \left(\frac{1}{2}\right)^x$

22. $2^y = x$ **23.** $\frac{2\log 2}{\log 3 - \log 2}$
24. 16

25.
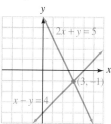
$(0, -1)$
$x^2 + (y + 1)^2 = 9$

26.
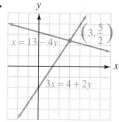
$x^2 - 9(y + 1)^2 = 9$
or
$\frac{x^2}{9} - (y + 1)^2 = 1$

Getting Ready (page 896)

1. 2   **2.** 5   **3.** -4 **4.** -3

Exercises 13.1 (page 906)

1. no solution   **3.** one solution   **5.** 2   **7.** 4   **9.** a^{22}
11. $\frac{1}{81x^{32}y^4}$ **13.** $r = \frac{A-p}{pt}$ **15.** $r = \frac{r_1 r_2}{r_2 + r_1}$ **17.** consistent
19. independent

21.
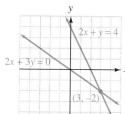
$2x + y = 5$
$(3, -1)$
$x - y = 4$

23.
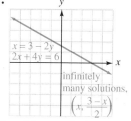
$x = 13 - 4y$
$\left(3, \frac{5}{2}\right)$
$3x = 4 + 2y$

25.
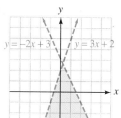
$2x + y = 4$
$2x + 3y = 0$
$(3, -2)$

27.
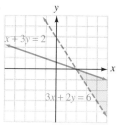
$x = 3 - 2y$
$2x + 4y = 6$
infinitely many solutions,
$\left(x, \frac{3-x}{2}\right)$

29. $(2, 2)$ **31.** $(5, 3)$ **33.** $(-2, 4)$ **35.** no solution
37. $(5, 2)$ **39.** $(-4, -2)$ **41.** infinitely many solutions, $(x, 2x - 4)$ **43.** no solution

45.
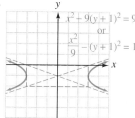
$y = -2x + 3$ $y = 3x + 2$

47.
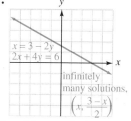
$x + 3y = 2$
$3x + 2y = 6$

49. $(2, 3)$ **51.** $\varnothing$ **53.** $(1, -2)$ **55.** $\left(5, \frac{3}{2}\right)$ **57.** $\left(-2, \frac{3}{2}\right)$

59. $(1, 2)$ **61.** $\left(\frac{1}{2}, \frac{2}{3}\right)$ **63.** $(4, 8)$ **65.** $(20, -12)$
67. $(-0.37, -2.69)$ **69.** $(-7.64, 7.04)$ **71. a.** $2 million
b. $3 million   **c.** 10,000 cameras   **73.** $57   **75.** 625 ohms
and 750 ohms   **77.** 16 m by 20 m   **85.** no

Getting Ready (page 909)

1. yes   **2.** yes   **3.** no   **4.** yes

Exercises 13.2 (page 916)

1. yes   **3.** $\frac{9}{5}$ **5.** 1   **7.** $2s^2 + 1$ **9.** plane
11. infinitely   **13.** yes   **15.** $(1, 1, 2)$ **17.** $(0, 2, 2)$
19. $\left(\frac{3}{4}, \frac{1}{2}, \frac{1}{3}\right)$ **21.** $\varnothing$ **23.** infinitely many solutions of the
form $(19 - 9z, 5 - 3z, z)$ **25.** $(3, 2, 1)$ **27.** $(2, 6, 9)$
29. $\varnothing$ **31.** infinitely many solutions of the form
$\left(\frac{1}{2}, \frac{5}{3} - \frac{4}{3}z, z\right)$ **33.** $-2, 4, 16$ **35.** $A = 40°$, $B = 60°$,
$C = 80°$ **37.** 1, 2, 3   **39.** 30 expensive, 50 middle-priced,
100 inexpensive   **41.** 250 $5 tickets, 375 $3 tickets,
125 $2 tickets   **43.** 3 poles, 2 bears, 4 deer   **45.** 78%, 21%,
1%   **47.** $y = x^2 - 4x$ **49.** $x^2 + y^2 - 2x - 2y - 2 = 0$
53. $(1, 1, 0, 1)$

Getting Ready (page 919)

1. 5   8   13   **2.** 0   3   7   **3.** -1 -1 -2
4. 3   3 -5

Exercises 13.3 (page 926)

1. $\begin{bmatrix} 3 & 2 \\ 4 & -3 \end{bmatrix}$ **3.** yes   **5.** 9.3×10^7 **7.** 6.3×10^4
9. matrix   **11.** 3, columns   **13.** augmented, coefficient
15. type 1   **17.** nonzero   **19.** 0   **21.** 8   **23.** $(1, 1)$
25. $(2, -3)$ **27.** $(1, 2, 3)$ **29.** $(-1, -1, 2)$ **31.** $\varnothing$
33. $(1, 2)$ **35.** $(2, 0)$ **37.** $\varnothing$ **39.** $(-6 - z, 2 - z, z)$
41. $(2 - z, 1 - z, z)$ **43.** $(0, -3)$ **45.** $(8, 8)$ **47.** $(4, 5, 4)$
49. $(1, 2)$ **51.** $(2, 3)$ **53.** $\varnothing$ **55.** $(2, 1, 0)$
57. $(x, 3x - 9)$ **59.** $(4 - z, 2, z)$ **61.** $(x, 0, 1 - x)$
63. $22°, 68°$ **65.** $40°, 65°, 75°$ **67.** $y = 2x^2 - x + 1$
69. $76°, 104°$ **71.** 20, 40, 4   **75.** $k \neq 0$

Getting Ready (page 928)

1. -22 **2.** 22   **3.** -13 **4.** -13

Exercises 13.4 (page 936)

1. 1   **3.** 0   **5.** $\begin{vmatrix} 5 & 2 \\ 4 & -1 \end{vmatrix}$ **7.** -3 **9.** 0   **11.** number,
square   **13.** $\begin{vmatrix} a_2 & c_2 \\ a_3 & c_3 \end{vmatrix}$ **15.** Cramer's rule   **17.** consistent,
independent   **19.** 8   **21.** -2 **23.** 0   **25.** -13 **27.** 26
29. 0   **31.** $(-1, 3)$ **33.** $(4, 2)$ **35.** $\varnothing$ **37.** dependent
equations, $\left(x, -\frac{2}{3}x + 3\right)$ **39.** $(1, 1, 2)$ **41.** $(3, 2, 1)$
43. $\varnothing$ **45.** dependent equations, $\left(\frac{1}{2}, \frac{5}{3} - \frac{4}{3}z, z\right)$
47. $x^2 - y^2$ **49.** $10a$ **51.** 0   **53.** -23 **55.** 26
57. $\left(-\frac{1}{2}, \frac{1}{3}\right)$ **59.** $(2, -1)$ **61.** $\left(5, \frac{14}{5}\right)$ **63.** $(3, -2, 1)$

65. $\left(\frac{3}{4}, \frac{1}{2}, \frac{1}{3}\right)$ **67.** $(-2, 3, 1)$ **69.** 2   **71.** 2   **73.** $50°, 80°$
75. $5,000 in HiTech, $8,000 in SaveTel, $7,000 in HiGas
81. -4

Getting Ready (page 939)

1. $7x^2 = 44$ **2.** $-3y^2 = 8$

Exercises 13.5 (page 944)

1. 0, 1, 2   **3.** 0, 1, 2, 3, 4   **5.** $-11x\sqrt{2}$ **7.** $\frac{t}{2}$
9. graphing, substitution   **11.** four
13. 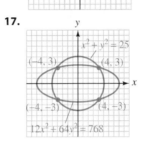   **15.**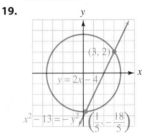

17. 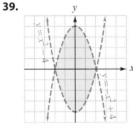   **19.**

21. $(3, 0), (0, 5)$ **23.** $(1, 1)$ **25.** $(1, 2), (2, 1)$
27. $(-2, 3), (2, 3)$ **29.** $\left(\sqrt{5}, 5\right), \left(-\sqrt{5}, 5\right)$
31. $(3, 2), (3, -2), (-3, 2), (-3, -2)$
33. $(0, -4), (-3, 5), (3, 5)$
35. $(-2, 3), (2, 3), (-2, -3), (2, -3)$
37.   **39.**

41. $(1, 2), (-2, -1)$ **43.** $(2, 4), (2, -4), (-2, 4), (-2, -4)$
45. $\left(-\sqrt{15}, 5\right), \left(\sqrt{15}, 5\right), (-2, -6), (2, -6)$ **47.** $(3, 3)$
49. $(6, 2), (-6, -2), \left(\sqrt{42}, 0\right), \left(-\sqrt{42}, 0\right)$ **51.** $\left(\frac{1}{2}, \frac{1}{3}\right), \left(\frac{1}{3}, \frac{1}{2}\right)$
53. 4 and 8   **55.** 7 cm by 9 cm   **57.** either $750 at 9% or
$900 at 7.5%   **59.** 68 mph, 4.5 hr   **63.** 0, 1, 2, 3, 4

Chapter Review (page 948)

1.

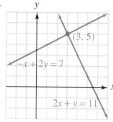

2.

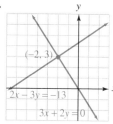

3.

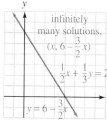

4.

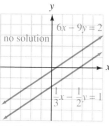

5. $(-1, 3)$ **6.** $(-3, -1)$ **7.** $(3, 4)$ **8.** $(-4, 2)$

9. $(-3, 1)$ **10.** $(1, -1)$ **11.** $(9, -4)$ **12.** $\left(4, \frac{1}{2}\right)$

13. $(1, 2, 3)$ **14.** no solution   **15.** $(2, 1)$ **16.** $(1, 3, 2)$

17. $(1, 2)$ **18.** $(3z, 1 - 2z, z)$ **19.** 18   **20.** 38   **21.** -3

22. 28   **23.** $(2, 1)$ **24.** $(-1, 3)$ **25.** $(1, -2, 3)$

26. $(-3, 2, 2)$ **27.** $(4, 2), (4, -2), (-4, 2), (-4, -2)$

28. $(2, 3), (2, -3), (-2, 3), (-2, -3)$

29.

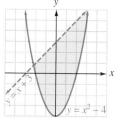

25.

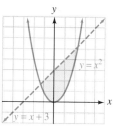

Getting Ready (page 958)

1. $x^2 + 4x + 4$ **2.** $x^2 - 6x + 9$ **3.** $x^3 + 3x^2 + 3x + 1$

4. $x^3 - 6x^2 + 12x - 8$

Chapter 13 Test (page 955)

1.

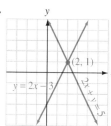

2. $(7, 0)$ **3.** $(2, -3)$

4. $(-6, 4)$ **5.** dependent

6. consistent   **7.** 6   **8.** -8

9. $\begin{bmatrix} 1 & 1 & 1 & 4 \\ 1 & 1 & -1 & 6 \\ 2 & -3 & 1 & -1 \end{bmatrix}$

10. $\begin{bmatrix} 1 & 1 & 1 \\ 1 & 1 & -1 \\ 2 & -3 & 1 \end{bmatrix}$ **11.** $(2, 2)$ **12.** $(-1, 3)$ **13.** 22

14. -17 **15.** 4   **16.** 13   **17.** $\begin{vmatrix} -6 & -1 \\ -6 & 1 \end{vmatrix}$

18. $\begin{vmatrix} 1 & -1 \\ 3 & 1 \end{vmatrix}$ **19.** -3 **20.** 3   **21.** 3   **22.** -1

23. $(2, 1), (2, -1), (-2, 1), (-2, -1)$ **24.** $(3, 4), (-3, 4)$

Index